Air Sampling Instruments

for evaluation of atmospheric contaminants

8th Edition
1995

Technical Editors

Beverly S. Cohen
Susanne V. Hering

ACGIH, Cincinnati, Ohio

First Edition 1960
Second Edition 1962
Third Edition 1966
Fourth Edition 1972
Fifth Edition 1978
Sixth Edition 1983
Seventh Edition 1989
Eighth Edition 1995

Second Printing

Library of Congress Catalog Card Number 83-70265

ISBN: 1-882417-08-9

Published in the United States of America by

American Conference of Governmental Industrial Hygienists, Inc.
1330 Kemper Meadow Drive
Cincinnati, Ohio 45240-1634

Contents

Procedures

Instrument Calibration and Quality Assurance

Gases and Vapors

Special Topics and Applications

Foreword

Air Sampling Instruments is a comprehensive guide to the sampling of airborne contaminants. It addresses both occupational and environmental air sampling issues and presents measurement methods for both gaseous and particulate air contaminants. In addition, this guide describes available air sampling instruments and provides information for their use.

This 8th Edition is divided into two major areas: "Part I. The Measurement Process" and "Part II. Instrumentation." Each part has then been further refined into specific topical sections, thus facilitating the learning/information process and access to the appropriate data.

"Part I. The Measurement Process" encompasses four sections and 11 chapters. The first section presents an overview of the sampling and analysis of air contaminants, while the second discusses occupational and environmental air sampling strategies. Air sampling procedures are the focus of the third section, including particulate and gas phase interactions, size-selective health hazard samplers, and measurement and presentation of aerosol size distributions. The fourth section is devoted to instrument calibration and quality assurance. It covers airflow, gas and vapor samplers, and aerosol samplers. This section also examines precision, accuracy, and validity in measurements as well as performance testing criteria.

"Part II. Instrumentation" offers 12 chapters under four main topic areas. In the first section, air movers and samplers are discussed. The second section is devoted to aerosols and covers such topics as filters and filter holders; impactors, cyclones, and other inertial and gravitational collectors; electrostatic and thermal precipitators; and direct-reading instruments. Gases and vapors are the subject of the third section. Topics include sample collectors; detector tubes, direct-reading passive badges, and dosimeter tubes; and direct-reading instruments. The final section addresses special topics and applications. Areas of discussion are denuder systems and diffusion batteries, sampling from ducts and stacks, sampling airborne radioactivity, and sampling airborne microorganisms and aeroallergens.

The instrument descriptions in Chapters 12–23 contain tables in addition to the individual instrument descriptions and photographs. These tables provide a concise list of available air sampling instruments and their major features; they are intended as a guide and supplement to the individual instrument descriptions. The descriptions are numbered and cross-referenced to the tables. Commercial vendors are listed in the concluding table of these chapters.

The instrument information in this manual was assembled based on literature submitted by the manufacturers. Every effort was made to assure that the data presented are factual and correct; however, the Air Sampling Instruments Committee does not assume responsibility for inaccuracies or false claims for the instruments described herein. Similarly, caution should be exercised with regard to calibration values which may be supplied. The Committee has not attempted to check the accuracy of instruments described in this manual. Furthermore, instrument calibrations can change due to use, handling, shipment, or use under conditions other than those assumed by the manufacturer. The user must take the responsibility for checking the calibration over the range of concentrations and conditions for which the instrument is to be used.

The Committee also wishes readers to be aware that mention of company names or products does not constitute endorsement by any federal agency with which the authors may be affiliated. Among these entities are the Centers for Disease Control and Prevention and the Department of Energy.

The preparation of *Air Sampling Instruments* is a continuing activity of the ACGIH Air Sampling Instruments Committee. The Committee asks for your comments to improve this volume. Information would be appreciated on new instruments or new uses for instruments as well as corrections, omissions, or inaccuracies.

Acknowledgments

The first compendium of air sampling instruments was the *Encyclopedia of Instrumentation for Industrial Hygiene,* published in 1956 by the University of Michigan, Institute of Industrial Health, Ann Arbor, Michigan. The *Encyclopedia* contained descriptive information on instruments exhibited at a symposium on "Instrumentation for Industrial Hygiene" held at the Institute in May 1954.

Air Sampling Instruments was first published by the American Conference of Governmental Industrial Hygienists (ACGIH) in 1960 as a successor to the *Encyclopedia.* Subsequent editions of *Air Sampling Instruments* appeared in 1962, 1967, 1972, 1978, 1983, and 1989. These volumes provided the basis for this edition, and the efforts of their authors are gratefully acknowledged.

This edition of *Air Sampling Instruments* was produced through the cooperative efforts of the members of the Air Sampling Instruments Committee of ACGIH, with the invaluable assistance of other industrial hygienists and air quality specialists in this country and abroad. This international pool of expertise and experience ensured the successful, responsive revision that is the 8th Edition.

The Committee wishes to recognize the significant contributions of authors from outside the Committee: Sidney C. Soderholm, Ph.D.; Bean T. Chen, Ph.D.; John G. Watson, Ph.D.; Peter K. Mueller; and Harriet A. Burge, Ph.D.

Many manufacturers and distributors provided literature and photographs for the instruments described here. We appreciate their cooperation. Many of the illustrations were taken from technical journals and books, as noted in the figure captions. We thank the publishers for their generally prompt response in granting permission for their reproduction.

Finally, we thank the many unnamed institutions that have provided support and the many unnamed colleagues of the Committee members who lent their services, suggestions, and encouragement in the production of this manual.

Air Sampling Instruments Committee Members

Charles E. Billings, Ph.D., CIH
Richard H. Brown, Ph.D.
Paul E. Caplan, PE, CIH
Mark A. Chatigny, Ph.D.
Yung-Sung Cheng, Ph.D.
Beverly S. Cohen, Ph.D.
Melvin W. First, Sc.D.
Susanne V. Hering, Ph.D.
Judson L. Kenoyer
Earl O. Knutson, Ph.D.
David Leong, Ph.D., CIH
Paul J. Lioy, Ph.D.
Morton Lippmann, Ph.D.
Dale A. Lundgren
Janet Macher, Ph.D.
Charles McCammon, Ph.D.
Lee E. Monteith, CIH
Owen R. Moss, Ph.D.
David Pui, Ph.D.
James Rock, Col., Ph.D., CIH
Kenneth Rubow, Ph.D.
Bernard E. Saltzman, Ph.D., CIH
David L. Swift, Ph.D.
Mary Lynn Woebkenberg

Chapter 1

Sampling and Analysis of Air Contaminants: An Overview

Melvin W. First, Sc.D.
Harvard University, School of Public Health, Boston, Massachusetts

CONTENTS

Introduction

The predecessor publication of *Air Sampling Instruments* is the *Encyclopedia of Instruments for Industrial Hygiene*, a compilation of papers presented at a conference entitled "Symposium on Instrumentation in Industrial Hygiene," which was held at the University of Michigan, Ann Arbor, May 24–27, 1954.[1] The scope of *Air Sampling Instruments* has been enlarged with each succeeding edition to encompass additional environmental health aspects. Fortunately, the basic principles of air sampling, and much of the equipment that is used, are common to all aspects, making it possible to keep the size of this book within reasonable bounds.

Air sampling equipment intended for evaluation of airborne exposures has undergone marked evolution over the past several decades in the direction of miniaturization and automation. The trend has been especially conspicuous for equipment intended for long period personal sampling in the workplace and in the indoor environment, and has been made possible by developments in diffusive sampling (often referred to as passive sampling) and in customized microelectronic circuitry. So universally has personal sampling been adopted as the most acceptable way to evaluate human exposures to airborne contaminants that it is a surprise to realize that the concept and equipment were first introduced in 1960 by Sherwood and Greenhalgh[2] who stated that, "The personal air sampler has been developed to permit more precise assessment of the average air concentration to which individuals are exposed."

The trend toward miniaturization of sampling equipment has also been assisted greatly by enormous improvements in the smallest quantity measurable by modern analytical methods (permitting satisfactory analytical procedures on microgram, and, in many cases, nanogram quantities of air contaminants) and made desirable by the vast array of sampling devices required to cope with an ever-increasing number and variety of chemical and biological substances of health significance. For example, the first list of Threshold Limit Values (TLVs) published by the American Conference of Governmental Industrial Hygienists (ACGIH) in 1951 contained 162 substances; the 1994–1995 schedule encompasses nearly 700 listings.[(3)]

By contrast with the shrinking size of personal sampling devices, stationary monitoring equipment used for radiation and air pollution measurements has grown. This has been most noteworthy with respect to instruments that incorporate size–selective inlets and the automatic analytical instruments that draw in samples continuously, perform many complex analytical steps automatically, instantly print the results and store them for a permanent record. Many are capable of displaying cumulative average concentrations at any time this information is called for. These kinds of analytical instruments not only conserve highly skilled manpower, they may even be essential for monitoring critical exposures having a well-defined ceiling limit designation in the ACGIH list of TLVs, e.g., hydrogen cyanide and cadmium oxide fume.[(3)] In addition, many automatic continuous air monitoring instruments perform functions that are impossible with older instruments and methods. For example, automatic particle sampling, counting, and sizing instruments, discussed in detail in Chapter 16, make it possible to examine airborne particles that have not been subjected to agglomeration or shattering in the sampling and analytical operations and to measure all the parameters that are needed to evaluate dust exposures. It is often exceedingly difficult to distinguish sampling from analytical operations in these complex automatic recording instruments, but, to the extent possible, it is desirable to do so to understand the exact nature of the results they display.

The sharp rise in the cost of energy during the 1970s resulted in drastic reductions in fresh air exchanges in residential and commercial buildings, whether ventilated by natural or mechanical means. As a direct consequence, indoor air pollutants that were formerly diluted and flushed out as they evolved now become concentrated. Sometimes, they produce acute discomfort, and a number may induce chronic diseases having a chemical (formaldehyde), radioactive (radon), or biological (mold spores) source. Diffusive samplers have found wide use for estimating levels of formaldehyde and radon in residences. The householder exposes the unit and returns it to the vendor at the conclusion of the recommended exposure period for analysis and a report.

Active sampling by professionals is more usual in commercial buildings experiencing what is popularly referred to as "sick building syndrome." Because such buildings are often equipped with heating, cooling, and humidifying facilities that represent a suitable habitat for a variety of molds and other microorganisms that release spores to the ventilation air when the systems cycle from wet to dry operation, microbiological sampling is likely to be undertaken in such facilities in addition to a search for irritants such as formaldehyde, systemic poisons such as mixed volatile organic compounds (VOCs), and indicators of deficient air exchange such as carbon dioxide. Air sampling for microbiological agents is an important activity in hospitals, microbiological laboratories, and research institutes, as well as in the vicinity of water cooling towers that may harbor Legionnaire's Disease bacteria. In response to these needs, a number of new microbiological sampling instruments have been developed and commercialized that impact airborne organisms directly onto culture media in a state ready for incubation. Details of instruments suitable for sampling and analyzing airborne microorganisms are described in Chapter 23.

Sampling and analysis of work atmospheres are simplified by two factors. First, industrial hygienists usually know the contaminants present in the workroom air from the nature of the process plus a knowledge of the raw materials, end products, and wastes. Therefore, identification of workroom contaminants is rarely necessary and, as a rule, only quantification is required. Second, usually, only a single contaminant of importance is present in the workroom atmosphere and, in the absence of obvious interfering substances, great simplification of procedures is possible. Nonetheless, one must be on guard continually to detect the presence of subtle and unsuspected interferences that may take the form of trace substances affecting color development or the shade of indicator dyes. By contrast, community air sampling, indoors and out, is made complex by the simultaneous presence of many substances of concern, plus the much lower concentrations that prevail compared to those observed in workroom atmospheres. A notable example is the need to identify and quantify specific components of total outdoor hydrocarbons for health assessment purposes.

Other reasons for sampling air include routine surveillance and evaluating the effectiveness of engineering control measures and process changes. The most frequent occupational health purpose is "to measure the dose of the hazardous agent absorbed by the worker at his place of work. This means that the assessment of the environment is not just an exercise in physical or chemical analysis but has its base in the biological characteristics of man, and the relevance of the results depends on the adequacy of the 'biological calibration' of the analytical procedures."[(4)] In addition, sampling is conducted to determine compliance with occupational and community air regulations or commonly accepted standards. Epidemiology of diseases of environmental origin and many other areas of research associated with environmental health are dependent on accurate evaluations of both occupational and nonoccupational exposures to toxic substances. Real-time sampling (with videotaping) may be used effectively to locate and evaluate sources and poor work practices, and to assist in the engineering design of work stations.[5]

Nature of Air Contaminants

Contaminants may be divided into a few broad categories depending on physical characteristics.

Gases and Vapors

Gases are fluids that occupy the entire space of their enclosure. They require increased pressure and decreased temperature for liquification, e.g., hydrogen sulfide and carbon monoxide, whereas vapors are the evaporation products of substances that are also liquid at normal temperatures, e.g., water and methanol. The sole reason for making the distinction is because in many instances they are collected by different devices, although thermodynamically they behave similarly.

Particulate Matter

Sampling considerations make it convenient to characterize particulate matter by size and phase (solid or liquid) as well as by chemical composition. Whether a particle is solid or liquid is important in determining its behavior in aerosol samplers and particle size is an important factor for evaluating deposition in the lung and transport in the environment.

Dusts are solid particles formed from inorganic or organic materials reduced in size by mechanical processes such as grinding, crushing, blasting, drilling, and pulverizing. These particles range in size from the visible to the submicroscopic, but the principal concern of industrial hygienists is with those below 10 μm because they reach the deepest parts of the lung and remain suspended in the atmosphere for a long period of time. Fibers are a special subcategory of dusts because of the effect of shape on their aerodynamic and toxic properties. Fiber exposures continue to be sampled by methods that permit evaluation by count, whereas other pneumoconiosis-producing dusts are sampled by methods that permit exposure evaluation by mass.

Fumes are fine particles formed from solid materials by evaporation, condensation, and gas phase molecular reactions. When heated, metals such as lead produce a vapor that condenses in the atmosphere to form metallic particles that oxidize, e.g., to lead oxide. These particles range in size from 1.0 μm to less than 0.01 μm. Solid organic materials, such as waxes (chlorinated naphthalenes), can form fumes by the same method. Current interest in atmospheric pollution studies has focused on solid particles in the size range below 2.5 μm, with a finding that they tend to be the fraction formed by gas phase reactions in the atmosphere. Their prevalence can be correlated with specific health effects.

Smokes and *soot* are products of incomplete combustion of organic materials and are characterized by optical density. The size of smoke particles is usually less than 0.5 μm.

Liquid particles are produced by atomization or by condensation from the gaseous state. Droplets formed from atomization are generally greater than 5 μm in diameter. Condensation of low volatility organic and inorganic species usually produces submicrometer aerosols, e.g., concentrated H_2SO_4. High boiling organic liquids, such as refined petroleum oils, are sometimes found as fine particles in the workroom atmosphere. Photochemical reactions in smoggy atmospheres lead to the production of secondary aerosols containing droplets $\leq$0.25 μm.

Odors

In some instances, the amount of material in the atmosphere is so small that it is only detectable by odor and the environmental health specialist should neglect no opportunity to exercise and sharpen the sense of smell. Because many substances of industrial hygiene importance have well-defined odor and irritation (nose, eyes) thresholds, the experienced hygienist is often able to distinguish nonacceptable air concentrations on this basis alone. Indeed, certain of the ACGIH TLVs are based on the criteria of eye and nose irritation or unpleasant odor. For example, the TLV and air quality standard for ozone is only a little above the odor threshold. Therefore, it may be concluded that, when this compound is detectable by odor, it would be desirable to test the atmosphere chemically to determine whether a standard is being exceeded.[6] Some substances, notably H_2S and ozone, rapidly anesthetize the odor receptors and for these substances, absence of odor is not a criterion of safety after the first few seconds of exposure.

Sampling Considerations

The volume of sample to be collected is dependent on an estimate of the amount of material to be found in the atmosphere, the sensitivity of the analytical method, and the hygienic or air quality standard. When dealing with occupational exposures, for example, sufficient sample must be collected for a reliable estimation of a concentration equal to one-half the hygienic standard, i.e., the proposed "action level," although a method capable of reliably estimating at least one-tenth the hygienic standard is preferable.

Personal and Area Sampling

Ideally, one wishes to characterize the environment in the breathing zone of individuals to evaluate their specific exposures. Passive dosimeters and compact, battery-operated personal sampling devices for particulate matter (filters) and gases (absorbers and adsorbers) are especially useful for monitoring those who move from place to place and engage in a variety of activities that involve interaction with different amounts of air contaminants. Sampling strategies for evaluating occupational exposures are contained in Chapter 2.

Formerly, the most frequent method of evaluating occupational exposure was to measure workroom contamination in the vicinity of workers at about the elevation of the breathing zone, but workroom sampling introduces uncertainty when evaluating the precise exposure of the most exposed worker and, therefore, fails to comply with Occupational Safety and Health Administration (OSHA) requirements.[7] Area sampling systems continue to have utility in workplaces to monitor the effectiveness of engineering controls. Short period personal samples are used to measure maximum exposures, and, when excessive levels are found, to help determine which machine or part of a process is responsible so that corrective actions may be taken.

As discussed in Chapter 3, fixed station sampling has been the predominant mode for outdoor environmental measurements up to the present. Over the past several years, a number of important studies have been conducted using 24-hr personal samplers to combine exposures to indoor and outdoor air pollutants into an integrated personal daily exposure level. Being a natural time-weighted average of outdoor, work or school, commuting, and residential conditions, this sampling method is believed to yield a better estimate of total exposure for epidemiologic purposes than widely spaced, fixed-station outdoor air monitors.[8] When combined with single source differential sampling at home, at work, etc., it becomes possible to identify the major contributors for purposes of control.

Small personal sampling instruments have been developed that incorporate a particle size-selective inlet with a collection stage for respirable particulate matter plus a stage for trapping gases and vapors. They make it increasingly possible to measure round-the-clock exposures to a wide variety of indoor and outdoor air contaminants. For example, a study of the exposure of children of elementary school age to environmental tobacco smoke used 24-hr personal samples collected in a multistage instrument consisting of a 10-mm nylon cyclone preseparator and a tared 37-mm Fluoropore filter for the respirable particulate fraction, followed by a sodium-bisulfate-treated, all-glass fiber final filter for retention of nicotine vapor.[9]

Sampling Duration

Brief period samples are often referred to as "instantaneous" or "grab" samples, whereas longer period samples are termed "average" or "integrated" samples. Although there is no sharp dividing line between the two categories, grab samples are obtained over a period of less than 5 min, usually less than 1 min, whereas average samples are taken for longer periods. *Threshold Limit Values and Biological Exposure Indices for 1994–1995*[3] defines sampling periods in relation to specific physiological responses. Brief period samples include the "Threshold Limit Value-Ceiling (TLV–C) — the concentration that should not be exceeded during any part of the working exposure" and the "Threshold Limit Value–Short-Term Exposure Limit (TLV–STEL) — the concentration to which workers can be exposed continuously for a short period of time without suffering from 1) irritation, 2) chronic or irreversible tissue damage, or 3) narcosis of sufficient degree to increase the likelihood of accidental injury, impair self-rescue or materially reduce work efficiency, and provided that the daily TLV–TWA is not exceeded." The longest period sample defined by ACGIH is the "Threshold Limit Value–Time-Weighted Average (TLV–TWA) — the time-weighted average concentration for a normal 8-hour workday and a 40-hour workweek, to which nearly all workers may be repeatedly exposed, day after day, without adverse effect." Closely similar short-term and long-term sampling periods are specified in Federal Regulations 29 CFR 1910.-1000, Tables Z-1 through Z-3, and are incorporated into current legal standards for evaluating the exposure of workers to airborne contaminants in the workplace. OSHA's legal, enforceable standards are referred to as PELs, permissible exposure limits. Recommended exposure limits (RELs), prepared by the National Institute for Occupational Safety and Health (NIOSH), usually refer to up to 10 hrs per day and 40 hrs per week. Workplace sampling strategies are covered in Chapter 2.

Environmental monitoring for community air pollution control is covered in Chapter 3. This sampling specialty has its own set of averaging times, dictated by custom and the physiological response of the body to specific pollutants. For example, ozone, an irritant, has a 1-hr averaging period; carbon monoxide has a 1-hr averaging time for high-level acute exposures plus an 8-hr averaging time for lower level exposures; suspended particulate matter has a 24-hr averaging period for maximum daily concentration and the daily results are averaged over a full calendar year for comparison with another air quality standard.

Brief sampling periods are best for following the phases of a cyclic process and for determining peak airborne concentrations of brief duration, but they usually require analytical methods capable of detecting and measuring very low concentrations of the collected airborne contaminants. Instantaneous sampling is a characteristic of most direct-reading instruments for gases and vapors (Chapter 19) as well as for aerosols (Chapter 16). Short period sampling may also be accomplished by trapping a small portion of the atmosphere in a suitable vessel such as a previously evacuated glass or stainless steel canister. Grab sampling methods can be used to investigate malodorous air pollution by organoleptic techniques. Short period sampling is suitable, physiologically, for primary irritants such as HCl, whereas continuous sampling methods are best for evaluating cumulative systemic poisons such as lead and mercury. Each method has special value and it is essential to develop a capability to do both. It is always important that the sample contain sufficient contaminant to be above the minimum quantity that can be measured reliably by the chosen analytical method.

Sampling Rate

Active gas sampling presents no special problems with respect to sampling rate and, more particularly, velocity of entry into a sampling device, because gas mixtures resist separation into components under the influence of usually applied centrifugal or inertial forces.

This is not the case for particulate matter and, more especially, for particles greater than 5 μm in aerodynamic equivalent diameter (AED), defined as the diameter of a hypothetical sphere of unit density having the same terminal settling velocity in air as the particle in question, regardless of its geometric size, shape, and true density. The need for isokinetic sampling rates in ducts and stacks, in which velocities are usually in excess of 5 m/s and often exceed 20 m/s, is unquestioned. The sampling errors introduced by anisokinetic sampling in rapidly moving air streams are detailed in Chapter 21. On the other hand, studies by Davies[10] have shown that most sampling rates give representative results when the sample is drawn from still or nearly still air whenever certain criteria for inlet conditions are met. This was found to be especially correct for particle sizes in the range of hygienic concern, i.e., <10 μm. Subsequently, Bien and Corn[11] applied Davies' criteria to the inlet configuration of commonly used air sampling devices and found a number that did not measure up, including the 10-mm cyclone of the coal mine personal sampler. Nevertheless, by test, these cyclones were found to give accurate results for respirable particles.[12] Additional empirical studies by Breslin and Stein[13] have shown "that published criteria for inlet conditions for correct sampling are overly restrictive and that respirable-size particles are sampled correctly in the normal range of operation of most dust sampling instruments." This observation was confirmed by Agarwal and Liu,[14] who concluded that there are no real inlet restrictions when sampling respirable particles in still air. There are still some with a contrary opinion, but "no restrictions" remains the mainstream view.

Although there is little evidence to show that interactions between typical indoor air velocity conditions, sample intake orientation, and inlet velocity are likely to affect the capture of particles in the respirable size range, this is not necessarily true for larger particles that can deposit in the nose and throat. When these larger particles are corrosive to tissues (e.g., chromic acid) or are systemic poisons (e.g., lead, arsenic), they may be absorbed where they deposit or be swallowed and exert their toxic action in that manner. For such substances, sampling errors associated with non-respirable, but inhalable, particles can become a matter of concern (see Chapter 5), but not enough is known about the systemic effects of exposures to particles larger than 10 μm to make firm judgments. The effects of sampling rate and inlet configuration for outdoor air sampling have been principally concerned with the effect of anisokinetic sampling velocities on particles greater than 10-μm AED in moderate wind velocity fields. Investigations of the combined effects of anisokinetic sampling velocity and angle of yaw have shown that when both are seriously awry simultaneously, undesirable effects on sample recovery can also occur for particle sizes below 10-μm AED.[15] Such conditions occur during outdoor air sampling but are minimized by the use of geometrically symmetrical inlets and careful control of sampling rate.

Size-selective Sampling

The AED of aerosol particles is of special importance for evaluating toxicologic effects because certain particle sizes deposit preferentially in different parts of the respiratory system. Evaluation of toxic potential can be simplified by the use of special sampling devices that select out of an aerosol cloud only those particle sizes that would reach specific compartments of the human lung. The characteristics of this type of sampler were first specified in 1970[16] by the joint Aerosol Hazards Evaluation Committee of ACGIH and the American Industrial Hygiene Association (AIHA). In the United States, miniature cyclones with carefully regulated characteristics have been used most frequently as sampling precollectors. They permit a predetermined fraction of each particle size to penetrate to a second sampling device that simulates the respiratory system and retains all particles passed by the size-selective cyclone. Multicompartmented gravitational settling chambers are also used as size-selective precollectors, e.g., the British MRE coal mine dust precollector,[17] but because they are relatively large devices and sensitive to orientation, a cyclone or impactor is preferred for use in conjunction with personal sampling devices. Although the particle size retention characteristics of size-selective presampling devices have been chosen to simulate as closely as possible a standardized human lung particle size rejection curve, it is important to keep in mind that the range of human variation for lung retention is probably as great as for most physiological characteristics and that changes in breathing rate and volume per breath profoundly affect the size retention characteristics of the respiratory system. Nevertheless, the use of size-selective samplers has been recognized in the Mine Safety Act of 1969 and the Occupational Safety and Health Act of 1970 as an important refinement in particle sampling for assessment of occupational risk. For similar reasons, the U.S. Environmental Protection Agency (U.S. EPA) modified its high-volume atmospheric sampling device for measuring total suspended particulate matter by adding a size-selective air intake with a cutpoint at 10 μm (referred to as a PM_{10} mass sampler inlet).[18] Current research interest in sampling suspended particulate matter for health effects is focused on developing instruments with cut sizes of 5 and 2.5 μm, inasmuch as the smallest particles originate from gas phase reactions in the atmosphere that produce acid aerosols, whereas the largest ones tend to come from stack emissions of solid particles plus windblown mineral particles. The importance of the fine particle fraction lies in correlations between elevated levels and increased mortality.[19] Size-selective sampling is treated in Chapter 5.

Other Sampling Techniques

Many other types of sampling are needed by environmental health scientists from time to time. Those most frequently used are:

1. Microbiological and aeroallergen sampling to evaluate occupational exposures to pathogenic bacteria, viruses (hospitals and microbiological laboratories), fungi (indoor air pollution studies), and biological matter formed by recombinant DNA techniques. This type of sampling is the subject of Chapter 23. It has been enlarged to reflect the growing importance of bioaerosols in indoor air pollution studies and the rapidly growing knowledge of the nature of aeroallergens, their effects, and methods for collection, culture, and quantification.
2. Rafter samples to determine the long-time average size distribution and composition (e.g., percent quartz) of settled airborne dusts.
3. Product samples to estimate the hazard potential associated with handling specific materials.
4. Bulk air samples by high volume sampling to obtain sufficient material for in-depth qualitative and quantitative analysis. Appropriate statistical criteria must be applied as a guide in obtaining representative samples.[20]
5. Multiday diffusive sampling for radon inside buildings with activated carbon-filled canisters followed by measurement of alpha-ray-emitting radon daughter products. This is a widely used screening procedure recommended by the U.S. EPA. More quantitative studies of radon in air are conducted with diffusion battery sampling to measure size distribution of the daughter products for evaluating differential lung deposition and by membrane filter sampling followed by prompt alpha activity counting with a bank of thermoluminescent detectors for short period measurements. Sampling for airborne radioactivity is covered in Chapter 22.
6. Air sampling to detect explosive concentrations. They are considerably higher than hygienic standards (usually in the % by volume range for gases and g/m^3 range for dusts). Some gas and vapor concentrations within the explosive range may also be anesthetic, asphyxial, or immediately dangerous to life and health (IDLH).
7. Analysis of a respirator pad or chemical cartridge worn by a worker. This type of analysis gives an integrated sample of the air that would have reached the lungs, although the exact air volume sampled can only be estimated.
8. An exposed worker without respiratory protection. Exposed workers have proven to be excellent, though involuntary, biological sampling devices. Analysis of appropriate body fluids or exhaled air gives an indication of absorbed dose and often reflects the average atmospheric concentrations of the exposure. For example, routine blood lead concentrations have been used for decades to supplement area and personal air samples and are particularly useful for locating individuals who may be exposed to the same toxic material during and outside working hours. Another example is the use of exhaled air samples at the conclusion of a work shift to measure the absorbed dose of toluene or carbon monoxide and esti-

mate from this value a TWA exposure.

Evaluating Sampling Results

Because it is impossible to examine the total air environment in which a person works, it is necessary to take small samples and generalize from them concerning the true nature of the entire environment. As might be expected, the larger the number of samples, the more faith can be put in the reliability of the derived information respecting the average concentration and the variability of the concentration from work station to work station and from time to time. Conversely, the degree of improvement in reliability obtainable by each additional sampling decreases as the total number of samples increases. Therefore, for economy, it is necessary to know the minimum number of samples required to characterize the environment to a degree of accuracy consistent with the maintenance of working comfort and safety. Information on sampling strategy is contained in Chapters 2 and 3.

Industrial hygienists use field sampling data to compare the measured values to a TLV, PEL, or REL. When evaluating how well air samples represent the working environment, it is necessary to recognize the presence of instrument and analytical errors as well as normal variations in workroom concentrations over space and time. There are two kinds of errors: systematic errors that relate to imperfectly representative sampling and result from the use of a finite number of sampling points and a limited sampling time[(21)] and nonsystematic errors that result from random fluctuations in the process under study. Random fluctuations may be of long duration relative to the sampling time and produce marked variability from sample to sample at the same location, or they may be randomly distributed in space and produce extreme and uncontrollable variations in samples taken simultaneously at different locations.

Although a larger number of replicate samples gives greater faith in the estimate of the true average concentration derived from them, small sample numbers are most frequent. For this reason, an "interval estimate" is a more useful measure of how well sample averages correspond with the true average in the entire environment than is a "single value estimate." Confidence intervals bracket the true average value and are associated with a confidence coefficient that defines the probability that the true average will be included within that confidence interval, i.e., for a 95% confidence interval, it may be stated with 95% confidence that the true average is greater than a lower interval value and less than an upper interval value. Larger numbers of samples tend to give narrower confidence intervals for the same level of confidence and come closer to the true average.

Action Level

NIOSH has developed "predictive and analytical statistical methods"[(22)] for the evaluation of field sampling results and has recommended to OSHA that these statistical methods be used to "minimize the probability that even a very low percentage of actual daily employee exposure (8-hr TWA) averages exceed the standard" when "only one day's exposure measurement is used to draw conclusions regarding compliance on unmeasured days."[(23)] It was noted, on the basis of numerous studies, that "concentrations in random occupational environmental samples are log normally and independently distributed both within one eight hour period and over many daily exposure averages" and, therefore, sample results are not distributed symmetrically around the average.[(22)] This comes about because, although airborne concentrations cover a wide range of values, most will lie closer to the zero concentration limit but a few will show very large values. Therefore, the distribution tends to peak toward the low concentration values with a long, flat "tail" on the high concentration side. This would be very difficult to handle mathematically were it not for the observation that a logarithmic transformation of the original data is often normally distributed and, by this transformation, a median and a geometric standard deviation can be easily determined. Those familiar with particle size analysis will recognize the statistical methodology. It has been found applicable to air pollution exposure data as well. More details will be found in Chapter 2, "Workplace Sampling Strategies" and in Chapter 6, "Aerosol Accuracy and Precision." The empirical observation that workroom measurements tend to follow a logarithmic probability distribution that has, on the average, a geometric standard deviation of 1.22 (i.e., slope of the distribution curve) has been used by NIOSH to recommend an "action level" when only a small number of samples is used to estimate the true average air concentration.[(23)] Figure 1-1 shows the effect that day-to-day variability in true daily exposure averages has on the probability that at least 5% of all unmeasured 8-hr TWA daily exposure averages will exceed the standard when a single day's measurement falls an identified fraction below the standard. This figure is the basis for the NIOSH recommendation that a measurement at or above one-half the standard should be the "action level" and calls for remeasurement of exposure at least every 2 months. Two consecutive exposure measurements (at least 1 week apart) showing employee exposures less than 50% of the federal limit are adequate to permit termination of the sampling program. Exposures above the federal limit call for more effective control measures and monthly remeasurements until the exposure is reduced to less than the federal limit. This obviously puts a premium on obtaining a low value for each

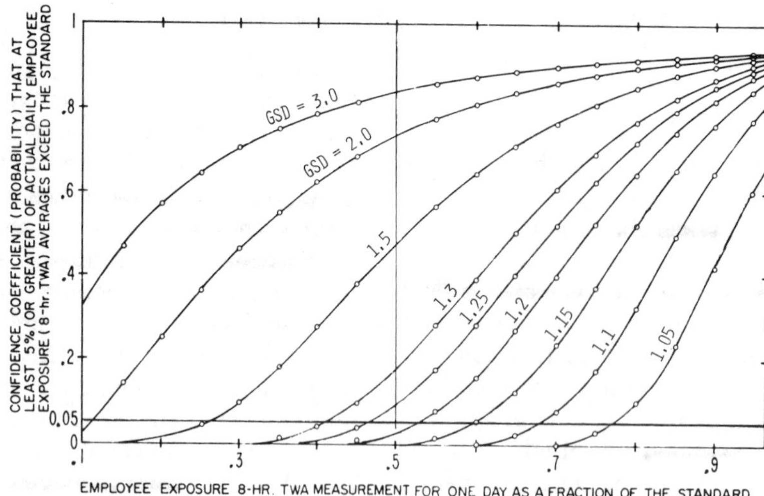

FIGURE 1-1. Probability that standard has been exceeded based on exposure measurements. (Reprinted with permission from Leidel *et al.*[23])

trial.[24]

A critique of the NIOSH action level and sampling strategy proposals was prepared by Rock and Cohoon.[25] They concluded that, "The OSHA implementation of a multiple sample decision strategy is arbitrarily stringent and by design ignores day-to-day variability. It is therefore not suitable for general use by industrial hygiene professionals other than OSHA compliance officers." This finding was based on their belief that "statistically sound strategies are elusive" and that "selection and proper use [of statistical strategies] requires disciplined professional judgment."[25] The authors emphasize their belief in the primacy of professional judgment over mechanistic evaluation schemes designed for subprofessionals and dictated by legal imperatives. The need for professional judgement in the design and conduct of all occupational-health-oriented sampling programs is emphasized in Chapter 2.

Chapter 10 deals more fully with sampling statistics and contains additional information on significance, variability, and correlation, as well as methods for their calculation and evaluation. It should be consulted for guidance and details in conjunction with other literature citations.[22–25]

It seems reasonable to believe that epidemiologic studies involving exposure assessments should include a detailed analysis of the reliability of the exposure values that have been employed (as well as a similar analysis of the "effects" data) so that the derived TLV may be expressed in terms of statistical confidence limits instead of a single number that implies a false degree of certainty regarding the accuracy of the cited value. In the United Kingdom, it is usual to take into account day-to-day variability errors when setting limit values.[26]

Sampling Methods

Methods of Sampling Gases and Vapors

Gases and vapors offer less difficulty in air sampling than aerosols because they diffuse rapidly, mix freely with the general atmosphere, and can, in a short time, reach equilibrium. For air sampling purposes, contaminants can be grouped with regard to solubility and vapor pressure. Many gases and vapors of hygienic significance are water soluble and can be collected in aqueous media with or without a dissolved reacting chemical to suppress the vapor pressure of the solute. Gases and vapors that are not water soluble, but are soluble or reactive in other agents, can be absorbed in a suitable solvent. Gases and vapors that are neither soluble nor reactive may be collected on adsorbents, e.g., activated charcoal, silica gel, and molecular sieves, in both active or diffusive (passive) samplers. Adsorbents have become the sample collection medium of choice for all gasses and vapors because of their convenience and generally high collection efficiency. (See also Chapter 17.)

Instantaneous gas and vapor samples may be collected in rigid glass or metal flasks or in soft plastic bags made of polyethylene, Saran®, Mylar®, Tedlar®, and combinations of these with aluminum foil in sizes up to 120 L.[27] For plastic bag sampling, "A sample is introduced into the bag by a hand or battery operated pump or a squeeze bulb. Bags can be re-used after purging with clean air and checking for any residual components. Certain contaminants cannot be sampled or stored in any type of plastic bag due to their reactivity with surrounding substances or with themselves, styrene being an example. Whether a substance can be sampled and stored in a plastic bag should be determined in the laboratory prior to field use."[28] (See discussion in Chapter 17.)

Pyrex® gas collecting tubes of 300-ml capacity with a capillary standard taper stopcock at each end may be used when the atmosphere sampled contains components incompatible with plastic bag materials. In practice, evacuation may be done in the laboratory and the flask opened in the environment to be sampled, or the flask may be evacuated in the field by a pump. In either case, it is necessary to know the volume of the sampling flask and the internal pressure prior to opening in order to calculate the volume of air sampled. This may be done easily when using evacuated flasks with stopcocks by connecting the flask to a mercury manometer or vacuum gauge and opening the stopcock for a reading just before sampling. Specially passivated stainless steel pressure vessels, known as "SUMMA canisters,"[A] are sometimes used for short period sampling of reactive gases and vapors. The quantity of material trapped by these techniques is small and reactions between trapped chemicals, water vapor, and the walls of the container can occur during storage.

Glass or metal sampling flasks not under vacuum are also used by purging them in the field with a pump or squeeze bulb. However, in this case, the amount trapped reflects the fact that concentration buildup is a semilogarithmic function. In addition, condensation can occur when sampling in saturated atmospheres and can result in continuous absorption in the condensate, thereby falsely increasing the apparent air concentration. Instantaneous gas and vapor sampling may also be done with direct-reading instruments that have a response time measured in seconds. Chapter 19 treats the subject of direct-reading instruments for gases and vapors and includes details of most of the commercially available items in this category.

Non-specific, direct-reading survey instruments such as photoionization and flame ionization meters that respond to broad classes of organic gases and vapors have found wide usage for investigations of leaking underground storage tanks and old chemical waste disposal sites. Detection of chemical vapors in gases found in shallow holes newly drilled in the ground in the vicinity of such facilities is a rapid and simple means of locating chemical leakage even when it is occurring deep underground.

For long-term, integrated sampling of gases and vapors, the sampling rate will depend on the type of collection device employed and the reaction speed of the contaminant. In some cases, the sampling rate will be as low as 50 cm^3/min. However, with the sensitive analytical methods now used, this imposes no handicap. Integrated gas and vapor samples may be collected in a solvent with wash bottles, impingers, and absorbers; on adsorbents, e.g., activated charcoal; by condensation; and in large plastic bags filled at the rate of 50 mL/min with the aid of low-volume, battery-operated personal sampling pumps that contain a built-in accumulator counter to record total air volume. After sampling, the contents may be analyzed in the field or laboratory by nondispersive infrared (CO), gas chromatography (hydrocarbons, chlorinated solvents), etc.

Absorbers vary in characteristics depending on the gas or vapor to be collected. Simple bubbling devices such as impingers and Drechsel bottles are adequate for readily soluble gases such as HCl, HF, and SO_2. For less easily absorbable materials such as Cl_2 and NO_2, multiple contact washing is required (as with fritted glass absorbers). Sometimes, it is desirable to burn the gas or vapor in a furnace and sample the oxidation products, e.g., for chlorinated hydrocarbons. Gas absorbers of this type were discussed and illustrated in earlier editions of this manual.[1]

Adsorption tubes are the method of choice for insoluble or nonreactive vapors. Commonly used adsorbents (in 6–20 mesh sizes) include activated charcoal, silica gel, and molecular sieves. Gas adsorption traps are sometimes preceded by one or two water vapor adsorption stages containing calcium chloride, calcium sulfate, or silica gel, all of which have excellent water vapor adsorption characteristics and poor adsorption capacity for most organic molecules. In the laboratory, the collected vapors may be desorbed thermally or stripped from the adsorbent with carbon disulfide and the recovered vapors quantified by gas chromatography using a suitable detector.

Adsorption tubes used for personal integrated sampling of many organic gases and vapors contain two interconnected chambers in series filled with gas adsorption charcoal. The first chamber, containing 100 mg of charcoal, is separated from a back-up section, containing 50 mg of carbon, by a plastic foam plug. Sampling can be conducted for as long as 8 hrs at 50 mL/min without saturating the first chamber when occupational exposures are at or below the TLV. The contents of the two chambers are analyzed separately to determine whether the first stage adsorbent has become saturated and lost an excessive amount of the sample to the second stage. Sampling results are discarded when the second adsorption stage contains more than 20% of the amount collected on the first stage. Personal sampling with two-chambered charcoal tubes is recommended by NIOSH for vinyl chloride, benzene, CCl_4, etc. Similar methods have been used for environmental and indoor, nonoccupational, sampling.

Gas chromatographic column packing materials (e.g., Tenax) are also used in adsorbent traps for field

[A]Molectrics, Inc., Cleveland, Ohio.

sampling of organic vapors. They are particularly useful for sampling high boiling compounds. The resealed trap is returned to the laboratory for analysis. Absorption of inorganic atmospheric constituents by liquid coatings on solid supports has been used to collect NO_2 on triethanolamine-coated molecular sieves.

Chemically active compounds may react with each other or with oxygen in the air after adsorption and make it difficult or impossible to recover and quantify the original adsorbed gases and vapors. In such instances, the best collection method may be to react them chemically to a stable derivative or to condense the contaminants at low temperature using a mixture of dry ice and acetone (–78°C) or liquid nitrogen (–196°C) as the coolant.

Methods of Sampling Aerosols

Collection methods for liquid and solid aerosol particles are likely to differ when particle loadings are high and the collection device is not designed to handle large liquid accumulations. In addition, liquid or solid aerosol particles that possess significant vapor pressure and are not in equilibrium with the conveying airstream will experience evaporation losses during the sampling period when filtration or dry inertial collection methods are used. For these conditions, the particle collector must be followed by an appropriate vapor collector to account for the entire sampled quantity. Samplers of this type are covered in Chapter 20. When particle loadings are light and evaporation after collection is not a concern, solid and liquid particles can often be sampled successfully by identical methods.

Dusts may be grouped into 1) relatively insoluble mineral dusts such as silica, granite, asbestos, and insoluble metal oxides; 2) soluble mineral dusts such as limestone and dolomite that dissolve in weak acids; and 3) organic dusts such as trinitrotoluene, flour, soap, leather, wood, and plastics. Many of the last group are explosive when the concentration in air is high.

Instantaneous dust samples may be collected with a device that takes in a small measured volume of air (25–50 ml) and blasts it at high velocity against a glass plate on which the particles are deposited. After deposition, the particles are examined and enumerated by bright or dark field microscopy. Today, these instruments are seldom used; they are discussed and illustrated in older publications on air sampling.[1,29]

For integrated or continuous sampling of particulate matter, several physical forces (gravity, impaction, electrophoresis, thermophoresis, and diffusion) are employed. Particle size determines the sampler to be used, and sample volume depends on the air concentration. Collectors for particulate matter can be divided into the following categories: 1) settling chambers, 2) centrifugal devices (e.g., cyclones), 3) impingers and impactors, 4) bubblers, 5) filters, 6) electrostatic precipitators, 7) thermal precipitators, and 8) diffusion batteries. The first four are the principal subject matter of Chapter 14; the fifth of Chapter 13; the sixth and seventh of Chapter 15, and the last one, Chapter 20.

Elutriators use gravitational sedimentation to collect or reject large particles. They are sometimes used for size-selective sampling.

Centrifugal devices include small cyclones and curved surface traps. Cyclones can be used to provide a size-selective separation upstream of another particle collector, such as a filter, or they may be cascaded together to separate particles into several size classes. Aerosol centrifuges are not commonly used for field studies; they are capable of a high degree of precision in the size segregation of particles.

Impingers and impactors use inertial properties of particles to effect collection. The impinger consists of a glass nozzle submerged in water or other liquid. The velocity at the nozzle ranges from 60 to 113 m/s. Particles are impacted on the bottom of the flask and trapped in the liquid.[30] Cascade impactors[31] collect particles on a dry or greased slide. They contain a number of impingement stages in series with graduated nozzle velocities and impaction distances to effect a progressive separation of smaller and smaller particles as the aerosol travels through the unit. Individual impactor stages may be of the single jet or multijet variety. Particles deposited on each stage may be examined microscopically, but when the impactor has been calibrated to define the AED 50% cutpoint of each stage, size distributions by mass can be measured more simply by using weighings, radioactivity, or chemical analysis to determine the amount of deposited material. Many types of cascade impactors are described in Chapter 14.

Absorbers designed for gas collection in a liquid medium are seldom effective for particulate material of small size, but small-scale models of commercial high-efficiency fume collecting devices (e.g., a Venturi scrubber) are useful for obtaining large dust samples from very hot gases.

Filters are among the best methods of sampling solid particulate matter. Many kinds of filter media are available and their use requires a minimum of equipment. The various types of filters are described in Chapter 13. Cellulose, Teflon®, and polyester membrane filters are often used for collecting metallic dusts for chemical analysis and mineral dusts for gravimetric or X-ray diffraction analysis. Absolute-type (HEPA), all-glass filter papers containing superfine glass fibers with diameters well below 0.25 µm are, as the name suggests, virtually 100% efficient for all particles of hygienic importance. Liquid particles, such as sulfuric acid mist, may be collected with equally good results on all-glass papers. Absolute-type, all-glass filters have low airflow resistance, adsorb little water vapor, and, because glass interferes with only a few analyses, have application for gravimetric, chemical, and physical analysis. They are widely used for air quality monitoring. Exceptions are noted in Chapter 13.

Membrane filters have been used for collecting sulfuric acid and similar mists but only for low concentrations. Membrane filters are widely used for collecting mineral dusts for mass respirable fraction evaluation, airborne fiber counting, and examination by optical and electron microscopy.

Electrostatic precipitators, homemade or commercial, have been used since the 1920s for industrial air sampling in workrooms.[29] A specially designed point-to-plane electrostatic precipitator, consisting of an ionizing needle with the point mounted directly above an opposite-polarity, carbon-coated electron microscope grid, is used to collect dust specimens onto grids for direct examination in the electron microscope (see Chapter 15). Some direct-reading instruments for aerosols use electrostatic precipitation as the sampling component.

Thermal precipitators were used in former times for particle enumeration and sizing to evaluate occupational dust exposures.[29] Collection efficiency is near 100% but the dust-free zone around the hot body is very limited and consequently sampling rate is only a few ml/min. At present, thermal precipitators are used as a research tool for collecting dust specimens directly onto grids for examination in the electron microscope. More information on thermal precipitators is contained in Chapter 15. Diffusion batteries are used for collecting and size-separating particles in the size range below the lower limit of optical airborne particle counters, i.e., those less than approximately 0.1 µm. Diffusion batteries are constructed in a variety of configurations. They are discussed and illustrated in Chapter 20.

Separating Volatile Aerosol Particles from Their Vapors

An air sampling task of considerable complexity arises when it is necessary to collect a vapor uncontaminated by its particulate phase in contact with it; or the reverse (see Chapter 4). It is not possible to remove the particulate phase first by filtration because unsaturated air passing through the filter will vaporize the liquid or sublimate the solid on the filter and contaminate the vapor phase collector that follows. It is equally unsatisfactory to pass the sampled air through a bed of gas-adsorbing granules as a first-stage vapor collector because the adsorbent will remove at least some of the particulate phase as well. A requirement of this nature arises when one wishes to evaluate separately the vapor phase and liquid phase workplace exposure to, for example, middle distillate fractions of petroleum. The reason for doing this is to evaluate the precise nature of the exposure of workers who handle these products: the vapor-only exposure is limited by the vapor pressure of the many specific compounds encompassed by the designation "middle distillates," whereas the particulate exposure is not so limited and inhalation will have different physiological and toxicological effects. A solution to this problem described by Bertoni *et al.*[32] is an "annular diffusive sampler" consisting of an annular inlet passage lined with activated charcoal to adsorb vapors by diffusion while the particulate phase penetrated the annular passage and collected on a filter. Samplers of this type are called diffusion denuders. When it is desirable to analyze both the vapor phase and the particulate phase of a volatile liquid, it is necessary to add a vapor adsorbing third stage to trap the vapors volatilized from the liquid droplets caught on the second stage filter as the sampled air passes through it.[33] Similar requirements occur when sampling outdoor air to separate nitrate and sulphate salts of ammonia from their precursor gases and from larger, inert particles, e.g., by the use of an impactor/honeycomb denuder/filter pack system.[34] Two honeycomb denuders in series, each containing over 200 hexagonal glass tubes sealed inside an outer glass tube of 4.7-cm diameter, were used to separate NH_3 from HNO_3 by coating the surfaces of the first denuder with a basic coating to collect acid gases and coating the second denuder with an acidic coating to collect basic gases. A diagram of the four-stage sampler is shown in Figure 1-2. The impactor has a 50% cut-off size of 2.1 µm. More information on "Denuder Systems and Diffusion Batteries" may be found in Chapter 20.

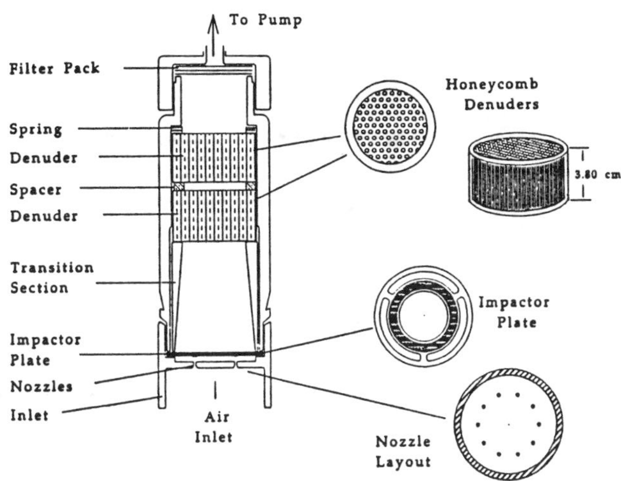

FIGURE 1-2. Honeycomb denuder sampler. (Source: Bertoni *et al.* Annali di Chimica 74:2497.[32])

Collection Efficiency

Collection efficiency is an important factor in the selection of sampling devices. Efficiency need not be 100% as long as it is high, known, and constant over the range of concentrations being evaluated. It should, preferably, be above 90%. An important advantage of evacuated sampling flasks is that efficiency is normally considered to be 100% provided wall adsorption is negligible and correction is made for completeness of evacuation of the container. For concentrating sampling devices, the collection efficiency of the concentrating device must be measured. A widely used method for measuring sampling efficiency for gases and vapors is to place two or more identical samplers in series and analyze the catch in each. When efficiency is independent of gas concentration, each sampler in the series will remove the same percentage of the concentration that reaches it, i.e., a log-decrement relationship. This may not be the case when sampling trace concentrations of gases and vapors by absorption or adsorption because collection efficiency is sometimes proportional to the concentration difference driving force. Therefore, it is often necessary to resort to other methods for measuring collection efficiency. These methods include the use of permeation and diffusion tubes of known emission strength, comparison sampling in parallel with a known high efficiency device utilizing a different measurement principle, measurement of the loss of material from a concentration accurately known at the start and end while sampling in a closed circuit at a known flow rate, sampling from pressurized cylinders containing known concentrations of various gases, and following the sampler under test with a different sampling device known to have close to 100% efficiency for the air contaminant under study. An example of the latter method would be the use of a high efficiency particulate air (HEPA) filter following a particle collection device of unknown efficiency. Chapter 8 is concerned with instrument calibrations of gas and vapor instruments and Chapter 9 is concerned with aerosol instrument calibrations.

Direct-reading Instruments

Direct-reading instruments combine sampling and analytical functions and usually display results rapidly. Many in this category are also capable of storing continuous readings and displaying on command averages for selected time intervals. Devices that provide an immediate answer are useful for industrial hygiene workroom appraisal. The value of an immediate measurement for prevention of further injury and the ability to demonstrate worker exposures to management cannot be overemphasized. An innovative teaching method that combines a direct-reading analytical instrument, such as a photoionization device for organic vapors or a light-scattering chamber for aerosols, with a videotape recorder makes it possible to instantly play back precisely how a production operation involving an exposure to a health hazard was conducted with a continuous record of the instrument readings superimposed.[5,35] This technique makes it possible to involve the workers as well as management in a unique safety education experience. Fortunately, the trend in recent years has been toward the development of more direct-reading devices (Chapters 16 and 19).

Direct-reading Instruments for Gases and Vapors

Numerous direct-reading instruments for gases and vapors have been in constant use by industrial hygienists for many decades. They include 1) a halide meter, 2) combustible gas detectors, and 3) thermal conductivity instruments. The halide meter produces an increase in the violet nitrogen spectrum from an electric arc in the presence of a halide vapor, e.g., methyl chloride. Recent versions of this instrument are capable of measuring concentrations below 1.0 ppm expressed as the halide. Combustible gas detectors measure the heat of combustion released when a gas or vapor is burned on a platinum wire. These detectors are not specific, but can be calibrated for a single vapor or known mixtures. Thermal conductivity instruments form the basis for most of the less expensive gas-detecting devices used for analyzing higher concentrations of carbon dioxide, such as in engine exhausts or oil burner flue gases.

Small, hand-carried direct-reading instruments are available commercially for measuring hydrogen and mercury vapor (using ultraviolet radiation). Mercury vapor in air may be measured directly with instruments that detect the fogging of a gold leaf as it amalgamates with mercury. Hand-operated instruments based on Orsat analytical methods have been used for measuring CO_2 and oxygen in tanks, manholes, and underground excavations to determine the life supporting properties of the atmosphere prior to entry of workers, but electrochemical meters have largely displaced them. Oxygen meters are often paired with combustible gas detectors and a toxic gas detector in a single compact instrument case for such gases as H_2S or CO. These instruments are portable and are designed to operate continuously. They contain microprocessor circuitry and software features that provide "automatic self-diagnostic check, automatic zeroing, and automatic calibration."[36] Oxygen measurements are needed not only to evaluate the presence of satisfactory concentrations for breathing, but to evaluate the readings of combustible gas indicators correctly. Combustible gas indicators give a false indication of safety when the oxygen concentration is less than 8%. However, when oxygen is low, the inlet to the combustible gas meter can be equipped with a tee connection and two sampling hoses of equal length, one of which is placed inside the enclosure to be tested, the other in outside air. The meter reading must then be multiplied by two.

Indicator (or detector) tubes are outstanding direct-reading industrial hygiene air analysis instruments because they are small, light, hand operated, safe in all atmospheres, and give an immediate readout. In addition, an indicator tube is the simplest and most economical air analysis method available for many common air contaminants. During World War II, the National Bureau of Standards (NBS) produced an improved CO indicator tube based on a reaction between CO and a palladium silicomolybdate complex that produces molybdenum blue; the intensity of the color being proportional to the concentration of CO. The success of the NBS CO indicator tube stimulated the development and commercial production of a large variety of reliable detector tubes in the sensitivity ranges useful to industrial hygienists. Detector tubes for more than 160 chemicals are currently available. Some are available in more than one concentration range and the most popular types are offered by many commercial sources. Most of the chemicals measurable by indicator tube are included in the current tabulation of ACGIH threshold limit values.

Because they are so simple to operate, it is commonly assumed by those ignorant of industrial hygiene theory and practice that indicator tubes can be used by unskilled personnel for monitoring work environments. It has been repeatedly demonstrated in practice that serious errors in sampler operation, in selection of sampling locations and times, and in interpretation of results occur unless the tubes are in the hands of a trained operator who is closely supervised by a competent professional. This point is also made in Chapter 18 and cannot be overemphasized.

Some indicator tubes have a long shelf life, e.g., H_2S, but many deteriorate within a year or two. It is customary to extend the shelf life of tubes by storing them under refrigeration, but because the speed of most chemical reactions is sensitive to temperature, the tubes must be warmed to ambient conditions prior to use if the calibration charts accompanying the tubes are to be relied upon. A general certification recommendation for the accuracy of tubes in the United States is ±25% of the true value when tested at 1–5 times the threshold limit value and ±35% at one-half the federal standard.[37] Although all tube manufacturers have improved their quality control, checking a suitable sample of each batch of tubes purchased is advisable and rechecking after a period equivalent to a large fraction of the normal shelf life is prudent.

NIOSH formerly certified detector tubes for a number of workroom exposures but they suspended their detector tube certification program in 1982. The Safety Equipment Institute (SEI), a nonprofit organization funded by safety equipment manufacturers, began a third-party certification program of their own in 1987. Tube testing is performed by contract laboratories holding AIHA laboratory accreditation status; the test protocols employed are those previously established by NIOSH and Military Standard 414.[38] In addition to tube testing in the laboratory, the contract laboratories conduct periodic quality assurance audits of each participant's manufacturing facility. A listing of SEI certified tubes will be found in Chapter 18.

One of the most important developments in air sampling technology for measuring exposures to low concentrations of airborne substances has been the commercial appearance of passive dosimeters for a broad list of volatile substances. Many use the principle of diffusion to a nonspecific adsorbent with subsequent laboratory analysis. Direct-reading devices use permeation through a plastic film barrier to a compound-specific chemical bonding color-developing reagent.

The adsorbent or reactive layer represents an infinite sink for the diffusing or permeating compound, preventing back pressure of the captured material. For that reason, the rate at which volatile airborne substances reach the sensitive surface is proportional to the air concentration in the immediate vicinity of the dosimeter. A review of passive dosimeters[39] cited potential sources of inaccuracy in the measurement of airborne concentrations of gases and vapors but concluded that "passive systems appear to be as reliable as the now accepted active sampling systems." Diffusive dosimeters are dealt with in Chapters 17 and 20. Although only a few passive dosimeters are direct-reading devices, e.g., CO, formaldehyde, and Hg vapor (most must be returned to a laboratory for analysis), the rapid commercialization of all types of passive dosimeters gives promise of an early appearance of additional direct-reading types.

Direct-reading Instruments for Aerosols

Direct-reading field instruments for aerosols are combination sampling and analytical instruments. In addition to the economy of effort and instantaneous readout they provide, many permit measurement of the principal characteristics of liquid and solid particles in an unaltered airborne state.

Airborne particle mass may be measured by depositing the particles on a piezoelectric sensor by electrostatic precipitation.[40] The rate of change of the resonant frequency of the sensor is directly proportional to the mass of material deposited on it. From a continuous trace of resonant frequency with time on a strip chart, short period slopes can be analyzed to measure concentration fluctuations, or the electrical output of the instrument can be digitized and averaged electronically to produce dust concentrations over an averaging period of 24–120 seconds. The instrument weighs approximately 9 kg and is capable of measuring particle concentrations in air as low as a fraction of a mg/m^3 at a sampling rate of 1.0 lpm over a 2-min sampling period. Another aerosol sampling and analyzing instrument, based on an oscillating crystal's response to changing mass loading, collects particles continuously on a filter attached to the crystal and displays aerosol concentration in μg/m^3 based on changes in oscillation frequency and air flow rate.[(41)] When fitted with a PM_{10} sampling head (most of the incoming air is bypassed), the instrument gives results in ambient air that qualify for certification by U.S. EPA as an equivalent air monitoring method.[(42)]

An automatic sampling and analyzing instrument based on beta-ray attenuation was developed through a contract issued by the U.S. Bureau of Mines for use in coal mines.[(43)] This unit is no longer manufactured, but others that use beta-ray detectors are available. The advantage of beta-ray measurement is that attenuation is directly related to the mass of collected particles in the beam. Sampling may be accomplished by membrane filtration or by electrostatic deposition of particles on a thin film. Either method produces a clearly defined dust deposit that can be evaluated quantitatively by beta-ray attenuation.

Another means of assessing airborne particle concentrations is by light scattering. A British unit, called SIMSLIN II (Safety in Mines Scattered Light Instrument), uses a single plate horizontal elutriator to separate the respirable dust fraction from the sampled aerosol and measures the light attenuation of the aerosol stream that penetrates the elutriator. The results are displayed to the machine operator at 1 second intervals, with a 15-min and full-shift cumulative average available on demand. A German unit, called Hund TM Digital μP[B], employs a scattering angle of 70° and monochromatic light of wave length 940 nm to optimize sensitivity to respirable dust. It also displays instantaneous and cumulative dust concentration data over full shift periods. When the instruments were evaluated using coal dust ranging in concentration from 1.0 to 9.9 mg/m^3 and the results were compared with the British MRE dust sampler, it was found that on average, the SIMSLIN II was 18% greater and the TM-Digital 25% less than the MRE.[(44)] Joining the list of portable, direct-reading aerosol survey instruments is a small, hand-held, battery-operated, light-scattering instrument called the Miniram, which stands for "Miniature Real-Time Aerosol Monitor."[(45)] Because light scattering intensity is influenced by particle size, color, shape, and index of refraction as well as by particle numbers, it is not possible to use light-scattering instruments for quantitative evaluations of aerosol concentrations of unknown composition and size distribution. After calibration with a specific aerosol, it may, however, be used as a semiquantitative survey instrument for repeat measurements of nonvarying operations to determine whether engineering controls have maintained their effectiveness.

Several automatic particle counting and sizing instruments capable of making measurements on flowing aerosols are available commercially. Most use optical systems and count light pulses scattered from particles that flow, one by one, through an intensely illuminated sensing zone. When instruments are equipped with an electronic pulse height analyzer, it is possible to obtain information on the size of each particle passing through the illuminated sensing zone. Sampling rate may be as high as 1 lpm. For conventional light particle counters, the smallest detectable size is about 0.3 μm. Portable models weighing about 10 kg are available that give a simultaneous readout of the entire size spectrum sensed by the instrument in 8–12 contiguous intervals. It is possible to make an airborne dust count and size analysis in 3–4 min with one of these instruments.

The use of laser illumination has improved the reliability of optical particle counters and sizers for the smallest particles because of the better collimation and greater light intensity that can be obtained with a laser beam. The most important advance in the use of lasers for counting and sizing airborne particles has been the development of intercavity lasers. The aerosol stream is introduced into the interior of the laser itself and only the scattered light is collected and reimaged at 10× or greater magnification against a dark field. In one commercial model,[(46)] the laser beam at the sensing volume is approximately 500 μm in diameter and produces a power density in excess of 500 Wcm^{-2}. It is capable of measuring particles as small as 0.08 μm in diameter and can cover the size range up to 20 μm (using two probes in series) in about 80 size intervals.

A notable development in automatic, real-time machine sampling and analysis of airborne dust is a battery-operated, portable (12 kg), Laser Fiber Monitor (FAM–7400).[(47)] In principle, it causes sampled airborne fibers to rotate rapidly in a rotating, high-intensity electric field and measures scattered light when illuminated by a 2-mW He-Ne polarized laser operated at 632.8 nm. "Each fiber generates a pulse train as it rotates in a helical trajectory that results from the combined effects of the rectilinear airflow [through the sensing volume] and the perpendicular field-induced rotation. Because longer fibers produce narrower pulses than shorter ones, the monitor is able to discriminate between fibers of different length by sensing the sharpness of individual pulses."[(47)] Tests at the U.S.

[B]Hund Corp., P.O. Box 63, D-6330 Wetzlar, Germany

Bureau of Mines' laboratory "showed that the instrument response is linearly correlated to concentration data obtained using the optical membrane filter count technique" recommended by NIOSH.[48] A later study concluded that the instrument is "recommended as a screening method for monitoring airborne asbestos fibers [but] the device cannot be used as a substitute for the standard monitoring and analysis method."[49] For counting fibers when large numbers of nonfibrous minerals are present, a virtual impactor accessory is available.

Areas for Development

Many sampling and analytical instruments of excellent characteristics and small size have been developed for air measurements. When carefully calibrated and intelligently operated, they are capable of measuring atmospheric contaminants with an accuracy and reliability that is well within the requirements of most environmental health needs. Unfortunately, testing for function and calibration is difficult, time consuming, or costly, and is frequently all three. The introduction of permeation tubes and diffusion tubes has been a major step forward in the calibration of some instruments at low gas concentrations, but the tubes require a prolonged equilibration period prior to use and the equipment to house them in a constant temperature environment is bulky. Storage of calibration gases in compressed gas cylinders is satisfactory for unreactive gases such as CO, but is unsuitable for many substances of interest. Calibration of gas sampling instruments in covered in Chapter 8.

No standard aerosols are available for calibration purposes. This is a serious deficiency because all devices depend on calibration for reliability. Monodisperse polystyrene spheres are aerosolized for calibration of automatic particle sizing instruments, but this hardly constitutes a calibration aerosol in the fullest sense. Test aerosol generation is covered in Chapter 9.

Even when correctly calibrated, it is important to remember that, in field usage, damage by vibration and impact from poor handling are factors that can alter the response of many components. In practical use, it is essential that recalibration be done at frequent intervals to ensure accuracy and reliability. Therefore, a continuing need exists for more simple, cheap, reliable, "off-the-shelf" field and laboratory calibration systems and devices to cover the wide range of gases, vapors, and aerosols of interest. A notable advance in the ability to test equipment in the field is the commercial appearance of small, battery-operated personal sampling pump calibrators.

Although a great deal of progress has been made in reducing the weight of field instruments, more must be done to reach the point where industrial hygenists can carry all the field instruments they need in their jacket pockets. In the area of environmental sampling instruments, considerably more miniaturization is needed. It seems reasonable to expect that solid state circuitry combined with greater instrument sensitivity will reduce electrical current needs and sample volume requirements (and hence, pumping power needs) to the point where increasing numbers of small, light, self-contained instruments of great versatility will become available soon. A step in the right direction is the "Micro Air Sampler,"[C] a 114-g battery-operated pump and electronics package for charcoal adsorber tubes that fits in a shirt pocket and samples up to 200 ml/min.

Standard methods of sampling and analysis are essential for demonstrating compliance with OSHA and U.S. EPA exposure standards. A great deal has been accomplished in this area by publication of approved methods by NIOSH[50] and U.S. EPA and concensus methods by the Intersociety Committee[51] and the American Society for Testing and Materials (ASTM) D-22 Standards Committee.[52] Completion of the program to standardize sampling and analytical methods for every substance of interest to environmental health scientists is occurring rapidly.

New methods for capturing chemical species of special interest and rejecting all others are on the horizon. Instruments employing these methods are especially powerful when they can be miniaturized and equipped with sensors that give a real-time readout, thereby combining selectivity with identification and quantification. For example, man-made zeolites are porous crystalline minerals that can be constructed with uniform pore diameters in the nanometer size range that are big enough to admit large molecules or are so small that only individual atoms can get through. A chemical sensor has been described that consists of "a thin layer of tiny zeolite crystals affixed to an acoustic wave device, a larger crystal that, because of a feedback mechanism, constantly vibrates at a set frequency. If molecules come along that fit into the cavities of the zeolite, they will subtly change the weight of the whole device, altering its resonance frequency. That change can be detected electronically. By assembling a number of such zeolite sensors, each with pores with different sizes and shapes, it should be possible to create a sensor that responds only to one or a few closely related molecules."[53]

From this single example, it can be concluded that many new and useful sampling and analytical devices are on the way to make environmental and occupational health monitoring easier, as well as instantaneous, more accurate, more convenient, and more specific.

[C] Spectrex, Redwood City, CA 94063

References

1. Yaffe, C.D.; Byers, D.H.; and Hosey, A.D.; Eds.: Encyclopedia of Instrumentation for Industrial Hygiene. University of Michigan, Ann Arbor, MI (1956).
2. Sherwood, R.J.; Greenhalgh, D.M.S.: A Personal Air Sampler. Ann. Occup. Hyg. 2:127 (1960).
3. American Conference of Governmental Industrial Hygienists: Threshold Limit Values and Biological Exposure Indices for 1994–1995. ACGIH, Cincinnati, OH (1993).
4. World Health Organization: Environmental and Health Monitoring in Occupational Health. WHO Technical Report Series No. 535. Geneva (1973).
5. Rosén, G.: PIMEX. Combined Use of Air Sampling Instruments and Video Filming: Experience and Results During Six Years of Use. Appl. Occup. Environ. Hyg. 8:344 (1993).
6. American Industrial Hygiene Association: Odor Thresholds for Chemicals with Established Occupational Health Standards. AIHA, Fairfax, VA (1989).
7. Occupational Safety and Health Administration: OSHA Technical Manual, Chapter 1. CPL 2–2.208. OSHA (Feb. 5, 1990).
8. Spengler, J.K.; Treitman, R.D.; et al.: Personal Exposures to Respirable Particulates and Implications for Air Pollution Epidemiology. Environ. Sci. Technol. 19:200 (1985).
9. McCarthy, J.: Physical and Biological Markers to Assess Exposure to Environmental Tobacco Smoke. Doctoral Dissertation, Harvard School of Public Health, Boston, MA (October 28, 1987).
10. Davies, C.N.: The Entry of Aerosols into Sampling Tubes and Heads. Brit. J. Appl. Phys. (J. Phys. D.) Sec. 2, 1:921 (1968).
11. Bien, D.T.; Corn, M.: Adherence of Inlet Conditions for Selected Aerosol Sampling Instruments to Suggested Criteria. Am. Ind. Hyg. Assoc. J. 32:453 (1971).
12. Pickett, W.E.; Sansone, E.B.: The Effect of Varying Inlet Geometry on the Collection Characteristics on a 10-mm Nylon Cyclone. Am. Ind. Hyg. Assoc. J. 34:421 (1973).
13. Breslin, J.A.; Stein, R.L.: Efficiency of Dust Sampling Inlets in Calm Air. Am. Ind. Hyg. Assoc. J. 36:576 (1975).
14. Agarwal, J.K.; Liu, B.Y.H.: A Criterion for Accurate Aerosol Sampling in Calm Air. Am. Ind. Hyg. Assoc. J. 41:191 (1980).
15. Tufto, P.A.; Willeke. K.: Dependence of Particulate Sampling Efficiency on Inlet Orientation and Flow Velocities. Am. Ind. Hyg. Assoc. J. 43:437 (1982).
16. American Industrial Hygiene Association Aerosol Technology Committee: Interim Guide for Respirable Mass Sampling. Am. Ind. Hyg. Assoc. J. 31:133 (1970).
17. Dunmore, J.H.; Hamilton, R.J.; Smith, D.S.G.: An Instrument for the Sampling of Respirable Dust for Subsequent Gravimetric Assessment. J. Sci. Inst. 41:669 (1964).
18. U.S. Environmental Protection Agency: Ambient Air Monitoring Reference and Equivalent Methods. Fed. Reg. 49(55):10454 (March 10, 1984).
19. Dockery, D.W.; Pope, A., III; et al.: An Association Between Air Pollution and Mortality in Six U.S. Cities. New Eng. J. Med. 329:1753 (1993).
20. Silverman, L.; Billings, C.E.; First, M.W.: Particle Size Analysis in Industrial Hygiene. Academic Press (1971).
21. MacDonald, J.R.: Are the Data Worth Owning? Science 176:1377 No. 4042 (June 1972).
22. Leidel, N.A.; Busch, K.A.: Statistical Methods for the Determination of Noncompliance with Occupational Health Standards. DHEW (NIOSH) Pub. No. 75-159. NIOSH, Cincinnati, OH (1975).
23. Leidel, N.A.; Busch, K.A.; Crouse, W.E.: Exposure Measurement Action Level and Occupational Environmental Variability. DHEW (NIOSH) Pub. No. 75-159. NIOSH, Cincinnati, OH (1975).
24. Leidel, N.A.; Busch, K.A.; Lynch, J.R.: Occupational Exposure Sampling Strategy Manual. Pub. No. PB-274-792. National Technical Information Service, Springfield, VA (1977).
25. Rock, J.C.; Cohoon, D.: Some Thoughts About Industrial Hygiene Sampling Strategies, Long Term Average Exposures, and Daily Exposures. Report OEHL 81-32. National Technical Information Service, Springfield, VA (July 1981).
26. Brown, R.H.: Personal Communication (1994).
27. VanderKolk, A.L.: Sampling and Analysis of Organic Solvent Emissions. Am. Ind. Hyg. Assoc. J. 28:588 (1967).
28. American Public Health Association Intersociety Committee: Methods of Air Sampling and Analysis, 2nd ed. M. Katz, Ed. APHA, Washington, DC (1977).
29. Drinker, P.; Hatch, T.: Industrial Dust, 2nd ed. McGraw–Hill, New York (1954).
30. Greenburg, L.; Smith, W.G.: A New Instrument for Sampling Aerial Dust. U.S. Bureau of Mines, Report. Invest. 2392 (1922).
31. Lodge, J.P.; Chan, T.L.; Eds.: Cascade Impactor Sampling and Data Analysis. American Industrial Hygiene Association, Akron, OH (1986).
32. Bertoni, G.; Febo, A.; Perrino, C.; Possanzini, M.: Annular Active Diffusive Sampler: A New Device for the Collection of Organic Vapors. Annali di Chimica 74:97 (1984).
33. Gottfried, G.; Yarko, J.; Olinger, C.; Lewis, R.D.: A Pilot Study to Develop a Method for Sampling and Analysis of Middle Distillate Fuels and Petroleum Solvents. Presented as Paper No. 148 at the American Industrial Hygiene Conference, San Francisco, CA, May 15–20, 1988.
34. Koutrakis, P.; Sioutis, C.; et al.: Development and Evaluation of a Glass Honeycomb Denuder/Filter Pack System to Collect Atmospheric Gases and Particles. Environ. Sci. Technol. 27:2497 (1993).
35. Gressel, M.G.; Heitbrink, W.A.; Eds.: Analyzing Workplace Exposures Using Direct Reading Instruments and Video Exposure Monitoring Techniques. DHHS(NIOSH) Pub. No. 92–104. NIOSH, Cincinnati, OH (August 1992).
36. Arenas, R.V.; Carney, K.R.; Overton, E.B.: Portable Multigas Monitors for Air Quality Evaluation, Part II: Survey of Current Models. Amer. Lab. p. 25 (July 1993).
37. National Institute for Occupational Safety and Health: Certification of Gas Detector Tube Units. Fed. Reg. 38:11458 (May 8, 1973).
38. National Institute for Occupational Safety and Health: Certified Equipment List. DHHS (NIOSH) Pub. No. 80-144. U.S. Government Printing Office, Washington DC (June 1980).
39. Rose, V.E.; Perkins, J.L.: Passive Dosimetry -- State of the Art Review. Am. Ind. Hyg. Assoc. J. 43:605 (1982).
40. TSI, Inc.: Model 3500 Respirable Aerosol Mass Monitor, Piezobalance. TSI, Inc., St. Paul, MN.
41. Patashnick, H.; Rupport, E.G.: Continuous PM–10 Measurements Using the Tapered Element Oscillating Microbalance. J. Air Waste Mgmt. Assoc. 41:1079 (1991).
42. U.S. EPA: Ambient Air Monitoring Reference and Equivalent Methods. 40 CFR Part 53.
43. MIE Corp.: Respirable Dust Monitor Model RDM-101. MIE Corp., Bedford, MA.
44. Thompson, E.M.; et al: Laboratory Evaluation of Instantaneous Reading Dust Monitors, USDL/MSHA. Presented at the American Industrial Hygiene Conference, Houston, TX, May 19–23, 1980.
45. Miniram, Model PDM–3: MIE, Bedford, MA 01730.
46. Particle Measuring System, Inc.: 1855 South 57th Court, Boulder, CO 80301.
47. Lilienfeld, P.: Selective Detection of Asbestos Fiber Aerosols by Electromagnetic Alignment and Oscillation. In: Proc. of the seminar, Trends in Aerosol Research II. Schmidt–Ott, A., Ed. University of Duisburg, Duisburg, Germany (June 17, 1991).
48. Page, S.J.: Correlation of the Fibrous Aerosol Monitor with the Optical Membrane Filter Count Technique. U.S. Bureau of Mines, Report of Investigations No. 8467. U.S. Dept. of the Interior, Washington, DC (1980).
49. Phanprasit, W.; Rose, V.E.; Oestenstad, R.K.: Comparison of the Fibrous Aerosol Monitor and the Optical Fiber Count Technique for Asbestos Measurement. Appl. Ind. Hyg. 3:28 (1988).

50. National Institute for Occupational Safety and Health: NIOSH Manual of Analytical Methods, 3rd ed. U.S. Gov't. Printing Office, Washington, DC (February 15, 1984). First Supplement, May 15, 1985. Second Supplement, August 15, 1987.
51. Intersociety Committee: Methods of Air Sampling and Analysis, 3rd ed. J.P. Lodge, Jr., Ed. Lewis Publishers, Inc., Chelsea, MI (1988).
52. American Society for Testing and Materials, D-22 Committee: Book of ASTM Standards, Part 23, Industrial Water; Atmospheric Analysis. ASTM, Philadelphia, PA (annual issue).
53. Pool, R.: The Smallest Chemical Plants. Science 263:1698 (1994).

Chapter 2

Occupational Air Sampling Strategies

James C. Rock, Ph.D., CIH, PE

Occupational Health and Safety Institute, Texas A&M University, College Station, Texas

CONTENTS

Introduction — Why Sample Workplace Air

Occupational air sampling is a key element of occupational exposure control programs. It is an effective tool for setting priorities for interventions to improve workplace health and safety. Air sampling also directly influences health and liability insurance eligibility and insurance rates, and supports compliance decisions based on occupational exposure limits.

Key Definitions

An **Acceptable** (or Tolerable) occupational exposure is one that is acceptable in light of available evidence, including applicable Occupational Exposure Limits (OELs).

The **Action Level (AL)** is defined here as 50% of the OEL.

An **Area Sample** is an air sample taken at a fixed location in a workplace.

Area Monitoring is the process of using real-time air monitoring devices to chart airborne concentration as a function of time at fixed locations.

A **Breathing Zone Sample** is an air sample taken in such a way that the air sampled is within 30 cm (1 ft) of the nostrils of the person being sampled. It is often called a breathing zone sample even when the subject is wearing a respirator.

A 100γ% **Confidence Interval** is a range of values that has a probability, γ, of including the true value of a parameter of the underlying probability distribution function. For example, a 95% confidence interval about the mean will include the mean in 19 of 20 trials. Contrast with Tolerance Interval, which bounds a proportion of the data (a range of data values).

A useful **Goal** is an observable, achievable, and exceedable endpoint.

A **Homogeneous Exposure Group (HEG)** is a group of employees having similar exposures in the sense that monitoring airborne exposures for any one of them provides data useful for evaluating the exposure conditions for all members of the group. An individual may be a member of several homogeneous exposure groups. An HEG may be confirmed by examining data from several of its members. Never assign one without verifying that the exposures are, indeed, homogeneous.

An **Occupational Air Sampling Strategy** is a plan to use available air sampling resources to quantify airborne concentrations in support of an Occupational Exposure Control Program. The strategy guides industrial hygiene actions and decisions toward the goal of accurate exposure estimates for each worker.[1]

An **Occupational Exposure Control Program** is that set of resources devoted by management to ensure that all airborne chemical concentrations are kept below appropriate OELs. Typically, it includes air sampling, biological monitoring, worker hazard communication training, mandatory work practices, material substitution, process isolation or enclosure, local exhaust ventilation, general ventilation, administrative work rules, and personal protective equipment (while better options are being installed or after all other exposure control options have been exhausted).

The **Occupational Exposure Limit (OEL)** is a generic term for a pair of numbers: 1) the criterion airborne concentration and 2) the time period over which workplace concentrations are averaged.[1] Some substances have more than one OEL: a Threshold Limit Value–time-weighted average (TLV–TWA) for 8-hr exposures, a Threshold Limit Value–short-term exposure limit (TLV–STEL) for 15-min exposures, and an absolute ceiling value. The OEL may be a consensus limit such as the American Conference of Governmental Industrial Hygienists (ACGIH) TLV, a regulated limit such as the Occupational Safety and Health Administration Permissible Exposure Limit (OSHA PEL), or an internal exposure limit set by a chemical supplier or by local management. The goal of an occupational exposure program should be to keep all exposures below OELs.

Random Sampling occurs when samples are selected from the statistical population of all relevant air samples so that each sample has an equal probability of being selected. This is a three-step process: 1) define the population of relevant samples, 2) randomly sample that population, and 3) verify that the data support the HEG hypothesis.

A **Strategy** is a careful plan to use available resources effectively to achieve a goal. This chapter outlines a coherent strategy for occupational air sampling that allows reasonable estimates of worker exposure levels with reasonable numbers of samples.

A 100γ% **Tolerance Interval** about the 100p percentile is a range of values that with a probability, γ, contains a fraction, p, of the data; γ is the probability that 100p% of data lies within the stated interval. For example, let UTL be the 90% one-sided upper tolerance limit about the 95th percentile of a distribution. When $UTL <$ OEL, there is 90% confidence that no more than 5% of all data are greater than OEL. Contrast with Confidence Interval, which bounds a range of probable values for a parameter of a parametric distribution representing the data.

Mathematical Symbols

This chapter uses a common statistical convention. Uppercase letters describe parameters estimated from data. Lowercase letters describe individual values of the data. Greek letters describe the true, and usually unknown, parameters of the population being sampled. A parameter preceded by G or g represents a statistic computed for a lognormal distribution.

x = value of a data point

X_p = the (100)(p) percentile, a proportion p of data is $\leq X_p$

M = arithmetic mean of data

Me = median of data, $Me = X_{0.5}$ or $X_{50\%}$

Mo = mode of data, the most probable value of data

S = sample standard deviation of data

GM = sample geometric mean of data

GS = sample geometric standard deviation of data

R = range of data, $[x_{max} - x_{min}]$

p = proportion of a population, $0 \leq p \leq 1$ and $0\% \leq 100p\% \leq 100\%$

$P(\ )$ = probability of the event in parentheses, $0 \leq P \leq 1$

μ = true population mean

σ = true population standard deviation

$g\mu$ = true population geometric mean

$g\sigma$ = true population geometric standard deviation

γ = confidence, probability that a hypothesis is true

n = number of data points in a sample of the population

υ = statistical degrees of freedom, $\upsilon = df = n-1$

UCL = upper confidence limit about the mean for normally distributed data

LCL = lower confidence limit about the mean for normally distributed data

UTL = upper tolerance limit for a proportion p; normal distribution

$GUCL$ = upper confidence limit about GM for lognormally distributed data

$GLCL$ = lower confidence limit about GM for lognormally distributed data

$GUTL$ = upper tolerance limit for a proportion p; lognormal distribution

$t_{p,n}$ = Students' t coefficient, two-sided interval with confidence = p

X_p = upper limit of sample proportion p, $P(x \leq X_p) = p$

$X_{75\%}$ = upper limit of sample percentile, $P(x \leq X_{75\%}) = 0.75$

z_p = normalized z variate, $z_p = [X_p - \mu]/\sigma \approx [X_p - M]/S$

$k_{p,n,\gamma}$ = coefficient for one-sided tolerance interval for normal data

The Cost of Air Sampling

The 20–80 rule is a great management principle to ensure proper investment of overall exposure control program resources. Devote about 20% of industrial hygiene resources to air sampling and priority setting. Devote 80% to training, engineering controls, process improvement, personal protective equipment, recordkeeping, and occupational medicine. This budget allows proper assessment of the relative risk of workplace exposures so that corrective action can be taken on a "worst first" basis.

It is reasonable to expect that over a period of time all airborne concentrations can be reduced below appropriate OELs and personal protective equipment can be eliminated in most workplaces. The half life for process changes is on the order of 3 years, meaning that exposure levels can be expected to drop by one-half about every 3 years once top management starts supporting such a program. As with all other aspects of quality engineering, resulting production efficiencies and product quality improvements generally more than pay for the cost of such efforts.

Purposes of Air Sampling

There are three purposes for occupational air sampling that merit attention in this publication:

- To characterize Air Quality for Occupational Exposure Control
- To characterize Process Emissions
- To characterize Air Quality for Regulatory Enforcement.

Sampling for Occupational Exposure Control — Breathing Zone Sampling

Breathing zone samples are used 1) by compliance officers to enforce OSHA regulations, 2) by insurance companies to assess underwriting risk, and 3) by industry to set priorities for process improvement and to establish locations and tasks requiring interim personal protective equipment. Direct-reading continuous monitors provide warning to workers with potential for exposure to conditions that are immediately dangerous to life and health (IDLH).

Sampling for Process Emissions — Area Sampling

Area samples are used 1) to continuously monitor for leaks to prevent fires, explosions, and IDLH airborne concentrations; 2) for process characterization for engineering control design and engineering control verification (such as laboratory safety hoods or biosafety cabinets); and 3) as basis for design and verification of breathing zone sampling strategies.

Area Monitoring for IDLH Conditions. The area samples that are most critically important in an occupational exposure control program are those that warn of and prevent IDLH exposures. These are provided by continuous monitors connected to both alarms and process control devices. These monitors may be networked to provide coverage not only of workplace emissions, but also of plant boundaries, providing community emergency responders with an early warning alarm as well.

Area Monitoring for Process Improvement and Verification of Installed Engineering Controls. Continuous area monitoring at fixed points in space can be used to correlate airborne contaminant concentrations and concentration gradients with process variables. This technique is widely used in nuclear industries.[2] There is a large and growing literature related to area monitoring as a means for confirming the satisfactory performance of ventilation and air cleaning systems. For principles of air movement, containment, evaporation rates, scrubbing, and filtration factors relevant to this task, see references such as Chapter 21 of this publication on stack and duct sampling,[3] *ASHRAE Handbooks,*[4] *Industrial Ventilation: Engineering Principles,*[5] and *The EPA Engineering Handbook.*[6]

Meteorological data and process data should be recorded simultaneously with area monitoring data. Ventilation systems that work as designed under prevailing wind conditions may fail to exhaust, or worse, may re-entrain contaminants through outside air intakes when winds approach from other directions. Careful area monitoring can reveal and quantify these problems, producing data directly useful to the process engineering team responsible for process improvements.

Sampling for Regulatory Compliance

Statistical tools for compliance sampling are well documented.[7–10] Compliance samples are seldom random samples. A compliance officer uses all available air sampling data, industrial hygiene reports, and his or her own observations of the workplace to identify locations of likely emissions, and selects a maximally exposed employee for a breathing zone sample. If that sample, corrected for all known bias and uncertainty in the sampling and analytical processes, exceeds the PEL, then a citation is possible. Although noncompliance decisions on the basis of one sample are common, it is unusual to reverse such a decision into a compliance decision on the basis of one sample. It is more likely that a statistically significant number of unbiased samples will be required as evidence that the observed sample is a rare event in a well-controlled workplace. The norm is that routine surveillance requires many samples to demonstrate the distribution of exposures, whereas noncompliance may be declared on the basis of one sample that exceeds the standard.

Reasons for an Air Sampling Strategy

A perfect axiomatic air sampling strategy exists.[11] Shannon's Sampling Theorem gives the number of samples needed to obtain perfect information about airborne concentrations in the workplace as a function of space and time.[12] More than 250,000 samples per cubic meter per hour are needed. Assuming a reasonable cost of $10 per data point, an axiomatic air monitoring program would cost $2.5 million per year per cubic meter.

The affordable alternative to perfect information is statistical sampling to estimate true exposure patterns from a small number of samples. The uncertainty associated with statistical exposure estimates is inversely proportional to a fractional power of the number of data points. More samples provide better information than fewer. The air sampling strategy of this chapter provides a framework for determining how many samples are needed. It also provides guidelines for corrective actions to be taken in the workplace based on the distribution of exposures about the applicable OEL.

Occupational Exposure Limits and Averaging Times

An OEL has two parts, a concentration and an averaging time. Common examples include a long-term average exposure, an 8-hr TLV–TWA, a 15-min TLV–STEL, or a 5-min ceiling limit (TLV–C), which should be measured instantaneously but may also be a 15-min average. It is inappropriate to pool, for statistical analysis, data collected with different averaging times. The statistical tools of this chapter work equally well for TLV–TWA, TLV–STEL, and TLV–C data sets. They do not work for a pooled data set containing a mixture of some TWA, some STEL, and some C values.

Occupational Exposure Control Program Goals

Primary Goal — Know and Control All Exposures

A primary goal of an occupational exposure control program is to **be sure that all hazardous exposures are known and controlled to a tolerable level.** This means that employees, supervisors, and managers know their exposures, know and accept their possible health consequences, and participate in mitigating the risk associated with these exposures. A credible occupational air sampling strategy is a necessary foundation for this goal.

Secondary Goal — Continuous Improvement

Establish priorities for remedial action based on air sample data and OELs. Keep the priority list current by adding new risks as they are identified and deleting older risks as engineering controls or process changes achieve tolerable exposure levels. Use the priority list to invest available remedial resources to maximize even marginal improvement of workplace health and safety. This results in continuous improvement of working conditions.

Components of a Sampling Strategy

The recommended air sampling strategy is a closed loop with six components:[1] 1) characterization, 2) risk assessment and sampling priorities, 3) air sampling and analysis, 4) data interpretation, 5) recommendations and reporting, and 6) the reevaluation schedule.

Characterization

The goal of this step is to completely characterize the workplace, the airborne stressors, and the workforce, for the purpose of designing a suitable sampling strategy. If homogeneous exposure groups exist, they provide the considerable benefit of permitting stratified sampling plans with reasonable statistical power from a small number of workplace measurements. Characterization should proceed cautiously, because a growing body of experience shows that each HEG must be confirmed by data analysis.[13]

Workplace characterization starts with a complete inventory of chemical, physical, and biological agents. Plant diagrams should be highlighted to show the location of all process steps and equipment likely to release contaminants into the workplace air. If prior air sampling data exist, those data should be used to confirm the inventory and improve the maps.

Stressor characterization uses OSHA-mandated material safety data sheet (MSDS) data and process models to compile estimates of airborne concentration levels under process conditions. Concentration estimates should be compared with applicable OELs and estimated concentration contours overlayed on plant and process diagrams to identify locations and personnel where air sampling may be needed.

Workforce characterization involves obtaining task assignment data, demographic data and health data for all members of the workforce. Evaluation of these data can discover clusters of occupationally related symptoms. If present, task locations should be compared with the concentration contours from the workplace characterization. This often leads directly to high priority sampling requirements.

An HEG is a group of employees who have comparable exposures. Each group may be tentatively identified from data on the workplace, the stressors, and the workforce. The HEG promotes air sampling efficiencies because a breathing zone air sample from any member of the group is considered representative of the exposures received by all members of the group. Each HEG must be confirmed by statistical analysis of breathing zone samples representing that group (see "Descriptive Statistics," page 24).

TABLE 2-1. Exposure Ranking

Rank	Description	Comment
0	No exposure	Observed concentrations less than 10% of the OEL
1	Low exposure	Observed concentrations less than the AL (50% OEL)
2	Moderate exposure	Frequent exposure at concentrations below the AL or infrequent exposure at concentrations between the AL and OEL
3	High exposure	Frequent exposure at concentrations near the OEL or infrequent contact with the stressor at concentrations above the OEL
4	Very high exposure	Frequent contact with the stressor at concentrations above the OEL

Risk Assessment and Sampling Priorities

Risk assessment is a multidimensional problem involving factors such as exposure levels, health consequences of overexposure, whether the risk is voluntarily accepted, whether the perception is that alternate risks are higher, the immediacy of consequences if the risk is accepted, and who is at risk. Two parameters suffice to manage an occupational air sampling strategy: the exposure ranking and the health effect ranking.

Exposure ranking is a monotonic semisubjective scale based on all available air sampling data and on process models that predict both airborne concentrations and their frequency of occurrence. There are many ways to define the scale, and an appropriate one should be selected in each instance. Table 2-1 illustrates the concept.

The **no exposure level** of OEL/10 is the level below which recurring sampling is not required. It is synonymous with the unexposed worker level in the 7th edition of this text.[14] It was based on an American Society of Heating, Refrigerating and Air-Conditioning Engineers, Inc. (ASHRAE) guideline that concentrations in office spaces should be kept below 10% of the OEL. For many years, the population standard for ionizing radiation has been 10% of the occupational standard.[15] A new report recommends 10% of the annual intake limit for radioisotopes as the threshold below which occupational breathing zone monitoring is not required.[2] The low exposure level is the level below which minimal recurring breathing zone sampling is required. It is based

TABLE 2-2. Health Effect Ranking

Rank	Description	Comment
0	NONE	No known permanent health effects. No treatment needed; no sick leave involved.
1	MILD	Reversible health effects with suspected consequences. Medical treatment usually not required for recovery. Sick leave is seldom involved.
2	SERIOUS	Severe reversible health effects. Medical treatment required for recovery. Lost time and sick leave are usually involved.
3	CRITICAL	Irreversible health effects; not treatable. New life style required to adapt to the disability.
4	IDLH	Life threatening or totally disabling injury or illness.

on the NIOSH action level concept (50% of the OEL).[7]

Health effect ranking is based on the consequences of exposure to the stressor. It, too, is structured on a five-point semisubjective scale that can be tailored to fit various situations. Table 2-2 displays commonly used definitions.

Sampling Priority

Sampling priorities should be set on the basis of the exposure ranking (ER) and the health effects ranking (HER) scales. As Table 2-3 shows, there is a very low priority for sampling exposures with a score of (ER,HER) = (0,0) and a very high priority for sampling exposures with a score of (4,4). In fact, it is good policy to require immediate cessation of any process producing a (4,4) ranking until steps can be taken to reduce the exposures. It is appropriate for an industrial hygienist to use professional judgment for intermediate priority scores and to move the assigned priority up or down one level depending on the size of the exposed population or other factors not considered by the health effect and exposure rankings.

TABLE 2-3. Breathing Zone Sampling Priorities

Health Effect	Sampling Priority*					
4	M	H	H	VH	VH	
3	L	M	H	H	VH	
2	L	M	M	H	H	
1	T	L	M	M	H	
0	T	T	L	L	M	
	0	1	2	3	4	Exposure

*T (trivial), L (low), M (medium), H (high), VH (very high)

Air Sampling and Analysis

The resources available for air sampling should be allocated in a way that ensures priority for the highest ranked classes while reserving adequate resources for lower priority classes because unexpected results do occur during sampling campaigns. About 80% of the available effort should be devoted to the high and very high risk categories and about 20% to the other categories, as in Table 2-4.

Data Interpretation

Air sampling data must be interpreted in the context of all available information. There are three decisions possible with regard to each exposure scenario:

- The exposures are acceptable (below the OEL)
- The exposures are unacceptably high (above the OEL)
- There are insufficient data to make a decision.

The sampling program should provide data for making one of the first two decisions. The goal of an exposure control program is to make process and administrative changes until all exposures become tolerable. Thus, the insufficient data problem must be dealt with by either collecting more data or making the decision that exposures are unacceptable.

Assuming there are sufficient data of sufficient quality, it must be determined whether the data support the decision of acceptable or unacceptable exposures. Statistical tools for making this decision are summarized below.

Descriptive Statistics

The first step in analysis of every data set is to compute descriptive statistics and plot the data on

TABLE 2-4. Budget Proportions for Air Sampling

Risk	Budget	20% for Sampling	80% for Intervention
Very High	55%	11.0%	44.0%
High	24%	4.8%	19.2%
Moderate	12%	2.4%	9.6%
Low	6%	1.2%	4.8%
Very Low	3%	0.6%	2.4%

probit and log-probit scales. Methods for computing descriptive statistics and confidence and tolerance intervals are given in "Statistical Tools for IH Decision-making," page 30. An example is provided in "Example of Data Interpretation," page 33. The descriptive statistics are used in setting priorities and at decision points in the decision flow diagram (Figure 2-1). The graphs are used to determine whether parametric hypothesis testing is appropriate. If the data do plot as a straight line on either graph, then the parametric tests described in the following sections can be used to make statistically sound decisions.

If the data do not plot as a straight line, or if the data have a *GS* > 4.5, it is likely that a bimodal or multimodal distribution exists.(2) Such data usually do not represent an HEG and an analysis of variance may be used to confirm the nonhomogeneity of the presumed HEG.(16) When data fail to support the hypothesis of an HEG, decisions cannot be based on parametric hypothesis testing. In these cases, a nonparametric tolerance interval test may be used to supplement a decision based on professional judgment (Table 2-12; located at the end of this chapter).

Statistics for Compliance

The NIOSH sampling strategy is at the heart of compliance decisions.(7) It is based on a 95% confidence interval about the mean of a group of samples. If the 95% upper confidence limit (*UCL*) is below the OEL, the exposure observed is in compliance. If the 95% lower confidence limit (*LCL*) is above the OEL, the exposure observed is out of compliance. If the OEL is between the *LCL* and the *UCL*, no decision is possible at 95% confidence.

An extension of this concept is applied to a single sample. Under the assumption that the relative standard deviation of a sample is less than 25% (the variability allowed for an approved air sampling method), a confidence interval is assumed for a single sample. This ignores spatial and temporal concentration gradients in the workplace air, and accounts only for random variation in air sampling and chemical analysis.

Statistics for Exposures to Chronic Stressors

For stressors that pose a chronic risk, the confidence interval around the mean is a good estimator of long-term risk. Exposures for which the 95% *UCL* < OEL are usually deemed acceptable.

The data used should be representative of long term exposures. This means that the sampling strategy should have an equal probability of sampling during all relevant conditions: day of the week, week of the year, under surge production or changeover production, and shift (if there is more than one).

Statistics for Exposures to Acute Stressors

For stressors that pose an acute risk, a one-sided tolerance interval (at 90% confidence) around the 95th percentile of the exposure distribution should be computed. A determination that the *UTL* < OEL establishes 90% confidence that no more than 5% of all exposures exceed the OEL.

Guidelines for the Number of Samples Needed

For **compliance sampling**, one or more samples determine whether the exposure sampled is in or out of compliance. This technique does not predict overall conditions in the workplace; it is valid only for estimating the meaning of the exposure(s) observed at the time and place of the compliance sampling campaign, as specified in a regulation.

For stressors posing **chronic risk**, a minimum of six samples is recommended to obtain reasonable estimates of the 95% *UCL* on the mean of all exposures in the workplace.

For **estimating the variance** of any data set, a minimum of 11 samples is recommended. For an HEG with n members, the larger of 11 samples or SQRT(n) samples should be collected.

For stressors posing **acute risk**, to test the hypothesis that no more than 100p% of exposures exceed the OEL, the one-sided *UTL* can be estimated from a minimum of $(1+1/p)$ samples. Thus, at least 21 samples are required to obtain a usable *UTL* (upper tolerance limit on the proportion p) to test that no more than $100p$ = 5% of all exposures exceed the OEL (see "Tolerance Interval on the nth Percentile," Table 2-11 [located at the end of this chapter], and Equation 8 for details of this parametric test).

Nonparametric data sets usually require 30–100 samples to achieve useful statistical power for decision-making. For data sets not suited to the hypothesis tests mentioned above (because the data do not fit established statistical distributions),[A] nonparametric forms of the tolerance interval test are recommended.

It is common to find IH reports that declare an HEG acceptable on the basis that all observed samples were below the OEL. When the data are nonparametric, the obtainable confidence level is surprisingly small. For example, if the largest observation of 21 nonparametric samples is less than the OEL, Table 2-12 shows that there is only 26% confidence that 95% of the population lies below the OEL (see "Nonparametric Tolerance Intervals," page 32, for more details).

If 90% confidence is needed with nonparametric data, information beyond the scope of this chapter is needed.

[A] IH data often fit either a normal or a lognormal distribution.

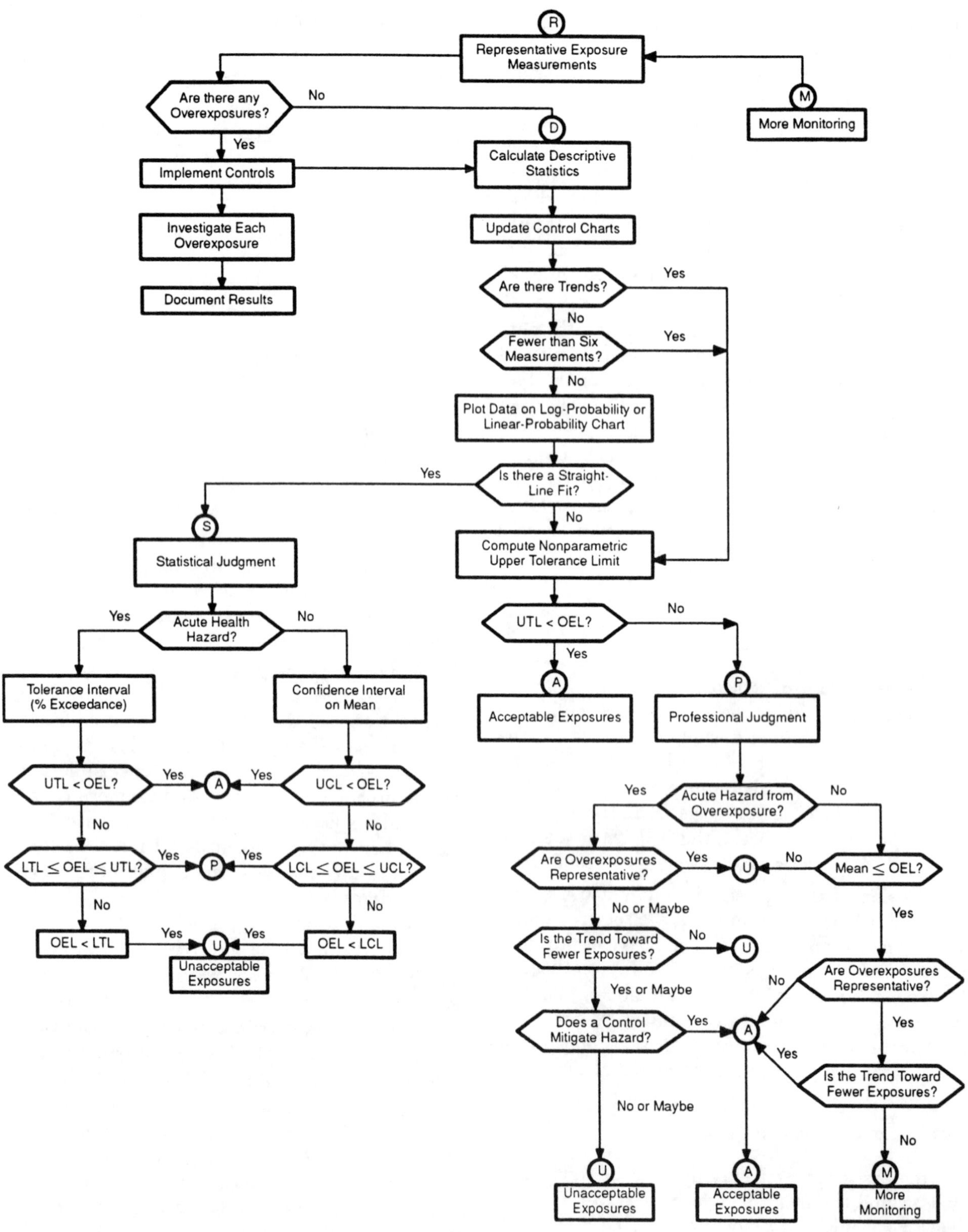

FIGURE 2-1. Decision Flow Diagram. Rectangles represent conclusions, processes leading to conclusions, or required actions. Hexagons represent decision points that branch through the decision flow diagram. Circles are connectors. Circles alone represent branching out of the decision flow diagram. Circles touching a rectangle represent the entry point for decisions that branched out elsewhere. Circles are identified by a letter loosely representing their function in the decision-making process: A - the exposures are acceptable (tolerable); M - more monitoring is needed; P - use professional judgment to decide; R - restart the monitoring process; S - use parametric statistical hypothesis testing; U - the exposures are unacceptable.

For example, to obtain 90% confidence that at least 95% of all exposures in an HEG are less than the OEL, 170 samples must be obtained, and all of them must be less than the OEL (see Table VI.1 of Reference 1).

For **IDLH situations**, higher confidence levels are required, and good practice dictates continuous monitoring. Statistical considerations confirm this. Ceiling values should be considered, and 99% confidence that no more than 1% of exposures exceed the OEL should be required.

If the data are parametric, Table 2-11 shows that 50 samples are required to obtain $K = 3.124$. Then, $UTL = M + K^*S$ for normal data or $\ln(GUTL) = \ln(GM) + K^*\ln(GS)$ for lognormal data. The desired confidence is obtained if $UTL <$ OEL or if $GUTL <$ OEL (see "Tolerance Interval on the nth Percentile").

For nonparametric data, Table 2-12 shows that with 100 samples, all below the OEL, there is only 26% confidence that 99% of all exposures are less than the OEL. Again resorting to an outside reference (Table VI.1 of Reference 1), all of 500 samples must be below the OEL to obtain 99% confidence that no more than 1% of all exposures exceed the OEL.

In an 8-hr shift, there is little difference between 500 samples and continuous monitoring. In fact, when using an instrument like a variable path infrared analyzer with a time constant of 50 seconds, there is no difference.

The Decision Flow Diagram

The decision flow diagram of Figure 2-1 systematizes the relationship between statistical data analysis and professional judgment. An earlier version was published in the AIHA Exposure Assessment Strategies Monograph.[1]

Figure 2-1 shows the overall flow diagram for deciding whether workplace exposures are tolerable. Starting at the top, in circle R, the first step is to collect representative samples. The small branch at the upper left emphasizes the importance of investigating and documenting every overexposure.[B] The main path emphasizes the importance of evaluating every data set, even when an observed overexposure requires stopping or altering the process. These two paths run parallel and both paths should be followed.

The second step is to compute the descriptive statistics. The third step is to select "Statistical Judgment" or "Professional Judgment." If Statistical Judgment is selected, the nature of the hazard determines whether a tolerance interval or a confidence interval test is to be applied. If Professional Judgment is selected, the decision is based on the data using rules of thumb established by a consensus of practicing industrial hygienists.[1] Such decisions should always be checked with nonparametric statistics so that the decision-maker understands the level of confidence associated with the decision.

The fourth step depends on the decision. If exposures are unacceptable, immediate action is required: the process must be stopped and changed before restarting. At a minimum, personal protective equipment should be issued until such time as engineering controls can be designed, budgeted, and installed. If more sampling is needed to make a decision, it should be done immediately. If the exposures are deemed acceptable, a time should be established for the next sampling campaign.

The flow diagram for descriptive statistics is entered through circle D touching the rectangle "Calculate Descriptive Statistics." Note that the first step is to update *X*-bar and *R* charts and check for trends (if prior data exist). If there are trends, prior data cannot be combined with present data for statistical decision-making; professional judgment is needed. Professional judgment is also used if there are fewer than six total samples. Finally, the data should be checked for fit to normal or lognormal distributions by plotting on linear probability or log probability paper and checking for a straight line. Note that a straight-line fit is unlikely if either of the following is true: the identified homogeneous exposure group is not homogeneous (could also be tested by an analysis of variance,[16] given sufficient data); or the exposure conditions are changing between samples. If a good straight-line fit is found, statistical decision making is entered through circle S. If the data are not well represented by either of these distributions, the nonparametric UTL is computed (Table 2-12). If $UTL <$ OEL, the workplace is considered acceptable; otherwise, professional judgment is the most likely decision-making tool.

The Professional Judgment aspect of the decision-making process is entered through circle P touching the Professional Judgment rectangle. If all observed samples are below the OEL and there are at least six of them, the workplace is acceptable.[C] If there is at least one overexposure, the decision depends on whether there is an acute hazard and whether the samples represent normal process conditions.

The Statistical Judgment aspect of the decision-making process is entered through circle S touching the Statistical Judgment rectangle. The first decision is whether the health effect is acute or chronic. If chronic,

[B] OSHA treats exposure as the measured breathing zone concentration, irrespective of personal protective equipment. Thus, overexposures observed in air sampling do not always represent health threats.

[C] When using this criterion for decision-making, be sure to check the table for the one-sided tolerance interval for nonparametric data. This will provide the level of confidence of the decision at hand.

TABLE 2-5. Reevaluation Frequency from Risk Ranking

Risk Ranking	Reevaluation Frequency
Very High	Continuous monitoring
High	Monthly to quarterly
Moderate	Quarterly to annually
Low	1–3 years
Trivial	3–5 years

hypothesis testing about the confidence interval on the mean (six samples minimum) is used. If acute, hypothesis testing about a chosen tolerance interval (90th or 95th percentile of the exposure distribution) is used. This usually requires at least 18 samples. If a decision can be made, the appropriate branch leads to that decision point: A for acceptable and U for unacceptable. If a statistically significant decision cannot be made, the appropriate branch is P for Professional Judgment.

The "Unacceptable Exposure" branch is entered through circle U. Note that each overexposure must be investigated and documented by both the industrial hygiene and the occupational medicine teams. The industrial hygiene purpose is to determine whether the events were representative or resulted from process upset conditions. The occupational medicine purpose is to treat the patient if disease or injury resulted and to document the clinical status for future epidemiology. Corrective measures are implemented before the offending process is restarted. Air sampling to verify the corrective measures is restarted at circle R.

The "Acceptable Exposure" branch is entered through circle A. Note that results are documented. More monitoring or investigation is called for if the data are acceptable but showing an adverse trend. Otherwise, scheduling the next sampling campaign may be based on program policies using guidelines in the "Reevaluation" section.

Recommendations and Reporting

The industrial hygiene decision about each stressor associated with each task must be recorded and communicated. The purpose of this step of the exposure assessment strategy is to document the air quality in the workplace, inform employees of their exposures, set priorities for process improvements, and schedule follow-up evaluations of each process.

If breathing zone samples represent environmental concentrations, but do not represent personnel exposures because of personal protective equipment, these conditions must be stated. Further guidance on written reports is available from a variety of sources.[1]

Reevaluation

An experienced industrial hygienist should walk through every process at least once a year and schedule air sampling of each process at least once every 3–5 years. Higher risk processes need more frequent attention in the form of air samples taken on monthly to annual intervals.

The risk ranking is a good basis for assigning frequency of reevaluation (see Table 2-5). Because the risk ranking changes with process changes, this linkage ensures appropriate changes in industrial hygiene sampling frequency in response to material substitutions and process improvements.

Obviously, there are circumstances that will accelerate scheduled review of a process, task, or homogeneous exposure group: 1) a diagnosed occupational illness, 2) an employee concern, or 3) any significant changes in operations or facilities.

It is recommended that policy require an industrial hygiene sign-off on all plans for facility or process changes. Otherwise, such process changes may go unnoticed until the next scheduled industrial hygiene walk-through (up to one year later). This is the primary reason for an annual walk-through of all areas, including those not otherwise scheduled for air sampling.

Professional Judgment versus Statistical Requirements

Number of Samples

The required number of samples depends on the goals for a specific sampling campaign. The original NIOSH sampling strategy monograph provides guidance for estimating peak exposures, short-term exposures, and 8-hr TWA exposures.[7] The resultant rules of thumb are that at least 6 samples are required for a valid estimate of the confidence interval around the mean and more than 11 are required to estimate the variance. At the upper end, one major corporation restricts to 18 the maximum number of samples for characterizing a single exposure scenario.[17]

An HEG with many workers should receive a higher proportion of the sampling budget than one with a few workers. It is reasonable to make the number of samples proportional to the square root of the number of workers in the HEG.[14] For example, 16 workers need 4 samples (rounded up to 6 if statistical analysis is needed), 36 workers need 6 samples, and 100 workers need 10 samples. If there is need to check the homogeneity of the HEG, it is appropriate to double these numbers for each HEG.

If each full-shift exposure estimate exceeding an OSHA PEL is treated as a violation, there are incentives to reduce the number of samples taken so that the number of such violations is minimized.[18] Under such conditions, too few samples are taken to adequately determine the degree of risk from airborne contaminants. A better policy would encourage voluntary samples so long as corrective measures are taken when justified by the data.

Finally, the number of samples needed depends on the rate of variation of concentrations over space and time. When this is the case, early papers discussing the concepts of correlation, covariance, and averaging time should be reviewed[19–21] and supplemented with current quality control and reliability references.[22,23]

Whom to Sample

The usual procedure for obtaining representative unbiased samples is to randomly pick the set of exposures for air sampling so that every possible exposure has an equal chance of being selected. The distribution of exposures observed in these random samples is assumed to be similar to the distribution of exposures in the sampled population. In contrast to this conventional wisdom, a recent report shows that there are circumstances where a random sampling strategy requires more samples than a properly selected deterministic sampling scheme.[24] For now, deterministic schemes for industrial hygiene sampling are rare.

Sometimes, biased samples are desired. In industrial hygiene, the worst-case exposures or the most exposed individual(s) are important.[25] If there exists a definable group of such exposures, then it is reasonable to sample them randomly and to apply statistical tests to the resulting data. Clearly, if such exposures are within the OEL, it can be safely concluded that ordinary exposures in the same homogeneous exposure group are acceptable. However, caution is in order if the samples are all drawn from the 2% of exposures that are truly the worst exposures, because it is unlikely that the data will fit either a normal or a lognormal distribution. The most likely distribution will be the exponential distribution.[26] The tools in "Example of Data Interpretation," page 33, will not help with analysis of such data.

To intentionally sample high exposure periods, it is necessary to identify those periods. Where there is visible dust, a powerful odor, or eye and upper respiratory irritation, the exposures are obvious. In these cases, the workers at the operation can furnish invaluable information, if asked. In other cases, there are operations, which by their nature, cause increased contaminant generation and higher concentrations; e.g., when a normally enclosed or covered operation is done with doors open or covers off, solvent is wiped or sprayed, or materials are handled outside of an enclosure. Such operations have inadequate control.

Limitations of Statistical Decision-making

The use of statistical criteria is based on the premise that the sample truly represents the population of interest. When some underlying feature of the sampled operation changes, previous data have limited utility for predicting the distribution of exposures in the "new" operation. Further, a data set containing 20 data points is unable to make usable predictions about the upper 5% of the distribution, and a data set containing 100 data points is useless for the upper 1% of the distribution (see "Guidelines for the Number of Samples Needed," page 26).

For example, high concentrations of metals in urban areas occur significantly more frequently than is predicted by the lognormal distribution that adequately describes the central tendencies of the metal samples.[27] Predicting the concentrations associated with the upper 1%, 2%, or even 5% of exposures from statistical air sampling data is seldom (if ever) justified.

Averaging Period

OELs are ordered pairs of numbers: an average allowable airborne concentration and an averaging period of time appropriate to the health hazard involved.[27] For pneumoconiosis-producing dusts, it is the cumulative exposure over a period of months and years which determines the probability of a diagnosis of pneumoconiosis and the severity of the adverse health effects. For coal mine dust exposures, an average over 10 working shifts was used in the legislation to determine the application of the mandatory respirable dust standard. For lead, in most cases, it is the integrated exposure over weeks which determines the probability of an excessive blood lead concentration. For carbon monoxide, averaging times measured in minutes are necessary to provide adequate protection at concentrations above 50 ppm.

There is a biological basis for single-shift averages for many chemicals. During nonworking hours, the body can metabolize and/or excrete the material inhaled over the work period. For this reason, the ACGIH Chemical Substances TLV Committee has used a TLV–TWA over full work shifts since the first TLV list.[14] However, these values may be modified by STEL or C requirements. In the enforcement of PELs, OSHA uses the average concentration over an 8-hr working shift.

Other OEL pairs are used by various standard setting bodies. The ACGIH TLV Committee defines 8-hr TLV–TWA, 15-min TLV–STEL, TLV–C, and excursion limits.[28] The TLV–TWA is measured over an 8-hr shift in a 5-day, 40-hr work week. The TLV–STEL is measured over a 15-min period during a shift, and that concentration should not occur more than 4 times per day nor be repeated within a period of 60 mins. The

TLV–C should not be exceeded at any time and should be measured over as short a period as possible, not exceeding 15 mins. When more than one TLV is assigned, each must be observed to protect against all possible pathways of injury and illness.[D]

The ACGIH guidance on styrene exposures is a useful means for illustrating how these values work together.[28] The average exposure over an 8-hr period is to be kept below the TWA of 213 mg/m^3 and no 15-min average is to exceed 426 mg/m^3. Further, the concentration of 426 mg/m^3 should not be approached more than 4 times per day and should not be approached more than once in any hour. Finally, the semiquantitative biological exposure index (BEI) limits the styrene in venous blood to 0.55 mg/L at the end of a work shift and to 0.02 mg/L at the beginning of a work shift. A properly designed workplace involving exposures near the STEL would need to keep other exposures well below the TWA to keep the 8-hr exposure below the TWA. If the full shift exposures approach the TWA, then 16 hrs of rest are likely to be needed to achieve the allowed beginning of shift BEI of 0.02 mg/L.

Statistical Tools for IH Decision-making

Any set of data can be characterized by its descriptive statistics and by its probability distribution as plotted on probability paper. This should always be the first step in data interpretation. The sections that follow provide a concise review of statistical concepts and the section entitled "Example of Data Interpretation," page 33, provides an example of the application of these concepts to industrial hygiene data.

Descriptive Statistics

Descriptive statistics are easily computed for any set of numbers and provide an invaluable starting point for data interpretation. Common and useful descriptive statistics include measures of central tendency (mean, median, mode, and geometric mean) and measures of dispersion (range, standard deviation, and geometric standard deviation).

Most scientific calculators and spreadsheets have a function, "Σ+," in which values can be accumulated. One or two additional commands will calculate the mean, *M*, and the sample standard deviation, *S*, for any data set. The geometric mean, *GM*, and the geometric standard deviation, *GS*, are calculated nearly as easily. First, the logarithm of every data point, ln(x), is computed. Using this transformed set of data, the calculator or spreadsheet returns ln(*GM*) from its function for the mean and ln(*GS*) from its function for the sample standard deviation. The antilog of these two numbers is the geometric mean, *GM*, and the geometric standard deviation, *GS*. Finally, the mode (*Mo*), the median (*Me*), and the range (*R*) are estimated. The mode is the value that occurs most frequently. The median is the value at the midpoint of the distribution: 50% of all data are larger and 50% are smaller. The range is the difference between the largest and smallest data point. The descriptive statistics for a set of n data points are summarized below.

$$R = [x_{max} - x_{min}]$$

$$Me = x_m; \quad \text{where } m = \frac{n+1}{2}, \text{ for } n \text{ odd}$$

$$= \frac{x_m + x_{m+1}}{2}; \text{ where } m = \frac{n}{2}, \text{ for } n \text{ even} \quad (1)$$

$$M = \frac{1}{n}\sum_1^n x_i$$

$$S = \sqrt{\frac{1}{n-1}\sum_1^n (x_i - M)^2} \quad (2)$$

$$\ln(GM) = \frac{1}{n}\sum_1^n \ln(x_i)$$

$$\ln(GS) = \sqrt{\frac{1}{n-1}\sum_1^n [(\ln(x_i) - \ln(GM)]^2} \quad (3)$$

A remarkable amount of insight is available from descriptive statistics. If $M = Me = Mo$, then the data are symmetrically distributed around the mean and the normal distribution is likely to fit the data fairly well. If [$Me = GM$], and [$Mo < GM < M$], then the data are skewed to the right and the lognormal distribution is likely to fit the data fairly well. If neither of these rules fit, or if $R < S$, the data are not satisfactorily modeled by either the normal or the lognormal distribution and nonparametric statistical tests are called for.

Because one or the other of these two distributions will fit almost any industrial hygiene data set, a brief review is presented in the following paragraphs. When data are symmetrically distributed around the average value, the normal distribution provides considerable computational advantage. When data are skewed so that they cluster between zero and the mean on the low side and spread out from the mean on the high side, the lognormal distribution is the distribution of choice. Its computational advantage is that after taking the loga-

[D]See also, 29 CFR 1910.1000, Tables Z-1, Z-2, and Z-3 for OSHA PELs using 8 hr, 15 min, and other specified averaging times.

rithm of each data point, the resulting transformed data set is normally distributed. Industrial hygienists competent with the statistical techniques for normally distributed data are qualified to interpret their air sampling data. Important statistical tools include hypothesis testing, confidence intervals on the mean, tolerance intervals about the $p\%$ point on the distribution, and analysis of variance (ANOVA) testing.

Normal Distribution

The normal distribution is a symmetrical distribution for which all three measures of central tendency are equal: $M = Me = Mo$. It has the "nice" property that it is entirely described by two parameters: its population mean, μ, and its population standard deviation, σ. It is widely tabulated[1,29,30] in terms of the normalized variable, $z = (x - \mu)/\sigma$. In most industrial hygiene situations, the true values of μ and σ are unknown and unknowable. Instead, their unbiased estimators, the sample mean, M, and the sample standard deviation, S, are used. The normalized variable for industrial hygiene becomes $z = (x–M)/S$. The probability that a sample is less than some value X can be read from a z-table entered at $z = (X–M)/S$.

The mathematical expression describing a normal distribution is:

$$f(z) = \frac{d\,F(z)}{d\,z} = \frac{1}{\sqrt{2\pi}}\; e^{-\left(\frac{z^2}{2}\right)} \qquad \textbf{(4)}$$

$$f(x) = \frac{d\,F(x)}{d\,x} = \frac{1}{S\sqrt{2\pi}}\; e^{-\frac{1}{2}\left(\frac{x-M}{S}\right)^2}$$

$$\text{with } z \equiv \frac{x-M}{S} \text{ and } dz = \frac{dx}{S}$$

where: $F(\bullet)$ = the probability distribution function
$f(\bullet)$ = the probability density function
M = the mean value of data
S = the sample standard deviation of data

Lognormal Distribution

The lognormal distribution is a skewed distribution with the "nice" property that it, too, is entirely described by two parameters: its population geometric mean, $g\mu$, and its population standard deviation, $g\sigma$. Further, the logarithmic transformation allows lognormal data to be analyzed as normally distributed data in terms of the standard normal variate defined as $z = (\ln\{x\}–\ln\{g\mu\})/(\ln\{g\sigma\})$. The true values of $g\mu$ and $g\sigma$ are seldom available for industrial hygiene air sample data. Instead, the unbiased estimates of the geometric mean, GM, and the geometric standard deviation, GS, are used. In this case, the normalized variable is $z = (\ln\{x\}–\ln\{GM\})/(\ln\{GS\})$. The probability that a sample is less than some value X can be read from a z-table entered at $z = (\ln\{X\}–\ln\{GM\})/(\ln\{GS\})$.

The lognormal distribution is easily used for hypothesis testing. First, the logarithm of each data point is computed. That computation produces a set of numbers that fit the normal distribution. Second, these normally distributed numbers can be used in all the standard tests, including hypothesis testing, confidence intervals, and tolerance intervals. Third, the log-transformed numbers must be transformed back to concentration units with an antilog function before reporting results. The procedure is more easily illustrated than described (see "Example of Data Interpretation," page 33).

There is one word of caution, however. For a lognormal distribution, the "nice" measure of central tendency is the geometric mean. It is equal to the median value of the data, not the mean value. The geometric mean should not be compared to exposure limits; rather, the arithmetic mean is compared to exposure limits. To emphasize the point, consider a set of data adequately characterized by two numbers, GM and GS. The mean, median, and mode for this distribution are given by:

$$M = e^{\left[\ln(GM) + \frac{[\ln(GS)]^2}{2}\right]}$$
$$Me = e^{[\ln(GM)]} \qquad \textbf{(5)}$$
$$Mo = e^{[\ln(GM) - [\ln(GS)]^2]}$$

Industrial hygiene standards are based on average exposures, and the average is computed as the sum of all data points divided by the number of those points, no matter the shape of the underlying probability distribution. Only like kinds of data may be averaged; that is, average all members of a set of 8-hr samples, or all members of a set of 15-min samples, but do not average some 8-hr with some 15-min samples.

Probability Plotting

Probability paper is available in two forms: linear versus probability axes and logarithmic versus probability axes. It is useful because data that are normally distributed plot as a straight line on linear versus probability paper and data that are lognormal plot as a straight line on log versus probability paper. From such plots, it is easy to accommodate missing data points, as from samples that were below the analytical detection limit or where breakthrough showed that the concentration was above the range of the sampling method.

Data are prepared for plotting by arranging data points in order of increasing value and numbering them from 1 to n. In a second column, the logarithms of the data points are arranged in order of increasing value. The plotting position on the probability axis is computed by the rank order of the data point divided by

(n+1). The data are then plotted and inspected for straight line behavior.

Standard scientific calculators or spreadsheets are sufficient to calculate the sample mean and the sample standard deviation from rank ordered data. The best fit straight line is then easily plotted by noting that [*M*–*S*] plots at 16%, *M* at 50%, and [*M*+*S*] at 84% for normal data on linear-probability paper, and that [*GM*/*GS*] plots at 16%, *GM* at 50%, and [*GM***GS*] at 84% for lognormal data on log-probability paper.

Truncated or Censored Data

In some exposure populations, several data points in each sample may be at or below the detection limit. In other samples, the true concentration is known to be above the reported concentration because breakthrough was detected at the time of analysis. In these cases, care is required to calculate an estimate for *GS*. It is not correct to assign some small value to samples below the detection limit and a large value to those with breakthrough and simply calculate descriptive statistics. If this is done, $GS \geq 5$ are often seen. A better technique is to assign a rank order to each data point, whether it has a usable value or not. The usable data points should be plotted in their assigned position and a line drawn through them. The intersection of that line with the plotting position for missing data is a usable estimate for the true value of those samples that were either below the detection limit or above the saturation limit.

Confidence Interval on the Mean

For normally distributed data, the confidence interval on the mean is computed using Students' *t* distribution (see Table 2-9 at the end of the chapter). Values for the coefficient $t_{p,n}$ are widely tabulated in terms of *n*, the number of data points in the sample and the probability, *p*, that the true mean, μ, lies between the *UCL* and the *LCL*. Using the value of *t* appropriate to a data set, *UCL* and *LCL* are easily computed:

for normal data:

$$UCL = M + \left(t_{p,\,df}\right)\left(\frac{S}{\sqrt{n}}\right);\ LCL = M - \left(t_{p,\,df}\right)\left(\frac{S}{\sqrt{n}}\right)$$

for lognormal data:

$$\ln(GUCL) = \ln(GM) + \left(t_{p,\,df}\right)\left(\frac{\ln(GS)}{\sqrt{n}}\right); \qquad (6)$$

$$\ln(GLCL) = \ln(GM) - \left(t_{p,\,df}\right)\left(\frac{\ln(GS)}{\sqrt{n}}\right)$$

Percentiles of a Distribution

When peak exposures are of concern rather than long-term average exposures, it is important to know the percentiles of normally distributed data (see Table 2-10 at the end of the chapter). These values are found by use of standard *z* tables. To find the value X_p such that the probability that a random sample *x* is less than X_p, is *p*, find z_p from the *z* table and then compute X_p:

$$X_p = M + (z_p)\,(S);\quad \text{for normal data}$$

and (7)

$$GX_p = e^{+[\ln(GM) + [z_p]\,[\ln(GS)]\,]};\quad \text{for lognormal data.}$$

Tolerance Interval on the nth Percentile

When peak exposures represent IDLH conditions, it is important to have higher confidence in exposure data than is given by the best estimate of the percentile. For that purpose, the one-sided tolerance interval provides a quantitative level of confidence (Table 2-11).[31] It says that the 100*p* percentile is less than the *UTL* with a probability γ when it is estimated from a sample containing n data points. The *UTL* is easily computed from a table of *k* factors. The value of $k_{p,n,\gamma}$ depends on the desired value of *p*, the number of data points (*n*) and the desired confidence (γ):

$$UTL = M + (k_{p,n,\gamma})\ \ (S);\quad \text{for normal data} \qquad (8)$$

$$GUTL = e^{+[\ln(GM) + (k_{p,n,\gamma})\,(\ln(GS))]};\ \text{for lognormal data}$$

Nonparametric Tolerance Intervals

When the available data fail to fit either the normal distribution or the lognormal distribution, professional judgment is needed to make a decision about the quality of the workplace. Although the decision flow diagram provides some guidelines in the professional judgment portion of the diagram, it should not be used in isolation. When a set of data has no measured exposures above the OEL, those data should be considered in terms of the tabulated confidence levels in the table of nonparametric tolerance intervals. Only after the level of confidence is evident should a decision be made that a workplace is acceptable with no further improvements.

On most occasions when data are neither normally nor lognormally distributed, there is a problem with the data. Often the data are from two or more HEGs. This important possibility is illustrated in the "Example of Data Interpretation." A second common possibility is that there are undetected changes in the workplace occurring between samples, so that the samples are not from a single distribution.

Workplace exposures vary both systematically and

randomly. Statistical analysis of data that contain systematic variations can be misleading, usually leading to an overestimate of the variance of the data and an overprediction of the *UCL* and the *UTL* as well as an overstatement of the acute health risk represented by the data.

Software and Useful References

All of the calculations described in this section are contained in a software package developed by Dupont and available for DOS-based computers.[17] The user interface is rather awkward, but it has remarkable features allowing decision-making with either normal or lognormal statistics for sample sizes from 6 to 18. If the data do not fit parametric assumptions very well, the program defaults to a nonparametric decision algorithm. Finally, it forces a decision with 18 samples instead of requiring the additional sampling called for by the NIOSH sampling strategy.

Example of Data Interpretation

The following sections present an example scenario incorporating the air sampling strategies discussed in this chapter. For this example, an HEG of 91 painters was surveyed. These workers sprayed paint two shifts per day. The data from the survey show that airborne solvent vapor concentrations were 49, 89, 24, 61, 287, 76, 72, 96, 83, 67, 54, 190, 50, 125, and 82 ppm. The question to be answered from the data is whether this HEG has acceptable solvent exposures. To determine the answer to this example scenario, the decision flow diagram in Figure 2-1 should be followed.

Calculate Descriptive Statistics

First, the descriptive statistics should be calculated and the data plotted on probability paper. This activity is recommended even in cases like the present example where some exposures are observed to be above the TLV.

Next, the data should be arranged for calculation by being placed in rank order (see Table 2-6). The data should be ranked from $r = 1$ to $r = n$ (see column 1 of Table 2-6). Then, the plotting position of $1/(n+1)$ should be calculated (column 2). After the plotting position is calculated, the data can be tabulated (column 3), and the logarithm of the ratio of the data values to some reference value (column 4) can be calculated. For this example, the reference value is 1 ppm. Statistical tables can be used to locate values for z_p, $t_{p,n}$, and $k_{p,n,\gamma}$.

The sample mean and the sample standard deviation for the numbers in columns 3 and 4 should be calculated using either a scientific calculator or spreadsheet (or other method of choice). For column 3, the calculation yields *M* and *S*. For column 4, the calculation yields ln(*GM*) and ln(*GS*). The median for both columns 3 and 4 should be estimated by inspection: the middle number of the data set should be used if *n* (the number of data points) is odd; the average of the middle two numbers should be used if n is even.

From the calculated values for *M* and *S* and the relevant values of z_p, $t_{p,n}$, and $k_{p,n,\gamma}$, it is a simple matter to calculate *LCL*, *UCL*, percentile, and *UTL* for both columns 3 and 4. Finally, the antilog function should be applied to the decision thresholds listed in column 4 to obtain the decision thresholds in concentration units as listed in column 5 of the data tables. Note that in concentration units, the thresholds are preceded by a *G* to signify that they are obtained from analysis assuming a lognormal distribution of data.

At this point, it is possible to make a preliminary judgment about whether a normal distribution is likely to fit either the data (column 3) or the log-transformed data (column 4). This is done by comparing the value of the calculated mean of the numbers in each column to the estimated median of each column. A useful test statistic is the ratio of the difference between *M* and *Me* to the sample standard deviation *S*. (This value is found in the last row of the data table.) A truly representative sample of a truly normal data set would return a value of zero because the mean equals the median for normal populations. Large values of this test statistic indicate significant asymmetry in the data. A poor fit to a normal distribution should be expected if the larger value is found in column 3; a poor fit to a lognormal distribution should be expected if the larger value is found in column 4.

For Table 2-6, the quality of fit test statistic on the last line is 6% of the standard deviation for the log-transformed data (column 4) and 27% of the standard deviation for the data (column 3). These results suggest that the lognormal distribution will fit these data better than the normal distribution. That assumption is verified by the plotted data, as shown in the next section.

Probability Plotting Exercise

For illustrative purposes, Figure 2-2 shows the data plotted on normal probit paper and Figure 2-3 shows the data plotted on lognormal probit paper. The straight line is the line plotted by use of the estimated parameters M, S, GM, and GS for the normal and lognormal distributions. The mean, *M*, occurs at the 50% point, *M–S* occurs at the 15.87% point, *M+S* occurs at the 84.13% point, and *M*+1.645**S* occurs at the 95% point for normal data. For lognormal data, *GM* occurs at the 50% point, *GM*/*GS* occurs at the 15.87% point, *GM***GS* occurs at the 84.13% point, and $GM*GS^{1.645}$ occurs at the 95% point.

From Table 2-6, $M–S = 28$, $M = 94$, and $M+S = 160$. Thus, the best fit line in Figure 2-2 goes through the points (28 ppm, 16%), (94 ppm, 50%), and (160 ppm, 84%). A glance at the data shows that they are not a good fit to the line, confirming the indication in the "Calculate Descriptive Statistics" section that the normal distribution would not be a good fit. When tested with the proprietary "omega" statistic with the

TABLE 2-6. Descriptive Statistics Example: Painters' Solvent Exposure Data Analysis

DATA PREPARATION

Rank [*r*]	Plot Position [*r*/(*n*+1)]	Exposure (ppm) [*x*]	ln(data/1ppm) (unitless) [ln(*x*)]	Tabulated Values [*t*, *z*, & *k*]
1	0.063	24.0	3.178	$p =$ 0.95
2	0.125	49.0	3.892	$n =$ 15.
3	0.188	50.0	3.912	$\gamma =$ 0.90
4	0.250	54.0	3.989	$z(p) =$ 1.645
5	0.313	61.0	4.111	$t(p,n-1) =$ 1.761
6	0.375	67.0	4.205	$k(p,n,\gamma) =$ 2.329
7	0.438	72.0	4.277	
8	0.500	76.0	4.331	
9	0.563	82.0	4.407	
10	0.625	83.0	4.419	
11	0.688	89.0	4.489	
12	0.750	96.0	4.564	
13	0.813	125.0	4.828	
14	0.875	190.0	5.247	
15	0.938	287.0	5.659	

DESCRIPTIVE STATISTICS

NORMAL	LOGNORMAL			
X	**ln(*GX*)**	***GX* = (1ppm)*exp[ln(*GX*)]**		
$S =$ 65.9	0.586	1.80	$= GS$	unitless
$M =$ 93.7	4.367	78.8	$= GM$	ppm
$M - S = X_{16\%} =$ 27.8	3.781	43.9	$= GX_{16\%}$	ppm
$M + S = X_{84\%} =$ 159.6	4.953	142.	$= GX_{84\%}$	ppm
OEL = 100.	4.605	100.	= OEL	ppm
$LCL =$ 63.7	4.101	60.4	$= GLCL$	ppm
$UCL =$ 124.	4.634	103.	$= GUCL$	ppm
$M + z_{95\%} * S = X_{95\%} =$ 202.	5.331	207.	$= GX_{95\%}$	ppm
$UTL =$ 247.	5.732	309.	$= GUTL$	ppm
$ME =$ median = 76.	4.331			
$(M - Me)/S =$ 0.268	**0.062**	(closer to 0 is better).		

$(M - Me)/S \Rightarrow$ lognormal fits better than normal distribution.

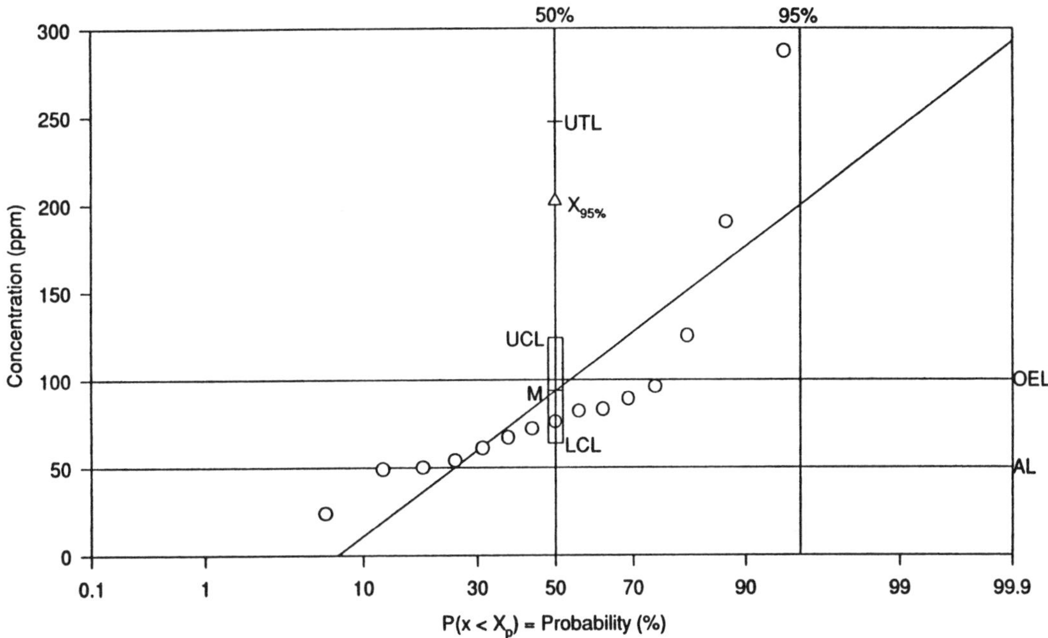

FIGURE 2-2. Normal probability plot, painter exposures.

Logan[17] software, this data set was declared unfit for analysis by the normal distribution.

For the data in column 4, the 50% point is given by ln(*GM*), the 16% point by [ln(*GM*)–ln(*GS*)], and the 84% point by [ln(*GM*)+ln(*GS*)]. Thus, the plotting points in log-transformed notation are (3.78, 16%), (4.37, 50%), and (4.95, 84%). Although these can be plotted directly on linear-probability paper, it is usually more intuitive to take the antilog of these numbers and plot the line on logarithm-probability paper in preferred concentration units. This is accomplished by taking the antilog and multiplying it by the reference concentration (1 ppm). The plotting positions for Figure 2-3 are (44, 16%), (79, 50%), and (142, 84%). Inspection of this line and the data confirms that there is a better fit under the lognormal assumption than was true under the normal assumption. The fit looks somewhat irregular, but adequate for making some decisions. In fact, the Logan software

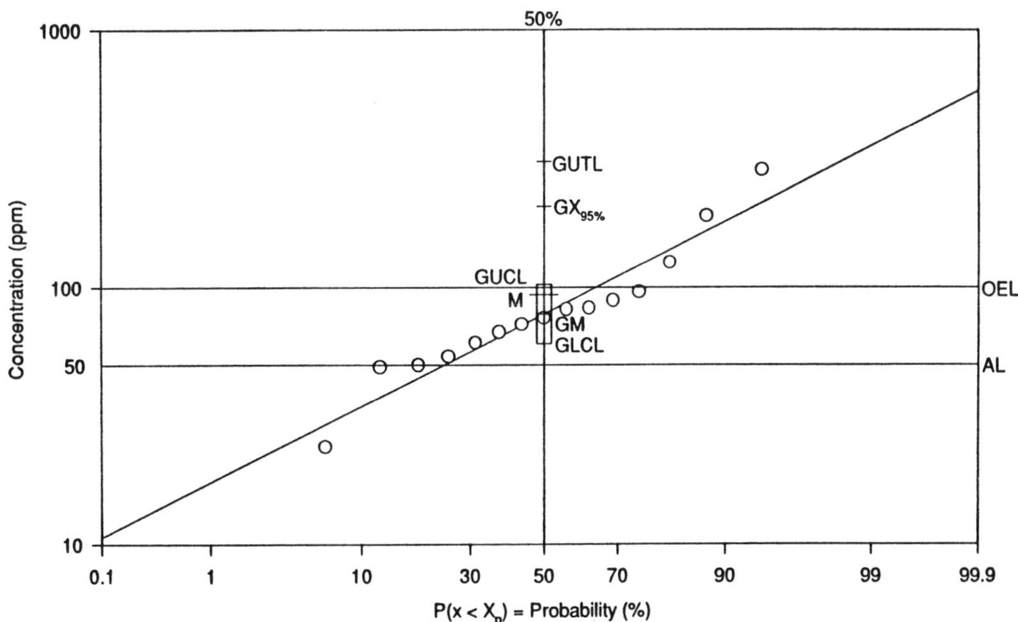

FIGURE 2-3. Lognormal probability plot, painter exposures.

TABLE 2-7. Descriptive Statistics Example: Solvent Exposure Data Analysis for Night Shift Painters

DATA PREPARATION

Rank $[r]$	Plot Position $[r/(n+1)]$	Exposure (ppm) $[x]$	ln(data/1ppm) (unitless) $[\ln(x)]$	Tabulated Values $[t, z, \& k]$
1	0.143	24.0	3.178	$p = 0.95$
2	0.286	50.0	3.912	$n = 6.$
3	0.429	82.0	4.407	$\gamma = 0.90$
4	0.571	125.0	4.828	$z(p) = 1.645$
5	0.714	190.0	5.247	$t(p,n-1) = 2.015$
6	0.857	287.0	5.659	$k(p,n,\gamma) = 3.091$

DESCRIPTIVE STATISTICS

NORMAL	LOGNORMAL		
X	$\ln(GX)$	$GX = (1\text{ppm})^*\exp[\ln(GX)]$	
$S =$ 98.1	0.906	2.47 = GS	unitless
$M =$ 126.	4.539	93.6 = GM	ppm
$M - S = X_{16\%} =$ 28.2	3.633	37.8 = $GX_{16\%}$	ppm
$M + S = X_{84\%} =$ 224.	5.445	232. = $GX_{84\%}$	ppm
OEL = 100.	4.605	100. = OEL	ppm
$LCL =$ 45.6	3.793	44.4 = $GLCL$	ppm
$UCL =$ 207.	5.284	197. = $GUCL$	ppm
$X_{95\%} =$ 288.	6.029	415. = $GX_{95\%}$	ppm
$UTL =$ 430.	7.339	1540. = $GUTL$	ppm
median = 72.0	4.618		
$(M - Me)/S =$ 0.554	**−0.087**	(closer to 0 is better).	

$(M - Me)/S \Rightarrow$ lognormal fits better than normal distribution.

calculates an "omega" of 0.103 (near the low end of the range recommended for decision-making).[17]

When evaluating the quality of fit visually, any substantial departure from linearity in the center 80% of the distribution should be cause for concern. A departure of this type indicates the distributional assumption is a poor approximation of the data. When predicting the probabilities that exposures exceed points in the upper end of the tail, predictions beyond the observed data should be made with caution. For this example, the highest observed data point was 287 ppm and it was estimated to represent the 93.8% point on the distribution. With 15 samples, any prediction above the 95% point is suspect. Likewise, with six samples, where the plotting position of the largest data point is 6/7, which equals 85.7%, it is wise to be cautious in estimating even the 90% point.

Decision-making with Descriptive Statistics

It is convenient to mark the action level, the OEL, the confidence interval about the mean (from *LCL* to *UCL*), and the range from the 95th percentile to the $\gamma = 90\%$ *UTL* right on the probability plot. Decision-making with an explicit knowlege of the level of confidence becomes a very intuitive process. The decisions identified in the statistical judgment portion of Figure 2-1 are all available by inspection.

Further, the line of best fit can be used to read estimated exceedance levels directly. Two levels of in-

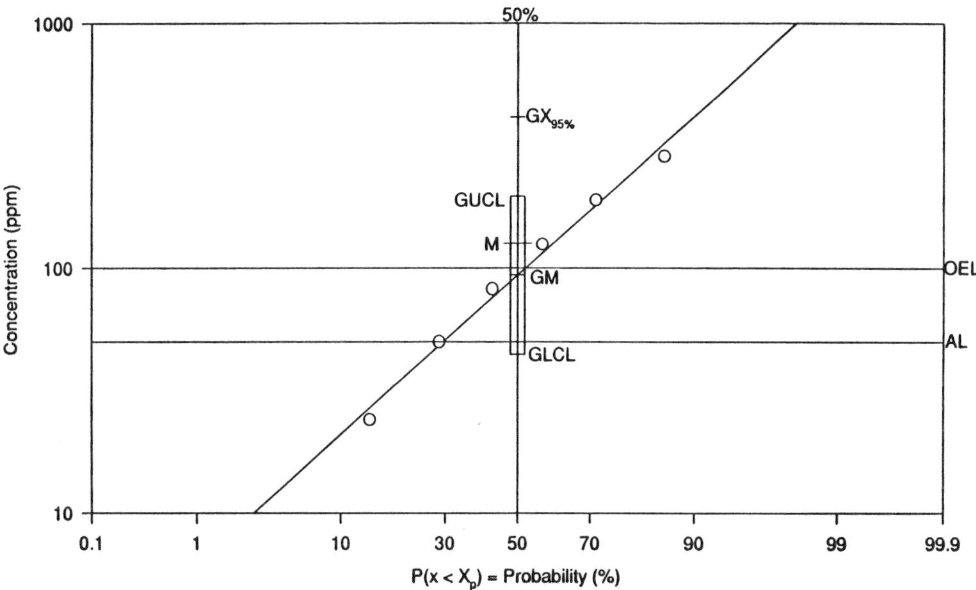

FIGURE 2-4. Lognormal probability plot, night shift. The *GUTL* = 1540 ppm plots above the axis on this figure because of the small number of samples (n=6).

terest are the proportion of exposures in the population[E] that exceed the OEL and the proportion that exceed the action level. For the data set in Table 2-6, Figure 2-3 shows that the 95% *UCL* is above the OEL, that less than 20% of exposures are below the action level, and less than 70% are below the OEL. It appears from all evidence at hand that these data represent an unacceptable workplace. Immediate intervention is required.

Professional Judgment in Statistical Interpretation

Even though the statistical judgment says this workplace is unacceptable, an experienced industrial hygienist might have misgivings about the decision. The data are scattered around the line of best fit to a lognormal distribution. Also, looking at Figure 2-2, there are nine points that seem to lie in a very straight line. If the other six were discarded, these would be a good fit to a normal distribution.

Upon careful investigation of the data, it is discovered that although there are 91 painters assigned to this shop, six of the samples were taken on the night shift and nine were taken during the day shift. Table 2-7 shows the descriptive statistical analysis for the night shift and Table 2-8 for the day shift. Sure enough, the nine samples that looked so neat on Figure 2-2 were all taken from the day shift!

These stratified samples clearly show that the exposures of individual painters, who often rotate between day and night shifts, are not homogeneous. The probability of overexposure at night far exceeds the probability of overexposure during the day. This may be due to lack of helpers or to lax supervision at night. Priority attention is needed to improve working conditions at night.

Further, it is apparent from Table 2-7 and Figure 2-4 that the nighttime exposures are lognormally distributed and from Table 2-8 and Figure 2-5 that the daytime exposures are normally distributed. Based on Figure 2-4, it is reasonable to classify the night shift as unacceptable because the average of observed exposures is above the OEL. Based on Figure 2-5, it is reasonable to classify the day shift exposures as tolerable, because the average of observed exposures, the 95% *UCL*, and the best estimate of the 95% of all exposures are all less than the OEL. The industrial hygienist making such a decision with the aid of Figure 2-5 would know that the level of confidence, γ, is less than 90% because the 90% *UTL* on the $X_{95\%}$ is above the OEL. This ability to understand the confidence with which industrial hygiene decisions are made illustrates the benefit of plotting data in the form of Figures 2-2 to 2-5.[F]

Summary

A formally defined air sampling strategy helps use available resources to provide maximum information for worker protection through good stewardship of available resources. A formal strategy ensures the re-

[E]This is the population of all exposures in the HEG. Its distribution is estimated from *GM* and *GS* in this example.

[F]This is the first publication of Dr. Rock's graphic decision aid.

TABLE 2-8. Descriptive Statistics Example: Solvent Exposure Data Analysis for Day Shift Painters

DATA PREPARATION

Rank [*r*]	**Plot Position** [*r*/(*n*+1)]	**Exposure (ppm)** [*x*]	**ln(data/1ppm) (unitless)** [ln(*x*)]	**Tabulated Values** [*t*, *z*, & *k*]
1	0.100	49.0	3.892	$p = 0.95$
2	0.200	54.0	3.989	$n = 9.$
3	0.300	61.0	4.111	$\gamma = 0.90$
4	0.400	67.0	4.205	$z(p) = 1.645$
5	0.500	72.0	4.277	$t(p,n-1) = 1.860$
6	0.600	76.0	4.331	$k(p,n,\gamma) = 2.649$
7	0.700	83.0	4.419	
8	0.800	89.0	4.489	
9	0.900	96.0	4.564	

DESCRIPTIVE STATISTICS

NORMAL			**LOGNORMAL**		
X			**ln(*GX*)**	**GX = (1ppm)*exp[ln(GX)]**	
$S =$	15.8		0.226	1.25 = GS	unitless
$M =$	71.9		4.253	70.3 = GM	ppm
$M - S = X_{16\%} =$	56.1		4.027	56.1 = $GX_{16\%}$	ppm
$M + S = X_{84\%} =$	87.7		4.479	88.1 = $GX_{84\%}$	ppm
OEL =	100.		4.605	100. = OEL	ppm
$LCL =$	62.1		4.113	66.1 = $GLCL$	ppm
$UCL =$	81.7		4.393	80.9 = $GUCL$	ppm
$X_{95\ \%ile} =$	97.9		4.625	102. = $GX_{95\%}$	ppm
$UTL =$	114.		4.852	128. = $GUTL$	ppm
Me = median =	72.00		4.277		
$(M - Me)/S =$	**−0.007**	(closer to 0 is better)	−0.105		

$(M - Me)/S \Rightarrow$ normal fits better than lognormal distribution.

sources needed to support a healthy industrial hygiene surveillance program. A successful strategy considers:

1. Whether an effect is acute or chronic
2. Government regulations and mandatory PELs
3. Consensus standards, recommended TLVs, and applicable OELs
4. Patterns of exposure
5. Presence of symptomatic workers
6. Classification of workers.

Statistical methods are helpful in designing the strategy and in interpreting the sampling data. The exact criteria to be used varies from one situation to another. There is no substitute for professional judgment. Air sampling is a major part of an exposure control program to protect workers against air contaminants. It is one of the tools used to ensure proper priorities for engineering controls, work practices, emergency response plans, and respiratory protection to reduce worker exposure.

A well-designed strategy includes criteria calling for additional control measures as necessary and specifies

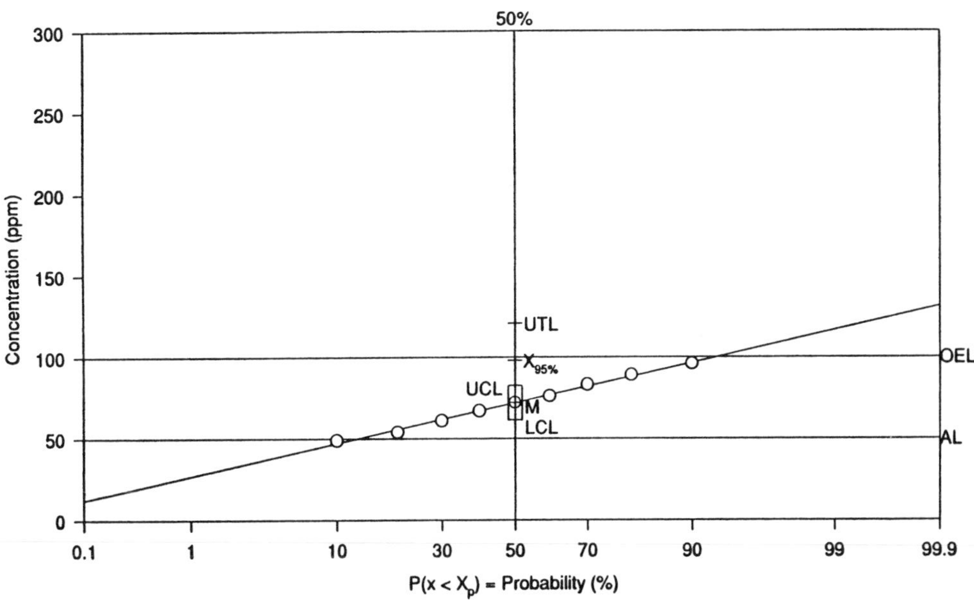

FIGURE 2-5. Normal probability plot, day shift.

the speed with which they must be implemented. The careful reader will have noted that the exposure rating scheme proposed here interacts with the decision flow diagram to reduce surveillance frequency only after representative exposures fall below the action level (50% OEL). The highest intensity air sampling efforts occur where the average exposure is between 50% and 100% of the OEL and the *UCL* on the mean is above the OEL. The lowest intensity air sampling efforts occur for those activities where the average exposure is below 10% OEL and the *UCL* is below the AL.

Finally, the use of statistical principles does not change the general basis for the health protection strategy used by industrial hygienists for many years. Although statistics assist the industrial hygienist in determining the relative uncertainty associated with any decision that is made, the criteria for such decisions still must be determined by consensus standards, by applicable regulations, or by the employer when external guidelines are unavailable. This chapter has outlined a structure that allows an improved level of quantifying IH decisions while retaining the traditional flexibility enjoyed by industrial hygienists who practice in a wide variety of occupational settings and provide safe and healthful working conditions in the face of an ever-growing number of potential stressors.

Useful Statistical Tables

- Table 2-9. Normal Distribution t values - for UCL
- Table 2-10. Normal Distribution z values - for X_p
- Table 2-11. Normal Distribution k values - for UTL
- Table 2-12. Nonparametric Tolerance Interval

References

1. Hawkins, N.C.; Norwood, S.K.; Rock, J.C.: A Strategy for Occupational Exposure Assessment. American Industrial Hygiene Association, Akron, OH (1991).
2. Hickey, E.E.; Stoetzel, G.A.; Strom, D.J.; et al.: Air Sampling in the Workplace, Final Report. NUREG-1400. U.S. Nuclear Regulatory Commission, Division of Regulatory Applications, Office of Nuclear Regulatory Research, Washington DC (September 1993).
3. Committee on Industrial Ventilation: Industrial Ventilation — A Manual of Recommended Practice, 20th ed. American Conference of Governmental Industrial Hygienists, Cincinnati, OH (1992).
4. American Society of Heating, Refrigerating and Air-Conditioning Engineers, Inc. (ASHRAE) Handbooks: Fundamentals Volume, Systems Volume, Equipment Volume, Applications Volume. ASHRAE, 1791 Tullie Circle, N.E., Atlanta, GA (Various Copyright Dates).
5. Heinsohn, R.J.: Industrial Ventilation: Engineering Principles. John Wiley & Sons, Inc., New York (1991).
6. U.S. Environmental Protection Agency: Chemical Engineering Branch Manual for the Preparation of Engineering Assessments, Vol I: CEB Engineering Manual. U.S EPA, Office of Toxic Substances, Washington, DC (1991).
7. Leidel, N.A.; Busch, K.A.; Lynch, J.R.: Occupational Exposure Sampling Strategy Manual. National Institute for Occupational Safety and Health, Cincinnati, OH (1977).
8. Leidel, N.A.; Busch. K.A.: Statistical Design and Data Analysis Requirements. In: Patty's Industrial Hygiene and Toxicology, 2nd ed., Vol. 3A, Theory and Rationale or Industrial Hygiene Practice: The Work Environment. L.J. Cralley and L.V. Cralley, Eds. John Wiley & Sons, New York (1985).
9. Rock, J.C.: The NIOSH Action Level — A Closer Look. In: Measurement and Control of Chemical Hazards in the Workplace Environment, Chap. 29. American Chemical Society, New York (1981).
10. Tuggle, R.M.: The NIOSH Decision Scheme. Am. Ind. Hyg. Assoc. J. 42:493 (July 1981).
11. Shannon, C. E.: Communication in the Presence of Noise, Proc IRE,

37(10):10-21 (1949). Referenced in Hancock, J.C.: An Introduction to the Principles of Communication Theory. Chapter 1. McGraw–Hill (1961).

12. Rock, J.C.: Can Professional Judgment be Quantified? Am. Ind. Hyg. Assoc. J. 47(6):A-370 (June 1986).
13. Heederik, D.; Hurley, F.: Occupational Exposure Assessment: Investigating Why Exposure Measurements Vary. Appl. Occup. Environ. Hyg. 9:71–76 (January 1994).
14. Ayer, H. E.: Occupational Air Sampling Strategies. In: Air Sampling Instruments, 7th ed., Chap. B. Susanne V. Hering, Ed. American Conference of Governmental Industrial Hygienists, Cincinnati, OH (1989).
15. National Council on Radiation Protection and Measurements: Recommendations on Limits for Exposure to Ionizing Radiation. NCRP Report No 91. NCRP, Bethesda, MD (June 1987).
16. Rappaport, S.M.; Kromhout, K.; Symanski, E.: Variation of Exposure Between Workers in Homogeneous Exposure Groups. Am. Ind. Hyg. Assoc. J. 54:654–662 (November 1993).
17. Dupont Statistics Group: LOGAN Workplace Exposure Evaluation System. American Industrial Hygiene Association, Fairfax, VA (1990).
18. Rappaport, S.M.: The Rules of the Game: An Analysis of OSHA's Enforcement Strategy. Am. J. Ind. Med. 6:291 (1984).
19. Roach, S.A.: A More Rational Basis for Air Sampling Programs. Am. Ind. Hyg. Assoc. J. 27:1–12. (January-February 1966).
20. Roach, S.A.: A Most Rational Basis for Air Sampling Programmes. Ann. Occup. Hyg. 20:65–84 (1977).
21. Spear, R.C.; Selvin, S.; Francis, M.: The Influence of Averaging Time on the Distribution of Exposures. Am. Ind. Hyg. Assoc. J. 47(6):365–368 (1986).
22. The 'MEMORY JOGGER'™ — A Pocket Guide of Tools for Continuous Improvement. GOAL/QPC, Methuen, MA (1988).
23. Grant, E.L.; Leavenworth, R.S.: Statistical Quality Control. 4th ed. McGraw–Hill Book Co., New York (1980).
24. Traub, J.F.; Wozniakowski, H.: Breaking Intractability. Scientific American, pp. 102–114 (January 1994).
25. Rock, J.C.: A Comparison Between OSHA — Compliance Criteria and Action-Level Decision Criteria. Am. Ind. Hyg. Assoc. J. 45:297 (May 1982).
26. Gumbel, E.J.: Statistics of Extremes. Columbia University Press, New York (1958).
27. Saltzman, B.E.; Cholak, J.; Shaefer,L.S.; et al.: Concentrations of Six Metals in the Air of Eight Cities. Environ. Sci Technol. 19:328 (April 1985).
28. American Conference of Governmental Industrial Hygienists: 1993–94 Threshold Limit Values for Chemical Substances and Physical Agents and Biological Exposure Indices. ACGIH, Cincinnati, OH (1993).
29. Natrella, M.G.: Experimental Statistics. National Bureau of Standards Handbook 91. U.S Government Printing Office, Washington, DC (1966).
30. Box, G.E.P.; Hunter, W.G.; Hunter, J.S.: Statistics for Experimenters. John Wiley & Sons, New York (1978).
31. Tuggle, R.M.: Assessment of Occupational Exposure Using One-sided Tolerance Limits. Am. Ind. Hyg. Assoc. J. 43:338 (May 1982).

TABLE 2-9. Percentiles of the t Distribution[A]

df	$t_{.60}$	$t_{.70}$	$t_{.80}$	$t_{.90}$	$t_{.95}$	$t_{.975}$	$t_{.99}$	$t_{.995}$
1	.325	.727	1.376	3.078	6.314	12.706	31.821	63.657
2	.289	.617	1.061	1.886	2.920	4.303	6.965	9.925
3	.277	.584	.978	1.638	2.353	3.182	4.541	5.841
4	.271	.569	.941	1.533	2.132	2.776	3.747	4.604
5	.267	.559	.920	1.476	2.015	2.571	3.365	4.032
6	.265	.553	.906	1.440	1.943	2.447	3.143	3.707
7	.263	.549	.896	1.415	1.895	2.365	2.998	3.499
8	.262	.546	.889	1.397	1.860	2.306	2.896	3.355
9	.261	.543	.883	1.383	1.833	2.262	2.821	3.250
10	.260	.542	.879	1.372	1.812	2.228	2.764	3.169
11	.260	.540	.876	1.363	1.796	2.201	2.718	3.106
12	.259	.539	.873	1.356	1.782	2.179	2.681	3.055
13	.259	.538	.870	1.350	1.771	2.160	2.650	3.012
14	.258	.537	.868	1.345	1.761	2.145	2.624	2.977
15	.258	.536	.866	1.341	1.753	2.131	2.602	2.947
16	.258	.535	.865	1.337	1.746	2.120	2.583	2.921
17	.257	.534	.863	1.333	1.740	2.110	2.567	2.898
18	.257	.534	.862	1.330	1.734	2.101	2.552	2.878
19	.257	.533	.861	1.328	1.729	2.093	2.539	2.841
20	.257	.533	.860	1.325	1.725	2.086	2.528	2.845
21	.257	.532	.859	1.323	1.721	2.080	2.518	2.831
22	.256	.532	.858	1.321	1.717	2.074	2.508	2.819
23	.256	.532	.858	1.319	1.714	2.069	2.500	2.807
24	.256	.531	.857	1.318	1.711	2.064	2.492	2.797
25	.256	.531	.856	1.316	1.708	2.060	2.485	2.787
26	.256	.531	.856	1.315	1.706	2.056	2.479	2.779
27	.256	.531	.855	1.314	1.703	2.052	2.473	2.771
28	.256	.530	.855	1.313	1.701	2.048	2.467	2.763
29	.256	.530	.854	1.311	1.699	2.045	2.462	2.756
30	.256	.530	.854	1.310	1.697	2.042	2.457	2.750
40	.255	.529	.851	1.303	1.684	2.021	2.423	2.704
60	.254	.527	.848	1.296	1.671	2.000	2.390	2.660
120	.254	.526	.845	1.289	1.658	1.980	2.358	2.617
∞	.253	.524	.842	1.282	1.645	1.960	2.326	2.576

[A]From National Bureau of Standards.

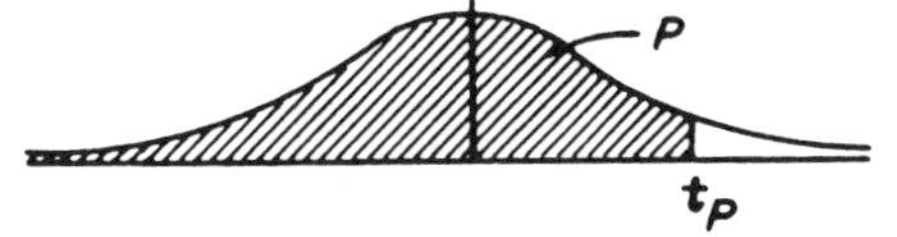

TABLE 2-10. Cumulative Normal Distribution — Values of P Corresponding to z_p for the Normal Curve

z is the standard normal variable. The value of P for $-z_p$ equals one minus the value of P for $+z_p$, e.g., the P for −1.62 equals 1−.9474 = .0526.

z_p	.00	.01	.02	.03	.04	.05	.06	.07	.08	.09
.0	.5000	.5040	.5080	.5120	.5160	.5199	.5239	.5279	.5319	.5359
.1	.5398	.5438	.5478	.5517	.5557	.5596	.5636	.5675	.5714	.5753
.2	.5793	.5832	.5871	.5910	.5948	.5987	.6026	.6064	.6103	.6141
.3	.6179	.6217	.6255	.6293	.6331	.6368	.6406	.6443	.6480	.6517
.4	.6554	.6591	.6628	.6664	.6700	.6736	.6772	.6808	.6844	.6879
.5	.6915	.6950	.6985	.7019	.7054	.7088	.7123	.7157	.7190	.7224
.6	.7257	.7291	.7324	.7357	.7389	.7422	.7454	.7486	.7517	.7549
.7	.7580	.7611	.7642	.7673	.7704	.7734	.7764	.7794	.7823	.7852
.8	.7881	.7910	.7939	.7967	.7995	.8023	.8051	.8078	.8106	.8133
.9	.8159	.8186	.8212	.8238	.8264	.8289	.8315	.8340	.8365	.8389
1.0	.8413	.8438	.8461	.8485	.8508	.8531	.8554	.8577	.8599	.8621
1.1	.8643	.8665	.8686	.8708	.8729	.8749	.8770	.8790	.8810	.8830
1.2	.8849	.8869	.8888	.8907	.8925	.8944	.8962	.8980	.8997	.9015
1.3	.9032	.9049	.9066	.9082	.9099	.9115	.9131	.9147	.9162	.9177
1.4	.9192	.9207	.9222	.9236	.9251	.9265	.9279	.9292	.9306	.9319
1.5	.9332	.9345	.9357	.9370	.9382	.9394	.9406	.9418	.9429	.9441
1.6	.9452	.9463	.9474	.9484	.9495	.9505	.9515	.9525	.9535	.9545
1.7	.9554	.9564	.9573	.9582	.9591	.9599	.9608	.9616	.9625	.9633
1.8	.9641	.9649	.9656	.9664	.9671	.9678	.9686	.9693	.9699	.9706
1.9	.9713	.9719	.9726	.9732	.9738	.9744	.9750	.9756	.9761	.9767
2.0	.9772	.9778	.9783	.9788	.9793	.9798	.9803	.9808	.9812	.9817
2.1	.9821	.9826	.9830	.9834	.9838	.9842	.9846	.9850	.9854	.9857
2.2	.9861	.9864	.9868	.9871	.9875	.9878	.9881	.9884	.9887	.9890
2.3	.9893	.9896	.9898	.9901	.9904	.9906	.9909	.9911	.9913	.9916
2.4	.9918	.9920	.9922	.9925	.9927	.9929	.9931	.9932	.9934	.9936
2.5	.9938	.9940	.9941	.9943	.9945	.9946	.9948	.9949	.9951	.9952
2.6	.9953	.9955	.9956	.9957	.9959	.9960	.9961	.9962	.9963	.9964
2.7	.9965	.9966	.9967	.9968	.9969	.9970	.9971	.9972	.9973	.9974
2.8	.9974	.9975	.9976	.9977	.9977	.9978	.9979	.9979	.9980	.9981
2.9	.9981	.9982	.9982	.9983	.9984	.9984	.9985	.9985	.9986	.9986
3.0	.9987	.9987	.9987	.9988	.9988	.9989	.9989	.9989	.9990	.9990
3.1	.9990	.9991	.9991	.9991	.9992	.9992	.9992	.9992	.9993	.9993
3.2	.9993	.9993	.9994	.9994	.9994	.9994	.9994	.9995	.9995	.9995
3.3	.9995	.9995	.9995	.9996	.9996	.9996	.9996	.9996	.9996	.9997
3.4	.9997	.9997	.9997	.9997	.9997	.9997	.9997	.9997	.9997	.9998

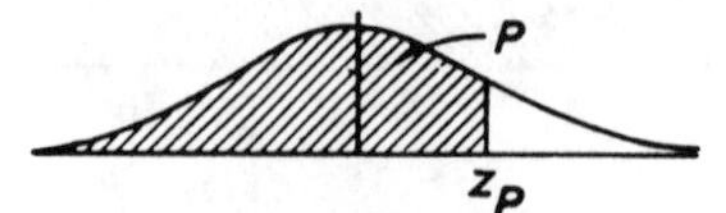

TABLE 2-11. Factors for One-Sided Tolerance Limits for Normal Distributions

Factors K such that the probability is γ that at least a proportion p of the distribution will be less than $M + KS$ (greater than $M - KS$), where M and S are estimates of the mean and the standard deviation computed from a sample size of n.

	$\gamma = 0.75$					$\gamma = 0.90$				
$n \setminus p$	0.75	0.90	0.95	0.99	0.999	0.75	0.90	0.95	0.99	0.999
3	1.464	2.501	3.152	4.396	5.805	2.602	4.258	5.310	7.340	9.651
4	1.256	2.134	2.680	3.726	4.910	1.972	3.187	3.957	5.437	7.128
5	1.152	1.961	2.463	3.421	4.507	1.698	2.742	3.400	4.666	6.112
6	1.087	1.860	2.336	3.243	4.273	1.540	2.494	3.091	4.242	5.556
7	1.043	1.791	2.250	2.126	4.118	1.435	2.333	2.894	3.972	5.201
8	1.010	1.740	2.190	3.042	4.008	1.360	2.219	2.755	3.783	4.955
9	0.984	1.702	2.141	2.977	3.924	1.302	2.133	2.649	3.641	4.772
10	0.964	1.671	2.103	2.927	3.858	1.257	2.065	2.568	3.532	4.629
11	0.947	1.646	2.073	2.885	3.804	1.219	2.012	2.503	3.444	4.515
12	0.933	1.624	2.048	2.851	3.760	1.188	1.966	2.448	3.371	4.420
13	0.919	1.606	2.026	2.822	3.722	1.162	1.928	2.403	3.310	4.341
14	0.909	1.591	2.007	2.796	3.690	1.139	1.895	2.363	3.257	4.274
15	0.899	1.577	1.991	2.776	3.661	1.119	1.866	2.329	3.212	4.215
16	0.891	1.566	1.977	2.756	3.637	1.101	1.842	2.299	3.172	4.164
17	0.883	1.554	1.964	2.739	3.615	1.085	1.820	2.272	3.136	4.118
18	0.876	1.544	1.951	2.723	3.595	1.071	1.800	2.249	3.106	4.078
19	0.870	1.536	1.942	2.710	3.577	1.058	1.781	2.228	3.078	4.041
20	0.865	1.528	1.933	2.697	3.561	1.046	1.765	2.208	3.052	4.009
21	0.859	1.520	1.923	2.686	3.545	1.035	1.750	2.190	3.028	3.979
22	0.854	1.514	1.916	2.675	3.532	1.025	1.736	2.174	3.007	3.952
23	0.849	1.508	1.907	2.665	3.520	1.016	1.724	2.159	2.987	3.927
24	0.845	1.502	1.901	2.656	3.509	1.007	1.712	2.145	2.969	3.904
25	0.842	1.496	1.895	2.647	3.497	0.999	1.702	2.132	2.952	3.882
30	0.825	1.475	1.869	2.613	3.454	0.966	1.657	2.080	2.884	3.794
35	0.812	1.458	1.849	2.588	3.421	0.942	1.623	2.041	2.833	3.730
40	0.803	1.445	1.834	2.568	3.395	0.923	1.598	2.010	2.793	3.679
45	0.795	1.435	1.821	2.552	3.375	0.908	1.577	1.986	2.962	3.638
50	0.788	1.426	1.811	2.538	3.358	0.894	1.560	1.965	2.735	3.604

	$\gamma = 0.95$					$\gamma = 0.99$				
$n \setminus p$	0.75	0.90	0.95	0.99	0.999	0.75	0.90	0.95	0.99	0.999
3	3.804	6.158	7.655	10.552	13.857	—	—	—	—	—
4	2.619	4.163	5.145	7.042	9.215	—	—	—	—	—
5	2.149	3.407	4.202	5.741	7.501	—	—	—	—	—
6	1.895	3.006	3.707	5.062	6.612	2.849	4.408	5.409	7.334	9.550
7	1.732	2.755	3.399	4.641	6.061	2.490	3.856	4.730	6.411	8.348
8	1.617	2.582	3.188	4.353	5.686	2.252	3.496	4.287	5.811	7.566
9	1.532	2.454	3.031	4.143	5.414	2.085	3.242	3.971	5.389	7.014
10	1.465	2.355	2.911	3.981	5.203	1.954	3.048	3.739	5.075	6.603
11	1.411	2.275	2.815	3.852	5.036	1.854	2.897	3.557	4.828	6.284
12	1.366	2.210	2.736	3.747	4.900	1.771	2.776	3.410	4.633	6.032
13	1.329	2.155	2.670	3.659	4.787	1.702	2.677	3.290	4.472	5.826
14	1.296	2.108	2.614	3.585	4.690	1.645	2.592	3.189	4.336	5.651
15	1.268	2.068	2.566	3.520	4.607	1.596	2.521	3.102	4.224	5.507
16	1.242	2.032	2.523	3.463	4.534	1.553	2.458	3.028	4.124	5.374
17	1.220	2.001	2.486	3.415	4.471	1.514	2.405	2.962	4.038	5.268
18	1.200	1.974	2.453	3.370	4.415	1.481	2.357	2.906	3.961	5.167
19	1.183	1.949	2.423	3.331	4.364	1.450	2.315	2.855	3.893	5.078
20	1.167	1.926	2.396	3.295	4.319	1.424	2.275	2.807	3.832	5.003
21	1.152	1.905	2.371	3.262	4.276	1.397	2.241	2.768	3.776	4.932
22	1.138	1.887	2.350	3.233	4.283	1.376	2.208	2.729	3.727	4.866
23	1.126	1.869	2.329	3.206	4.204	1.355	2.179	2.693	3.680	4.806
24	1.114	1.853	2.309	3.181	4.171	1.336	2.154	2.663	3.638	4.755
25	1.103	1.838	2.292	3.158	4.143	1.319	2.129	2.632	3.601	4.706
30	1.059	1.778	2.220	3.064	4.022	1.249	2.029	2.516	3.446	4.508
35	1.025	1.732	2.166	2.994	3.934	1.195	1.957	2.431	3.334	4.364
40	0.999	1.697	2.126	2.41	3.866	1.154	1.902	2.365	3.250	4.255
45	0.978	1.669	2.092	2.897	3.811	1.122	1.857	2.313	3.181	4.168
50	0.961	1.646	2.065	2.863	3.766	1.096	1.821	2.269	3.124	4.096

Adapted by permission from Industrial Quality Control, Vol. XIV, No. 10, April 1958, from article entitled "Tables for One-Sided Statistical Tolerance Limits" by G.J. Lieberman.

TABLE 2-12. Confidence Associated With a Tolerance Limit Statement

Confidence γ with which we may assert that 100*p* percent of the population lies between the largest and smallest of a random sample of *n* from that population (continuous distribution assumed).

n	*p* = .75	*p* = .90	*p* = .95	*p* = .99	*n*	*p* = .75	*p* = .90	*p* = .95	*p* = .99
3	.16	.03	.01	.00	17	.95	.52	.21	.01
4	.26	.05	.01	.00	18	.96	.55	.23	.01
5	.37	.08	.02	.00	19	.97	.58	.25	.02
6	.47	.11	.03	.00	20	.98	.61	.26	.02
7	.56	.15	.04	.00	25	.99	.73	.36	.03
8	.63	.19	.06	.00	30	1.00–	.82	.45	.04
9	.70	.23	.07	.00	40	—	.92	.60	.06
10	.76	.26	.09	.00	50	—	.97	.72	.09
11	.80	.30	.10	.01	60	—	.99	.81	.12
12	.84	.34	.12	.01	70	—	.99	.87	.16
13	.87	.38	.14	.01	80	—	1.00–	.91	.19
14	.90	.42	.15	.01	90	—	—	.94	.23
15	.92	.45	.17	.01	100	—	—	.96	.26
16	.94	.49	.19	.01					

Adapted with permission from The Institute of Mathematical Statistics, *Annals of Mathematical Statistics*, Vol. 29, No. 2, June 1958, pp. 599–601, from article entitled "Tables for Obtaining Non-Parametric Tolerance Limits" by Paul N. Somerville.

Chapter 3

Approaches for Conducting Air Sampling in the Community Environment

Paul J. Lioy, Ph.D.

Division of Exposure Measurement and Assessment, Environmental and Occupational Health Sciences Institute, UMDNJ–Robert Wood Johnson Medical School and Rutgers University, Piscataway, New Jersey

CONTENTS

Introduction

A number of different approaches can be used to study community air pollution problems and each has evolved substantially since the passage of the Clean Air Act (CAA) of 1970. Earlier activities in community air sampling used very simple monitoring tools, including the dustfall bucket, and collected data primarily in specific geographic-population centers. The location studied could have been a rural center, a small town or a city, a suburb of a large urban center, or a selected portion of a city. Usually, one or more fixed monitoring stations measuring a few pollutants (e.g., particulate matter, sulfur dioxide) were placed at selected locations and these comprised a sampling program. Some of these evolved into well-established monitoring programs for examining attainment of National Ambient Air Quality Standards (NAAQS). The techniques also evolved from simple manual monitoring techniques, such as the high volume sampler and spot samplers, into networks that have multiple continuous and integrating monitors.[1]

Today, depending on the information needs, a number of pollutants can be measured continuously at a site, and the continuous monitoring data are usually telemetered to a central data acquisition and validation center. For pollutants measured routinely with integrating samplers (e.g., volatile organic compounds, size-selected particulate matter), a statistically de-

TABLE 3-1. National Ambient Air Quality Standards[A]

Pollutant	Averaging Time	Primary Standard	Secondary Standard	Measurement Method
Carbon monoxide	8 hrs	10 mg/m^3 (9 ppm)	Same	Nondispersive infrared spectroscopy
	1 hr	40 mg/m^3 (35 ppm)	Same	
Nitro dioxide	Annual average	100 μg/m^3 (0.05 ppm)	Same	Calorimetric using Saltzman method or equivalent
Sulfur dioxide	Annual average 24 hrs	80 μg/m^3 (0.03 ppm) 365 μg/m^3 (0.14 ppm)		Pararosaniline method or equivalent
	3 hrs		1300 μg/m^3 (0.5 ppm)	
PM_{10} (≤10 μm)	Annual arithmetic mean 24-hr	50 μg/m^3 150 μg/m^3	50 μg/m^3	Size-selective samplers
Ozone	1 hr	235 μg/m^3 (0.12 ppm)	Same	Chemiluminescent method or equivalent
Lead	3-month average	1.5 μg/m^3	Same	Atomic absorption

[A]Standards, other than those based on the annual average, are not to be exceeded more than once a year.

signed sampling schedule is needed for population-based sampling.

Since the promulgation of the 1970 CAA,[(2)] one of the basic objectives of community air sampling has been to measure the concentrations of one or more pollutants originating from a number of different sizes and types of sources. This premise remains a cornerstone of the evaluation tools in the 1990 CAA amendments.[(3)] For most state and local agencies, the minimum set includes criteria pollutants, i.e., carbon monoxide, ozone, nitrogen dioxide, lead, suspended thoracic particulate matter (PM_{10}), and sulfur dioxide; however, other pollutants, especially air toxics, and pollutant indicators are also measured at specific sites. The actual techniques are outlined or illustrated in many chapters throughout this manual. Data from these types of routine monitoring programs are normally used to evaluate compliance with the NAAQS, but can be used in epidemiological or long-term trend studies. When specific problems are addressed, the data from the routine monitoring programs are usually augmented by more detailed community air sampling programs.

Overall, community air sampling programs have been designed to examine the following: compliance with the NAAQS and National Emissions Standards for Hazardous Air Pollutants (NESHAPS); human exposures to pollutants or pollutant classes; pollutant formation, transport, and deposition; and the potential for human health effects, damage to vegetation and materials, etc. The primary NAAQS are based on the prevention of adverse human health effects, whereas the secondary NAAQS are based on prevention of ecological disturbance and resource degradation effects. The current 1993 NAAQS are shown in Table 3-1. In addition, community air pollution studies can also be designed and conducted to investigate and understand basic chemical and physical processes in the atmosphere to assist risk managers in attempts to reduce the intensity of air pollution episodes and develop more effective control strategies.[(4)]

Types of Community Studies

Some of the air sampling programs developed to address the above issues are categorized as special short-term studies. Other special survey studies have evolved into the current National Air Monitoring Station (NAMS) network or the State and Local Air Monitoring Station (SLAMS) network for examining attainment of criteria pollutants monitored by regulatory agencies. Both of these networks are important because they measure indicators of various emission sources, including fossil fuels, combustion and industrial processes, and other sources of national impact. In recent years, the Urban Air Toxic Monitoring Program (UATAP) for volatile organics has been initiated, and in future years, the U.S. Environmental Protection Agency (U.S. EPA) will be employing enhanced monitoring networks for identifying and tracking the individual volatile organic and nitrogen oxide constituents in the air that lead to the formation of ozone in many nonattainment areas.[(5)]

Research investigations on community air pollution use short-term exposure studies to assess the acute exposures that produce health effects and the chemical characteristics of the atmosphere. Long-term studies are used to investigate the nature of acid rain, visibility or pollutant trends, and chronic health risks among the general population. Depending on the objectives of any particular study and the resources available, variations from program to program will be noted in the size of the area studied, the specific site locations, the number of samplers at each site, the pollutants measured, the frequency and length of sampling, and the duration of the sampling intervals. The area associated with a community air sampling program can be defined by the meteorological influence on a microscale, mesoscale, and/or synoptic scale, which translate, for community air pollution, to radial distances of ~10 km, ~100 km, and ~3000 km.[6] The microscale investigations can have subcategories because problems may exist in a specific neighborhood, in a section of a city, around a group of small sources (<10 tons/year emission), or downwind of a single point source. The mesoscale influence can involve emissions from a number of points or line sources, which ultimately combine to produce the urban plume and its downwind impacts. Synoptic scale events are associated with high or low pressure weather systems and the contributions from secondary pollutants such as ozone, sulfate, and nitrates.

The preceding discussion has described a traditional approach to community air sampling. In recent years, concerns about community air pollution have also been extended to the indoor environment[7,8] and, in some cases, the total exposure of an individual to specific pollutants.[9–11] These new study issues have developed because of the potential for the accumulation of high pollutant concentrations in indoor environments.[12] Increased indoor pollution has been partly a result of activities designed to reduce energy costs by sealing up homes, the construction of public and commercial buildings with windows that do not open, and the use of synthetic materials for furniture and other personal products. In other cases, it has been due to the migration of hazardous wastes under a house and volatilization of organics within a basement or first floor.[13] Because there are no indoor air standards at the present time, community-based studies are directed toward source identification and reduction, pollutant characterization, indoor–outdoor relationships, risk assessment, and health effects.

The intent of the remainder of the chapter is to examine the features of various types of community air sampling programs and the parameters that must be considered in the design of individual programs. A discussion of representative examples of different community air sampling studies is also presented.

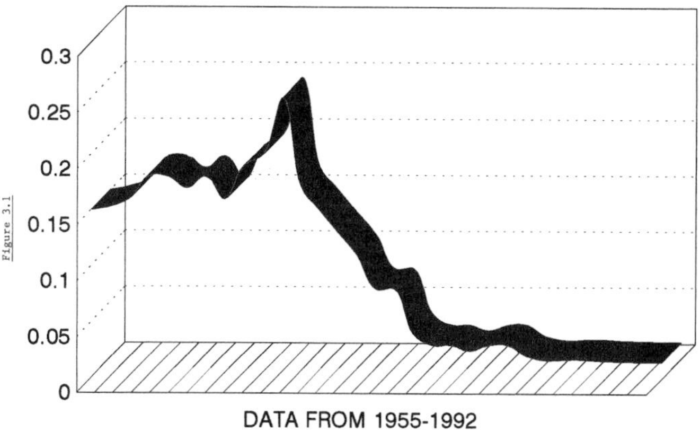

FIGURE 3-1. Annual average sulfur dioxide in northern Manhattan, New York (adapted from Eisenbud[14]).

Community Air Sampling

Fixed Outdoor Sampling Sites

The selection of protocols and methods for measuring air pollution is mainly dependent upon the specific goals of the investigation. The earliest efforts in air monitoring focused on a central monitoring station; for instance, in New York City, it was the 121st Street Laboratory.[14] Various pollutants were measured, and originally, mechanized sampling techniques, such as bubblers and high-volume samplers, integrated ambient concentrations of pollutants for periods of 24 hrs or longer. This was done on a daily basis or on a statistically selected number of days (e.g., every sixth day) at regular intervals throughout the year. Air quality data from these types of monitoring networks provided valuable information on long-term trends and now provide a basis for assessing compliance with local and national standards. An example of the value of such a long term network is shown in Figure 3-1 for the concentrations of sulfer dioxide found at the New York City site from the 1950s until today. It is a historical record that places current concerns within an overall frame of reference for previously reported health and environmental effects. The original network was called the National Air Surveillance Network (NASN) and was a community-based voluntary effort conducted at selected locations throughout the United States.[15] It was superseded by the NAMS and SLAMS networks, which select sites and pollutants to be measured using specific siting criteria, and by standard reference methods for sampling of criteria pollutants. Many of the standard methods or equivalent methods for sampling the criteria pollutants are described in this manual.

The siting documents were developed by the U.S. EPA for ambient air criteria pollutants such as photochemical oxidants.[16] Ott[17] recommended six types of outdoor sites, or monitoring categories, that could assist in identifying situations where a variety of human exposures could be measured in the community (Table 3-2). These still provide an excellent approach for establishing the initial criteria for site selection. The specific criteria will depend on the nature and accumulation patterns for individual pollutants; however, the general concepts can be applied for both compliance and research studies.

Although a standardized approach may be suitable for an air monitoring network, other approaches to sampling may be more appropriate for site-specific types of studies. For example, a state or local control agency may initially conduct a short-term, multiple station, intensive survey for particular ambient air pollutants. In recent times, this has been done for specific pollutant classes such as polycyclic aromatic hydrocarbons (PAHs) and volatile organic compounds (VOCs) and for specific pollutants such as ozone, acid sulfates, and nitric acid. After assessing the measured concentrations, the network can be reduced in number to a few strategically located stations. At a minimum, monitoring should be performed in an area that frequently receives the maximum ambient concentration, as well as in an area that periodically receives only background ambient concentrations. Any monitoring strategy can be modified as required to examine impacts from emissions increases (or decreases) as new control technology is applied to a source, process characteristics are altered, or fuel reformulations or conversions are implemented at the facility. Sometimes, monitoring strategies are designed to measure the amount of a particular pollutant transported into a state, country, or province from another jurisdiction.

Industry may at times take a different approach to ensure compliance with existing air quality standards. Managers of an industrial plant responsible for the control of a single pollutant may be most interested in averaging concentrations from their own source over specific sampling times when it is operating at different production levels. Therefore, the industry may design short-term studies. In fact, a plant's total monitoring effort may be focused on relating fenceline pollution concentrations to production emissions as a basis for choosing the correct control devices. Consequently, these monitoring efforts could evolve into long-term studies that measure levels both before and after the implementation of a control strategy. The sites would be located primarily at the plant fenceline and at particular locations either upwind or downwind of the facility. The 1990 revisions of the CAA will require more emissions and fenceline monitoring efforts to quantify reductions of the approximately 189 air toxics targeted for reduction in Title III.[3]

In the past 10 years, fixed outdoor sampling studies have been designed to investigate the nature of pollut-

TABLE 3-2. Recommended Criteria for Siting Monitoring Stations

TYPE A	Downtown Pedestrian Exposure Station. Locate station in the central business district (CBD) of the urban area on a congested, downtown street surrounded by buildings (i.e., a "canyon" type street) and having many pedestrians. Average daily travel (ADT) on the street must exceed 10,000 vehicles/day, with average speeds less than 15 mph. Monitoring probe is to be located 0.5 m from the curb at a height of 3 ± 0.5 m.
TYPE B	Downtown Background Exposure Station. Locate station in the CBD of the urban area but not close to any major streets. Specifically, no street with ADT exceeding 500 vehicles/day can be less than 100 m from the monitoring station. Typical locations are parks, malls, or landscaped areas having no traffic. Probe height is to be 3 ± 0.5 m above the ground surface.
TYPE C	Residential Population Exposure Station. Locate station in the midst of a residential or suburban area but not in the CBD. Station must not be less than 100 m from any street having a traffic volume in excess of 500 vehicles/day. Station probe height must be 3 ± 0.5 m.
TYPE D	Mesoscale Meteorological Station. Locate station in the urban area at appropriate height to gather meteorological data and air quality data at upper elevations. The purpose of this station is not to monitor human exposure but to gather trend data and meteorological data at various heights. Typical locations are tall buildings and broadcasting towers. The height of the probe, along with the nature of the station location, must be carefully specified along with the data.
TYPE E	Nonurban Background Station. Locate station in a remote, nonurban area having no traffic and no industrial activity. The purpose of this station is to monitor for trend analyses, for nondegradation assessments, and large-scale geographical surveys. The location or height must not be changed during the period over which the trend is examined. The height of the probe must be specified.
TYPE F	Specialized Source Survey Station. Locate station very near a particular air pollution source under scrutiny. The purpose of the station is to determine the impact on air quality, at specified locations, of a particular emission source of interest. Station probe height should be of 3 ± 0.5 m unless special considerations of the survey require a nonuniform height.

Reprinted with permission from J. Air Pollut. Control Assoc. 27:543 (1977).[17]

TABLE 3-3. Spatial Considerations: Summary of Sampling Designs and When They Are Most Useful

Sampling Design	Condition for Most Useful Applications
Haphazard sampling	Only valid when target population is homogeneous in space and time; hence, not generally recommended
Purposive sampling	Target population well defined and homogeneous so sample-selection bias is not a problem; or specific environmental samples selected for unique value and interest rather than for making inferences to wider populations
Probability sampling	
Simple random sampling	Homogeneous population
Stratified random sampling	Homogeneous population within strata (subregions); might consider strata as domains of study
Systematic sampling	Frequently most useful; trends over time and space must be quantified
Multistage sampling	Target population large and homogeneous; simple random sampling used to select continguous groups of population units
Cluster sampling	Economical when population units cluster (e.g., schools of fish); ideally, cluster means are similar in value, but concentrations within clusters should vary widely
Double sampling	Must be strong linear relation between variable of interest and less-expensive or more easily measured variable

Source: NRC, 1991

ants deposited in acid rain and their relationship to potential ecological effects in lakes and on forest vegetation.[18,19] In addition, visibility degradation in the scenic areas of the western United States and in the urban–rural areas of the eastern United States and problems associated with compliance with prevention of significant deterioration of statutes have been the subject of multipollutant, fixed site, and platform sampling studies.[20]

Epidemiological and field health effects studies require an understanding of the distribution of a pollutant and the potential locations of maximum impact. However, each health investigation requires sampling over time periods and in locations that are appropriate for relating species or pollutant exposures to a potential effect. At a minimum, the information derived for health purposes should be appropriate for estimating the incremental inhalation exposure, $c(t)dt$, of an individual in a particular environment; where $c(t)$ is the time varying concentration and dt is the differential interval of time associated with a biologically plausible effect used to define a sampling interval. Table 3-3 illustrates the general types of studies that can be considered to define exposures and develop exposure–response relationships.[21,22]

Indoor and Personal Sampling

Many pollutants may have both outdoor and indoor sources. Situations involving exposures to a particular chemical that lead to health effects may require a thorough evaluation of a person's total inhalation exposure or, at a minimum, the quantification of the important microenvironments and exposures. This will ensure that the major sources of exposure can be accurately identified for risk assessment and/or health effects studies. Confounding factors, such as occupation, weather, secondary products, etc., must also be explored to be sure that any potential effect is associated with air pollution.[22]

For pollutants with major indoor sources, the use of a fixed outdoor monitoring site in a population center may not accurately reflect the exposures for any given individual or for the population as a whole.[23] Prior to major initiatives on outdoor emission controls in the 1970s, this measurement design was probably more reasonable for compounds such as sulfur dioxide, benzo(a)pyrene, or particulate matter. However, in most areas of the United States, strict pollution control regulations have reduced the levels of a number of pollutants to the point where indoor concentrations (e.g., nitrogen dioxide, VOCs) are often equivalent to or higher than the outdoor concentrations.[8,21] In developing or third world nations, the outdoor levels for some pollutants may still be well above indoor concentrations; however, for situations in which unvented cooking occurs, the indoor concentrations of both criteria and noncriteria pollutants can be excessively high.[23] For some pollutants, especially VOCs, radon, nitrogen dioxide, and carbon monoxide, indoor and personal air sampling will be required to identify situations where high concentration exposures occur. For secondary pollutants such as ozone and acid aerosols, outdoor monitors may still provide adequate metrics of population exposures.[24,25]

Chronic health effects studies would require identifying areas or subpopulations that would be subjected to conditions conducive to high, medium, and low pollution exposure. Acute effects studies may be designed in one location where significant temporal changes are possible and are on a scale comparable to the potential effect. Personal monitoring of individuals is very desirable in many situations. For some pollutants, the monitors have become inexpensive to produce and inconspicuous to wear (e.g., passive diffusion monitors).[26,27]

Pollutant Characterization Sampling

Other common types of community air sampling studies are directed toward understanding the physical, chemical, and biologically active nature of the atmosphere (both indoor and outdoor). For an outdoor situation, the focus or foci can be 1) the formation or decay processes of individual compounds, 2) the transport and transformation of pollutants in industrial or urban plumes, 3) the wet or dry deposition of pollutants, 4) the dynamics of pollution accumulation and removal in urban and rural locales, 5) photochemical smog and other types of episodes, and 6) source tracer measurements. These can involve fixed-site sampling, mobile vans and trailers, and airborne sampling platforms.

Indoor studies may emphasize characterization of sources, outdoor pollution penetration, adsorption, absorption, transformation products, and transformation rates. In these cases, samplers will be located in one or more rooms throughout a house or more commonly, a group of houses. An important example that is outside the realm of traditional air pollution is the infiltration of contaminated groundwater within the vadose zone (unsaturated soil) into the basement of a home.[5] This will lead to the emission of volatile species into the basement and living quarters.

General Features of Community Studies

Using the previous section as a guide, it is immediately apparent that a number of factors must be considered when designing a community air pollution sampling program. Key articles or books can be useful in designing the details of a specific type of study and representative examples are found in the reference list. There are some basic or fundamental steps that must be considered prior to any community air sampling study, and these are outlined in the following sections.

Sampler Location

Selection of an outdoor air monitoring site requires addressing a number of considerations that will affect pollution values recorded at any given time. These include 1) the type(s) of point or area sources; 2) obstructions or changes to air flow caused by tall buildings, trees, etc.; 3) abrupt changes in terrain; 4) height above ground for a sampler or sampler probe; and 5) topography.

Beyond considerations of the physical location of the monitor, each site must be representative in terms of the questions to be answered by the study. All too often, an agency or the investigator can select a location that seems practical in terms of availability, security, and electrical needs, yet would severely compromise the intent of the study. At times, these practical problems cannot be resolved easily, but the suitability of the site for answering pollutant-related questions (e.g., regulatory or health) must be the prime consideration.

For example, if the objective is to monitor the outdoor air concentrations of carbon monoxide (or other emission or evaporative compounds) derived from automobile emissions within the center of a city, the concentrations inhaled would be found in a breathing zone approximately 1–2 m above the street, and some of the highest values would be found between tall buildings forming a street canyon. In addition, personal exposure to carbon monoxide may be enhanced by the driving habits of an individual, time spent in parking garages, and time spent outdoors. Thus, the maximum carbon monoxide concentration for a specific subpopulation may be due to exposure in a specific microenvironment like the cabin area of a car or bus, or an office above a parking garage.[28–30]

In contrast, ozone monitors are normally placed at some distance from the primary sources of its precursors, nitrogen oxides and hydrocarbons. In the early 1970s, Coffey and Stasiuk made a major observation in a rural area of New York State.[31] Their results showed the presence of ozone concentrations in a rural area to be at or above levels found in major urban areas. This finding required the scientific and regulatory community to reevaluate where and when high ozone would occur in the Eastern United States, where population exposures could be significant, and what is required to achieve attainment.[32] Today, ambient ozone monitors are located in rural and suburban areas throughout the United States and other countries. During the summer, the 8-hr averages of ozone can be above the occupational threshold limit value (TLV) of 100 ppb, which creates concern about possible health effects in the general population.[4,33] Because high ozone concentrations occur in both rural and suburban areas, a study could be conducted that is not confounded by the presence of many locally generated pollutants.

Acid aerosol studies display many design features characteristic of ozone, e.g., maximum during the summer; outdoor exposure during periods of activity.[34] In addition, it is imperative that the monitors are located at a distance from local ammonia sources to obtain an accurate regional characterization of the potential exposure. However, a site near an ammonia source might be useful because ammonia neutralizes the acidity. The site may identify the population unaffected by the acid aerosol (a local control).

Sampler Location for Health Studies

Generally, air sampling conducted in support of health effects studies requires the data to be representative of population exposures. Ideally, the measurements should be completed coincidentally with any measurements of a health outcome. Once a population or populations are defined, the need for indoor sampling or personal monitoring must be assessed. Further, the number of central sampling stations, personal monitors, and/or indoor air samplers must be positioned to obtain adequate representation of where the selected population (affected and control) lives.[35] The size of the population to be studied, as well as the number of homes to be used, can be determined from epidemiologic principles.[36,37] The need for personal versus microenvironmental monitoring and the use of questionnaires and biological markers must be examined. The investigator must also evaluate a variety of typical personal habits and lifestyles that could confound analysis. A typical confounder is the exposure attributable to environmental tobacco.[38]

The positioning of the outdoor monitors requires a full understanding of the nature of pollutant accumulation under ambient conditions. From our previous examples, adequate measurement of the distribution of ambient carbon monoxide in an urban environment requires the placement of many more samplers than are required to measure exposure to ozone. The basic reason is that carbon monoxide accumulates in confined spaces and produces a large range in concentrations over a short spatial range. A personal carbon monoxide monitor provides data that are more closely coupled to the biological marker of internal dose: carboxyhemoglobin. In contrast, ambient ozone concentrations will vary rather uniformly over a large area, although some local differences will be observed because of high local concentrations of nitric oxide. Thus, for the latter, a few well-placed samplers may provide data adequate for both exposure and health analyses.

The mobility of the study population is important in defining the outdoor sampling situations. Consideration must be given to the variations in exposure to a pollutant emitted near a residence, a place of employment, transportation routes, a school, and recreational activities (Figure 3-2).

Sampling Frequency and Duration

In a community air pollution study, the length of the sampling program is shaped by a number of factors, not the least of which is the amount of resources available to conduct the study. However, this perennial problem aside, the purpose of a community air pollution research program will have a major influence on the duration of the sampling activities. For example, long-term trend studies should be conducted for multiple years to obtain data on the range of concentrations, overall influence of meteorology, and changes in emission strength.[39] Examination of peak concentrations, diurnal variations, and episode conditions requires a study design that ensures a sufficient number of sampling days or hours to include a representative number and range of events. In many instances, only one or two major events will occur. For example, the study of photochemical smog exposures requires sampling to be conducted for an extensive period during the summer (approximately 45 days). This provides a sufficient number of sampling days for measuring the impact of one or more episodes.[40] If continuous samplers are used for reactive hydrocarbons, ozone, selected organic species, and nitrogen oxide measurements, the kinetic processes associated with the accumulation of oxidant species can be examined and subsequently modeled.[4,41]

Another example is the examination of local source impacts on the surrounding neighborhood. In this case, an intensive community air sampling program would have an array of sampling sites placed around the facility. The size of the emission source would dictate the extent of the array, e.g., an industrial source versus a gasoline station versus wood burning, but the number should be sufficient to detect concentration variability due to changes in wind direction and source strength (Figure 3-3). This type of spatial coverage provides an investigator with an opportunity to determine the contributions in background or upwind air. The duration of the study would have to be sufficient to identify the meteorological conditions conducive to maximum plume impact.[1] The study could be at least 1 or 2 years in duration, but the approach could include an intensive period of study for gathering baseline information, and then a second phase that is primarily activated when specific meteorological conditions are anticipated to occur. Determining this time frame is not an easy task. For individual pollutants present in a plume, it may be important to consider the use of indoor and/or personal samplers within an impacted area. The true picture of the pollutant loading contributed by a plant to a community is better assessed by quantifying the extent of outdoor pollutant(s) penetration indoors.

In some cases, such as lead emissions, the deposition of particulate matter on the soil or in water may be potentially the most important indirect source of air pollutant exposure to people, plants, or animals. Obvi-

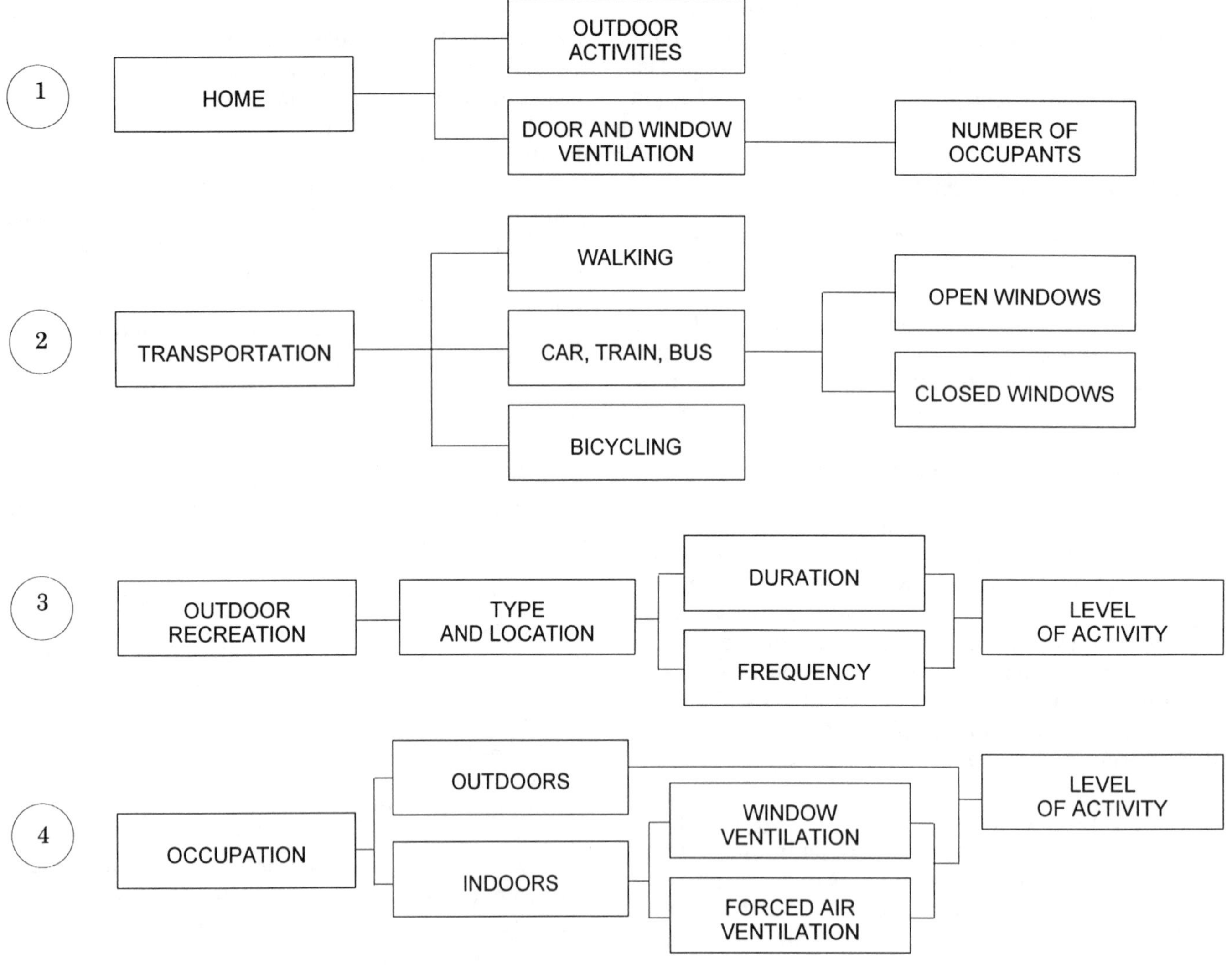

FIGURE 3-2. Personal activities with potential outdoor pollution exposure. 1: Home; 2: Transportation; 3: Recreation; 4: Occupation.

ously, this situation will require determining a pollutant's concentration in the surface soil and/or the groundwater, and then estimating exposure from ingestion and dermal contact in addition to inhalation.(22)

Averaging Time

Sample averaging time is dependent upon the instrumentation available to conduct a study, the detection limits for a particular compound, and the time resolution required to discriminate particular events or effects. For many of the gaseous criteria pollutants, this will not pose a problem because most devices are continuous samplers.(42)

For VOCs, the devices primarily integrate a sample over an interval that is usually 24 hrs in duration.(43) Unfortunately, there is a wide range of artifact formation, breakthrough, and equilibrium problems associated with VOCs that limit the number of compounds that can be measured reliably. At the present time, some state agencies have set up routine air monitoring networks for VOCs. U.S. EPA initiated a Toxic Air Monitoring system (TAMs) that measured approximately 15 VOCs using a stainless steel canister or a set of four distributed-volume Tenax® samplers for 24 hrs on an every sixth day sampling cycle.(44) Currently, the Summa® canister is the sampling methodology of choice for routine VOC investigations.(45)

The results of the Total Exposure Assessment Methodology (TEAM) studies have indicated that the major route of population exposure to VOCs is indoor air, suggesting a different focus for future investigations.(9) Further development of VOC sampling techniques, such as continuous monitors, canisters, and human breath analysis as a biological marker of exposure, will occur as more researchers attempt to measure concentrations within specific or new volatile compounds present in the outdoor and indoor environment. Included would be areas around specific toxic pollutant sources, landfills, and hazardous waste sites.

Particulate matter sampling has normally been conducted with devices that integrate samples, although continuous monitors exist that measure specific particle size ranges (Chapter 5). For most routine U.S. EPA and state regulatory monitoring efforts through the early 1980s, total suspended particulate (TSP) samples were collected on a statistically based every sixth day schedule and were 24 hrs in duration. This approach is marginally adequate for the determination of mass and selected inorganic and organic constituents. For other material, such as semivolatile organics and hydrogen ion (which represents aerosol acidity), other samplers with much shorter (<6 hrs) and more frequent samples (four/day) may be needed for a community air sampling program. For some compounds, gas and vapor denuders are required upstream of a filter; for others, additional samplers are required after the filter to reduce artifacts due to filter absorption or desorption of compounds during a specific sampling period.

The need for conducting size-selective particle sampling is discussed in Chapter 5, which also identifies instruments and methods for sampling. Presently, a number of size-selective devices are used in ambient, personal, and indoor studies. These are designed to collect particles presented to various regions of the lung (see Figure 5-5, in Chapter 5). The most common are the thoracic samplers (d_{50} = 10 μm), respirable samplers (d_{50} = 4.0 μm), and fine particle samplers (d_{50} = 2.5 μm). D_{50} is the aerodynamic diameter of particles collected by a sampler with an efficiency of 50%. Devices have been developed that can be used to detect particle size fractionated mass and many inorganic and organic constituents in time intervals of 4 hrs or less. In addition, for the dichotomous filter sampler,[46] automated models are available that provide the opportunity to obtain up to 36 consecutive samples over various time durations. The minimum or maximum duration of any particular sample would depend on the detection limits for the compounds measured and the range of pollution levels present in a particular area.

As of July 1987, U.S. EPA replaced the TSP standard with a standard for PM_{10} (particulate mass collected with a 50% cut size of 10 μm). Community air pollution sampling for attainment is now conducted for this particulate fraction every third day. In areas where exceedances of the NAAQS occur, it is anticipated that the sampling schedule can be increased to every day. This can be a very labor-intensive program and some communities opt to replace it with the use of a continuous particle monitor (see Chapter 16).

Personal samplers with respirable particle inlets are presently used in indoor air pollution studies.[47] Recently, personal samplers for PM_{10} have also become available (see Chapter 14). An excellent summary of the recent data available on PM_{10} measurements throughout the United States is found in Chow *et al.*[48]

An important current need is for measurements of particulate matter from fugitive dust emissions at hazardous waste sites. This is much more complicated than routine monitoring of particles because high levels are usually sporadic and dependent upon local conditions, including wind speed and direction, unpaved road traffic density, and personal activities. Long-term data would probably not find the PM_{10} concentrations much above those typically found in ambient air, but sporadic events could lead to high concentrations of toxics redistributed through the air (inhalation exposure) and deposited at offsite surfaces (ingestion exposure).

Chemical Analyses

Presently, community air sampling surveys for particulate matter can require analyses beyond a traditional mass determination. Some fairly routine measurements include the concentrations of numerous trace elements (e.g., Pb, Cd, Cs, Fe, Se, As, and Br) and water-soluble ions (sulfate, ammonium, chloride, and

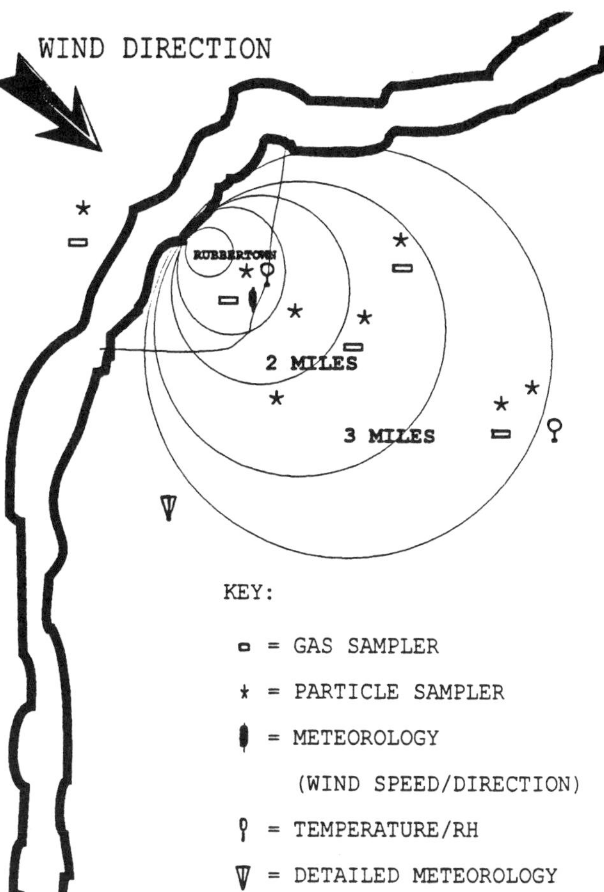

FIGURE 3-3. Site locations for air samplers and meteorology around a major source (adapted from Stern[1]).

nitrate).[49] More sophisticated studies may measure the acidity of sulfate particles,[50] the organic mass fractions,[51] specific organic species,[52] and elemental carbon.[53] Such measurements have been instrumental in the development of receptor-based modeling approaches, which quantify the contributions made by particular sources to the ambient air.[54]

Samplers have been developed for outdoor studies that can also routinely collect particulate organics on a filter and have a vapor trap that contains polyurethane foam. The trap collects semivolatile species that evaporate from the filter during sampling. These devices are housed in a Hi-volume sampler shell and operate at 40 ft.^{3}/min (1.13 m^3/min).

Area particulate matter samplers for indoor air pollution measurements have been developed by a number of investigators. The most sophisticated are the Marple–Spengler–Turner samplers, which collect mass on a Teflon® filter and can have single or multiple aerodynamic cut sizes between 10 and 1 μm.[55] The samples are collected for various time intervals from <1 day to 4 days. Most analyses performed for ambient samples can be conducted on indoor impactor filters if the mass loading is sufficiently high and if a limited number of destructive analyses are completed on the samples.

A careful review of analytical tools for air sampling can be found in an Air and Waste Management Association (AWMA) critical review.[49] Other useful information is found in the works of a number of authors listed in the reference section and from the many instrument chapters in this manual.

Biological Assay of Air Samples

The identification of potentially carcinogenic compounds in the atmosphere has led to the development and application of techniques for the measurement of the biological activity of particulate and gaseous samples. In principle, actual animal bioassays of carcinogenic air pollution are the most direct measure of potential effect;[56] however, these assays are difficult to conduct on ambient air. As an alternative to actual animal bioassays, short-term *in vitro* bioassays have been used to examine the mutagenic properties of organic materials. Of the known carcinogens, over 80% have been shown to be mutagenic in the Ames Assay,[57] a short-term *in vitro* technique that uses alterations in the *Salmonella* DNA to demonstrate the mutagenic properties of organic material in particulate matter. The Ames Assay has been the method of choice for application to air pollution samples.[58] The concentration results of such assays have been reported as revertant colonies per cubic meter of air; for mutagenic potency, these have been reported as revertant colonies per microgram of sample. Through 1985, over 50 studies have used the Ames Assay on air pollution samples, and the results with references have been summarized by Louis *et al.*[59] At present, further research is being directed to the identification of the actual compounds contributing to the mutagenic activity of the air pollution samples.[60] An excellent investigation called the Integrated Air Cancer Study was conducted to assess the contributions made by wood smoke and automobiles to the biologically active portions of particulate matter. The study employed a variety of chemical and biological assays to quantify the contributions to ambient air.[61]

The field application of biological measures as markers of exposure is beginning to evolve. It is anticipated that techniques will continue to be developed which will permit the precise measurement of biologically effective exposure and dose to individuals in a community. This could include the use of cytotoxicity tests as well as the application of breath analyses.[26,28,61,62]

Data Retrieval and Analysis

For the state monitoring networks required to assess attainment of the NAAQS, most data are sent by telemetry to a central station for computerized data recording, validation, and processing of many of the continuously measured pollutants. At a minimum, the NAAQS pollutants NO_x, O_3, SO_2, and CO are monitored continuously. These data are formatted with identifying parameters and are sent to the National Aerometric Data Bank. The format used for data that are archived by the U.S. EPA is called SAROAD. Manually collected particulate pollution data are eventually entered by tape or by hand into a computer after a number of chemical analyses have been performed on a series of samples.

Intensive field studies conducted at a given location have become much more sophisticated in both study design, monitoring equipment, and data gathering practices. The former will be discussed in a separate section; however, improvements in the use and application of sampling and data retrieval equipment have been significant. This should continue in the future with the advent of optical fiber transmission, high speed microcomputers, and CD-ROM storage of data.

Beyond the construction of fixed monitoring sites with telemetry systems, a number of groups have developed and utilized fully equipped mobile vans or trailers. One of the most sophisticated mobile units used in field studies was a trailer designed as the Atmospheric Research Laboratory of General Motors Research Laboratories, which has a complete computerized system for continuous samplers, calibration facilities, and integrated samplers.[63] The interior of the trailer is shown in Figure 3-4. It has been used in field studies on atmospheric chemistry and air pollution throughout the United States. Another mobile unit was developed cooperatively by the New York University

FIGURE 3-4. Atmospheric Research Laboratory of General Motors Research Laboratories (GMRL) (supplied by G. Wolff, GMRL, Warren, Michigan).

and U.S. EPA. This van houses both monitoring equipment and health measurement equipment in separate sections of the same vehicle. The continuous environmental exposure monitors (O_3, NO_x, SO_2, H_2SO_4) and the Total Sulfur Analyzer use a data logger that feeds a cassette recorder. Designed for acute health effects studies, this van is equipped to make measurements of pulmonary function parameters (Forced Vital Capacity, Forced Expiratory Volume in 1 second, Peak Expiratory Flow Rate) from a spirometry system. The spirometry is conducted on two computerized systems with memory to store the lung function tracings and calculate function parameter values for an individual. The information is displayed on a monitor for visual observation during actual tests.[64]

Air Pollution Modeling

When a community air pollution program or study is designed, one of the primary activities to be considered for use of the collected data is model development. Models play an important role in the examination of air pollution because they can be used to: 1) determine the effectiveness of control strategies, 2) predict pollutant concentrations downwind of sources, 3) examine chemical processes; 4) examine regional transport questions; 5) establish source-receptor relationships; and 6) estimate human exposure. In all cases, though, an important final step is the validation of a model using community sampling data. The acquisition of these types of pollution data requires carefully selected protocols because an application of a model(s) poses certain constraints on the selection of variables, study duration, sampling frequency, number of samples, and sampling site selection.

The most common form of models applied to air pollution is based on the Gaussian dispersion model. It estimates the contributions at a downwind receptor site of a pollutant emitted by a source after dispersal in the atmosphere under a variety of meteorological conditions. The technique has been used in community air pollution for many years and is available for specific source and terrain applications as off-the-shelf models. Turner[65] in 1979 published a review of dispersion modeling that covers the general features of the technique and the source and meteorological information necessary to apply the various types of models. In 1984, Hidy[66] completed a review of air pollution modeling issues but focused on regional models and their application to the source–receptor relationships of acid deposition.[67,68] In 1988, Seinfeld examined the status of available models for predicting the behavior of photochemical smog.[69]

Another modeling approach that has been used extensively since the late 1970s is receptor–source apportionment. The general technique involves constructing a model that determines the sources that contribute to pollution levels observed at a receptor location. In contrast to dispersion modeling, it derives information from compositional data collected at the receptor (sampler). The significance of the source is obtained by measuring the concentration of a source tracer at the receptor and other pollutants emitted by the source by using the principle of conservation of mass.

A number of different approaches are available that can be used to develop receptor models, including Chemical Element Balance,(70) Factor-Analysis Multiple Regression,(71) and Target Transformation.(72) Applications of these models are summarized by Hopke,(73) and a review of their use in transport modeling studies has been published by Thurston and Lioy.(74)

A more recent approach to modeling that examines the frequency and distribution of a pollutant among a population is *human exposure modeling*.(4,21) This type of modeling involves the acquisition of pollutant concentration data, identification of the activity patterns of an individual or a target population, and the estimation of time spent by an individual in a particular microenvironment. From these data, a model can be constructed that links the presence of an individual at a location in a microenvironment to the concentration of a pollutant present at that location for a certain length of time.(75–77) The exposures estimated are usually the average or integrated values for each microenvironment. A recent application of this technique was completed by Ott for carbon monoxide.(10) Advances and needs associated with the complex area of individual and population distribution exposure modeling were recently detailed in the NRC Report "Human Exposures to Airborne Pollutants: Advances and Opportunities."(21)

Examples of Community Air Pollution Studies Since 1970

The following section briefly describes some important ambient air quality studies designed to examine specific types of community air pollution problems. Some are dated in terms of the usefulness of the scientific information and instrumentation, but the basic approach for completing the study is sound and survives. Where possible, examples of recent studies that have built upon previous research are mentioned briefly and cited for future review and analysis. Clearly, the reader should attempt to select those aspects of one or more study designs that can be of value in implementing a new study or monitoring survey. It is important that the more recent references are examined to ensure that state-of-the-art instrumentation is selected or evaluated for use in a study. The instruments discussed in this manual provide a valuable starting point for an investigator.

California Aerosol Characterization Experiment (ACHEX)

One of the most comprehensive early investigations of outdoor air pollution, which is still a classic, was ACHEX(78) (see Table 3-4). The major objectives of the study focused on describing the physical and chemical characteristics of photochemical smog aerosols and establishing relationships with the reduction of visibility in Southern California. As an adjunct to this study, the three-dimensional distribution and transport of a number of pollutants were examined in the region.

The approach involved very intensive case study sampling for attainment protocols within a particular 24-hr (midnight to midnight) period. Conduct of actual experiments was based on the results of a meteorological forecast 1 day before an experiment and the potential for high ozone levels. Depending upon the instrumentation used for a particular pollutant, the sample durations were from 10 min to 2 hrs. This provided an opportunity to obtain detailed information on the origin and evolution of the smog aerosol. The basic ACHEX study lasted from 1972 through 1973, with most of the field activity concentrated in the summer and the early fall. In contrast to other studies, the measurement systems were located in a mobile van that took samples at a number of locations. These sites were areas with either high source emission densities, or receptors of reacted species, or nonurban areas. The measurements in the van were supplemented with data from a number of fixed sites in Southern California.

In addition to the particulate mass, a number of species were measured, including sulfates, organic compounds, and trace elements. Particle size distributions were obtained from a series of analyzers that covered the nuclei through the coarse particle size ranges(79) and were processed as 10-min averages. Continuous measurements were obtained for a number of gases including total hydrocarbons and ozone. A complete listing of the chemical constituents measured and the techniques used is found in Hidy *et al.*(80)

Some major findings in the study included information on the duration and multimodal nature of the particle size distribution, the chemical composition of different size fractions, the episode intensity, the source apportionment of the particulate mass in the atmosphere, and the particle size fractions and sources causing visibility reduction.

A more recent version of this study was The Southern California Air Quality Study (SCAQS), which involved several government and industry laboratories and universities. It was conducted in 1987, and the results are found in a number of publications.(81,82)

Before ACHEX, almost nothing was known about the

TABLE 3-4. Site Locations for the Mobile Van During the ACHEX Study

Occupancy Date	Site	Location	Environment
A. 1972			
July 15–30	Berkeley	College of Agriculture tract 2175 Hearsat Avenue Berkeley, California	Acceptance tests and preliminary checkout
Aug. 1–13	Richmond	San Pueblo Water Pollution Control Plant 2377 Garden Tract Road San Pueblo, California	Urban–industrial (downwind from chemical complex)
Aug. 15–27	San Francisco airport	On the airport property at Bayshore Drive and end of north–south runway	Aircraft-enriched aerosol; receptor of aerosol from west San Francisco Bay area
Aug. 28–Sept. 11	Fresno	Fresno County Fairgrounds 1121 Chance Avenue Fresno, California	Photochemical–agricultural
Sept. 12–18	Hunter–Liggett Military Reservation	Meadow areas, 1 mile south of the public road connecting Hunter–Liggett with Route 1	Vegetarian-enriched (expected photochemical aerosol production from vegetation organic emissions)
Sept. 19–Oct. 2	Freeway Loop	May Company parking lot 3rd Street and Hope Street Los Angeles, California	Auto-enriched (100 ft east of Harbor Freeway)
Oct. 3–30	Pomona	Los Angeles County Fairgrounds Pomona, California	Los Angeles photochemical (receptor)
Oct. 30–Nov. 4	Goldstone	Goldstone Tracking Station Barstow, California	Desert background
Nov. 6–10	Point Arguello	U.S. Coast Guard LORAN Station	Marine-enriched
B. 1973			
July 11–Aug. 9	West Covina	Hospital on Sunset Avenue West Covina, California	Los Angeles photochemical (receptor)
Aug. 11–25	Pomona	Los Angeles, County Fairgrounds Pomona, California	Los Angeles photochemical (receptor)
Aug. 27–Sept. 26	Rubidoux (Riverside)	Rubidoux Water Treatment Plant Rubidoux, California	Los Angeles photochemical (receptor)
Sept. 29–Oct. 11	Dominguez Hills	California State College Dominguez Hills, California	Source-dominated (refineries, chemical industry)

From Hidy *et al.*[80] Reprinted by permission of John Wiley & Sons, Inc.

ambient particulate pollutants, and that study gained an overall picture of particulate pollutants. In contrast, SCAQS was designed to gather measurement inputs needed to improve basinwide modeling of the formation of particulate and gaseous pollutants. The SCAQS used intensive, simultaneous, ground-based monitoring at nine sites, with 4- to 7-hr time resolution for particulate samples. It also included wind and temperature profiled aloft (by radio-equipped weather balloons called rawinsondes), and gaseous pollutant profiles aloft (measured by aircraft).

Denver "Brown Cloud" Study

The "Brown Cloud" study was a study that characterized the ambient atmosphere during the winter. This mesoscale (<100 km) pollution phenomenon is topographically induced and affects the metropolitan Denver area. There have been several "Brown Cloud" studies, including programs in 1973,[83] 1978, [84–87] 1982,[88] and 1987–1988.[89] A major feature of the 1978 investigation, which was conducted in November and December, was the measurement of both the organic and elemental carbon content of size-fractionated particulate mass. Chemical analyses similar to those conducted in ACHEX provided the opportunity to conduct source apportionment studies. In addition, the species contributing to visibility reduction in Denver were estimated.

A very elaborate community sampling program was established for this intensive investigation (Figure 3-5).

It included surface-based sites to measure 1) the maximum impact of the pollution contained in the cloud, 2) the background concentrations, and 3) the characteristics of the cloud throughout various parts of the city. Aircraft measurements were made in the vertical and horizontal direction to examine cloud dynamics.

Measurements were made of the fine and coarse particle mass, which was composed of sulfate, nitrate, and ammonium ions; trace elements; and the carbon fractions. Source apportionment studies were conducted using the chemical element balance technique and regression models were developed to estimate the contributors to visibility reduction.

Airborne Toxic Element and Organic Substance (ATEOS) Project

The ATEOS project was an extensive community air pollution characterization study that was designed to investigate not only the atmospheric dynamics and distribution of pollutants, but also the potential risks to human health from biologically active materials present in the outdoor air.[90] More than 50 pollutants were measured simultaneously at fixed monitoring sites within three urban areas in New Jersey and at a rural location. Each site was selected to reflect a different type of industrial–commercial–residential interface that was representative of a different type of exposure situation rather than the entire city. For example, the Newark site was within a residential area surrounded by small and moderately sized industrial facilities, e.g., body shops and chemical manufacturers (Figure 3-6). The site was a surrogate for the exposures to ambient pollutants in the local community rather than the central business district and its residents.

Each day measurements were completed in Newark, Elizabeth, Camden, and Ringwood (the latter is the rural site) over the course of 6 weeks in the summers of 1981 and 1982 and the winters of 1982 and 1983. Most samples were 24 hrs in duration, and these included inhalable particulate mass ($d_{50} = 15\ \mu m$) and VOCs. The mass was analyzed for a number of components, including nonpolar through polar organics, PAHs, sulfates, trace elements, mutagenicity, and alkylating agents. A total of 26 VOCs were measured, including benzene, toluene, chlorinated hydrocarbons, and vinyl chloride.

The study produced useful information on potential human exposures to biologically active compounds in different types of community settings and identified target populations for future epidemiological studies. Other results defined seasonal and interurban variations, the intensity of summer and winter episodes, and the sources of the mass and its organic fractions.[91] The ATEOS results eventually led to the Total Human Environmental Exposure Study (THEES),[11,92] which examined the influence of multimedia pathways on an individual's exposure to benzo(a)pyrene (BaP).

Harvard Six-City and Multicity Studies

The community air sampling conducted in the Harvard study, which is familiar to many as the Harvard Six Cities Study, included outdoor, indoor, and personal air monitoring.[93] The air sampling was in support of the 10-year prospective examination of respiratory symptoms and pulmonary function of children and adults living in the six communities of Topeka, Kansas; Portage, Wisconsin; Watertown, Massachusetts; Kingston, Tennessee; St. Louis, Missouri; and Steubenville, Ohio. Indices of acute and chronic respiratory effects and pulmonary function performances were examined in relation to any adverse effects of ambient and indoor air pollutants.

Fixed outdoor air sampling sites were located in each community. However, because exposure to a number of air pollutants, such as nitrogen dioxide, respirable particles, and formaldehyde, can be associated with a number of microenvironments, indoor and personal samples are required for individuals participating in the study. The use of each of the above types of samples provides microenvironment and personal pollution data for the development of exposure models as well as estimation of the influence of various activity patterns. The most extensive indoor database developed in the Harvard study is for nitrogen dioxide and respirable particles. As shown in Figure 3-7, the respirable particles measured or monitored indoors can contribute the dominant proportion of the personal exposure.

The fixed monitoring sites measured total suspended particulates, respirable particles, trace elements, sulfate, acid sulfates, ozone, and other pollutant gases. The indoor particulate samples were analyzed for a number of the above and, in special studies, they were analyzed for tracers specific to tobacco smoke. The Harvard study has provided an opportunity to conduct a number of supplementary studies and add pollutants as the measurement technology; the potential for pollutants to affect public health is defined. For instance, measurement of acid sulfates was added after a number of researchers conducted investigations and determined that significant concentrations of acid-sulfate species are present at times in the outdoor atmosphere. This led to the 24 cities health study which examined the health effects related to ambient acid aerosols and ozone exposures in moderately sized cities in North America. Information on the study design required to collect acid aerosol data that were relevant to the health measurements was described by Speizer.[94]

Total Exposure Assessment Methodology (TEAM) Study

The last study that will be examined in this chapter,

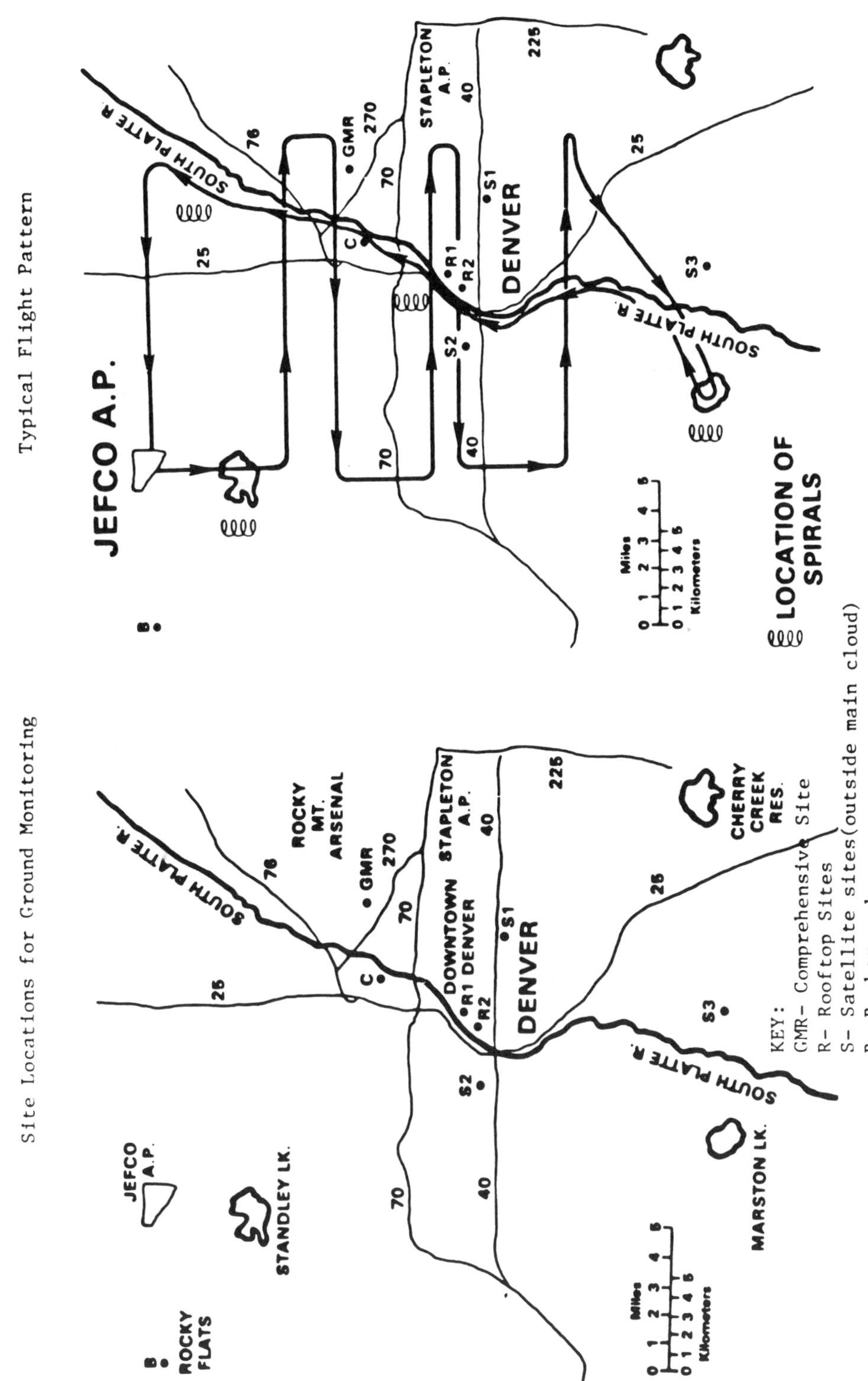

FIGURE 3-5. The Denver "Brown Cloud" Study (reproduced from Wolff *et al.*[55] with permission).

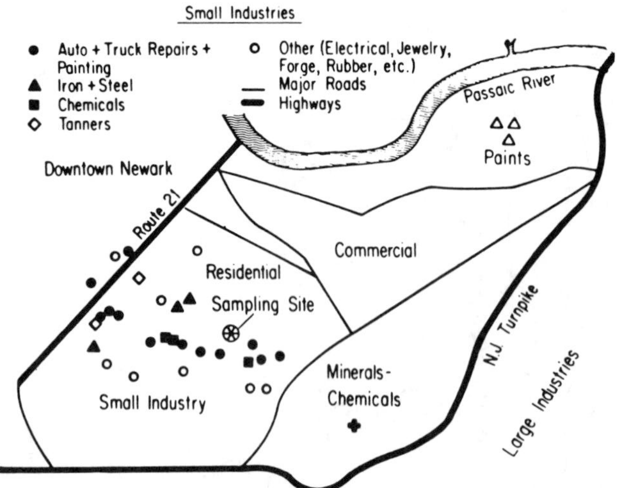

FIGURE 3-6. The distribution of sources around the subpopulation studied in ATEOS (from Lioy and Daisey;[61] adapted from Final Report to N.J. DEP. 1985).

although there are many other examples, is the TEAM Study.[9] At the time, it provided another unique approach to the study of community pollution. The investigation was actually a series of studies conducted in 10 cities in the United States from 1980 through 1984. Because the TEAM was a statistically designed study, inferences could be drawn about the general population living in certain areas of Elizabeth/Bayonne, New Jersey; the South Bay of Los Angeles, California; and Antioch/Pittsburgh, Pennsylvania.

The investigation primarily involved measuring the personal exposures of 700 individuals to 20 VOCs and the corresponding body burden. Fixed-site, outdoor sampling was conducted next to the homes of the participants. Personal monitoring was completed on each individual, and the levels of the compounds were measured in exhaled breath as an indication of levels that could be found in an individual's blood. Drinking water and beverage concentrations of the VOCs were determined, and detailed questionnaires were administered concerning occupation, hobby, and home VOC sources. Other substudies conducted in the TEAM included indoor microenvironmental sampling.[95]

A major result of the TEAM Study has been that the outdoor environment is not the primary contributor to personal VOC exposures (Figure 3-8). In many cases, the concentrations were 10 to 100 times higher indoors than those observed outdoors. Also, significant vari-

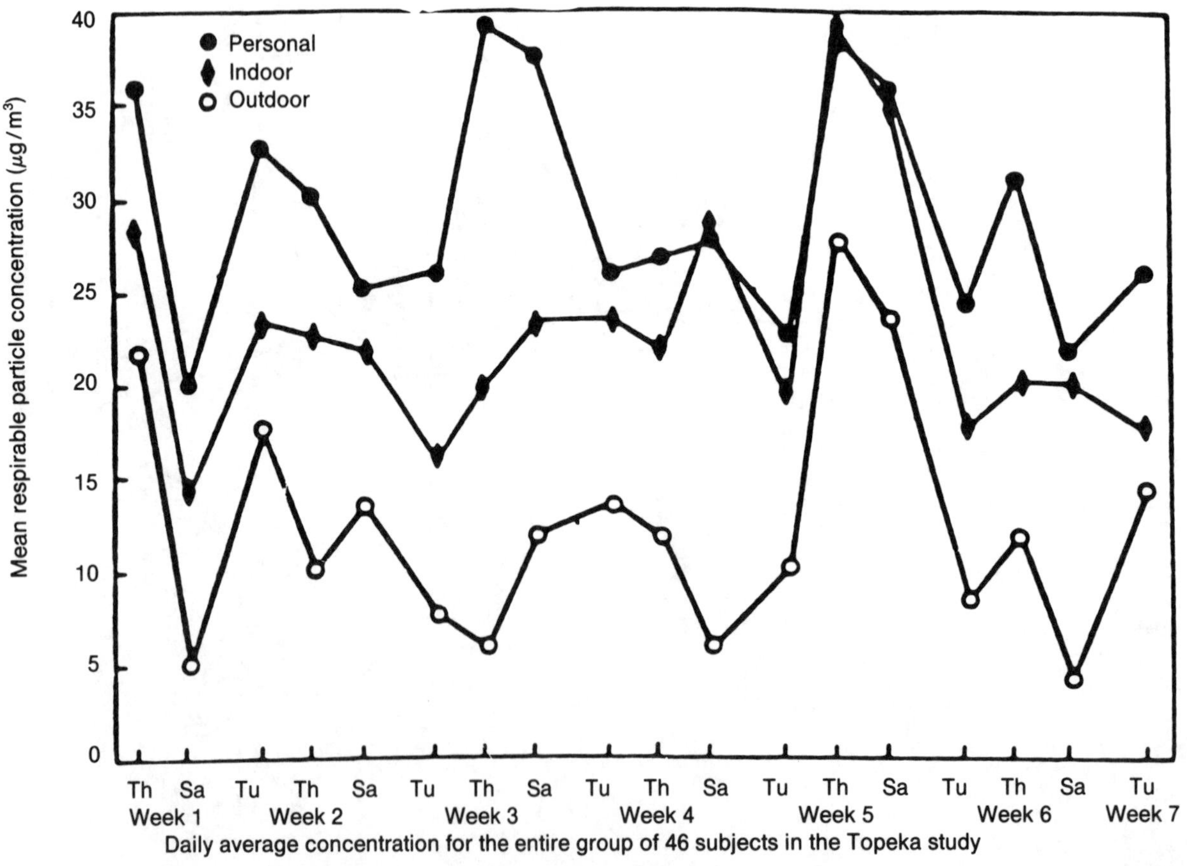

FIGURE 3-7. Personal, indoor, and outdoor levels of respirable particles in Topeka, Kansas, during the Harvard Health Study (reprinted with permission. J. Spengler, Harvard School of Public Health, 1987).

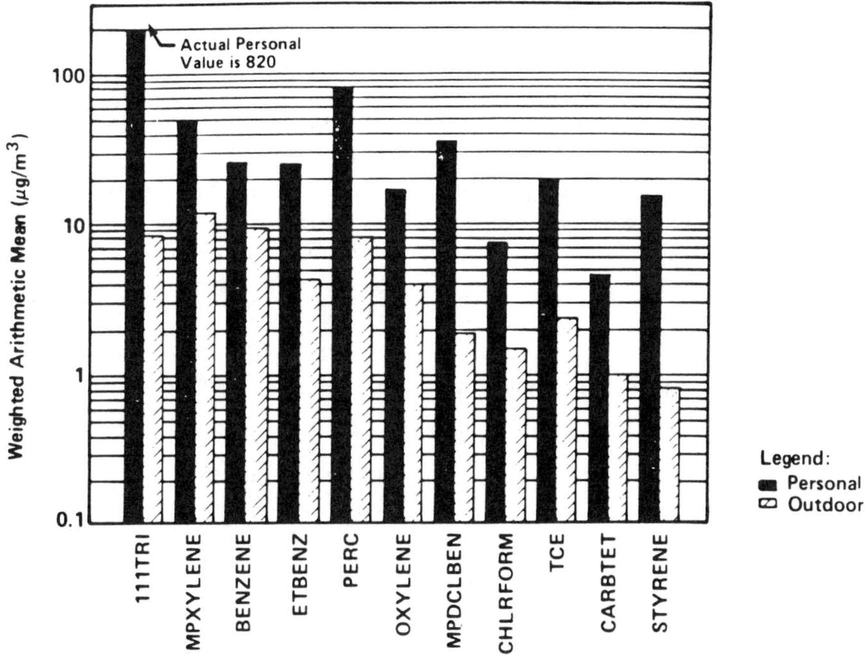

FIGURE 3-8. Estimated arithmetic means of 11 toxic compounds in daytime (6:00 am to 6:00 pm) air samples for the target population (128,000) of Elizabeth and Bayonne, New Jersey, between September and November 1981. Personal air estimates based on 340 samples; outdoor air estimates based on 88 samples (from Wallace;[6] reprinted with permission).

ations in the VOC concentrations can occur in a small geographic area during the day. Therefore, when planning epidemiological studies, investigators will have to consider the possibility of not having uniform exposures for VOCs.

A second phase of TEAM studies was conducted in the late 1980s to follow up on the hypotheses generated in the initial experiments. Included was a much more extensive use of breath analysis as a biological marker of exposure.[96–99]

Community Air Sampling at Hazardous Waste and Landfill Sites

Chemical waste disposal in the United States has been a significant problem for many years. Historically, the methods of disposal were not responsibly developed, and the disposal was usually controlled by industry, with insufficient regulation by governments.[100] With the passage of a number of federal and state regulations, numerous (>900) National Priorities List (NPL) chemical disposal sites have been identified across the nation, and 109 are associated with human health risk.[101] A few of the more well-known examples are the Rocky Mountain Arsenal, Colorado;[102] the Love Canal, New York; Hyde Park Landfill, Niagara Falls, New York; Rollins Landfill, Baton Rouge, Louisiana; Chemical Control, Elizabeth, New Jersey; and Jersey City Landfill, New Jersey.[103] In addition to the NPL sites, there are thousands of sites controlled by the states and other federal agencies.[101,104,105]

The individuals exposed to any air emissions from the many types of disposal sites include persons living and working in communities adjacent to the area. Their air pollution exposures may result from the inhalation of particles (fugitive dusts), fumes, or vapors dispersed in the ambient air from a dump before remediation, or during the mitigation stage. Volatilization of VOCs may also occur as a result of contaminated leachate moving through groundwater to a well that provides water used for showering and tap water in a home, or the evaporation of VOCs in basements and their circulation throughout the house.

Documentation of air pollution exposure requires a number of activities similar to those described in previous sections. These include a screening stage as well as an intensive study and a follow-up, long-term investigation. The study design would, of necessity, need a component that characterizes the emissions from the site. The usual approach includes borehole testing for potential volatile organic emissions, surface soil sampling, and groundwater sampling for compounds that could be dispersed away from the site. This type of information satisfies the requirements of a typical hazardous waste site. Because a remedial investigation establishes the magnitude and extent of the onsite contamination, extensive sampling could be made of the surface soil to determine the content of organics and trace elements dispersed as fugitive emissions to the surrounding neighborhood.

In contrast to general community air sampling studies, the nature of the emissions may be quite variable because the waste will generally not be homogeneous within a dump. Also, any active or continuing deposition of wastes or any activities associated with waste removal could change the emission rates (e.g., active landfills). Thus, a series of emissions tests may be required throughout the period encompassed by the study. Other screening activities would involve the use of hydrogeologists and meteorologists to model the movement of contaminants through the water and air, respectively.

During the second stage of a study; the nature and extent of the offsite population exposure to the pollution needs to be documented. This would primarily involve microenvironmental sampling. A study should include the identification of the most probable downwind directions for outdoor air and indoor air contamination, the downstream direction of flow for groundwater contamination, and the identification of a control area. After a series of samples are taken, the most exposed area could be subject to follow-up investigation. This approach can provide the basis for the development of epidemiological studies on specific health end points, and provide information needed to complete a risk assessment. Recent documentation on risk assessment for hazardous waste sites is beginning to lead to the use of techniques to characterize exposure.[106] However, this is not widely done, and the deficiencies in current exposure assessments have been noted in site-specific health assessments by the Agency for Toxic Substances and Disease Registry (ATSDR).[107]

The analytical approaches used would probably follow those presently available for both air pollution and industrial hygiene investigations. However, specific protocols are dependent upon the scope of the investigation. The sensitivity of the techniques used would probably be that required for ambient air sampling because ambient air usually contains the lowest concentrations of contaminants such as VOCs.

Summary

The purpose of air pollution measurements within the community environment is multidimensional. The basic type of program is used to examine source compliance with regulations and the progress toward attaining national or other ambient air quality standards for health or welfare effects. There are, however, a wide variety of research-based strategies to assess human or ecological exposure or effects. These can become very sophisticated in terms of number of measurements, sites, and duration of the study. Because of financial costs as well as personnel and time commitments, the investigators must clearly establish the hypotheses and data quality objectives prior to the development of a study. Each of the research studies described in this chapter was conducted to examine a community air pollution problem. Although these are by no means inclusive of all the types of investigations that can be designed, they do demonstrate 1) the breadth and depth to which studies of these types can examine the nature of the outdoor or indoor community atmosphere, 2) the advances in instrumentation and analyses for measuring pollutants, and 3) the flexibility available for finding appropriate sampling locations and for conducting experiments of adequate duration to obtain meaningful exposures.

Acknowledgments

The author wishes to thank Ms. Malti Patel for her efforts in editing and processing the manuscript and Mr. Jason Lioy for the graphics. Dr. Lioy's work is in part supported by NIEHS Center Grant #451-44-7121 and ATSDR Cooperative Agreement #451-44-8021.

References

1. Stern, A.C., Ed.: Air Pollution, Vol. I–V. Academic Press, New York (1977).
2. U.S. Federal Register 36:8186 (1971).
3. Public Law 101-549, 104 Stat. 2399, Clean Air Act. U.S. Government Printing Office, Washington, DC (Nov. 15, 1990).
4. National Research Council: Rethinking the Ozone Problem in Regional Air Pollution. National Academy Press, Washington, DC (1991).
5. U.S. Environmental Protection Agency: Enhanced Ozone Monitoring Network Design and Siting Criteria Guidance Document. EPA-45/4-9/-033. OAQPS, Research Triangle Park, NC (November 1991).
6. Wolff, G.T.: Mesoscale and Synoptic Scale Transport of Aerosols. In: Aerosols: Anthropogenic and Natural — Sources and Transport, pp. 338, 379–388. T.J. Kneip and P.J. Lioy, Eds. Ann. N.Y. Acad. of Sciences (1980).
7. National Research Council, Committee on Indoor Pollutants: Indoor Pollutants. National Academy Press, Washington, DC (1981).
8. Yocum, J.: Indoor-Outdoor Air Quality Relationships — A Critical Review. J. Air Pollut. Control Assoc. 32:500 (1982).
9. Wallace, L.: Total Exposure Assessment Methodology (TEAM) Study: Summary and Analysis, Vol. I. Final Report. Contract #68-0-02-3679. U.S. Environmental Protection Agency, Washington, DC (1986).
10. Ott, W.: Exposure Estimates Based Upon Computer Generated Activity Patterns. J.Toxicol. Clin. Toxicol. 21:97 (1983–84).
11. Lioy, P.; Waldman, J.; Greenberg, A.; et al.: The Total Human Environmental Exposure Study (THEES) to Benzo(a)pyrene: Comparison of the Inhalation and Food Pathways. Arch. Environ. Health 43:304 (1988).
12. Quackenboss, J.L.; Spengler, J.D.; Kanarek, M.S.; et al.: Personal Exposure to Nitrogen Dioxide: Relationship to Indoor/Outdoor Air Quality and Activity Patterns. Environ. Sci. Technol. 20:775–783 (1986).
13. Little, J.C.; Daisey, J.M.; Nazaroff, W.: Transport of Subsurface Contaminants Into Buildings. Environ. Sci. Technol. 26:2058–2065 (1992).
14. Eisenbud, M.: Levels of Exposure to Sulfur Oxides and Particulates in New York City and their Sources. Bull. N.Y. Acad. Med. 54:99 (1978).

15. U.S. Environmental Protection Agency: Air Quality Criteria for Particulate Matter and Sulfur Oxides, Vol. I–IV. EPA-600/8-82-029a. ECAO, Research Triangle Park, NC (December 1982).
16. U.S. Environmental Protection Agency: Site Selection for the Monitoring of Photochemical Air Pollutants. EPA-450/3-78-013. OAQPS, Research Triangle Park, NC (April 1978).
17. Ott, W.: Development of Criteria for Siting of Air Monitoring Stations. J. Air Pollut. Control Assoc. 27:543 (1977).
18. U.S. Environmental Protection Agency: The Acid Deposition Phenomenon and Its Effects. EPA-600/8-83-016BF. OAQPS, Research Triangle Park, NC (July 1984).
19. National Deposition Study: U.S. National Acid Precipitation Assessment Program, Acid Deposition State of Science and Technology, Vol. I–IV. U.S. Government Printing Office, Washington, DC (December 1990).
20. White, W.H., Ed.: Plumes and Visibility: Measurements and Model Components. Atmos. Environ. 15:1785 (1981).
21. National Research Council, Committee on Advances in Assessing Human Exposure to Airborne Pollutants: Human Exposure Assessment for Airborne Pollutants: Advances and Opportunities. National Academy Press, Washington, DC (1991).
22. Lioy, P.J.: Assessing Total Human Exposure to Contaminants. Environ. Sci. Technol. 24:938–945 (1990).
23. National Research Council, Committee on Air Pollution Epidemiology: Epidemiology and Air Pollution. National Academy Press, Washington, DC (1985).
24. Lioy, P.J.; Waldman, J.M.: Acidic Sulfate Aerosols: Characterization of Exposure. Environ. Health Persp. 79:15–34 (1989).
25. Brauerm, M.; Kontrakis, P.; Spengler, J.D.: Personal Exposure to Acidic Aerosols and Gases. Environ. Sci. Technol. 23:1408–1412 (1989).
26. Wallace, L.; Ott, W.R.: Personal Monitors: A State of the Art Survey. J. Air Pollut. Control Assoc. 32:601 (1982).
27. Lioy, P.J.: Measurement of Personal Exposure to Air Pollution: Status and Needs. In: Measurement Challenges in Atmospheric Chemistry, #232. L. Newman, Ed. American Chemical Society (1993).
28. Akland, G.G.; Hartwell, T.D.; Johnson, T.R.; Whitemore, R.W.: Measuring Human Exposure to Carbon Monoxide in Washington, D.C. and Denver, CO during the Winter of 1982–1983. Environ. Sci. Technol. 19:911 (1985).
29. Ott, W.R.; Mage, D.T.; Thomas, J.: Comparison of Microenvironmental CO Concentrations in Two Cities for Human Exposure Modeling. J. Exposure Anal. Environ. Epidem. 2:249–267 (1992).
30. Cortese, A.M.; Spengler, J.D.: Ability of Fixed Monitoring Stations to Represent Personal Carbon Monoxide Exposure. J. Air Pollut. Control Assoc. 26:1144–1150 (1976).
31. Coffey, P.E.; Stasiuk, W.N.: Evidence of Atmospheric Transport of Ozone into Urban Areas. Environ. Sci. Technol. 9:59 (1975).
32. U.S. Environmental Protection Agency: Review of the NAAQS for Ozone. Preliminary Assessment of Scientific and Technical Information. OAQPS, Research Triangle Park, NC (March 1986).
33. Rombout, P.J.A.; Lioy, P.J.; Goldstein, B.: Rationale for an Eight-Hour Ozone Standard. J. Air Pollut. Control Assoc. 36:913 (1986).
34. Spengler, J.D.; Keeler, G.J.; Koutrakis, P.; et al.: Exposures to Acid Aerosols. Environ. Health Perspectives 79:43–51 (1989).
35. Lioy, P.J.: Exposure Analysis and Assessment for Low Risk Cancer Agents. Intern. J. Epid. 19(Suppl. 1)553–561 (1990).
36. Morris, J.: Uses of Epidemiology. Churchill Livingston, New York (1975).
37. Lilenfeld, A.M.; Lilenfeld, D.E.: Foundations of Epidemiology, 2nd ed. Oxford University Press, New York (1980).
38. Leaderer, B. P.: Assessing Exposure to Environmental Tobacco Smoke. In: Risk Analysis, pp. 10, 19–28, 1990.
39. Lioy, P.J.; Mallon, R.P.; Kneip T.J.: Long Term Trends in Total Suspended Particulates, Vanadium, Manganese, and Lead at a Near Street Level and Elevated Sites in New York City. J. Air Pollut. Control Assoc. 30:153 (1980).
40. Lioy, P.J.; Samson, P.J.: Ozone Concentration Patterns Observed During the 1976–1977 Long Range Transport Study. Environ. Int. 2:77 (1979).
41. Seinfeld, J.H.: Atmospheric Chemistry and Physics of Air Pollution. Wiley Interscience, John Wiley & Sons, New York (1986).
42. American Conference of Governmental Industrial Hygienists: Air Sampling Instruments for the Evaluation of Atmospheric Contaminants, 6th ed. P.J. Lioy and M.J. Lioy, Eds. ACGIH, Cincinnati, OH (1983).
43. Thompson, R.: Air Monitoring for Organic Constituents. In: Air Sampling Instruments for the Evaluation of Atmospheric Contaminants, 6th ed. P.J. Lioy and M.J. Lioy, Eds. American Conference of Governmental Industrial Hygienists, Cincinnati, OH (1983).
44. Walling, J.F.: The Utility of Distributed Air Volume Sets When Sampling Ambient Air Using Solid Adsorbents. Atmos. Environ. 18:855 (1984).
45. U.S. Environmental Protection Agency: Compendium Method TO-14μ: The Determination of Volatile Organic Compounds (VOC's) in Ambient Air Using Summa® Passivated Canister Sampling and Gas Chromatographic Analysis. U.S. EPA, Washington, DC (May, 1988).
46. Lou, B.W.; Jaklevic, J.M.; Goulding, F.S.: Dichotomous Virtual Impactors for Large Scale Monitoring of Airborne Particulate Matter. In: Fine Particles: Aerosol Generation Measurement, Sampling and Analysis, pp. 311–350. B.Y.H. Liu, Ed. Academic Press, New York (1976).
47. Spengler, J.D.; Treitman, R.D.; Losteson, T.D.; et al.: Personal Exposures to Respirable Particulates and Implications for Air Pollution Epidemiology. Environ. Sci. Technol. 19:700 (1985).
48. Chow, J.C.; Watson, J.G.; Ono, D.M.; Mathai, C. V.: PM_{10} Standards and Non-Traditional Particulate Source Controls: A Summary of the AWMA/EPA Conference, pp. 43, 74–84 (1993).
49. Katz, M.: Advances in the Analysis of Air Contaminants: A Critical Review. J. Air Pollut. Control Assoc. 30:528 (1980).
50. Lioy, P.J.; Lippmann, M.: Measurement of Exposure to Acidic Sulfur Aerosols. In: Aerosols, pp. 743–752. S.D. Lee, Ed. Lewis Publishers, Chelsea, MI (1986).
51. Daisey, J.J.: Organic Compounds in Urban Aerosols. In: Aerosols: Anthropogenic and Natural Sources and Transport. T.J. Kneip and P.J. Lioy, Eds. Ann. N.Y. Acad. Sci. 338:50 (1980).
52. Lee, M.L.; Goates, S.R.; Markides, K.E.; Wise, S.A.: Frontiers in Analytical Techniques for Polycyclic Aromatic Compounds. In: Polynuclear Aromatic Hydrocarbons: Chemistry Characterization and Carcinogenesis, 9th International Symposium, pp. 13–40. M. Cooke and A.J. Dennis, Eds. Battelle Press, Columbus, OH (1986).
53. Cadle, S.H.; Groblicki, P.J.: An Evaluation of Methods for the Determination of Organic and Elemental Carbon in Particulate Samples. In: Particulate Carbon: Atmospheric Life Cycle, pp. 89–110. G.T. Wolff and R.L. Klimesch, Eds. Plenum Press, New York (1982).
54. Watson, J.G.: Overview of Receptor Model Principles. J. Air Pollut. Control. Assoc. 34:619–623 (1984).
55. Marple, A.; Rubow, K.L.; Spengler, J.D.: Low Flow Rate Sharp Cut Impactors for Indoor Air Sampling: Design and Calibration. Particle Technology Laboratory Pub. No. 623 (December 1986).
56. U.S. Environmental Protection Agency: Review and Evaluation of the Evidence for Cancer Associated with Air Pollution. EPA 450/5-83-006R. QAQOS, Research Triangle Park, NC (1984).
57. Maron, D.M.; Ames, B.N.: Revised Methods for the Salmonella Mutagenicity Test. Mutat. Res. 113:173 (1983).
58. Ames, B.N.; McCann, J.; Yamasaki, E.: Methods for Detecting Carcinogens and Mutagens with the Salmonella/microsomal Mutagenicity Test. Mutat. Res. 113:347 (1974).
59. Louis, J.B.; McGeorge, L.J.; Atherholt, T.B.; et al.: Mutagenicity of Inhalable Particulate Matter at Four Sites in New Jersey. In: Toxic Air Pollution. P.J. Lioy and J. M. Daisey, Eds. Lewis Publishers,

Inc., Chelsea, MI (1987).

60. Butler, J.P.; Kneip, T.P.; Daisey, J.M.: An Investigation of Interurban Variations in the Chemical Composition and Mutagenic Activity of Airborne Particulate Organic Matter Using an Integrated Chemical Class Bioassay System. Atmos. Environ. 21:883 (1987).
61. Cupitt, L.J.; Glen, W.G.; Lenta, J.: Integrated Air Cancer Boise Field Program: Proceedings of the 1988 EPA/APCA Symposium on Measurement of Toxic and Related Pollutants, pp. 799–803. Air Pollution Control Association, Pittsburgh, PA (1988).
62. Lioy, P.J.: Exposure Analysis and the Biological Response to a Contaminant: A Melding Necessary for Environmental Health Sciences. J. Exposure Anal. Environ. Epidem. 2(Suppl. 1)19–24 (1992).
63. Wolff, G.T.: Personal communication. General Motors Research Laboratories, Warren, MI (1984).
64. Lioy, P.J.; Spektor, D.; Thurston, G.; et al.: The Design Consideration for Ozone and Acid Aerosol Exposure and Health Investigations: The Fairview Lake Summer Camp. Photochemical Smog Case Study. Environ. Int. 13:271 (1987).
65. Turner, D.B.: Atmospheric Dispersion Modeling: A Critical Review. J. Air Pollut. Control Assoc. 29:502 (1979).
66. Hidy, G.M.: Source-Receptor Relationships for Acid Depositing: Pure and Simple. J. Air Pollut. Control Assoc. 34:518 (1984).
67. Nazaroff, W.W.; Cass, G.R.: Mathematical Modeling of Chemically Reactive Pollutants in Indoor Air. Environ. Sci. Technol. 20:924–934 (1986).
68. Henry, R.C.; Lewis, C.H.; Hopke, P.K.; Williamson, H.J.: Review of Receptor Model Fundamentals. Atmos. Environ. 18:1507–1515 (1984).
69. Seinfeld, J.H.: Ozone Air Quality Models: A Critical Review. J. Air Pollut. Control Assoc. 38:616–645 (1988).
70. Miller, M.S.; Fiedlander, S.K.; Hidy, G.M.: A Chemical Balance for the Pasadena Aerosol. J. Coll. Interface Sci. 47:165 (1972).
71. Kleinman, M.T.; Pasternack, B.; Eisenbud, M.; Kneip, T.J.: Identifying and Estimating the Relative Importance of Sources of Airborne Particles. Environ. Sci. Technol. 14:62 (1980).
72. Hopke, P.E.; Alpert, D.J.; Roscoe, B.A.: Fantasia — A Program for Target Transformation Factor Analysis to Apportion Sources in Environmental Samples. Computers in Chem. 7:149 (1983).
73. Hopke, P.E.: Receptor Modeling in Environmental Chemistry. J. Wiley & Sons, New York (1985).
74. Thurston, G.D.; Lioy, P.J.: Receptor Modeling and Aerosol Transport. Atmos. Environ. 21:687 (1987).
75. Price, P.S.; Sample, J.; Strieter, R.: Determination of Less than Lifetime Exposures to Point Source Emissions, pp. 12, 367–382 (1992).
76. Thompson, K.M.; Burmaster, D.E.; Crouch, E.A.C. Monte Carlo: Techniques for Quantitative Uncertainty Analysis in Public Health Risk Assessments. In: Risk Analysis, pp. 12, 53–63 (1992).
77. Duan, N.: Models for Human Exposure to Air Pollution. Environ. Inter. 8:305–309 (1982).
78. Hidy, G.M.; et al.: Summary of the California Aerosol Characterization Experiment. J. Air Pollut. Control Assoc. 25:1106 (1975).
79. Lippman, M.: Size-Selective Health Hazard Sampling. In: Air Sampling Instruments for the Evaluation of Atmospheric Contaminants, 6th ed. P.J. Lioy and M.J. Lioy, Eds. American Conference of Governmental Industrial Hygienists, Cincinnati, OH (1983).
80. Hidy, G.M.; Mueller, P.K.; Grosjean, D.; et al.: The Character and Origin of Smog Aerosols: A Digest of Results from the California Aerosol Characterization Experiment (ACHEX). John Wiley & Sons, New York (1980).
81. Hering, S.V.; Blumenthal, D.L.: Southern California Air Quality Study (SCAQS), Description of Measurement Activities. Sonoma Technology, Final Report to California Air Resources Board, Sacramento, A5-151-32.
82. Lawson, D.R.: The Southern California Air Quality Study. J. Air Waste Manag. Assoc. 40:156–165 (1990).
83. Russell, P.A.: Denver Air Pollution Study–1973. Proceedings of a Symposium, Vol. 1: EPA Report No. 600/9-76-007a; Vol. 2: EPA Report No. 600/9-77-001.
84. Wolff, G.T.; Groblicki, P.J.; Countess, R.J.; Ferman, M.A: Design of the Denver Brown Cloud Study. GMR-3050. General Motors Research Laboratories, Larsen, MI (August 1979).
85. Countess, R.J.; Wolff, G.T.; Cadle, S.H.: The Denver Winter Aerosol: A Comprehensive Chemical Characterization. J. Air Pollut. Control Assoc. 30:1194 (1980).
86. Countess, R.J.; Cadle, S.H.; Groblicki, P.J.; Wolff, G.T.: Chemical Analysis of Size Segregated Samples of Denver's Ambient Particulate. J. Air Pollut. Control Assoc. 31:247 (1981).
87. Wolff, G.T.; Countess, R.J.; Groblicki, P.J.; et al.: Visibility Reducing Species in the Denver Brown Cloud, Part II, Sources and Temporal Patterns. Atmos. Environ. 15:2485 (1981).
88. Lewis, C.W.; Baumgardner, R.E.; Stevens R.K.: Receptor Modeling Study of Denver Winter Haze. Environ. Sci. Technol. 20: 1126 (1986).
89. Watson, J.G.; Chow, J.C.; Richards, L.W.; et al.: The 1987-88 Metro Denver Brown Cloud Study, Vol. 1, Program Plan; Vol. 2, Measurements; Vol. 3, Data Interpretation. Final Report from the Desert Research Institute, DRI Document No. 8810-F (October 1988).
90. Lioy, P.J.; Daisey, J.M.: Airborne Toxic Elements and Organic Substances. Environ. Sci. Technol. 20:8 (1986).
91. Lioy, P.J.; Daisey, J.M., Eds.: Toxic Air Pollutants: Study of Non-Criteria Pollutants. Lewis Publishers, Inc., Chelsea, MI (1986).
92. Waldman, J.; Lioy, P.J.; Greenberg, A.; Butler, J.: Analysis of Human Exposure to Benzo(a)pyrene Via Inhalation and Food Ingestion in the Total Human Environmental Exposure Study (THEES). J. Exposure Anal. Environ. Epidem. 1:197–226, 1991.
93. Ferris, B.G.; Spengler, J.D.: Harvard Air Pollution Health Study in Six Cities in the USA. Tokai J. Exp. Clin. Med. 10:263 (1985).
94. Speizer, F.E.: Studies of Acid Aerosols in Six Cities and in a New Multi-city Investigation — Design Issues. Environ. Health Persp. 79:61–67 (1989).
95. Pellizzari, E.; Sheldon, L.; Sparcino, C.; et al.: Volatile Organic Levels in Indoor Air. In: Indoor Air, Vol. 4, Chemical Characterization and Personal Exposure, pp. 303–308. Swedish Council for Building Research, Stockholm, Sweden (1984).
96. Lioy, P.J.; Wallace, L.; Pellizzari, E.: Indoor/Outdoor and Personal Monitoring and Breath Analysis Relationships for Selected Volatile Organic Compounds Measured at Three Homes During New Jersey TEAM - 1987. J. Exposure Anal. Environ. Epidem. 1:45–61 (1991).
97. Raymer, J.H.; Pellizzari, E.D.; Thomas, K.W.; Cooper, S.D.: Elimination of Volatile Organic Compounds in Breath After Exposure to Occupational and Environmental Microenvironments. J. Exposure Anal. Environ. Epidem. 1:439–451 (1991).
98. Wallace, L.A.; Pellizzari, E.D.; Hartwell, T.D.; et al.: The California TEAM Study: Breath Concentrations and Personal Exposures to 26 Volatile Compounds in Air and Drinking Water of 188 Residents of Los Angeles, Antioch and Pittsburgh. Atmos. Environ. 22:2141–2163 (1988).
99. Thomas, K.W.; Pellizzar, E.D.; Clayton, C.A.; et al.: Particle Team Exposure Assessment Methodology (PTEAM) Study: Method Performance and Data Quality for Personal, Indoor and Outdoor Aerosol Monitoring for 178 Homes in Southern California. J. Exp. Anal. Environ. Epid. 3:203–226 (1993).
100. Landrigan, P.J.: Epidemiologic Approaches to Persons with Exposures to Waste Chemicals. Environ. Health Persp. 48:93 (1983).
101. National Research Council, Environmental Epidemiology: Public Health and Hazardous Wastes. National Academy of Sciences, Washington, DC (1991).
102. Campbell, D.L.; Quintrell, W.N.: Cleanup Strategy for Rocky Mountain Arsenal. In: Proceedings 6th National Conference on Management of Uncontrolled Hazardous Waste Sites, pp. 36–42 (November 4–6, 1985).

103. Melius, J.M.; Costello, R.J.; Kominsky, J.R.: Facility Siting and Health Questions: The Burden of Health Risk Uncertainty. Natural Resources Lawyer 17:467 (1985).
104. Hawley, J.K.: Assessment of Health Risk from Exposure to Contaminated Soil. Risk Analysis 5:289–302 (1985).
105. Lioy, P.J.; Freeman, N.C.G.; Wainman, T.: Microenvironmental Analysis of Residential Exposure to Chromium Laden Wastes In and Around New Jersey Homes. J. Risk Analysis 12:287–299 (1992).
106. U.S. Environmental Protection Agency: Risk Assessment Guidance for Superfund, Vol. 1, Human Health Evaluation Manual, Parts A-C. EPA/5401/1-85/002. OERR (December 1989).
107. Agency for Toxic Substances and Disease Registry: Public Health Assessment Guidance Manual. Lewis Publishers, Inc., Chelsea, MI (1992).

Chapter 4

Particle and Gas Phase Interactions in Air Sampling

Sidney C. Soderholm, Ph.D.
National Institute for Occupational Safety and Health, Morgantown, West Virginia

CONTENTS

Introduction

An aerosol consists of airborne particles and surrounding gases. The particle phase may include solids and liquids. The gas phase normally includes air and water vapor and may include vapors of organic and inorganic compounds as well as contaminant gases, such as sulfur dioxide. Following common practice, the term "vapor" refers to the gas phase portion of a material which can exist as a liquid or solid at room temperature and atmospheric pressure. A "gas" cannot exist as a liquid or solid at normal conditions. The distinction between a vapor and a gas is somewhat arbitrary and has little physical significance in this discussion.

Molecules of each species in the gas phase continually bombard the surface of each particle, giving ample opportunity for chemical reactions, i.e., formation of new molecules, and physical interactions, e.g., transfer of mass between the particle and gas phases. This chapter does not emphasize the most general case in which both chemical reactions and physical interactions occur simultaneously in the atmosphere and during sampling. This is important in particular situations, e.g., when sampling ammonia, acids, and ammonium salts in the ambient atmosphere, and has been discussed elsewhere.[1,2] This chapter emphasizes information needed to make decisions about which phase(s) to sample and techniques for avoiding erroneous sampling results when chemical reactions or condensation/evaporation may occur during sampling. The words "condensation" and "evaporation" are used to indicate the net transport of mass from the gas phase to the particle phase or from the particle phase to the gas phase, respectively.

Air sampling errors being considered include allowing unwanted chemical reactions to occur during sampling, measuring the concentration of a contaminant only in the particle or gas phase when there is a significant fraction in the unsampled phase, and using inappropriate techniques to measure the distribution of a contaminant between the two phases. Avoiding unwanted chemical reactions with reactive gases during sampling is discussed briefly in the next section. This

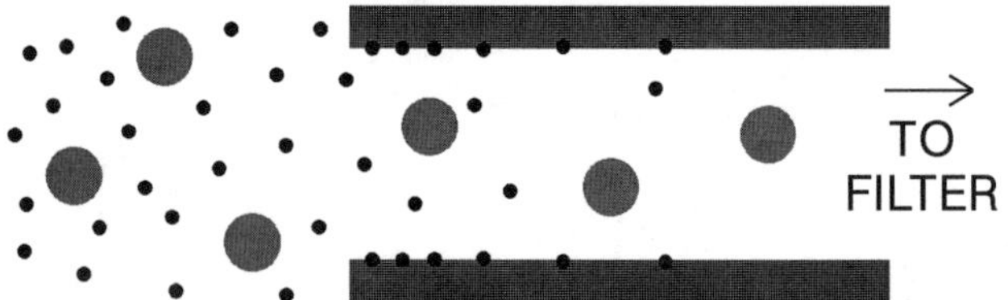

FIGURE 4-1. Schematic diagram of a denuder showing the collection of a reactive gas (small black circles) at the wall by adsorption or chemical reaction. Particles (large gray circles) penetrate the denuder and are transmitted to the filter.

issue has received substantial attention in the literature of environmental air sampling. In the remaining sections, the emphasis is on effects of interphase mass transfer in sampling.[3] The term "semivolatile" is sometimes associated with compounds for which such effects are important. First, the equilibrium distribution of a material between the particle and gas phases will be discussed. Several factors that tend to disturb equilibrium and the time-scale of the approach to equilibrium will then be presented. Finally, techniques for measuring a contaminant's total airborne concentration (concentration in both the particle and gas phases) and approaches to measuring a contaminant's distribution between the two phases will be offered.

Much of this chapter contains detailed discussions intended to aid the reader who needs a deeper understanding of how particle-gas interactions can influence air sampling. Readers who wish to focus on the practical implications may be most interested in the following: 1) the "Chemical Reactions" section for a brief discussion of how to avoid chemical reactions between collected material and reactive gases; 2) the "General Guidance" subsection of the "Physical Equilibrium" section for rules-of-thumb to guide decisions about whether to sample the particle, gas, or both phases of an aerosol; and 3) the "Sampling Approaches" section for a review of the applicability of different types of sampling instrumentation.

Chemical Reactions

Gases, such as HNO_2, HNO_3, NH_3, NO_2, SO_2, HCl, and HF, in an atmosphere may react with sampled particulate or the filter material and lead to erroneous results. This is a more serious problem when sampling times are long as is often the case when sampling outdoors.

A common approach to avoiding these problems is to remove the reactive gas from the air stream with a denuder before the air reaches the filter (see Chapter 20). A recent review summarizes developments in this field.[4] The sampled air passes through an open tubular or annular channel in the denuder before reaching the filter. The channel walls are coated with a chemical that will adsorb or react with the unwanted gas and retain it at the wall (Figure 4-1). A properly designed denuder removes the reactive gas from the air stream without removing a significant fraction of the particles being sampled.[5] Annular denuders of convenient size can be designed for relatively high flow rate samplers and for low flow samplers worn by an individual (personal samplers).[6,7] Recently, coated porous metal disks and honeycomb glass structures have also been proposed as convenient and efficient denuders.[8,9]

A denuder reduces artifacts caused by a gas reacting with collected particles on the filter. However, calculations illustrate the potential for a denuder to introduce artifacts. A denuder section of a sampler collecting particulate from an atmosphere containing HNO_3 and NH_3 gases and NH_4NO_3 particulate in equilibrium with the gases would remove the NH_3, disturb the equilibrium, and tend to cause the chemical species in the particulate to change, possibly leading to an incorrect assessment of the aerosol mass concentration and chemical species.[10] Denuders can be very helpful in avoiding sampling artifacts due to chemical reactions between a reactive gas and collected particles or the filter, but all the possible influences of a denuder should be considered and tested before deciding to include one in a sampling system.[11]

Physical Equilibrium

Gas molecules collide with the surface of suspended particles. At the same time, molecules are ejected from particle surfaces due to thermal energy. At equilibrium, there is no net flux of any species across any solid/gas, liquid/gas, or solid/liquid interface. A solid/liquid interface occurs within particles containing a liquid and undissolved material.

Experimental data relevant to the equilibrium between identical particles and the gas phase can be written in the form:

$$C_{G,i} = f(d_p, C_{P,1}, C_{P,2}, \ldots) \quad \textbf{(1)}$$

The symbol C will always imply a mass concentration in this chapter. The subscript G or P refers to the gas or particle phase, respectively. The mass concentration of the ith contaminant in the gas phase just outside the particle surface $C_{G,i}$ is some function of the composition of the particle surface, which is described here by the mass concentration $C_{P,i}$ of each species in the particle phase of the aerosol. A relation like Equation 1 holds for each species in the gas phase. All the relations are linked because each depends on all constituents in the particle phase. Additional relations exist between the concentration in the liquid phase and the surface composition of solid constituents, if there are any solid/liquid interfaces within particles.

The particle diameter d_p appears in the function because of the Kelvin effect, which increases the equilibrium concentration above a convex surface compared to a planar surface.[12] This factor can be significant for particles that are submicrometer in diameter. For example, a pure submicrometer droplet in an atmosphere which is saturated with the vapor is expected to evaporate completely because it requires a supersaturated atmosphere to reach equilibrium.

When an aerosol consists of particles that differ markedly in composition or size, the equilibrium of each particle class should be considered separately. Each particle class may influence the composition of the other classes through the gas phase that they share.

In principle, it is possible to predict the distribution, gas, and particle phase of a material between the particle and gas phases if the total airborne mass concentration of each constituent is known and if each of the possible liquid/gas, solid/gas, and solid/liquid interfaces in the system has been sufficiently characterized. Typically, this information is obtained by measuring the concentrations of each constituent on both sides of the interface in a laboratory system. It is often not clear whether available experimental data are relevant because the equilibrium distribution is sensitive to temperature and pressure and may be sensitive to the addition or removal of small quantities of other constituents. Because real atmospheres are often complex and contain many constituents, rigorous prediction of equilibrium conditions is a difficult task. The approach taken here is to present the general form of the relations needed to predict equilibrium and to make some general observations for guidance when making sampling decisions.

Absorption

For aerosols, absorption refers to the dissolution of gas phase materials in droplets. The relation between the gas phase concentration of one of the components adjacent to a droplet surface and the composition of the droplet surface can be expressed in terms of an activity coefficient γ_i[13,14]

$$C_{G,i} = \gamma_i \, \chi_i \, C_{G,i}^S \tag{2}$$

where χ_i is the mole fraction of the ith material in the droplet surface and $C_{G,i}^S$ is its saturated vapor concentration at the droplet temperature. The superscript S indicates saturation. The saturated vapor concentration is the mass concentration of the vapor above a planar surface of the pure material and can be calculated from the saturated vapor pressure using the Ideal Gas Law. In general, γ_i is a function of the droplet composition, but it is constrained to assume the value of unity when χ_i is unity (pure droplet). The Kelvin effect is not included explicitly in Equation 2, although it should be included for submicrometer particles.[13]

Saturated vapor pressure is a property of the pure material. Caution should be exercised if using saturated vapor pressure data from the literature. The value is temperature sensitive, often changing by an order of magnitude for a 10 to 20°C change in temperature, so application of predictive equations for temperature correction, e.g., the Clausius–Clapeyron equation, may be necessary.[14] In many cases, a literature search may be worthwhile; early measurements of small saturated vapor pressures may be in substantial error and yet may be widely cited. Some saturated vapor pressure information may be available in material safety data sheets, handbooks, and exposure limit documentation.

Equation 2 can be expressed in terms of mass concentrations which are commonly measured when describing an atmosphere

$$C_{G,i} = \gamma_i \frac{M_P}{M_i} \frac{C_{P,i}}{C_P} C_{G,i}^S \quad \text{droplets} \tag{3}$$

where a substitution has been made for the mole fraction

$$\chi_i = \frac{M_P \, C_{P,i}}{M_i \, C_P} \tag{4}$$

The molecular weight of the ith material is M_i and the average molecular weight of the droplet M_P is

$$M_P^{-1} = \frac{M_1^{-1} \, C_{P,1} + M_2^{-1} \, C_{P,2} + \ldots}{C_P} \tag{5}$$

The concentration of all materials in the particle phase C_P is

$$C_P = C_{P,1} + C_{P,2} + \ldots \tag{6}$$

Equation 3 is very general. It can be used to summarize experimental data on liquid/gas equilibria for most systems across the whole range of possible mole fractions for each component, even when the liquids are not completely miscible.[13,14]

Specifying the activity coefficient as a function of droplet composition can be quite complex. Simpler and less general relations can successfully characterize liquid/gas equilibria in special cases that commonly occur. Three such special cases will be discussed: ideal liquids, Raoult's Law for solvents, and Henry's Law for dilute solutions.

For ideal liquids, the activity coefficient for each component is unity for all compositions. This is likely to occur for similar liquids, for example, propylene glycol and water.[13,15] The equilibrium of an airborne system of ideal liquids in uniform droplets can be described by

$$C_{G,i} = \frac{M_P}{M_i} \frac{C_{P,i}}{C_P} C^S_{G,i} \quad \text{ideal liquids} \tag{7}$$

Very few aerosols are likely to consist of ideal liquids.

Raoult's Law has been found to apply to the solvent in many liquid systems even if the solution is not ideal. It can be derived from Equations 2 or 3 by setting the activity coefficient to unity (it should be nearly equal to unity for any material that is nearly pure in the liquid) and applying the resulting equation only to the solvent in a dilute solution[15]

$$C_{G,solv} = \frac{M_P}{M_{solv}} \frac{C_{P,solv}}{C_P} C^S_{G,solv} \quad \text{solvents} \tag{8}$$

The ratio of the molecular weights and the ratio of the particle phase mass concentrations are both near unity for the solvent in a dilute solution. The Kelvin effect should be included for submicrometer droplets. A common application of Raoult's Law is to describe the relationship between the composition of aqueous droplets and relative humidity RH (in percent) where

$$RH = \frac{C_{G,water}}{C^S_{G,water}} 100 \tag{9}$$

Henry's Law often applies to a solute in a dilute solution. It states that the gas phase concentration of the material is proportional to its mole fraction in the solution[15]

$$P_i = \chi_i H_i \tag{10}$$

The proportionality constant H_i is the Henry's Law coefficient.

Henry's Law is compatible with Equation 2, the general equation for liquids. As the mole fraction of a material approaches zero, the activity coefficient approaches a constant γ^0_i.[14] Thus, for a material in a dilute solution, Equation 2 becomes

$$C_{G,i} = \gamma^0_i \chi_i C^S_{G,i} \tag{11}$$

Converting the gas phase mass concentration to partial pressure P_i by the Ideal Gas Law

$$P_i = C_{G,i} \frac{R\,T}{M_i} \tag{12}$$

(R is the universal gas constant and T is the absolute temperature) gives for a dilute solution

$$P_i = \gamma^0_i \chi_i C^S_{G,i} \frac{R\,T}{M_i} \tag{13}$$

The last result is in the form of Henry's Law. Comparing Equations 10 and 13 shows that the Henry's Law coefficient H_i is related to the activity coefficient for a material in a dilute solution γ^0_i by

$$H_i = \gamma^0_i C^S_{G,i} \frac{R\,T}{M_i} = \gamma^0_i P^S_i \tag{14}$$

The saturated vapor pressure P^S_i has been related to the saturated vapor concentration $C^S_{G,i}$ by the Ideal Gas Law, Equation 12, applied to the saturated state. Solving Equation 14 for γ^0_i and substituting for γ_i in Equation 3 gives the relation for materials in droplets as dilute solutions in terms of the Henry's Law coefficient

$$C_{G,i} = \frac{H_i}{P^S_i} \frac{M_P}{M_i} \frac{C_{P,i}}{C_P} C^S_{G,i} \quad \text{dilute solutions} \tag{15}$$

The form has been chosen to be similar to that for ideal solutions and solvents.

Many liquid/gas systems, especially those consisting of water and an organic liquid, have been characterized in terms of Henry's Law coefficients either by direct measurement or by extrapolation from measurements in similar systems. All Henry's Law coefficients that have been tabulated have something in common: each is a proportionality constant between the amount in the gas phase and the amount in a dilute (usually aqueous) solution at equilibrium. Unfortunately, different authors define the proportionality constant differently, so Henry's Law coefficients have a variety of units and some Henry's Law coefficients are related to the inverse of another. For example, one list is limited to aqueous solutions and tabulates a Henry's Law coefficient that is related to the inverse of that defined here.[15] For that tabulation, the units of the quantity specifying the amount of the material in the dilute aqueous solution are moles per liter and the units of the quantity specifying the amount in the gas phase (partial pressure) are atmospheres, so the Henry's Law coefficient is tabulated with units of moles per liter per atmosphere. The relationship between that Henry's Law coefficient and the one defined in Equation 10 can be derived by relating the concentration of a contaminant in a dilute aqueous solution to its mole fraction. Great care must be taken in applying Henry's Law coefficients obtained from the literature because of the confusing number of definitions and units. The Henry's Law coefficient used in Equations 10, 14, and 15 has units of pressure.

Adsorption

Gas phase materials may adsorb onto the surface of solid particles. Adsorption theories have been discussed in the environmental literature, but there seems to be no definitive compilation of experimental results. One problem has been the difficulty in obtaining valid data on the distribution of an airborne substance between the particle and gas phases due to the artifacts discussed later in this chapter. Some data have been summarized by a relation of the form

$$\log\left(\frac{C_{G,i}\,C_P}{C_{P,i}}\right) = \frac{m_Y}{T} + b_Y \quad (16)$$

where m_Y and b_Y are constants determined by fitting the data.(16) This relation has been shown to be consistent with the Junge equation which had been proposed earlier.(17) The Junge equation relates the fraction of the material of interest in the particle phase to the saturated vapor pressure of the material at that temperature, P_i^S; the surface concentration of particles, C_S (the total surface area of particles per volume of air); and the Junge constant, c_J, which is determined experimentally,

$$\frac{C_{P,i}}{C_{T,i}} = \frac{c_J C_S}{P_i^S + c_J C_S} \quad (17)$$

where the total airborne concentration of the contaminant $C_{T,i}$ is

$$C_{T,i} = C_{P,i} + C_{G,i} \quad (18)$$

Pankow(17) has derived the theoretical temperature dependence of the Junge constant assuming linear Langmuir adsorption and has shown that the resulting equation describing equilibrium conditions is equivalent to Equation 16. Solving Equations 17 and 18 for $C_{G,i}$ results in the equilibrium relation

$$C_{G,i} = \frac{P_i^S\,C_{P,i}}{c_J C_S} \quad (19)$$

For materials with a melting point higher than the temperature of the atmosphere being sampled, it has often been found preferable to use the saturated vapor pressure of the liquid extrapolated down to the atmospheric temperature (called the subcooled liquid saturated vapor pressure) rather than the saturated vapor pressure above the pure crystalline solid.(3) Application of the Ideal Gas Law and straightforward algebraic manipulation leads to a form similar to Equations 3, 7, 8, and 15 for the equilibrium relation for adsorption

$$C_{G,i} = \frac{R\,T}{M_i c_J \sigma_p}\,\frac{C_{P,i}}{C_P}\,C_{G,i}^S \quad \text{adsorption} \quad (20)$$

where the specific surface area (area per mass) of the particle phase σ_P is

$$\sigma_P = \frac{C_S}{C_P} \quad (21)$$

Sorption

The association of gas phase material with particles by either absorption or adsorption is called sorption. It has been suggested that it may be adequate to describe the gas phase mass concentration of an air contaminant in equilibrium with either solid or liquid particles by a fairly simple relation:(18)

$$C_{G,i} = B\,\frac{C_{P,i}}{C_P}\,C_{G,i}^S \quad (22)$$

$C_{P,i}$ is the mass concentration of the ith contaminant in the particle phase. C_P is the mass concentration of all materials in the particle phase. $C_{G,i}^S$ is the saturated vapor concentration of the ith material or the extrapolated saturated vapor concentration for the subcooled liquid, if the melting point of the pure material is above the temperature of the atmosphere. The Kelvin correction may be needed for submicrometer particles. The proportionality "constant" B is temperature dependent and also depends on the materials involved. One utility of this approximation is that although B depends on a variety of characteristics of the particles and contaminant gases, it may be slowly varying. For example, it may be nearly constant for similar solid/gas and liquid/gas systems.(18)

Equation 22 emphasizes that the distribution, gas, and particle phase of a material between the particle and gas phases depends strongly on its saturated vapor concentration and the amount of particulate available. One advantage of this equation for summarizing air sampling data on the distribution of a particular contaminant of interest between the particle and gas phases is that it asserts a relationship between the equilibrium concentration of the contaminant in the gas phase and the particle phase mass concentrations that might be measured in a field study, as well as the contaminant's saturated vapor concentration. Generally, B and its variability (including its temperature dependence) will be determined experimentally for the particular situation.

Formulating the particle/gas distribution relationship in terms of a new proportionality constant B does not mean that all the previous data on such systems must be discarded. Available data on adsorption of material onto solid particles and absorption into droplets can be converted to information about B. Comparing Equation 22 with Equations 3, 7, 8, 15, and 20 shows that the form of each is similar and gives relationships which can be expected to hold between the proportionality constant B in Equation 22 and other experimental quantities that are sometimes tabulated for solid/gas and liquid/gas systems

$$B = \gamma_i\,\frac{M_P}{M_i} \quad \text{droplets} \quad (23)$$

$$B = \frac{M_P}{M_i} \quad \text{ideal liquids} \quad (24)$$

$$B = \frac{M_P}{M_{solv}} \quad \text{solvents} \qquad (25)$$

$$B = \frac{H_i}{P_i^S} \frac{M_P}{M_i} \quad \text{dilute solutions} \qquad (26)$$

$$B = \frac{R\,T}{M_i c_J \sigma_p} \quad \text{adsorption} \qquad (27)$$

Additional field studies will be needed to indicate whether the relatively simple form of Equation 22 is adequate to describe particle-gas equilibria in real systems. However, it seems to have a solid theoretical basis for both adsorption and absorption and is related to previously tabulated quantities, as shown in Equations 23–27.[18] The form of Equation 22 suggests that quantities may be important to measure when dealing with the distribution of materials between the particle and gas phases and indicates a relationship which should be tried when attempting to summarize experimental data.

Activity coefficients for two-component liquid/gas systems often seem to fall in the range of 0.01 to 100, so B is approximately in the same range, according to Equation 23.[14] The results of one review of data on partitioning between the gas and particle phase in a variety of locations outdoors can be reinterpreted to reveal that values of B lie in a range between 1 and 100 for alkanes, polycyclic aromatic hydrocarbons (PAHs), and organochlorines.[19] B values can be derived from the information in that review by requiring that their parameter m_r must be −1 and noting that their parameter b_r lies in the range from −9 to −7.[18,19] Assuming that a typical molecular weight is 200 allows calculation of the range for B.

Single Component System

Consider the case of a single component aerosol. This occurs when the airborne particles consist of only one constituent because none of the other constituents of the gas phase dissolve into or adsorb onto the particles. Calculation of the distribution of the contaminant between the gas and particle phases at equilibrium is straightforward. If the total airborne concentration, i.e., the concentration in the particle phase plus that in the gas phase, is larger than the saturated vapor concentration, the difference between the two is the mass concentration in the particle phase. The saturated vapor concentration is the concentration in the gas phase. Otherwise, if the total airborne mass concentration is less than the saturated vapor concentration, any particles evaporate completely and all the contaminant is in the gas phase. For small particles, the gas phase concentration that is in equilibrium with the pure droplet may be significantly higher than the concentration over a planar surface (the saturated vapor concentration), so a Kelvin effect correction may be needed.

Multiple Component System

In most cases, particles are not pure and two or more materials must be considered. For example, water vapor is ubiquitous on Earth and dissolves into or adsorbs onto most particles to some extent. Some general discussions of the equilibrium of simplified airborne systems have been presented in the literature of environmental and occupational air sampling.[20–22] Calculation of the Kelvin effect is more complicated for a two-component droplet than for a single component.[23] The correction for the equilibrium vapor concentration above a curved surface is often small for droplet diameters larger than a micrometer and will not be explicitly included here.

Ignoring the Kelvin effect and assuming identical particles, there are four unknowns in describing the equilibrium of a two-component system: a particle phase and a gas phase mass concentration for each of the components. If the total mass concentrations of both components are specified and the two interdependent relations between the mass concentrations of the two components in the gas phase and the composition of the particles similar to Equations 1 or 22 are known, then the four equations can be solved for the four unknowns.[20] In principle, the equilibrium of a system consisting of more than two components can be predicted using analogous information for each component.

General Guidance

Consideration of two-component systems emphasizes the importance of four basic facts that also hold for more complex systems:

A. The mass concentration of a contaminant in the gas phase is less than or equal to its saturated vapor concentration at that temperature.

B. If the particle phase has significant excess capacity to adsorb or dissolve the contaminant, the mass concentration of the contaminant in the gas phase is significantly less than its saturated vapor concentration.

C. The mass concentration of a contaminant in the particle phase is the difference between the mass concentration in the gas phase and its total mass concentration in the atmosphere.

D. The mass concentration of each contaminant in the particle phase is less than or equal to the total mass concentration of all airborne particles.

Applying these somewhat elementary facts leads to three useful generalizations (rules-of-thumb):

1. Sample only the particle phase when the saturated vapor concentration of a substance $C^S_{G,i}$ is

TABLE 4-1. Examples of Sampling Decisions in a Range of Assumed Atmospheres

Mass concentration of all airborne particulate, C_P (mg/m^3)	Total airborne mass concentration of contaminant, $C_{T,i}$ (mg/m^3)	Saturated vapor concentration of contaminant at 25°C, $C_{G,i}^S$ (mg/m^3)			
		0.0001	0.01	1	100
0.05	0.0001	PG	PG	PG	PG
0.05	0.01	P	PG	PG	PG
0.05	1	*	*	G	G
0.05	100	*	*	*	G
5	0.0001	PG	PG	PG	PG
5	0.01	P	PG	PG	PG
5	1	P	P	PG	PG
5	100	*	*	*	G

P = Sample particulate phase only, because $C_{G,i}^S << C_{T,i}$.
G = Sample gas phase only, because $C_P << C_{T,i}$.
PG = Sample both phases because neither condition is met.
* = Unphysical, because no atmosphere can meet both conditions.

much less than its total airborne mass concentration $C_{T,i}$

$$C_{G,i}^S << C_{T,i} \quad (28)$$

2. Sample only the gas phase when the total mass concentration of all constituents in the particle phase C_P is much smaller than the total airborne mass concentration of a contaminant $C_{T,i}$

$$C_P << C_{T,i} \quad (29)$$

3. Sample both the particle and gas phases when neither of the above two conditions is met.

When the saturated vapor concentration of a substance is of the same order as or is larger than its total airborne mass concentration, much of the mass might be expected to be in the gas phase. However, if the material occurs as a dilute solution in the particle phase or is strongly bound to particle components, a significant fraction of the mass may be in the particle phase. For example, both observations and calculations suggest that some pesticides and other organic compounds can have a significant fraction of the total airborne material in the particle phase at high humidities.[20,21,24]

The three rules-of-thumb can be applied once some information is known about the system under consideration. The most helpful pieces of information are the identities of the major constituents and their saturated vapor concentrations and some estimate of their total airborne mass concentrations. These ideas are consistent with previous publications that emphasized considering the ratio of the saturated vapor concentration to the exposure limit for the material under consideration when deciding whether to sample the particle, gas, or both phases of an atmosphere.[20,21] This ratio has also been called the "vapor/hazard ratio number."[25]

Substances for which the American Conference of Governmental Industrial Hygienists had established Threshold Limit Values were reviewed to provide examples of materials for which too little might be known to judge whether the particle, gas, or both phases should be sampled as well as examples of substances for which the available information might seem to suggest erroneously that only one phase should be sampled.[21]

Table 4-1 illustrates the results from applying the rules-of-thumb to a number of assumed atmospheres when deciding whether to sample the particle, gas, or both phases. Each atmosphere contains a contaminant with a known saturated vapor concentration of 0.001, 0.01, 1, or 100 mg/m^3. For an assumed molecular weight of 100, the Ideal Gas Law gives the corresponding saturated vapor pressures: 3×10^{-6}, 3×10^{-4}, 3×10^{-2}, and 3 Pa (2×10^{-8}, 2×10^{-6}, 2×10^{-4}, and 2×10^{-2} mm Hg). The mass concentration of all airborne particles, C_P, is assumed to be either 0.05 mg/m^3, which may be typical of the general outdoor environment and many workplaces, or 5 mg/m^3, which may be typical of dusty workplaces or light fog. Table 4-1 illustrates the large range of conditions for which both the particle and gas phases should be sampled. Whenever it is not clear that only one phase should be sampled, both phases should be sampled.

The discussion in this section applies if an airborne system is in or near equilibrium. Sometimes a system is not near equilibrium. The following two sections consider conditions that disturb the equilibrium of a system and the time a system needs to reach equilibrium.

Disturbance of Equilibrium

Some kinds of changes will disturb the equilibrium of an airborne system and require mass to be transferred between the phases to attain a new equilibrium consistent with the new conditions. For example, an atmosphere may not be in equilibrium immediately after a source injects a gaseous or particulate contaminant into it or just after it is pulled into a sampler. Detailed calculations of the system dynamics can be performed using similar experimental information to that needed to predict equilibrium (equilibrium concentrations across interfaces), plus information about transport through a phase, e.g., the diffusion of gas molecules through air.[13,26] The equations are complicated by the transport of latent heat which occurs during condensation and evaporation. The formulation and results of detailed computational models are beyond the scope of this discussion.

Atmospheric Changes

Conditions that may disturb an airborne system's equilibrium include a change in temperature or atmospheric pressure, addition or removal of contaminant mass, or addition of clean air (dilution). The direction in which each of these changes tends to move the equilibrium will be discussed briefly.

An increase in temperature tends to increase the fraction of a substance in the gas phase due to higher thermal energy promoting the ejection of molecules from surfaces. A decrease in temperature tends to decrease the fraction in the gas phase.

A decrease in atmospheric pressure with no change in temperature, for example, due to the slow expansion of a volume, decreases the gas phase concentration at a particle surface and tends to lead to evaporation of material from the particle. The decrease in the mass concentration of the particle phase due to the expansion does not influence the new equilibrium, because equilibrium depends most fundamentally on gas phase concentrations and particle phase composition, not particle phase concentration. Increases in atmospheric pressure have an opposite effect.

Sources or sinks of vapor disturb the equilibrium and may lead to significant condensation onto or evaporation from particles. For example, an increase in humidity is likely to lead to increased water in the particle phase. The loss of particles, for example, by sedimentation, or the addition of particles which have the same composition as the particles that are already equilibrated with the atmosphere does not disturb the equilibrium of the system. However, the addition of particles of a different composition will disturb the equilibrium in general.

Dilution with clean air decreases the vapor concentration at the particle surface and tends to promote evaporation of volatile contaminants from the particles.

Sampling

The process of sampling an atmosphere has the potential to disturb the particle-gas equilibrium in the sampled air. This can lead to biased sampling results. Characteristics of four types of sampling instruments, filter samplers, cascade impactors, denuders, and electronic monitors, will be discussed briefly. Some effects of inhaling an aerosol will also be mentioned.

After a filter sampler collects particles (see Chapter 13), they remain on the filter surface and are exposed to the air that is sampled subsequently. Even if there are no chemical changes due to reactive gases, physical changes in the particles can occur. During extended sampling, the atmosphere is likely to change in temperature or in the concentration of gas phase species, including water vapor. Such changes will require volatile components to evaporate from or absorb/adsorb onto the particles collected on the filter, possibly leading to substantial decreases or increases in the overall mass or the mass of volatile components. For example, ammonium nitrate evaporates from filters, if the air sampled subsequently is relatively clean. Much less evaporation into clean air occurs from ammonium nitrate collected in an impactor than in a filter, apparently because of the relatively thick boundary layer of air and the decreased surface area of the collected material.[27,28] Another situation that can occur with extended sampling times is clogging of the filter with particulate. The decreased pressure experienced by some of the collected particulate may lead to evaporation of some materials.

Another type of error can occur in filter sampling. Some filter materials adsorb some vapors from the air stream.[29–31] This contributes to an increase in mass and may allow the materials to be extracted from the filter for chemical analysis. Such errors lead to an overestimate of the mass of material in the particle phase. This problem can be reduced by choosing a filter material that is not prone to adsorbing the types of vapors which are in the atmosphere to be sampled. Filter adsorption can be detected in the field by placing a second filter downstream of the first and checking for an increase in mass, assuming the first filter is not such an efficient adsorber that all the vapor is scrubbed from the air stream. Adsorption on the back-up filter may not parallel that on the front filter, so correction of the mass increase on the front filter by that on the back-up filter may not be accurate.[30] Inefficient particle collection by the first filter would confound detection of vapor adsorption by this method, because it would also lead to an increase of mass of the second filter.

In a cascade impactor (see Chapter 14), the sampled air is drawn through a nozzle to accelerate the particles, so the larger ones will impact on a collection surface and be separated from the smaller particles and the air stream. Then the process is repeated with smaller nozzles that achieve higher air velocities and allow smaller particles to be collected on other surfaces. During its passage through each nozzle, the air experiences a pressure drop. The decrease in pressure tends to promote evaporation of volatile components from particles.[27] In smaller nozzles and higher speed jets, the air may be cooled somewhat. This tends to promote condensation of volatile materials onto particles.[32] Because the two effects act in opposite directions, predicting the net effect of passage through a cascade impactor depends on the details of the situation, but the potential for significant particle-gas interactions should not be overlooked.

If a sampler incorporates a denuder as the first stage to remove reactive gases (see Chapter 20), any particle components that are in equilibrium with that gas will tend to adjust to the removal of the gas from the sampled air stream.[10] Some have suggested that measuring the distribution of a material between the particle and gas phases of an atmosphere could be accomplished using a denuder to collect material from the gas phase followed by a filter to collect particulate. One difficulty with this approach is that there will be a tendency for the particles to evaporate in the denuder. This situation will be considered in more detail later in this chapter.

Electronic sampling instruments, e.g., real-time monitors, may contain pumps, motors, and lights that generate heat. Drawing air into warm instruments will heat the air and promote evaporation of volatile components from particles.[32]

Inhaling air typically warms and humidifies it. Warming the air tends to cause volatile materials to evaporate from particles. High humidity tends to cause water-soluble particles to absorb water vapor. This typically dilutes other constituents in the particles and causes other volatile components to be absorbed also.[13] However, more complex interactions can occur. For example, water might drive off less polar compounds adsorbed on some materials. If the particles consist entirely of substances that are immiscible with water, high humidity may have little effect. It is difficult to generalize about the effects of inhaling an atmosphere on the distribution of material between the gas and particle phases. It is clear that the distribution of a material between the particle and gas phases that is measured in the atmosphere may not be the same distribution that occurs in the respiratory tract.

Time-scale of Evaporation and Condensation

When considering the effects of evaporation and condensation on sampling results, it is often useful to know the time-scale, an estimate of the time required for a significant fraction of the evaporation or condensation to occur as the system approaches its new equilibrium. This can be helpful in judging whether a recently generated system, e.g., one consisting of droplets that were ejected into relatively clean air, has had sufficient time to approach equilibrium. One approach for estimating the time-scale for evaporation of a contaminant from the particle phase is to divide the decrease in contaminant mass in the particle phase by the initial evaporation rate.[13] The resulting time-scale for evaporation t_e is

$$t_e = \frac{C^o_{P,i} - C^f_{P,i}}{C_P} \; \frac{\rho_p\, d_p^2}{12\, \mathcal{D}_i C^S_{G,i} \left(B \dfrac{C^o_{P,i}}{C_P} - S_i \right)} \tag{30}$$

The initial and final mass concentrations of the contaminant in the particle phase are $C^o_{P,i}$ and $C^f_{P,i}$, respectively. The particle density is ρ_p and the diffusion coefficient of the vapor in air is $\mathcal{D}_i$. The saturation S_i is the gas phase concentration of the contaminant (far from a particle surface) divided by the saturated vapor concentration. It has been assumed that the mass concentration of vapor at the particle surface can be described successfully by Equation 22. Equation 30 neglects the slower evaporation that occurs due to the latent heat of the evaporating material cooling the particles as well as the Kelvin effect and the correction for gas transport from small particles.[13]

Substituting plausible values for the density (1 g/cm^3) and the diffusion coefficient (0.1 cm^2/s) and applying the equation to the special case of complete evaporation of the contaminant ($C^f_{P,i} = 0$) into air that is substantially depleted of vapor (S_i negligible) results in the order-of-magnitude estimate:

$$t_e \approx 8\ \text{sec} \frac{\left(\dfrac{d_p}{1 \mu\text{m}} \right)^2}{\left(\dfrac{B\, C^S_{G,i}}{1\ \text{mg/m}^3} \right)} \tag{31}$$

If the value of B is unknown, a first estimate of the time-scale of evaporation can be obtained by assuming B is unity. For pure droplets ($B = 1$) near room temperature, the time-scale for evaporation of a 1-µm water droplet ($C^S_{G,i} = 17{,}000$ mg/m^3) into dry air is about a half millisecond; that of a 10-µm glycerol droplet ($C^S_{G,i} = 0.5$ mg/m^3) is about 27 min. Equation 31 also provides a reasonable estimate for the time-scale of growth by condensation for a particle that contains no contaminant initially and grows into one with diameter d_p.[13]

Sampling Approaches

There has been little discussion of the issue in the literature, but it could be argued that in most health-related air sampling, the quantity that is the most important to measure accurately is the total airborne mass concentration without regard to whether the material is in the gas or particle phase. Volatile materials may move between the gas and particle phases because of a change in conditions, including after inhalation, but the total airborne mass concentration is unchanged.[13] This makes it a practical first choice for measurement.

In some cases, it may be desirable to measure the distribution of a compound between the two phases instead of only the total airborne mass concentration. For example, there may be compounds for which the toxic effects are known to differ significantly depending on whether the material existed in the particle or gas phase just prior to inhalation. Also, the choice of control technology may depend on which phase dominates. Both sampling the total airborne concentration and sampling the distribution between the two phases are discussed in the following sections.

Total Airborne Concentration

Measuring the total airborne concentration requires an efficient particle collector and an efficient vapor collector. Two approaches have been found suitable. One is to place the vapor collector, such as a tube containing an efficient sorbent, downstream of an efficient particle collector, such as a filter.[33–35] One problem with the reverse configuration, placing the vapor collector upstream of the particle collector, is that material might evaporate from the particles which are collected on the filter and be lost. The second approach that has been used successfully is to apply a coating of a material to the filter that either adsorbs or reacts chemically with the air contaminant being sampled.[36] A variation of this approach is to preload the filter with a particulate sorbent.[37] If done properly, the approach of using a coated or preloaded filter results in a compact and convenient sampler with all the collected material on one substrate for analysis.

Other approaches might provide satisfactory results, but care must be taken to ensure that the collection efficiency is sufficiently high for both phases in each sampling situation. Impingers are versatile in allowing the liquid to be changed to match the compound being collected, but the collection efficiency for submicrometer particles is low. The particle collection efficiency of some sorbent beds may be sufficient to allow measurements of the total airborne concentration of some compounds.[38] These devices should not be used without experimental validation of their suitability for the specific application.

Techniques for measuring the total airborne concentration have been much less widely discussed in the literature of workplace air sampling than in the literature of air sampling in the general environment. However, such techniques have been proposed recently for organophosphorus pesticides, fluoride, formaldehyde, and isocyanates.[39]

Particle/Gas Distribution

In cases where high precision is not required and some experimental phase distribution data are available to validate a relation like Equation 22, it would be possible to estimate the distribution between the particle and gas phases after measuring only the total airborne concentration of the contaminant and the concentration of all airborne particulate. In order to use a relation like Equation 22, it would be necessary to assume that the atmosphere is near equilibrium, i.e., sufficient time has passed since the atmosphere's equilibrium was last disturbed, as discussed in the previous section. In most cases, reliable information about the distribution of a material between the particle and gas phases of an atmosphere can only be obtained by measurements in that or similar atmospheres.

There does not appear to be any universally accepted method for measuring the mass concentrations of an air contaminant in the particle and gas phases separately. Many approaches have been described in the literature, but questions arise about the accuracy of the results. Three approaches are presented here that seem suitable for a range of sampling conditions, but each has characteristics that might lead to erroneous results in some sampling situations. Because of the ease with which the particle/gas equilibrium is disturbed and mass is transferred between the two phases, measurement of the distribution of an air contaminant between the particle and gas phases is much more difficult than measurement of the total airborne mass concentration.

A sampling system consisting of an efficient particle collector followed by an efficient vapor collector was one of the two configurations recommended for measuring the total airborne mass concentration of a contaminant. It has also been used in attempts to measure the distribution of a contaminant between the gas and particle phases. The vapor collector must be removed from the particle collector at the end of the sampling period and stored separately to avoid evaporation of the volatile contaminant from the particles and transport to the vapor collector.

The most common configuration, called a "filter

pack," consists of a filter as the particle collector and a sorbent as the vapor collector. The particle phase concentration is calculated from the mass collected on the filter and the gas phase concentration from that collected in the sorbent (Figure 4-2).[3,22] A filter pack might be suitable for measuring the average concentration in each phase over the sampling period if two conditions are met: 1) the filter does not adsorb the vapor and 2) the chemical composition and physical characteristics of the sampled atmosphere are constant during the entire sampling period.[40] If the filter adsorbs vapor, the particle phase mass concentration will be overestimated and the gas phase underestimated.[29–31] As mentioned previously, adsorption onto a filter might be detected by placing a second filter downstream of the first, but correcting for such adsorption is problematic.[30] If the sampled atmosphere does not stay constant, mass collected from the particle phase onto the filter will tend to evaporate and be transferred into the vapor collector whenever the mass concentration of the contaminant in the gas phase decreases. Also, mass in the gas phase of the air being sampled will be transferred to collected particles on the filter whenever the mass concentration in the gas phase increases. As a result, filter packs may not be valid for health-related sampling from the occupational or general environment, although they may be valid for sampling from a controlled atmosphere, e.g., inhalation exposure chambers or a process line.

Replacing the filter by a cascade impactor appears to reduce the interaction between particles that have deposited on the collection surfaces and the air drawn through the device subsequently, reducing the severity of some of the artifacts.[41] The problem remains that the air which enters the vapor collector has passed over all the previously collected particles and significant mass transfer between the gas and collected particles may have occurred.

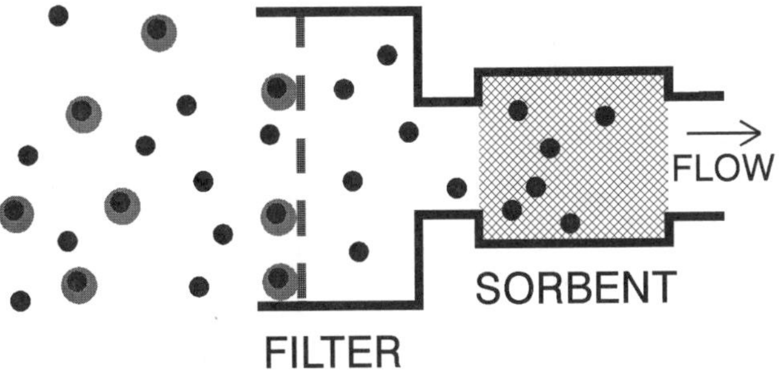

FIGURE 4-2. Schematic diagram of a common approach to measuring the distribution of a contaminant between the particle and gas phases of an atmosphere. Particles (large gray circles) with associated molecules of a contaminant in the gas phase (small black circles) are collected on the filter. Vapor penetrating the filter is collected in the sorbent. Particle and gas phase concentrations are calculated from the masses collected on the filter and in the sorbent, respectively. Potential errors include vapor adsorption by the filter material and transfer of contaminants between the gas phase and particles already collected on the filter if the atmosphere changes temperature, humidity, or composition.

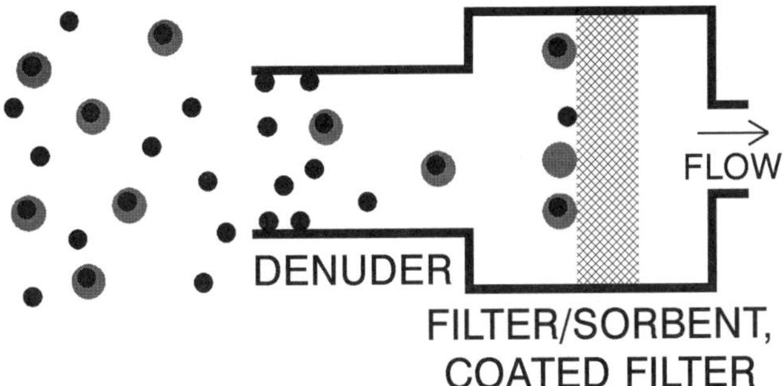

FIGURE 4-3. Schematic diagram of a denuder-based approach to measuring the distribution of a contaminant between the particle and gas phases of an atmosphere. Vapor molecules (small black circles) are collected at the wall of the denuder. Particles (large gray circles) with associated volatile contaminants are collected by a filter that is either treated or followed by a suitable sorbent to trap vapor molecules. Potential errors include particle deposition in the denuder and significant evaporation of the particles while surrounded by vapor-depleted air.

Replacing the filter by a virtual impactor reduces this problem because the larger particles are not collected on a surface over which air subsequently passes on the way to the vapor collector.[42,43] Instead, the particles are diverted to a filter that is some distance away.

A second approach uses a denuder to remove vapor from the sampled air stream (see Chapter 20), followed by an efficient collector of both particles and vapor (Figure 4-3). The particle and vapor collector may be a treated filter or a filter followed by an adsorbent. The gas phase concentration is calculated from the mass collected in the denuder and the particle phase concentration from that collected in the particle and vapor collector.[44–47]

If the material collected in the denuder cannot be removed quantitatively for analysis, the "denuder difference method" may be used.[48] Two samplers are operated in parallel. One is a particle and vapor collector and the other consists of a denuder to collect the material from the gas phase followed by a particle and vapor collector. The difference between the masses of material collected in the two particle and vapor collectors is taken to be the mass in the gas phase.

In another variation, the vapor may be transported preferentially into a parallel air stream because it has a higher diffusion coefficient than the particles.[49]

These denuder-related approaches might be expected to give valid results if: 1) there is insignificant particle deposition in the denuder,[5] 2) the denuder collects all or a known fraction of the contaminant mass which was in the gas phase when the air entered the sampler, and 3) there is insignificant particle evaporation and subsequent transfer of that contaminant mass to the denuder walls. Item 2 is easier to attain using denuders with narrow channels because the small distance between the bulk of the sampled air and the coated walls allows efficient collection of vapor at higher flow rates.[(6–10)] The third item is the most troublesome and may be impossible to attain for some materials. During the time the particles reside in an atmosphere that has been depleted of vapor, some material will evaporate from the particles. In order to have this mass transfer be negligible, the amount that evaporates must be a negligible fraction of the amount in the particle phase and must be a negligible fraction of the amount that was in the gas phase before the aerosol entered the denuder.

Consideration of a simple case, particles with a single volatile component and the vapor in equilibrium with them, is instructive. The sampled air's residence time in the denuder t_r can be estimated as the denuder's volume divided by the sampling flow rate. The characteristic time for complete evaporation/desorption into vapor-depleted air is given in Equation 31. Only a negligibly small fraction of the volatile component's mass in the particles will evaporate during the transit time if

$$t_r << t_e = 8 \text{ sec} \frac{\left(\dfrac{d_p}{1\ \mu\text{m}}\right)^2}{\left(\dfrac{B\, C^S_{G,i}}{1\ \text{mg/m}^3}\right)} \quad (32)$$

Another condition is necessary to ensure that the mass of contaminant that does evaporate from the particles is negligibly small compared to the mass of material which was initially in the gas phase. Otherwise, the mass of contaminant collected at the denuder walls will be in error. Recalling that the characteristic time of evaporation is defined here as the volatile contaminant's mass in the particle phase divided by the initial evaporation rate, an order of magnitude estimate of the mass of material that evaporates from the particles per volume of air can be written as the particle mass divided by the characteristic time of evaporation times the residence time. A relationship sufficient to ensure that the amount of evaporated contaminant is negligibly small compared to the amount originally in the gas phase, expressed in terms of saturation, is:

$$\frac{C_{P,i}}{t_e} t_r << S_i\, C^S_{G,i} \quad (33)$$

Substituting for t_e using Equation 31 and substituting $C_{G,i}$ using Equation 22 for $S_i\, C^S_{G,i}$ under the assumption that the particles were in equilibrium with the vapor before entering the denuder gives:

$$t_r << 8 \text{ sec} \frac{\left(\dfrac{d_p}{1\ \mu\text{m}}\right)^2}{\left(\dfrac{C_P}{1\ \text{mg/m}^3}\right)} \quad (34)$$

The residence time cannot be made arbitrarily small because all or a known fraction of the vapor molecules must have time to diffuse to the wall of the denuder and be collected (see Chapter 20). Evaporation of particles in a denuder will lead to negligible errors if both the contaminant's saturated vapor concentration and the concentration of all materials in the particle phase are sufficiently small according to Equations 32 and 34, given the assumptions stated in their derivation. Negligible evaporation of particles in a denuder is more likely for outdoor environmental sampling than for sampling in dusty/misty workplaces where C_P is likely to be higher. These generalizations should hold even for atmospheres containing several volatile and nonvolatile components.

A third approach to measuring the distribution of a contaminant between the gas and particle phases has been described.[(50–52)] The approach is to measure the total concentration in both phases by methods outlined already and place a suitable passive sampler nearby to measure the vapor concentration (Figure 4-4). The concentration in the particle phase would be estimated by subtraction. If only a small fraction of the total airborne contaminant were in the particle phase, this estimate might be quite imprecise, because it is determined by subtracting two measurements. Another source of significant error might be the deposition of particles on the front surface of the diffusive sampler. If such particles were allowed to remain in that position sufficiently long

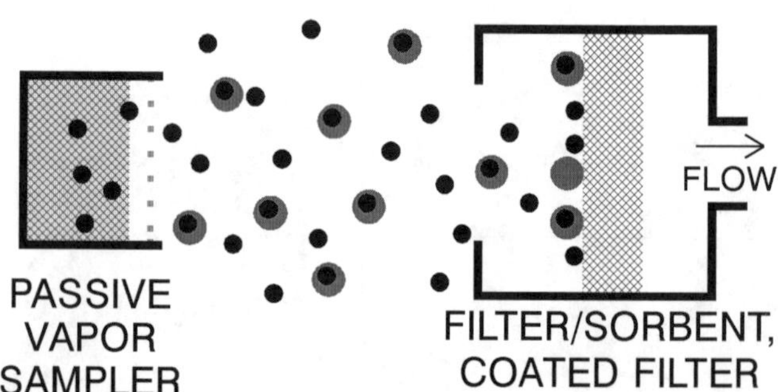

FIGURE 4-4. Schematic diagram of an approach to measuring the distribution of a contaminant between the particle and gas phases of an atmosphere. Vapor molecules (small black circles) and particles (large gray circles) are collected in an active sampler containing a treated filter or filter followed by a sorbent to measure the total airborne concentration of the contaminant. Vapor only is collected in the passive sampler. The particle concentration is estimated by subtraction. Potential errors include deposition of particles on the passive sampler and high uncertainty in estimating the particle concentration when it is much smaller than the vapor concentration.

and the surrounding vapor concentration fluctuated, material in the particles might evaporate during periods of lower vapor concentration and erroneously contribute a significant amount to the mass collected on the sorbent of the diffusion sampler. This would lead to an overestimate of the fraction of contaminant in the gas phase.

Summary and Conclusions

Particle and gas phase interactions can lead to errors in air sampling results. Some errors include allowing unwanted chemical reactions to occur during sampling, measuring the concentration of a contaminant only in the particle or gas phase when there is a significant fraction in the unsampled phase, and using inappropriate techniques to measure the distribution of a contaminant between the two phases.

Errors due to chemical reactions between a reactive gas and particles that have been collected on a filter can be reduced by passing the air through a suitable denuder before it reaches the filter.

It is important to understand the distribution of an air contaminant between the particle and gas phases and the potential for changes in that distribution during sampling. Three pieces of information are helpful in judging whether it is necessary to sample the gas, particle, or both phases of an atmosphere: the saturated vapor concentration of the contaminant, a rough estimate of the total airborne concentration of the contaminant in the atmosphere being sampled, and a rough estimate of the concentration and composition of the particles in the atmosphere. The distribution of a contaminant between the particle and gas phases depends on temperature, pressure, particle composition, and the gas phase concentration of the contaminant. The processes of sampling or inhalation may change the distribution between the phases significantly.

It is arguably more important to measure the total airborne concentration of a contaminant, i.e., the concentration in the particle phase plus that in the gas phase, than to measure the distribution between the phases. The total airborne concentration can be measured by a sampler consisting of an efficient filter followed by an efficient sorbent or can be measured by a filter that is treated with a material which adsorbs or reacts with the vapor.

When it is necessary to measure the distribution of a contaminant between the particle and gas phases, no universally acceptable technique appears to be available. The common approach of placing a sorbent downstream of a filter is prone to errors if the filter adsorbs vapor or if the atmosphere's composition changes. Replacing the filter with a virtual impactor reduces many of these errors. The approach of placing a denuder capable of collecting the vapor upstream of a collector of the particles and vapor that penetrate the denuder is prone to errors if the denuder is not optimized for the application. In some cases, it may be difficult to avoid significant errors due to evaporation of the contaminant from the particles while they reside in vapor–depleted air in the denuder. A third approach to measuring the distribution of a contaminant between the gas and particle phases is available. The total airborne concentration is measured by an active sampler and the vapor concentration is measured by a passive sampler. This approach has not been widely used, yet. Other approaches are likely to be suggested in the future, but measuring the distribution will always be much more difficult than measuring the total airborne concentration.

References

1. Tanner, R.L.; Harrison, R.M.: Acid–base Equilibria of Aerosols and Gases in the Atmosphere. In: Environmental Particles. Vol. I, pp. 75–106. J. Buffle and H.P. van Leeuwen, Eds. Environmental Analytical and Physical Chemistry Series. Lewis Publishers, Inc., Boca Raton, FL (1992).
2. Wexler, A.S.; Seinfeld, J.H.: The Distribution of Ammonium Salts Among a Size and Composition Dispersed Aerosol. Atmos. Environ. 24A:1231–1246 (1990).
3. Bidleman, T.F.: Atmospheric Processes: Wet and Dry Deposition of Organic Compounds are Controlled by their Vapor-Particle Partitioning. Environ. Sci. Technol. 22:361–367 (1988).
4. Slanina, J.; de Wild, P.J.; Wyers, G.P.: The Application of Denuder Systems to the Analysis of Atmospheric Components, Chapter 3, Gaseous Pollutants: Characterization and Cycling, pp. 129–154. J.O. Nriagu, Ed. John Wiley & Sons, New York (1992).
5. Ye, Y.; Tsai, C.-J.; Pui, D.Y.H.; Lewis, C.W.: Particle Transmission Characteristics of an Annular Denuder Ambient Sampling System. Aerosol Sci. Tech. 14:102–111 (1991).
6. Possanzini, M.; Febo, A.; Liberti, A.: New Design of a High-Performance Denuder for the Sampling of Atmospheric Pollutants. Atmos. Environ. 17:2605–2610 (1983).
7. Koutrakis, P.; Fasano, A.M.; Slater, J.L.; et al.: Design of a Personal Annular Denuder Sampler to Measure Atmospheric Aerosols and Gases. Atmos. Environ. 23:2767–2773 (1989).
8. Poon, W.S.; Pui, D.Y.H.; Lee, C.-T.; Liu, B.Y.H.: A Compact Porous Denuder for Atmospheric Sampling of Inorganic Aerosols. J. Aerosol Sci. 25:923–934 (1994).
9. Koutrakis, P.; Sioutas, C.; Ferguson, S.T.; Wolfson, J.M.: Development and Evaluation of a Glass Honeycomb Denuder/Filter Pack System to Collect Atmospheric Gases and Particles. Environ. Sci. Technol. 27:2497–2501 (1993).
10. Pratsinis, S.E.; Xu, M.; Biswas, P.; Willeke, K.: Theory for Aerosol Sampling through Annular Diffusion Denuders. J. Aerosol Sci. 20:1597–1600 (1989).
11. Perrino, C.; DeSantis, F.; Febo, A.: Criteria for the Choice of a Denuder Sampling Technique Devoted to the Measurement of Atmospheric Nitric and Nitrous Acids. Atmos. Environ. 24A:617–626 (1990).
12. Hinds, W.C.: Aerosol Technology: Properties, Behavior, and Measurement of Airborne Particles. John Wiley & Sons, New York (1982).
13. Soderholm, S.C.; Ferron, G.A.: Estimating Effects of Evaporation and Condensation on Volatile Aerosols during Inhalation Exposures. J. Aerosol Sci. 23:257–277 (1992).
14. Reid, R.C.; Prausnitz, J.M.; Poling, B.E.: The Properties of Gases & Liquids, 4th ed., Chapter 8. McGraw–Hill, New York (1987).

15. Betterton, E.A.: Henry's Law Constants of Soluble and Moderately Soluble Organic Gases: Effects on Aqueous Phase Chemistry, Chapter 1, Gaseous Pollutants: Characterization and Cycling, pp. 1–50. J.O. Nriagu, Ed. John Wiley & Sons, New York (1992).
16. Yamasaki, H.; Kuwata, K.; Miyamoto, H.: Effects of Ambient Temperature on Aspects of Airborne Polycyclic Aromatic Hydrocarbons. Environ. Sci. Technol. 16:189–194 (1982).
17. Pankow, J.F.: Review and Comparative Analysis of the Theories on Partitioning Between the Gas and Aerosol Particulate Phases in the Atmosphere. Atmos. Environ. 21:2275–2283 (1987).
18. Pankow, J.F.: An Absorption Model of Gas/Particulate Partitioning in the Atmosphere. Atmos. Environ. 28:185–188 (1994).
19. Pankow, J.F.; Bidleman, T.F.: Interdependence of the Slopes and Intercepts from Log–Log Correlations of Measured Gas-Particle Partitioning and Vapor Pressure — I. Theory and Analysis of Available Data. Atmos. Environ. 26A:1071–1080 (1992).
20. Soderholm, S.C.: Aerosol Instabilities. Appl. Ind. Hyg. 3:35–40 (1988).
21. Perez, C.; Soderholm, S.C.: Some Chemicals Requiring Special Consideration when Deciding Whether to Sample the Particle, Vapor, or Both Phases of an Atmosphere. Appl. Occup. Environ. Hyg. 6:859–864 (1991).
22. Pankow, J.F.; Bidleman, T.F.: Effects of Temperature, TSP and Per Cent Nonexchangeable Material in Determining the Gas-Particle Partitioning of Organic Compounds. Atmos. Environ. 25A:2241–2249 (1991).
23. Nair, P.V.N.; Vohra, K.G.: Growth of Aqueous Sulphuric Acid Droplets as a Function of Relative Humidity. J. Aerosol Sci. 6:265–271 (1975).
24. Gotfelty, D.E.; Seiber, J.N.; Liljedahl, L.A.: Pesticides in Fog. Nature 325:602–605 (1987).
25. McFee, D.R.; Zavon, P.: Solvents. In: Fundamentals of Industrial Hygiene, 3rd ed., p. 103. B.A. Plog, G.S. Benjamin, and M.A. Kerwin, Eds. National Safety Council, Chicago (1988).
26. Kulmala, M.; Vesala, T.: Condensation in the Continuum Regime. J. Aerosol Sci. 22:337–346 (1991).
27. Zhang, X.Q.; McMurry, P.H.: Theoretical Analysis of Evaporative Losses from Impactor and Filter Deposits. Atmos. Environ. 21:1779–1789 (1987).
28. Wang, H.-C.; John, W.: Characteristics of the Berner Impactor for Sampling Inorganic Ions. Aerosol Sci. Tech. 8:157–172 (1988).
29. McDow, S.R.; Huntzicker, J.J.: Vapor Adsorption Artifact in the Sampling of Organic Aerosol: Face Velocity Effects. Atmos. Environ. 24A:2563–2571 (1990).
30. Cotham, W.E.; Bidleman, T.F.: Laboratory Investigations of the Partitioning of Organochlorine Compounds between the Gas Phase and Atmospheric Aerosols on Glass Fiber Filters. Environ. Sci. Technol. 26:469–478 (1992).
31. Hart, K.M.; Pankow, J.F.: Comparison of n-Alkane and PAH Concentrations Collected on Quartz Fiber and Teflon Membrane Filters in an Urban Environment. J. Aerosol Sci. 21(Supp. 1):S377–S380 (1990).
32. Biswas, P.; Jones, C.L.; Flagan, R.C.: Distortion of Size Distributions by Condensation and Evaporation in Aerosol Instruments. Aerosol Sci. Tech. 7:231–246 (1987).
33. Hill, Jr., R.H.; Arnold, J.E.: A Personal Air Sampler for Pesticides. Arch. Environ. Contam. Toxicol. 8:621–628 (1979).
34. König, J.; Funke, W.; Balfanz, E.; Grosch, B.; Pott, F.: Testing a High Volume Air Sampler for Quantitative Collection of Polycyclic Aromatic Hydrocarbons. Atmos. Environ. 14:609–613 (1980).
35. Kirton, P.J.; Ellis, J.; Crisp, P.T.: Investigation of Adsorbents for Sampling Compounds Found in Coke Oven Emissions. Fuel 70:4–8 (1991).
36. Levin, J.-O.; Fängmark, I.: High-Performance Liquid Chromatographic Determination of Hexamethylenetetramine in Air. Analyst 113:511–513 (1988).
37. Markell, C.; Hagen, D.F.; Bunnelle, V.A.: New Technologies in Solid-Phase Extraction. LC•GC 9:332–337 (1991).
38. Kogan, V.; Kuhlman, M.R.; Coutant, R.W.; Lewis, R.G.: Aerosol Filtration by Sorbent Beds. J. Air Waste Manag. Assoc. 43:1367–1373 (1993).
39. Streicher, R.P.; Kennedy, E.R.; Lorberau, C.D.: Strategies for the Simultaneous Collection of Vapours and Aerosols with Emphasis on Isocyanate Sampling. Analyst 119:89–97 (1994).
40. Hart, K.M.; Isabelle, L.M.; Pankow, J.F.: High-Volume Air Sampler for Particle and Gas Sampling. 1. Design and Gas Sampling Performance. Environ. Sci. Technol. 26:1048–1052 (1992).
41. Kaupp, H.; Umlauf, G.: Atmospheric Gas-Particle Partitioning of Organic Compounds: Comparison of Sampling Methods. Atmos. Environ. 26A:2259–2267 (1992).
42. Sioutas, C.; Koutrakis, P.: Development of a Low Cutpoint Slit-Nozzle Virtual Impactor for Collection of Semi-Volatile Organic Compounds. J. Aerosol Sci. 24(Supp. 1):S363–S364 (1993).
43. Sioutas, C.; Koutrakis, P.: Development of a Low Cutpoint Size Slit Virtual Impactor for Sampling Ambient Fine Particles. J. Aerosol Sci. (in press, 1994).
44. Gunderson, E.C.; Anderson, C.C.: Collection Device for Separating Airborne Vapor and Particulates. Am. Ind. Hyg. Assoc. J. 48:634–638 (1987).
45. Caka, F.M.; Eatough, D.J.; Lewis, E.A.; et al.: An Intercomparison of Sampling Techniques for Nicotine in Indoor Environments. Environ. Sci. Technol. 24:1196–1203 (1990).
46. Krieger, M.S.; Hites, R.A.: Diffusion Denuder for the Collection of Semivolatile Organic Compounds. Environ. Sci. Technol. 26:1551–1555 (1992).
47. Gundel, L.A.; Daisey, J.M.; Mahanama, K.R.R.; et al.: Polycyclic Aromatic Hydrocarbons in Indoor Air and Environmental Tobacco Smoke Measured with a New Integrated Organic Vapor-Particle Sampler. In: Indoor Air '93: Proceedings of the 6th International Conference on Indoor Air Quality and Climate, Volume 3, Combustion Products, Risk Assessment, Policies, July 5–8, 1993, Helsinki, Finland, pp. 81–86. M. Jantunen, P. Kalliokoski, E. Kukkonen, et al., Eds. Indoor Air '93 (1993).
48. Coutant, R.W.; Brown, L.; Chuang, J.; Lewis, R.G.: Field Evaluation of Phase Distribution of PAH. Proceedings of the 1986 EPA/APCA Symposium on Measurement of Toxic Air Pollutants, pp. 146–155. Report No. 600/9-86-013. U.S. Environmental Protection Agency, Washington, DC (1986).
49. Turpin, B.J.; Liu, S.-P.; Podolski, K.S.; et al.: Design and Evaluation of a Novel Diffusion Separator for Measuring Gas/Particle Distributions of Semivolatile Organic Compounds. Environ. Sci. Technol. 27:2441–2449 (1993).
50. Malek, R.F.; Daisey, J.M.; Cohen, B.S.: The Effect of Aerosol on Estimates of Inhalation Exposure to Airborne Styrene. Am. Ind. Hyg. Assoc. J. 47:524–529 (1986).
51. Cohen, B.S.; Brosseau, L.M.; Fang, C.-P.; et al.: Measurement of Air Concentrations of Volatile Aerosols in Paint Spray Applications. Appl. Occup. Environ. Hyg. 7:514–521 (1992).
52. Brosseau, L.M.; Fang, C.-P.; Snyder, C.; Cohen, B.S.: Particle Size Distribution of Automobile Paint Sprays. Appl. Occup. Environ. Hyg. 7:607–612 (1992).

Chapter 5

Size-Selective Health Hazard Sampling

Morton Lippmann, Ph.D.
Nelson Institute of Environmental Medicine, New York University Medical Center, Tuxedo, New York

CONTENTS

Introduction

Sampling for Respiratory Hazard Evaluation

Air sampling techniques have been used to obtain information for a variety of purposes. The following discussion concerns the specific purpose of sampling for the evaluation of the toxicological insult arising from the inhalation of airborne particles and compliance with particle size-selective Threshold Limit Values (PSS–TLVs™) recommended by the American Conference of Governmental Industrial Hygienists (ACGIH). Air sampling techniques used to obtain information for other purposes (e.g., performance testing of ventilation systems and air cleaners, contamination monitoring in so-called "white room" or "cleanroom" operations, and basic scientific studies of atmospheric reactions, composition, and capacity for pollutant dispersion) may differ and are beyond the scope of this discussion.

If the objective is to obtain information on the nature and magnitude of the potential health hazard resulting from the inhalation of airborne particles, the techniques must be capable of providing data on the contaminant concentration within the size range that reaches the critical organ for toxic action. In other words, the choice of methods must be based on a recognition of the size-selecting characteristics of the human respiratory tract in addition to the usual factors affecting the selection of methods, e.g., the physical limitations of the collection process, and the sensitivity and specificity of the analytical procedures.

There has been an increasing recognition of the importance of the selective sampling of airborne particles. The size-selecting characteristics of the human respiratory tract were largely ignored before 1952. The only standard method that had provided a means for discriminating against nonrespirable particles was the impinger sampling–light field counting technique for pneumoconiosis-producing dusts. The Greenburg–Smith impinger, developed in 1922–1925 through the cooperative efforts of the U.S. Bureau of Mines, the U.S. Public Health Service, and the American Society of Heating and Ventilating Engineers,[1] and the midget impinger, developed in 1928 by the Bureau of Mines,[2] collect particles larger than about 0.75 µm in a liquid medium. Such samples were analyzed by counting the particles that settled to the bottom of an aqueous counting cell and were visible when viewed through a 10X objective lens. Particles larger than 10 µm observed during the count were rejected as "nonrespirable." The alternative approach was gravimetric analysis of the total airborne particulate sample, in which there was no practical way to discriminate against oversized particles.

The use of the terms "respirable" and "nonrespirable" were first applied to those mineral dusts known to produce pneumoconioses, i.e., dust diseases of the nonciliated gas-exchange region of the lungs (also referred to as the alveolar or pulmonary region). The particles that deposit in the oral or nasal airways of the upper respiratory tract (head airways region) or in the conductive airways of the tracheobronchial region are cleared from the deposition sites by mechanical processes such as mucociliary transport and cough; they do not contribute to the pathogenesis of the pneumoconioses. Such particles, which are generally considered "nonrespirable," can, however, contribute to the development of other diseases such as bronchitis and cancers of the nasal and bronchial airways. The section that follows outlines the factors affecting the deposition of particles within the major functional regions of the human respiratory tract and the quantitative data available on deposition in these regions as a function of aerodynamic particle size. This will be followed by a discussion of the criteria that have been proposed and/or used for sampling "respirable" dusts and for sampling particles that can deposit in the head airways and tracheobronchial airways.

Regional Deposition, Clearance, and Dose

The hazard from airborne particles varies with their physical, chemical, and/or biological properties. These properties determine the fate of the particles and their interactions with the host after they are deposited. A basic consideration is that this fate, in any given individual, varies greatly with the site of deposition within the respiratory tract.

There are a number of major subdivisions within the respiratory tract that differ markedly in structure, size, and function, and they have different mechanisms for particle elimination. Thus, a complete determination of dose from an inhaled toxicant depends on the regional deposition and the retention times at the deposition sites and along the elimination pathways, in addition to the chemical and surface properties of the particles.

Anatomical and Physiological Factors in Respiratory Tract Particle Deposition and Clearance

The succeeding paragraphs present a brief summary of the factors controlling particle deposition and clearance. More complete descriptions of the anatomy of the respiratory tract and of some of the factors controlling particle deposition and clearance are presented elsewhere.[3–5]

Head Airways Region

Nasal Passages. Air enters through the nares or nostrils, passes through a web of nasal hairs, and flows posteriorly toward the nasopharynx while passing through a series of narrow passages winding around and through shelflike projections called turbinates. The air is warmed and moistened in its passage and partially depleted of particles. Some particles are removed by impaction on the nasal hairs and at bends in the air path; others are removed by sedimentation and diffusion. Except for the anterior nares, the surfaces are covered by a mucous membrane composed of ciliated and goblet cells. The mucus produced by the goblet cells is propelled toward the pharynx by the beating of the cilia, carrying deposited particles along with it. Particles deposited on the anterior unciliated portion of the nares and at least some of the particles deposited on the nasal hairs usually are not carried posteriorly to be swallowed, but rather are removed mechanically by nose wiping, blowing, sneezing, etc.

Oral Passages, Pharynx, Larynx. In mouth breathing, some particles are deposited, primarily by impaction, in the oral cavity and at the back of the throat. Diffusion may also be important for ultrafine particles. These particles are rapidly eliminated to the esophagus by swallowing.

Tracheobronchial Region

The conductive airways in the tracheobronchial region have the appearance of an inverted tree, with the trachea analogous to the trunk and the subdividing bronchi to the limbs. The branching pattern is normally asymmetric in a regular pattern, as described by Horsfield *et al.*(6) However, for purposes of discussion, it will be clearer if Weibel's simplified anatomic model,[7] in which there are 16 generations of bifurcating airways, is adopted. As illustrated by Table 5-1, the diameter decreases from generation to generation, but because of the increasing number of tubes, the total cross section for flow increases and the air velocity decreases toward the ends of the tree. In the larger airways, particles too large to follow the bends in the air path are deposited by impaction. At the low velocities in the smaller airways, particles deposit by sedimentation and, if small enough, by diffusion.

Ciliated and mucus-secreting cells are found at all levels of the tracheobronchial tree. Most of the inert, nonsoluble particles deposited in this region are thus carried within hours toward the larynx on the moving mucous sheath that is propelled proximally by the beating of the cilia. Beyond the larynx, the particles enter the esophagus and pass through the gastrointestinal tract.

Cigarette smoke and air contaminants can affect mucociliary transport along the tracheobronchial tree. As demonstrated by Lippmann *et al.*,[8] brief exposures at low doses of irritants such as cigarette smoke and submicrometer H_2SO_4 can accelerate mucus transport, while higher doses of the same pollutants can slow or temporarily halt mucus transport. Chronic exposures to these pollutants can result in more variable rates of clearance and persistent changes in clearance rates which may predispose the individual to, or initiate a sequence of changes leading to, the development of chronic bronchitis.

Persistent defects in clearance of particles from the bronchial tree would also lead to increased residence times for particles containing toxic and carcinogenic chemicals, thereby increasing the dose to the underlying tissues from those chemicals and resulting in increased systemic uptake. In this manner, defective clearance may contribute to a variety of disease conditions.

Gas-Exchange Region

The region beyond the terminal bronchioles is the region in which gas exchange takes place. The epithelium is nonciliated and, therefore, insoluble particles deposited in this region by sedimentation and diffusion are removed at a very slow rate, with clearance half-times on the order of a month or more. The mechanisms for particle clearance from this region are only partly understood, and their relative importance remains a matter of some debate. Some particles are engulfed by phagocytic cells which are transported onto the ciliary "escalator" of the bronchial tree in an undefined manner. Others penetrate the alveolar wall and enter the lymphatic system. Still others dissolve slowly *in situ.* "Insoluble" dusts all have some finite solubility, which is greatly enhanced by the large surface-to-volume ratio characteristic of particles small enough to penetrate to the alveolar region of the lung. Morrow *et al.*[9] demonstrated that the late-phase clearance half-times of many "insoluble" dusts in the lung are proportional to their solubilities in simulated lung fluids. Alveolar clearance rates may differ for different dusts. Jammet *et al.*[10] studied the clearance of hematite, silica, and coal in cats, rats, and hamsters. Three clearance phases were observed. The first phase, representing bronchial clearance, had a half life of less than 1 day. An intermediate phase, with a half life of 10–12 days was seen in all species for hematite and in the cat for coal dust. When silica dust was inhaled, this phase was not seen. The slow third clearance phase, with a half life of >100 days, was unaffected, except that it accounted for more of the clearance. Further tests on cats and rats with carbon, quartz, titanium dioxide, and hematite were reported by LeBouffant.[11] The alveolar clearance was found to be a function of the species used, the pulmonary dust load, the time since exposure, and the nature of the particles. Coal, even in small quantities, slowed clearance in the rat. With heavy exposures, the clearance rate did not recover appreciably.

For asbestos and man-made mineral fibers, long-term fiber retention in the lungs depends on fiber length, fiber diameter, and leaching rates of various elements from the fibers. Bellmann *et al.*[12] showed that crocidolite fibers longer than 5 μm did not clear from rat lungs in 1 year, whereas chrysotile fibers longer than 5 μm increased in numbers, presumably due to longitudinal splitting. The glass fibers longer than 5 μm were lost, with a half-time of 55 days, primarily by dissolution. Short fibers of all types were cleared rapidly by comparison.

TABLE 5-1. Architecture of the Lung Based on Weibel's[A] Model A: Regular Dichotomy Average Adult Lung With Volume 4800 cm^3 at About Three-Fourths Maximal Inflation

Name of Airway	Generation[A]	Number/ Generation[A]	Diameter (mm)[A]	Length (mm)[A]	Cumulative Length (mm)[A]	Total Cross Section (cm^2)[A]	Volume (cm^3)[A]	Cumulative Volume (cm^3)[A]	Velocity (cm/s)[B,C]	Residence Time (m/s)[B,C]	Cumulative Time (m/s)[B,C]	Pressure Difference ($\mu m\ H_2$)[B,C,D]	Cum. Press. Diff. ($\mu m\ H_2$)[B,C,D]	Reynolds Number[B,E]
Trachea	0	1	18.0	120.0	120.0	2.54	30.5	30.5	393	30.5	31	87	87	4350
Main bronchus	1	2	12.2	47.6	167.4	2.33	11.3	41.8	427	11.1	41	82	169	3210
Lobar bronchus	2	4	8.3	19.0	186.6	2.13	4.0	45.8	462	4.11	45	76	246	2390
	3	8	5.6	7.6	194.2	2.00	1.5	47.2	507	1.50	47	73	320	1720
Segmental bronchus	4	16	4.5	12.7	206.9	2.48	3.5	50.7	392	3.23	50	147	467	1110
	5	32	3.5	10.7	217.6	3.11	3.3	54.0	325	3.29	53	170	638	690
Bronchi with	6	64	2.8	9.0	226.6	3.96	3.5	57.5	254	3.55	57	174	812	434
cartilage in wall	7	128	2.3	7.6	234.2	5.10	3.9	61.4	188	4.04	61	162	974	277
	8	256	1.86	6.4	240.6	6.95	4.5	54.8	144	4.45	65	160	1134	164
	9	512	1.54	5.4	246.0	9.56	5.2	71.0	105	5.15	80	143	1277	99
	10	1.02K	1.30	4.6	250.6	13.4	6.2	77.2	73.6	6.25	77	120	1397	60
Terminal bronchus	11	2.05K	1.09	3.9	254.5	19.6	7.6	84.8	52.3	7.45	85	103	1500	34
	12	4.10K	0.95	3.3	257.8	28.8	9.8	94.6	34.4	9.58	94	75	1576	20
Bronchioles with	13	8.19K	0.82	2.7	260.5	44.5	12.5	1.6	23.1	11.7	106	55	1632	11
muscle in wall	14	16.4 K	0.74	2.3	262.8	69.4	16.4	123	14.1	16.2	122	35	1667	6.5
	15	32.8 K	0.66	2.0	264.8	113	21.7	145	8.92	22.4	144	24	1692	3.6
Terminal bronchiole	16	65.5 K	0.60	1.65	266.5	180	29.7	175[F]	5.40	30.6	175	14	1707	2.0
Respiratory bronchiole	17	131 K	0.54	1.41	267.9	300	41.8	217	3.33	42.3	217	10	1716	1.1
Respiratory bronchiole	18	262 K	0.50	1.17	269.0	534	61.1	278	1.94	60.2	277	5	1722	0.57
Respiratory bronchiole	19	524 K	0.47	0.99	270.0	944	93.2	371	1.10	90.0	368	3	1725	0.31
Alveolar duct	20	1.05M	0.45	0.83	270.9	1.60K	140	510	0.60	138	506	1.4	1726	0.17
Alveolar duct	21	2.10M	0.43	0.70	271.6	3.22K	224	735	0.32	213	719	0.74	1727	0.08
Alveolar duct	22	4.19M	0.41	0.59	272.1	5.88K	350	1085	0.18	326	1047	0.37	1727	0.04
Alveolar sac	23	8.39M	0.41	0.50	272.6	11.8 K	591	1675	0.09	553	1602	0.16	1728	—
Alveoli, 21 per duct		300M[C]	0.28[C]	0.23[C]	272.9[C]		3200[C]	4875[C]						

[A]From Weibel.(7)
[B]At flow rate = 1.0 L/sec = 60 L/min.
[C]Added by W. Briscoe (personal communication).
[D]Pressure difference from mouth if flow were laminar.
[E]Added by B. Altshuler (personal communication).
[F]Dead space from larynx.

Gaseous air contaminants can also affect the clearance of particles from the alveolar region. Brief periods of exposure to irritant gases such as SO_2[13] and O_3[14] have been shown to stimulate the early alveolar clearance of rats, while prolonged exposure to SO_2 slowed clearance.[13] McFadden *et al.*[15] showed that cigarette smoke reduced the more rapid phase of alveolar clearance of asbestos fibers in guinea pigs.

Considering the recognized importance of the alveolar retention of relatively insoluble particles in the pathogenesis of chronic lung disease, it is somewhat surprising that examination of the literature yields so little useful data on the rates or routes of alveolar particle clearance in people.

In a study reported by Albert and Arnett,[16] eight normal human males inhaled neutron-activated metallic iron particles. For three subjects, there was sufficient residual activity after the completion of the bronchial clearance for continued measurement of retention. For a 32-year-old nonsmoking male and a 27-year-old male who was a moderate smoker, the postbronchial clearance occurred in two phases, a fast phase lasting about 1 month and a much slower terminal phase. The faster phase was missing in a 38-year-old, two pack-a-day cigarette smoking male with chronic cough. Although it is not possible to draw firm conclusions from these limited data, they are consistent with the findings of Cohen *et al.*,[17] who studied the alveolar clearance rates of magnetite particles in nine nonsmokers and three smokers using an external magnetometer for the particle retention measurements. The clearance rates in all three smokers were much lower than in any of the nine nonsmokers. Thus, it appears that the fast alveolar phase can be detected in man, and that cigarette smoking may increase dust retention beyond the retention of the smoke particles themselves. Low doses of cigarette smoke have been shown to inhibit macrophage phagocytosis.[18]

Another study that provides confirmation for the hypothesis that cigarette smoking can severely retard the clearance of particles from the alveolar region was performed by Bohning *et al.*[19] They exposed five healthy nonsmokers, six healthy ex-smokers, eight smokers, and six persons with chronic obstructive lung disease to 3.6-µm-diameter polystyrene latex particles tagged with ^{85}Sr. The nonsmokers and ex-smokers essentially had the same clearance patterns. There were two clearance phases: one with a $T_{1/2}$ of 30 ± 23 days, which accounted for 27% ± 13% of the total alveolar clearance. The $T_{1/2}$ of the slower phase was 296 ± 98 days. Only three smokers had a measurable fast phase, accounting for 6% to 13% of the clearance, with $T_{1/2}$ of 4, 18, and 20 days. The average $T_{1/2}$ for the slower phase for the eight smokers was 534 days. The slow phase $T_{1/2}$ was linearly correlated ($r = 0.99$) with the amount of smoking, increasing 14.7 ± 3.0 days per pack-year. The obstructive lung disease subjects had an average $T_{1/2}$ for the faster phase of 26.6 days and an average $T_{1/2}$ for the slower phase of 660 days.

It is difficult to imagine that prolonged retention of particles in the alveolar regions of the lungs is beneficial. Therefore, it is important to develop a better understanding of the normal patterns and rates of particle clearance from the alveoli as well as the dose-related influences of air contaminants on that clearance. Prolonged retention of inhaled particles in the alveolar regions increases both the doses of those particles to the underlying tissues and the potential for systemic uptake. If the particles are fibrogenic, they could contribute to the development of pneumoconiosis and emphysema. Cigarette smoke from either passive or active smoking contains a variety of carcinogens, and greater retention in the alveoli could cause an increased risk from both lung cancer and cancer in other organs that accumulate these chemicals after their dissolution in the lungs.

Much of the preceding remains speculative. It is unfortunate that our current knowledge of the quantitative aspects of the normal rates of clearance and of the effects of inhaled pollutants on clearance rates and pathways is too meager to permit a more definitive assessment.

Whereas variations in clearance dynamics for particles deposited in the alveoli may be critical determinants of toxicity and should be considered in the establishment of TLVs, these variables cannot be simulated by size-selective samplers that can only subdivide the airborne suspension on the basis of where the particles are expected to deposit. Thus, the establishment of size-selective sampling criteria has been dependent primarily on regional deposition data in healthy adults.

Regional Deposition and Clearance Dynamics

To estimate toxic dose from inhaled particles, the respiratory tract can be divided into five functional regions that differ grossly from one another in retention time at the deposition site, the elimination pathway, or both. These regions are:

1. Gas-exchange region (for both nose and mouth breathing).
2. Tracheobronchial region (for both nose and mouth breathing).

3a. Oral cavity, pharynx, and larynx (for mouth breathing).

3b. Nasopharynx, pharynx, and larynx (for nose breathing).

4. Ciliated nasal passages (for nose breathing).
5. Anterior unciliated nares (for nose breathing).

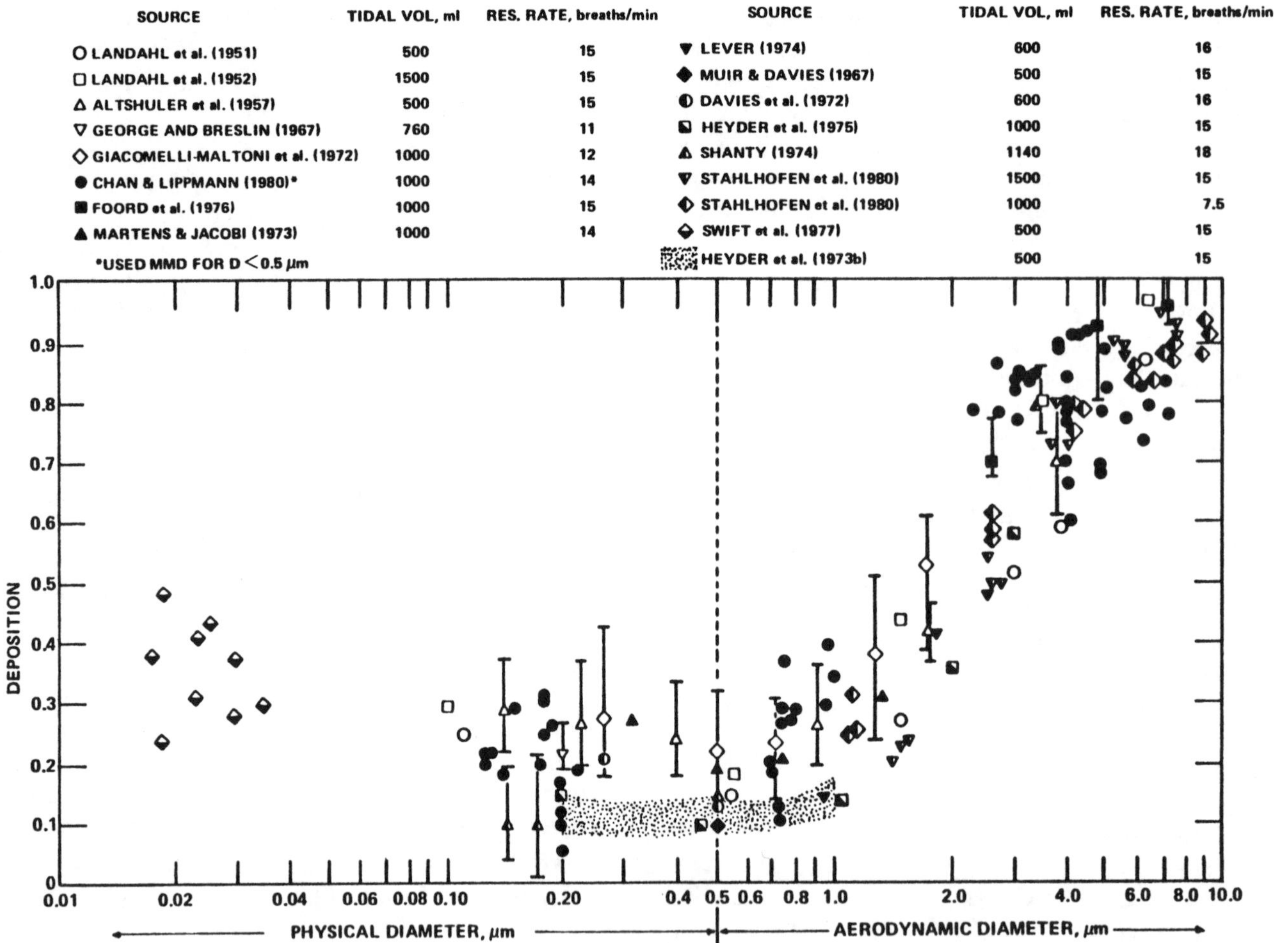

FIGURE 5-1. Deposition of monodisperse aerosols in the total respiratory tract for mouth breathing in humans as a function of aerodynamic diameter, except below 0.5 μm, where deposition is plotted versus physical diameter. The data are individual observations, averages, and ranges as cited by various investigators.

The fractional deposition in each of these regions is dependent on the aerodynamic particle size and the subject's airway dimensions and respiratory characteristics (e.g., flow rate, breathing frequency, tidal volume). Ideally, air sampling data should provide data on the deposition to be expected in each functional region or at least in regions 1, 2, and 3–5 inclusive.

Experimental Deposition Data

Total Deposition

There have been relatively few studies of regional particle deposition in humans. For particles between approximately 0.1- and 2-μm aerodynamic diameter, deposition in the conductive airways is generally small compared to deposition in the alveolar regions, and thus total deposition approaches alveolar deposition. Total deposition as a function of particle size and respiratory parameters has been measured experimentally by numerous investigators. Many previous reviews on deposition have called attention to the very large difference in the reported results.[3–5,20–23]

Figure 5-1 shows data from studies done with mouth breathing. Tidal volumes varied from 0.5 to 1.5 L. All appear to show the same trend with a minimum of deposition at approximately 0.5 μm diameter.

It is also apparent that in most studies involving more than one subject, there was considerable individual variation among the subjects. Davies *et al.*[24] showed that some of this variation could be eliminated by standardizing the expiratory reserve volume (ERV) and thereby the size of the air spaces. They found that deposition decreases as ERV increases. This was confirmed by Heyder *et al.*,[25] who reported that there was little intrasubject variation among six subjects when their deposition tests were performed at their normal ERVs. Some of the variability was also due to the variations in breathing frequency and flow rate among the various subjects, and Heyder *et al.*[26] showed how these variable factors affect total respiratory tract deposition. However, when all of the controllable fac-

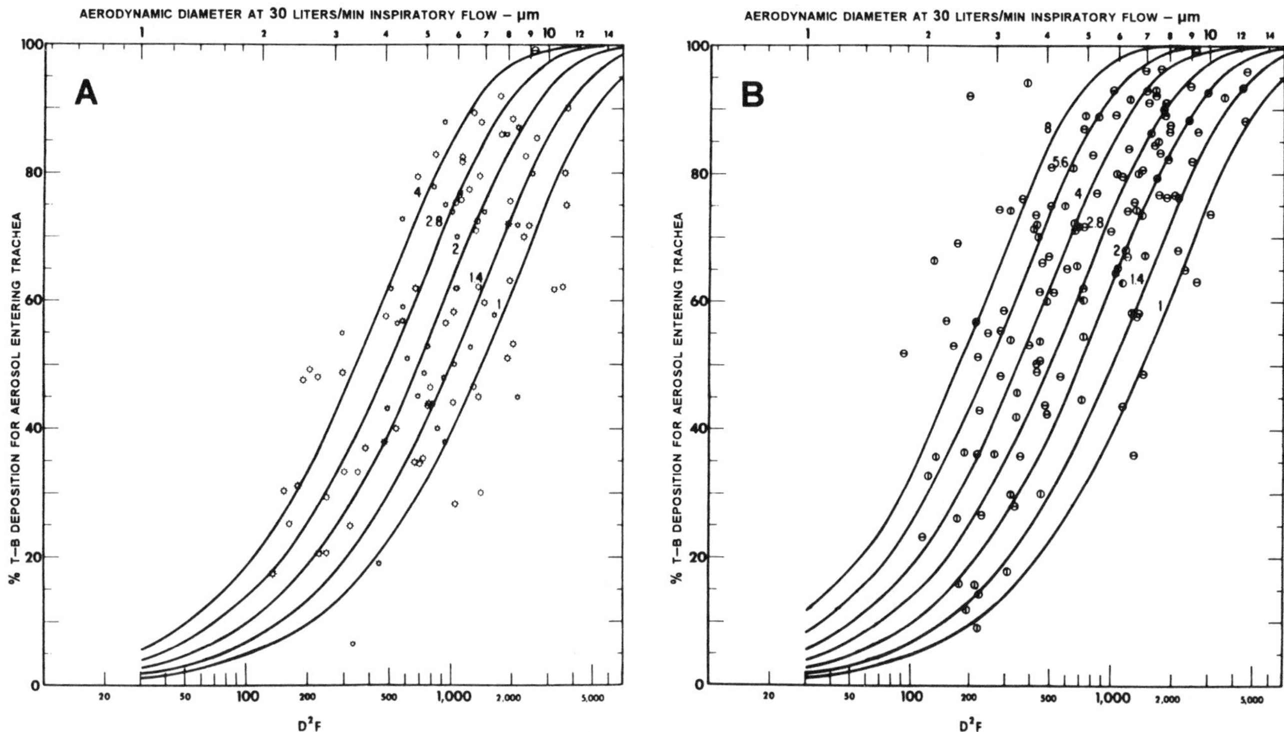

FIGURE 5-2. Deposition in the ciliated tracheobronchial (TB) region during mouthpiece breathing, in percent of the aerosol entering the trachea. Panel A shows data for nonsmoking normal human males; Panel B contains data for cigarette smokers. The curves represent the change in TB deposition as a function of D^2F for different values of the characteristic airway dimension parameter developed by Palmes and Lippmann.[37] A comparison of the two panels demonstrates that many cigarette smokers have increased TB deposition.

tors are taken into consideration, there is still variability in deposition due to the intrinsic variability of airway and air space sizes among individuals in a population. The extent and significance of such variability has been discussed.[27–30] Using aerosol deposition data to estimate bronchial airway sizes, Chan and Lippmann[29] reported a coefficient of variation of 0.23 among healthy young nonsmokers. For alveolar air space dimensions, Lapp *et al.*[31] found a coefficient of variation of 0.21 using an aerosol deposition technique, while Matsuba and Thurlbeck[32] reported a coefficient of variation of 0.25 based on measurements of lung sections taken at autopsy.

The data of Heyder *et al.*,[25,33] Muir and Davies,[34] and Davies *et al.*[24] appear to represent deposition minima for normal men. Their test protocols were precisely controlled. Their aerosols were charge neutralized. With more natural aerosol and respiratory parameters, higher deposition efficiencies would be expected. The deposition data in Figure 5-1 were based on the difference between inhaled and exhaled particle concentrations, except for the data of Lippmann,[21] Foord *et al.*,[35] and Stahlhofen *et al.*,[36] which are based on external *in vivo* measurements of γ-tagged particle retention. The large amount of scatter among the individual data points for the larger particles is due to a quite variable deposition in the head and tracheobronchial tree. Cigarette smokers have a similar median behavior for head deposition, but even more scatter. Figure 5-2 shows that the median and upper limits of tracheobronchial deposition are higher for cigarette smokers than for nonsmokers, but the lower limit is about the same.

Regional Deposition

Some inhaled particles deposit within the air passages between the point of entry at the lips or nares and the larynx. The fraction depositing can be highly variable, being dependent on the route of entry, the particles' sizes, and the flow rates. In most cases, the nasal route is a more efficient particle filter than the oral, especially at low and moderate flow rates. Thus, those people who normally breathe part or all of the time through the mouth may be expected to deposit more particles in their lungs than those who breathe entirely through the nose. During exertion, the flow resistance of the nasal passages causes a shift to mouth breathing in almost all people.

Available data on the regional deposition of inhaled particles in the human respiratory tract were summarized by the U.S. Environmental Protection Agency (U.S. EPA) in their 1982 criteria document for particulate matter and sulfur oxides.[38] The data considered reliable for deposition in the head (extrathoracic), tracheobronchial (TB) tree, and nonciliated pulmonary (alveolar) regions of healthy humans are summarized in Figures 5-3 through 5-6. There is a great amount of intersubject variability in deposition in all regions, due both to their inherent variability in airway and air space dimensions, and the variability in breathing rates and patterns. Deposition in the head is primarily by impaction, and a comparison of Figures 5-3 and 5-4 shows how much more efficient particle collections in the nasal passages are than those in the oral passages. In the TB airways, impaction is the dominant removal mechanism for particles larger than about 2.0 μm under most conditions, while sedimentation is the major collection mechanism for particles between about 0.5 and 2.0 μm. As an impactor, the TB region is much more efficient than the oral airways, but somewhat less efficient than the nasal airways. Thus, particle deposition within the lungs for 1.0- to 10-μm particles is very much dependent on whether the individual breathes through the nose or mouth. Deposition in the pulmonary region is primarily by sedimentation for particles larger than 0.5 μm and by diffusion for smaller particles. Particles of approximately 0.5 μm, having a minimal intrinsic mobility, have a minimum in deposition probability. For particles larger than approximately 3 μm, there is less pulmonary deposition with increasing size because these larger particles have a diminishing penetration through the conductive airways.

Figure 5-6 also shows an estimate of the alveolar deposition that could be expected when aerosol is inhaled via the nose. This estimate is based on the difference in head retention during nose breathing and mouth breathing from the straight line relations developed by Lippmann.[21] It can be seen that for mouth breathing, the size for maximum deposition is approximately 3 μm and that approximately one-half of the inhaled aerosol at this size deposits in this region. For nose breathing, there is a much less pronounced maximum of approximately 25% at 2.5 μm, with a nearly constant alveolar deposition averaging about 20% for all sizes between 0.1 and 4 μm.

Predictive Deposition Models

Mathematical models for predicting the regional deposition of aerosols were developed by Findeisen[41] in 1935, Landahl in 1950[42] and 1963,[43] and by Beeckmans[44] in 1965. Findeisen's simplified anatomy, with nine sequential regions from the trachea to the alveoli, and his impaction and sedimentation deposition equations were used in the International Commission on Radiological Protection (ICRP) Task Group's 1966 model.[23] For diffusional deposition, the Task Group used the Gormley–Kennedy[45] equations, and for head deposition, they assumed entry through the nose with a deposition efficiency given by the empirical equation of Pattle.[39]

The ICRP Task Group's 1966 model was adopted by ICRP Committee II in 1973, with numerical changes in some clearance constants. The Task Group report has been widely quoted and used within the health physics field. One of the significant conclusions of the Task Group study was that the regional deposition within the respiratory tract can be estimated using a single aerosol parameter, the activity median aerodynamic diameter (AMAD). For a tidal volume of 1450 cm^3, there are relatively small differences in estimated deposition over a very wide range of geometric standard deviations ($1.2 < \sigma g < 4.5$).

None of these earlier models provide reliable estimates of aerosol deposition in healthy normal adults. Their predictions for total and alveolar deposition efficiencies differ from the best available experimental data for adult normals illustrated in Figures 5-1 through 5-6. Furthermore, they do not give any measure of the very large variability in deposition efficiencies among normals, nor of the changes produced by cigarette smoking and lung disease. However, there have been significant advances in the measurement of deposition in recent years, and considerable effort is underway to improve theoretical understanding and predictive models. As shown in Figure 5-6, the regional deposition model of Yu[40] fits the available experimental data quite well.

New Predictive Deposition Models of ICRP and NCRP

In 1984, both the ICRP and the National Council on Radiation Protection (NCRP) appointed task groups to review the dosimetric model of the respiratory tract to propose revisions or a new model. Although intergroup liaison members were appointed, each task group produced its own model with significant differences between them.

ICRP Deposition Model[46]

The new ICRP Task Group directed its efforts toward improving the model adopted in 1973 rather than developing a completely new model. The objective was a model that would 1) facilitate calculation of biologically meaningful doses; 2) be consistent with the morphological, physiological, and radiobiological characteristics of the respiratory tract; 3) incorporate current knowledge; 4) meet all radiation protection needs; 5) be no more sophisticated than necessary to meet dosimetric objectives; 6) be adaptable to development of computer software for calculation of relevant radiation doses from knowledge of a few readily measured expo-

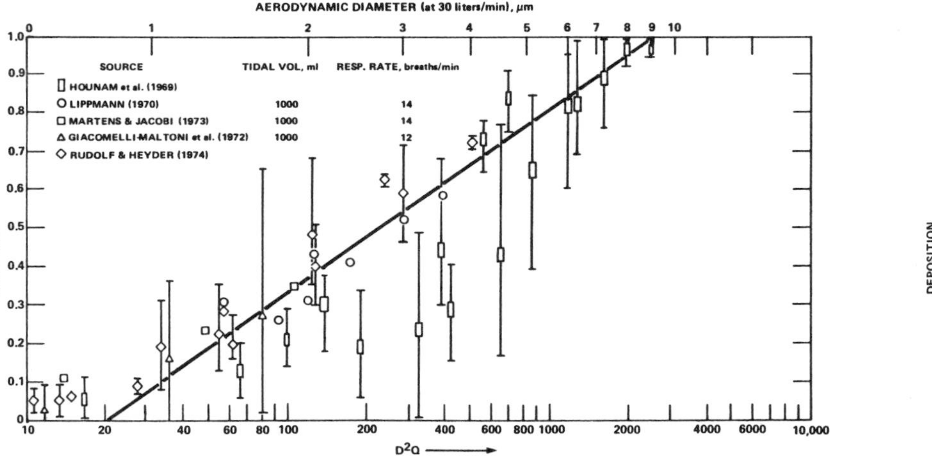

FIGURE 5-3. Deposition of monodisperse aerosols in the extrathoracic region for nasal breathing in humans as a function of D^2Q, where Q is the average inspiratory flow rate in L/min. The solid line is ICRP deposition model based on the data of Pattle.[39] Other data show the median and range of the observations as cited by the various investigators.

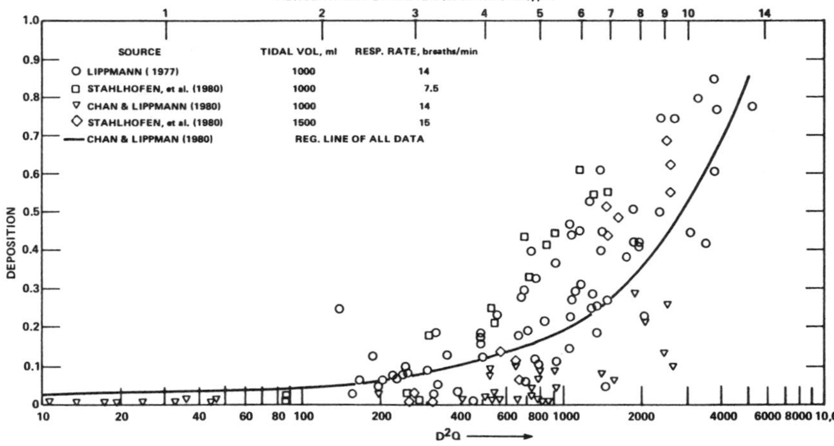

FIGURE 5-4. Deposition of monodisperse aerosols in extrathoracic region for mouth breathing in humans as a function of D^2Q, where Q is the average inspiratory flow rate in L/min. The data are the individual observations as cited by various investigators. The solid line is the overall regression derived by Chan and Lippmann.[29]

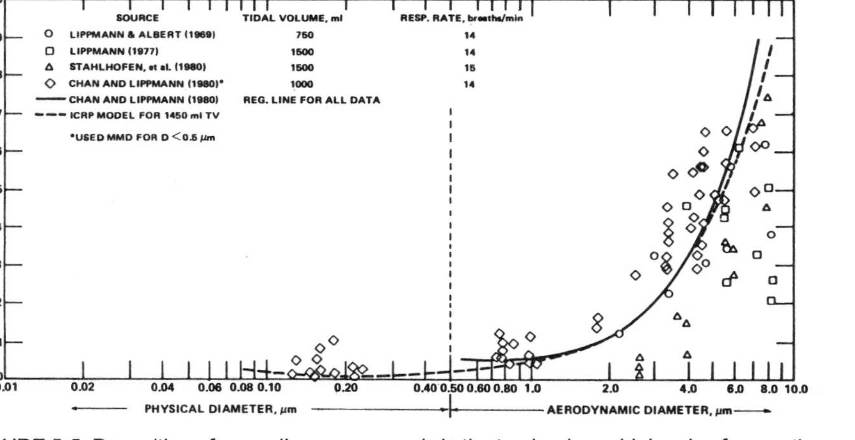

FIGURE 5-5. Deposition of monodisperse aerosols in the tracheobronchial region for mouth breathing in humans in percent of the aerosols entering the trachea as a function of aerodynamic diameter, except below 0.5 μm, where deposition is plotted versus physical diameter, as cited by different investigators. Dashed line is ICRP model for 1450-ml tidal volume. The solid line is the overall regression derived by Chan and Lippmann.[29]

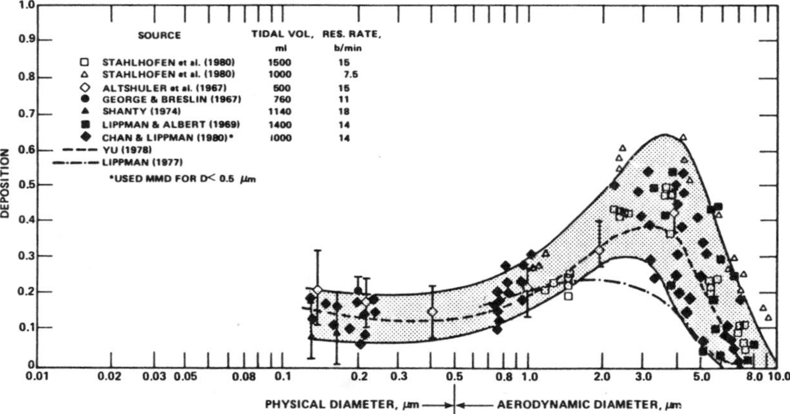

FIGURE 5-6. Deposition of monodisperse aerosols in the pulmonary region for mouth breathing in humans as a function of aerodynamic diameter, except below 0.5 μm, where deposition is plotted versus physical diameter. The eye-fit band envelops deposition data cited by the different investigators. The dashed line is the theoretical deposition model of Yu,[40] and the broken line is an estimate of pulmonary deposition for nose breathing derived by Lippmann.[21]

sure parameters; 7) be equally useful for assessment purposes as for calculating recommended values for limits on intake; 8) be applicable to all members of the world population; 9) allow for use of information on the deposition and clearance of specific materials; and 10) consider the influence of smoking, air pollutants, and diseases on the inhalation, deposition, and clearance of radioactive particles from the respiratory tract. Although it was intended that this new or revised model be applicable to all members of the world's population, i.e., to both sexes for all ages, to smokers and nonsmokers, and to those with healthy and diseased respiratory tracts, the lack of data prevented the full achievement of this goal.

The revised ICRP Task Group's clearance model identifies the principal clearance pathways within the respiratory tract that are important in determining the retention of various radioactive materials, and thus doses received, by respiratory tissues and/or other organs. The deposition model is required to estimate the amount of inhaled material that enters each clearance pathway. These discrete pathways are represented by the compartment model shown in Table 5-2 and Figure 5-7.

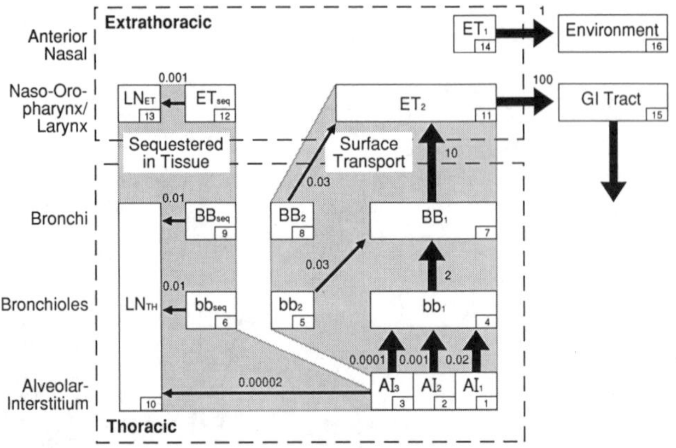

FIGURE 5-7. Compartment model to represent time-dependent particle transport from each region in 1994 ICRP model. Particle transport rate constants shown beside the arrows are reference values in d^{-1}. Compartment numbers (shown in the lower right-hand corner of each compartment box) are used to define clearance pathways. Thus, the particle transport rate from bb_1 to BB_1 is denoted $m_{4,7}$ and has the value 2 d^{-1}.

Extrathoracic airways

The extrathoracic airways are partitioned into two distinct clearance and dosimetric regions: the anterior nasal passages (ET_1) and all other extrathoracic airways (ET_2), i.e., the posterior nasal passages, the naso- and oropharynx, and the larynx. Particles deposited on the surface of the skin lining the anterior nasal passages are assumed to be subject only to removal by extrinsic means (e.g., nose blowing, wiping). The bulk of material deposited in the naso-oropharynx or larynx (ET_2) is subject to fast clearance in the layer of fluid that covers these airways. The new model recognizes that diffusional deposition of ultrafine particles in the extrathoracic airways can be substantial, whereas the earlier models did not.

Thoracic airways

Activity deposited in the thorax is divided between bronchial (BB) and bronchiolar (bb) regions, which are subject to relatively fast ciliary clearance, and the alveolar-interstitial (AI) region, which is not subject to fast ciliary clearance.

For dosimetry purposes, deposition of inhaled material is divided between the trachea and bronchi (BB), and in the more distal, small airways, the bronchioles (bb). However, the subsequent efficiency with which cilia in either type of airway are able to clear deposited particles is controversial. In order to be certain that doses to bronchial and bronchiolar epithelia will not be underestimated, the Task Group assumes that as much as half the number of particles deposited in these airways is subject to "slow" clearance. The likelihood that a particle is cleared slowly by the mucociliary system appears to depend on its physical size.

Material deposited in the AI region is subdivided among three compartments (AI_1, AI_2, and AI_3) that are each cleared slowly but at different characteristic rates.

NCRP Deposition Model

The new NCRP deposition model[47] made fewer changes in the old ICRP Task Group model format than did the new ICRP model. The original name of the head airways region was changed from nasopharynx (NP) to naso-oro-pharyngo-laryngeal (NOPL) to be more fully descriptive of the nature of the region. The names of the other regions remained tracheobronchial (TB) for the trachea and the conductive airways within the thorax, and pulmonary (P) for the gas exchange and interstitial lung areas. NCRP also retained the lymph nodes as a separate compartment for clearance and dose calculations. Their model permits assumptions about different proportions depositing in each region, and different rate constants for clearance from subcompartments within each region, but does not designate them as separate compartments. Thus, NCRP's NOPL corresponds to ICRP's ET_1 + ET_2, and their TB region corresponds to ICRP's BB + bb regions. The new NCRP model also recognizes that substantial deposition of ultrafine particles in the NP region can take place.

TABLE 5-2. Morphometry, Cytology, Histology, Function, and Structure of the Respiratory Tract and Regions Used in the 1992 ICRP Dosimetry Model

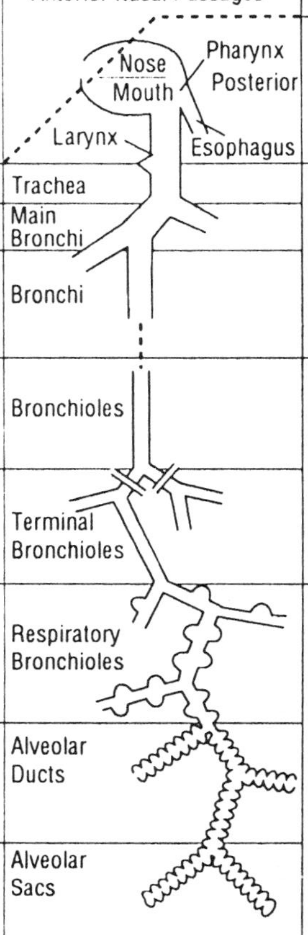

Functions	Cylology (Epithelium)	Histology (Walls)	Generation Number	Anatomy	Regions used in Model: New	Regions used in Model: Old*	Zones (Air)	Location	Airway Surface	Number of Airways
Air Conditioning; Temperature and Humidity, and Cleaning; Fast Particle Clearance; Air Conduction	Respiratory Epithelium with Goblet Cells: Cell Types: - Ciliated Cells - Nonciliated Cells: • Goblet Cells • Mucous (Secretory) Cells • Serous Cells • Brush Cells • Endocrine Cells • Basal Cells • Intermediate Cells	Mucous Membrane, Respiratory Epithelium (Pseudostratified, Ciliated, Mucous), Glands		Anterior Nasal Passages	ET_1		Conditioning; 0.175 x $10^{-3}m^3$ (Anatomical Dead Space)	Extrathoracic; Extrapulmonary	2 x $10^{-3}m^2$	—
		Mucous Membrane, Respiratory or Stratified Epithelium, Glands		Nose, Mouth, Pharynx, Posterior, Larynx, Esophagus	ET_2; LN_{ET}	(N-P)			4.5 x $10^{-2}m^2$	—
		Mucous Membrane, Respiratory Epithelium, Cartilage Rings, Glands	0	Trachea	BB	(T-B)		Thoracic; Extrapulmonary	3 x $10^{-2}m^2$	511
			1	Main Bronchi						
		Mucous Membrane, Respiratory Epithelium, Cartilage plates, Smooth Muscle Layer, Glands	2 - 8	Bronchi				Thoracic; Pulmonary		
	Respiratory Epithelium with Clara Cells (No Goblet Cells) Cell Types: - Ciliated Cells - Nonciliated Cells • Clara (Secretory) Cells	Mucous Membrane, Respiratory Epithelium, No Cartilage, No Glands, Smooth Muscle Layer	9 - 14	Bronchioles	bb		Conduction		2.6 x $10^{-1}m^2$	6.5 x 10^4
		Mucous Membrane, Single-Layer Respiratory Epithelium, Less Ciliated, Smooth Muscle Layer	15	Terminal Bronchioles	LN_{TH}†					
Air Conduction; Gas Exchange; Slow Particle Clearance	Respiratory Epithelium Consisting Mainly of Clara Cells (Secretory) and Few Ciliated Cells	Mucous Membrane, Single-Layer Respiratory Epithelium of Cuboidal Cells, Smooth Muscle Layers	16 - 18	Respiratory Bronchioles	AI	P	Gas-Exchange Transitory; 0.2 x $10^{-3}m^3$		7.5m^2	4.6 x 10^5
Gas Exchange; Very Slow Particle Clearance	Squamous Alveolar Epithelium Cells (Type I), Covering 93% of Alveolar Surface Areas	Wall Consists of Alveolar Entrance Rings, Squamous Epithelial Layer, Surfactant	**	Alveolar Ducts			4.5 x $10^{-3}m^3$		140m^2	4.5 x 10^7
	Cuboidal Alveolar Epithelial Cells (Type II. Surfactant-Producing), Covering 7% of Alveolar Surface Area Alveolar Macrophages	Interalveolar Septa Covered by Squamous Epithelium, Containing Capillaries, Surfactant	**	Alveolar Sacs						
				Lymphatics		L				

* Previous ICRP Model
** Unnumbered because of imprecise information
† Lymph nodes are located only in BB region but drain the bronchial and alveolar interstitial regions as well as the bronchial region.

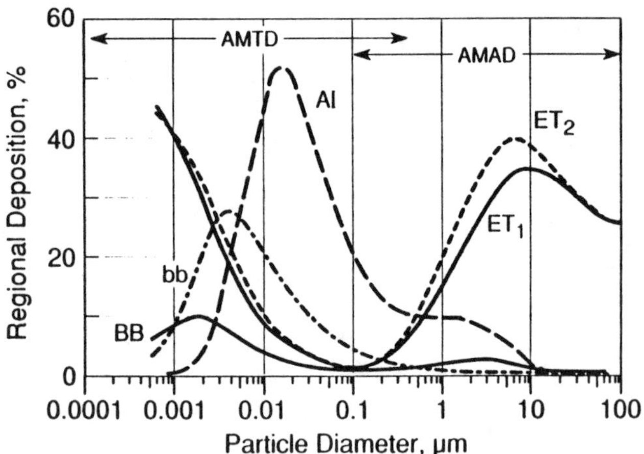

FIGURE 5-8. Fractional deposition in each region of respiratory tract for reference light worker (normal nose breather) in 1994 ICRP model.[46] Deposition is expressed as a fraction of activity present in volume of ambient air that is inspired, and activity is assumed to be lognormally distributed as a function of particle size (for particles of density 2.25 g/cm^3 and shape factor 1.5). The activity median particle diameter (AMAD) applies to larger particles, while the activity median thermal diameter (AMTD) applies to smaller particles where deposition is by diffusion.

Comparison of ICRP and NCRP Predictive Models

Both NCRP and ICRP used the same databases in formulating their mathematical predictive regional deposition models, but they made some different decisions about the appropriate formulations and mathematical forms to fit the available data. Figure 5-8 shows the size dependence of the deposition fractions for the light exercise category of ICRP. Figure 5-9 shows the corresponding curves for the NCRP model, along with those of ICRP when ET_1 is combined with ET_2, and when BB is combined with bb. It can be seen that the inclusion of the inspirability factor, i.e., the aspiration efficiency for entry of ambient particles into the human nose or mouth, strongly affects the predicted deposition in the head airways. Notable differences are the modal particle size and maximal efficiencies for AI versus P and for TB versus BB + bb.

Some of the other differences between the two deposition models are:

- The NCRP model's code permits a wider range of user flexibility.
- The NCRP model uses generation-by-generation data for calculating deposition and clearance; the ICRP model uses broad classes of airways.
- The ICRP model provides for early sequestration in bronchial airways; the NCRP model does not.
- The NCRP model provides more guidance for evaluation of novel materials and situations.

Perhaps the message from this intercomparison of the careful work of two distinguished expert committees is that considerable uncertainty remains about regional deposition, reflecting our incomplete understanding of airway anatomy, flow factors, and pathways for particle clearance, and their variability among individuals in the population. As techniques improve for controlled experimental studies of deposition, and as more data from carefully designed and executed studies accumulate, it should be possible to reduce current uncertainties.

Because total and regional deposition are particle-size dependent, changes in size due to droplet growth can cause significant changes in deposition pattern and

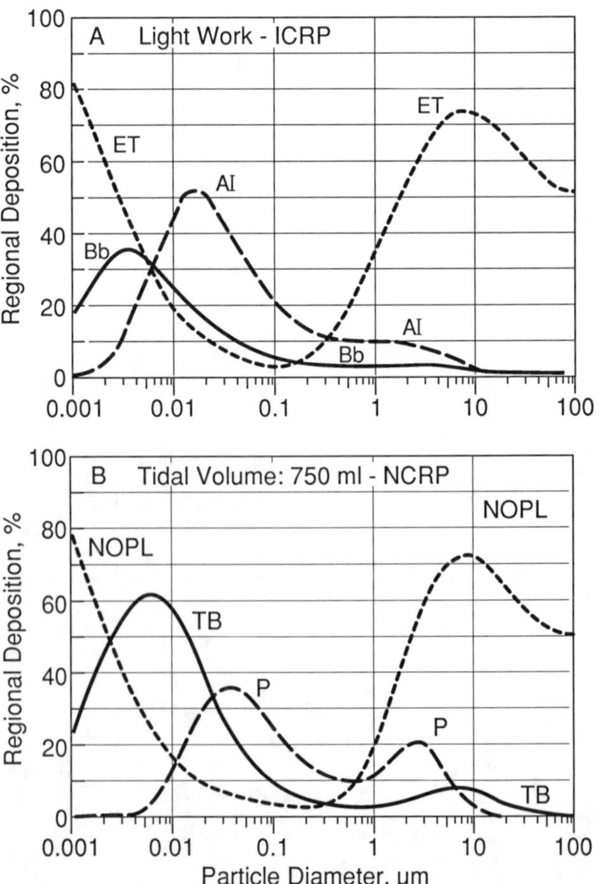

FIGURE 5-9. Panel A shows the results when the ICRP regions ET_1 and ET_2 are combined as ET and regions BB and bb are combined as Bb. Panel B shows the corresponding models of NCRP for the corresponding activity level (750-ml tidal volume). The 1994 NCRP model[47] is not corrected for inspirability. The relation of particle diameter to calculated regional deposition is for spherical particles of density 1 g/cm^3.

efficiency. If a hygroscopic aerosol with a dry size of 1.0 μm or larger is released, its growth in the atmosphere[48–52] or the respiratory tract[53–56] could have a major effect on its regional deposition. For the larger droplets, the fractional deposition in the head and tracheobronchial zones increases rapidly with increasing droplet size (see Figures 5-3, 5-4, and 5-5).

Respirable Dust versus Lung Dust

For the pneumoconiosis-producing dusts, the aerosol of direct interest is that fraction retained in the alveoli for long periods of time. All of the dust that penetrates the ciliated airways and reaches the alveolar region is not retained. Some is exhaled without deposition, and some of the dust that does deposit in the alveoli is cleared out relatively rapidly. Thus, it might seem that the best and most direct way to determine how much dust has a long retention time is to compare the size-mass distribution of inhaled dust with dust actually retained in the lungs. Unfortunately, such studies are difficult to perform in animals and cannot be performed in humans. Human lungs obtained after accidental deaths could be analyzed, but the amount of dust inhaled would not be accurately known.

Cartwright and Skidmore[57] exposed rats to well-characterized clouds of coal dust and glass microspheres. The comparison of airborne, respirable coal dust levels (determined by Hexhlet thimble samples) with lung dust was limited in accuracy because the thimble samples included aggregate particles, whereas lung dust can be sized only after complete redispersion. The glass sphere aerosols lacked this complication. They found that the lung dusts from animals with high dust retentions had the same size distributions as the lung dust from animals with low dust retention. Also, comparisons of the recoveries of glass spheres from animals killed 6 months after the exposure with those killed 5 days after the exposure showed that one-half of the dust retained at 5 days was eliminated 6 months later, without any change in size distribution. Thus, they concluded that a sampler following the British Medical Research Council (BMRC) criteria for "respirable" dust, as defined in the next part of this review, had retention characteristics corresponding reasonably well with rat-lung retention.

Carlberg et al.[58] measured total dust, free silica, and trace metal concentrations in 65 West Virginia bituminous coal miners' lungs and compared the values obtained with those reported by others for English, Welsh, and German miners. Although coal and total dust had nearly equal concentrations in the lungs and hilar lymph nodes, the silica was more concentrated in the lymph nodes by a factor of about 3.6.

Total or Gross Air Concentration Measurements

Aerosol sampling is most commonly performed using single-stage collectors, and the collected samples are analyzed to determine the mass concentration of the overall sample or constituents thereof. It is also often used for determining number concentration, as for fiber counting and viable aerosol counting after incubation and growth of colonies (see Chapter 23).

In the past, reports of air concentration measurements often implied that there was something called "total airborne dust" or "total suspended particulate" that could be measured simply by drawing air through a collector, without regard to the design of the inlet. Because most aerosols are polydisperse, with a geometric standard deviation (σg) > 2, the mass median size approaches the diameter of the largest particles in the sample. However, particles above a certain size may not be aspirated into the sampler inlet. When the aerosol being sampled contains very large particles, the gross air concentrations determined using various samplers may differ from one another and from the true total concentration. The aerosol could include large particles that dominate the measured mass concentration and yet have little biological significance. Alternatively, when large particles are important, representative samples may not be collected. Very large particles may be important; for example, wood dusts that cause nasal cancers, or highly soluble materials that deposit in the nasal or oral passages and are taken up systemically.

There has been progress toward defining "total" dust for workplace and community air sampling purposes. One approach has been to define the biologically important fraction, i.e., the "inspirable" or "inhalable" fraction, defined as the fraction of the total aerosol that enters the nose and mouth. This principle has been adopted by the International Standards Organization (ISO)[59] and the American Conference of Governmental Industrial Hygienists (ACGIH).[60] They both proposed that future exposure limits be based on the "inspirable" fraction. An alternate approach to the biological one is to define a standard sampling method without prejudging what is thereby collected. A separate proposal to ISO was that "total" dust should be defined as that collected by a sampling device into which air enters at a velocity of between 1.1 and 3 m/s and in which the volumetric flow rate is between 0.5 and 4 L/min. Ogden[61] examined the results of three computational studies in order to estimate what particle size-range such a device would collect provided that it is sharp-edged and operating in calm air. He found that a particle of aerodynamic diameter d_a (cm) would be collected with better than 90% efficiency by a sharp-edged sampler of diameter D (cm) and entry velocity V

(cm/s) in an external wind W (cm/s) provided that

$$d_a < 0.003\, D^{0.2}\, V^{0.09}$$

and

$$w < 0.002\, (D^2\, V/d_a^{\,4})^{1/3}$$

Thus, a sharp-edged sampler with this proposed ISO specification would efficiently collect particles up to about 40-µm aerodynamic diameter, but this would be limited to winds less than about 10 cm/s. For blunt samplers, the diameter limit may be about half as much. The theory for moving air is less well-developed, and sampler shape would affect efficiency. One cannot, therefore, say what the ISO "total" dust proposals correspond to in moving air. However, experience gained from efficiency measurements on practical samplers should make it possible to make static and personal samplers that meet the "inspirable" specification, and the indications are that such a sampler would, under most conditions, collect more than a sampler meeting the proposed "total" specification.

In practice, there is a broad range of inlet efficiencies among the samplers used in the field. Buchan *et al.*(62) described the inlet penetration of open- and closed-face 37-mm filter cassettes. Chung *et al.*[(63)] reported on the inlet penetration of 12 different personal samplers mounted on a tailor's dummy in a wind tunnel. Vincent and Mark[(64)] did additional wind tunnel tests on nine personal samplers and five static samplers, and summarized their results along with those of Chung *et al.*[(63)] There is clearly an enormous range of inlet efficiencies for large particles among the commonly used samplers.

Measurement of Mass Concentrations Within Size-Graded Aerosol Fractions

Because the dose from inhaled toxicants is dependent on the regional deposition, which is dependent on particle size, the best dose estimates for a material whose toxicity is proportional to absorbed mass can be derived from a knowledge of the mass concentrations within various size ranges. Such information can be obtained in several ways: 1) by separating the aerosol into size fractions corresponding to anticipated regional deposition during the process of collection; 2) by making a size distribution analysis of the airborne aerosol, e.g., with a conifuge, cascade impactor, or light-scattering aerosol spectrometer; and 3) by making a size distribution analysis of a collected sample.

The most reliable information can be obtained using methods in which the aerosol is fractionated on the basis of aerodynamic diameters in much the same manner as it is fractionated within the respiratory tract. Thus, differences in particle shape and density are compensated for automatically.

Light-scattering instruments that sort the pulses resulting from the scattered light from individual particles can provide information on the distribution of airborne particle diameters. In converting this information to a size-mass distribution, an average particle density must be assumed. Furthermore, the accuracy of the diameter distribution is dependent on the particle shape, index of refraction, and surface roughness. For example, Whitby and Vomela[(65)] reported that for India ink particles, which absorb light and have a rough surface, the indicated size was one-half to one-fifth of the true size for the three different instrument designs tested.

Further opportunities for error arise when the size distribution analysis is performed on collected samples. It is almost impossible to examine the sample in the original state of dispersion. Thus, particles that were unitary in the air may be analyzed as aggregates and vice versa. Furthermore, particles analyzed by microscopy will be graded by a linear dimension or by projected area diameter, and these are normally larger than the true average diameter. Also, there is no way to distinguish between toxic and nontoxic particles.

Standards and Criteria for Respirable Dust Samplers — Historical Review (1952–1980)

British Medical Research Council

In 1952, the BMRC adopted a definition of "respirable dust" applicable to pneumoconiosis-producing dusts. It defined respirable dust as that reaching the alveolar region. The BMRC selected the horizontal elutriator as a practical size selector, defined respirable dust as that passing an ideal horizontal elutriator, and selected the elutriator cutoff to provide the best match to experimental lung deposition data. The same standard was adopted by the Johannesburg International Conference on Pneumoconiosis in 1959.[(66)]

To implement these recommendations, it was specified that

1. For purposes of estimating airborne dust in its relation to pneumoconiosis, samples for compositional analysis or for assessment of concentration by a bulk measurement, such as that of mass or surface area, should represent only the "respirable" fraction of the cloud.
2. The "respirable" sample should be separated from the cloud while the particles are airborne and in their original state of dispersion.
3. The "respirable fraction" is to be defined in terms of the free falling speed of the particles, by the equation $C/C_o = 1-(f/f_c)$, where C and C_o are the concentrations of particles of falling speed, f, in the "respirable" fraction and in the whole cloud, respectively, and f_c is a constant equal to twice the falling speed in air of a sphere of unit density 5 µm in diameter.

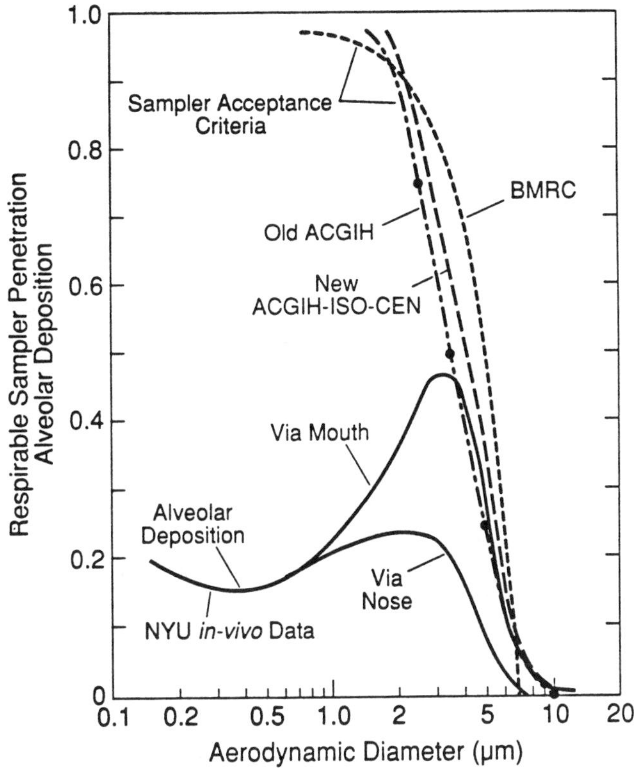

FIGURE 5-10. Comparison of respirable sampler acceptance curves of BMRC and ACGIH with new ACGIH–ISO–CEN criteria, and with median human *in vivo* alveolar deposition data.[21]

A sampling device meeting these requirements would have a sampling efficiency versus size curve suggested by Davies,[67] as illustrated in Figure 5-10.

U.S. Atomic Energy Commission

A second standard, established in January 1961 at a meeting sponsored by the U.S. Atomic Energy Commission (AEC), Office of Health and Safety,[3] defined "respirable dust" as that portion of the inhaled dust penetrating to the nonciliated portions of the lung. This application of the concepts of respirable dust and concomitant selective sampling were intended only for "insoluble" particles that exhibit prolonged retention in the lung. They were not intended to include dusts having appreciable solubility in body fluids and those that are primarily chemical intoxicants. Within these restrictions, "respirable dust" was defined as being 0% at 10 μm, 25% at 5 μm, 50% at 3.5 μm, 75% at 2.5 μm, and 100% at 2.0 μm, all sizes being aerodynamic diameters.

American Conference of Governmental Industrial Hygienists

The application of respirable dust sampling concepts to other toxic dusts and the relationships between respirable dust concentrations and accepted standards such as the ACGIH TLVs are more complicated. Unlike the exposure limits for radioisotopes, which are based on calculation, most TLVs are based on animal and human exposure experience. Thus, even if the data on which these standards were based could be related to the particle size of the dust involved, which unfortunately is unlikely, there probably would be a different correction factor for each TLV rather than a uniform factor.

ACGIH initiated the process of adopting "respirable" dust limits at its 1968 annual meeting by including, in their "Notice of Intended Changes," alternate mass concentration TLVs for quartz, cristobalite, and tridymite (three forms of crystalline free silica) to supplement the TLVs based on particle count concentrations. For quartz, the alternative mass values proposed were:[68]

1. For respirable dust in mg/m^3,

$$\frac{10 \text{ mg/m}^3}{\% \text{ Respirable Quartz} + 2}$$

Note: Both concentration and % quartz for the application of this limit are to be determined from the fraction passing a size-selector with the following characteristics:

(Aerodynamic Diameter) – μm ≤	2.0	2.5	3.5	5.0	10
% Passing Selector –	90	75	50	25	0

2. For "total dust" (respirable and nonrespirable),

$$\frac{30 \text{ mg/m}^3}{\% \text{ Quartz} + 2}$$

For both cristobalite and tridymite, use one-half the value calculated from the count or mass formula for quartz.

The size-selector characteristic specified by ACGIH was almost identical to that of the AEC, differing only at 2 μm, where it allowed for 90% passing the first stage collector instead of 100%. The difference reflected a recognition of the characteristics of real particle separators. For practical purposes, the two standards may be considered equivalent.

The proposed mass concentration limits were obtained by a comparison of simultaneous impinger and size-selective samples collected in the Vermont granite sheds.[69] Because the original impinger sampling and microscopic particle counting standards were based on epidemiological investigations, which had been performed 3–4 decades earlier in some of the same granite cutting sheds, it was possible to make a valid comparison of "respirable" mass and particle count.

In 1969, the U.S. Department of Labor adopted the ACGIH size-selector criteria for respirable dust and extended its application to coal dust and inert or nuisance dust. In the revised Safety and Health Standards for Federal Supply Contracts published in the Federal Register,[70] the ACGIH quartz, tridymite, and cristobalite TLVs were adopted along with the following respirable dust limits:

Coal Dust — 2.4 mg/m^3 or

$$\frac{10 \text{ mg/m}^3}{\% \text{ SiO}_2 + 2} \text{ (Respirable fraction} < 5\% \text{ SiO}_2\text{)}$$

Inert or Nuisance Dust—15 million particles per cubic foot (mppcf) or

5 mg/m^3 (Respirable fraction)

The Federal Coal Mine Health and Safety Act of 1969[71] specified that

> References to concentrations of respirable dust in this title means the average concentration of respirable dust if measured with an MRE instrument or such equivalent concentrations if measured with another device approved by the Secretary (of Interior) and the Secretary of Health, Education and Welfare. As used in this title, the term 'MRE instrument' means the gravimetric dust sampler with four channel horizontal elutriator developed by the Mining Research Establishment of the National Coal Board, London, England.

Although the 1969 Act specified the MRE instrument, which closely follows the BMRC sampling criteria, the Federal Mine Safety and Health Act of 1977,[72] which superceded it, did not. The National Research Council Committee on Measurement and Control of Respirable Dust in Mines[73] noted that it may be more appropriate to use the definition of respirable dust adopted by ACGIH because human deposition data demonstrate that the ACGIH curve is a better representation of respirable dust than the BMRC curve.

The Occupational Safety and Health Act of 1970[74] has led to the adoption of only a few permanent standards, and none of them addressed the issue of "respirable" dust. As a result, the Occupational Safety and Health Administration (OSHA) enforced numerous interim permissible exposure limits (PELs), including 22 maximum allowable concentrations (MACs) of the American National Standards Institute (ANSI) and approximately 280 of the ACGIH 1968 TLVs,[68] including the silica TLVs which specify either dust counts or respirable mass concentrations. The Mine Safety and Health Administration (MSHA) of the U.S. Department of Labor operates under different enabling legislation and uses the 1973 TLVs as PELs which, for silica, are the same as the 1968 values. Most of the transitional OSHA PELs were superceded by the adoption of permanent PELs in 1989,[75] but this rulemaking was overturned by the U.S. Eleventh Circuit Court of Appeals in 1992, thus restoring the transitional PELs.

Comparison of Standards for Respirability

Basically, there are two sampler acceptance curves described in the preceding discussion, and they have similar, but not identical characteristics (see Figure 5-10). The shapes of the curves differ because they are based on different collector types. The BMRC curve was chosen to give the best fit between the calculated characteristics of an ideal horizontal elutriator and lung deposition data, whereas the AEC curve was patterned more directly after the Brown *et al.*[76] upper respiratory tract deposition data and is simulated by the separation characteristics of cyclone-type collectors. In most field situations, where the geometric standard deviation of the particle size distribution is > 2, samples collected with instruments meeting either criterion will be comparable. For example, Mercer[77] calculated the predicted pulmonary (alveolar) deposition according to the ICRP Task Group deposition model[23] for a tidal volume of 1450 cm^3 and aerosols with $1.5 < \sigma g < 4$. He found that a sampler meeting the BMRC acceptance curve would have about 10% more penetration than a sampler meeting the AEC curve.[77]

Other comparisons of samples collected on the basis of the two criteria have been reported. Knight and Lichti[78] made an experimental comparison of the penetrations through the Dorr–Oliver 10-mm nylon cyclone and the MRE elutriator for a variety of mineral dusts. Comparisons were made for four different constant cyclone flow rates: 1.3, 1.65, 1.95, and 2.64 L/min. The corresponding ratios of the cyclone/elutriator penetrations were 1.06, 0.90, 0.83, and 0.64.

Maguire and Barker[79] made eight coal mine tests with SIMPEDS cyclones adjacent to MRE elutriators. The average respirable dust ratio was 0.97, with a standard deviation of 0.11; i.e., there was no statistical difference.

Comparative "respirable" mass sampling in the Vermont granite sheds for granite cutters operating their equipment without exhaust ventilation produced the following concentrations: a 10-L/min NIOSH elutriator — 11.6 mg/m^3; the MRE (Isleworth) 2.5-L/min sampler — 10.7 mg/m^3; the HASL 1/2-in. cyclone at 10 L/min — 10.9 mg/m^3; and the 10-mm nylon cyclone at 1.7 L/min — 10.7 mg/m^3. Thus, for practical purposes, they were equivalent in performance.[80]

It is apparent from the preceding discussions that the various definitions of respirable dust are somewhat arbitrary. The BMRC and AEC definitions are based on the aerosol that reaches the alveolar region. Thus, they do not predict alveolar deposition, because part of the aerosol that penetrates to the alveoli remains suspended in the exhaled air. The portion that does not deposit is a variable that depends on particle size.

Standards and Criteria for Health-based, Size-selective Samplers — Recent Developments

Comprehensive definitions are clearly needed for particles that deposit in the head and tracheobronchial regions, causing diseases such as nasal and bronchial cancers and chronic bronchitis. Three groups have addressed this need. The first was the U.S. EPA on the basis of its responsibility to protect the public health from diseases associated with the inhalation of airborne particles. The second was the ISO on the basis of their desire to have better sampling specifications for test methods used to determine potential inhalation hazards in both the workplace and general community atmospheres. Similar criteria were adopted by ACGIH for use with PSS–TLVs.

U.S. Environmental Protection Agency

In developing a revised primary ambient air quality standard for particulate matter (PM) to protect the public health, U.S. EPA concluded that the diseases which could be related to the inhalation of ambient aerosols were associated with particles that penetrated through the upper respiratory tract and were available for deposition in the tracheobronchial and/or alveolar regions. They initially called this fraction "inhalable" dust.[81] Because they were only concerned about the particles entering the trachea, they took a conservative position on the selection of the appropriate cut size for a precollector, proposing a D_{50} (50% cut size) at an aerodynamic diameter of 15 μm on the basis of published data indicating that about 10% of the particles of this size would enter the trachea of a mouth-breathing person.

The use of the word "inhalable" to designate particles penetrating though the upper respiratory airways and entering the thorax was in conflict with the usage of the word in Europe, where it was defined as the particles that entered the nasal or oral air passages.[82,83]

On the basis of public comment, the subsequent recommendations of an ISO Task Group (discussed in the next paragraph), and the recommendation of the U.S. EPA Clean Air Scientific Advisory Committee, the U.S. EPA Office of Air Quality Planning and Standards recommended to the U.S. EPA Administrator that U.S. EPA revise the criterion for the particulate matter primary standard for ambient air to include a D_{50} of 10 μm. The fraction below the 10-μm cut, designated by ISO as thoracic particulate (TP) or by U.S. EPA as PM_{10} (particulate matter below a 10-μm cut size), replaced total suspended particulate (TSP) as the basic ambient air particulate pollution parameter. The adoption of the PM_{10} standard in 1987 provided a basis for the collection of ambient air concentration data of better relevance to potential inhalation hazards.[84] The actual specification for inlets matching the PM_{10} criteria is shown in Table 5-3. The ideal sampler is one that matches particle penetration to the thorax, as defined by U.S. EPA and illustrated in Figure 5-11.

TABLE 5-3. U.S. EPA's Performance Specifications for PM_{10} Samplers

Performance Parameter	Units	Specification
1. Sampling effectiveness		
A. Liquid particles	%	Such that the expected mass concentration is within ± 10% of that predicted for the ideal sampler.
B. Solid particles	%	Sampling effectiveness is no more than 5% above that obtained for liquid particles of same size.
2. 50% cutpoint	μm	10 ± 0.5-μm aerodynamic diameter.
3. Precision	μg/m³ or %	5 μg/m³ or 7% for three collocated samplers.
4. Flow rate stability	%	Average flow rate over 24 hours within ± 5% of initial flow rate; all measured flow rates over 24 hours within ± 10% of initial flow rate.

International Standards Organization (ISO)

Technical Committee 146 — Air Quality of the ISO appointed an *ad hoc* working group to prepare recommendations on size definitions for particle sampling to be used in preparing standard methods for the sampling and analysis of air contaminants in both occupational and general environmental settings. The working group used the available human regional deposition data to define a series of aerosol fractions related to particle deposition within specific regions of the human respiratory tract.[57] To avoid conflict with the proposed U.S. EPA definition of "inhalable," the fraction drawn in by the nose or mouth was called "inspirable," that part collected in the head was called "extrathoracic," and that part penetrating through the larynx was called "thoracic" and was further subdivided into "tracheobronchial" and "alveolar." The ISO adopted a thoracic D_{50} cut of 10 μm. They also provided two

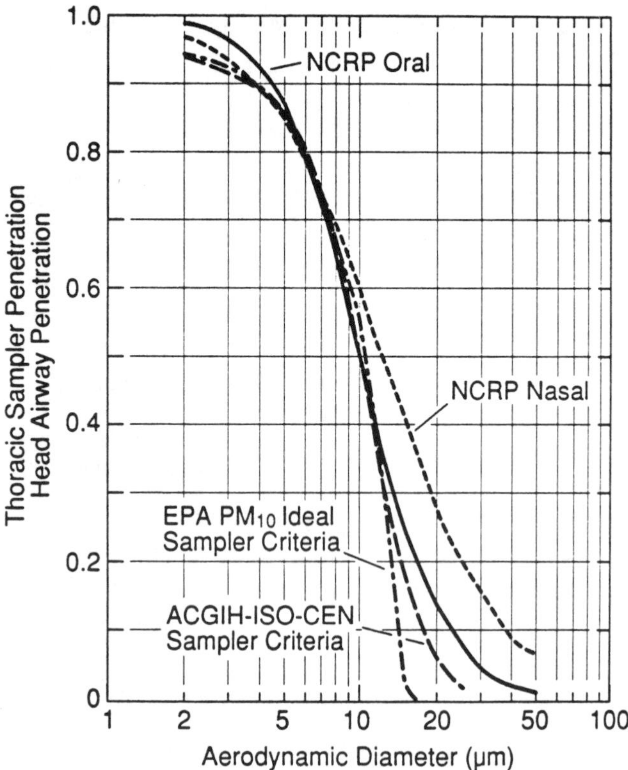

FIGURE 5-11. Comparison of thoracic sampler acceptance curves of U.S. EPA (PM_{10}) and ACGIH–ISO–CEN with NCRP thoracic penetration models for nasal and oral inhalation based on curves fitted to *in vivo* experimental data for aerosol penetration through the airways in the human head.[47]

options for the "respirable" size cut. Their recommendations accommodated both the BMRC and ACGIH criteria, according to national preference. They also endorsed an alternate alveolar convention for ambient air sampling where the target population is very young or infirm and may be expected to have greater tracheobronchial deposition. It is very similar in shape to the ACGIH "respirable" dust criteria, but with all the diameter values reduced by 29%. The ISO thoracic cut is essentially consistent with U.S. EPA's new PM_{10} standard that specifies a 10-µm D_{50}, but differs in that the 10-µm cut is applied to the aerosol penetrating a precollector following the "inspirable" cut convention.

The recommendations of the ISO working group also provided a basis for a thorough reexamination of air concentration limits for occupational exposures. For some, such as droplets or soluble components of solid particles, deposition anywhere in the respiratory tract leads to absorption by the tissues, and the current total concentration limits may be appropriate. For other particles, biological effect may depend on the region of deposition. For example, particles depositing extrathoracically that are not expelled through the nose or mouth are likely to be swallowed and may cause a hazard by absorption in the gastrointestinal tract. Particles depositing in the tracheobronchial region and cleared by the mucociliary escalator are also likely to be swallowed, so that gastrointestinal absorption is a possible route for these particles also. Particles depositing in the alveolar region may also be cleared by this route, or through the lymphatic system, or may cause a reaction in the alveolar region itself.

American Conference of Governmental Industrial Hygienists

In 1982, the ACGIH Board appointed an *ad hoc* Committee on Air Sampling Procedures (ASP) to prepare general recommendations for size-selective sampling appropriate to size-selective TLVs for particulate materials.

The ASP Committee of the ACGIH had as its primary charge

> . . . to recommend size-selective aerosol sampling procedures which will permit reliable collection of aerosol fractions which can be expected to be available for deposition in the various major subregions of the human respiratory tract, e.g., the head, tracheobronchial region, and the alveolar (pulmonary) region.

It was anticipated from the outset that the work of this committee would lead to an approach for establishing PSS-TLVs for many airborne agents. The ASP Committee reviewed the relevant literature and the recommendations of other groups on size-selective aerosol sampling; its report and recommendations were presented to the Board of Directors and the ACGIH membership at the 1984 Annual Membership Meeting. The report of the ASP Committee and its background documentation were published in the 1984 *Transactions of the American Conference of Governmental Industrial Hygienists*[85] and are available as a separate document entitled *Particle Size-Selective Sampling in the Workplace.*[60]

The following paragraphs summarize the recommendations of the ASP Committee in 1984.

The ASP Committee report is a background document summarizing the available data on 1) airway anatomy and physiology that influence the deposition and retention of inhaled particles, 2) penetration of inhaled particles into the major functional regions of the respiratory tract, 3) the particle size collection characteristics of available size-selective aerosol samplers, and 4) evaluation of the performance of samplers. The ASP Committee also reviewed the basis for its particular recommendations on size-selective sampling criteria and how and why they differed from the recommendations of others.

The major functional regions of the human respiratory tract were given different names and/or abbreviations than those used by others, but were anatomically equivalent, as indicated in Figure 5-12 and Table 5-4. The designations chosen were, in the ASP Committee's view, more anatomically correct and unambiguous.

Deposition within the head airways region (HAR) was associated with an increased incidence of nasal cancer in wood and leather workers and in ulceration of the nasal septum in chrome refinery workers. Within the tracheobronchial region (TBR), deposited particles can contribute to the pathogenesis of bronchitis and bronchial cancer. Particles depositing within the gas-exchange region (GER) can cause emphysema and fibrosis. On the other hand, the hazards from inhaled materials that exert their toxic effects on critical sites outside the respiratory tract, after dissolution into circulating fluids, depend on total respiratory tract deposition rather than on deposition within one region.

The ASP Committee considered several options for size-selective sampling of fractions of the aerosol that represent hazards for specific health endpoints. The major options were 1) samplers that would mimic deposition in the specific regions of interest and 2) samplers that would collect those particles that would penetrate to, but not necessarily deposit in, the specific region of interest. The ASP Committee opted for the latter approach as the one requiring simpler and less expensive samplers. They also concluded that it would be more practical because this approach had proven to be effective in "respirable" dust sampling. It was recognized that "respirable dust" concentrations may be as much as 5–10 times greater than the fraction actually depositing in the lungs because 80% to 90% of particles in the 0.1-μm- to 1.0-μm-diameter range may be exhaled. However, because the fraction deposited in the GER is relatively constant over the whole "respirable dust" size range, the "respirable dust" concentration is an adequate index of the hazard. A sampler that would mimic GER deposition would be much more difficult to design and operate, and it would not give a materially better

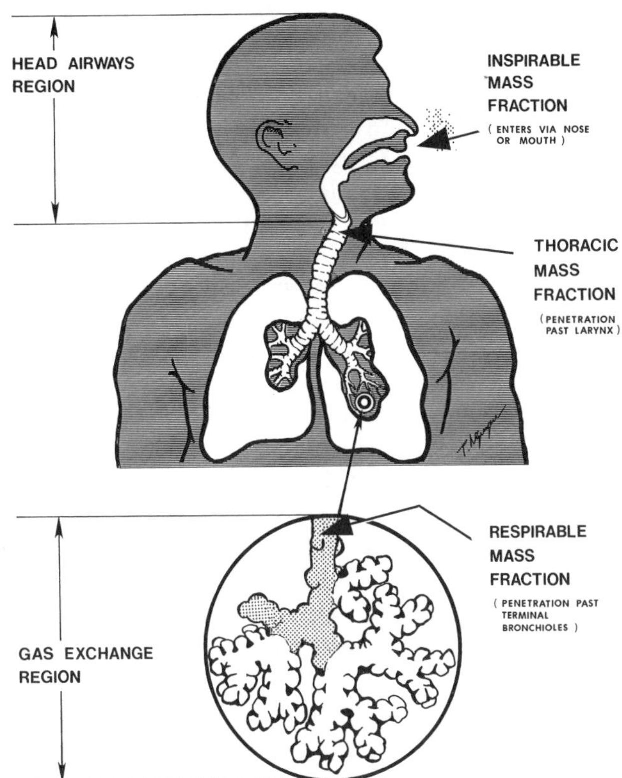

FIGURE 5-12. Schematic representation of the major respiratory tract regions of ACGIH, i.e., head airways region (HAR), tracheobronchial region (TBR), and gas-exchange region (GER).

TABLE 5-4. Respiratory Tract Regions as Defined in Particle Deposition Models

ACGIH Region	Anatomic Structure Included	ISO Region	1966 ICRP Task Group Region	1994 ICRP Task Group Region	1994 NCRP Task Group Region
1. Head airways (HAR)	Nose Mouth Nasopharynx Oropharynx Laryngopharynx	Extrathoracic (E)	Nasopharynx (NP)	Anterior nasal passages (ET_1) All other extrathoracic (ET_2)	Naso-oro-pharyngo-laryngeal (NOPL)
2. Tracheobronchial (TBR)	Trachea Bronchi Bronchioles (to terminal bronchioles)	Tracheobronchial (B)	Tracheobronchial (TB)	Trachea and large bronchi (BB) Bronchioles (bb)	Tracheobronchial (TB)
3. Gas-exchange (GER)	Respiratory bronchioles Alveolar ducts Alveolar sacs Alveoli	Alveolar (A)	Pulmonary (P)	Alveolar-interstitial (AI)	Pulmonary (P)

index of hazard.

The aerosol that enters the HAR is called the inspirable particulate mass (IPM) fraction. The aerosol that penetrates the HAR and enters the TBR is called the thoracic particulate mass (TPM) fraction. Here, the ASP Committee chose to define the thoracic mass fraction on the basis of data for HAR deposition during mouth breathing. The difference between the IPM and the TPM fractions approximates the deposition fraction in the HAR occurring during mouth breathing. Therefore, because nasal inhalation would almost always produce more HAR deposition than oral inhalation, actual HAR deposition during nasal breathing would be greater than that calculated. Similarly, the TPM fraction would overestimate the hazard to the TBR region for nose-breathing workers.

The ASP Committee's selection of a mouth-breathing model rather than a nose-breathing model was made in order to be conservative. Occupational diseases of the lung airways are much more common than are diseases of the head airways. Also, heavy work in industry is believed to cause a significant fraction of workers to engage in mouth breathing during periods of maximal activity, which may coincide with maximal levels of airborne dust. The algebraic difference between TPM and respirable particulate mass (RPM) approximates tracheobronchial region deposition during oral breathing. For nasal breathing individuals, the difference between TPM and RPM is a poor estimate of tracheobronchial deposition.

In general, mass concentrations tend to be dominated by the largest size-fraction collected. In consideration of all these factors, the ASP Committee recommended samplers that follow its IPM criteria be used for sampling those materials which are hazardous when deposited in the HAR or when systemic toxicity can follow from deposition anywhere in the respiratory tract. For those materials that represent a hazard when deposited on the conductive airways of the lungs, the ASP Committee recommended using a sampler that follows its criteria for TPM. Finally, for those materials, such as silica, which are hazardous only after deposition in the GER, the ASP Committee recommended using a sampler that follows its RPM sampling criteria.

The ASP Committee's recommendations for the performance specifications of samplers that would mimic aerosol penetration into these regions are similar, but not identical, to those of ISO. The most notable differences are in the IPM criteria and the RPM criteria. In terms of the former, the ACGIH ASP Committee had the advantage over ISO of access to deposition data in the head for particles larger than 40 µm in aerodynamic diameter that were not available to the ISO Working Group. The ISO Group made the reasonable, but inadequate, assumption that the <40-µm data could be extrapolated to zero deposition at 185 µm. For RPM, the major difference was in not having the alternate criteria based on the BMRC recommendations.

The ASP Committee's recommendations for sampling TPM were quite similar to those of ISO[57] and U.S. EPA.[84] The recommendations also contained sampler acceptance envelopes about the recommended curves.

Following acceptance of the ASP Committee's recommendations by the ACGIH Board of Directors in 1984, activities to implement the recommendations proceeded in two ACGIH Technical Committees. The Chemical Substances TLV Committee addressed the use of the Particle Size-Selective Criteria for Airborne Particulate Matter by listing the criteria as an issue under study in the TLV/BEI booklet for 1986–1987. In the following year, ACGIH adopted these criteria as a separate appendix in the booklet. This appendix, reproduced below, incorporated the original sampling definitions and rationale recommended by the ASP Committee.

> For chemical substances present in inhaled air as suspensions of solid particles or droplets, the potential hazard depends on particle size as well as mass concentration because of: 1) effects of particle size on deposition site within the respiratory tract, and 2) the tendency for many occupational diseases to be associated with material deposited in particular regions of the respiratory tract.
>
> ACGIH has recommended particle size-selective TLVs for crystalline silica for many years in recognition of the well established association between silicosis and respirable mass concentrations. It now has embarked on a re-examination of other chemical substances encountered in particulate form in occupational environments with the objective of defining: 1) the size-fraction most closely associated for each substance with the health effect of concern, and 2) the mass concentration within that size fraction which should represent the TLV.
>
> The Particle Size-Selective TLVs (PSS–TLVs) will be expressed in three forms, e.g.,
>
> a. *Inspirable Particulate Mass TLVs (IPM–*TLVs) for those materials which are hazardous when deposited anywhere in the respiratory tract.
>
> b. *Thoracic Particulate Mass TLVs (TPM–*TLVs) for those materials which are hazardous when deposited anywhere within the lung airways and the gas-exchange region.
>
> c. *Respirable Particulate Mass TLVs (RPM–*TLVs) for those materials which are hazardous when deposited in the gas-exchange region.
>
> The three particulate mass fractions described above are defined in quantitative terms as follows:

a. Inspirable Particulate Mass consists of those particles that are captured according to the following collection efficiency regardless of sampler orientation with respect to wind direction:

$$E = 50\ (1 + \exp\ [-0.06\ d_a]) \pm 10;$$
$$\text{for } 0 < d \leq E\ 100\ \mu m$$

Collection characteristics for d_a>100 µm are presently unknown. *E* is collection efficiency in percent and d_a is aerodynamic diameter in µm.

b. Thoracic Particulate Mass consists of those particles that penetrate a separator whose size collection efficiency is described by a cumulative lognormal function with a median aerodynamic diameter of 10 µm ± 1.0 µm and with a geometric standard deviation of 1.5 (± 0.1).

c. Respirable Particulate Mass consists of those particles that penetrate a separator whose size collection efficiency is described by a cumulative lognormal function with a median aerodynamic diameter of 3.5 µm ± 0.3 µm and with a geometric standard deviation of 1.5 (± 0.1). This incorporates and clarifies the previous ACGIH Respirable Dust Sampling Criteria.

These definitions provide a range of acceptable performance for each type of size-selective sampler. Further information is available on the background and performance criteria for these particle size-selective sampling recommendations.[60]

In 1989, Soderholm, Chair of the ASP Committee, with the endorsement of the full ASP Committee, proposed modified particle size-selective sampling criteria for adoption by ACGIH, ISO, and the European Community (CEN), with the objective of international harmonization.[86] In effect, his revised sampling criteria split the difference between the ACGIH and ISO criteria consistent with matching the best available total and regional human deposition data. His initiative was well received by the interested parties and is being implemented by all concerned.[87–89]

The Soderholm revisions to Appendix D of the TLV/BEI booklet *Particle Size-Selective Sampling Criteria for Airborne Particulate Matter* were adopted by ACGIH in 1993. The three particulate mass fractions were redefined according to the following equations:

A. *Inhalable Particulate Mass* consists of those particles that are captured according to the following collection efficiency regardless of sampler orientation with respect to wind direction:

$$SI(d) = 50\% \times (1 + e^{-0.06d})$$
$$\text{for } 0 < d \leq 100\ \mu\text{m}$$

where: *SI(d)* = the collection efficiency for particles with aerodynamic diameter *d* in µm

B. *Thoracic Particulate Mass* consists of those particles that are captured according to the following collection efficiency:

$$ST(d) = SI(d)\ [1 - F(x)]$$

where: $x = \dfrac{\ln (d/\Gamma)}{\ln (\Sigma)}$

Γ = 11.64 µm
Σ = 1.5
$F(x)$ = the cumulative probability function of a standardized normal variable, x

C. *Respirable Particulate Mass* consists of those particles that are captured according to the following collection efficiency:

$$SR(d) = SI(d)\ [1 - F(x)]$$

where: $F(x)$ has the same meaning as above with Γ = 4.25 µm and Σ = 1.5

The most significant difference from previous definitions is the increase in the median cut point for a respirable dust sampler from 3.5 µm to 4.0 µm; this is in accord with the International Standards Organization/European Standardization Committee (ISO/CEN) protocol.[87,88] At this time, no change is recommended for the measurement of respirable dust using a 10-mm nylon cyclone at a flow rate of 1.7 liters per minute. Two analyses of available data indicate that the flow rate of 1.7 liters per minute allows the 10-mm nylon cyclone to approximate the dust concentration which would be measured by an ideal respirable dust sampler as defined herein.[90]

Collection efficiencies representative of several sizes of particles in each of the respective mass fractions are shown in Table 5-5. References 86 and 87 provide documentation for the respective algorithms representative of the three mass fractions. The respirable and thoracic sampling criteria are illustrated in Figures 5-10 and 5-11.

An issue initially raised in Appendix F of the 1986–87 TLV/BEI booklet concerned the changing of all TLVs that were explicitly defined in terms of "total dust" to "inspirable particulate mass" without changing the numerical values. A decision to make this change for particulates not otherwise classified (PNOC) was made by ACGIH in 1994. At its 1993 Annual Meeting, ACGIH endorsed the need to examine each TLV for airborne particles for conversion to PSS–TLVs.

The ASP Committee undertook several additional activities related to the development of size-selective TLVs. By extension of its initial activities, it responded

TABLE 5-5. Inhalable, Thoracic, and Respirable Dust Criteria of ACGIH–ISO–CEN

Inhalable		Thoracic		Respirable	
Particle Aerodynamic Diam. (μm)	Inhalable Particulate Mass (IPM) (%)	Particle Aerodynamic Diam. (μm)	Thoracic Particulate Mass (TPM) (%)	Particle Aerodynamic Diam. (μm)	Respirable Particulate Mass (RPM) (%)
0	100	0	100	0	100
1	97	2	94	1	97
2	94	4	89	2	91
5	87	6	80.5	3	74
10	77	8	67	4	50
20	65	10	50	5	30
30	58	12	35	6	17
40	54.5	14	23	7	9
50	52.5	16	15	8	5
100	50	18	9.5	10	1
		20	6		
		25	2		

to comments received and made some modifications to its recommendations.

Bartley and Doemeny[91] of the National Institute for Occupational Safety and Health (NIOSH) objected to the original ACGIH sampler acceptance criteria. The ASP Committee had recommended that calibrations be performed at equal size intervals between 2- and 10-μm aerodynamic diameter, and that the correlation coefficient (r^2) of the linear fit be larger than 0.90.

The Bartley and Doemeny critique had two primary concerns: 1) that the statistical tests required for determining satisfactory sampler performance were too difficult to meet for real samplers, and 2) that the criteria would, for certain aerosol size distributions, permit instruments that differed too greatly in their measured RPM concentration. In part, these criticisms arose because of differences in perspective. Although NIOSH and ACGIH both provide technical information and professional guidance to facilitate the protection of worker health, NIOSH has the further role of certifying samplers for compliance purposes. In this regard, NIOSH develops performance criteria for size-selective samplers.

Bartley and Doemeny's concern about the sampler performance criteria was well founded and was addressed by changes to the criteria for acceptable test performance adopted by the ASP Committee. The simplified performance criteria for an RPM sampler required only that tests be performed at 10 monodisperse particle sizes between 2 and 10 m, and that 9 out of the 10 points fall within the acceptance bands given. A point is considered to be within the band if more than 50% of replications at that particle size lie within the acceptance band.

The simplification of the criteria greatly reduced the range of RPM concentration that could be measured with instruments meeting the criteria. When an RPM sampler performing according to the lower bound is compared to a sampler performing according to the upper bound (a worst-case difference in performance which is extremely unlikely in practice), there is only about a factor of two difference in RPM for the worst-case size distribution given by Bartley and Doemeny, a size distribution for coal mine dust with mass median diameter (MMD) of 18.5 μm and geometric standard deviation (σ_g) of 2.3. For this condition, the RPM represents only 2.3% to 4.7% of the total mass. The nuisance dust TLV of 10 mg/m^3, if enforced, would limit dust concentration such that RPM would be well below the coal mine dust TLV of 2 mg/m^3, and the twofold difference in measured RPM concentration would therefore be relatively insignificant.

Bartley and Doemeny[91] and Liden and Kenny[92] have recommended that sampler equivalence be measured by simulated performance with various test particle size distributions for known types of dust exposure such as coal mine dust. However, the ASP Committee has reservations that the sampler equivalence approach is appropriate for professional practice recommendations that would be applied to an extremely wide range of size distributions as is anticipated for the particle size-selective sampling recommendations.

McCawley[93] argues that "respirable" dust is not a good index for inhalation hazard for dust that deposits in the gas-exchange region of the lung, and that it would be better to design a sampler that collects a dust fraction more closely related to that which actually deposits in that region. This approach to hazard evaluation has a long history of application in Germany.[94]

Knight[95] presented a rationale for an approach to the specification of size-selective sampling criteria, which had been considered and rejected by the ASP Committee. He suggested that "The mean anatomical regional depositions can be obtained with a reasonable degree of accuracy" from linear combinations (adding, subtracting, and scaling) of the three sampler results. Although the regional dose approach is conceptually sound, the ASP Committee maintained that its regional exposure approach has several advantages and no serious disadvantages. It is simpler, more operationally reliable, and, in many cases, more conservative (i.e., protective).

The development of PSS–TLVs for specific substances other than mineral dusts has advanced slowly. Technical papers have documented the basis for particle size-selective sampling for beryllium,[96] wood dust,[97] and sulfuric acid aerosol.[98] In developing new TLVs for these and other substances, the decision flow diagram developed by the ASP Committee should prove to be useful and help to ensure a uniform documentation for the new PSS–TLVs.

As shown in Figure 5-13, the first step in deriving a PSS–TLV is the identification of the chemical substance that constitutes a potential air pollutant, including examination of all available physicochemical properties related to its airborne and biological behavior. Concomitantly, the literatures of epidemiology, industrial hygiene, and toxicology should be searched to identify diseases that may be associated with the chemical substance affecting specific regions of the respiratory tract or systemic organ systems. New data gathered from these searches, including experimental animal studies, especially on recently developed substances, should be incorporated with existing TLV documentation for insight into possible disease mechanisms.

If no potential diseases related to the chemical substance are found, then the evaluation can be terminated. If a disease potential exists, but the physicochemical nature of the chemical substance is such that no airborne particle phase can be produced, the procedure can revert to the traditional procedure for establishing a TLV.

However, if the physicochemical properties of the chemical substance suggest that it may become airborne as an aerosol, the analysis proceeds. At this stage, the physical and chemical properties of the substance are evaluated under conditions likely to be encountered by workers.

The aerodynamic particle size distribution will determine the mass fraction of the workplace aerosol that will enter the head airways, tracheobronchial, or gas-exchange regions of the respiratory tract. Particle size-selective sampling is then used to estimate the actual quantity of chemical substance that will be presented to the three principal regions of the respiratory tract during the course of each working day. Thus, the mass of the substance presented to each region will be established as the critical value in airborne hazard evaluation. Once the chemical substance is deposited in a particular region or regions of the respiratory tract, the critical factor in selecting the appropriate particle mass fraction (respirable, thoracic, or inspirable) is the extent of dissolution of the substance within each region.

Concurrent examination of the clinical diseases that may affect any systemic organ will identify extrapulmonary sites of action. Subsequently, it will be determined whether the incorporated dose of the substance is a critical dose that is likely to cause acute or chronic injury. Once the particle size and particulate mass fraction are determined and the hazard analyses are completed, a critical mass concentration will be determined for an appropriate size fraction. This review will result in a recommendation for a PSS–TLV.

If the inhaled chemical material is likely to dissolve only slowly or is essentially insoluble after deposition in any of the three principal regions of the respiratory tract, selection of the appropriate particle size-selective sample should be based on the specific site of action within the respiratory tract that is associated with the most restrictive PSS–TLV, as based on comparing each potential disease.

A more detailed discussion of the use of this decision flow diagram for specific substances was prepared by Stuart, Lioy, and Phalen.[99]

Other Size-selective Criteria for Specific Occupational Hazards

Size-selective criteria in widespread use for cotton dust and asbestos are different from those previously discussed. A brief review of the rationale and practice used for each of these special cases follows.

Cotton Dust Sampling

Because byssinosis or "brown lung" is characterized by an allergic response producing airway constriction, it was recognized that particles depositing in the tracheobronchial airways should not be excluded. Thus, conventional "respirable" dust criteria were judged to be inappropriate. On the other hand, the mass of the dust in cotton ginning and textile operations tends to be dominated by very large cotton fibers which are too large to be inspirable. These considerations led to the recommendation of a vertical elutriator with a nominal 50% cut size at 15 μm as the first stage of a standard sampler.[100] The second stage filter is analyzed for the

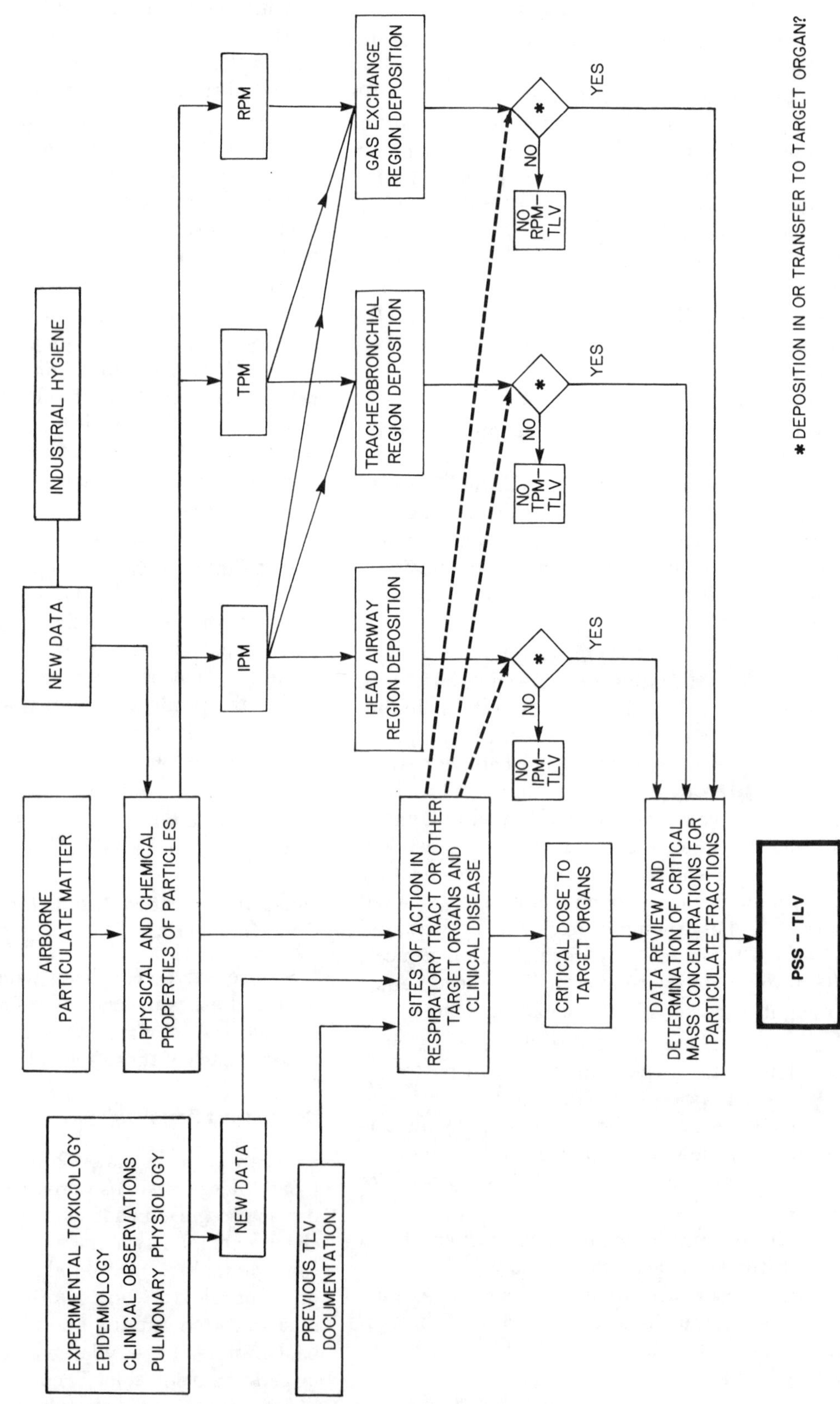

FIGURE 5-13. Flow diagram of the information to be considered in the development of ACGIH Particle Size-Selective Threshold Limit Values (PSS-TLVs).

mass concentration of the particles judged most likely to be related to the health effects.

Asbestos Sampling

In asbestos and other mineral fiber analyses, the size-selectivity is applied after the sampling. There is no sampling selectivity specified in the NIOSH[101] or ACGIH–American Industrial Hygiene Association (AIHA)[102] sampling recommendations, although the specified inlet configurations to the filter holders will, of course, impose some. In the analyses by phase contrast optical microscopy, there is an effective lower limit for fiber diameter imposed by the resolving power of the objective lens. There are also other limits specified by the methods, whereby particles with an aspect ratio (length to diameter) of less than 3 or a length of less than 5 μm, are not counted. The rationale for these exclusions is based on toxicological and epidemiological studies which showed that the toxic effects were primarily associated with long thin fibers. Asbestosis, a pneumoconiosis, and mesothelioma, a cancer of the pleural or peritoneal surfaces, are presumably related to long fibers depositing in the alveolar regions, while bronchial cancer may be related to the long fibers depositing on bronchial airways.

In a critical review of the literature on asbestos toxicity and human disease in relation to the dimensions of the fibers, Lippmann[103] identified the critical dimensions for each of the asbestos-associated diseases. These are summarized in Table 5-6.

TABLE 5-6. Summary of Recommendations on Asbestos Exposure Indices

Disease	Relevant Exposure Index
Asbestosis	Surface area of fibers with: Length >2 μm, diameter >0.15 μm
Mesothelioma	Number of fibers with: Length >5 μm, diameter <0.1 μm
Lung cancer	Number of fibers with: Length >10 μm, diameter >0.15 μm

Instruments for Size-selective Sampling

The goal of obtaining air concentration data related to health hazards can be approached in several ways. For "insoluble" dusts, multistage samplers, consisting of one or more collectors with cutoff characteristics like those of the upper respiratory and tracheobronchial airways, followed by an efficient final stage, can provide the desired information with minimal sampling and analytical effort. For other toxic materials or for aerosols where the contaminant of interest is a minor mass constituent, it may be necessary to obtain the overall size-mass concentration within different size ranges appropriate to the sites of toxic action.

Because the size-selective particle criteria outlined in the preceding sections were intended for "insoluble" dusts, most of the samplers developed to satisfy them have been relatively simple two-stage devices. In recent years, multistage samplers designed to simulate deposition within more restricted subdivisions of the respiratory tract have been developed. These and other multistage samplers will be discussed in the sections to follow.

Two-Stage, "Respirable" Particulate Mass Samplers

A two-stage respirable dust sampler consists of a first stage, whose collection efficiency falls from very high to very low as the aerodynamic particle size decreases from approximately 10 to 2 μm, and a second stage with a high collection efficiency for all particle sizes. Horizontal elutriators and cyclones have been most widely used as first-stage collectors, whereas filters have been used as the second stage in most two-stage samplers.

Other first-stage collectors that have been used for "respirable" dust sampling include the helical tube of Hatch and Hemeon;[104] the pre-impinger of May and Druett;[105] the Personal Centripeter of Langmead and O'Connor;[106] the multiple-nozzle, single-stage impactors of Marple[107] and Willeke;[108] and an inefficient filter. Roessler[109] and Gibson and Vincent[110] proposed using plastic foam filters to simulate the respirable cut, while Parker *et al.*[111] and Cahill *et al.*[112] proposed using large pore Nuclepore filters. The use of Nuclepore filters for this purpose is inadvisable for two reasons. One, their primary collection mechanism in the size range and face velocity of interest is interception; therefore, they collect particles according to their linear dimensions more than on the basis of their aerodynamic diameters. Second, solid particles tend to bounce or be re-entrained off Nuclepore filter surfaces as demonstrated by Spurny,[113] Buzzard and Bell,[114] and Heidam.[115] On the other hand, the porous foam filter sampler of Gibson and Vincent[110] offers some interesting advantages for "respirable" dust sampling. It has a collection efficiency close to that of the MRE elutriator over a broad range of filter face velocities. At the lower velocities, particle collection by sedimentation increases while collection by impaction decreases. At the higher flow rates, the reverse is true, and the overall efficiency is about the same. In some devices there is no actual first-stage collector. Instead, the sampler has entry conditions that prevent oversize "nonrespirable" particles from being drawn into the inlet. One such device is the conicycle,[116] an air centrifuge that collects "respirable" particles smaller than the

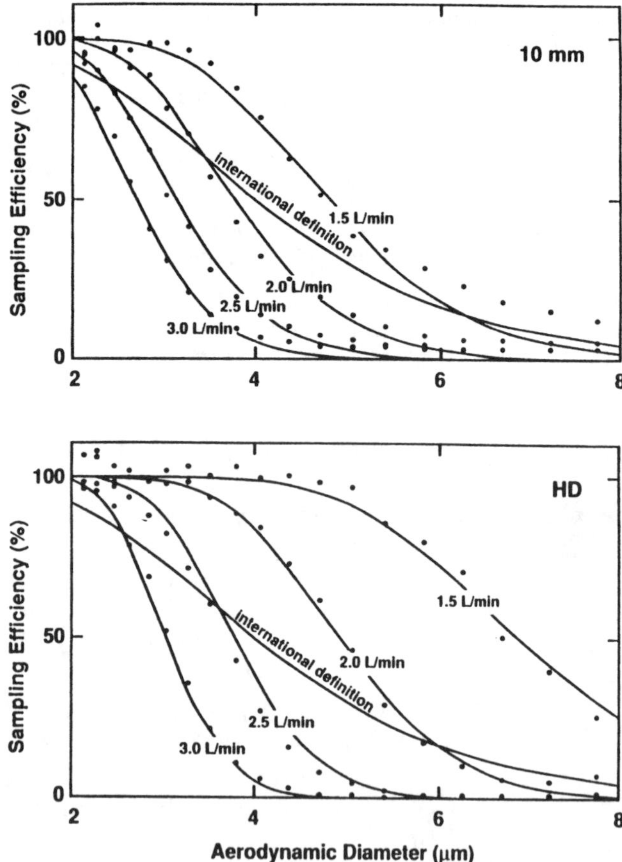

FIGURE 5-14. Aerodynamic particle diameter versus collection efficiency for the 10-mm nylon cyclone (top) and the Higgins and Dewell (HD) type of cyclone made by Casella and BGI, Inc. (bottom), in relation to the recently adopted ACGIH–ISO–CEN respirable mass sampling criteria (from Bartley *et al.*[125]).

inlet cutoff size but larger than a lower cutoff of approximately 1.0 μm diameter.

In addition to filters, other second-stage collectors that have been used include impingers, impactors, cyclones, bubblers, thermal precipitators, and electrostatic precipitators. Table 5-7 summarizes the pertinent characteristics of two-stage, "respirable" dust samplers.

Cyclones are the most commonly used respirable mass samplers. They are available in a wide range of flow rates, including miniature sizes for personal sampling. The sampling efficiency can be closely matched to that of a respirable curve (Figure 5-14). Cyclones have important practical advantages, such as minimal particle bounce and re-entrainment, large capacity for loading, and insensitivity to orientation. A disadvantage of the cyclone is the lack of a fundamental theory that can predict performance. However, empirical theories are available to assist the designer.[128,133,134]

Considerable data are available on the performance of the widely used 10-mm nylon cyclone.[125,135–137] The latest study, using an aerodynamic particle sizer to measure cyclone penetration, has been reported by Bartley *et al.*[125] Their results for the 10-mm nylon cyclone and the Higgins and Dewell design made by Casella and BGI, Inc. are shown in Figure 5-14. Based on their analyses, they have concluded that the 10-mm nylon cyclone will most closely match the revised ACGIH–ISO–CEN criteria for respirable dust sampling at 1.7 L/min, while the best match for the Casella and BGI cyclones is 2.2 L/min.

Small cyclones have been designed to approximate the separation characteristics specified by the BMRC. The Casella SIMPEDS, widely used in Europe, is a modified version of a design by Higgins and Dewell[127] that was fabricated for the British Cast Iron Association (BCIRA). In Sweden, SKC has produced a series of similar cyclones, i.e., SKCα, SKCβ, and SKCγ. These cyclones have recently been evaluated by Liden.[138] Figure 5-15 and Table 5-8 show the critical dimensions of these cyclones. Figure 5-16 shows performance data reported by Liden for the SIMPEDS and SKCα in relation to the BMRC and new ACGIH–ISO–CEN criteria. He also reported that the SKCγ is closest in performance to the SIMPEDS; however, the SKCα and SKCβ gave the closest performance to the new criteria of ACGIH–ISO–CEN.

Larger miniature cyclones with nominal diameters between 1/2 and 3 in. (1.2 to 7.6 cm), which make comparable particle-size cuts at larger flow rates, have also been widely used for "respirable" dust sampling.[125,127,128,133–139]

An inertial spectrometer personal sampler that sorts the sampled aerosol onto a 47-mm membrane filter according to aerodynamic diameter has been developed by Prodi *et al.*[140,141] The filter can be cut into strips with cut sizes ranging from >10 μm to <2.5 μm. It was reported that its performance for sampling TPM and RPM matches the ACGIH criteria and suggests that, when worn on the lapel, its inlet efficiency matches the IPM criteria.

Horizontal elutriators have been widely used outside of the United States. Their main advantage is the predictable performance based on gravitational settling of the particles during passage between horizontal collecting plates. Disadvantages include the restriction to a fixed orientation, the possible re-entrainment of particle deposits, and the difficulty of miniaturization.

The collection efficiency of an impactor can be accurately predicted by theory.[142] On the other hand, important details such as wall losses cannot be reliably predicted. Also, impactors suffer from the problems associated with particle bounce and re-entrainment. Impactors can be designed over a wide range of flow rates and can be operated in any orientation. Particle bounce and re-entrainment can be minimized by using

TABLE 5-7. Size-Selective Samplers for Respirable, Thoracic (PM_{10}), and Inhalable Sampling

Type of First-Stage Collector	Type of Second-Stage Collector	Instrument or Precollector Name	Sampling Rate (L/min)	Suction Source	Reference	Commercial[A] Sources	Descriptions in Other Sections
A. Two-Stage "Respirable" Dust Samplers and Monitors							
Elutriator	Filter thimble	Hexhlet	50[B]	Air ejector	Wright[117]	CAS	14-38
Elutriator	Thermal ppt	Long period thermal ppt	0.002	Piston pump	Hamilton[118]		
Elutriator	Filter	SMRE semiautomatic hand pump	80 ml/stroke	Hand-pump	Dawes & Winder[119]		
Elutriator	Filter	High-volume elutriator	1250	Turbine blower	Shanty & Hemeon[120]		
Elutriator	Filter	MRE gravimetric dust sampler (Isleworth)	2.5	Diaphragm pump	Dunmore *et al.*[121]	CAS	14-39
Elutriator	Photometer[C]	Simslin	0.625	Vane pump	Blackford & Harris[122]	RML	
Spiral tube	Midget impinger		2.8	Impinger pump	Hatch & Hemeon[104]		
Pre-impinger	Porton impinger	Pre-impinger	11	Various	May & Druett[105]		
Centripeter	Filter	Personal centripeter	2	Diaphragm pump	Langmead & O'Conner[106]	BGI	14-16
Filter	Filter	Polyurethane foam prefilter	1130	Turbine blower	Roesler[109]		
Impactor	Filter		28.3	Pump	Marple[107]		
Impactor	Filter	Personal environmental monitoring impactor	4 10	Pump		MSP	14-15
Impactor	Electrostatic[C]	Respirable aerosol mass monitor	1	Pump	Sem *et al.*[123]	TSI	
Impactor	Photometer[C]	Respirable aerosol photometer	4	Pump		TSI	
Cyclone	Filter	Aerotec 3/4	25	Various	Lippmann & Chan[124]	AA	
Cyclone	Filter	Aerotec 2	430	Turbine blower	Lippmann & Chan[124]	GMW, BGI	
Cyclone	Filter	10-mm Dorr–Oliver Cyclone	1.7	Various	Bartley *et al.*[125]	MSA, SEN, SKC	14-34, 14-35, 14-36
Cyclone	Filter	1/2" HASL cyclone	9	Various	AIHA Aerosol Technology Committee[126]	SEN	14-35
Cyclone	Filter	1" HASL cyclone	75	Turbine blower	Lippmann & Chan[171]	SEN	14-35
Cyclone	Filter	Personal dust sampler, SIMPEDS 70 MK2	2.2	Diaphragm pump	Higgins & Dewell[127]	BGI, CAS RML	14-31
Cyclone	Filter		15.4	Pump	John & Reischl[128]		
Cyclone	Cyclone	Gravimetric dust sampler vT/BF	50	Air ejector	Breuer[94]		
Cyclone	Impactor[C]	Respirable dust mass monitor	2	Pump		MIE	
Cyclone	Photometer[C]	RAM	2	Pump		MIE	

TABLE 5-7 (con't). Size-Selective Samplers for Respirable, Thoracic (PM_{10}), and Inhalable Sampling

Type	Type of Size Selector	Nominal Cut-Size	Downstream Collector(s)	Sampling Rate (L/min)	Reference	Commercial[A] Source(s)	Descriptions in Other Sections
B. Samplers and Monitors with Inlet Cut-Sizes at 10–15 μm							
Cotton dust samplers	Vertical elutriator	100% @ 15 μm	Filter - 37 mm	7.4	NIOSH[(100)]	GMW	14-40
PCAM	Vertical elutriator	100% @ 15 μm	Photometer	7.4	Shofner *et al.*[(129)]	PPM	
Wedding PM_{10} inlets:							
Dichotomous sampler	Cyclone	50% @ 10 μm	37-mm virtual impactor filters collecting 10-15 μm, < 2.5 μm	16.7		N/A	
High vol. PM_{10}	Cyclone	50% @ 10 μm	Filter - 8 × 10 in.	1130		WED	14-29
PM_{10} ambient samplers:							
Dichotomous samplers	Impaction baffles	50% @ 10 μm	37-mm virtual impactor filters 10-2.5 μm, < 2.5 μm	16.7		GRA, GMW	14-28
Medium flow samplers	Impaction baffles	50% @ 10 μm	Filter - 102 mm	113		GRA, GMW	14-27
Size-selective hi-vols.	Impaction baffles	50% @ 10 μm	Filter - 8 × 10 in.	1130		GRA, GMW	14-26
PM_{10} personal sampler	Impactor	50% @ 10 μm	Filter	4	Buckley *et al.*[(130)]	MSP	14-15
C. Samplers with Inhalable Inlet Cut-Sizes							
IOM/STD 1	Rotating slit	ACGIH IPM	Filter capsule	3	Mark *et al.*[(131)]	RML	
IOM personal sampler	15-mm inlet tube	ACGIH IPM	Filter capsule	2	Mark & Vincent[(132)]	SKC	

[A]See Table 5-9 for explanation of manufacturer's codes.
[B]For revised design - original unit had smaller plate spacing and operated at 100 L/min.
[C]Provides for direct readout of "respirable" mass concentration.

virtual impactors. It should be emphasized, however, that the cutoff curves of most existing impactors are sharp, and hence do not conform to the human respirable curve.

The deposition models proposed by the ICRP[23,46] and NCRP[47] Task Groups, which were previously discussed, define deposition in the head airways, tracheobronchial airways, and gas-exchange regions on the basis of a single parameter that they call the AMAD. This parameter is a type of mass median diameter, specifically for radioactive aerosols, and it can be determined in industrial environments using cascade impactor samplers under some circumstances. However, cascade impactors cannot be used effectively to monitor materials with very low concentration limits because background dust will overload the collection plates, resulting in unacceptable re-entrainment and wall losses long before detectable levels of the radioisotope of interest are collected. Two-stage samplers cannot provide an estimate of the aerosol AMAD and might appear to be inapplicable to the estimation of "respirable" concentrations as defined by the original Task Group model. However, Mercer[77] demonstrated that the second-stage collection of a two-stage sampler, whose first stage conforms to the BMRC or AEC criteria, could be related to the original Task Group deposition prediction by a simple fraction. For a variety of lognormal aerosol distributions with σ_g between 1.5 and 4, the predicted pulmonary (alveolar) deposition was very close to 30% of the fraction collected on the second-stage collector for both elutriator and cyclone.

TABLE 5-8. Dimensions (mm) of Three SKC Cyclone Generations, Single-hole Vortex-Outlet SIMPEDS Cyclone, and Original Drawing by Higgins and Dewell (HD) (from Liden[138])

	HD	SIMPEDS	SKCα	SKCβ	SKCγ
D	9.5	9.5	9.3	9.3	9.5
D_e	3.2	3.2	3.9	3.1	3.2
D_p	4.7	5.0	4.9	4.5	4.7
b	1.6	1.5	0.9	1.6	1.7
a	9.5	10.3	9.6	9.1	9.5
S	9.5	10.3	9.3	19.5	9.5
H	12.1	12.8	12.2	9.3	12.1
L_c	25.4	26.2	36.8	23.7	25.4
z	0.0	0.0	4.3	0.0	0.0
B	2.4	2.3	2.2	2.4	2.4

Inspirable Particulate Mass Samplers

It is desirable that IPM sampling eventually replace the present method of total dust sampling using open-face filter holders. So-called total dust samplers, such as open-face filter cassettes, do not measure total dust and are unsuitable for most monitoring of airborne particles larger than a few micrometers because their sampling efficiency for large particles is sensitive to wind velocity and direction. Implementation of IPM sampling will require the development and testing of suitable sampling instruments.

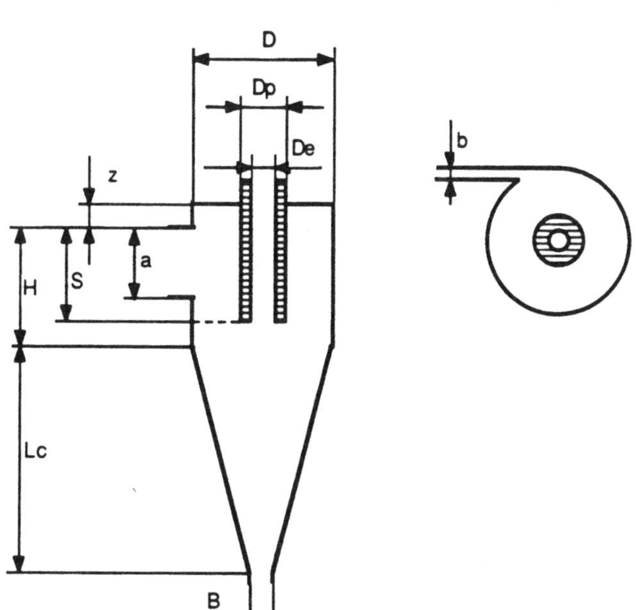

FIGURE 5-15. Critical cyclone dimensions (see Table 5-8).

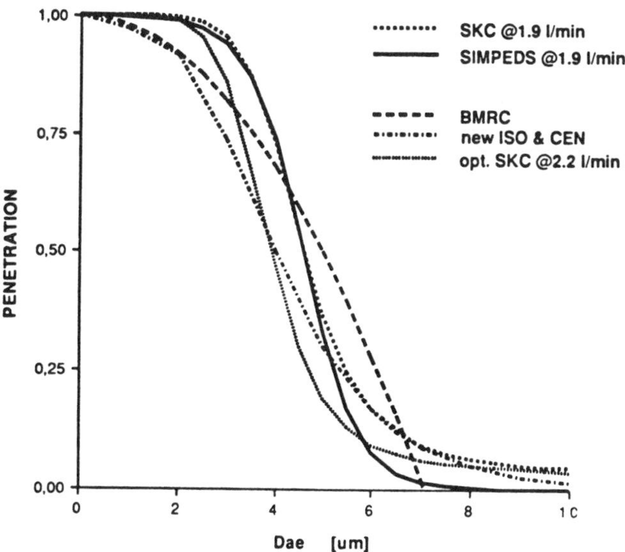

FIGURE 5-16. Average penetration for the SKCα and SIMPEDS cyclones at 1.9 L/min, together with the BMRC and the new ACGIH–ISO–CEN-proposed respirable sampling conventions, and optimum SKCα flow rate for proposed ACGIH–ISO–CEN respirable sampling convention (from Liden[138]).

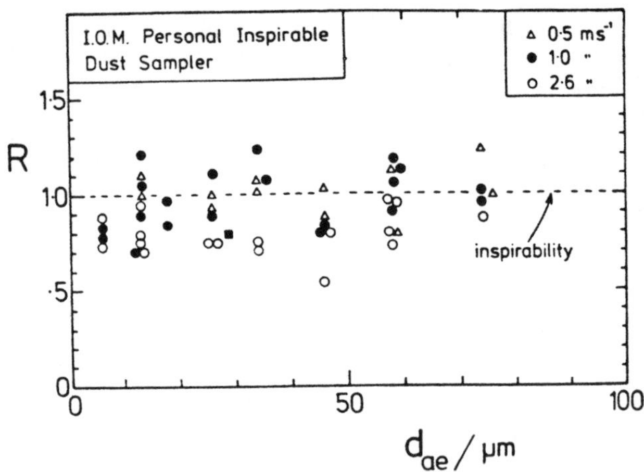

FIGURE 5-17. Collection ratio (R) to the IPM personal "inspirable" dust sampler as a function of particle aerodynamic diameter (d_{ae}).[132] Reprinted with permission from the British Occupational Hygiene Society.

Sampling in calm air has been evaluated by several investigators.[143–145] These studies deal with the effect of sedimentation and particle inertia on sampling losses. In the workplace environment, it is rare for the air to be sufficiently calm for this still air analysis to hold. The situation is more complicated for the case of blunt samplers sampling in calm air. Studies of blunt samplers lead to the conclusion that for calm air the particle aerodynamic diameter that results in a 90% sampling efficiency is roughly one-half that predicted for thin-walled tube samplers.[61]

When sampling in moving air for particles whose settling velocities are small compared to the air velocity, accurate samples of large particles can be obtained by using thin-walled probes aligned with the gas streamlines using entering air velocities that match the approaching wind velocity. When these conditions are met, sampling is said to be isokinetic and sampling efficiency is 100% for all particle sizes. Blunt samplers operating in a wind present a complicated situation, and there is no unique probe velocity that permits sampling with 100% efficiency for all particle sizes in a given wind.

The inlet characteristics of currently used personal and static samplers under various conditions were previously discussed in the section of this chapter on "Total or Gross Air Concentration Measurements."[63,64]

The Orb sampler was considered for use as an inspirable mass sampler, but it was found to undersample particles larger than about 13 μm in diameter.[146] Mark *et al.*[131] developed an area sampler, the IOM/STD1, that comes close to matching the recommended IPM criteria over the range of 0- to 100-μm aerodynamic diameter. The sampling head of their device is a vertical axis cylinder about 5 cm in diameter and 6 cm high. A horizontal axis, oval-shaped inlet slot (about 3 mm high × 16 mm wide) is located midway up the side of the cylinder. The device samples at 3 L/min through a 37-mm filter mounted in a weighable cassette inside the cylinder. The sampling head is mounted on a larger vertical axis cylinder about 15 cm in diameter and about 18 cm high that houses batteries, pump, and flow control. The sampling head rotates continuously at about 2 rpm. Test results indicate reasonable agreement with the ACGIH IPM criteria. Mark and Vincent[132] described a 2 L/min personal lapel sampler whose collection characteristics closely match the ACGIH IPM criteria (Figure 5-17).

Thoracic Particulate Mass Samplers

Probably the simplest approach to sampling for TPM is to use a sampler whose collection efficiency as a function of particle aerodynamic diameter falls within the acceptance envelope. Such a TPM sampler consists of an inlet, a size-fractionating stage, which is sometimes integral with the inlet, and a particle collector, which is usually a filter.

One of the principal criteria used in the selection of samplers is the flow rate. TPM samplers can be classified into low volume ($Q < 20$ L/min), medium volume (20 L/min $< Q <$ 150 L/min), and high volume ($Q >$ 150 L/min) samplers. In the low volume category, the dichotomous sampler[147] is a virtual impactor having a flow rate of 16.7 L/min. The TPM fraction is selectively passed through the inlet; the virtual impactor further fractionates the aerosol into coarse and fine fractions with a d_{50} of 2.5 μm.

Several inlet designs are available. The UMLBL inlet[148,149] is a single-stage impactor with a grooved impaction surface and an internal flow pattern designed to suppress particle bounce. Independence of wind direction is assured by cylindrical symmetry about the vertical axis. For TPM sampling alone, the virtual impaction stage of the dichotomous sampler is unnecessary. The fractionating inlet can be coupled directly to a filter to form a sampler which has been called the PASS (Particulate Automatic Sampling System [Graseby Andersen, Atlanta, GA]). Such a sampler, using the earlier U.S. EPA 15-μm cutpoint dichotomous sampler inlet, performed well.[150]

Medium volume samplers have been developed. One version employs a sampler geometry that fractionates particles by a combination of impaction and sedimentation.[151] The tortuous air path also suppresses particle bounce. A high volume sampler based on a similar geometry, called the Size-Selective Inlet (SSI), converts a standard hi-vol into a thoracic mass sampler.[152] The SSI can be used only with quartz or glass fiber filters.

A small, portable sampler has been developed within a thoracic cut provided by the inlet, which contains a single-stage impactor with an oil-soaked porous plate to suppress particle bounce.[153]

The foregoing samplers are all area samplers. Personal samplers designed for the collection of the TPM fraction have been developed.[130,154] The miniature impactor[155] could also be used to determine the TPM fraction.

The measured sampling efficiencies of two of the samplers discussed above are compared to the TPM sampling criteria in Figure 5-18. The data points lie within the tolerance band. These particular samplers were chosen for illustrative purposes only; a number of other samplers also satisfy the criteria.

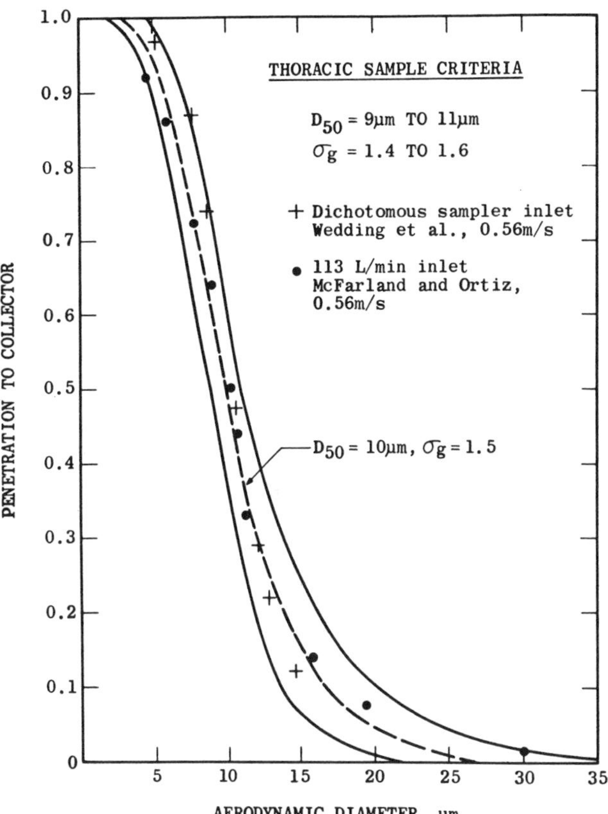

FIGURE 5-18. TPM sampling criteria with data for two thoracic particulate mass samplers.[151,156]

Other Multistage Aerosol Samplers

A filter pack sampler that provides estimates of the deposition in each of the ICRP Subcommittee II Task Group subdivisions was described by Shleien *et al.*,[157] who calculated their regional deposition estimates using a linear programming approach in which they combined their calibration data on the relative collection efficiencies of the stages in the filter pack and the characteristics of the Task Group's deposition model. The filter stage collections themselves do not correspond to particular regions of the respiratory tract.

Reiter and Potzl[158] developed a filter pack in which the particle penetration characteristics of each filter were selected so that the particles retained on each filter represent deposition in a particular region of the respiratory tract. Their calibration data indicate that the stages of their filter pack are similar to the regional deposition estimates from the calculations of Findeisen[41] and Landahl.[42] Thus, the first filter collection represents the deposition in the trachea and bronchi of the first order, the second filter represents the remainder of the bronchial deposition, the third filter represents alveolar deposit, and the fourth or final filter represents the exhaled aerosol. Air enters the filter pack through a moistening vessel which serves to maintain a selected water vapor partial pressure. The filter pack is housed within a Faraday cage and the electric charge deposited on each filter by the collected particles can be measured. This model does not consider nasopharyngeal deposition and thus appears to represent deposition during mouth breathing.

Other Airborne Particle Classifiers

There are a number of inertial particle classifier samplers whose cutoff characteristics were not designed to match human respiratory tract deposition or penetration. These include two-stage samplers designed to make some other specific size cut and multiple-stage instruments which make a series of specific cuts and/or an estimate of the overall size-mass distribution.

Samplers with a single impaction stage include the single-stage impactors. These impactors deposit the large particle fraction on adhesive-coated plates or agar-filled dishes.

To overcome the limited collection capability of agar and adhesive-coated collection plates, Conner[159] directed the impaction jet into a still air region. Most of the flow must pass through an annular slit in the sampling tube and on to the back-up filter, carrying with it the smaller particles. The large particles continue down the tube beyond the slit along with a small volume of bleed air and are retained on a filter at the exit of the still air chamber. With a sampling rate of 39.7 L/min and a bleed rate of 0.5 L/min, the 50% cutoff is at 1.4 µm for polystyrene latex spheres. With other jet dimensions and flow rates, this type of sampler could make other particle size cuts, e.g., a "respirable" size cut.

Multiple-stage samplers that project large particles into still air have also been described. The cascade centripeter of Hounam and Sherwood[160] consists of three such inertial separation stages followed by a final filter stage. At the back of each still air chamber is a filter which collects the oversize particles and limits the amount of bleed air flow.

A similar approach is followed in the so-called "virtual impactors" recently developed for two-stage air pollution sampling applications.[161,162] Samplers used in aerosol characterization studies have had a 2.5-µm design cutoff, whereas others, used in health-effects studies, have operated with a 3.5-µm cutoff.

The most widely used type of multistage sampler is the cascade impactor, which is available commercially in a variety of designs. One major limitation to its application is that only limited sample masses can be collected without re-entrainment. Further limitations, which are shared by other multistage instruments such as the cascade centripeter, are wall losses between collection stages and the increased number of analyses per sample which are required. Their major advantage is that the full particle size-mass distribution can be determined. Recent developments include cascade impactors small enough for use as personal samplers.[163,164]

The first development of a portable sampler using a parallel array of cyclone-filter series samplers was described by Lippmann and Kydonieus.[165] Each cyclone had a different cut size and the overall size-mass distribution of the total aerosol or any of its chemical constituents could be determined from analyses of the collection on the filter following each cyclone and a parallel filter sampler operated without a cyclone precollector. The performance characteristics of an improved version of this sampler were described by Blachman and Lippmann.[166] A much larger version of this sampler for fixed-station, ambient air pollution sampling was described by Bernstein *et al.*[167] A parallel multicyclone sampling train for stack sampling applications was described by Chang;[168] in addition, Smith *et al.*[169] developed a five-stage series cyclone sampler for the same purpose.

The major advantage in using cyclones instead of impactors for such applications is that their performance is not significantly affected by the amount of sample collected.[166] They share with impactors the advantage of relatively low fabrication cost.

Air centrifuges such as the Stöber spinning spiral centrifuge,[170] Conifuge,[171] and Goetz Aerosol Spectrometer,[172] and the horizontal elutriators of Timbrell[173] and Walkenhorst[174] deposit the aerosol sample in a continuous trace that can be subdivided into particle size subgroups. These instruments have very low sampling rates, and their use in the field is usually restricted to research studies rather than routine monitoring.

Other Techniques for Size Classification

All of the preceding methods separated the airborne particles according to their aerodynamic diameters. This parameter is of primary interest when considering the deposition probabilities of aerosols. However, useful data can be obtained by measuring other size parameters, such as light scatter,[175,176] provided that a basis can be established for reliable conversion of the diameter measured to aerodynamic diameter.

Limitations of Selective Sampling and Selective Samplers

The effective application of selective sampling concepts to respiratory hazard evaluation requires 1) adequate knowledge of the regional deposition and clearance of particles in man and 2) reliable, reproducible, and accurately calibrated selective samplers. In both areas, the current state-of-the-art leaves much to be desired.

It is apparent from the review of the human deposition and clearance data and models presented earlier that the data are far from consistent and that the available models are, at best, crude approximations. Furthermore, as recent studies have demonstrated, there are very large variations in both regional deposition efficiencies and clearance rates among normal populations. Thus, even if the data were highly precise and reproducible, and population average figures met with general acceptance, the potential toxicity from the inhalation of a given aerosol would vary over a wide range.

The technology for designing a size-selective sampler and characterizing its collection characteristics is relatively more advanced than that for determining regional deposition and clearance dynamics in the human respiratory tract. Yet, even here, there are many conflicting data in the literature, and many instrument designs have required modifications to meet their original specifications. Also, some laboratory calibration data have been found to be erroneous, due to differences between laboratory test and field conditions as well as errors in measurement and/or data conversion errors.

For example, the original standard British elutriator sampler, the Hexhlet,[117] when operated at its design flow rate of 100 L/min, was found to be passing oversize particles onto the filter thimble. One major cause was re-entrainment of settled dust from the plates. To minimize this problem, the plate spacing was increased and the sampling rate reduced to 50 L/min.

The chief advantage of the horizontal elutriator over the cyclone as a precollector is that its performance can be predicted on the basis of gravitational sedimentation theory and the physical dimensions of the device. Thus, it was sometimes claimed that laboratory calibrations with carefully characterized test aerosols were not needed. This generalization was true, at least in a relative sense, in comparison to cyclone collectors where no adequate predictive relations exist for collection efficiency. However, in an absolute sense, the prediction of performance of actual elutriator samplers is not completely reliable, as discussed in the preceding paragraphs. Thurmer[177] presented a theoretical basis for describing some of the discrepancies observed in elutriator performance on the basis of technical shortcomings in the manufacture of the elutriators, especially in the nonuniformity of the plate spacings.

One of the major limitations of all elutriator precollectors is that it is difficult if not impossible to recover the collected material for analysis. In many cases, it is even difficult to periodically clean out the collected dust to minimize contamination of the second-stage collection by re-entrained dust. In most cases, the use of elutriators has been restricted to sampling for pneumoconiosis-producing dusts where the hazards and concentration standards are based entirely on the "respirable" fraction. For research studies and other situations where the concentrations of both fractions are to be determined, cyclone precollectors are generally used.

Another limitation of the elutriator type of sampler is that it must be operated in a fixed horizontal position. The same limitation also applies to the water-filled preimpinger. Cyclones, on the other hand, can be operated in any orientation without significant change in their collection characteristics.[166,178] The only precaution necessary is to avoid turning them upside down during or after sampling, which could cause dust from the cyclone to fall onto the filter or out through the inlet. This independence of orientation, combined with their smaller physical size at comparable flow rates, is one of the reasons that most of the recent two-stage, personal sampler designs have been built around miniature cyclones as the precollectors. These samplers, combined with filter collectors as the second stage and miniature battery-powered air pumps, are small and light enough to be worn throughout a work shift.

Most of the miniature battery-powered pumps are diaphragm or piston-type air movers and therefore produce a pulsating flow. This could render them unsuitable for pulling air through precollectors whose collection characteristics are flowrate dependent. Initially, personal gravimetric samplers distributed in the United States did not have pulsation dampers. Caplan *et al.*[179] demonstrated that the instantaneous flow was as much as 4 times the average for some units. There was a greater increase in collection efficiency at flows above the average than there was a decrease for flows below it. The net effect was to produce reduced cyclone penetration in pulsating flow as compared to a constant flow at the average rate. As a result, field samplers with pulsating flows underestimated the respirable mass. In recent years, all of the manufacturers have been producing samplers with built-in pulsation dampers. The performance of pulsation dampers used in personal sampling pumps and the effects of the residual pulsations on cyclone penetration were reviewed by Berry.[180]

For small variations in flow rate, changes in cyclone collection efficiency are not a severe problem, at least for those applications when the parameter of interest is the "respirable" mass measured on the second stage. Knight and Lichti[78] demonstrated that variations in air flow are corrected to some extent by changes in cyclone collection efficiency. For nonfibrous test aerosols, including mica and silica, there was essentially no change in the mass collected on the filter for flow rates between 1.3 and 2.65 L/min. As the flow rate increases, the aerosol mass entering the cyclone increases proportionally, but apparently so does the collection efficiency. In an elutriator, the effect would be the opposite; an increase in sampling rate would result in an increase in penetration to the filter.

One potential problem with the 10-mm nylon cyclone is that, being an insulator, it can accumulate a static charge. When sampling aerosols with very high charge levels, this can significantly affect collection efficiency. Blachman and Lippmann[166] showed that highly charged aerosols with aerodynamic diameters below approximately 4 μm were collected with higher efficiencies than charge-neutralized aerosols of the same aerodynamic diameter. Almich and Carson[181] reported that the average collection efficiency for 4- to 5-μm charged particles was not significantly increased, but the variability in collection efficiency in replicate runs was increased. This variability was absent when using 10-mm cyclones of the same design which were constructed of stainless steel.

Lippmann and Chan[124] calibrated three larger, commercially available cyclones. They found that the 1/2-in. HASL, the Aerotec 3/4, the 1-in. HASL, and Aerotec 2 cyclones matched the original ACGIH criteria at 9, 25, 75, and 430 L/min, respectively. Other calibrations of these cyclones at the flow rates recommended by Lippmann and Chan have been inconsistent. Yablonsky *et al.*[182] reported that the concentration of a clay dust cloud passing the Unico 240 (HASL 1-in.) was 1.3 times the concentration passing the Aerotec 3/4 when both were operated at the flow rates recommended by Lippmann and Chan. Thompson *et al.*,[183] in using the Unico 240 and the Aerotec 3/4 at recommended flow rates, noted that the Unico 240 passed 1.24 times as much dust as the Aerotec 3/4. Using an Andersen Impactor, Yablonsky determined that the Aerotec 3/4 was passing essentially that fraction of the total dust which would be expected for a cyclone with characteristics that corresponded to the retention criteria specified by ACGIH. Thompson *et al.* used a Coulter counter to determine the efficiency of the cyclone for various size fractions and determined that the Aerotec 3/4, operating at its recommended flow rate, performed very close to the ACGIH criteria. Thus, independent analyses by differing methods confirmed the calibration of Lippmann and Chan for the Aerotec 3/4, but produced rather different results for the Unico 240.

It is suggested that many of the inconsistent results which have been observed in "respirable" dust cyclone calibration are not the result of experimental error or because of minor variations in construction between the experimental cyclones. The way Lippmann and Chan connected the cyclone outlet to the filter holder was used by Thompson and Yablonsky for the Aerotec 3/4 cyclones, and comparable results were observed. However, whereas Lippmann and Chan used a close-coupled filter for both the Unico 240 and the Unico 18, this configuration was not used by Thompson *et al.* in their experiments and the results were not comparable. Likewise, Yablonsky did not use a close-coupled filter for the Unico 240 and again the penetration was some 25% greater. These findings are consistent with those of Knight,[(184)] who observed different penetration through the 10-mm nylon cyclone in the two MSA configurations, i.e., the coal mine dust cassette and the silica dust apparatus which uses the Millipore field monitor cassette.

Although the relationship of the outlet configuration of miniature cyclones to efficiency has not yet been investigated in detail, it is already quite clear that cyclone outlet configurations are important, and that standardizations of pump and cyclone for a personal sampler will not characterize the performance of the sampler unless the outlet configuration through the filter is also standardized.

The remaining uncertainty about the collection characteristics of such simple devices is unfortunate, because if the correct cut is not made during the process of collection, it cannot be made with much assurance later. A rough approximation could be made on the basis that an equivalent mass would have been collected on the filter at another flow rate, as previously discussed. In this respect, multistage collectors, such as the cascade impactor, have an advantage over the two-stage collector, even though there are conflicting data in the literature on the collection efficiencies of the various collection stages. In this case, even if the stage constants and the resulting size-mass distribution are incorrect, the basic stage collection data are valid, and a corrected size-mass plot can be made at a later time using more reliable stage calibrations. Also, as discussed previously, a major advantage of multistage sampling is that overall size-mass distributions can be used to estimate deposition at all levels of the respirable tract, not just the nonciliated level. Also, the MMD, as determined from multistage sampling data, can serve as an indicator of the percent "respirable" dust.

It is unfortunate that there are few multistage samplers which can provide useful data. Cascade impactors can make reasonably sharp particle size cuts, but those with collection plates cannot collect large sample masses without overloading them.

It appears that the best prospects for successful multistage sampling lie in the further development and application of parallel cyclone-filter systems and virtual impactor-filter systems.

Applications

The wide variety of equipment available for two-stage respirable, thoracic, and inhalable dust sampling is amply documented in Table 5-7, with reference to commercial suppliers (Table 5-9). All of these instruments have similar purposes; however, they differ in cutoff characteristics and sampling rates, which often imposes restrictions on the types of analyses that can be performed.

Conclusions

The potential health hazards arising from the inhalation of insoluble toxic aerosols can be related to the concentration of "inspirable" particles. The term "inspirable" in this context can refer to those particles which are sufficiently small to be aspirated into the human respiratory tract. More commonly, especially when considering pneumoconiosis-producing dusts and other insoluble dusts whose site of toxic action is the alveolar region of the lung, the term "respirable" dust is used to refer to a more restricted size spectrum, i.e., the particles small enough to penetrate the tracheobronchial region of the lung.

In either case, the commonly measured parameter of air concentration, i.e., the gross air concentration, provides a crude and sometimes misleading indication of inhalation hazard. Samplers designed to separate particles during the process of collection into "respirable" and "nonrespirable" fractions are available and have the potential of providing more realistic measurements of pneumoconiosis hazard.

In practice, there are several factors that limit the precision of "respirable dust" samples as hazard indicators. One is the questionable accuracy of the standardized deposition curves whose cutoff characteristics the samplers attempt to simulate. Human deposition studies using monodisperse spherical test aerosols indicate large individual differences in regional deposition among normal, nonsmoking males, as well as indications that tracheobronchial deposition is increased among some cigarette smokers. Thus, the "respirable" fraction of a given aerosol will differ with the individual.

TABLE 5-9. List of Instrument Manufacturers

BGI	BGI Incorporated 58 Guinan Street Waltham, MA 02154 (617)891-9380 FAX (617)891-8151	MIE	MIE, Inc. 1 Federal St. #2 Billerica, MA 01821 (508)663-7900 FAX (508)663-4890	SEN	Sensidyne, Inc. 16333 Bay Vista Drive Clearwater, FL 34620 (813)530-3602 or (800)451-9444
CAS	Casella London, Ltd. Regent House, Brittania Walk London NI 7ND, England	MSP	MSP Corporation 1313 Fifth Street SE, Suite 206 Minneapolis, MN 55414 (612)379-3963 FAX (612)379-3965	SKC	SKC Inc. 863 Valley View Road Eighty Four, PA 15330-9614 (412)941-9701 or (800)752-8472 FAX (412)941-1396
GRA	Graseby Andersen 500 Technology Court Smyrna, GA 30082-5211 (404)319-9999 or (800)241-6898 FAX (404)319-0336	PPM	ppm Enterprises, Inc. 11428 Kingston Pike Knoxville, TN 37922 (615)966-8796 FAX (615)675-4795	TSI	TSI Incorporated 500 Cardigan Road P.O. Box 64394 St. Paul, MN 55164 (612)483-0900
GMW	Graseby GMW General Metal Works, Inc. 145 S. Miami Ave. Cleves, OH 45002 (513)941-2229 FAX (513)941-1977	RML	Rotheroe and Mitchell Ltd. Victoria Road Ruislip, Middlesex HA4 OYL England	WED	Wedding & Associates, Inc. 209 Christman Drive, #2 Fort Collins, CO 80524 (303)221-0678 or (800)367-7610 FAX (303)221-0400

Finally, there are instrumental uncertainties arising from several sources. One is the basic design and calibration of size-selective samplers. There is still disagreement about the collection efficiency characteristics of some of the instruments used in the field. Other uncertainties arise from field applications. Because the efficiency of these devices is flow-rate dependent, operation at nonstandard flows will cause erroneous results in both total concentration and percent inspirable, thoracic, or "respirable." With elutriators, errors can arise from re-entrainment, departures from the desired orientation, and high velocity pressures at the inlet. With cyclones, very high dust concentrations may cause particle agglomeration and an increased collection efficiency within the cyclone.

Multistage aerosol sampler data can provide estimates of the fractions depositing in several functional regions, as well as an overall particle size distribution curve. However, field sampling application of these devices has been limited for several reasons. One is the increased number and cost of sample analyses. More important perhaps is the lack of suitable instrumentation. Most of the commercially available instruments of this type are cascade impactors, which as a group suffer from a very limited mass collection capability, especially for aerosols of respirable size.

One of the major factors limiting the application of selective sampling concepts in the United States has been the absence of recognized criteria for size-selective mass concentrations. With the introduction of an alternate respirable mass concentration limit for quartz in 1968 by ACGIH, and the specification of respirable mass limits for coal dust by the U.S. Department of Labor in 1969, larger-scale applications of "respirable" sampling began. Now, with the harmonization of definitions and guidelines by ISO, CEN, and ACGIH,[87–89] much more activity and development of size-selective exposure criteria can, and should be, expected.

Despite all of the uncertainties and instrumental problems, inhalation hazard evaluations based on inspirable, thoracic, and/or "respirable" mass are clearly superior to estimates based on gross air concentrations for insoluble dusts whose site of toxic action is the deep lung. Gross concentration sampling protocols should be redefined as "inspirable" particulate mass sampling and be limited to situations where the entire aerosol is absorbed, e.g., for some highly soluble aerosols, or where the particle size distribution is relatively constant, and there is a known fixed ratio between the "inspirable" concentration and the concentration in the size range of interest.

References

1. Katz, S.H.; Smith, G.W.; Myers, W.M.; et al.: Comparative Tests of Instruments for Determining Atmospheric Dust. Public Health Bull. No. 144. DHEW, Public Health Service, Washington, DC (1925).
2. Littlefield, J.B.; Schrenk, H.H.: Bureau of Mines Midget Impinger for Dust Sampling. Bureau of Mines RI 3360. U.S. Department of the Interior, Washington, DC (1937).
3. Hatch, T.F.; Gross, P.: Pulmonary Deposition and Retention of Inhaled Aerosols. Academic Press, New York (1964).
4. Brain, J.D.; Valberg, P.A.: Deposition of Aerosol in the Respiratory Tract. Am. Rev. Resp. Dis. 120:1325 (1979).
5. Lippmann, M.; Yeates, D.B.; Albert, R.E.: Deposition, Retention, and Clearance of Inhaled Particles. Br. J. Ind. Med. 37:337 (1980).

6. Horsfield, K.; Dart, G.; Olson, D.E.; et al.: Models of the Human Bronchial Tree. J. Appl. Physiol. 31:207 (1971).
7. Weibel, E.R.: Morphometry of the Human Lung. Academic Press, NewYork (1963).
8. Lippmann, M.; Schlesinger, R.B.; Leikauf, G.; et al.: Effects of Sulphuric Acid Aerosols on Respiratory Tract Airways. In: Inhaled Particles V, pp. 677-690. W.H. Walton, Ed. Pergamon Press, London (1982).
9. Morrow, P.E.; Gibb, F.R.; Johnson, L.: Clearance of Insoluble Dust from the Lower Respiratory Tract. Health Phys. 10:543 (1964).
10. Jammet, H.; Lafuma, J.; Nenot, J.C.; et al.: Lung Clearance: Silicosis and Anthracosis. In: Pneumoconiosis — Proceedings of the International Conference, Johannesburg, 1969, pp. 435–437. H.A. Shapiro, Ed. Oxford University Press, Capetown (1970).
11. LeBouffant, L.: Influence de la Nature des Poussieres et de la Charge Pulmonaire sur l'Epuration. In: Inhaled Particles III, pp. 227–237. W.H. Walton, Ed. Unwin Bros., London (1971).
12. Bellmann, B.; Konig, H.; Muhle, H.; Pott, F.: Chemical Durability of Asbestos and of Man-Made Mineral Fibers *In Vivo*. J. Aerosol Sci. 17:341 (1986).
13. Ferin, J.; Leach, L.J.: The Effect of SO_2 on Lung Clearance of TiO_2 Particles in Rats. Am. Ind. Hyg. Assoc. J. 34:260 (1973).
14. Phalen, R.F.; Kenoyer, J.L.; Crocker, T.T.; McClure, T.R.: Effects of Sulfate Aerosols in Combination with Ozone on Elimination of Tracer Particles by Rats. J. Toxicol. Environ. Health 6:797 (1980).
15. McFadden, D.; Wright, J.L.; Wiggs, B.; Chung, A.: Smoking Inhibits Asbestos Clearance. Am. Rev. Resp. Dis. 133:372 (1986).
16. Albert, R.E.; Arnett, L.C.: Clearance of Radioactive Dust from the Lung. Arch. Ind. Health 12:99 (1955).
17. Cohen, D.; Arai, S.F.; Brain, J.D.: Smoking Impairs Long Term Dust Clearance from the Lung. Science 204:514 (1979).
18. Haroz, R.K.; Mattenberger-Kreber, L.: Effects of Cigarette Smoke on Macrophage Phagocytosis. In: Pulmonary Macrophages and Epithelial Cells, pp. 36–57. C.L. Sanders et al., Eds. CONF-76092. National Technical Information Service, Springfield, VA (1977).
19. Bohning, D.E.; Atkins, H.L.; Cohn, S.H.: Long Term Particle Clearance in Man: Normal and Impaired. Ann. Occup. Hyg. 26:259 (1982).
20. Davies, C.N.: Deposition and Retention of Dust in the Human Respiratory Tract. Ann. Occup. Hyg. 7:169 (1964).
21. Lippmann, M.: Regional Deposition of Particles in the Human Respiratory Tract. In: Handbook of Physiology, Section 9. D.H.K. Lee, H.L. Falk, and S.D. Murphy, Eds. The American Physiological Society, Bethesda, MD (1977).
22. Stuart, B.O.: Deposition of Inhaled Aerosols. Arch. Intern. Med. 131:60 (1973).
23. International Commission on Radiological Protection, Task Group on Lung Dynamics Committee II: Deposition and Retention Models for Internal Dosimetry of the Human Respiratory Tract. Health Phys. 12:173 (1966).
24. Davies, C.N.; Heyder, J.; Subba Ramu, M.C.: Breathing of Half Micron-Aerosols; 1: Experimental. J. Appl. Physiol. 32:592 (1972).
25. Heyder, J.; Armbruster, L.; Stahlhofen, W.: Deposition of Aerosol Particles in the Human Respiratory Tract. In: Aerosole in Physik, Medizin und Technik, pp. 122–125. Gesellschaft fur Aerosolforschung, Bad Soden, Federal Republic of Germany (1973).
26. Heyder, J.; Gebhart, J.; Rudolf, G.; Stahlfofen, W.: Physical Factors Determining Particle Deposition in the Human Respiratory Tract. J. Aerosol Sci. 11:505 (1980).
27. Tarroni, G.; Melandri, C.; Prodi, V.; et al.: An Indicator on the Biological Variability of Aerosol Total Deposition in Humans. Am. Ind. Hyg. Assoc. J. 41:826 (1980).
28. Yu, C.P.; Nicolaides, P.; Soong, T.T.: Effect of Random Airway Sizes on Aerosol Deposition. Am. Ind. Hyg. Assoc. J. 40:999 (1979).
29. Chan, T.L.; Lippmann, M.: Experimental Measurements and Empirical Modelling of the Regional Deposition of Inhaled Particles in Humans. Am. Ind. Hyg. Assoc. J. 41:399 (1980).
30. Stahlhofen, W.; Gebhart, J.; Heyder, J.: Biological Variability of Regional Deposition of Aerosol Particles in the Human Respiratory Tract. Am. Ind. Hyg. Assoc. J. 42:348 (1981).
31. Lapp, N.L.; Hankinson, J.L; Amandus, H.; Palmes, E.D.: Variability in the Size of Airspaces in Normal Human Lungs as Estimated by Aerosols. Thorax 30:293 (1975).
32. Matsuba, K.; Thurlbeck, W.M.: The Number and Dimensions of Small Airways in Non-emphysematous Lungs. Am. Rev. Resp. Dis. 104:516 (1971).
33. Heyder, J.; Gebhart, J.; Heigwer, G.; et al.: Experimental Studies of Total Deposition of Aerosol Particles in the Human Respiratory Tract. Aerosol Sci. 44:191 (1973).
34. Muir, D.C.F.; Davies, C.N.: The Deposition of 0.5-μm Diameter Aerosols in the Lungs of Man. Ann. Occup. Hyg. 10:161 (1967).
35. Foord, N.; Black, A.; Walsh, M.: Regional Deposition of 2.5–7.5 μm Diameter Particles in Healthy Male Nonsmokers. J. Aerosol Sci. 9:343 (1978).
36. Stahlhofen, W.; Gebhart, J.; Heyder, J.: Experimental Determination of the Regional Deposition of Aerosol Particles in the Human Respiratory Tract. Am. Ind. Hyg. Assoc. J. 41:385 (1980).
37. Palmes, E.D.; Lippmann, M.: Influence of Respiratory Air Space Dimensions on Aerosol Deposition. In: Inhaled Particles IV, W.H. Walton, Ed. Pergamon Press, Oxford (1977).
38. U.S. Environmental Protection Agency: Air Quality Criteria for Particulate Matter and Sulfur Oxides, Vol. III. EPA-600/882-029c. Environmental Criteria and Assessment Office, U.S. Environmental Protection Agency, Research Triangle Park, NC (December 1982).
39. Pattle, R.E.: The Retention of Gases and Particles in the Human Nose. In: Inhaled Particles and Vapors, C.N. Davies, Ed. Pergamon Press, Oxford (1961).
40. Yu, C.P.: A Two-Component Theory of Aerosol Deposition in Lung Airways. Bull. Math. Biol. 40:693 (1978).
41. Findeisen W.: Uber das Absetzen Kleiner, in der Luft Suspendierten Teilchen in der Menschlichen Lunge bei der Atmung. Pfluger Arch. fd. ges. Physiol. 236:367 (1935).
42. Landahl, H.D.: On the Removal of Airborne Droplets by the Human Respiratory Tract; 1: The Lung. Bull. Math. Biophys. 12:43 (1950).
43. Landahl, H.D.: Particle Removal by the Respiratory System. Bull. Math. Biophys. 25:29 (1963).
44. Beeckmans, J.M.: The Deposition of Aerosols in the Respiratory Tract; 1: Mathematical Analysis and Comparison with Experimental Data. Can. J. Physiol. Pharmacol. 43:157 (1965).
45. Gormley, P.G.; Kennedy, M.: Diffusion from a Stream Flowing through a Cylinder. Proc. Roy. Irish Acad. A52:163 (1949).
46. International Commission on Radiological Protection: Human Respiratory Tract Model for Radiological Protection. Report of Committee II of the ICRP (1994).
47. National Council on Radiation Protection: Deposition, Retention and Dosimetry of Inhaled Radioactive Substances. Report S.C. 57-2. NCRP, Bethesda, MD (1994).
48. Charlson, R.J.; Vanderpol, A.H.; Covert, D.S.; et al.: $H_2SO_4(NH_4)_2SO_4$ Background Aerosol: Optical Detection in St. Louis Region. Atmos. Environ. 8:1257 (1974).
49. Cooper, D.W.; Byers, R.L.; Davis, J.W.: Measurements of Laser Light Backscattering vs. Humidity for Salt Aerosols. Environ. Sci. Technol. 7:142 (1973).
50. Orr, C.; Hurd, F.K.; Corbett, W.J.: Aerosol Size and Relative Humidity. J. Coll. Sci. 13:472 (1958).
51. Winkler, P.; Junge, C.: The Growth of Atmospheric Aerosol Particles as a Function of the Relative Humidity. Part I: Method and Measurements at Different Locations. J. Recherches Atmospheriques 6:617 (1972).
52. Winkler, P.: The Growth of Atmospheric Aerosol Particles as a Function of the Relative Humidity. Part II: An Improved Concept of Mixed Nuclei. Aerosol Sci. 4:373 (1973).
53. Milburn, R.H.; Crider, W.C.; Morton, S.D.: The Retention of Hygro-

scopic Dusts in the Human Lungs. AMA Arch. Ind. Health 15:59 (1957).

54. Porstendorfer, J.: Untersuchungen zur Frage des Wachstums von Inhalierten Aerosolteilchen im Atemtrak. Aerosol Sci. 2:73 (1971).
55. Held, J.L.; Cooper, D.W.: Theoretical Investigation of the Effects of Relative Humidity on Aerosol Respirable Fraction. Atmos. Environ. 13:1419 (1979).
56. Austin, E.; Brock, J.; Wissler, E.: A Model for Deposition of Stable and Unstable Aerosols in the Human Respiratory Tract. Am. Ind. Hyg. Assoc. J. 40:1055 (1979).
57. Cartwright, J.; Skidmore, J.W.: The Size Distribution of Dust Retained in the Lungs of Rats and Dust Collected by Size-Selective Samplers. Ann. Occup. Hyg. 7:151 (1964).
58. Carlberg, J.R.; Crable, J.V.; Limtiaca, L.P.; et al.: Total Dust, Coal, Free Silica, and Trace Metal Concentrations in Bituminous Coal Miners' Lungs. Am. Ind. Hyg. Assoc. J. 32:432 (1971).
59. International Standards Organization: Air Quality-Particle Size Fraction Definitions for Health Related Sampling. ISO/TR 7708-1983 (E). ISO (1983).
60. American Conference of Governmental Industrial Hygienists, Air Sampling Procedures Committee: Particle Size-Selective Sampling in the Workplace, 80 pp. ACGIH, Cincinnati, OH (1985).
61. Ogden, T.L: Inhalable, Inspirable, and Total Dust. In: Aerosols in the Mining and Industrial Work Environment, Vol. 1, pp. 185–205. V.A. Marple and B.Y.H. Liu, Eds. Ann Arbor Science Publishers, Ann Arbor, MI (1983).
62. Buchan, R.M.; Soderholm, S.C.; Tillery, M.I.: Aerosol Sampling Efficiency of 37-mm Filter Cassettes. Am. Ind. Hyg. Assoc. J. 47:825 (1986).
63. Chung, K.Y.K.; Ogden, T.L.; Vaughan, N.P.: Wind Effects on Personal Dust Samplers. J. Aerosol Sci. 18:159 (1987).
64. Vincent, J.H.; Mark, D.: Entry Characteristics of Practical Workplace Aerosol Samplers in Relation to the ISO Recommendations. Ann. Occup. Hyg. 34:249 (1990).
65. Whitby, K.T.; Vomela, R.A.: Response of Single Particle Optical Counters to Nonideal Particles. Environ. Sci. Technol. 1:801 (1967).
66. Proceedings of the Pneumoconiosis Conference, Johannesburg, 1959, A.J. Orenstein, Ed. J. and A. Churchill, Ltd., London (1960).
67. Davies, C.N.: Dust Sampling and Lung Disease. Br. J. Ind. Med. 9:120 (1952).
68. Threshold Limit Values for Airborne Contaminants for 1968, p. 17. American Conference of Governmental Industrial Hygienists, Cincinnati, OH (1968).
69. Sutton, G.W.; Reno, SJ.: Respirable Mass Concentrations Equivalent to Impinger Count Data. Presented at American Industrial Hygiene Conference, St. Louis, MO (May 1968).
70. U.S. Dept. of Labor: Public Contracts and Property Management. Fed. Reg. 34(96):7946 (May 20, 1969).
71. Public Law 91 - 173, Federal Coal Mine Health and Safety Act of 1969, 91st Congress (December 10, 1969).
72. Public Law 95- 164, Federal Mine Safety and Health Act of 1977, 95th Congress (November 9, 1977).
73. National Research Council: Measurement and Control of Respirable Dust in Mines. NMAB-363. National Academy of Sciences, Washington, DC (1980).
74. Public Law 91 -596, Occupational Safety and Health Act of 1970, 91st Congress (December 29, 1970).
75. 29CFR Part 1910. Air Contaminants; Final Rule. Federal Register 54(12):2329–2984 (January 19, 1989).
76. Brown, J.H.; Cook, K.M.; Ney, F.G.; Hatch, T.: Influence of Particle Size Upon the Retention of Particulate Matter in the Human Lung. Am. J. Pub. Health 40:450 (1950).
77. Mercer, T.T.: Air Sampling Problems Associated with the Proposed Lung Model. Presented at the 12th Annual Bioassay and Analytical Chemistry Meeting, Gatlinburg, TN (October 13, 1966).
78. Knight, G.; Lichti, K.: Comparison of Cyclone and Horizontal Elutriator Size Selectors. Am. Ind. Hyg. Assoc. J. 31:437 (1970).
79. Maguire, B.A.; Barker, D.: A Gravimetric Dust Sampling Instrument (SIMPEDS): Preliminary Underground Trials. Ann. Occup. Hyg. 12:197 (1969).
80. Ayer, H.E.; Dement, J.M.; Busch, K.A.; et al.: A Monumental Study-Reconstruction of a 1920 Granite Shed. Am. Ind. Hyg. Assoc. J. 34:206 (1973).
81. Miller, F.J.; Gardner, D.E.; Graham, J.A.; et al.: Size Considerations for Establishing a Standard for Inhalable Particles. J. Air Pollut. Control Assoc. 29:610 (1979).
82. Vincent, J.H.; Armbruster, L.: On the Quantitative Definition of the Inhalability of Airborne Dust. Ann. Occup. Hyg. 24:245 (1981).
83. Vincent, J.H.; Mark, D.: The Basis of Dust Sampling in Occupational Hygiene: A Critical Review. Ann. Occup. Hyg. 24:375 (1981).
84. Ambient Air Monitoring Reference and Equivalent Methods. Fed. Reg. 52(126):24727 (July 1,1987).
85. ACGIH Technical Committee on Air Sampling Procedures: Particle Size-Selective Sampling in the Workplace. Ann. Am. Conf. Govt. Ind. Hyg. 11:21 (1984).
86. Soderholm, S.C.: Proposed International Conventions for Particle Size-Selective Sampling. Ann. Occup. Hyg. 33:301–320 (1989).
87. International Organization for Standardization (ISO): Air Quality — Particle Size Fraction Definitions for Health-Related Sampling. Approved for publication as CD 7708. ISO, Geneva (1991).
88. European Standardization Committee (CEN): Size Fraction Definitions for Measurement of Airborne Particles in the Workplace. Approved for publication as prEN 481. CEN, Brussels (1991).
89. 1994–1995 Threshold Limit Values and Biological Exposure Indices. ACGIH, Cincinnati, OH (1993).
90. Lidén, G.; Kenny, L.C.: Optimization of the Performance of Existing Respirable Dust Samplers. Appl. Occup. Environ. Hyg. 8(4):386–391 (1993).
91. Bartley D.L.; Doemeny, L.J.: Critique of 1985 ACGIH Report on Particle Size-Selective Sampling in the Workplace. Am. Ind. Hyg. Assoc. J. 47:443 (1986).
92. Liden, G.; Kenny, L.C.: The Performance of Respirable Dust Samplers: Sampler Bias, Precision, and Inaccuracy. Ann. Occup. Hyg. 36:1 (1991).
93. McCawley, M.A.: Should Dust Samplers Mimic Human Lung Deposition. Appl. Occup. Environ. Hyg. 5:829 (1990).
94. Breuer, H.: Problems of Gravimetric Dust Sampling. In: Inhaled Particles III, pp. 1031–1042. W.H. Walton, Ed. Unwin Bros., London (1971).
95. Knight G.: Definitions of Alveolar Dust Deposition and Respirable Dust Sampling. Ann. Occup. Hyg. 29:526 (1985).
96. Raabe, O.G.: Basis for Particle Size-Selective Sampling for Beryllium. Chapter 4. In: Advances in Air Sampling, pp. 39–51. ACGIH, Lewis Publishers, Inc., Chelsea, MI (1988).
97. Hinds, W.C.: Basis for Particle Size-Selective Sampling for Wood Dust. Appl. Ind. Hyg. 3:67 (1988).
98. Lippmann, M.; Gearhart, G.M.; Schlesinger, R.B.: Basis for a Particle Size-Selective TLV for Sulfuric Acid Aerosols. Appl. Ind. Hyg. 2:188 (1987).
99. Stuart, B.O.; Lioy, P.J.; Phalen, R.F.: Particle Size-Selective Sampling in Establishing Threshold Limit Values. Appl. Ind. Hyg. 1:138 (1986).
100. NIOSH: Criteria for a Recommended Standard - Occupational Exposure to Cotton Dust. DHEW (NIOSH) Pub. No. 75-118. U.S. Government Printing Office, Washington, DC (1975).
101. Leidel, N.A.; Bayer, S.G.; Zumwalde, R.D.; Busch, K.A.: USPHS/ NIOSH Membrane Filter Method for Evaluating Airborne Asbestos Fibers. DHEW (NIOSH) Pub. No. 79-127. NIOSH, Rockville, MD (February 1979).
102. ACGIH–AIHA Aerosol Hazards Evaluation Committee: Recommended Procedures for Sampling and Counting Asbestos Fibers. Am. Ind. Hyg. Assoc. J. 36:83 (1975).
103. Lippmann, M.: Asbestos Exposure Indices. Environ. Res. 46:86

(1988).

104. Hatch, T.; Hemeon, W.C.L.: Influence of Particle Size in Dust Exposure. J. Ind. Hyg. Toxicol. 30:172 (1968).
105. May, K.R.; Druett, HA.: The Pre-Impinger. Br. J. Ind. Med. 10:142 (1953).
106. Langmead, W.A.; O'Connor, D.T.: The Personal Centripeter — A Particle Size-Selective Personal Air Sampler. Ann. Occup. Hyg. 12:185 (1969).
107. Marple, V.A.: Simulation of Respirable Penetration Characteristics by Inertial Impaction. J. Aerosol Sci. 9:125 (1978).
108. Willeke, K.: Selection and Design of an Aerosol Sampler Simulating Respiratory Penetration. Am. Ind. Hyg. Assoc. J. 39:317 (1978).
109. Roessler, J.F.: Application of Polyurethane Foam Filters for Respirable Dust Separation. J. Air Pollut. Control Assoc. 16:30 (1966).
110. Gibson, H.; Vincent, J.H.: The Penetration of Dust Through Porous Foam Filter Media Ann. Occup. Hyg. 24:205 (1981).
111. Parker, R.D.; Buzzard, G.H.; Dzubay, T.G.; Bell, J.P.: A Two-Stage Respirable Aerosol Sampler Using Nuclepore Filters in Series. Atmos. Environ. 11:617 (1977).
112. Cahill, T.A.; Ashbaugh, L.L; Barone, J.B.; et al.: Analysis of Respirable Fractions in Atmospheric Particulate via Sequential Filtration. J. Air Pollut. Control Assoc. 27:675 (1977).
113. Spurny, K.: Discussion: A Two-Stage Respirable Aerosol Sampler Using Nuclepore Filters in Series. Atmos. Environ. 11:1246 (1977).
114. Buzzard, G.H.; Bell, J.P.: Experimental Filtration Efficiencies of Large Pore Nuclepore Filters. J. Aerosol Sci. 435 (1980).
115. Heidam, N.Z.: Review: Aerosol Fractionation by Sequential Filtration with Nuclepore Filters. Atmos. Environ. 15:891 (1981).
116. Woolf, H.S.; Roach, S.A.: The Conicyle Selective Sampling System. In: Inhaled Particles and Vapors, C.N. Davies, Ed. Pergamon Press, Oxford (1961).
117. Wright, B.M.: A Size-Selecting Sampler for Airborne Dust. Br. J. Ind. Med. 11:284 (1954).
118. Hamilton, R.J.: A Portable Instrument for Respirable Dust Sampling. J. Sci. Inst. 33:395 (1956).
119. Dawes, J.G.; Winder, G.F.: A Semi-automatic Handpump for Obtaining a Sample of Respirable-Size Airborne Dust. S.M.R.E. Research Report No. 198. Safety in Mines Research Establishment, Sheffield, England (April 1961).
120. Shanty, F.; Hemeon, W.C.L.: The Inhalability of Outdoor Dust in Relation to Air Sampling Network. J. Air Pollut. Contr. Assoc. J.:211 (1963).
121. Dunmore, J.H.; Hamilton, R.J.; Smith, D.S.G.: An Instrument for the Sampling of Respirable Dust for Subsequent Gravimetric Assessment. J. Sci. Instr. 41:669 (1964).
122. Blackford, D.B.; Harris, G.W.: Field Experience with Simslin. II: A Continuously Recording Dust Sampling Instrument. Ann. Occup. Hyg. 21:301 (1978).
123. Sem, G.J.; Tsurubayashi, K.; Homma, K.: Performance of the Piezoelectric Microbalance Respirable Aerosol Sensor. Am. Ind. Hyg. Assoc. J. 38:580 (1977).
124. Lippmann, M.; Chan, T.: Calibration of Dual-Inlet Cyclones for "Respirable" Mass Sampling. Am. Ind. Hyg. Assoc. J. 35:189 (1974).
125. Bartley, D.; Chen, C-C.; Song, R.; Fischbach, T.J.: Respirable Aerosol Performance Testing. Am. Ind. Hyg. Assoc. J. 55:1036 (1994).
126. Aerosol Technology Committee: AIHA Guide for Respirable Mass Sampling. Am. Ind. Hyg. Assoc. J. 31:133 (1970).
127. Higgins, R.I.; Dewell, P.: A Gravimetric Size-Selecting Personal Dust Sampler. In: Inhaled Particles and Vapours II, pp. 575–585. C.N. Davies, Ed. Pergamon Press, London (1967).
128. John, W.; Reischl, G.: A Cyclone for Size-Selective Sampling of Ambient Air. J. Air Pollut. Control Assoc. 30:872 (1980).
129. Shofner, F.M.; Neefus, J.D.; Smoot, D.M.; Beck, J.M.: Electrooptical Isokinetic Sampling of Microdust in Process Air Flows. In: Aerosols in the Mining and Industrial Work Environment, Vol. 3, pp. 1205–1222. Ann Arbor Science, Ann Arbor, MI (1983).
130. Buckley, T.J.; Waldman, J.M.; Freeman, N.C.G.; Lioy, P.J.: Calibration, Intersampler Comparison, and Field Application of a New PM_{10} Personal Air Sampling Impactor. Aerosol Sci. Tech. 14: 380 (1991).
131. Mark, D.; Vincent, J.H.; Gibson, H.; Lynch, G.: A New Static Sampler for Airborne Total Dust in Workplaces. Am. Ind. Hyg. Assoc. J. 46:127 (1985).
132. Mark, D.; Vincent, J.H.: A New Personal Sampler for Airborne Total Dust in Workplaces. Ann. Occup. Hyg. 30:89 (1986).
133. Chan, T.; Lippmann, M.: Particle Collection Efficiencies of Air Sampling Cyclones: An Empirical Theory. Environ. Sci. Technol. 11:377 (1977).
134. Saltzman, B.: Generalized Performance Characteristics of Miniature Cyclones for Atmospheric Particulate Sampling. Am. Ind. Hyg. Assoc. J. 45:671 (1984).
135. Blachman, M.W.; Lippmann, M.: Performance Characteristics of the Multicyclone Aerosol Sampler. Am. Ind. Hyg. Assoc. J. 35:311 (1974).
136. Caplan, K.J.; Doemeny, L.; Sorenson, S.D.: Performance Characteristics of the 10 mm Cyclone Respirable Mass Sampler. Part 1 - Monodisperse Studies. Am. Ind. Hyg. Assoc. J. 38:83 (1977).
137. John, W.: Thoracic and Respirable Particulate Mass Samplers: Current Status and Future Needs. In: Advances in Air Sampling, pp. 25–38. ACGIH, Lewis Publishers, Inc., Chelsea, MI (1988).
138. Liden, G.: Evaluation of the SKC Personal Respirable Dust Sampling Cyclone. Appl. Occup. Environ. Hyg. 8:178 (1993).
139. Fabries, J.F.; Wrobel, R.: A Compact High-Flowrate Respiratory Dust Sampler: The CPM_3. Ann. Occup. Hyg. 31:195 (1987).
140. Prodi, V.; Belosi, F.; Mularoni, A.: A Personal Sampler Following ISO Recommendations on Particle Size Definitions. J. Aerosol Sci. 17:576 (1986).
141. Prodi, V.; Sala, C.; Belosi, F.: PERSPEC, Personal Size Separating Sampler: Operational Experience and Comparison with Other Field Devices. Appl. Occup. Environ. Hyg. 7:368 (1992).
142. Marple, VA.; Willeke, K.: Impactor Design. Atmos. Environ. 10:891 (1976).
143. Davies, C.N.: The Entry of Aerosols into Sampling Tubes and Heads. Br. J. Appl. Phys. D. 2s(1):921 (1968).
144. Yoshida, H.; Uragami, M.; Masuda, H.; Linoya, K.: Particle Sampling Efficiency in Still Air. Kagaku Kagalcu Robunshu 4:123 (1978).
145. Agarwal, J.K.; Liu, B.Y.H.: A Criterion for Accurate Sampling in Calm Air. Am. Ind. Hyg. Assoc. J. 41:191 (1980).
146. Ogden, T.L.; Birkett, J.L.: An Inhalable-Dust Sampler for Measuring the Hazard from Total Airborne Particulate. Ann. Occup. Hyg. 21:41 (1978).
147. Loo, B.W.; Adachi, R.S.; Cork, C.P.: A Second Generation Dichotomous Sampler for Large-Scale Monitoring of Airborne Particulate Matter. LBL-8725. Lawrence Berkeley Laboratory, Berkeley, CA (January 1979).
148. Liu, B.Y.H.; Pui, D.Y.H.: Aerosol Sampling Inlets and Inhalable Particles. Atmos. Environ. 15:589 (1981).
149. Shaw, Jr., R.W.; Stevens, R.K.; Lewis, C.W.; Chance, J.H.: Comparison of Aerosol Sampling Inlets. Aerosol Sci. Technol. 2:53 (1983).
150. John, W.; Wall, S.M.; Wesolowski, J.J.: Validation of Samplers for Inhaled Particulate Matter. EPA-600/4-83-010. National Technical Information Service Report No. PB 83-191395. Springfield, VA (March 1983).
151. McFarland, A.R.; Ortiz, C.A.: A 10 μm Cutpoint Ambient Aerosol Sampling Inlet. Atmos. Environ. 16:2959 (1982).
152. McFarland, A.R.; Ortiz, C.A.; Bertch, Jr., R.W.: A High Capacity Preseparator for Collecting Large Particles. Atmos. Environ. 13:761 (1979).

153. Bright, D.S.; Fletcher, R.A.: New Portable Ambient Aerosol Samplers. Ind. Hyg. Assoc. J. 44:528 (1983).
154. Lioy, P.J.; Waldman, J.M.; Buckley, T.; Butler, J.; Pietarinen, C.: The Personal Indoor and Outdoor Concentrations of PM_{10} Measured in an Industrial Community During the Winter. Atmos. Environ. 24B: 57 (1990).
155. Marple, V.A.; McCormack, J.E.: Personal Sampling Impactor with Respirable Aerosol Penetration Characteristics. Am. Ind. Hyg. Assoc. J. 44:916 (1983).
156. Wedding, J.B.; Weigand, M.A.; Carney, T.C.: A 10-μm Cutpoint Inlet for the Dichotomous Sampler. Environ. Sci. Technol. 16:602 (1982).
157. Shleien, B.; Friend, A.G.; Thomas, H.A.: A Method for the Estimation of the Respiratory Deposition of Airborne Materials. Health Phys. 13:513 (1967).
158. Reiter, R.; Potzl, K.: The Design and Operation of a Respiratory Tract Model. Staub 27:19 (English Translation) (1967).
159. Conner, W.D.: An Inertial-Type Particle Separator for Collecting Large Samples. J. Air Pollut. Control Assoc. 16:35 (1956).
160. Hounam, R.F.; Sherwood, R.J.: The Cascade Centripeter: A Device for Determining the Concentration and Size Distribution of Aerosols. Am. Ind. Hyg. Assoc. J. 26:122 (1965).
161. Dzubay, T.G.; Stevens, R.K.: Ambient Air Analysis with Dichotomous Sampler and X-ray Fluorescence Spectrometer. Environ. Sci. Technol. 9:663 (1975).
162. Loo, B.W.; Jacklevic, J.M.; Goulding, F.S.: Dichotomous Virtual Impactors for Large Scale Monitoring of Airborne Particulate Matter. In: Fine Particles, pp. 311–350. B.Y.H. Liu, Ed. Academic Press, New York (1976).
163. Gibson, H.; Vincent, J.H.; Mark, D.: A Personal Inspirable Aerosol Spectrometer for Applications in Occupational Hygiene Research. Ann. Occup. Hyg. 31:463 (1987).
164. Rubow, K.L.; Marple, V.A.; Olin, J.; McCawley, M.A.: A Personal Cascade Impactor: Design, Evaluation, and Calibration. Am. Ind. Hyg. Assoc. J. 48:532 (1987).
165. Lippmann, M.; Kydonieus, A.: A Multi-Stage Aerosol Sampler for Extended Sampling Intervals. Am. Ind. Hyg. Assoc. J. 31:730 (1970).
166. Blachman, M.W.; Lippmann, M.: Performance Characteristics of the Multicyclone Aerosol Sampler. Am. Ind. Hyg. Assoc. J. 35:311 (1974).
167. Bernstein, D.; Kleinman, M.T.; Kneip, T.J.; et al.: A High-Volume Sampler for the Determination of Particle Size Distributions in Ambient Air. J. Air Pollut. Control Assoc. 26:1069 (1976).
168. Chang, H-c.: A Parallel Multicyclone Size-Selective Particulate Sampling Train. Am. Ind. Hyg. Assoc. J. 35:538 (1975).
169. Smith, W.B.; Wilson, Jr., R.R.; Harris, D.B.: A Five-Stage Cyclone System for *In-Situ* Sampling. Environ. Sci. Technol. 13:1387 (1979).
170. Stöber, W.; Flachsbart, H.: Size Separating Precipitation of Aerosols in a Spinning Spiral Duct. Environ. Sci. Tech. 3:1280 (1969).
171. Sawyer, K.F.; Walton, W.H.: The Conifuge - A Size Separating Sampling Device for Airborne Particles. J. Sci. Instr. 27:272 (1950).
172. Goetz, A.; Stevenson, H.J.R.; Preining, O.: The Design and Performance of the Aerosol Spectrometer. J. Air Poll. Control Assoc. 10:378 (1960).
173. Timbrell, V.: The Terminal Velocity and Size of Airborne Dust Particles. Br. J. Appl. Phys. Suppl. No. 3:86 (1954).
174. Walkenhorst, W.; Bruckmann, E.: Mineral Analysis of Suspended Dusts Classified According to Particle Sizes. Staub 26:45 (English Translation) (1966).
175. Armbruster, L.: A New Generation of Light-Scattering Instruments for Respirable Dust Measurement. Ann. Occup. Hyg. 31:181 (1987).
176. Roebuck, B.; Vaughn, N.P.; Chung, K.Y.K.: Performance Testing of the Osiris Dust Monitoring System. Ann. Occup. Hyg. 34:263 (1990).
177. Thurmer, H.: Investigations with the Horizontal Plate Precipitator. Staub 29:35 (English Translation) (1969).
178. Watson, H.H.: Dust Sampling to Simulate the Human Lung. Br. J. Ind. Med. 10:93 (1953).
179. Caplan, K.J.; Doemeny, L.J.; Sorenson, S.D.: Performance Characteristics of the 10 mm Cyclone Respirable Mass Sampler; Part I: Monodisperse Studies; Part II: Coal Dust Studies. Am. Ind. Hyg. Assoc. J. 38:83-162 (1977).
180. Berry, R.D.: The Effect of Flow Pulsations on the Performance of Cyclone Personal Respirable Dust Samplers. J. Aerosol Sci. 22:887 (1991).
181. Almich, B.P.; Carson, G.A.: Some Effects of Charging on 10-mm Nylon Cyclone Performance. Am. Ind. Hyg. Assoc. J. 35:603 (1974).
182. Yablonsky, J.; Ayer, H.E.; Svetlik, J.; Horstman, S.W.: Calibration System for Dust Sampling. Final Report, Contract No. DAMD 17-74-c-4024. University of Cincinnati, Cincinnati, OH.
183. Thompson, E.M.; Treaftis, H.N.; Tomb, T.F.: Comparison of Recommended Respirable Mass Dust Sampling Devices. Presented at American Industrial Hygiene Conference, Atlanta, GA (May 1976).
184. Knight, G.: Personal communication (1978).

Chapter 6

Measurement and Presentation of Aerosol Size Distributions

Earl O. Knutson, Ph.D.,[A] Paul J. Lioy, Ph.D.[B]

[A]*Environmental Measurements Laboratory, U.S. Department of Energy, 376 Hudson St., New York, New York;* [B]*UMDNJ Robert Wood Johnson Medical Center, Piscataway, New Jersey*

CONTENTS

Introduction

It is widely agreed among aerosol, environmental, and health scientists that the two most important properties of an aerosol particle are its size and its chemical composition. This chapter will survey the types of apparatus that have been found useful for measuring particle size, as well as the methods that have been found useful for communicating particle size information. Chemical composition is beyond the scope of this chapter and, therefore, will be treated only incidentally. However, the techniques used for communicating particle size information are the same.

Methods for measuring particle size in aerosols have been used since the early days of dust, fume, and aerosol studies in this century. This search has been particularly intense during the past 30 years, spurred by the increasing use of aerosols in industry and medicine, as well as by growing concern about the health effects of aerosols in industrial hygiene, outdoor and indoor air pollution, and product defects in manufacturing cleanrooms. During this period, many new methods of sizing particles have been developed and others have been refined. In the process, emphasis has shifted from microscopy methods to automated instrumental methods.

It is safe to say that at least 100,000 size distribution measurements have been made in the past 30 years.

The new measurement methods also have spawned new ways of presenting particle size data. Terminology and definitions have changed—"size" has taken on a more general meaning, and "number" has diminished in importance as a means of specifying the quantity of particles. The classical texts on particle size data and statistics, such as Herdan,(1) are oriented to powder technology and are, therefore, difficult to apply to modern data on aerosols. A more recent presentation, applicable to aerosol science, is given in Hinds.(2)

In the following, it is convenient to reverse the normal order by discussing the presentation of particle size data first. This permits the early introduction of modern views and definitions regarding particle size, which are an integral part of the methods for presenting these data.

Presentation of Particle Size Data

Particle size data are most often presented in some form of x–y plot or in the form of a table. The point to be made here is that two variables are needed: the two variables may be called particle "size" and particle "amount." The use of quotation marks here indicates that both terms have evolved somewhat generalized meanings in connection with aerosols.

Particle Size

For spherical particles, the most common and fundamental definition of particle size is the diameter of the sphere. For solid spherical particles, the preferred reference method for measuring size is microscopy. Microscopes can be calibrated against diffraction gratings, so that size measured by microscope is traceable to national physical standards for length. Liquid particles are by nature spherical so the same definition applies, but measurement by microscope is now more difficult and less accurate.

For nonspherical particles, the definition of particle size is more problematic and often depends on the instruments available for measurement. For microscopy, easily visualized geometric properties such as Martin's diameter, Feret's diameter, the projected area diameter, and the perimeter diameter have been used as definitions of particle size.(1) These concepts and definitions continue to be useful in powder technology.

As already mentioned, modern technology has had an effect on definitions of particle size. As an example, the differential electric mobility analyzer (DEMA) can measure the diameter of spherical particles, solid or liquid, with an accuracy that rivals microscopy.(3) Calibration against microscopy is reassuring, but not absolutely necessary.

When applied to nonspherical particles, the DEMA provides its own definition of particle size. This definition should not be considered arbitrary because it is based on an important property, namely the drift velocity of the particle when airborne and subjected to a force field. Emerging technology is one of the compelling reasons to adopt a more general definition of particle size—one not based exclusively on geometry.

In this chapter, particle size is defined as any single-number parameter that in some way describes the size of a single particle. (However, cases where two-number parameters would be quite useful in defining particle size can be foreseen.) The key point is that the definition must make sense as applied to individual particles.

One widely used measure of particle size is the *aerodynamic equivalent diameter*, often denoted by d_{ae}. Its importance stems from the fact, discussed by Mercer,(4) that it is the single most useful parameter for predicting the probability of particle deposition in the human lung. The formal definition is:

The diameter of a unit density sphere which has the same settling velocity as the particle in question.

The definition is based on physics rather than on geometry. It works equally well for spherical and nonspherical particles, and it takes into account the intrinsic density of the particle material. Similarly, the term "thermodynamic equivalent diameter" is gradually gaining acceptance, especially when dealing with particles smaller than 0.1 µm. The definition here is:

The diameter of a sphere having the same diffusion coefficient as the particle in question.

Some definitions of particle size were literally brought into being by emerging technology. One such is the "light-scattering equivalent diameter," defined as the diameter of a polystyrene latex sphere that scatters the same amount of light in an optical particle counter as the particle in question. This definition was made in response to the development of convenient and reliable single-particle optical counters. It is a weak definition in that it depends too much on the design of the particular optical counter.

Table 6-1 gives some of definitions of particle size in common use. To some extent, it is possible to convert from geometry-based to physics-based size definitions by means of shape factors or through calibration of sampling devices using spheres.

In any practical situation, particles are found to be present over a range of sizes. To characterize the full range, the particles must first be separated into smaller subsets, or classes, usually 10 or so. If particle size is thought of as being represented on an x-axis, the size classes would be represented by dividing this axis into contiguous intervals. This is also the way the term "classes" is used in statistics.

TABLE 6-1. Quantities Used to Represent Size of Individual Aerosol Particles

Derived from microscopy	
Diameter, radius	Minimum chord
Area, projected area diameter	Maximum chord
Perimeter	Fiber length
Feret's diameter	
Derived from other sizing techniques	
Terminal settling velocity (in air)	Thermodynamic equivalent diameter
	Electrical equivalent diameter
Aerodynamic equivalent diameter	Optical equivalent diameter
	Particle volume
Stokes equivalent diameter	Particle mass

In graphs, the particle size axis can be either linear or logarithmic. The most common choice of size classes is represented by equal increments on a logarithmic scale. For example, Mitchell and Pilcher[5] designed their cascade impactor so that the increment of log particle diameter would be 0.301. On the other hand, the example could be cited of the active-scattering aerosol spectrometer,[6] which was designed to have equal linear increments in particle diameter. Size classes of equal width are preferred, but are not always possible. In some cases, as in some optical particle counters, the law of physics may dictate the choice of size classes.

Particle Amount

The second variable needed to present size distributions is the quantity of particles, or amount, in each size class. By amount, a number is meant, which describes the property of concern associated with a given collection of particles. Like size, amount must be meaningful as applied to individual particles. Furthermore, it must be an additive property so that the total amount can be obtained by summing up the amounts in each size class or, for that matter, the amounts associated with the individual particles.

Table 6-2 lists several characteristics used to represent particle amount, listed roughly in the order of importance, or frequency of use. It is stressed that the choice to represent amount depends on the use of the data.

Mass is important as a measure of particle amount, as can be seen from its use in the National Ambient Air Quality Standards for Particulate Matter[7] and in the Occupational Safety and Health regulations[8] for inert dusts. (In this paragraph, "mass" is used to mean total mass without regard to chemical composition. Composition-related definitions are described below.)

The number of particles is a simple measure of particle amount when microscopy is used in aerosol measurements. Certain automated instruments such as optical particle counters and condensation nucleus counters also respond to number (with some limitations based on particle size). Single-particle optical counters were developed largely to fill a need in cleanrooms and, in turn, the standards for cleanrooms were written in terms of particle number (particles of diameter <0.5 μm exempt).

In some cases, such as in places with high concentrations of radon gas, radioactivity is the particle property of concern. Measurements of number or mass will not reveal the important features of such aerosols, so it is prudent to measure activity as directly and accurately as possible. Activity, expressed for example as Bq, is a legitimate measure of particle amount. In other cases, a particular mineral (e.g., free silica) or class of chemical species (e.g., polycyclic aromatic hydrocarbons) is the particle property of concern. Typically, these properties are not related to number or mass of particles, so there is no way to proceed other than direct measurement of the property of concern.

To summarize, there are many acceptable ways to express the amount of particles in a given size class, and these should be accorded equal status. It should be noted that not all definitions of particle amount are independent and unrelated. For example, the surface area, a measure of particle amount that is of interest to combustion engineers, can be approximated by computation from a carefully measured number distribution. This is discussed in a later section.

Generalized Histograms

Histograms, borrowed from statistics but modified for aerosol use, are a very convenient way for presenting particle size data. The process will be explained with the help of an example, which provides an opportunity to illustrate the concepts of particle size and amount.

Figure 6-1 depicts a cascade impactor, a device widely used in aerosol measurements to physically separate particles by size. Aerosol is drawn by a pump through a series of stages; only two stages are shown in this

TABLE 6-2. Quantities Frequently Used to Represent Particle Amount

Mass of particles	Sulfate content
Number of particles	Lead content
Particle radioactivity	Graphitic carbon content
Particle surface	Crystalline silica content
Particle volume	Many others

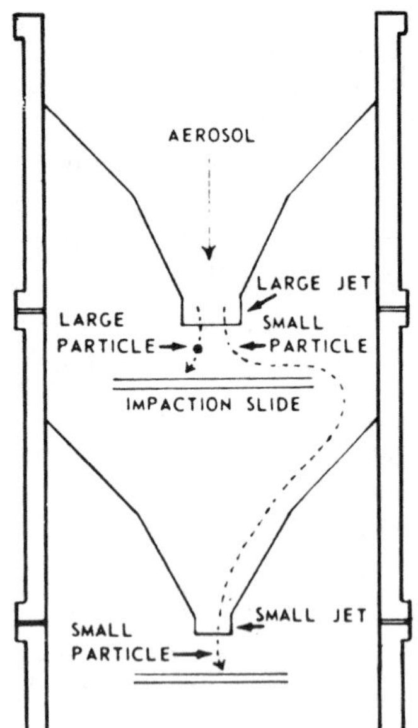

FIGURE 6-1. Two stages of a cascade impactor (courtesy of Delron Research Products Company).

figure. At the first stage, particles larger than a certain critical size strike the collection plate and are retained there, while smaller particles remain airborne and move to the second stage. Similarly, the second stage collects particles down to another (smaller) critical size. At each stage, particles are collected that were too small to be collected by the previous stage, but too large to escape collection by the present stage. Thus, when the sampling is finished, the successive collection plates hold particles belonging to successive size classes. (This is an idealized picture of the performance of cascade impactors; departures from the ideal will be discussed later in this chapter and also in Chapter 14.)

To specify the amount of particles in each size class of an impactor sample, it is necessary to measure or analyze the material on each of the successive collection plates. Among the many possibilities are 1) weighing to determine the total mass, 2) analyzing for a particular radioactive isotope or for a particular chemical species, 3) analyzing for surface area, or 4) counting by microscope to determine either gross number or number of a particular type of particle. Each of these procedures yields a different but equally valid definition of particle amount in each size class.

Table 6-3 gives results for a sample collected in a multistage impactor sampler in Los Angeles, as reported by Miguel and Friedlander.[9] The first column of Table 6-3 shows the size classes defined by their impactor, which was specially designed to permit classifying very small particles. The values given are aerodynamic diameters because this is the size measure by which impactors classify samples. The second column shows that the deposit on each stage was analyzed for benzo(a)pyrene (BaP). The result given is the mass of BaP divided by the volume of air sampled, i.e., the concentration corresponding to each size class in the air. The symbol M refers to the total concentration of BaP in air, whereas ΔM refers to the portion within the given size class.

Figure 6-2 shows the histogram constructed from the data in Table 6-3. In statistics, the vertical axis represents the number of cases per class, and the classes are of equal width. For aerosol size distributions, the vertical axis represents amount, not necessarily number, and the size classes are frequently not equal. To deal with unequal class widths, it has become standard practice to normalize by dividing the amount in each size class by the width of that size class. This makes the amount in each size class proportional to the area of the rectangle, rather than its height. This normalization step permits comparison of results obtained using different instruments by simply overlaying the plots.

TABLE 6-3. Example Aerosol Distribution Data: Benzo(a)pyrene in Los Angeles Air

Particle Size Range[A,B] (μm)	Mass in Range[A] (ng/m³)	$\Delta \log d_p$	$\Delta M/\Delta \log d_p$ (ng/m³)[A]	Cumulative Mass (ng/m³)	% of Mass
0.05 –0.075	0.030	0.176	0.170	0.030	7.1
0.075–0.12	0.196	0.204	0.961	0.226	53.6
0.12 –0.26	0.079	0.336	0.235	0.305	72.5
0.26 –0.5	0.028	0.284	0.099	0.333	78.9
0.5 –1.0	0.036	0.301	0.120	0.369	87.4
1.0 –2.0	0.016	0.301	0.053	0.385	91.2
2.0 –4.0	0.016	0.301	0.053	0.401	95.0
4.0 –8.0[C]	0.021	0.301	0.070	0.422	100.0

[A]Data from Miguel and Friedlander.[9]
[B]Particle size in aerodynamic diameter.
[C]Estimated value.

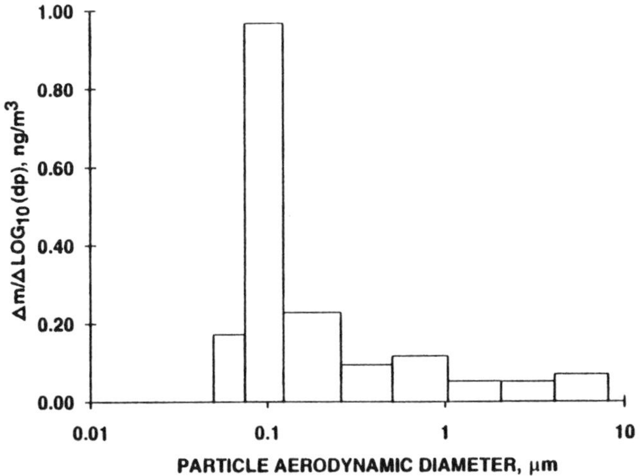

FIGURE 6-2. Example of a generalized histogram plot of aerosol particle size (benzo[a]pyrene, Los Angeles, 10/25 to 10/28/76).

The steps needed to form the histogram are shown in columns three and four of Table 6-3. The third column gives the width of each class in logarithmic terms, $\Delta\log_{10}(d_p)$, where d_p is the particle diameter. (This is used if the particle size is to be represented on logarithmic axis, as in Figure 6-2. If a linear scale is used, the class width should be the arithmetic difference between the upper and lower endpoints of the size class rather than the difference of logarithms.) The fourth column, $\Delta M/\Delta\log_{10}(d_p)$, is the ratio of the previous two and is the quantity plotted as the height of the rectangles in Figure 6-2.

The type of plot shown in Figure 6-2 (amount plotted vertically on a linear scale and size plotted horizontally on a logarithmic scale) was popularized by Kenneth Whitby[10] and has been widely accepted in the aerosol research community. However, as yet there is no widely accepted name for this plot. In this chapter, this construct will be referred to as the Whitby histogram.

Instead of the volume of air sampled, some researchers prefer to divide the amount in each size class by the total amount of particles. This is acceptable if the total is known. Often, however, practical difficulties in aerosol sampling make it impossible to fully collect all sizes of particles, in which case the total cannot be accurately known. It is usually preferable to divide amount by volume, as in Table 6-3.

Figure 6-3, taken from Whitby,[11] shows an elaborate histogram depicting an atmospheric aerosol. Particle amount is specified in terms of particulate volume. To cover the nearly four decade range of particle size, three separate instruments were used, each with a different definition of size and size classes. The ability to combine data in this way is one of the virtues of the Whitby histogram.

Notice that the atmospheric aerosol depicted in Figure 6-3 has three relative maxima, called modes. This term was also adopted from statistics. Thus, the size distribution depicted in Figure 6-3 has become known as the trimodal distribution of the atmospheric aerosol. Each of these modes has a separate significance, as described by Whitby.[11] However, the mode at 0.018 μm is not always as prominent as shown in the figure; it is characteristic of freshly produced combustion aerosols.

In summary, histograms make use of two axes to present particle size data. The x-axis, usually logarithmic but sometimes linear, is used for particle size and the y-axis is used for particle amount. The y-axis should be a linear scale; otherwise, the plot loses much of its visual descriptive value. Similarly, the visual value of the histogram is enhanced by the generalizing step of dividing each amount by the width of the size class.

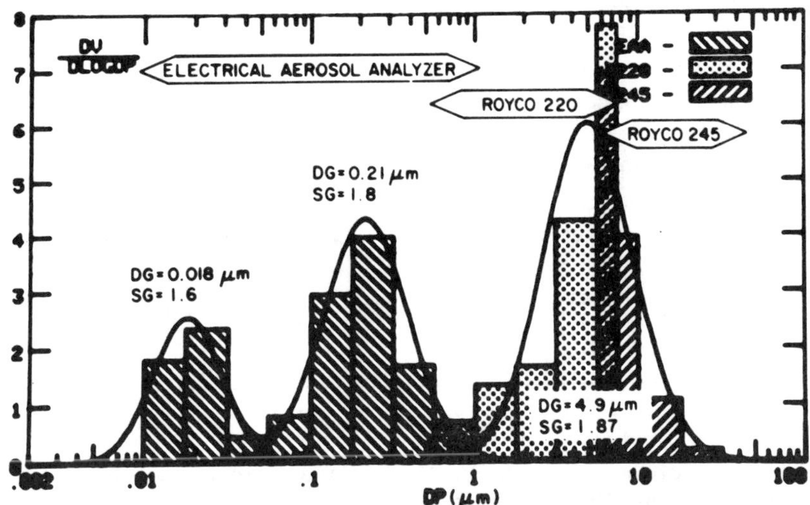

FIGURE 6-3. Generalized histogram plot of atmospheric aerosol size distribution (reprinted with permission from Atmos. Envir. 12:135–159, Whitby, K.T., The Physical Characteristics of Sulfur Aerosols, Copyright 1978, Pergamon Press, Ltd.).

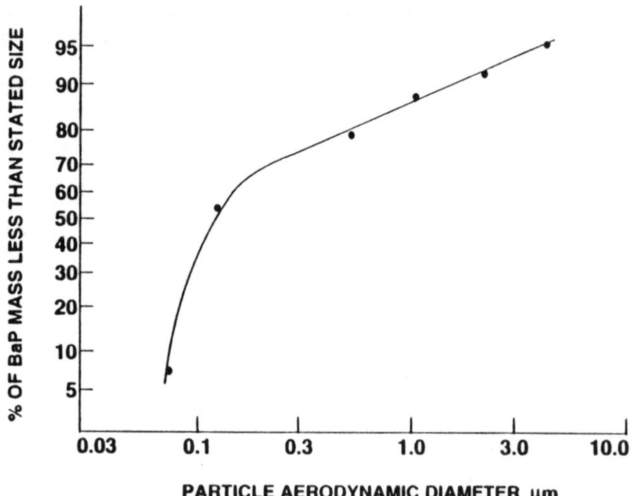

FIGURE 6-4. Log probability plot of aerosol particle size (benzo[a]pyrene, Los Angeles, 10/25 to 10/28/76).

Cumulative Plots

There is an alternative to the histogram, called the cumulative plot. Cumulative plots have been used widely in some areas of aerosol technology such as in connection with industrial hygiene. Cumulative plots avoid some of the pitfalls of histograms, but they have a few disadvantages of their own.

Figure 6-4 shows one form of a cumulative plot, as a means of displaying the BaP data already discussed. Data of this plot were prepared as shown in the last two columns of Table 6-3. The first entry of the final column, for example, means that 7.1% of the BaP mass is associated with particles smaller than 0.075 µm.

In Figure 6-4, the particle size is plotted on a logarithmic scale, and the particle amount (expressed in percent of the total) is plotted on a special scale called the probit scale. This combination of scales is called log-probability graph paper. Any particle size data that plot as a straight line on this graph paper are called a lognormal distribution (to be discussed later). Note that the distribution in Figure 6-4 is definitely not lognormal.

The probit scale is derived from the normal probability integral $P(x)$:

$$P = \frac{1}{\sqrt{2\pi}} \int_{-\infty}^{x} \exp(-y^2/2)dy \qquad (1)$$

Values of the integral are shown in Table 6-4, and more complete tables may be found in statistics or mathematics handbooks. The x values in Table 6-4 are called probits. Comparison of the x and P values in this table shows why the amount axis in Figure 6-4 is so severely stretched at either end.

TABLE 6-4. Comparison of *x* and *P* Values in the Normal Probability Integral

x	*P*	*x*	*P*
−2.5	0.006	0.5	0.692
−2.0	0.023	1.0	0.841
−1.5	0.067	1.5	0.933
−1.0	0.159	2.0	0.977
−0.5	0.308	2.5	0.994
0	0.500		

Other scales can be used for plotting cumulative size distributions. Sometimes a linear scale is substituted for the logarithmic scale in Figure 6-4, and the result is called a linear probability plot. Other combinations of linear and logarithmic scales are used occasionally.

The cumulative plot, which requires expressing each amount as a percentage of the total amount, should not be used unless there is a reasonable certainty that the total has been fully and accurately measured. For example, data taken with an optical particle counter are seldom suitable for cumulative plots because these counters see only the "tip of the iceberg"; large numbers of particles are too small to be counted. Dividing by the "total" in this case would be very misleading. For such data, the Whitby histogram would be more appropriate because the volume sampled, rather than the "total," is used as the normalizing factor.

Size Distribution Statistics

As already discussed, a single number will usually suffice to describe the size of an individual aerosol particle. It is often desirable to have the same simplicity when describing the size of collections of particles such as an aerosol. This simplicity is made possible by using descriptive statistics.

The simplest and most useful single-number description of particle size in an aerosol is the median. The median can be defined as that particle size which splits the population into two equal parts. That is, one-half the particle amount is associated with particles smaller than the median size, and one-half is associated with particles larger than the median size. The median is most easily determined with the help of a cumulative plot by locating the particle size corresponding to 50% of the amount. For the example of the Los Angeles BaP study, Figure 6-4 gives about 0.11 µm for the median size.

For a given aerosol or other collection of particles, the value of the median depends on the measures that were selected for the particle size and the particle amount. The following four measures are in common use and are very important: 1) count median diameter, 2) mass median diameter, 3) count median aerodynamic diameter, and 4) mass median aerodynamic diameter. These terms completely specify how the median size was obtained. The proper terminology for the BaP example is mass median aerodynamic diameter of BaP. Another median that is seen quite frequently is activity median aerodynamic diameter. This means that particle amount was obtained by a radioactivity measurement and the size measurement yielded aerodynamic diameter. Other combinations are possible and are seen occasionally. Unless otherwise stated, the size is understood to be geometric size, as determined by microscopy or its equivalent. The term "number" is often used in place of count. The median is best determined, as above, from a cumulative plot, but it can also be estimated from a properly constructed histogram: the median is that size which divides the total area under the curve into two equal parts. In Figure 6-3, the volume median diameter is estimated to be about 0.4 μm, just above the location of the center mode.

Another important single-number description of particle size in an aerosol is the mean, or average, size. If the particle size is determined by microscopy, the familiar definition of mean is easy to apply — add the particle diameters and divide by the number of particles. This case is treated in great detail in textbooks such as the one by Herdan[1]. Statistical concepts such as the maximum likelihood principle can be readily applied to determine the most accurate value of the mean diameter, as well as the uncertainty in that value.

For particle size data determined by means other than microscopy, mean sizes are still very important but are more complicated to define. A procedure is used which is similar to that used in statistics for "grouped data." The general definition is:

$$\bar{x} = \frac{\sum A_i x_i}{\sum A_i} \qquad \textbf{(2)}$$

where: $\bar{x}$ = the arithmetic mean diameter
x_i = the mid-point of the ith size class
A_i = the amount of particles in the ith class
Σ = summation over all size classes

As with the median, each combination of size and amount leads to a different mean. For example, if x is represented by a linear diameter and A is measured in terms of number, the number-weighted mean diameter is then obtained (as in the microscopy example mentioned above). The amount could equally well be given in terms of mass or radioactivity, in which case the above terminology would be modified to say mass-weighted or activity-weighted.

There is another family of mean sizes, for which the definition is:

$$x_g = \text{antilog}\left(\frac{\sum A_i \log x_i}{\sum A_i}\right) \qquad \textbf{(3)}$$

This is called the geometric mean size. The geometric mean diameter has long been a staple of aerosol and powder technology, probably because it is one the parameters of the lognormal distribution (to be discussed later).

Table 6-5 shows how to apply the equations just given to calculate the arithmetic and geometric mean diameters for the BaP data. It is shown that $\Sigma A_i = 0.422$ ng/m^3 and that $\Sigma A_i x_i = 0.257$ μm-ng/m^3. The arithmetic mean (full name: BaP-weighted arithmetic mean aerodynamic diameter) is therefore 0.257/0.422 = 0.61 μm. For the geometric mean, application of Equation 3 yields x_g = 0.21 μm. Note that there is a large difference between the two mean diameters and that both differ from the median diameter, found earlier to be 0.11 μm.

Many textbooks on particle size give a generalized definition of mean diameter, involving the pth moment and the qth weighting. In these definitions, there is a tacit assumption that the size distribution data were obtained by microscopy, i.e., size is assumed to be given in terms of linear dimension and amount by number of particles. Because microscopy is no longer the principal method of measuring particle size in aerosols, the definition will not be repeated here. See Herdan, [1] Cadle,[12] Orr,[13] or other books for discussions of the generalized means.

Although the single number representation of particle size in an aerosol is very convenient, it is often a serious oversimplification. This is certainly the case in Figure 6-3. A substantial improvement is made by giving a two-number representation. To supplement any one of the mean sizes mentioned above, the standard deviation could be cited, either arithmetic or geometric. The geometric standard deviation (σg) is particularly common and useful. It is defined as

$$\sigma g = \text{antilog}\sqrt{\frac{\sum A_i \log^2(x_i/x_g)}{\sum A_i}} \qquad \textbf{(4)}$$

The symbols used were defined previously. Although not shown in Table 6-5, when this formula is applied to the BaP data, it is found that σ_g = 3.38. As with the geometric mean, the popularity of the geometric standard deviation is in part because it is one of the parameters of the lognormal distribution. A less common two-number description of the particle size distribution is the first and third quartile. These are the two sizes corresponding to 25% and 75%, respectively, of the total

TABLE 6-5. Example Calculation of Arithmetic and Geometric Mean Particle Size[A]

Size Class Boundaries (μm)[B]	Mass BaP, A_i (ng m^{-3})[B]	Class Mid-point, x_i (μm)	A_ix_i	$\log(x_i)$	$A_i\log(x_i)$
0.05 –0.075	0.030	0.061	0.002	–1.213	–0.036
0.075–0.12	0.196	0.095	0.019	–1.023	–0.200
0.12 –0.26	0.079	0.177	0.014	–0.753	–0.059
0.26 –0.5	0.028	0.361	0.010	–0.443	–0.012
0.5 –1.0	0.036	0.707	0.025	–0.151	0.002
1.0 –2.0	0.016	1.414	0.023	0.151	0.002
2.0 –4.0	0.016	2.828	0.045	0.452	0.007
4.0 –8.0[C]	0.021	5.657	0.119	0.753	0.016
Total	0.422		0.257		–0.289

Arithmetic mean aerodynamic diameter = 0.257/0.422 = 0.61 μm

Geometric mean aerodynamic diameter = antilog (–0.289/0.422) = 0.21 μm

[A]Weighted by mass of benzo(a)pyrene, BaP.
[B]From Miguel and Friedlander.[(9)]
[C]Estimated value.

amount of a particle descriptor (mass, number, etc.).

A common misconception is that the geometric mean size and the geometric standard deviation cannot be defined for aerosols which are not lognormally distributed. The truth is that these quantities are defined by summation formulas (Equations 3 and 4) independent of the shape of the size distribution. For BaP, Table 6-5 shows that the geometric mean diameter can be calculated, even though Figure 6-4 shows that the size distribution is not lognormal. However, if the distribution is lognormal, a simple graphical method is available to determine the geometric mean and standard deviation (see discussion after Equation 6).

A note of caution should be raised with regard to size distribution statistics: all the median and mean size definitions discussed here assume that the total amount of particles is known. The truth of this assumption depends on the sampling and analysis employed to measure the particles. The factor A (the total amount) is needed to compute any of the means, and the total amount is also needed to define the median. Therefore, these statistical representations should be used only when there is a reasonable certainty that the full amount of the aerosol is known. The same point was raised earlier with respect to cumulative plots.

Mathematical Transformations

As mentioned earlier, it is possible, to a limited extent, to mathematically transform between representations of the particle size distribution. This practice should not be encouraged because experimental errors often become magnified to the point where the final result is untrustworthy. However, used with caution, the procedure can be illuminating. Such a transformation was used, for example, in preparing the histogram in Figure 6-3.

Table 6-6 illustrates the steps necessary to transform between selected representations of the aerosol size distribution, using data from aerosol measurements in New York City.[(14)] Column A gives the size class boundaries, as defined by the electrical aerosol analyzer (upper block of data) and an optical particle counter (lower block of data). Column B gives class geometric midpoints, formed by taking the square root of the product of the upper and lower boundaries of the class. It is assumed that the midpoint is representative of the particles in its class. (Some prefer to use the arithmetic midpoint, the class mark, as the representative size for the class.) Column C gives the number-weighted size distribution, which was the primary result of the measurements.

Column D is the surface area of a single particle, computed from the expression πx^2. It is assumed that this surface area is valid for particles within the indicated size class. Obviously, this assumption could be far from the truth if the particles are not spherical or if the midpoint is not representative of the particles in the class. If these uncertainties are accepted, it is straightforward to form the surface-area weighted distribution, Column E, by multiplying C and D.

Column F in Table 6-6 gives the volume of a single particle, computed from the expression $\pi x^3/6$. It is assumed that this value is typical of particles in the corresponding size class, but the same reservations

TABLE 6-6. Example Transformation from Number Distribution to Surface and Volume Distribution*

A	B	C	D	E	F	G
0.0100						
	0.0133	79200.0	0.000556	44.0	0.00000123	0.0974
0.0178						
	0.0237	106300.0	0.00176	188.0	0.00000697	0.741
0.0316						
	0.0422	28700.0	0.00559	161.0	0.0000393	1.31
0.0562						
	0.075	31900.0	0.0177	564.0	0.000221	7.05
0.100						
	0.133	15600.0	0.0556	867.0	0.00123	19.2
0.178						
	0.237	2860.0	0.176	505.0	0.00697	19.9
0.0316						
	0.422	270.0	0.559	151.0	0.0393	10.6
0.562						
0.50						
	0.56	114.0	0.985	112.0	0.0920	10.5
0.063						
	0.905	10.6	2.57	27.3	0.388	4.11
1.30	1.97	0.87	12.2	10.6	4.00	3.48
3.0						
	3.87	0.20	47.1	9.4	30.3	6.06
5.0						

Explanation of columns:

A. Size class boundaries, in μm.

B. Class mid-point, in μm. The authors use the geometric mid-point, i.e., the square root of the product of the upper and lower boundaries. Some prefer to use the arithmetic mid-point, i.e., the average of the upper and lower bounds.

C. $\Delta N/\Delta \log d_p$, the number-weighted size distribution as obtained from the measurement. Units: 1/cm^3.

D. The surface area of a single spherical particle, computed as πx_i^2; assumed to be valid for an average particle in the size class. Units: μm^2.

E. The surface-area-weighted particle size distribution, $\Delta S/\Delta \log d_p$, formed by multiplying C and D. Units: μm^2/cm^3.

F. The volume of a single spherical particle, computed as $\pi x_i^3/6$. Units: μm^3

G. The volume-weighted size distribution, $\Delta V/\Delta \log d_p$, formed by multiplying C and F. Units: μm^3/cm^3, or parts per trillion by volume.

*Data from Knutson, Sinclair, and Leaderer;[14] average of 314 hrs of measurements on the New York City aerosol in August 1976.

stated with respect to the surface area apply here as well. Again accepting these uncertainties, it is straightforward to compute how the volume is distributed over the particle size range, Column G.

Although not shown in Table 6-6, the data could be used to calculate an approximation to the mass-weighted size distribution. This requires a knowledge or estimate of particle density, which may vary over the particle size range. Multiplication of the volume-weighted distribution, Column G, by the particle density gives the mass-weighted size distribution.

Durham *et al.*[15] describe a complex transformation between representations of aerosol size distributions. They sought to compare size data obtained by a cascade impactor to data obtained with a system comprised of an electrical aerosol analyzer and two optical counters.

It was necessary to convert both particle amount, as described in this section, and particle size. The authors found agreement between the two types of instruments, over at least part of the particle size range.

Size Distribution Functions

As an alternative to graphs, it is often possible to represent particle size data by means of a mathematical function. This method is concise and has advantages when there are subsequent mathematical computations to be performed. For these reasons, this subject has been pursued with great ingenuity by many individuals over the last century.

To clarify how mathematical functions relate to experimental size data, the histogram in Figure 6-2 should again be considered. For the sake of argument, the assumption could be made that the sampling was redone using an impactor with twice as many collection stages covering the same overall size range. This would yield a histogram with twice the number of size classes, each narrower, packed into the same range. If the number of stages was doubled and the sample was repeated, with each doubling, the new histogram would more nearly approximate a smooth curve. It is this limiting curve that is described by means of a mathematical function. The mathematical task is a little easier to visualize for the cumulative plot (Figure 6-4) where a smooth curve has already been drawn through the data points.

Ingenuity and varied experience has led to a number of size distribution functions, with one, two, or more parameters that can be adjusted as needed for particular cases. The names of some functions that have found use are Dalla Valle–Orr–Blocker, gamma, Gates–Gaudin–Schumann, Gates–Meloy, Junge, Krumbein, lognormal, normal, Nukiyama–Tanasawa, Roller, Rosin–Rammler, Rosin–Rammler–Bennett, Sehmel, self-preserving, upper-limit lognormal, and Weibull. To this list, an eight-parameter distribution function could also be added, the trimodal distribution shown by smooth curve in Figure 6-3.

The normal distribution, which is important in many branches of science and mathematics, has already been mentioned in connection with the probit scale. It is of some importance to aerosol science, both in its own right and as a point of departure for the lognormal distribution.

For aerosol science, the most important of the above distributions is the lognormal. Textbooks give references for this distribution dating back to 1879. Papers by Hatch and Choate in 1929 and 1933 established some of the remarkable mathematical properties, encapsulated in the Hatch–Choate equations, of this distribution. In 1941, Kolmogoroff predicted from theory that dusts formed by grinding should conform to the lognormal distribution, and papers by Kottler in the early 1950s elaborated further on this distribution.

Equation 5 is the mathematical expression for the cumulative form, $F(x)$, of the lognormal distribution.

$$F(x) = P\left[\frac{\log (x/x_g)}{\log \sigma g}\right] \quad \textbf{(5)}$$

$F(x)$ is the fractional amount of particles associated with particles of size less than x, and P is the normal probability integral defined earlier in Equation 1. Equation 5 shows clearly that the lognormal distribution is derived from the normal by a substitution of variables: the function $\log(x/x_g)/\log \sigma g$ is substituted for the variable x found in Equation 1.

The differential form, $f(x)$, of the lognormal distribution is obtained by differentiating $F(x)$. Caution is advised here because some authors use x as the independent variable in this differentiation and some use $\log(x)$. The latter is preferred. Equation 6 is the mathematical expression for $f(x)$, as obtained using $\log(x)$ as the differentiating variable.

$$f(x) = \frac{dF}{d(\log x)} = \frac{1}{\sqrt{2\pi}} \; \frac{1}{\log \sigma g} \exp\left[\frac{-\log^2 (x/x_g)}{2 \log^2 \sigma g}\right] \quad \textbf{(6)}$$

The two parameters of the lognormal distribution are geometric mean size, x_g, and the geometric standard deviation, σg, both defined earlier. On log probability graph paper such as that in Figure 6-4, Equation 5 plots as a straight line. This is a convenient, widely used test for lognormality. For data that are lognormally distributed, the geometric mean size coincides with the median size, which is the 50% point on a cumulative plot. It is equally easy to determine the geometric standard deviation for lognormal distribution data: it is the ratio of the 84.1% size to the 50% size, or the ratio of the 50% size to the 15.9% size. This graphical method for determining the two parameters is valid only for lognormally distributed aerosols, but Equations 3 and 4 are valid for any distribution.

Before personal computers, it was very common to analyze particle size data by plotting in cumulative form on lognormal graph paper, as in Figure 6-4. After drawing a straight line through these data, it was easy to determine the lognormal parameters. This was such a useful crutch that many data sets were labeled lognormal even when the points did not fit on a line. In fact, some workers regarded points not on the line as evidence of experimental error!

It is a safe bet that lognormal distributions (note the plural) will continue to be useful in aerosol work. In many cases, especially where the aerosol particles are predominantly from a single source, a single-mode lognormal will provide a very good description of the data. In most other cases, size data can be well approximated by combining two, or if needed, three, lognormals. Sometimes these modes are well separated (see Figure 6-3), but in other cases the lognormals are overlapped so that there is only one clear mode. The geometric mean diameters and geometric standard deviations, as shown in Figure 6-3, are very useful for summarizing and communicating particle size information.

Computer Methods of Analyzing and Presenting Data

Advantages

In recent years, high-performance personal computers have become common in the laboratory and on sampling trips. This has opened new possibilities with regard to analyzing and presenting particle size data. Advantages include:

1. Tedious calculations such as those in Table 6-5 can be automated.
2. Curve fitting and other mathematics methods that are impractical for hand calculation can be applied to summarize and reduce particle size data.
3. The effect on instrument calibration of sampling at nonstandard temperature and pressure can be taken into account, thereby increasing the accuracy of information derived from the data.
4. Detailed information on the sampling device itself (e.g., nonideal performance expressed as calibration curves) can be programmed into the data analysis, again increasing accuracy of the results.
5. Information on the uncertainty in particle size data can be generated, either by propagating the input uncertainties or by Monte Carlo error studies.
6. The graphics and text-formatting capabilities of these computers can be used to present the results in a concise, readable form.

The first item, and to some extent the next two, are relatively simple tasks that can also be accomplished by a hand calculator. Hinds [16] presents four programs for a programmable calculator that address these items in the context of cascade impactors.

The real value of personal computers comes to the fore starting with item 4 above. The issue addressed here is that all real aerosol samplers misclassify particles to some extent. As an example, the data in the upper part of Table 6-6 should be considered: there is a dip in the column C value adjacent to the diameter value 0.0422. The dip is due to a nonideal feature of the device used to collect these data; the device tends to discriminate against particles with diameters near 0.04 µm, placing these particles into the two adjacent size classes, thus producing the artificial dip. For further discussion of nonideal performance, see the later section entitled "Size Selective, I and II."

To correct for nonideal behavior, it is first necessary to describe nonideal behavior in mathematical terms. The basic equation is:

$$D_i = \int \Phi_i A f(x) dx, \quad i = l,m \tag{7}$$

In this equation:

D_i = the data determined from the ith stage or channel of the sampler
m = the number of channels or stages
$\Phi_i(x)$ = the response of the ith stage or channel of the sampler to a unit amount of monodisperse aerosol of size x
A = the total amount of aerosol
$f(x)$ = the normalized differential size distribution of the aerosol

The set of functions $\Phi_i(x)$, which must be known either from theory or experiment, contains the required detailed information concerning the sampler. The goal is to solve for the function $f(x)$ which appears inside the integral sign. This equation, or rather this set of equations, is often referred to as a Fredholm integral equation of the first kind. The process of solving it is variously called data inversion, deconvolution, unfolding, or reconstruction.

Methods of Data Inversion

Fitting. In this approach, a function with several free parameters is selected in advance to represent the differential size distribution $f(x)$. A mathematical algorithm is then applied to determine the parameter values that provide the best fit to the data.

The lognormal distribution function has proven very useful in fitting. By using two or three overlapping lognormal distributions, it is possible to portray even quite complicated size distributions with good accuracy. For example, in Figure 6-3, three lognormal distributions are used. This overcomes the objection stated earlier that force-fitting a single lognormal to data often suppresses important details.

Raabe[17] has given a concise yet complete description of the fitting approach to data inversion. If a given sampler provides m pieces of data related to particle size, as in Equation 7, the recommended technique allows fitting a function with as many as $m-1$ parameters. Special cases such as incomplete, censored, or overlapping data can be accommodated. The three examples given by Raabe are well fit by a single lognormal mode, but Raabe stresses that the same technique can be extended easily to multimodal fits.

To use this approach properly, it is important to have valid information on data quality; i.e., the experimental uncertainty of each data point. Given this, Raabe's method provides an estimate of the standard error for each fitted parameter, as well as a Chi-square statistic that measures the goodness-of-fit.

Dzubay and Hasan[18] report generally good success in fitting up to three lognormal distributions to data taken with a cascade impactor. A technique very similar to that of Raabe[17] was used, except that Dzubay and Hasan further limit the number of parameters that can be fit, based on data quality.

A note of caution was sounded by Helsper *et al.*,[19] whose objective was to fit size distribution functions to data from the Electrical Aerosol Analyzer (EAA). In fitting bimodal lognormals, the authors noted that the algorithm (which was not the same as that used by Raabe) occasionally became stuck in a local minimum, i.e., it produced incorrect results. The practical remedy was to rerun the calculation several times from random starting positions.

The present authors recommend the Raabe approach for general use in data inversion. The advantages are:

- A long history of use and broad acceptance by aerosol scientists and by mathematicians.
- Results obtained are the parameters of one or more lognormal distributions that are easy to visualize, understand, and communicate.
- Standard errors are derived for each parameter.
- Experience indicates that the method works well in most cases.
- Dzubay and Hasan[18] have presented a good implementation of this method as applied to cascade impactors.

However, in view of the local minima problems noted by Helsper *et al.*,[19] each set of data should be recalculated several times, starting from different initial points.

Unfolding. This approach to data inversion is based on the fact that an integral, such as in Equation 7, can be approximated by a sum, as follows:

$$D_i = \sum_j \Phi_i(x_j)A_j \quad i = 1,m; j = 1,n \tag{8}$$

In this equation:

x_j = one of a set of n preselected discrete values of x;

A_j = the amount of aerosol associated with the discrete size x_j.

This approximation corresponds to the "mid-point rule," which is a numerical analysis technique for evaluating definite integrals. Equation 8 is a set of linear algebraic equations, which replaces the set of integral equations, 7.

Solving Equation 8 has proven to be a very thorny mathematical problem. Among many others, Cooper[20] has shown the difficulties that can arise when applying standard methods such as the Gauss–Jordan (applicable where $n = m$) or linear least squares (for the case $n < m$). Either method often leads to physically impossible results, in which many of the A_j are assigned negative values. The results obtained are very sensitive to small errors in the input data D_i.

It is only recently that rigorous and satisfactory methods for solving Equation 8 have become available.[21–23] These methods are too complicated for the occasional user. Short of this, aerosol professionals have found certain iterative algorithms to be useful, even though some are more intuitive than rigorous. Markowski[23] and Winklmayr *et al.*[24] report good success applying Twomey's algorithm, or variants thereof, to impactor and electrical aerosol analyzer data. The expectation–maximization (EM) algorithm discussed by Maher and Laird,[25] or variants thereof, has also proved useful.

The present authors recommend that the unfolding methods should be used only by aerosol professionals, not by the occasional user. For nonspecialists, the use of the fitting methods described in the last section is recommended.

Software for Inverting and Presenting Aerosol Data

DISTFIT.[26] This professionally written software is available from TSI, Inc., St. Paul, Minnesota. It is meant to be used as a tool for manipulating size distribution data, as in Tables 6-3, 6-5, and 6-6, and for constructing graphs, as in Figures 6-2, 6-3, and 6-4.

In addition to mathematical transformations, the software provides for fitting of single-mode or multimode lognormal distributions to the data. On the other hand, the software does not do data inversion because this is different for each type of aerosol sampler or instrument.

Graphs are produced in a standardized format and can be annotated similar to Figure 6-3. Graphs can be printed out on laser printers, thus producing publication-quality finished graphs.

The present authors suggest that DISTFIT would be worthwhile for a user who needs to study size distribution data and produce graphs on a weekly basis. This is particularly true if the data come from a variety of sources, so that no single format is best for all. If the need is less frequent, or if the data are very similar each time, one of the many good computer graphics programs, or spreadsheet programs, might serve nearly as well.

STWOM. This is the computer program developed by Markowski to do the calculations described in Reference 23. As of this writing, it consists of FORTRAN source code, one version for impactors and another for the electrical aerosol analyzer. Those interested in information about current status should write the author, Greg Markowski, at the Department of Meteorology, Texas A&M University, College Station, TX 77843.

EVE.[27] This program, available for a fee from P. Paatero at the University of Helsinki in Finland, performs data inversion using a technique called *extreme value estimation*. Rather than calculate a single solution for a given data inversion problem, the program calculates the family of acceptable solutions. A companion program is available for plotting graphs, or standard graphing programs can be used. EVE is an unfolding type of program and, as mentioned before, the present authors consider it too complicated for the occasional user.

MICRON. This program was developed by Wolfenbarger and Seinfeld in the course of their study.[21] For information on status and availability, the authors should be contacted directly.

Features of Aerosol Measurement Instruments and Methods

In the first part of this chapter, it was stressed that two quantities—particle size and particle amount—are necessary to describe aerosol size distribution. This carries over into the measurement process: the measurement of particle size is often made by a different physical principle and at a different time than the measurement of particle amount. As a consequence, there is great variety in the instruments and methods available for aerosol measurements. Here, some of the main "dimensions" that can be used to describe instruments and methods will be identified and discussed. These dimensions can be used to rank different instruments or methods for a particular application. They also provide a framework for a general survey of instruments and methods, to be discussed later in this chapter.

Type and Degree of Size Resolution

In keeping with the emphasis in this chapter on particle size measurement, the type and degree of size resolution provided is a very important "dimension" of aerosol instruments and methods. However, because this dimension will be used as a means of categorizing instruments/methods in the next major part of this chapter, the discussion of size resolution will be deferred until then.

Time Resolution and Response Time

The time resolution is the time required for an instrument or method to obtain an amount of aerosol sufficient for reliable measurement. For example, in the standard high volume method[5] for measuring total suspended particles, several hours of sampling are needed to collect a reliable measurable mass (the standard period is 24 hrs). At the opposite extreme, optical particle counters often obtain an adequate sample in a few minutes. Obviously, the time resolution depends on the concentration of the aerosol at the time of measurement. In the experience of the authors, time resolution of less than a few hours is rarely needed. In fact, time-integrated samples covering 8, 24, or even 40 hrs are often just as good as a series of samples covering the same period of time. Final selection should be based on the data quality objectives of the experiment or study.

Response time is a different concept that refers to the length of time between the sampling and the availability of the result. In aerosol measurements, the term "real time" is appropriate when the response time is less than a few minutes. Although important in laboratory aerosol research and in diagnostic measurements, there are many situations in which real-time measurements are not necessary.

Sample Preservation, Integrity, and Artifacts

It often happens that aerosol particles are volatile or chemically reactive and therefore susceptible to change in the process of measurement. Sulfuric acid droplets, for example, change size with changing humidity and are also subject to chemical change by reaction with ammonia. Accurate measurement of these droplets requires attention to recording humidity during the particle sizing part of the process and to preserving chemical identity until the amount of acid is determined. In other cases, solid or liquid material can be produced as an artifact of the measurement process, and this material can be mistaken for the aerosol sample. Formation of sulfate and nitrate species from atmospheric gases during sampling with glass fibers is an example.

These considerations have caused a high value to be attached to *in situ* measurements, i.e., methods in which the critical part of the measurement is made without removing the particles from their normal environment. Much work has been done, for example, to design samplers that can be placed inside smokestacks and allowed to reach the temperature of the flue gas before the sample is taken.

When it became desirable to examine the physical form of aerosol particles just after they were released from a stack, a new form of stack sampler was developed, called a dilution sampler. This device brings the stack gases to ambient conditions, then collects the particles by means of appropriate samplers.

Convenience of Use

Aerosol measuring instruments differ greatly in the extent to which they are self-contained. The modern trend is toward complete instruments in which both the size and amount determination are performed in the same unit. Highly integrated, self-contained instruments often feature sufficient electronics to permit continuous, near-real-time display of measurement results. Often, these instruments can be programmed to operate unattended according to a prescribed schedule, recording the data on magnetic tape or disk. In some instruments, there are on-board microcomputers that do mathematical data manipulation on line.

Another class of aerosol measurements provides for the size-selective collection of particles, with subsequent and separate analysis to determine the amount in each size fraction. In this way, samples can be collected in many field locations and brought to a central laboratory for amount determination, and the amount analysis can be performed using laboratory instruments too complicated and expensive to be located at multiple field sites. Neutron activation analysis, requiring proximity to a small nuclear reactor, is one example.

Physical Principle

Another way to categorize aerosol measurement instruments or methods is the physical principle by which they work. For example, in their book *Aerosol Measurement*, Lundgren *et al.*[28] make use of four main sections: 1) inertial classification, 2) light-scattering particle counters, 3) electrical aerosol analyzer, and 4) condensation nucleus counter and diffusion battery. These authors contend that these four techniques are the only ones in widespread use for making particle size distribution measurements in aerosols.

Ruggedness and Reliability

Yet another difference among instruments and methods is their tolerance to the operating environment. Some instruments have ambient temperature and humidity specifications that preclude all but indoor or fair weather operation. Other apparatus can be operated outdoors, even in extremes of weather.

As an example of equipment designed to operate in hostile environments, the impactors[29] and condensation nucleus counters[30] designed for use in the stratosphere where the temperature is –50°C and the pressure might be 20 Pa. Another example of design for extreme conditions, mentioned earlier, is the equipment designed for operations inside smokestacks.

The maintenance required to keep instruments in top operating condition and the support received from the manufacturer when trouble occurs are also important factors. If aerosol measurements are a project in themselves due to lack of convenience, reliability, or support, progress in environmental or industrial aerosol research will be slow.

General Survey of Instruments and Methods for Aerosol Measurements

In his table of contemporary methods and instruments for aerosol measurements, Whitby[11] makes use of two main categories—integral and size resolving. The specialized size-selective samplers, defined and discussed in Chapter 5, qualify as a third instrument category. These categories differ primarily in the type of size resolution provided.

Nonselective (Integral) Methods

The term integral, or nonselective, means that the measurement is based on amount alone, embracing all particle sizes. Even here, however, the question of particle size cannot be completely suppressed. Aerosols frequently involve a very broad range of particle sizes which should be proportionately included in the measurement of amount. Practical difficulties, however, often prevent both very large and very small particles from being fully represented. Consequently, as mentioned in the first part of this chapter, the "total" amount of aerosol is often not well known. The terms "unbiased sampling" and "representative sampling" are synonymous with integral sampling.

Chapter 21 of this manual describes techniques for obtaining unbiased samples from ducts and stacks; sampling in so-called still air requires analogous precautions. Chapter 13 describes the properties and use of filters, a very important, nonselective method of sampling. Chapter 15 covers electrostatic and thermal precipitators, which also collect a broad range of particle sizes. Chapter 16 presents direct-reading instruments, some of which are non-size-selective.

Size-Selective, I and II

Size resolving methods, which provide information on particle size, are more of interest here than the integral methods. Two main types of methods, Types I and II, can be identified. These are depicted in Figure 6-5. In Type I, the particles are separated into two groups based on size, and the measurement of amount is made on one or both groups. Usually, provision is made to adjust the cutpoint so that the full size distribution can be developed by repeated sampling.

There is an obvious kinship between the Type I device and the cumulative plot previously discussed in this chapter. Mercer uses the term "cumulative type" in discussing this class of method or instrument.[31] Some others use the term "first order analyzer."

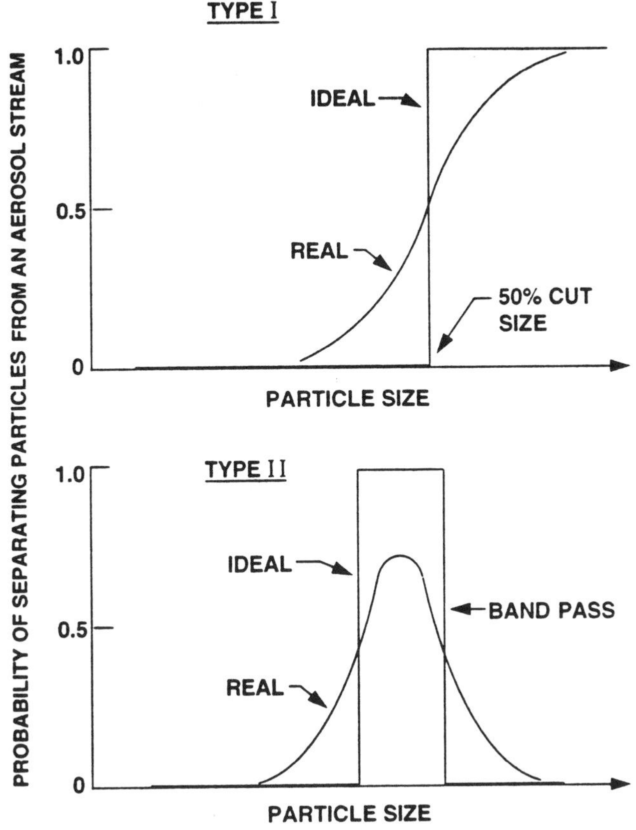

FIGURE 6-5. Particle size resolving characteristics of Type I and Type II classifiers.

In Type II size-selective instruments or methods, a narrow band of sizes comprising a size class is isolated and the amount determination is made for that class. As with Type I, provision is usually made to adjust the pass-band so that a histogram can be developed by repeated sampling. Other terms used to describe Type II are spectrometric, discrete, second order, and differential.

A logical extension of Type II, perhaps worthy of a category of its own, is a device in which several size classes are treated simultaneously. This eliminates the need for sequential sampling, which is awkward when the aerosol concentration is fluctuating. A similar logical extension could also be proposed for Type I.

Figure 6-5 also shows the difference between the ideal and the real performance of both Type I and Type II classifiers. In ideal performance, each aerosol particle is assigned to its proper size class. This is indicated by the sharp vertical boundaries in Figure 6-5. The real situation always entails some misclassification in which particles are assigned to the wrong size class. This is a fact of life in aerosol measurements. The smooth curves in Figure 6-5 depict probabilities. For example, the smooth curve at the top of Figure 6-5 represents the probability, as a function of size, that a particle will be assigned to the larger size class.

Aerosol measuring methods and instruments differ greatly in their size resolving characteristics. They differ both in type and in the degree to which they approach ideal behavior. As already discussed under *Computer Methods,* nonideal size resolution can be ameliorated to some extent by mathematics applied after sampling. There are limits, which are currently being studied.

Inertial Methods

Chapter 14 of this handbook describes a family of methods—the inertial and gravitational methods—which are capable of separating particles into size classes according to their aerodynamic diameter. The single stage impactor (including the virtual impactor) is a close approximation to the Type I size selective sampler, in the terminology used above. Cascade impactors closely approximate the Type II sampler.

The spiral duct centrifuge shown and discussed in Chapter 14 is a very high-resolution Type II sampler. Centrifuges can be designed as either Type I or Type II. Cyclones are Type I, and some recent designs provide near ideal classification. (As discussed in Chapter 14, cyclones have been designed that have very desirable, nonideal classifying characteristics.) Elutriators are also Type I, with typically poor classification characteristics.

Chapter 16 describes instruments that combine optical and inertial principles to measure aerodynamic diameter on a particle-by-particle basis.

Noninertial Methods

For particles smaller than about 0.2 μm, diffusion replaces inertia as the most important mechanism for particle deposition. To size-classify these small particles, diffusion batteries have been developed. Although diffusion battery results are usually given in terms of particle linear diameter, the quantity that governs classification is the diffusion coefficient. Thus, whether spherical or not, the particles are classified according to a definition of size which is of great physical significance. Diffusion batteries are Type I classifiers, retaining small particles and allowing larger ones to pass. Several stages, in series or parallel configuration, are needed to develop complete size distribution.

Diffusion batteries classify only, and the measurement of particle amount must be made separately. The most common method is a condensation nucleus counter, but the penetrating aerosol also can be collected on filters for subsequent chemical or radioactivity analysis.

Electrical methods for achieving aerosol particle size

classification are discussed in Chapter 16. One commercially available electrical aerosol analyzer consists of a section to charge the particles in a standard way, a Type I electrostatic classifier, and an electrometer to measure particle amount. Type II classifiers, often called differential mobility analyzers, are also commercially available and have gained wide acceptance. Much research has been done on and with the electrical methods in the past 30 years.

For particles larger than about 0.2 µm, optical particle counters have become a fixture in aerosol research and aerosol measurements. The Owl, an early type of optical device (not a counter), is still useful for its intended purpose of measuring the size of near-monodisperse aerosols in the laboratory. Single particle counters are described in Chapter 16. Depending on the electronic design, these can be either Type I or Type II classifiers. The principles of optics place some limits on the selection of size classes.

Respirable, Inhalable, and Thoracic Particle Samplers

These Type I classifiers are discussed in detail in Chapter 5 and are mentioned here only for completeness. They have a deliberately nonideal size classification characteristic, designed to match certain characteristics of the human nose and throat.

Summary

Two variables are required to present data on the size distribution of aerosols. These are particle size and particle amount. There are many diverse and equally valid ways of measuring both of these quantities.

The Whitby histogram has some advantages over other graphical forms for presenting size distribution data, especially when the total amount of aerosol is not accurately known or when comparing results obtained by different instruments. The log-probability plot is useful when the aerosol size distribution is not too broad or when a single aerosol source is dominant.

Among the statistical descriptions of particle size, there are four median diameters that are very important. These are: the count median diameter, the mass median diameter, the count median aerodynamic diameter, and the mass median aerodynamic diameter. Other medians are used occasionally. The geometric mean diameter and the geometric standard deviation, the second of which is a measure of the spread of the distribution, are two more very important statistics. The latter two are well defined even for size distributions which are not lognormal!

Although it is often possible to mathematically convert from one measure of particle amount to another, it is usually better to make the measurement directly.

The lognormal distribution is by far the most important of the mathematical distribution functions for aerosol use. However, not all aerosols are lognormally distributed. In some cases, it is necessary to superimpose two, or even three, lognormals to adequately describe the data.

Aerosol measurement instruments and methods have many "dimensions" to be considered when selecting one for a particular task. No one instrument or method is suitable for all tasks.

Additional Reading

The following textbook (especially Chapters 1 and 4) further explains many of the concepts presented in this chapter: Hinds, William C., Aerosol Technology. John Wiley & Sons, Inc., New York (1982).

References

1. Herdan, G.: Small Particle Statistics. Butterworth and Co., London (1960).
2. Hinds, W.C.: Aerosol Technology: Properties, Behavior and Measurement of Airborne Particles. John Wiley & Sons, New York (1982).
3. Knutson, E.O.; Whitby, K.T.: Accurate Measurements of Aerosol Electric Mobility Moments. J. Aerosol Sci. 6:453–460 (1975).
4. Mercer, T.T.: Aerosol Technology in Hazard Evaluation. Academic Press, New York (1973).
5. Mitchell, R.; Pilcher, J.: Improved Cascade Impactor for Measuring Aerosol Particle Sizes in Air Pollutants, Commercial Aerosols, Cigarette Smokes. Ind. Eng. Chem. 47:1039 (1959).
6. Knollenberg, R.G.; Luehr, R.: Open Cavity Laser "Active" Scattering Particle Spectrometry from 0.05 to 5 microns. In: Fine Particles: Aerosol Generation, Measurement, Sampling and Analysis, B.Y.H. Liu, Ed. Academic Press, New York (1976).
7. National Primary Ambient Air Quality Standards for Particulate Matter. 40 CFR 50.6 (July 1992).
8. Occupational Safety and Health Administration: Table G-3, Mineral Dust. Federal Register 58(142):40191 (July 27, 1974).
9. Miguel, A.H.; Friedlander, S.K.: Distribution of Benzo(a)pyrene and Coronene with Respect to Particle Size in Pasadena Aerosols in the Submicron Range. Atmos. Environ. 12:2407–2411 (1968).
10. Whitby, K.Y.; Husar, R.B.; Liu, B.Y.H.: The Aerosol Size Distribution of the Los Angeles Smog. J. Colloid Interface Sci. 37:177 (1972).
11. Whitby, K.T.: The Physical Characteristics of Sulfur Aerosols. Atmos. Environ. 12:125–159 (1978).
12. Cadle, R.D.: Particle Size. Reinhold Publishing Co., New York (1965).
13. Orr, Jr., C.: Particulate Technology. MacMillan Company, New York (1966).
14. Knutson, E.O.; Sinclair, D.; Leaderer, B.: New York Summer Aerosol Study: Number Concentration and Size Distribution of Atmospheric Particles. In: The New York Summer Aerosol Study, 1976. T. Kniep and M. Lippmann, Eds. Ann. New York Acad. Sci. 322:11–28 (1979).
15. Durham, J.L.; Wilson, W.E.; Ellestad, T.G.; et al.: Comparison of Volume and Mass Distributions for Denver Aerosols. Atmos. Environ. 9:717 (1975).
16. Hinds, W.C.: Data Analysis. In: Cascade Impactors: Sampling and Data Analysis, Chapter 3. J.P. Lodge, Jr. and T.L. Chan, Eds. American Industrial Hygiene Association, Akron, OH (1986).
17. Raabe, O.G.: A General Method for Fitting Size Distributions to Multicomponent Data Using Weighted Least Squares. Environ. Sci. Technol. 12:1162–1167 (1978).
18. Dzubay, T.G.; Hasan, H.: Fitting Multimodal Lognormal Size Distri-

butions to Cascade Impactor Data. Aerosol Sci. Technol. 13:144–150 (1990).

19. Helsper, C.; Fissan, H.; Kapadia, A.; Liu, B.Y.H.: Data Inversion by Simplex Minimization for the Electrical Aerosol Analyzer. Aerosol Sci. Technol. 1:135–146 (1982).
20. Cooper, D.W.; Wu, J.J.: The Inversion Matrix and Error Estimation in Data Inversion: Application to Diffusion Battery Measurements. J. Aerosol Sci. 21:217–226 (1990).
21. Wolfenbarger, J.K.; Seinfeld, J.H.: Inversion of Aerosol Size Distribution Data. J. Aerosol Sci. 21:227–247 (1990).
22. Wolfenbarger, J.K.; Seinfeld, J.H.: Estimating the Variance in Solutions to the Aerosol Data Inversion Problem. Aerosol Sci. Technol. 14:348–357 (1991).
23. Markowski, G.: Improving Twomey's Algorithm for Inversion of Aerosol Measurement Data. Aerosol Sci. Technol. 7:127–142 (1987).
24. Winklmayr, W.; Wang, H.C.; John, W.: Adaptation of the Twomey Algorithm to the Inversion of Cascade Impactor Data. Aerosol Sci. Technol. 13:322–331 (1990).
25. Maher, E.J.; Laird, N.M.: EM Algorithm Reconstruction of Particle Size Distributions from Diffusion Battery Data. J. Aerosol Sci. 16:557–570 (1985).
26. DISTFIT Aerosol Data Fitting Program. Product Information Sheet, TSI Incorporated, St. Paul, MN (1991).
27. Paatero, P.: EVE Reference Manual 04.03.1991. University of Helsinki, Helsinki, Finland (1991).
28. Lundgren, D.A.; et al.: Aerosol Measurements. D.A. Lundgren, F.S. Harris, Jr., W.H. Marlow, et al., Eds. University of Florida Press, Gainesville, FL (1979).
29. Leifer, R.; Hinchliffe, L.; Fisenne, I.; et al.: Measurements of the Stratospheric Plume from the Mount St. Helens Eruption: Radioactive and Chemical Composition. Science 214:904–907 (1981).
30. Cadle, R.D.; Langer, G.; Haberl, J.B.; et al.: A Comparison of the Larger, Rosen, Nolan-Pollak and SANDS Condensation Nucleus Counters. J. Appl. Meteorol. 14:1566–1571 (1975).
31. Mercer, T.T.: Gravitational and Inertial Separation of Particles. In: Particle Size Analysis in Estimating the Significance of Airborne Contamination. Technical Reports Series No. 179. International Atomic Energy Agency, Vienna, Austria (1978).

Chapter 7

Airflow Calibration

Morton Lippmann, Ph.D.

Nelson Institute of Environmental Medicine, New York University Medical Center, Tuxedo, New York

CONTENTS

Flow Rate and Volume Metering Instruments

Accurate measurement of air flow rate and volume is an integral part of the calibration of most air sampling instruments. The various instruments and techniques involved in the measurement of flow rate and volume are discussed in this chapter and elsewhere.[1,2] These can be divided into two general categories: primary and secondary standards. Primary measurements generally involve a direct measurement of volume on the basis of the physical dimensions of an enclosed space. Secondary standards are reference instruments or meters that trace their calibration to primary standards and which have been shown to be capable of maintaining their accuracy with reasonable handling and care in operation (Table 7-1).

Primary Standards

Spirometers

The spirometer (Figure 7-1) is a cylindrical bell with its open end under a liquid seal. The bell is supported by a chain or cord and is balanced by a counterweight. The volume of air entering the spirometer is determined by calculating the change in height times the cross section. With the gas valve open, the cylindrical bell should remain stationary. If it does not, the counterweight should be adjusted accordingly. Some spirometers do not have a cycloid counterpoise and, in these units, the bell will not remain stationary with the valve open to ambient air, but rather will slowly move toward the geometric center of the bell. Spirometers are often calibrated by the manufacturer; however, it

TABLE 7-1. Apparatus for Air Sampling Flow Rate Calibration

Type of Meter	Quantity Measured	Range	Commercial Sources*
Spirometer	Integrated volume	0.2–20 ft^3 (6–600 L)	AMC, BRO, GRA, WEC
Soap film flowmeter	Integrated volume	2–10,000 ml	BIO, BUC, GIC, SEN, SKC, SPE
Mercury sealed piston	Integrated volume	1–12,000 ml	BRO
Wet test meter	Integrated volume	Unlimited volumes; max. flow rates from 1–480 ft^3/hr (0.5–230 L/min)	AMC, PSC
Dry test meter	Integrated volume	Unlimited volumes; max. flow rates from 20–325 ft^3/hr (10–150 L/min)	AMC, GRA
Electronic mass flow rate	Mass flow rate	0–10 ml/min up to 0–3000 L/min	BRO, KRZ, MGE, SIE, SKC, THR
Laminar flowmeter	Volumetric flow rate	0.00005–2000 ft^3/hr (0.02 ml/min–1 m^3/min)	AFP, CME, MIC, RAD
Venturi meter	Volumetric flow rate	Depends on pipe and orifice diameters	HIQ, RAD, TSI
Orifice meter	Volumetric flow rate	Depends on pipe and orifice diameters	BGI, MIC
Rotameter	Volumetric flow rate	From 1.0 ml/min up	AFP, BRO, FPC, GIC, GIL, KEY, MGE, SKC, SKD
Thermo-anemometer	Velocity	From 10 fpm (0.3 m/min) up	ALN, KRZ, SIE, TSI
Pitot tube	Velocity	From 1000 fpm (300 m/min) up	DWY, GRA, MIC

*Refer to Table 7-2 at the end of this chapter for the full company names and addresses for these sources.

is prudent to check the calibration after proper alignment by measuring the spirometer bell's inside dimensions.

The Mariotte bottle (Figure 7-2) is an instrument similar to the spirometer that measures displaced water instead of air. When the valve at the bottom of the bottle is opened, water drains out of the bottle by gravity, and air is drawn into the bottle via a sample collector to replace it. The volume of air drawn in is equal to the change in water level multiplied by the cross section at the water surface.

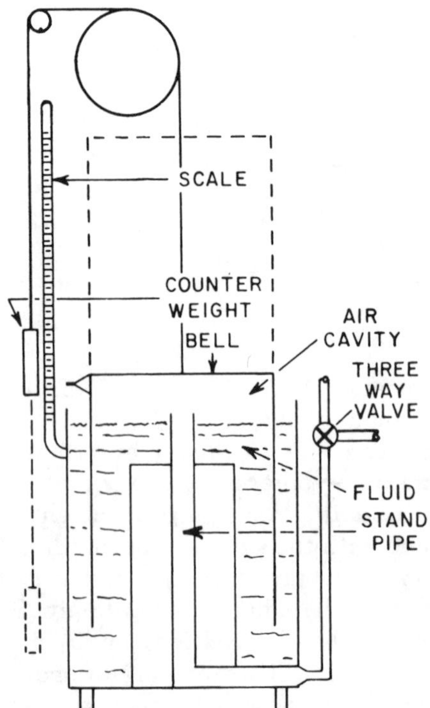

FIGURE 7-1. Schematic of a spirometer or gasometer (reprinted from *The Industrial Environment — Its Evaluation and Control*[1]).

"Frictionless" Piston Meters

Cylindrical air displacement meters with nearly frictionless pistons are frequently used for primary flow calibrations at flow rates of 0.001–10 L/min. The simplest of these is the soap bubble meter illustrated in Figure 7-3. A soap bubble is created in a graduated tube (i.e., volumetric laboratory burette) by squeezing a rubber bulb and raising the soap solution above the gas inlet level. As the gas passes through the soap solution, it creates bubbles that are then timed as they traverse through a known volume within the tube. In this case, the bubbles act as the frictionless pistons.

Soap film flowmeters are generally accurate to within 1.0%, although greater accuracy can be achieved under select conditions. However, a correction may be needed for the humidification of the air during contact with the soap solution. Also, at high flow rates, the accuracy of soap bubble meters declines because of gas permeation through the soap film.

Pitot Tubes

The spirometer and frictionless piston are considered the primary standard for measuring volume and flow

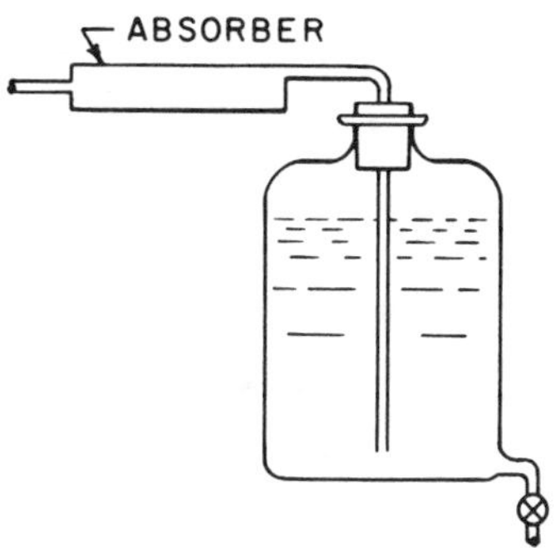

FIGURE 7-2. Mariotte bottle (reprinted from *The Industrial Environment — Its Evaluation and Control*[1]).

rate. The Pitot static tube (commonly referred to as Pitot tube) is the primary standard for measuring gas velocities, and it needs no calibration. It consists of a tube (the Pitot tube) whose opening faces directly into the flow and a static tube formed by a concentric tube with holes placed equally around it in a plane that is 8 diameters from the impact opening. The pressure in the Pitot tube is the impact pressure, whereas that in the static tube is the static pressure. The difference between the static and impact (total) pressure is the velocity pressure. Bernoulli's theorem applied to a Pitot tube in an air stream simplifies to the formula:

$$V = \left(\frac{2\, g_c\, P_V}{\rho}\right)^{\frac{1}{2}} \tag{1}$$

where: V = linear velocity
P_V = velocity pressure = impact pressure – static pressure
g_c = gravitational constant (English units)
r = gas density

If the Pitot tube is to be used with air at 70°F and 1 atm, Equation 1 reduces to the convenient dimensional formula

$$V = 4005\sqrt{h_V} \tag{2}$$

where: h_V = velocity pressure in inches of water
V = velocity in feet per minute (fpm)

For air at 20°C and 1 atm, the equation in metric form reduces to

$$V = 12.8\sqrt{h_V} \tag{3}$$

where: h_V = velocity pressure in cm of water
V = velocity in m/s

The acceptable accuracy of the Pitot tube is limited by the ability to measure the velocity pressure. Above 2500 fpm (12.7 m/s), a U-tube manometer is satisfactory. However, for lower velocities, an inclined manometer or low-range Magnehelic® gauge is necessary. With such a manometer, velocities of 1000 fpm (5.1 m/s) can be measured accurately (at 1000 fpm [5.08 m/s], h_V

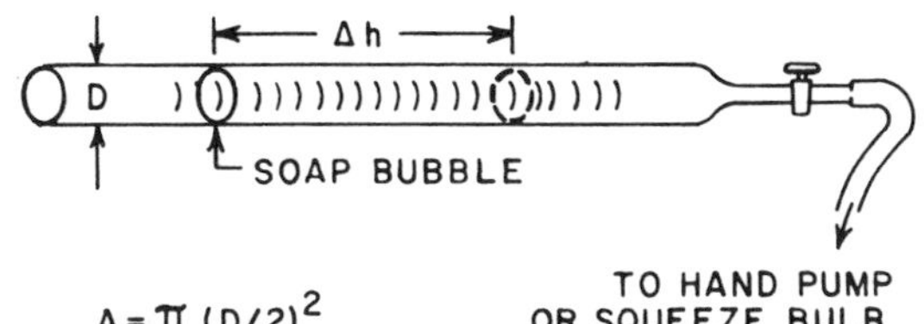

FIGURE 7-3. Soap bubble meter (reprinted from *The Industrial Environment — Its Evaluation and Control*[1]).

= 0.1 in. H_2O [0.25 cm H_2O]). Electronic capacitance pressure gauges permit measurements of h_V down to 0.001 in. H_2O, corresponding to a velocity of about 100 fpm (0.5 m/s or 50 cm/s).

Secondary Standards

Secondary standards are reference instruments that trace their calibration to primary standards. Among secondary standards, however, there are a number of instruments that provide an accuracy nearly comparable to that of primary standards but which, of themselves, cannot be calibrated by internal volume measurement. These instruments are sometimes referred to as intermediate standards, and provide an accuracy of approximately 1.0%. These instruments include wet test meters and dry gas meters.

Wet Test Meter

A typical wet test meter is shown in Figure 7-4. It consists of a cylindrical container in which there is a partitioned drum half submerged in water with openings at the center and periphery of each radial chamber. Air or gas enters at the center and flows into an individual compartment with the buoyant force causing it to raise, thereby producing rotation. This rotation, and therefore the volume, is indicated by a dial on the face of the instrument. The volume measured will depend on the fluid level in the meter because the liquid is displaced by air. This liquid level must be maintained

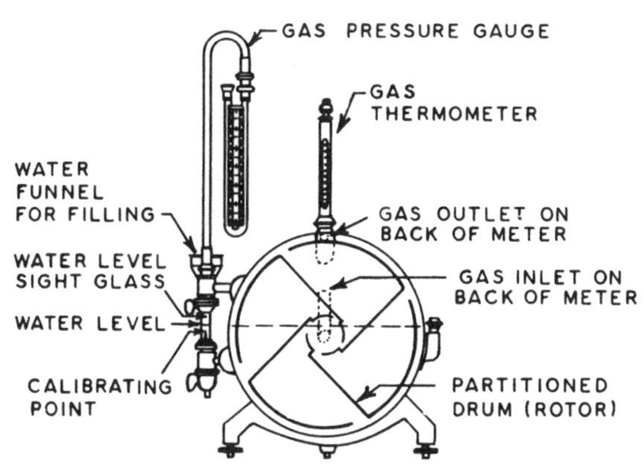

FIGURE 7-4. Wet test meter (reprinted from *The Industrial Environment — Its Evaluation and Control*[1]).

at a calibrated height that is indicated by a sight gauge. In addition, level screws and a sight bubble are provided to level the instrument horizontally. Once the instrument is fllled with water, the water should be saturated with the gas in question by running the gas through the instrument for several hours. When calibrated against a spirometer, wet test meters should exhibit an accuracy of 0.5% or better. However, they can only be used within a narrow pressure range near ambient pressure. The manometer used with the instrument acts, in effect, as a pressure limiting valve.

Care has to be taken in the use of wet test meters. If they are used with gas that can produce a potentially corrosive solution upon contact with water, the internal drum and moving parts may corrode. In addition, it is necessary to overcome the inertia of the mechanical parts at low flow rates, and there is the possibility that the liquid might surge and break the water seal at the inlet or outlet at high flow rates.

Dry Gas Meter

The dry gas meter shown in Figure 7-5 is similar to that used for domestic natural gas metering. It consists of two bags interconnected by mechanical valves and a cycle-counting device. The air or gas fills one bag while the other bag empties itself. When the cycle is completed, the valves are switched, and the second bag fills while the first one empties.

In using dry gas meters, operators should be cognizant of the mechanical drag of the instrument, especially at low flow rates, and of the resulting pressure drop and the possibility of leaks. Instruments of this type, however, can be used to measure flow rates from 5 to 5000 L/min. At pressures up to 250 lb/in.^{2} (17 atm, 1717 kPa), an accuracy of approximately 1.0% can readily be obtained, and when calibrated against a spirometer, the accuracy can be improved. If calibration indicates an error in flow rate, the dry gas meter can be adjusted by means of tangential adjusting weights associated with the linkage to the volume dials.

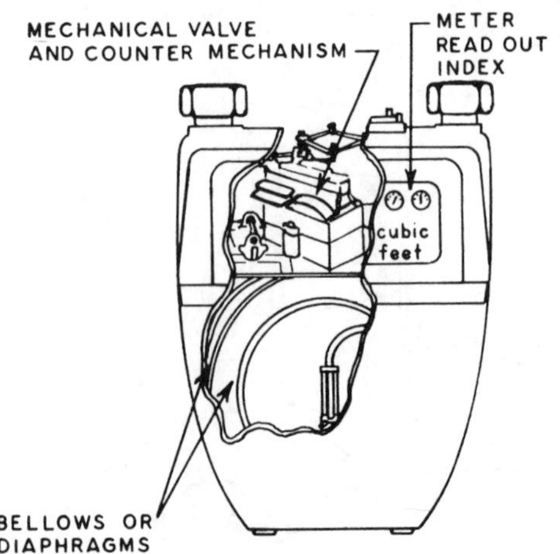

FIGURE 7-5. Dry gas meter (reprinted from *The Industrial Environment — Its Evaluation and Control*[1]).

Additional Secondary Standards

The remaining secondary standards have an accuracy that is usually less than that of the preceding instruments. Among these are a variety of positive displacement meters as well as air velocity meters and electromechanical devices.

Positive Displacement Meters

Positive displacement meters consist of a tight-fitting, moving element with individual volume compartments that fill at the inlet and discharge at the outlet ports. A lobed rotor design is illustrated in Figure 7-6. Another multicompartment continuous rotary meter uses interlocking gears. When the rotors of such meters are motor driven, these units become positive displacement air movers.

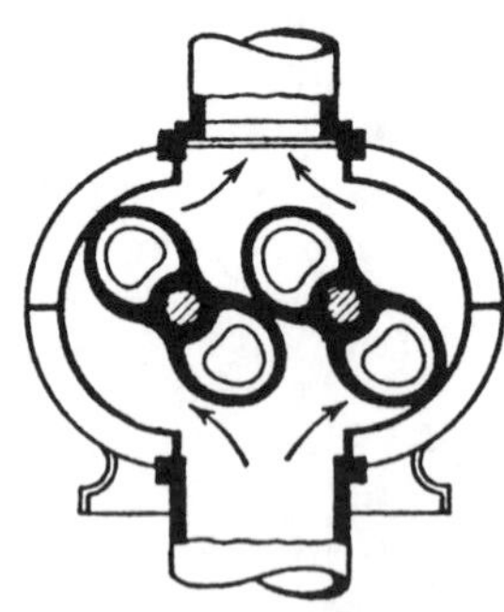

FIGURE 7-6. Cycloidal or roots-type gas meter.

Exchange of Potential and Kinetic Energy

The following secondary standards for flow rate operate on the principle of the conservation of energy. Specifically, they utilize Bernoulli's theorem for the exchange of potential energy for kinetic energy and/or frictional heat. Each consists of a flow restriction within a closed conduit. The restriction causes an increase in the fluid velocity and therefore an increase in kinetic energy, which requires a corresponding decrease in potential energy, i.e., static pressure. The flow rate can be calculated from a knowledge of the pressure drop, the flow cross section at the constriction, the density of the fluid, and the coefficient of discharge, which is the ratio of actual flow to theoretical flow and makes allowance for stream contraction and frictional effects.

Flowmeters that operate on this principle can be divided into two groups. The larger group includes orifice meters, Venturi meters, and flow nozzles; these have a fixed restriction and are known as variable-head meters because the differential pressure head varies with flow. Flowmeters in the other group, which includes rotameters, are known as variable-area meters because a constant pressure differential is maintained by varying the flow cross section.

Rotameters

A rotameter consists of a "float" that is free to move up and down within a vertical tapered tube that is larger at the top than the bottom. The fluid flows upward, causing the float to rise until the pressure drop across the annular area between the float and the tube wall is just sufficient to support the float. The floats achieve stability through their rotation within the tapered tube, providing the basis for the term "rotameter." The tapered tube is usually made of glass, metal, or clear plastic and has a flow rate scale etched directly on it. The height of the float indicates the flow rate. Floats of various configurations have been used, as indicated in Figure 7-7. Such shaped floats are conventionally read at the highest point of maximum diameter of the float, unless otherwise indicated. The float used in most rotameters now is spherical and is read at the center of the ball.

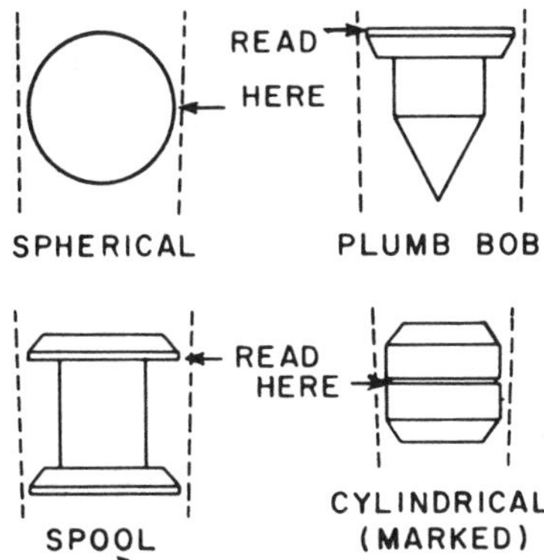

FIGURE 7-7. Types of rotameter floats (reprinted from *The Industrial Environment — Its Evaluation and Control*[1]).

Most rotameters have a range of 10:1 between their maximum and minimum flows. The range of a given tube can be extended by using heavier or lighter floats. The tubes are made in sizes from about 1/8 to 6 in. (0.32–15 cm) in diameter, covering ranges from a few mL/min to over 1000 cfm (28.3 m^3/min).

Both in the laboratory and in commercial air sampling devices, rotameters are the most commonly used devices for measuring flow rate. Depending on the accuracy required, they range in length from about 5 cm to approximately 50 cm. Whereas very small rotameters may not have very good accuracy, most laboratory rotameters are supplied with a calibration curve by the manufacturer that is accurate to ±5%. Accuracies of ±1% to 2% are obtainable when the rotameters are calibrated in the system. Most rotameters are calibrated against a primary or an accurate secondary standard. These calibrations are usually performed with one port of the rotameter at standard "room" temperature (20°C) and pressure (760 torr). The accuracy is therefore limited by the reproducibility or correction to these conditions. If one side of the rotameter is not at standard temperature and pressure, the calibration supplied with the rotameter is no longer valid. In this case, the instrument has to be calibrated in the system in which it is used (temperature and pressure) against a known standard, or the supplied calibration must be corrected for these variations. It should be noted that not correcting for these factors is one of the most common errors encountered in the use of rotameters. At excessive pressure differences, inaccuracies of a factor of 5 to 10 can readily be encountered.

For rotameters with linear flow rate scales, the actual sampling flow will approximately equal the indicated flow rate times the square roots of the ratios of absolute temperatures and pressures of the calibration and field conditions.[3] The ratios change when the field pressures and temperatures differ from those in the calibration laboratory. Thus, if the flowmeter was accurate at standard conditions and the flow resistance of the sampling medium was relatively low (e.g., 30 torr), the flow rate that would be indicated on the rotameter for a standard flow rate of 11 L/min would be $11 \times (760/730)^{1/2} = 10.8$ L/min, a difference of only 1.8%. On the other hand, for a 25-mm diameter AA Millipore filter with a 3.9-cm^2 filtering area and a flow resistance of 190 torr, the indicated flow rate would be $11 \times (760/570)^{1/2} = 9.5$ L/min, 14% above the standard flow rate.

A further correction will be needed when the sampling is done at atmospheric pressures and/or temperatures that differ substantially from those used for the calibration. For example, at an elevation of 5000 ft above sea level, the atmospheric pressure is only 83% of that at sea level. Thus, the actual flow rate would be 9.6% greater than that of standard air, based on the altitude correction alone. If the temperature in the field was 35°C while the meter was calibrated at 20°C, the actual flow rate in the field would be $[(273 + 35)/(273 + 20)]^{1/2} \times 100 = 2.5\%$ greater than that of standard air.

These corrections can be summarized as follows:

$$Q_{ind} = Q_{std}\left(\frac{T_{amb}}{T_{std}} \cdot \frac{P_{std}}{P_{amb}} \cdot \frac{P_{amb}}{P_{rot}}\right)^{\frac{1}{2}}$$

where: Q_{ind} = rotameter reading on site
Q_{std} = flow rate at 760 torr and 20°C

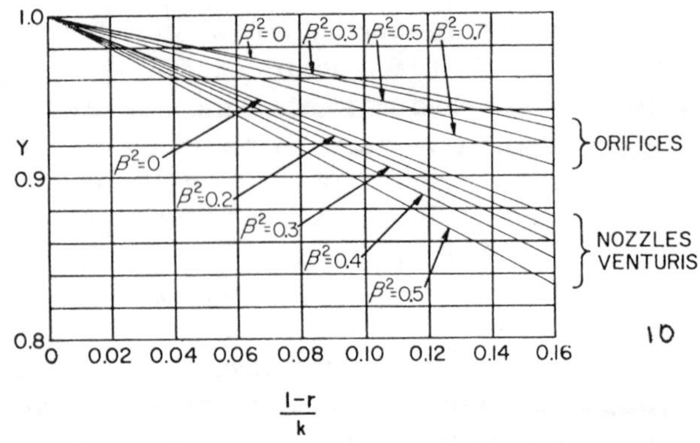

FIGURE 7-8. Expansion factor *Y* for variable head meters (reprinted from *Chemical Engineering Handbook*[(2)]).

T_{amb}= ambient temperature – °K
T_{std} = 20°C = 293°K
P_{std} = 760 torr
P_{amb} = ambient pressure – torr
P_{rot} = pressure at rotameter inlet – torr

In a situation where there were corrections needed for the pressure drop of the sampler, high altitude, and high temperature, the overall correction could be, for the examples cited, 1.14 × 1.096 × 1.025 = 1.28 or 28%.

Head Meters

For a closed channel with a stream of fluid flowing within it, an increase in velocity is experienced whenever the fluid passes through a restriction with a corresponding increase in kinetic energy at the point of constriction. The overall energy balance as determined by the first law of thermodynamics (Bernoulli's theorem) indicates that there must be a corresponding reduction in pressure as a result of the constriction. The mass rate of discharge from such a constriction can be determined by the following general working equation that is applied to both orifice and Venturi meters.

$$W = q_1 \rho_1 = KYA_2 \sqrt{2\, g_c\, (P_1 - P_2)}\ \rho_1 \qquad (4)$$

where: W = weight–rate of flow (lb/s) for English units
= mass–rate of flow (kg/s) for metric units
q_1 = volumetric flow at upstream pressure and temperature (ft³/s or m³/s)
ρ_1 = density at upstream pressure and temperature (lb/ft³ or kg/m³)
$K = C/(1-\beta^4)^{1/2}$
C = coefficient of discharge, dimensionless
β = ratio of throat diameter to pipe diameter, dimensionless
Y = expansion factor (dimensionless, see Figure 7-8)
A_2 = cross-sectional area of throat (ft² or m²)
g_c = 32.17 ft/sec² for English units
= 1 for metric units
P_1 = upstream static pressure (lb/ft² or Pa)
P_2 = downstream static pressure (lb/ft² or Pa)

This equation should be used with caution because it is sometimes difficult to determine the actual coefficients for a given system.

Orifice Meters

The simplest form of variable-head meter is the square-edged or sharp-edged orifice illustrated in Figure 7-9. It is also the most widely used because of its ease of installation and low cost. If it is made with properly mounted pressure taps, its calibration can be determined from Equation 4 and Figures 7-8 and 7-10. However, even a nonstandard orifice meter can serve as a secondary standard, provided it is carefully calibrated against a reliable reference instrument.

The five most common tap locations for square-edged orifice meters are:

1. Flange taps: taps located 1.0 in. (2.54 cm) upstream and 1.0 in. (2.54 cm) downstream from the plate.
2. Radius taps: taps located 1.0 pipe diameter upstream and 0.5 pipe diameters downstream from the plate.
3. Vena Contracta taps: taps located upstream 0.5 to 2 pipe diameters from the plate. Downstream tap located at position of minimum pressure.
4. Corner taps: taps drilled one in the upstream and one in the downstream flange with openings as close as possible to the orifice plate.
5. Pipe taps: taps located 2.5 pipe diameters upstream and 8 pipe diameters downstream from the plate.

The permanent pressure loss for a square-edged orifice meter with either radius or vena contracta taps is approximated by the following equation:

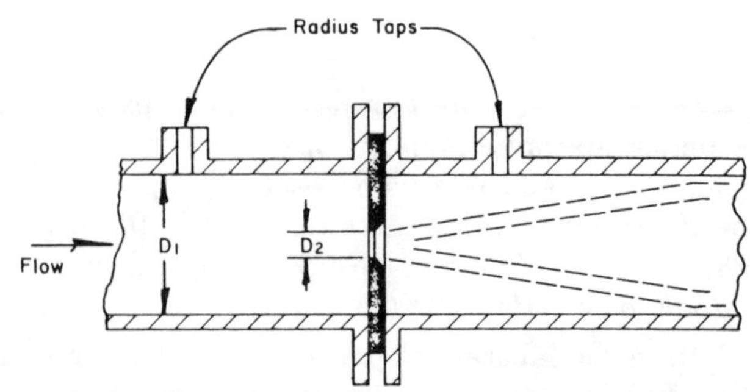

FIGURE 7-9. Square-edged or sharp-edged orifice meter. The plate at the orifice opening must not be thicker than 1/30 of pipe diameter, 1/8 of the orifice diameter, or 1/4 of the distance from the pipe wall to the edge of the opening. The orifice can be cylindrical or have a taper as shown above (reprinted from *Chemical Engineering Handbook*[(2)]).

$$\frac{P_1 - P_4}{P_1 - P_2} = 1 - \beta^2 \tag{5}$$

where: P_1 = upstream pressure
P_2 = downstream pressure
P_4 = fully recovered pressure (4–8 diameters downstream of orifice)
β = diameter ratio (orifice to pipe)

If, for air, the downstream pressure P_2 is less than 0.53 P_1 (the upstream pressure) and the ratio of the upstream cross-sectional area to the orifice area is greater than 25, the orifice is said to be critical, producing a sonic velocity at the orifice gas exit. With these conditions, a constant flow is obtained. However, a critical orifice meter should be calibrated against a primary or secondary standard because it is difficult to take into account all the factors that affect the flow rate through such a system.

Venturi Meters

The large energy loss of an orifice is, for the most part, a result of the sudden increase of area after the air has passed through the orifice restriction.[4] This pressure loss occurs because of the dead space in the corners between the pipe and orifice plate directly downstream of the orifice. This dead space causes large eddies that account for much of the energy loss. The Venturi meter minimizes this energy loss by essentially eliminating the dead space area by using a cone as shown in Figure 7-11. Venturi meters have optimal converging and diverging angles of 21 and 5 to 15, respectively. The potential energy that is converted to kinetic energy at the throat is reconverted to potential energy at the discharge, with an overall energy loss of only about 10%.

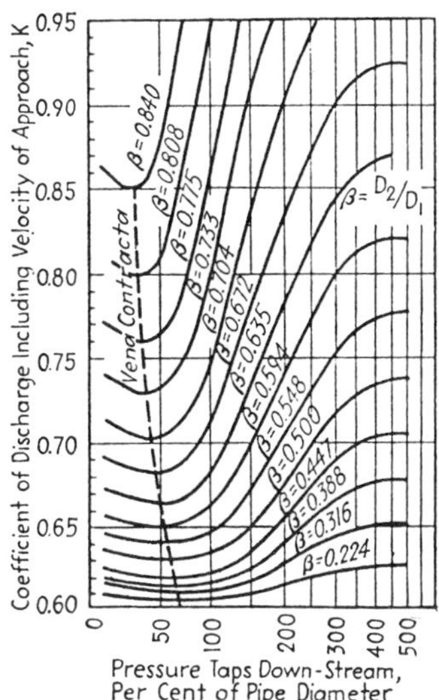

FIGURE 7-10. Coefficient of discharge for square-edged circular orifices (NRE 30,000), with upstream tap located between 1 and 2 pipe diameters from orifice plate (reprinted from *Chemical Engineering Handbook*[2]).

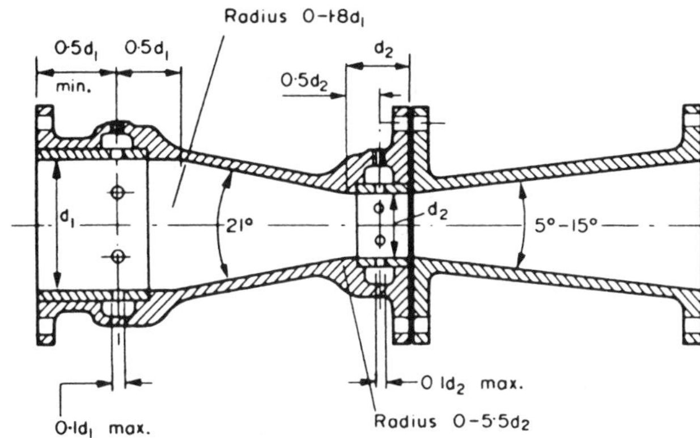

FIGURE 7-11. Standard Venturi (reprinted from *The Measurement of Air Flow*[4]).

For air at 70°F and 1.0 atm and for $1/4 < \beta < 1/2$, a standard Venturi has a calibration described by

$$Q = 21.2\, \beta^2 D^2 \sqrt{\Delta h} \tag{6}$$

where: Q = flow (cfm)
β = ratio of throat to duct diameter, dimensionless
D = duct diameter (inches)
Δh = differential pressure (inches of water)

In metric units Equation 6 becomes

$$Q = 58.4\, \beta^2 D^2 \sqrt{\Delta h} \tag{7}$$

where: units of Q are L/min
units of D are cm
units of Δh are cm H_2O

Laminar Flow Meters

In the laminar flow type of variable-head meter, the pressure drop is directly proportional to the flow rate. In orifice meters, Venturi meters, and related devices, the flow is turbulent and flow rate varies with the square root of the pressure differential.

Laminar flow restrictors used in commercial flowmeters consist of egg-crate or tube bundle arrays of parallel channels. Alternatively, a laminar flowmeter can be constructed in the laboratory using a tube packed with beads or fibers or a filter as the resistive element. Figure 7-12 illustrates this homemade kind of flowmeter. It consists of a "T" connection, pipet or glass tubing, cylinder, and packing material. The outlet arm of the "T" is packed with a porous plug and the leg is attached to a tube or pipet projecting down into the cylinder filled with water or oil. A calibration curve of the depth of the tube outlet below the water level versus the rate of flow should produce a linear curve. Saltzman[5] has used such tubes to regulate and measure flow rates as low as 0.01 cm^3/min.

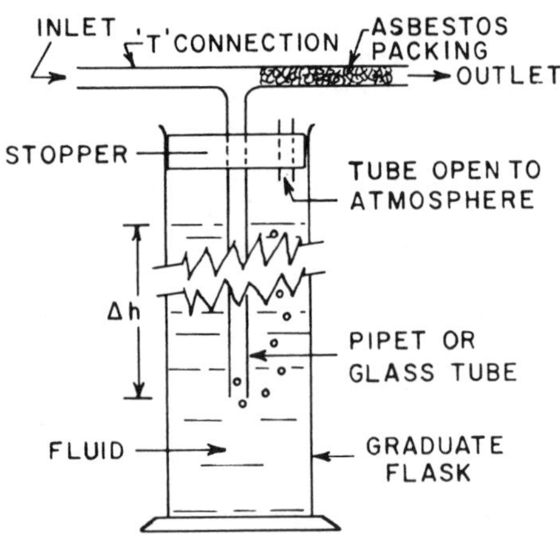

FIGURE 7-12. Packed plug flowmeter (reprinted from *The Industrial Environment — Its Evaluation and Control*[1]).

Pressure Transducers

All of the variable-head meters require a pressure sensor, sometimes referred to as the secondary element. Any type of pressure sensor can be used, with the three most common types being manometers, mechanical gauges, and electrical transducers.

Liquid-filled manometer tubes, when properly aligned and filled with a liquid whose density is accurately known, provide the most accurate measurement of differential pressure. In most cases, however, it is not feasible to use liquid-filled manometers in the field, and pressure differentials are measured with mechanical gauges with scale ranges in centimeters or inches of water. For the low pressure differentials most often encountered in air flow measurement, the most commonly used gauge is the Magnehelic (see DWY, Table 7-2). These gauges are accurate to ±2% of full scale and are reliable provided they and their connecting hoses do not leak and their calibration is periodically rechecked. More sensitive measurements of pressure can be made with electronic capacitance pressure gauges.

Bypass Flow Indicators

In most high-volume samplers, the flow rate is strongly dependent on the flow resistance, and flowmeters with a sufficiently low flow resistance are usually bulky or expensive. A commonly used metering element for such samplers is the bypass rotameter, which actually meters only a small fraction of the total flow; a fraction, however, that is proportional to the total flow. As shown schematically in Figure 7-13, a bypass flowmeter contains both a variable-head element and a variable-area element. The pressure drop across the fixed orifice or flow restrictor creates a proportionate flow through the parallel path containing the small rotameter. The scale on the rotameter generally reads directly in cfm or L/min of total flow. In the versions used on portable high-volume samplers, there is usually an adjustable bleed valve at the top of the rotameter that should be set initially and periodically readjusted in laboratory calibrations so that the scale markings can indicate overall flow. If the rotameter tube accumulates dirt, or the bleed valve adjustment drifts, the scale readings can depart greatly from the true flows.

Heated Element Anemometers

Any instrument used to measure velocity can be referred to as an anemometer. In a heated element (hot wire) anemometer, the flow of air cools the sensor in proportion to the velocity of the air. Instruments are available with various kinds of heated elements, e.g., heated thermometers, thermocouples, films, and wires. They are all essentially nondirectional (i.e., with single element probes); they measure the airspeed but not its direction. They all can accurately measure steady-state airspeed, and those with low mass sensors and appropriate circuits can also accurately measure velocity fluctuations with frequencies above 100,000 Hz. Because the signals produced by the basic sensors are dependent on ambient temperature as well as air velocity, the probes are usually equipped with a reference element that provides an output which can be used to compensate or correct errors due to temperature variations. Some heated element anemometers can measure velocities as low as 10 fpm (0.05 m/s) and as high as 8000 fpm (40.6 m/s). Arrays of point sensors can be coupled electronically to provide indications of flow rate as well as velocity.

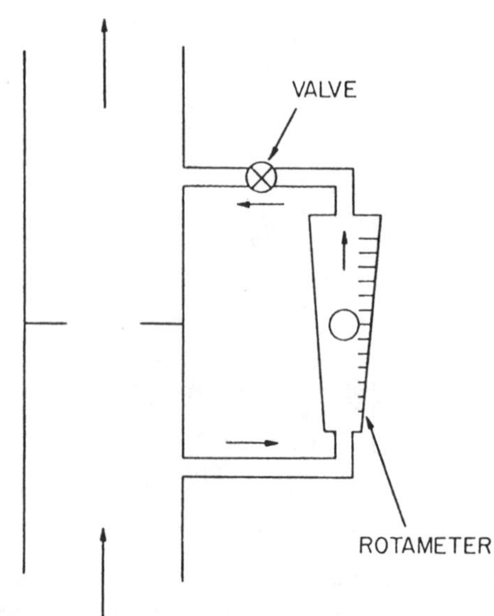

FIGURE 7-13. Bypass flow indicator.

Other Velocity Meters

Vane Anemometers

There are several other ways to utilize the kinetic energy of a flowing fluid to measure velocity besides the Pitot tube. One way is to align a jeweled-bearing turbine wheel axially in the stream and count the number of rotations per unit time. Such devices are generally known as rotating vane anemometers. Some are very small and are used as velocity probes. Others are sized to fit the whole duct and become indicators of total flow rate. These are sometimes called turbine flowmeters.

Automated vane anemometers are currently available that permit measurement of air flow in circular tubes in the range from 7 to 2500 cfm (0.2–71 m^3/min). The systems are generally included with a sensor and associated electronics which provide a digital readout of velocity or flow rate. The systems also have a linearity of between 0.5% and 1.0% with a pressure drop of a few inches of H_2O depending on pipe diameter and flow rate.

The velometer or swinging vane anemometer is widely used for measuring ventilation air flows, but it has few applications in sampler flow measurement or calibration. It consists of a spring-loaded vane whose displacement is indicative of velocity pressure. Its value is in its simplicity, lack of power requirement, and intrinsic safety in explosive atmospheres. These instruments are more fully described in *Industrial Ventilation: A Manual of Recommended Practice.*[6]

Mass Flow and Tracer Techniques

Thermal meters measure mass air or gas flow rate with negligible pressure loss. A unit consists of a heating element in a duct section between two points at which the temperature of the air or gas stream is measured. The temperature difference between the two points is dependent on the mass rate of flow and the heat input.

Mixture metering has a principle similar to that of thermal metering. A contaminant is added and its increase in concentration is measured, or clean air is added and the reduction in concentration is measured. This method is useful for metering corrosive gas streams. The measuring device may react to some physical property such as thermal conductivity or vapor pressure.

Ion flowmeters generate ions from a central disc which flow radially toward the collector surface. Air flow through the cylinder causes an axial displacement of the ion stream in direct proportion to the mass flow.

Procedures of Calibrating Flow and Volume Meters

In this limited space, it is not possible to provide a complete description of all of the techniques available or to go into great detail on those that are commonly used. This discussion will be limited to selected procedures which should serve to illustrate recommended approaches to some calibration procedures commonly encountered.

Comparison for Primary and Secondary Standards

Figure 7-14 shows the experimental setup for checking the calibration of a secondary standard (in this case a wet test meter) against a primary standard (in this case a spirometer). The first step should be to check out all of the system elements for integrity and proper functioning and to determine that there are no leaks within each system or in the interconnections between them. Both the spirometer and wet test meter require specific internal water levels and leveling. The operating manuals for each should be examined because they will usually outline simple procedures for leakage testing and operational procedures.

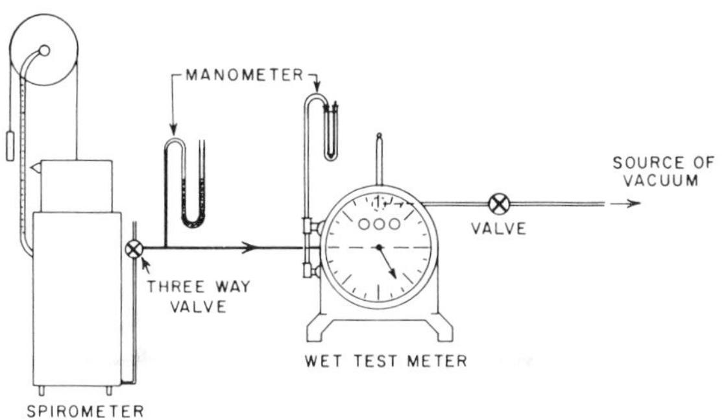

FIGURE 7-14. Calibration of wet test meter with a spirometer (reprinted from *The Industrial Environment — Its Evaluation and Control*[1]).

After all connections have been made, it is a good policy to recheck the level of all instruments and determine that all connections are clear and have minimum resistance. If compressed air is used in a calibration procedure, it should be cleaned and dried.

Actual calibration of the wet test meter shown in Figure 7-14 is accomplished by opening the bypass valve and adjusting the vacuum source to obtain the desired flow rate. The optimum range of operation is between one and three revolutions per minute. Before actual calibration is initiated, the wet test meter should be operated for several hours in this setup to stabilize the meter fluid relative to temperature and absorbed gas, and to work in the bearings and mechanical linkage. After all elements of the system have been adjusted, zeroed, and stabilized, several trial runs should be made. During these runs, should any difference in pressure in the sampling system be indicated, the cause should be determined and corrected. The actual procedure would be to instantaneously divert the air to the spirometer for a predetermined volume indicated by the wet test meter (minimum of three revolutions) or to near the maximum capacity of the spirometer, then return to the bypass arrangement. Readings, both quantity and pressure of the wet test meter, must be taken and recorded while it is in motion, unless a more elaborate system is set up. In the case of a rate meter, the interval of time that the air is entering the spirometer must be accurately measured. The bell should then be allowed to come to equilibrium before displacement readings are made. A sufficient number of different flow rates are used to establish the shape or slope of the calibration curve with the procedure being repeated three or more times for each point. For an even more accurate calibration, the setup should be reversed so that air is withdrawn from the spirometer. In this way, any unbalance due to pressure differences would be canceled.

A permanent record should be made of a sketch of the setup, data, conditions, equipment, results, and personnel associated with the calibration. All readings (volume, temperature, pressures, displacements, etc.) should be legibly recorded, including trial runs or known faulty data, with appropriate comments. The identifications of equipment, connections, and conditions should be so complete that the exact setup with the same equipment and connections could be reproduced by another person solely by use of the records.

After all of the data have been recorded, the calculations, such as corrections for variations in temperatures, pressure, and water vapor, are made using the ideal gas laws:

$$V_S = V_1 \times \frac{P_1}{760} \times \frac{273}{T_1} \quad (8)$$

where: V_S = volume at standard conditions (in this case: 760 mm at 0°C)
V_1 = volume measured at conditions P_1 and T_1
T_1 = absolute temperature of V_1 (K)
P_1 = pressure of V_1 (mm Hg)

In most cases, the water vapor portion of the ambient pressure is disregarded. Vapor pressure, however, can be a source of error when using such an instrument following a collection bubbler that contains a high vapor pressure liquid. In this case, an appropriate dryer should be placed between the bubbler and flowmeter. Also, the standard temperature of the gas in most industrial hygiene applications is normal room temperature, i.e., 25°C rather than 0°C. The manipulation of the instruments, data reading and recording, calculations, and resulting factors or curves should be done with extreme care. Should a calibration disagree with previous calibrations or the supplier's calibration, the entire procedure should be repeated and examined carefully to assure its validity. Upon completion of any calibration, the instrument should be tagged or marked in a semipermanent manner to indicate the calibration factor and, where appropriate, the date and who performed the calibration.

Reciprocal Calibration by Balanced Flow System

In many commercial instruments, it is impractical to remove the flow-indicating device for calibration. This may be because of physical limitations, characteristics of the pump, unknown resistance in the system,[7] or other limiting factors. In such situations, it may be necessary to set up a reciprocal calibration procedure; that is, a procedure where a controlled flow of air or gas is compared first with the instrument flow, then with a calibration source. Often a further complication is introduced by the static pressure characteristics of the air mover in the instrument.[8] In such instances, supplemental pressure or vacuum must be applied to the system to offset the resistance of the calibrating device. An example of such a system is illustrated in Figure 7-15.

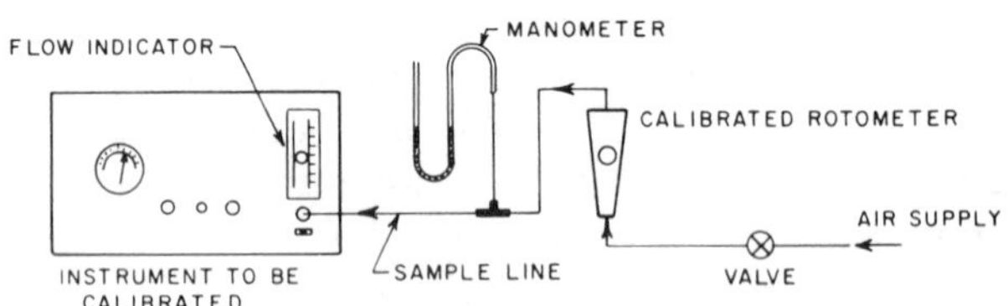

FIGURE 7-15. Schematic for balanced flow calibration (reprinted from *The Industrial Environment — Its Evaluation and Control*[1]).

The instrument is connected to a calibrated rotameter and a source of compressed air. Between the rotameter and the instrument, an open-end manometer is installed. The connections, as in any other calibration system, should be as short and as resistance-free as possible.

In the calibration procedure, the flow through the instrument and rotameter is adjusted by means of a valve or restriction at the pump until the manometer indicates zero pressure difference from the atmosphere. When this condition is achieved, the instrument and rotameter are both operating at atmospheric pressure. The indicated and calibrated rates of flow are then recorded and the procedure repeated for other rates of flow.

Dilution Calibration

Normally, gas-dilution techniques are employed for instrument response calibrations; however, several procedures[9,10] have been developed whereby sampling

TABLE 7-2. Sources for Calibration Instruments and Apparatus Code

Code	Source
AFP	AccuRa Flow Products, Inc. P.O. Drawer 100 Warminster, PA 18974-0100
ALN	Alnor Instrument Company 7555 N. Linder Avenue Skokie, IL 60077
AMC	American Meter Company 300 Welsh Road, Bldg. 1 Horsham, PA 19044-2234
BGI	BGI Incorporated 58 Guinan Street Waltham, MA 02154 (617)891-9380 FAX (617)891-8151
BRO	Brooks Instrument Division 407 W. Vine Street Hatfield, PA 19440
BIO	BIOS International 230 West Parkway – Unit 1 Pompton Plains, NJ 07444-1029 (201)839-6960
BUC	A.P. Buck, Inc. 3139 S. Orange Avenue Orlando, FL 32806 (407)851-8602
CME	CME, Inc. 1314 West 76th St. Davenport, IA 52806-1305
DWY	Dwyer Instruments, Inc. P.O. Box 373 Michigan City, IN 46360
FPC	Fischer & Porter Company 125 E. County Line Road Warminster, PA 18974
GRA	Graseby Andersen 500 Technology Court Smyrna, GA 30082-5211 (404)319-9999 or (800)241-6898 FAX (404)319-0336
GIC	Gilian Instrument Corporation 35 Fairfield Place West Caldwell, NJ 07006 (201)808-3355 FAX (201)808-6680
GIL	Gilmont Instruments Div. Barnant Company 28W 092 Commercial Avenue Barrington, IL 60010
HIQ	HI-Q Environmental Products Co. 7386 Trade Street San Diego, CA 92121 (619)549-2820 FAX (619)549-9657
KEY	Key Instruments 250 Andrews Road Trevose, PA 19053
KRZ	Kurz Instruments, Incorporated 2411 Garden Road Monterey, CA 93940
MGE	Matheson Gas Equipment 166 Keystone Drive Montgomeryville, PA 18936
MIC	Meriam Instrument Company 10920 Madison Avenue Cleveland, OH 44102
PSC	Precision Scientific 2777 West Washington Bellwood, IL 60104
RAD	SAIC-RADeCO 1461 Campus Point Ct. San Diego, CA 92121-9416
SEN	Sensidyne, Inc. 16333 Bay Vista Drive Clearwater, FL 34620 (813)530-3602 or (800)451-9444
SIE	Sierra Instruments, Inc. 5 Harris Court, Bldg. L Monterey, CA 93940
SKC	SKC Incorporated 863 Valley View Road Eighty Four, PA 15330-9614 (412)941-9701 or (800)752-8472 FAX (412)941-1396
SKD	Schutte and Koerting Div. Ametek 2233 State Road Bensalem, PA 19020
SPE	Spectrex Corporation 3580 Haven Avenue Redwood City, CA 94063 (415)365-6567 or (800)822-3940 FAX (415)365-5845
THR	Teledyne Hastings Raydist P.O. Box 1275 Hampton, VA 23661
TSI	TSI Incorporated 500 Cardigan Road P.O. Box 64394 St. Paul, MN 55164 (612)483-0900
WEC	Warren E. Collins, Inc. 220 Wood Road Braintree, MA 02184

rates of flow could be determined. The principle is essentially the same except that different unknowns are involved. In air flow calibration, a known concentration of the gas (i.e., carbon dioxide) or submicrometer-sized aerosol tracer is contained in a vessel. Uncontaminated air is introduced and mixed thoroughly in the chamber to replace that removed by the instrument to be calibrated. The resulting depletion of the agent in the vessel follows the theoretical dilution formula:

$$C = C_o e^{-bt} \tag{9}$$

where: C = concentration of agent in vessel at time t
C_o = initial concentration at $t = 0$
e = base of natural logarithms
b = air changes in the vessel per unit time
t = time

The concentration of the gas or aerosol in the vessel is determined periodically by an independent method. A linear plot should result from plotting concentration of agent against elapsed time on semi-log paper. The slope of the line indicates the air changes per minute (b), which can be converted to the rate (Q) of air withdrawn by the instrument from the following relationship: $Q = bV$, where V is the volume of the vessel.

This technique offers the advantage that virtually no resistance or obstruction is offered to the air flow through the instrument; however, it is limited by the accuracy of determining the concentration of the agents in the air mixture.

Summary and Conclusions

Because the accuracy of air sampling instruments is dependent on the precision of measurement of the sampled volume, extreme care should be exercised in performing all flow calibration procedures. The following comments summarize the key features of airflow calibration:

1. Use standard devices with care and attention to detail.
2. All calibration instruments and procedures should be checked periodically to determine their stability and/or operating condition.
3. Perform calibrations whenever a device has been changed, repaired, received from a manufacturer, subjected to use, mishandled or damaged, and at any time when there is a question as to its accuracy.
4. Understand the operation of an instrument before attempting to calibrate it, and use a procedure or setup that will not change the characteristics of the instrument or standard within the operating range required.
5. When in doubt about procedures or data, ensure their validity before proceeding to the next operation.
6. All calibration train connections should be as short and free of constrictions and resistance as possible.
7. Extreme care should be exercised in reading scales, timing, adjusting and leveling, and in all other operations involved.
8. Allow sufficient time for equilibrium to be established, inertia to be overcome, and conditions to stabilize.
9. Enough data should be obtained to give confidence in the calibration curve for a given parameter. Each calibration point should be made up of at least three readings to ensure statistical confidence in the measurement.
10. A complete permanent record of all procedures, data, and results should be maintained. This should include trial runs, known faulty data with appropriate comments, instrument identification, connection sizes, barometric pressure, temperature, etc.
11. When a calibration differs from previous records, the cause of change should be determined before accepting the new data or repeating the procedure.
12. Calibration curves and factors should be properly identified as to conditions of calibration, device calibrated and what it was calibrated against, units involved, range and precision of calibration, data, and who performed the actual procedure. Often, it is convenient to indicate where the original data are filed and attach a tag to the instrument indicating the above information.

Acknowledgment

The author wishes to thank D.M. Bernstein and R.T. Drew for their dedicated work and collaboration on this chapter for previous editions of this manual.

References

1. The Industrial Environment — Its Evaluation and Control, 2nd ed. P.H.S. Pub. No. 614 (1965).
2. Perry, J.H.; et al., Eds.: Chemical Engineering Handbook, 6th ed. McGraw–Hill, New York (1984).
3. Leidel, N.A.; Busch, K.A.; Lynch, J.R.: Occupational Exposure Strategy Manual. USDHEW, PHS, CDC, NIOSH, Cincinnati, OH (January 1977).
4. Ower, E.; Pankhurst, R.C.: The Measurement of Air Flow, 5th ed. Pergamon Press, New York (1977).
5. Saltzman, B.E.: Preparation and Analysis of Calibrated Low Concentrations of Sixteen Toxic Gases. Anal. Chem. 33:1100 (1961).
6. American Conference of Governmental Industrial Hygienists: Industrial Ventilation: A Manual of Recommended Practice, 21st ed. ACGIH, Cincinnati, OH (1992).
7. Tebbens, B.D.; Keagy, D.M.: Flow Calibration of High Volume Samplers. Am. Ind. Hyg. Assoc. Q. 17:327 (September 1956).
8. Morley, J.; Tebbens, B.D.: The Electrostatic Precipitator Dilution Method of Flow Measurement. Am. Ind. Hyg. Assoc. J. 14:303 (December 1953).
9. Setterlind, A.N.: Preparation of Known Concentrations of Gases to Vapors in Air. Am. Ind. Hyg. Assoc. J. 14:113 (June 1953).
10. Brief, R.S.; Church, F.W.: Multi-Operational Chamber for Calibration Purposes. Am. Ind. Hyg. Assoc. J. 21:239 (June 1960).

Chapter 8

Calibration of Gas and Vapor Samplers

Owen R. Moss, Ph.D.
Chemical Industry Institute of Toxicology, Research Triangle Park, North Carolina

CONTENTS

Introduction

Our understanding of the impact of an airborne contaminant is based on the accurate measure of concentration; the amount present in a unit volume of air. Calibration apparatus and techniques used to accurately measure a volume of air are discussed in Chapter 7, "Airflow Calibration." The following discussion, on the calibration of both sampling equipment and techniques used to measure the amount of contaminant present, will dwell on the generation of the gas and vapor contaminant and the operation of static or dynamic calibration atmosphere systems.

Units of Gas and Vapor Concentration

In the field of Industrial Hygiene, gas or vapor concentrations are usually discussed in terms of parts per million (ppm); a measure of the number of contaminant molecules per million molecules of total atmosphere present. The ideal gas law can be used to show that a concentration given in "ppm" is equivalent to the volume-to-volume relationship of milliliters contaminant per cubic meter (ml/m^3) or microliters per liter (µL/L) of atmosphere. A concentration of 1.0 µL of SO_2 vapor per liter of air mixture thus becomes 1.0 ppm SO_2.

$$1.0\left(\frac{\mu\text{L SO}_2}{\text{L air}}\right) = 1.0\left(\frac{\text{ml SO}_2}{\text{m}^3\text{ air}}\right) = 1.0\ (\text{ppm SO}_2) \quad (1)$$

Occasionally, with direct-reading instruments and, more frequently, with chemical analysis of a sample collected from the atmosphere, confusion and subsequent errors arise in converting to "ppm" from concentration measured as mass per unit volume. A two-step process can be used to make this conversion.

Step 1: Calculate $C(\text{milli-moles}_x/\text{m}^3)$ given:

$C(\text{mg}_x/\text{m}^3\text{ air})$

x = trace contaminant

G_x = gram molecular weight of the trace contaminant

$$C\left(\frac{\text{milli–moles}_x}{\text{m}^3}\right) = C\left(\frac{\text{mg}_x}{\text{m}^3\text{ air}}\right)\cdot\frac{1}{G_x}\left(\frac{\text{milli–moles}_x}{\text{mg}_x}\right) \quad (2)$$

Step 2: Calculate $C(\text{ml/m}^3)$ given:

$C(\text{milli-moles}_x/\text{m}^3)$

T = temperature (°K)

P = pressure (mm Hg)

$$C\left(\frac{\text{ml}_x}{\text{m}^3}\right) = C\left(\frac{\text{milli–moles}_x}{\text{m}^3}\right) \cdot 22.4\left(\frac{\text{ml}_x \text{ at STP}}{\text{milli–mole}_x}\right)$$

$$\cdot \frac{T}{273}\left(\frac{°\text{K}}{°\text{K}}\right) \cdot \frac{760}{P}\left(\frac{\text{mm Hg}}{\text{mm Hg}}\right) \quad \textbf{(3)}$$

$$C\,(\text{ppm}_x) = C\left(\frac{\text{ml}_x}{\text{m}^3}\right)$$

When the two steps are combined, the concentration in ppm becomes:

$$C\,(\text{ppm}_x) = C\left(\frac{\text{mg}_x}{\text{m}^3 \text{ air}}\right) \cdot \frac{1}{G_x} \cdot 22.4 \cdot \frac{T}{273} \cdot \frac{760}{P} \quad \textbf{(4)}$$

Conversely, given the concentration of "x" in ppm (1 ppm = 1 ml/m^3), the mass concentration is:

$$C\left(\frac{\text{mg}_x}{\text{m}^3 \text{ air}}\right) = C\left(\frac{\text{ml}_x}{\text{m}^3}\right) \cdot G_x \cdot \frac{1}{22.4} \cdot \frac{273}{T} \cdot \frac{P}{760} \quad \textbf{(5)}$$

Sample Calculation: A field sample of SO_2 was taken on a hot day in July (99°F, with barometric pressure of 586 mm Hg). The concentration obtained was 0.06 mg SO_2 per m^3 of air. What is the SO_2 concentration in ppm?

$$99°\text{F} = 37.2°\text{C} = 37.2 + 273 \text{ or } 310°\text{K}$$

$$C\,(\text{ppm}) = 0.06\left(\frac{\text{mg SO}_2}{\text{m}^3 \text{ air}}\right) \cdot \frac{1}{64} \cdot 22.4 \cdot \frac{310}{273} \cdot \frac{760}{586} \quad \textbf{(6)}$$

$$C = 0.03\ (\text{ppm SO}_2)$$

Generation of Gas and Vapor Calibration Contaminants

Gases or vapors that comprise a pollutant must be generated specifically for the calibration of air sampling instruments. The accurate analysis of pollutant concentration, whether it be through direct-reading instrumentation, wet chemical techniques, or indirect methods, is only as good as the calibration system. In order to test the collection efficiency of a sampler for a given contaminant, it is necessary either: 1) to conduct the test in the field using a proven reference instrument or technique as a reference standard; or 2) to reproduce the expected field atmosphere in a calibration chamber or flow system. Techniques and equipment for producing such test atmospheres are discussed here and in detail in various other sources.

Accurate calibration standards of a known contaminant gas or vapor are needed either in temporary storage containers or in continuously generated streams. Temporary storage containers, or "*static* calibration systems," may be composed of flexible or solid walled containers used to provide calibration atmospheres that can be "grabbed" by the monitoring instrument or sampling system. In the case of an instrument being operated in a closed loop configuration, the static calibration system is contained completely within the sensing device. The continuously generated stream of calibration atmosphere produced by a "*dynamic* calibration system" may be directly sampled by the sensing device, or the calibration atmosphere may completely surround the instrument as it sits in a chamber. The following description of both of these systems draws heavily from the recent publication by Nelson,[1] and from past overviews by others.[2–6]

Test atmospheres generated for the purpose of calibrating instrument response and collection efficiency should be checked for accuracy by using mass balance relations or, where applicable, by using reference instruments or sampling and analytical procedures whose reliability and accuracy are well documented. Professional groups and governmental agencies that publish such recommendations, guidelines, and standards are listed in Table 8-1.

Static Calibration Systems

The term "static" is used to describe a gas and vapor calibration system where the calibration gas is stored in a container for periodic delivery of an aliquot to the sensing instrument or sampling train. Static calibration systems are operated with the calibration atmosphere stored either at or near atmospheric pressure or at elevated pressures.

Storage of Calibration Atmosphere at Atmospheric Pressure

Storage containers with flexible or rigid walls have been used to hold calibration atmospheres temporarily. When there is no adsorption or diffusion of material through the walls, these containers will hold a calibration standard when a known amount of gas, or liquid that can be vaporized, is injected into a known volume of dilution air.

Flexible Walled Storage Containers

Bags composed of a wide variety of material from Tedlar® and Teflon® to aluminized Mylar® have been used as flexible walled containers for temporary storage of calibration atmospheres.[1] Usually these bags come with a valved inlet port that can accept some type of gas chromatograph septum. The O-rings in the valve and the septum must have very little or no affinity for the components of the calibration atmosphere.

The bag should first be evacuated as thoroughly as possible prior to metering in the dilution gas and injection of calibration gas or liquid. Calibrated syringes provide a simple method for injection of these materi-

TABLE 8-1. Organizations Publishing Recommended or Standard Methods and/or Test Procedures Applicable to Air Sampling Instrument Calibration

Abbreviation	Full Name and Address
ANSI	American National Standards Institute, Inc. 1430 Broadway New York, NY 10018
AWMA	Air and Waste Management Association (formerly the Air Pollution Control Association) P.O. Box 2861 Pittsburgh, PA 15230
ASTM	American Society for Testing and Materials D-22 Committee on Sampling and Analysis of Atmospheres and E-34 Committee on Occupational Health and Safety 1916 Race Street Philadelphia, PA 19103
EPA/EMSL	U.S. Environmental Protection Agency Environmental Monitoring Systems Quality Assurance Division (MD-77) Research Triangle Park, NC 27711
ISC	Intersociety Committee on Methods for Air Sampling and Analysis Sampling and Analysis c/o Dr. James P. Lodge, Editor Intersociety Manual — 3rd edition 385 Broadway Boulder, CO 80303
NIOSH	National Institute for Occupational Safety and Health NIOSH Manual Coordinator Division of Physical Sciences and Engineering 4676 Columbia Parkway Cincinnati, OH 45226

als. Just prior to use, the syringe should be flushed several times with the component of interest.

Side-port needles should be used to penetrate septa that have an inert surface, like Teflon, coating a material, such as rubber, that may absorb the calibration gas or vapor. The side port will ensure that no piece of the latter material is cut out and injected into the bag along with the gas or liquid to be vaporized. The actual injection should be performed by gently depressing the syringe one time.

A rigid container such as a bottle can be modified to function as a collapsible bag by insertion of a balloon. Inflation and deflation of the balloon allows loading and unloading of the calibration atmosphere with no dilution. The fittings necessary for controlling the sampling can be attached directly to the exposure container, separate from the air source for the balloon.

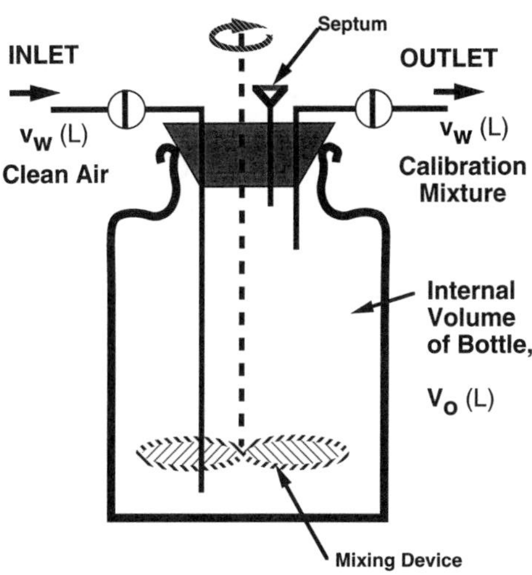

FIGURE 8-1. Single bottle gas and vapor static calibration system.

Rigid Walled Storage Containers

Single and multiple rigid walled containers, for calibration gases held at atmospheric pressure, are used in the few cases where flexible walled bags are not available or are not appropriate due to loss of material on the walls or diffusion of the components of the calibration atmosphere through the walls of the bag. Even though the concentration will be diluted with replacement air whenever gas is transferred for analysis, the concentration can be accurately determined provided fan blades or stirring devices are present to ensure that instantaneous mixing occurs in each rigid walled container. The storage bottles are usually equipped with a valved inlet and a similar outlet (Figure 8-1). A third inlet or pass-through port for introduction of the contaminant may also be provided.

An alternative method of introducing a calibration atmosphere is to produce glass ampoules containing a known amount of pure contaminant and then to break them within the fixed volume of the static system. Setterlind[7] has discussed the preparation of ampoules in detail. Other devices, such as gas burettes, displacement manometers, and small pressurized bombs, have all been used successfully.[8,9] Gaseous concentrations can also be produced by adding stoichiometrically determined amounts of reacting chemicals to the bottle. Some instruments, such as gas chromatographs, may be calibrated by direct injection of standard solutions.

In practice, after the mixture inside the bottle has come to equilibrium, samples are drawn from the outlet while replacement air is allowed to enter through the inlet tube, diluting the contents of the bottle during the process of getting the sample. Under ideal conditions, the concentration remaining is a known fraction of the number of air changes removed from the bottle. If one assumes instantaneous and perfect mixing of the incoming air with the entire sample volume in the bottle, the concentration change, dC, as a small volume, dv_w, is withdrawn, is equal to the residual concentration, C, times the fraction, dv_w/V_o, of the total volume withdrawn:

$$dC = C\frac{dv_w}{V_o} \tag{7}$$

The residual concentration, C, is:

$$C = C_o e^{-\left(\frac{v_w}{V_o}\right)} = C_o e^{-a}, \tag{8}$$

$$\text{for } a = \frac{v_w}{V_o}$$

$$\ln\left(\frac{C_o}{C}\right) = a \tag{9}$$

where: C = the residual concentration in the bottle at any time
v_w = total volume of sample withdrawn
C_o = original concentration
V_o = volume of the chamber
a = ratio of v_w to V_o
ln = logarithm to the base e ($\ln(x) = 2.3 \log_{10}(x)$)

If one-tenth the volume is removed from the bottle and replaced with clean air ($v_w = 0.1\ V_o$), the residual concentration, C, of air sampled when v just equals v_w is:

$$C = C_o e^{-0.1} = 0.9047\ C_o \tag{10}$$

The average concentration of a sample withdrawn from a single container is

$$\overline{C}_1 = C_o \frac{\left(1 - e^{-\left(\frac{v_w}{V_o}\right)}\right)}{\left(\frac{v_w}{V_o}\right)} = C_o \frac{(1 - e^{-a})}{a}, \text{ for } a = \frac{v_w}{V_o} \tag{11}$$

For the case of $v_w = 0.1\ V_o$, $\overline{C}_1 = 0.953\ C_o$ and, as expected, is larger than the residual concentration, $C = 0.9047\ C_o$. If instantaneous mixing does not occur, the average concentration, $\overline{C}_1$, for the time of sampling may be even higher.

If the concentration of the sample must be held to within 5% of the initial concentration, only about 10% of the volume of the bottle can be sampled. Setterlind[7] has shown that this limitation can be overcome by using two or more bottles of equal volume (V_o) in series, with the initial concentration in each bottle being the same. When the mixture is withdrawn from the last bottle, it is not displaced by air but by the mixture from the preceding bottle. If, as above, a maximum of 5% drop in concentration can be tolerated, two identical bottles in series provide a usable sample of 0.6 V_o. With five bottles in series, the usable sample will increase to about 3 V_o. The general relations for the residual concentration in the last of n containers and the average concentration of the withdrawn sample can be extracted from the discussions by Setterlind,[7] Lodge[10] and Nelson:[1]

$$C_n = C_o\left\{1 + \left(\sum_{j=1}^{n-1}\frac{1}{j!}a^j\right)e^{-a}\right\} \tag{12}$$

and

$$\overline{C}_n = C_o\left\{n + \left(\sum_{j=1}^{(n-1)}\frac{(n-j)}{j!}a^{j-1}\right)e^{-a}\right\} \tag{13}$$

$$\text{for, } n > 1, j < n - 1, \text{ and } a = \frac{v_w}{V_o}$$

When an analysis instrument such as the Miran infrared gas analysis unit can be operated in a closed loop configuration, the body of the unit can be used as the rigid calibration atmosphere container. The unit is set to sample itself and a known amount of contaminant is injected into the internal volume.

Storage of Calibration Atmosphere at Elevated Pressure

Rigid storage containers for calibration atmospheres can be filled to pressures significantly greater than atmosphere pressure. During preparation, these standard cylinders are evacuated and then filled with 1) a measured mass, 2) a measured partial pressure, or 3) a known volume of gas or liquid, and then, as required, repressurized with a diluent gas, such as air or nitrogen to produce the concentration required. Nelson[1] has recently reviewed these three main techniques (gravimetric, partial pressure, volumetric) for producing pressurized standard cylinders. These techniques have also been previously discussed by Cotabish *et al.*[11] and reviewed by Roccanova.[8]

Gravimetric

Measuring the weight of compound that is placed inside the standard cylinder is the most accurate method of producing a calibration atmosphere. In fact, when purchasing standard cylinders from a commercial source, the calibration is usually provided in terms of gravimetric analysis of the weight of the cylinder before and after the pure compound was introduced. The cylinder is repressurized with a known number of moles of diluent gas such as air or nitrogen. The actual cylinders should always be checked by an independent analysis procedure because the trace gas may not be adequately mixed or may be partially lost due to wall adsorption. The mixture of the gas produced in cylinders cannot be assumed to be uniform. In fact, the cylinders have to be rolled, or otherwise treated, in order to ensure that the injected gases are thoroughly mixed.

Partial Pressure

In this method, the relative concentrations of the different component gases that comprise the calibration atmosphere are determined by the partial pressure used to introduce each gas into the cylinder. The cylinder or cylinders are filled in sequence beginning with the component that will have the lowest partial pressure (concentration) in the gas mixture.

Volumetric

Standard cylinders can be filled with known volumes of contaminant gas and diluent gas by having known flows of each of these gases supplying the input line to the compressor. The concentration in the standard cylinder will be the same as that determined by the ratio of these flows.

Dynamic Calibration Systems

The term "dynamic" is used to describe a gas and vapor calibration system where the calibration gas is continuously produced and fed into a sampling train or calibration chamber following vaporization, dilution, and mixing. The air sampling instrument is placed to sample either the output of the system or it is completely immersed in the calibration atmosphere. In either case, the generation, dilution, and operation of the calibration system must be incorporated in the documentation along with the nature and frequency of calibration checks. This information must be present to support the scientific measurements and are often necessary to meet legal requirements. Any measurements made to document the presence or absence of excessive exposures will only be as reliable as the calibrations upon which they are based.

Gases or vapors that comprise the atmosphere normally monitored by an air sampling instrument can be continuously generated for the purpose of calibration. All instruments should be checked against such standard calibration atmospheres immediately upon receipt and periodically thereafter. Verification of the concentrations of such test atmospheres should be performed whenever possible using analytical techniques that are referee-tested or otherwise known to be reliable. Procedures for establishing such atmospheres involve dilution of gas streams produced from "static" sources, generation and dilution of atmospheres produced from liquid sources through active vaporization, or controlled diffusion or permeation of gas molecules. The calibration atmosphere is introduced into systems that may be as simple as a single delivery line into the inlet of the air sampling instrument or as complex as a calibration system that includes a chamber of sufficient size to allow the air sampling instrument to be completely immersed in the calibration atmosphere. Less frequently used approaches to calibration atmosphere generation, in addition to the ones presented here, are discussed by Nelson.[1]

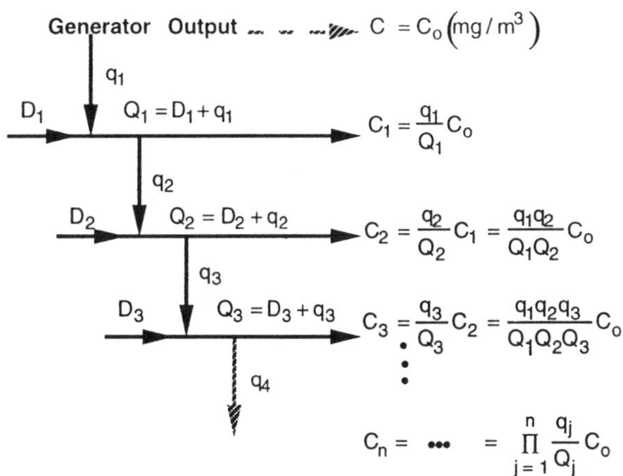

FIGURE 8-2. Basic schematic of a multi-stage dilution system. (D_j is the dilution air flow, in L/min, for the jth stage of the dilution system. Likewise, q_j is the flow of airborne mixture from the previous stage.)

Gas Dilution

Dilution of the sample may be necessary when the concentration from the generator is above the range of the analytical instrument. In each stage of a dilution system, air and the contaminant gas are metered through restrictions and then mixed. The output is used as is, or it is diluted further by passing it through a similar system (Figure 8-2). Such dilution systems are subject to instabilities that make them difficult to control. The precision of the output concentration is very sensitive to the variations inherent in controlling each of the flows. This sensitivity, plus constraints on the acceptable variation in the calibration concentration, limits the number of "dilutions" that can be made in series. The schematic in Figure 8-2 includes the generalized equation for the diluted concentration at the nth stage. In practice, n is seldom larger than three.

Most dilution units operate on the assumption that the pressure drop across each restriction to flow is constant. Cotabish *et al.*[11] have described a system originally patented by Mase for compensation of back

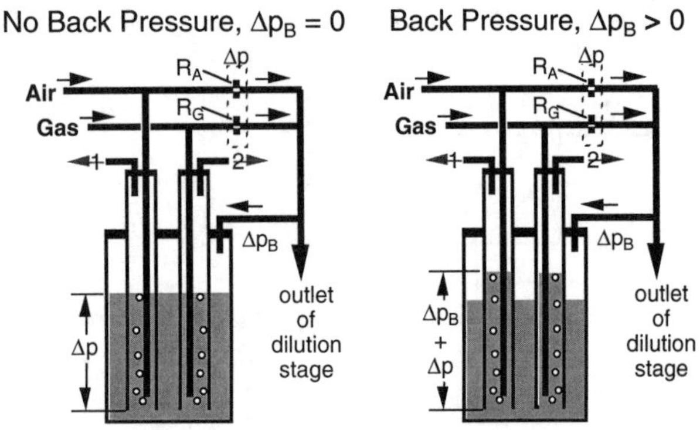

FIGURE 8-3. Automatic back-pressure compensator. (R_A and R_G are air and gas line restrictions with pressure drop Δp. Excess dilution air and gas vent at "1" and "2.")

pressure (Figure 8-3). In this system, both the air and contaminant gas flow are regulated by the height of a water column which, in turn, is controlled by the back pressure of the calibration system. Thus, an increase in back pressure causes an increase in the delivery pressure of both air and contaminant gas. This system is limited to those gases that are not significantly soluble in the water or oils used to regulate the pressure drop. This concept is also included, in part, in devices described by Saltzman.[12–14]

In general, commercially available dilution units (for example, from MEL and MGP, Table 8-2) use constant sources of flow that are relatively insensitive to back pressure (Figure 8-2). These dilution units control flow with such devices as positive displacement pumps and mass flow controllers.

Generation of Dynamic Calibration Atmospheres

Static systems are limited by two factors: loss of vapor by surface adsorption and the finite volume of the mixture. Although the influences of the latter can be included in the calculations, the loss to the walls may be significant.

In dynamic systems, the rate of air flow and the addition of contaminant to the air stream are both carefully controlled to produce a known dilution ratio. Dynamic systems offer a continuous supply of material,

TABLE 8-2. Sources for Calibration Instruments and Apparatus

Code	Source
AID	Analytical Instrument Development, Inc. Division of Thermo Environmental Instruments, Inc. 8 West Forge Parkway Franklin, MA 02038
APC	Air Products and Chemicals, Inc. Specialty Gas Department 7201 Hamilton Blvd. Allentown, PA 18195
BGI	BGI Incorporated 59 Guinan Street Waltham, MA 02154 (617)891-9380 FAX (617)891-8151
CAL	Calibrated Instruments, Inc. 200 Saw Mill River Road Hawthorne, NY 10532 (914)741-5700 or (800)969-2254 FAX (914)741-5711
CSI	Columbia Scientific P.O. Box 203190 Austin, TX 78720 (512)258-5191
HAM	Hamilton Company P.O. Box 10030 Reno, NV 89520
HOR	Horiba Instruments, Inc. 1021 Duryea Avenue Irvine, CA 92714
KEC	KECO R & D Inc. 10034 Clay Road Houston, TX 77080
KTK	Kin-Tek Laboratories, Inc. 504 Lourel LaMarque, TX 77568
LCC	Liquid Carbonic Corp. 901 Embarcadero Oakland, CA 94606
MDC	Mast Development Company Suite 3, 736 Federal Street Davenport, IA 52803
MEL	Meloy Laboratories, Inc. 6715 Electronic Drive Springfield, VA 22151
MGP	Matheson Gas Products 30 Seaview Drive P.O. Box 1587 Secaucus, NM 07096 (201)867-4100
MSA	Mine Safety Appliances P.O. Box 427 Pittsburgh, PA 15230 (412)776-8600 or (800)MSA-INST FAX (412)776-3280
NBS	National Bureau of Standards Office of Standard Reference Materials Room B311 Chemistry Bldg. National Institute of Standards and Technology Gaithersburg, MD 20899
SEN	Sensidyne, Inc. 16333 Bay Vista Dr. Clearwater, FL 34620 (813)530-3602 or (800)451-9444
SKC	SKC Incorporated 863 Valley View Road Eighty Four, PA 15330-9614 (412)941-9701 or (800)752-8472 FAX (412)941-1396
SKD	Schutte and Koerting Div. Ketema Inc. 2233 State Rd. Bensalem, PA 19020
SSG	Scott Specialty Gases 6141 Easton Rd. P.O. Box 310 Plumsteadville, PA 18949
UNI	Univetrics Corp. 501 Earl Road Shorewood, IL 60436
VCM	VICI Metronics 2991 Corvin Drive Santa Clara, CA 95051

allow for rapid and predictable concentration changes, and minimize the effect of wall losses as the contaminant comes to equilibrium with the interior surfaces of the system. Both gases and liquids can be used with dynamic systems. With liquids, however, provision must be available for conversion to the vapor state.

Liquid Delivery: Vapor Generation

When the contaminant is a liquid at normal temperature, a vaporization step must be included. One procedure is to use a motor-driven syringe [2,9,11] and meter the liquid onto a wick or a heated surface. Such systems consist of an air cleaner, a solvent injection device, a heating/vaporizing/dilution zone, and a zone for mixing and cooling. A large range of solvent concentrations can be produced (0.01 to 50,000 ppm). These devices permit rapid changes in the concentrations and can be accurate to better than 1.0%.

A second generation method is to saturate an air stream with vapor and then dilute the air stream to the desired concentration. The amount of vapor in the saturated air stream is directly proportional to the ratio of the vapor pressure, p_v, to the atmospheric pressure P_o;

$$C(\text{ppm}) = \frac{p_v}{P_o} 10^6 \tag{14}$$

The vapor pressure is proportional to the temperature and can be estimated from equations such as the Antione relationship for those gases where the characteristic constants A, B, and C have been reported (Nelson;[1] Reid, Prausnitz, and Sherwood[15]).

$$\ln(p_v) = A - \frac{B}{C+T} \tag{15}$$

A simple vapor saturator is shown in Figure 8-4. The carrier gas passes through two gas washing bottles in series which contain the liquid to be volatilized. The first bottle is kept at a higher temperature than the second one, which is immersed in a constant temperature bath. By using the two bottles in this fashion, saturation of the exit gas is assured. A filter is sometimes included to remove any droplets entrained in the air stream as well as any condensation particles. Such a system has even been used to generate a constant concentration of mercury vapor (Nelson[16]).

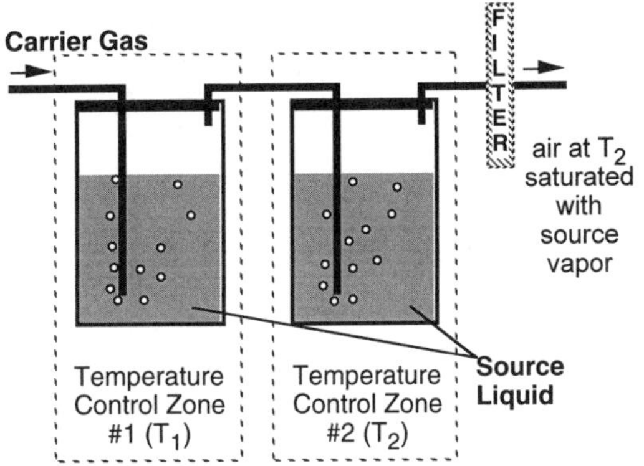

FIGURE 8-4. Schematic of a two-stage vapor saturator (T_1 is usually greater than T_2).

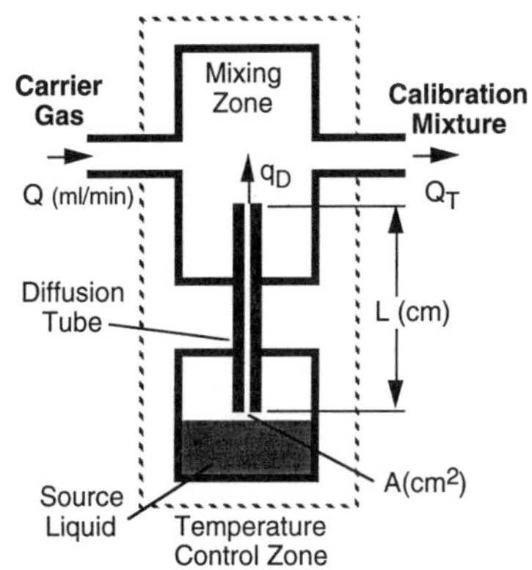

FIGURE 8-5. Basic design of all diffusion cells.

Diffusion of Vapors: Diffusion Cells

Diffusion cells have been used to produce known concentrations of gaseous vapors.[1,17] All such devices have the basic design shown in Figure 8-5. Liquid is placed in a reservoir that is connected to a mixing zone by a tube of known length and cross section. The concentration in the outlet of the diffusion cell is a function of the diffusion rate of the vapor, q_d, and the total flow, Q_T, in the system.

$$C(\text{ppm}) = \frac{q_d}{Q_T} 10^6 \tag{16}$$

When designing a diffusion cell for a specific application or output rate, the diffusion rate of the vapor produced above the liquid in the reservoir can be calculated from the environmental conditions in the system, the diffusion coefficient of the vapor, and the length and cross sectional area of the diffusion tube. If the diffusion coefficient is unknown, it can be estimated from the molecular weights of the vapor and the diluent gas.[1] In general, these calculations for estimating the diffusion rate are subject to assumptions that cause a significant difference between the calculated and measured values.

In practice, the diffusion rate of the vapor through the specific geometry of the diffusion tube can be estimated for a given temperature by measuring the change in weight of the reservoir or by measuring the output concentration with calibrated chemical detectors. In operating such devices, the accuracy and stability of the output concentrations are directly proportional to the ability to control temperature in the reservoir, diffusion tube, and mixing zone.

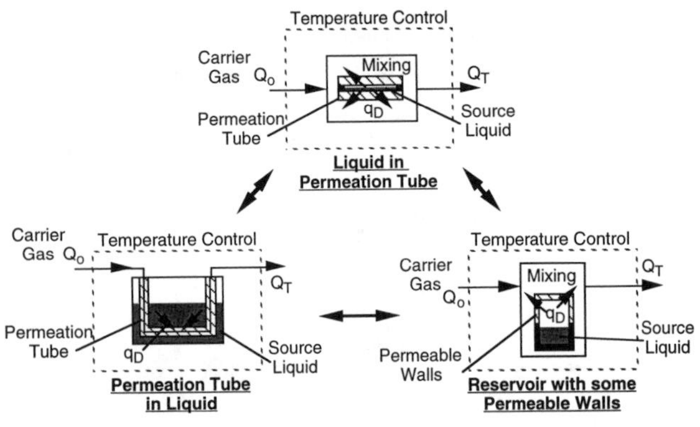

FIGURE 8-6. Three basic formats of permeation devices.

Diffusion of Vapors: Permeation Devices

Permeation methods for producing controlled atmospheres used in calibrating air sampling instruments have recently been reviewed by Nelson[1] in addition to previous discussions by O'Keefe and Ortman[18] and Lodge.[10] In general, the permeation of molecules of a source material through plastics can be used to reproducibly generate a controlled atmosphere provided the critical temperature of the source material is above 20 to 25°C. Plastics such as fluorinated ethylene propylene (FEP Teflon), tetrafluoroethylene (TFE Teflon), polyethylene, polyvinyl acetate, and polyethylene terephthalate (Mylar) are a few of the materials that have been used in permeation devices.[1] In the operation of these devices, the source material will usually dissolve in the plastic and permeate through it. The rate of permeation is primarily a function of the thickness of the plastic material, the total internal area exposed to the source material, and the temperature.

These devices are sensitive to the temperature to the extent that a 0.1°C change in temperature can result in a 1% change in the permeation rate through the plastic container.

All existing permeation devices have one of three basic formats (Figure 8-6): source liquid in a permeation tube, permeation tube in the source liquid, and source liquid reservoir with permeable and impermeable walls. In all cases, diluent air at flow rate Q_o (L/min) passes over or through the device and the source liquid held at constant temperature. The concentration in the output flow is proportional to the ratio of the permeation rate of the source material, q_p, to the output flow rate, Q_T.

Like diffusion devices, the output of a permeation device can be estimated from the thickness of the wall material, the type of the wall material, the source liquid, the magnitude of the permeable areas exposed to the source material, the pressure drop, and the temperature.[1] These approximations can be accurate to within 10% and are useful mainly in designing a device with specific output capabilities.

For permeation devices to be used in calibration of air sampling instruments, they must be either weighed before and after use, calibrated with chemical detectors just prior to use, or purchased as precalibrated units. Table 8-3 lists manufacturers who produce permeation devices for applicable source materials that may be of interest in calibration of air sampling instruments. The advantage of permeation devices are that they are extremely simple and, under adequate temperature control, can be highly precise. A wide range of concentrations in the high (hundreds of ppm) to very low (hundredths of ppm) range can be produced. However, the total output rate and, thus, the achievable concentrations from these permeation devices, is low.

Dynamic Calibration

Calibration systems for air sampling instruments may be as simple as a single delivery line from the generator to the inlet of the air sampling instrument, or they may be as complex as an exposure system that includes a chamber of sufficient size to allow several air sampling instruments to be completely immersed in the calibration atmosphere. Sampling conditions encountered in the industrial environment can often be duplicated by placing instruments inside a calibration chamber or wind tunnel. When such facilities are not available, the instruments are tethered about a gas distribution system in a manner much like that used for nose-only exposure of animals to test atmospheres. Techniques, insights, and pitfalls common in whole body and nose-only exposure of animals to test atmospheres are directly applicable to completing accurate air sampling instrument calibrations.[19]

Regardless of whether a calibration duct or calibration chamber is used, the operator should have a basic understanding of the air flow through the calibration

TABLE 8-3. Commercially Available Items for Gas and Vapor Calibration.

Types	Sources*
Microsyringes	HAM, UNI
Calibrated ampoules	MSA, KEC
Compressed gases	APC, LCC, MGP, SSG
Permeation devices and systems	AID, KEC, KTK, MDC, CSI, VCM
Gas blenders and diluters	CAL, CSI, HOR, MGP
Gas phase titration	CSI
Gas sampling bags	BGI, CAL

*See Table 8-2.

system, the assumptions contained in the equations used to predict concentration at different points in the calibration system as a function of time, and the influence of deviations from optimal operating conditions on the stability of the calibration atmosphere.[20–27]

Operation of an Ideal Calibration Chamber

Calibration systems in which the air sampling instrument will be placed (immersed in the calibration atmosphere) can have one of three basic configurations (push-only, push–pull, and pull-only) with respect to the total flow of calibration atmosphere through the chamber (Figure 8-7). The simplest and most commonly used configuration is the latter case where the output from the generator is mixed with dilution air whose flow is controlled by a system pulling air from the exhaust of the calibration chamber (Figure 8-8).

When there is instantaneous mixing of each incremental volume of calibration atmosphere entering the chamber, an exponential buildup of concentration is seen:

$$C = \frac{W}{Q}\left[1 - e^{-\left(\frac{Q}{V}t\right)}\right] \quad (17)$$

where: C = concentration (mass/unit volume)
W = output of the test atmosphere generator (mass/unit time)
Q = total flow through the chamber (volume/unit time)
V = calibration chamber volume
t = time since the generator started

Silver[21] credited this equation to ventilation engineers; however, the relation is universal, occurring whenever the rate of change of a quantity is directly proportional to its current value:

$$\frac{dC}{dt} = \frac{(W - QC)}{V} \quad (18)$$

Dilution air mixes with and begins to dilute the test or calibration atmosphere when the generator in Figure 8.8 is shut off. In this case, the concentration within the

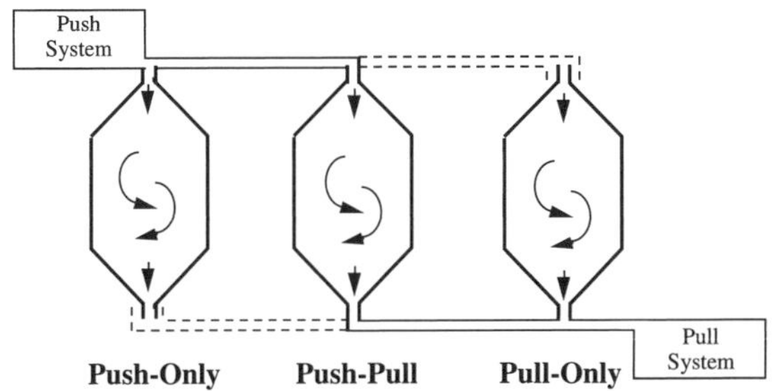

FIGURE 8-7. Calibration chamber systems for "immersion" of air sampling instruments (push-only, push–pull, pull-only).

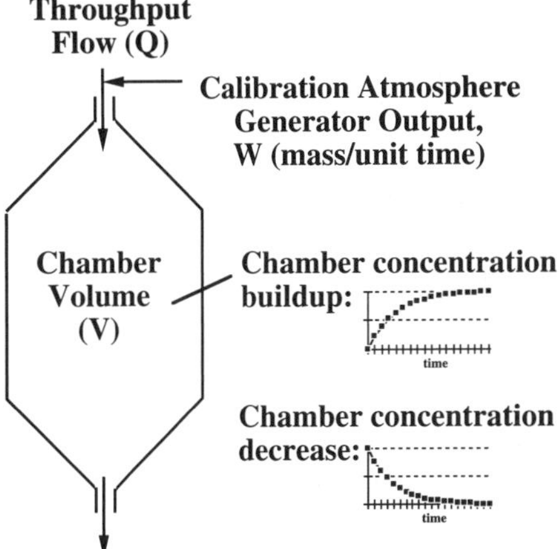

FIGURE 8-8. Air flow and concentration change in a dynamic calibration system.

chamber decreases at a rate, dC/dt, directly proportional to a multiple of its current value, $-(Q/V)C$. The concentration within the chamber decreases exponentially from an initial value, C_o:

$$C = C_o\, e^{-\left(\frac{Q}{V}t\right)} \quad (19)$$

where: t = time since the generator stopped

The time for concentration to approach 50% closer to its equilibrium value when the generator is on, or the time for concentration to reduce to one-half of its current value when the generator is off, will be the same for the system shown in Figure 8-8 provided that, in both cases, the total flow, Q, and volume, V, are constant. Operation of the system can be described by a characteristic response time because the exponential terms are the same in the equations for buildup (Equation 17) and clearance (Equation 19). When the test atmosphere generator is first turned on, the concentration in the test box increases from zero to an equilibrium concentration, C_e. The expected time or "half time" ($t_{1/2}$) for the concentration to become 50% closer to an equilibrium concentration is calculated from the ratio of V/Q:

$$t_{1/2} = \frac{V}{Q}\ln(2) \quad (20)$$

where: ln(2) = the natural logarithm of 2 (= 0.693)

If it takes 6 min, V/Q=6, for one chamber volume of air to be sucked into the chamber inlet, then the half time for concentration change in this chamber will be 0.693 × 6 or 4.16 min. Every 4.16 min, the chamber concentration will come 50% closer to equilibrium concentration. Within two half times, or 8.32 min from the start, the concentration will be 75% of the equilibrium concentration [50% + (100%–50%)/2]. These "times" are independent of whether the test atmosphere generator is on, causing the concentration in the chamber to increase to an equilibrium level, or off, causing the equilibrium level in the chamber to decrease toward zero. The relations can be generalized—the time it takes the concentration to change some percentage, P, of the difference between the current (or initial) and equilibrium concentration is:

$$t_{P/100} = -\frac{V}{Q}\ln\left(\frac{100-P}{100}\right) \tag{21}$$

when: $P = 50\%$

$t_{0.50} = t_{1/2} = 0.693(V/Q)$

Likewise:

$t_{0.75} = 1.386\ (V/Q)$
$t_{0.90} = 2.30\ (V/Q)$
$t_{0.95} = 3.00\ (V/Q)$
$t_{0.99} = 4.61\ (V/Q)$

If the air exchange in the calibration chamber is three air changes an hour, then $V/Q = 20$ min, and it will take 92 min (4.61×20) to clear the air to 1% of the original concentration.

These relations (Equations 17–21) are valid only if the following two conditions are met:

1. The output of the source or calibration atmosphere generator is thoroughly mixed with the clean dilution air within the inlet line before entering the chamber.
2. Mixing of all air inside the worksite or chamber is rapid and thorough and there is little or no loss to surfaces.

Both conditions are difficult to achieve in practice.

Sampling from an Ideal Calibration Chamber

Ideally, a sample of test atmosphere should be obtained without changing the concentrations anywhere in the chamber.[25] When a percentage, P, of the flow through the chamber is removed for sampling purposes and replaced with clean dilution air, the equilibrium concentration in the system will shift to a new level:

$$C = C_o\left(1 - \frac{P}{100 + P}\right) \tag{22}$$

The half time for this shift will be shorter than the normal half time for the chamber by the same percentage $[P/(100 + P)]$. By keeping P small, the effect becomes negligible.

The problem of diluting the concentration within the chamber during sampling can be solved by returning the sample air to the exhaust line, if possible, or by operating the calibration system in the push-only mode (i.e., pushing the calibration atmosphere from the generator, past the sampling point, to an exit that is open to atmosphere; Figure 8-7). In either case, when this is done, the total flow into the chamber remains constant, as does the equilibrium concentration, ($C_o = W/Q$). Specific strategies[28] for sampling from a calibration chamber are discussed in the book by Willeke and Baron.[20]

When self-contained air sampling instruments are placed in a test chamber, their exhaust often must be directed into the chamber volume instead of into the exhaust line. The dilution effect should be undetected if the sample flow is less than 2% of the total flow through the chamber, Q, and if the instrument exhaust is directed away from sampling points.

Calibration Chamber Performance: Poor Mixing in the Inlet

When the output of the calibration atmosphere generator is not thoroughly mixed with the clean dilution air before entering the chamber, at least two air streams will enter: one relatively clean and the other having a concentration higher than the expected equilibrium concentration.

The two streams may actually travel separate and distinct paths in the chamber, especially if the energy provided for mixing is not large. Consequently, there will be zones in the chamber that are continually diluted by clean air and zones that are continually fed by air having a higher concentration of calibration material than desired. The mean concentration obtained from different sampling points will equal the target equilibrium concentration, $C_o = W/Q$ (Figure 8-8), but the variation between sampling points would be large and would adversely affect any comparison between air sampling instruments being calibrated instantaneously.

An air leak into the chamber produces the same effect as little or no mixing of dilution air in the inlet line. Concentrations upstream from the leak should be stable and higher than concentrations below the leak. Initially, if the inlet air is several degrees centigrade higher than the chamber air, mixing within the chamber will be less because portions of the warm air will tend to remain above the colder air. Even with the temperature differences, the equilibrium concentration will be the same throughout the chamber, although the half time needed to reach them will be longer.

Calibration Chamber Performance: Poor Mixing in the Chamber

Uniform mixing within a chamber is achieved with fans, baffles, cyclone injectors, or manifolds.[22] When this is not done, zones of little or no air movement, i.e., stagnant zones, are created in the chamber. The equilibrium concentration throughout the chamber will still be the same as expected, $C_o = W/Q$, and will be independent of sampling position, provided enough time has passed. The half time for buildup or decline of concentration at a given point will not be the same throughout the chamber. Concentration at sampling points within stagnant zones will change at a slower rate than the concentration at sampling points within the major streamlines of flow that exist, in such cases, between chamber inlet and exhaust.

A self-contained monitor placed within a stagnant zone in the chamber would tend to clean the air in that zone if it captures the contaminant. The instrument would suck in the test atmosphere and expel partially clean air back into the chamber. A new and lower equilibrium concentration would be reached in the stagnant zone around the monitor. Any alteration that provides for an improvement of mixing within the chamber, such as the addition of a fan, will resolve the problem by breaking up the stagnant zone and carrying the instrument exhaust away from the sampling port.

Measurement of Chamber Performance

Four areas should be tested in evaluating chambers before use in an instrument calibration program:

1. Uniform mixing of the test atmosphere before it reaches the chamber inlet.
2. Excessive loss of test material to chamber surfaces.
3. Possible leaks of air into the chamber.
4. Uniform mixing within the chamber.

Uniform mixing at the inlet is the most difficult to evaluate, and it is usually the area least considered. A process of elimination to evaluate mixing of dilution air with calibration atmosphere in the inlet line is recommended. If there are no leaks of clean air into the chamber, and if enough time has passed to reach some percent of the equilibrium concentration but a concentration distribution is seen within the chamber, then the cause must be poor mixing of test atmosphere in the inlet line. Poor mixing in the inlet line can be compensated by inserting simple deflectors or by inserting a surge chamber with a volume large enough to have 2–5 air changes per min.

Measurement of Chamber Performance: Loss of Material to Walls

Excessive loss of test material to surfaces inside the chamber is specific for the compound and the materials composing the surface. Silver[(21)] provides the most complete discussion to date, devoting over a third of his paper to this subject. He gives experimental results on the effects of walls, animal fur (in inhalation chambers), and even clothing (in walk-in chambers) on concentration levels. Concentration drops can be due to absorption, adsorption, or chemical reaction at the surfaces. Silver[(21)] reported that the concentration can be reduced over 80% if an absorbing surface is used on the walls. He also concluded that "excessive concentration lowering occurs when the volume of animals is more than 5% of the chamber volume." Actual deposition rates (μg/min/m^2) cannot be estimated from his paper because only relative concentrations are given. Nonetheless, Silver clearly demonstrates the magnitude that surface effects can reach. Wall loss should be considered when setting up a calibration system for a source gas or vapor and should be estimated by measuring concentration at the inlet and exhaust of the chamber when empty and when the air sampling instruments being calibrated are in place.

Measurement of Chamber Performance: Leaks

Chamber leaks can be evaluated in several ways. A messy but simple test is to pressurize the chamber slightly (about 1.0 cm of water) and squirt a soap solution along all the edges where leaks might occur. The bubbles produced by escaping air locate the problem area but do not quantitate the magnitude of the leak. This is appropriate for chambers operated at a slightly positive pressure but not for calibration chambers operated slightly below atmosphere pressure unless an observer enters the chamber during the test.

Another approach is to measure the rate at which air leaks into a chamber that is sealed under slight vacuum.[(29)] The change in vacuum or pressure difference, Δp, between chamber and room is measured over some preset time period. A slow change in pressure difference would indicate an inward leak, Q (L/min), given by:

$$f = \frac{V \Delta p \ln 2}{P_r T_{1/2}} \tag{23}$$

where: V = volume of the chamber
Δp = pressure difference between chamber pressure, P, and room pressure, P_r
$T_{1/2}$ = time for the pressure difference to change from p to $p/2$

In practice, a decision must be made on what leak rate is acceptable. In general, this should be less than 2% of the total flow through the chamber.

Measurement of Chamber Performance: Uniform Concentration

Measurements of the uniformity or degree of mixing within a chamber have been made by using dynamically similar models,[(22)] sampling from many different points within the chamber (point tests), and monitoring the entrance and exit of a bolus of gas (dynamic flow tests).[(30,31)] In practice, it is only practical to conduct point tests and dynamic flow tests.

TABLE 8-4. Summary of Recommended and Standard Methods on Air Sampling and Instrument Calibration Related to Gases and Vapors

Organization	Type of Methods
ANSI	Sampling airborne radioactive materials
AWMA (APCA)	Recommended standard methods for continuous air monitoring of fine particulate matter
ASTM	Test methods for sampling and analysis of atmospheres
ASTM	Recommended practices for sampling and calibration procedures, nomenclature, guides, etc.
EPA/EMSL	Reference methods for air contaminants
ISC	Methods of air sampling and analysis
NIOSH	Analytic methods for air contaminants

Point tests (sampling many different points within a chamber) should always indicate uniform concentration regardless of the type of the chamber, provided enough time has passed for equilibrium to be reached. A measure of degree of mixing within the chamber is obtained from the difference between buildup half times at each sampling point; the greater the difference, the poorer the mixing.

Dynamic flow tests[22,30] consist of continuously monitoring a bolus of gas injected into the air stream as it passes the inlet and exhaust ports of the chamber. The mean time of the concentration versus time plot is calculated for the sampling point at the chamber inlet, t_1, and at the exhaust port, t_2. Chamber operation is evaluated from these numbers by calculating the percent dead space, $\%DS$,

$$\%DS = 100\left(\frac{T - T_m}{T}\right) \tag{24}$$

where: T = the theoretical residence time, V/Q

T_m = the measured residence time, $t_2 - t_1$

The percent dead space is a direct measure of uniformity of mixing within the chamber. A high percent dead space indicates that stagnant zones exist and that a fraction of the inlet air is being directly shunted through the chamber.

Summary

Calibration of gas and vapor samplers involves the production of a stable calibration atmosphere. The calibration atmosphere may be stored in a container for periodic delivery of an aliquot to the air sampling instrument or it may be continuously generated through vaporization, diffusion, or permeation, and then diluted prior to delivery into the instrument being calibrated or into a calibration chamber containing several air sampling instruments that are being compared. Further discussions on the techniques for calibration of gas and vapor sampling instruments may be found in recommendations from organizations (Tables 8-1 and 8-4) and in reviews such as those by Nelson,[6] Willeke and Baron,[10] McClellan and Henderson,[5] and Lodge.[4]

References

1. Nelson, G.O.: Gas Mixtures Preparation and Control. Lewis Publishers, Chelsea, MI (1992).
2. Barrow, C.S.: Generation and Characterization of Gases and Vapors. In: Concepts in Inhalation Toxicology, pp. 63–84. R.O. McClellan and R.F. Henderson, Eds. Hemisphere Publishing Corp., Washington, DC (1989).
3. Lippmann, M.: Calibration of Air Sampling Instruments. In: Air Sampling Instruments for Evaluation of Atmospheric Contaminants, 7th ed., pp. 73–109. S.V. Hering, Ed. American Conference of Governmental Industrial Hygienists, Cincinnati, OH (1989).
4. Chapman, R.L.; Sheesley, D.C.: Calibration in Air Monitoring. ASTM Pub. 598. American Society for Testing and Materials, Philadelphia, PA (1976).
5. Hersch, P.A.: Controlled Addition of Experimental Pollutants to Air. J. Air Poll. Control Assoc. 19:164 (March 1969).
6. Raabe, O.G.: The Generation of Aerosols of Fine Particles. In: Fine Particles, pp. 50–110. B.Y.H. Liu, Ed. Academic Press, New York (1976).
7. Setterlind, A.N.: Preparation of Known Concentrations of Gases to Vapors in Air. Am. Ind. Hyg. Assoc. Q. 14:113 (June 1953).
8. Roccanova, G.: The Present State-of-the-Art of the Preparation of Gaseous Standards. Presented at the Pittsburgh Conference on Analytical Chemistry and Spectroscopy; available from Scientific Gas Products, Inc. (1968).
9. Silverman, L.: Experimental Test Methods. In: Air Pollution Handbook, pp. 12:1–12:48. P.L. Magill, F.R. Holden, and C. Ackley, Eds. McGraw-Hill, New York (1956).
10. Lodge, J.P.: Methods of Air Sampling and Analysis, 3rd ed. Lewis Publishers, Inc., Chelsea, MI (1989).
11. Cotabish, H.N.; McConnaughey, P.W.; Messer, H.C.: Making Known Concentrations for Instrument Calibration. Am. Ind. Hyg. Assoc. J. 22:392 (1961).
12. Saltzman, B.E.: Preparation and Analysis of Calibrated Low Concentrations of Sixteen Toxic Gases. Anal. Chem. 33:1100 (1961).
13. Saltzman, B.E.; Gilberg, N.: Microdetermination of Ozone in Smog Mixtures: Nitrogen Dioxide Equivalent Method. Am. Ind. Hyg. Assoc. J. 20:379 (1959).
14. Saltzman, B.E.; Wartburg, Jr., A.F.: Precision Flow Dilution System for Standard Low Concentrations of Nitrogen Dioxide. Anal. Chem. 37:1261 (1965).
15. Reid, R.C.; Prausnitz, J.M.; Sherwood, T.K.: The Properties of Gases and Liquids, 3rd ed. McGraw–Hill, New York (1977).
16. Nelson, G.O.: Simplified Method for Generating Known Concentrations of Mercury Vapor in Air. Rev. Sci. Instr. 41:776(1970).
17. Altshuller, A.P.; Chohe, L.R.: Applications of Diffusion Cells to the Production of Known Concentrations of Gaseous Hydrocarbons. Anal. Chem. 32:802 (1960).
18. O'Keefe, A.E.; Ortman, G.O.: Primary Standards for Trace Gas Analysis. Anal. Chem. 38:760 (1966).
19. McClellan, R.O.; Henderson, R.F.: Concepts in Inhalation Toxicology. Hemisphere Publishing Corp., New York (1989).
20. Willeke, K.; Baron, P.Q.: Aerosol Measurement Principles, Tech-

niques and Application. Van Nostrand Reinhold, New York (1993).

21. Silver, S.K.: Constant Gassing Chambers: Principles Influencing Design and Operation. J. Lab. Clin. Med. 31:1153 (1946).
22. Moss, O.R.: Comparison of Three Methods of Evaluating Inhalation Toxicology Chamber Performance. In: Proceedings of the Inhalation Toxicology and Technology Symposium, pp. 19–28. B.K.J. Leong, Ed. Ann Arbor Science Publishers, Inc., Ann Arbor, MI (1981).
23. Drew, R.T.; Laskin, S.: Environmental Inhalation Chambers. In: Methods of Animal Experimentation, Vol. IV, Environmental and Special Senses, pp. 1–42. W.I. Gray, Ed. Academic Press, New York (1973).
24. Griffis, L.C.; Wolff, R.K.; Beethe, R.L.; et al.: Evaluation of a Multitiered Inhalation Exposure Chamber. Fund. Appl. Toxicol. 1:8 (1981).
25. MacFarland, H.N.: Design and Operational Characteristics of Inhalation Exposure Equipment: A Review. Fund. Appl. Toxicol. 3:603 (1983).
26. Carpenter, R.L.; Beethe, R.L.: Airflow and Aerosol Distribution in Animal Exposure Facilities. In: Generation of Aerosols and Facilities for Exposure Experiments, pp. 459–474. K. Willeke, Ed. Ann Arbor Science Publishers, Inc., Ann Arbor, MI (1980).
27. Cheng, Y.S.; Moss, O.R.: Inhalation Exposure Systems. In: Concepts in Inhalation Toxicology. R.O. McClellan and R.F. Henderson, Eds. Hemisphere Publishing Corporation, Washington, DC (1989).
28. Moss, O.R.: Inhalation Toxicology: Sampling Techniques Related to Control of Exposure Atmospheres. In: Aerosol Measurement Principles, Techniques, and Applications, pp. 833–842. K. Willeke and P.A. Baron, Eds. Van Nostrand Reinhold, New York (1993).
29. Mokler, B.V.; White, R.K.: Quantitative Standard for Exposure Chamber Integrity. Am. Ind. Hyg. Assoc. J. 44(4):292 (1983).
30. Hemenway, D.R.; Carpenter, R.L.; Moss, R.R.: Inhalation Toxicology Chamber Performance: A Quantitative Model. Am. Ind. Hyg. Assoc. J. 43:120 (1982).
31. Whitaker, S.: Introduction to Fluid Mechanics. Prentice-Hall, Englewood Cliffs, NJ (1968).

Chapter 9

Aerosol Sampler Calibration

Yung-Sung Cheng, Ph.D., Bean T. Chen, Ph.D.
Inhalation Toxicology Research Institute, Lovelace Biomedical and Environmental Research Institute, Albuquerque, New Mexico

CONTENTS

Introduction

Before aerosol sampling instruments are used in any study, the user must ensure that these instruments perform according to the specifications and that the data obtained from the instruments are of high quality, reproducible, and defendable for the intended purposes. Ideally, instrument performance should be evaluated in the laboratory under controlled conditions and/or tested in the field. For some instruments, including optical counters, impactors, and condensation nucleus counters (CNCs), instrument responses can be predicted theoretically. However, practical considerations, such as compactness, portability, and convenience of operation, may influence instrument design. As a result, instrument response may deviate from the theoretical prediction based on ideal conditions. For example, although 50% effective cutoff diameters and collection efficiencies for an impactor stage can be computed, the phenomena of particle bounce, re-entrainment, electrostatic charge effects, and wall losses do occur.[1,2] Therefore, the measured impaction efficiency may be different from the theoretically determined collection efficiency and, thus, experimental calibration is essential. For other instruments, empirical data using standard test aerosols are needed to generate calibration curves.

Most instruments are calibrated and evaluated by the manufacturer or the inventor before being used by others. For an instrument intended to collect and analyze an aerosol, collection efficiency and wall losses are generally determined in the calibration. For a real-time, direct-reading instrument, calibration establishes the relationship between instrument response (e.g., electronic signal or channel number) and the value of the property (e.g., particle size, number concentration, or mass concentration) being measured. However, the operating conditions and the parameters used during the original calibration can vary from those under which the eventual user operates. As a result, the original calibration data may not apply, and the user must recalibrate the instrument to operate it with confidence. In general, a reliable and accurate calibration process requires 1) sufficient knowledge of the capabilities and limitations of an instrument, 2) appropriate test facilities, 3) proper selection of a desired test aerosol, 4) thorough investigation of relevant parameters, 5) sufficient knowledge about the conditions that can be encountered during operation, and 6) a quality assurance program that is followed throughout the test.

In the last two decades, developments in the generation and classification of monodisperse aerosols, along with the improvement of test facilities, have made instrument calibration easier and the results more reproducible. Calibration methods for air sampling instruments have been reviewed.[3,4] The calibration and use of flow monitoring devices that play an integral role in aerosol sampling and instrument calibration are discussed in Chapter 7. This chapter reviews the calibration techniques relevant to aerosol samplers, such as sizing instruments, devices for concentrations, and size-selective samplers. Test facilities, generation of test aerosols, and testing procedures will be emphasized.

General Considerations

Before embarking on a rigorous instrument testing/calibration program, decisions must be made on the frequency of calibration. General descriptions of instrument components and the measured parameter for each aerosol instrument are also discussed here. Finally, the sampling environments, which will influence the selection of the appropriate test facility and procedures, must also be considered.

Components of Aerosol Samplers

An aerosol sampler usually consists of a sampling inlet, a detection or collection section, an air mover, and flow controllers. The sampling inlet, which is the entrance to the instrument, is connected to the detection section with a short transport line. The air mover (usually a pump) moves air into the sampler, and flow controllers control flow rates. Personal samplers and some area samplers, including impactors and filters, have separate pumps and flowmeters. A few passive samplers, such as personal photometers, do not have the air mover and flowmeters. They rely on air current in the atmosphere to bring the aerosol into the detector. Most direct-reading aerosol instruments, such as optical counters, CNCs, and photometers, include the sampling inlet, transport line, detector, pump, and flowmeter in a single unit. Each unit is indeed a complete system. For other systems such as filter samplers, individual components must be assembled.

It is important to know that there can be significant particle losses in the sampling inlet (aspiration efficiency) and transport lines (transport losses), especially for very large (>5 µm) and small particles (<0.01 µm). Also, every instrument has finite detection limits and detection efficiency. The flowmeter controls a constant volumetric flow rate so that the instrument can be operated properly, and accurate sampling volume and, therefore, aerosol concentration can be determined. Calibration of the flowmeters is a part of the total instrument calibration. Recalibration of a flowmeter is required when it is used at a high altitude or under ambient conditions (temperature, pressure, and gas composition) different from the original factory calibration. Calibration of the flowmeter is usually the first step in the process of instrument calibration.

Measured Parameters

Depending on the function of the instrument, the measured parameter can be separated into particle concentration (number or mass) and particle size distribution. For size-selective samplers, mass concentrations for inspirable, thoracic, or respirable fractions will be determined. Often, both parameters have to be considered in the instrument calibration. For example, in impactor calibration, the collection efficiency as a function of particle size has to be determined, taking into account the sampling and transport losses. It is recommended that the investigator measure the detection efficiency of the whole system, including the aspiration efficiency of the inlet, losses in the transport lines, and efficiencies of the detector or sensor.

Each instrument has a finite detection range and is therefore useful in that range. The applicable size range is based on the sampling principle, the detector efficiency, and inlet design. For example, inertial-type instruments such as impactors usually collect particles between 0.5 and 15 µm; for diffusion batteries, the size ranges between 0.005 and 0.5 µm. For optical instruments, the lower detection limit is about 0.1 µm. Therefore, the instrument influences the selection of the test aerosol. In most calibrations, particles having the size in the applicable range of the instrument are required to establish the calibration curves. Also, most instruments have minimum and maximum detection limits in aerosol concentration. For example, instruments that are based on the detection of scattered light for single particles have very low maximum concentration limits (in the order of 100 particles/cm^3). At higher concentrations, increased coincidence errors are due to the presence of two or more particles in the sensing volume of the detector. For aerosol collectors, overloading the substrates causes sampling errors; therefore, appropriate sampling time and mass concentration have to be considered.

Sampling Environments

Depending on the wind speed in an environment, the sampling procedure can be classified as calm air sampling or sampling in the flow stream. Calm air sampling generally refers to a wind speed less than 50 cm/sec and applies to indoor environments, including residential homes, offices, and factories. Flow stream sampling refers to environments with higher wind speed, such as ambient atmosphere or inside ventilation ducts and stacks. The air flow pattern in an environment affects particle movement and, therefore, is an important parameter for the inlet aspiration efficiency. Criteria for calm air and flow stream sampling have been discussed by Davies,[(5)] Hinds,[(6)] and Brockmann.[(7)] To simulate various flow conditions in the environment, test facilities with different capabilities should be considered. Instrument chambers with uniform, low air speeds are suitable for testing samplers under calm air conditions, and aerosol wind tunnels are required for testing samplers under flow stream conditions.

Test Programs

Aerosol instruments can be tested on several levels for performance. The decision on the appropriate test program is largely driven by regulatory and/or scientific needs. The three levels of test programs include:

1. Flow calibration and system integrity
2. Single point check
3. Full-scale calibration.

The simplest test procedure checks flow rates and system leaks. Scheduled and frequent checks are recommended for routine use of any instrument. However, passive samplers such as the personal mass monitor, MINIRAM, do not require flow calibration.

The next level of testing involves instrument response for a single point. For an aerosol sizing instrument, a test aerosol (usually polystyrene latex [PSL] particles) of a defined size is used, and the response is compared to an existing calibration curve. This procedure assumes that a full-response calibration curve is available, and the user performs the test to make sure it is functioning normally. A full-scale calibration requires testing the instrument response over its full operational range. Therefore, the calibration curve in terms of response as a function of particle size or concentration can be established. The efforts, equipment, and test facility needed to perform these programs increase substantially from the simple flow calibration to the full-scale test. Only a standard flowmeter and a pressure gauge are needed for a flow calibration and system check. The effort is minimal, and the benefit to the user in terms of improved quality of data is high. For a single point test, aerosol generation and monitoring systems are needed, but if they are available in the laboratory, the effort required is relatively small. A full-scale calibration requires more elaborate test facilities and extensive efforts in terms of time and labor for the exercise. Essentially, any user can perform a regular flow check, and any laboratory with experience in aerosol instruments can check a single point. However, only aerosol laboratories with appropriate facilities and equipment can perform a full-scale calibration.

When Should an Instrument Be Calibrated?

Full-scale calibration is needed to establish a calibration curve for each new instrument. Therefore, it is usually assumed that the manufacturer or instrument developer would provide such data. However, there are some commercial instruments without calibration data. In many cases, independent investigators provide careful evaluation and calibration of such instruments, and their results are usually published in the open literature.

A user needs to obtain aerosol measurement data of high quality in order to meet scientific guidelines or regulatory standards established by government agencies. The user must ensure that the instrument performs according to its specifications. The flow and system integrity should be checked whenever possible, and a single-point check should be considered for scientific validation. To a large extent, decisions on full-scale calibration depend on the scientific justifications and regulatory requirements for each study. Aerosols are usually measured for scientific research, regulatory compliance for health protection purposes, and toxicity testing.

For scientific research, calibration data provided by

the manufacturer or published in a scientific journal can be used, when the instrument is used under normal conditions. If the instrument is used under different ambient pressures or flow rates, then it may need to be recalibrated under the actual operating conditions. At a minimum, the flowmeter must be calibrated and a single-point check be performed to see whether the instrument responds differently than the original calibration.

Aerosols in work environments are measured by industrial hygienists because of mandates by government agencies including the Occupational Safety and Health Administration (OSHA) or Mine Safety and Health Administration (MSHA). Similarly, U.S. Environmental Protection Agency (U.S. EPA) regulations require determination of release of aerosols to the ambient atmosphere from fixed-point and mobile sources. These regulations often specify standard sampling methods or equivalent methods that follow the same performance specifications. For example, the U.S. EPA performance specifications and test procedures applicable to a size-selective instrument, PM_{10}, are contained in 40 CFR Part 53–Ambient Air Monitoring Reference and Equivalent Methods.[8] The PM_{10} samplers should be tested in a wind tunnel with liquid particles (10 sizes ranging from 3 to 25 μm in aerodynamic diameter) at wind speeds of 2, 8, and 24 km/h. The 50% cutoff determined for each speed must be 10 ± 0.5 μm. The precision for determination of concentration and flow stability is also specified.[9]

Finally, toxicity tests using inhalation exposures for new products or chemicals must be conducted under Good Laboratory Practice Standards for FDA[10] and Toxic Substances Control Act test guidelines.[11] Based on these guidelines, specific procedures for the calibration of mass monitors to determine aerosol concentrations in exposure chambers are required. For example, the laboratory must provide data on instrument responses of real-time aerosol monitors for the test material, with filter samples as a reference standard in the concentration range used for the study.

Calibration Standards

Calibration curves are generated by comparing responses from the test instrument to those of a calibration standard. Several standard methods are now available for calibrating aerosol instruments. The primary standard method for particle size and number concentration determination is the microscopic examination, whereas the gravimetric method is the primary standard for mass concentration determination. However, several secondary standard methods have been developed and frequently used because they are often easier to use than the primary method. Table 9-1 lists aerosol instruments and test standards that have been used for their calibration. The following paragraphs describe each test standard in detail.

Direct Measurement with Microscopy

The primary standard method of instrument calibration is direct measurement of collected particles under an optical or electron microscope. This technique provides information on particle size distribution and particle number concentration. For example, a number concentration determined from an aerosol collected in a liquid impinger has long been used to determine dust levels in occupational environments. Also, the response of a CNC was calibrated against a photographic CNC,[12] in which the particles are photographed and the total number of the particles counted to yield the number concentration. However, this technique is labor-intensive, and the observations varied substantially among different operators. With advanced imaging techniques, the procedure can be automated, and the accuracy of the measurements in both size and number concentration determinations is greatly improved. The microscopic technique is still used routinely in determination of particle size and number concentration of fiber aerosols. It is also used to determine the number concentrations of bioaerosols. It is a good quality assurance practice to check the size of standard test aerosols with the primary method during the test.

One problem in using the microscopic method to determine the diameter of a liquid droplet is deformation of the droplet on a collection surface. Because of surface tension, a droplet loses its spherical shape and forms a shape similar to a segment of sphere with a height of h and diameter of D, as shown in Figure 9-1. This diameter, D, is larger than the actual diameter, d, and the ratio of the projected and the actual diameter, $B = d/D$ is called the spread factor. This factor is a function of the surface tension of the droplet and the adhesion force between the particle and the surface; the spread factor is needed for accurate size measurement of droplets using the microscopic technique. For routine collection of known test aerosols such as dioctyl phthalate (DOP), oleic acid, and dibutyl phthalate (DBP) on glass slides coated with a special agent, spread factors can be developed.[13–15] Using a test aerosol generated from a vibrating orifice aerosol generator (VOAG) as described in the section on "Test Aerosol Generation," the spread factor can be determined by comparing the measured diameter, D, and the theoretically calculated aerosol diameter, d. A more general but direct method has been described by Cheng *et al.*[16] This technique is used to determine the volume of a deformed droplet by examining the droplet under a microscope with an angle other than 90° (Figure 9-1). From the measured axes of the projected image, the height of the spherical segment is calculated; therefore, the volume equivalent diameter d is also calculated.

TABLE 9-1. Calibration Standards of Aerosol Instruments

Instrument	Measured Parameter	Particle Size Range (μm)	Calibration Standard
Size Measurement			
Cascade impactor	Flow rate, gas medium, physical dimension in and around the nozzle	0.05–30	Monodisperse, spherical particles with a known size and density
Aerodynamic particle sizing instrument	Flow rate, pressure, gas medium	0.5–20	Monodisperse, spherical particles with a known size, shape, and density
Optical particle counter	Wavelength of the light source, range of scattering angles, sensitivity of detector	0.3–15	Monodisperse, spherical particles with a known size and refractive index
Electrical mobility analyzer	Flow rate, charging mechanism, electric field strength	0.001–0.1	Monodisperse, spherical particles with a known size
Diffusion battery	Flow rate, temperature, deposition surface	0.001–0.1	Monodisperse, spherical particles with a known size
Number Concentration Measurement			
Condensation nuclei counter	Flow rate, saturation ratio, temperature gradient	0.001–0.5	Electrical classifer with electrometer
Mass Concentration Measurement			
Photometer	Wavelength of the light source, range of scattering angles, sensitivity of detector	0.3–1.5	Gravimetric measurement of filter samples
β-Attenuation monitor	Uniformity of particle deposit	1–15	Gravimetric measurement of filter samples
Quartz crystal mass balance	Sensitivity of the sensor	0.02–10	Gravimetric measurement of filter samples

Particle Size

Monodisperse, spherical solid particles of PSL have been used widely as a secondary test standard to determine the responses of aerosol sizing instruments, including optical counters, impactors, and other real-time monitors. These particles are uniform, spherical, and smooth with very small standard deviations. The particle sizes have been determined by the manufacturer using microscopic techniques. They have well-defined physicochemical properties, including the refractive index, density, and chemical composition. They are commercially available in the size range of 0.03 to 200 μm and are relatively easy to use.

A VOAG or an electrostatic classifier (EC) is also frequently used to produce monodisperse spherical test aerosols with well-defined characteristics. The VOAG produces particles in the size range of 1.5 to 30 μm and the EC in the size range of 0.003 to 1 μm. The sizes of these test particles can be accurately predicted from the operational principles, when the devices are operated appropriately. Theoretical sizes have been verified with the primary standard using microscopic techniques.[17,18]

Number Concentration

The primary standard for calibration of number concentration is to collect aerosol particles using a high-efficiency filter and then to count the particles in a microscope. From the number of particles counted in a

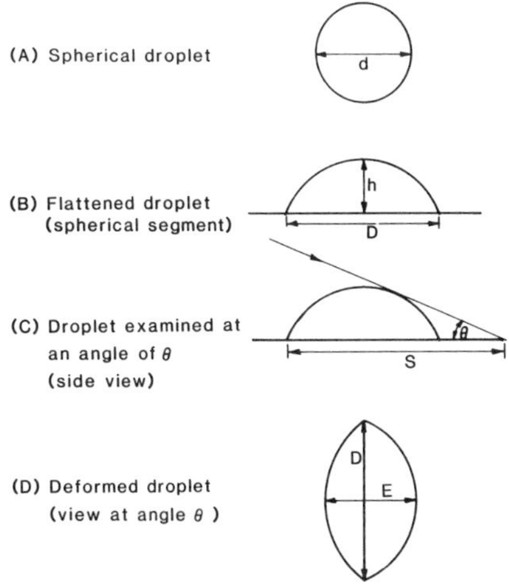

FIGURE 9-1. Schematic of drop particles collected on a surface.

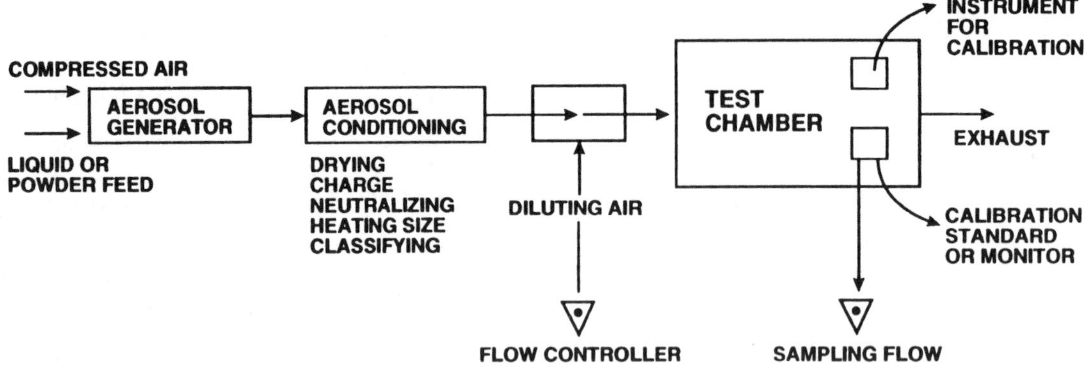

FIGURE 9-2. Schematic of a typical calibration system for aerosol samplers.

unit area, the total collection area, and the volume of air sample, the number concentrations (particles/cm^3) can be estimated. A secondary standard and more commonly used method is the electrometer technique, which measures the electrical current of mobility-classified aerosols produced by the EC.[19] A monodisperse test aerosol generated by an EC carries mostly a single positive charge. By measuring the electrical current with an electrometer, the aerosol concentration can be determined by dividing the measured current with the volumetric flow rate and the elementary electric charge.[18] For particles greater than 0.05 µm, a significant portion of the charged particles (depending on the aerosol size distribution) would include doubly charged particles and, therefore, corrections for the doubly charged particles are needed to obtain an accurate number concentration from this method.[18] The electrometer technique is very useful for particles smaller than 1 µm.

For micrometer-size particles, a secondary method is to determine the mass concentration by the gravimetric or colorimetric method of monodisperse, spherical test particles, then to convert the mass concentration (C_m, mass/volume) to the number concentration (C_n, particles/volume):

$$C_n = \frac{C_m}{\frac{\pi}{6} \rho_p d_{avg}^3} \tag{1}$$

where: ρ_p = the particle density
d_{avg} = the particle diameter of the average volume

Mass Concentration

The primary standard for aerosol mass concentration is to pass a known volume of an aerosol through a high-efficiency filter and determine the increase in mass of the substrate due to the collected aerosol particles. The mass can be determined using either an analytical balance (10-µg precision) or an electronic balance (1-µg precision). Mass concentration is obtained by dividing the increased mass by the gas volume sampled. Colorimetric or fluorescent techniques can be used to determine the mass concentration of test aerosols tagged with dye. Generation of tagged particles will be discussed in the section on "Test Aerosol Generation." Criteria for representative samples in either the flow stream or calm air sampling conditions should be followed to minimize sampling biases.

Calibration Systems and Test Facilities

Components of Calibration Systems

Figure 9-2 is a schematic diagram of a typical calibration apparatus for aerosol instruments. It includes an aerosol generator, conditioning devices, a flow mixer, a test chamber, pressure and air flow monitoring equipment, the instrument to be calibrated, and the calibration standard. The aerosol from the generator can be monodisperse or polydisperse, solid or liquid, wet or dry, charged or uncharged, or spherical or nonspherical (described later). Generally, this aerosol requires several steps of conditioning before use. For an aerosol containing volatile vapors or water droplets, a diffusion dryer with desiccant and/or charcoal is commonly used to remove the solvent. In some cases, a heat treatment using a high-temperature furnace is required for the production of a test aerosol.[20,21] The heat treatment involves either sintering or fusing the particles to reach the desired particle morphology and chemical form, or initiating particle evaporation and subsequent condensation to produce monodisperse particles. Because aerosol particles are usually charged by static electrification during formation, a neutralizer containing a bipolar ion source (e.g., ^{85}Kr, ^{241}Am, or ^{63}Ni) is often used in the aerosol treatment. This reduces the number of charges on the particles and results in an aerosol with charge equilibrium.[22] In addition, a size-classifying device is often used in the aerosol treatment to segregate particles of a similar size or of a desired size fraction.[23–25] Furthermore, a concentrator or a dilutor is often used to adjust the aerosol concentration.[26,27]

Test Facilities

The desired test aerosol is then delivered to the test chamber, where the instrument under testing and the test standard are located. Test facilities may include mixing chambers, instrument chambers for calm air sampling, and aerosol wind tunnels. All test chambers require uniform aerosol concentrations in the test section where the aerosol instrument is located. However, the aerosol wind tunnel can provide a test section with various wind speeds for testing a size-selective aerosol sampler under simulated ambient flow conditions. Vertical instrument chambers with low velocity are used for calm air sampling. Mixing chambers with small, simple plenums are used to provide steady aerosol streams for limited calibration of the detection or collection efficiency of the instrument detector. These chambers usually do not provide performance data for calm air or flow stream sampling conditions. The space, facility requirements, and cost associated with these three types of test chambers are quite different. Mixing chambers are usually placed on top of a laboratory bench, whereas the instrument chamber requires a much larger space, and the wind tunnel often occupies the whole room. A vacuum cleaner or pump is sufficient to move air within the mixing chamber. For vertical chambers, air movers with capacities between 200 and 1000 L/min are required, whereas larger fans are part of the wind tunnel systems.

Mixing Chambers

A mixing chamber is usually a small cylindrical chamber made of glass, plastic, or metal, where the aerosol can be uniformly distributed (Figure 9-3). The aerosol instrument is placed outside the chamber. Samples are taken via sampling probes inside the chamber and delivered to both the instrument to be calibrated and the calibration standard or monitor. Pressure in the chamber and flow rates through instruments are monitored. Multiple samples can be taken simultaneously to characterize the test aerosol, including aerosol concentration and size distribution. The key to successful calibration is to ensure that the same aerosol (size and concentration) is delivered to both the instrument to be calibrated and the test standard/monitor. The same sampling probes and transport line between the probe and the instrument inlet should be used. Also, the same flow rate through the instrument and the test

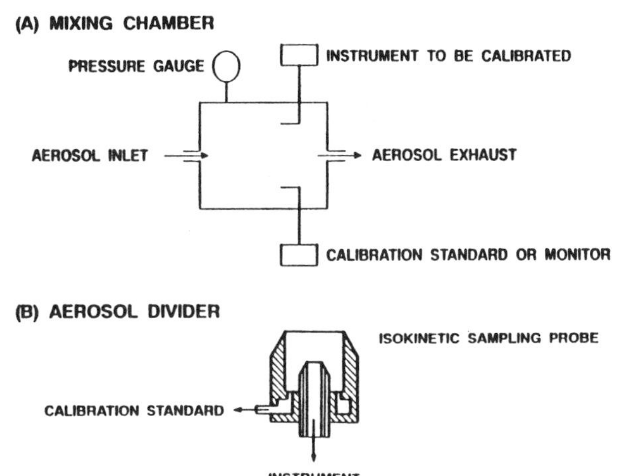

FIGURE 9-3. Schematic of a setup for instrument calibration using a mixing chamber (A) and an aerosol divider (B).

standard/monitor is preferred. If the same flow rate can be used for the tested instrument and the standard, it is recommended to sample a single aerosol flow from the chamber, then split the flow in half with a three-way valve. Alternative sampling by switching the valve between the tested instrument and the calibration standard minimizes experimental errors. Also, an aerosol divider is a common sampling port for calibrating a mass monitor.[28] In the aerosol divider, the flow is split isokinetically into two streams: one passes directly into the instrument to be calibrated; the other flows through the calibration standard (Figure 9-3).

The mixing chamber is an inexpensive piece of equipment, easy to set up, and does not require a large working area. Therefore, many instruments including factory calibration have been tested in this fashion. The mixing chamber can be used to obtain detector efficiency, such as the counting efficiency of a CNC, and collection efficiency, as well as internal losses of impactors and response of real-time monitors. It is especially useful for smaller particles; for particles larger than 3–5 μm, it is increasingly difficult to provide a stable aerosol stream in sufficiently high concentrations. Because the instrument is placed outside the chamber, it is not possible to test the aspiration efficiency of the instrument inlet under different wind conditions.

Test Chambers for Calm Air Conditions

Another way of calibrating an instrument is to introduce an aerosol into a test chamber that contains the subject instrument and the test standard/monitor. This type of chamber usually has a large cross-sectional area in the test section, and therefore a low air velocity(<50 cm/sec), simulating quiescent atmosphere. For example, large exposure chambers for inhalation experiments[29] have been used for calibration of real-time

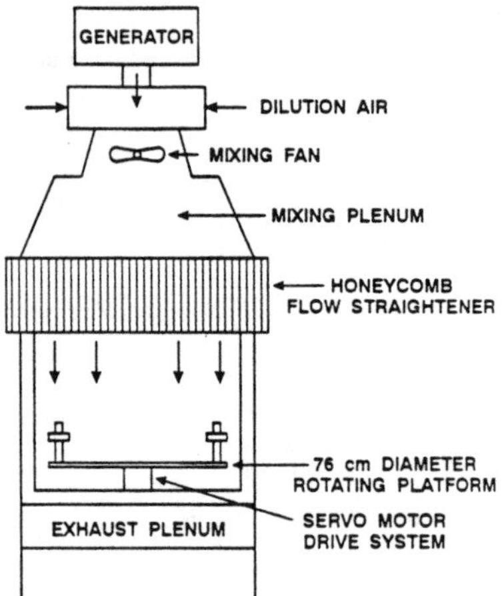

FIGURE 9-4. Schematic of a vertical aerosol instrument chamber.

aerosol monitors.[30] In addition, dedicated instrument chambers have been designed for calibration of several instruments simultaneously.[31–33] A vertical flow instrument chamber with large test volume (1.8 m^3) similar to the design of Marple and Rubow[33] is shown in Figure 9-4. The test aerosol enters vertically from the top of the chamber. The opposing air jets create turbulence to mix the aerosol. To improve the uniformity of aerosol distribution, a 10-in. box fan is placed underneath the chamber entrance for mixing. A 10-cm-thick honeycomb structure is inserted above the test section of the chamber to reduce eddy created by flow turbulence and present the sampling area with a well-defined downward air flow. To ensure that spatial variations of concentration and size distribution are minimized, samplers are placed on a 30-in. platform rotating at 0.5 or 1 rpm. Variations of aerosol concentrations in the sampling platform based on filter samples are less than 5.5% for particles of 12 μm.

This type of instrument chamber provides uniform concentrations of aerosols in the test section for large particles. Several instruments could be placed inside the chamber for simultaneous calibration and comparison. The flow rate and turbulence intensity in the chamber are low, simulating calm air sampling conditions.

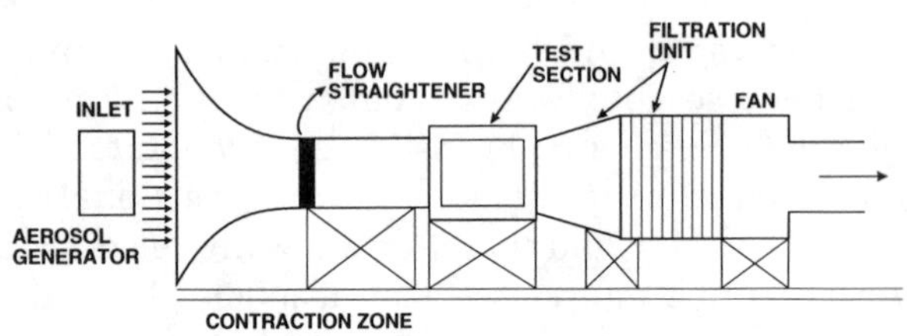

FIGURE 9-5. Schematic of an open circuit aerosol wind tunnel.

Aerosol Wind Tunnels

Aerosol wind tunnels have been used to test many aerosol samplers for wind speeds between 0.5 to 10 m/sec.[9,34–36] Two types of wind tunnels are commonly used: an open circuit tunnel and a closed circuit tunnel. Figure 9-5 shows a diagram of an open circuit tunnel. Room air is taken into the system with the test aerosol and then passed through honeycomb screens to reduce the turbulence and to provide uniform velocity. A section of contraction cone connects the test section and the screens. The test section usually has a rectangular shape and is large enough to accommodate the instrument and filter samplers with isokinetic inlets. The cross-sectional area of the test instrument should not occupy more than 10–15% of the test section so that the uniform velocity and aerosol profiles will not be affected. The aerosol then is filtered through a high-efficiency particulate air (HEPA) filter bank, and clean air is exhausted to the room. A fan with sufficient capacity is used to move the air through the tunnel. Large open circuit wind tunnels that can accommodate a manikin are also used extensively to study the inspirability of large particles.[34,37,38]

Figure 9-6 shows a schematic of a closed-circuit wind tunnel which has a continuous path for the air. The HEPA filter removes aerosols after the test section, and the air is recirculated. Consistent flow profiles are easier to maintain in the recirculating tunnel, and less energy consumption is required for a given test section size and velocity as compared to an open tunnel. It is also less noisy than the open tunnel. However, it occupies at least twice the space and has a higher initial installation cost. To dissipate the heat produced, the closed tunnel may need to be cooled for continuous

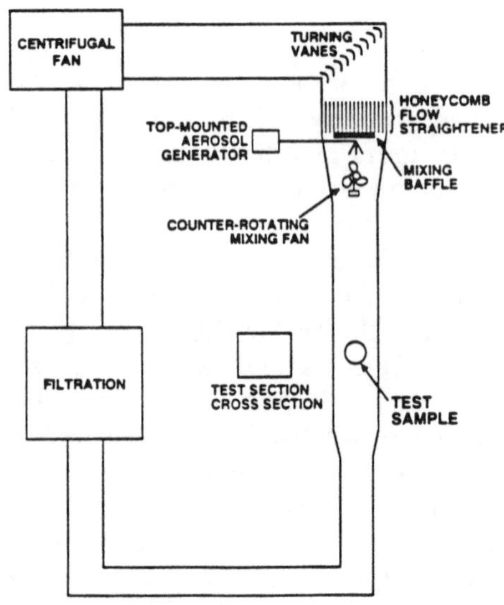

FIGURE 9-6. Schematic of a closed circuit aerosol wind tunnel.

TABLE 9-2. Test Aerosols and Generation Methods Used for Instrument Calibration

Test Aerosol	Particle Morphology	Size Range[A,B] VMD (μm)	Size Range[A,B] σ_g	Density (g/cm³)	Refractive Index[C]	Generation Method	Aerosol Output (particles/cm³)
PSL (PVT)	Spherical, solid	0.01–30	≤1.02	1.05 (1.027)	1.58	Nebulization	<10⁴
Fluorescent uranine	Irregular, solid	<8	1.4–3	1.53	—	Nebulization	<10⁹
Dioctyl phthalate	Spherical, liquid	0.5–40	≤1.1	0.99	1.49	Vibrating atomization	<10⁵
Oleic acid	Spherical, liquid	0.5–40	≤1.1	0.89	1.46	Vibrating atomization	<10⁵
Ammonium fluorescein	Spherical, solid	0.5–50	≤1.1	1.35	—	Vibrating atomization	<10⁵
Fused ferric oxide	Spherical, solid	0.2–10	≤1.1	2.3	—	Spinning disc (top) atomization	<10⁷
Fused aluminosilicate	Spherical, solid	0.2–10	≤1.1	3.5	—	Spinning disc (top) atomization	<10⁷
Fused cerium oxide	Spherical, solid	0.2–10	≤1.1	4.33	—	Spinning disc (top) atomization	<10⁷
Sodium chloride	Irregular, solid	0.002–0.3	≤1.2	2.17	1.54	Evaporation/ condensation	<10⁶
Silver	Irregular, solid	0.002–0.3	≤1.2	10.5	0.54	Evaporation/ condensation	<10⁶
Coal dust	Irregular, solid	~ 3.3	~ 3.2	1.45	1.54–0.5i	Dry powder dispersion	<30 mg/m³
Arizona road dust	Irregular, solid	~ 3.8	~ 3.0	2.61	—	Dry powder dispersion	<30 mg/m³

[A]Aerosol treatment of drying, charge neutralization, and size classification is generally used.
[B]VMD = volume median diameter; σ_g = geometric standard deviation.
[C]— indicates refractive index (RI) unknown; i indicates imaginary RI for absorption coefficient.

operation during the summer months.

Aerosol wind tunnels are similar to those used in aerodynamic tests, but they require provisions to introduce aerosols in the test section and remove test aerosols after the test section. In addition to a uniform velocity profile in the section, a uniform aerosol concentration profile is also required. For example, U.S. EPA testing requirements specify that air velocity and aerosol concentration through the test section must be within ± 10% of the mean values in the test section.(9)

Test Aerosol Generation

Test aerosols contain either monodisperse or polydisperse, spherical or nonspherical, solid, or liquid particles.(3,6,39–41) The characteristics of an ideal generator are a constant and reproducible production of monodisperse and stable aerosol particles whose size and concentration can be easily controlled. For general instrument calibration, the test aerosol often contains monodisperse, spherical particles. To calibrate an instrument for a specific environment, the test aerosol should have similar physical and chemical properties to those of the aerosol of interest. In addition, the environment in which the instrument is to be operated must be considered when selecting the test aerosol. For example, if the instrument is to be operated in a high-temperature environment, the desired test aerosol could be a refractory metal oxide, such as cerium oxide, because of its thermal stability and chemical inertness. Generally, as long as the desired aerosol is determined, the appropriate method of generation can be identified. Table 9-2 lists the test aerosols frequently used for instrument calibration. Monodisperse aerosols containing spherical particles are the most widely used. Parti-

TABLE 9-3. Operating Parameters of Air-Blast and Ultrasonic Nebulizers

Nebulizer	Operating Conditions: Orifice Diameter (mm)	Operating Conditions: Air Pressure (psig)	Operating Conditions: Frequency (mHz)	Flow Rate[A] (L/min)	Aerosol Output (μL/L)	Droplet Size Distribution: VMD (μm)	Droplet Size Distribution: σ_g	Commercial Source
Airblast type								
Collison	0.35	15		2.0	8.8	2.5–3	—	BGI
		25		2.7	7.7	1.9–2	—	
DeVilbiss[B] D-40	0.84	15		12.4	15.5	4.2	1.8	DEV
		30		20.9	12.1	2.8	1.9	
DeVilbiss D-45	0.76	15		9.4	23.2	4.0	—	DEV
		30		14.5	22.9	3.4	—	
Lovelace	0.26	20		1.5	40	5.8	1.8	INT
		50		2.3	27	2.6	2.3	
Retec X-70/N	0.46	20		5.0	46	5.7	1.8	INT
		50		9.7	47	3.2	2.2	
Ultrasonic Type								
DeVilbiss 880	(2)[C]		1.35	41.0	54	5.7	1.5	DEV
	(4)[C]		1.35	41.0	150	6.9	1.6	
Sono-Tek			0.025–0.12	10^{-6}–0.44	—	18–80	—	SON

[A]Output per orifice.
[B]Vent closed.
[C]Power settings.

cles with nonspherical shapes are sometimes used in calibration to study the possible effect of shape on the instrument response. Polydisperse dust particles have also been used in calibrating dust monitors. This is important, because most real aerosols contain nonspherical particles of different sizes and densities.

The size distribution and concentration of a test aerosol depend on the characteristics of the generator and the feed material. The information given in this section is intended to assist in the selection of appropriate generation techniques. The actual size distribution in each application should always be measured directly with the appropriate instruments.

Polydisperse Aerosols

Polydisperse aerosols are seldom used as test aerosols to calibrate sizing instruments; however, some polydisperse aerosols, such as coal dust and Arizona road dust, are frequently used in calibrating dust monitors, which provide information on the mass concentration of total and/or respirable dust. There are two ways to generate polydisperse aerosols: wet droplet dispersion and dry powder dispersion.

Wet Dispersion

The simplest way to disperse a droplet aerosol is by wet nebulization. Two types of nebulizers are often used to produce droplet aerosols. Air-blast nebulizers[42] use compressed air (15–50 psig, 1 psig = 6.87 × 10^4 dyne/cm^2) to draw bulk liquid from a reservoir as a result of the Bernoulli effect. The high-velocity air breaks up the liquid into droplets, then suspends the droplets as part of the aerosol. Droplets produced from this method have a volume median diameter (VMD) of 1–10 μm and a geometric standard deviation (σ_g) of 1.4–2.5 (Table 9-3). The aerosol size distribution can be modified by varying the pressure in the compressed air or the dilution ratio in the solution. One problem arises when the bulk liquid contains a volatile solvent that evaporates rapidly after formation of a droplet. The continuous loss of solvent increases the solute concentration in the reservoir and causes the particle size to increase gradually with time. This problem can be circumvented by circulating the solution through a large reservoir,[43] delivering the solution at constant rate,[44] and cooling the nebulizer. Figure 9-7 shows a modified reservoir for the Retec nebulizers that maintains stable aerosol generation.

In the ultrasonic nebulizer, the mechanical energy necessary to atomize a liquid comes from a piezoelectric crystal vibrating under the influence of an alternating electric field produced by an electronic high-frequency oscillator. The vibrations are transmitted through a coupling fluid to a nebulizer cup containing the solution to be aerosolized. At a certain frequency (1.3–1.7 mHz), a heavy mist appears above the liquid surface of the cup. The diameter of the droplets making up the mist is related to the wavelength of the capillary waves, which decreases with increasing frequency of the ultrasonic vibrations. Normally, the VMD is 5–10 μm, with a σ_g of 1.4–2.0 (Table 9-3).

Aerosol particles with chemical properties different from those of the liquid feed material can be produced through wet dispersion by using suitable gas phase reactions, such as polymerization or oxidation. Production of spherical particles of insoluble oxides and aluminosilicate particles with entrapped radionuclides has been described.[20,45]

Dry Dispersion

Aerosolization of dry powders and fibers requires different techniques than aerosolization of droplets or suspensions. The dry powder generation methods usually include a two-step operation: 1) feeding or delivery of dry powder at a constant rate to the disperser and 2) dispersing the powder pneumatically in the aerosol form. The ease of dispersing a powder depends on the powder material, particle size, particle shape, electrostatic charge, and moisture content. Dry powder usually forms clumps or aggregates. A sticky powder is difficult to generate because the powder usually clogs the feeding system and requires high energy from the disperser to break apart the agglomerates into individual aerosol particles. Aerosols generated from dry powder dispersers are also highly charged and, therefore, require discharging to reduce the electrostatic charge.

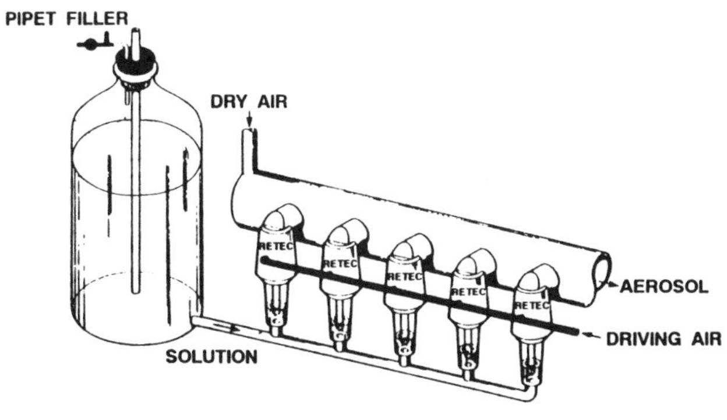

FIGURE 9-7. Schematic of a modified Retec Nebulizer for constant output.

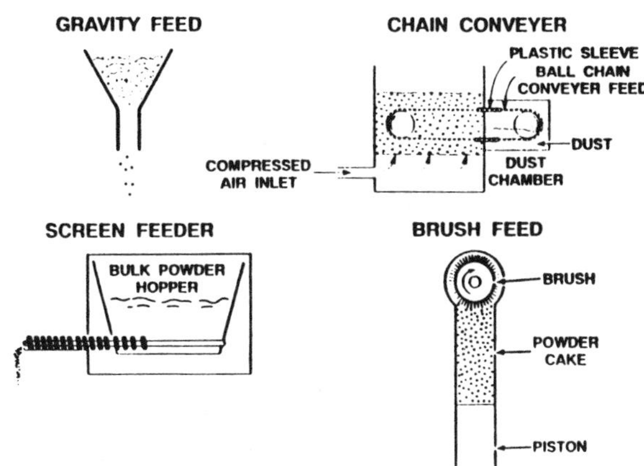

FIGURE 9-8. Schematic of dry powder delivery mechanisms.

Powder delivery systems,[6,46] in which powder is delivered by scraping off the top layer, can use hoppers, screw feeders, rotating disks, conveyor belts composed of chains, tubing, brushes, troughs, or compressed cylindrical packs (Figure 9-8). Gravity delivery systems are composed of simple hoppers designed to drop their contents into grooves cut in a plate or directly into a fluidized bed. The TSI fluidized-bed system uses a chain to deliver a powder from a hopper to the multicomponent bed. Commercial screw feeders[47] and flexible-walled, brush-bristle augers[48,49] have been used to successfully deliver powders to an airstream. In the instrument calibration and aerosol generation for inhalation exposures, the dry powder aerosol generator most often used is the Wright dust feeder mechanism. Figure 9-9 is a view of the Wright dust feeder mechanism that consists of a cup in which the material is packed and a scraper blade that moves through the packed material. As it moves, the blade removes material from the pack to the central tube. This generator is very dependable if the material can be uniformly compressed into the cup. If the cup is not well packed, air blowing across the blade of the scraper may cause large amounts of material to slough off and become airborne. The TSI small-scale powder generator uses a rotational table in which the powder is loaded. Aerosol concentration from any powder generator is to a large extent controlled and adjusted by the feeding rate. A device for dispersing fibers, similar to the Wright dust feeder, has been designed by Timbrell *et al.*[50] and is commercially available. The fibers are compressed into a cylindrical plug which is advanced by a threaded piston into the path of rotating blades. The motion of the blades disperses the fibers throughout the small chamber; air flowing through the chamber carries the dispersed fibers out of the device.

The powder is delivered to the disperser for aerosoli-

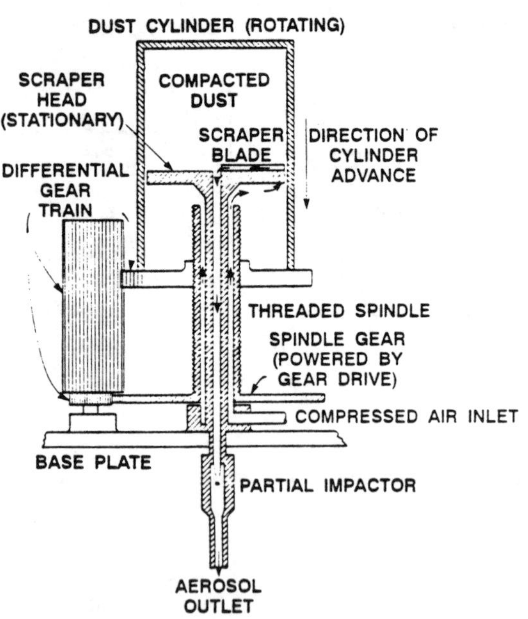

FIGURE 9-9. Schematic of the Wright dust feeder.

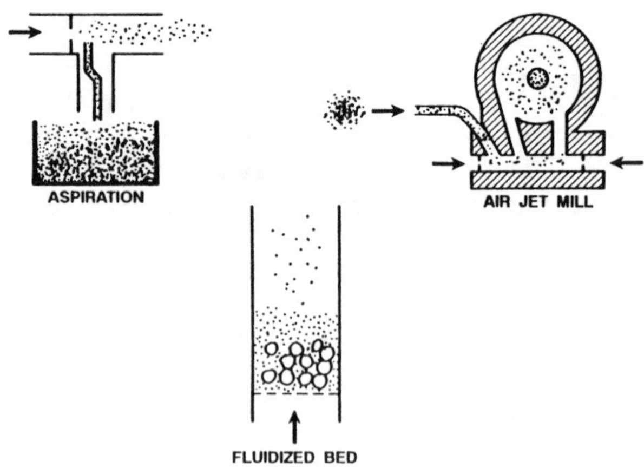

FIGURE 9-10. Schematic of dry powder dispersing mechanisms.

zation, dilution, and deagglomeration. Airstreams, Venturi tubes, air jet mills, and fluidized beds have been used to disperse powders as fine aerosols (Figure 9-10). The most common methods are to feed the dust into a high-velocity airstream or to blow air over the powder. The shear forces in the turbulent airstream disperse powder and break up agglomerates. In the Venturi design, a high-velocity air jet blows across a nozzle or restriction in the pipe to produce suction, which draws clumps of powders into the shear flow of air (Figure 9-11). Both the Venturi dry powder generator[51] and the TSI small-scale powder generator use this principle. Fluid energy mills used for dispersion include the Trost jet mill,[49] the Jet-O-Mizer,[47] and the microjet mill.[52] The fluid energy is delivered in high-velocity streams, which circulate around a grinding and classifying chamber, where turbulence and centrifugal forces deagglomerate particles. Fine particles carried by the fluid exit at the center of the chamber; coarse particles are recirculated for further size reduction. The Trost jet mill uses two opposing jets to grind and reduce particles with higher efficiency. In a one- or two-component fluidized bed, the minimal air flow required to cause the bed to fluidize is used so that only the smallest particles are released.

Commercial and laboratory powder generators listed in Table 9-4 consist of a combination of these delivery and dispersion mechanisms. Figure 9-12 shows an example of a fluidized bed generator with gravity feed system. Other delivery systems, including a screw feed[53] and a chain belt,[54] have been used with the

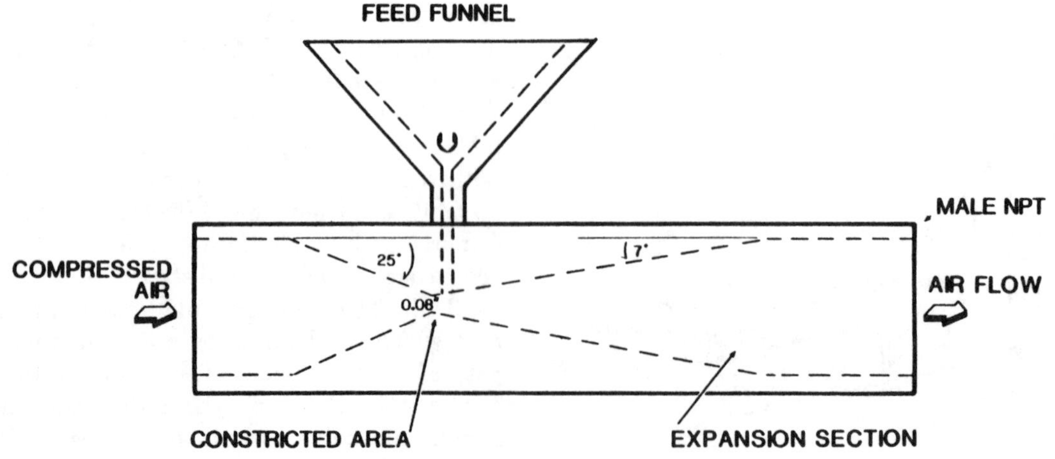

FIGURE 9-11. A Venturi powder disperser.

TABLE 9-4. Operating Parameters of Commercial Dry Powder Dispersers

	Wright Dust Feed	Fluidized Bed	NBS II Dust Generator	Small-Scale Powder Disperser	Jet-O Mizer Model 00
Type of operation	Scraping the packed plug and dispersing it with air	Feeding the powder to the bed on a conveyor and air fluidizing it	Using metering gear to deliver the powder and air dispersing it	Using rotating plate to deliver the powder and dispersing it with Venturi suction	Using Venturi suction to feed the powder into a fluid energy mill in which centrifugal force and air velocity are used to break up the agglomerate and disperse the powder
Air flow rate, L/min	8.5–40	5–20	50–85	12–21	14–113
Feed flow rate, mm^3/min	0.24–210	1.2–36	1200–50,000	0.9–2.5	2000–30,000
Output mass concentration, g/m^3 (ρ = 1 g/cm^3)	0.012–11.5	0.13–4.0	15–200	0.0003–0.04	10–1500
Source	BGI	TSI	BGI	TSI	FLU

fluidized bed generator. The Jet-O-Mizer and Venturi with the screw feed are used to disperse sticky organic powders.[47,51] Most dry powder generators are material-specific, because delivery strongly depends on the bulk powder properties, including size, shape, compactness, and stickiness. For example, sticky powder tends to stay on a gravity feed tube or rotating disk, resulting in a reduced feed rate or complete stoppage. The bulk material must be compact for delivery by a Wright dust feeder, where the powder is packed under pressure to form a solid cylinder. Loose or uneven packing causes the packed powder to break up during the generating process.

Most dry dust generators work best for nonsticky, dry powders. When sticky materials are dispersed as powder, they tend to form clumps that require more energy for dispersion, or they cannot be broken up, thus clogging the generator. The kinetic energy of an air dispersion system is proportional to the square of the air velocity. The fluidized bed has the least kinetic energy and therefore cannot be used to generate sticky powders. The Venturi and fluid energy mills have the highest velocity; therefore, they are more suitable for sticky powders.

One advantage of this dry dispersion method is that the aerosol generated has a similar size distribution as single powder particles when they are suspended in the air. In addition, because no solvent or heat treatment is required, the physical and chemical forms of the material are preserved. A problem common to dry-dispersion aerosols is the buildup of charge on particles as they touch and separate from the surface in the generator. This process reduces the output concentration due to particle losses to the wall of the system. The problem can be solved by passing the aerosol through a chamber containing a bipolar ion source, as described earlier.

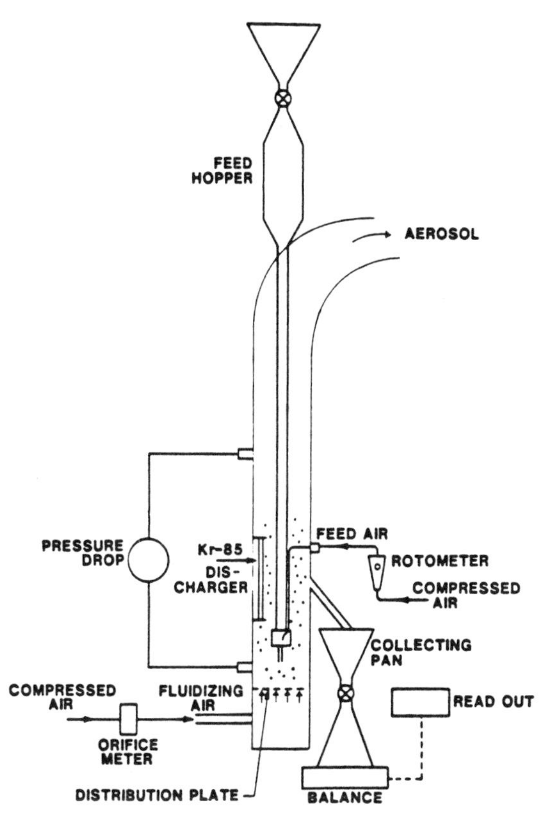

FIGURE 9-12. A fluidized bed powder generator with a gravity feed.

Monodisperse Aerosols with Spherical Particles

The methods of producing monodisperse aerosols with spherical particles have been reviewed.(39,40,55) These methods include the atomization of a suspension of monodisperse particles; the formation of uniform droplets by dispersion of liquid jets with periodic vibration, electrical fields, or a spinning disc (top); and the growth of uniform particles or droplets by controlled condensation.

Atomization of Suspensions of Monodisperse Particles

The simplest way to produce monodisperse aerosols is by air-blast nebulizing a dilute liquid suspension containing monodisperse PSL or polyvinyltoluene (PVT) latex spheres. These spheres are commercially available in a size range from 0.01 to 30 μm (Duke Scientific, Palo Alto, California; Dyno Industrier A. S., Lillestrom, Norway; Japan Synthetic Rubber, Tokyo, Japan; Polysciences, Warrington, Pennsylvania; Seragen Diagnostics, Indianapolis, Indiana; 3M, Minneapolis, Minnesota). PSL particles of different sizes have also been concurrently produced in an aerosol to obtain more than one data point per experimental run. Monodisperse latex particles containing fluorescent dye or radiolabeled isotopes are also used in calibrations when quantitative measurements by fluorometric or radiometric techniques are needed.(45,56)

Three problems arise in the generation of these latex particles: measurement of particle size, formation of aggregates, and existence of residual particles. The diameters of the particles reported by the manufacturer can be different from those measured by an electron microscope, because the particles tend to evaporate and shrink due to electron irradiation, or to increase in size due to absorption of a contaminant under irradiation. Porstendörfer and Heyder(57) and Yamada *et al.*(58) recommend measurement of these particles by an electron microscope, but the particle size should be determined without particle shadowing and with minimal electron beam intensity and short exposure time.

The second problem in generating latex particles is the formation of aggregate latex particles in the aerosol. The percentage of aggregates can be reduced by diluting the suspension. Assuming that the probability of the number of particles in an atomized droplet can be described by Poisson statistics, and that the droplet-size distribution can be approximated by a lognormal distribution, Raabe(59) derived the following equation to calculate the latex dilution factor, Y, necessary to give a desired singlet ratio, R, which is the number of droplets containing single particles relative to the total number of droplets containing particles:

$$Y = \frac{F\,(\mathrm{VMD})^3\, exp\,[4.5(\ln \sigma_g)^2]\,[1 - 0.5\, exp\,(\ln \sigma_g)^2]}{(1-R)d_p^3} \quad (2)$$

where: F = volumetric fraction of individual particles of diameter d_p in the original latex suspension
VMD = volume median diameter
σ_g = geometric standard deviation of the droplet size distribution

The VMD and σ_g values of commonly used air-blast atomizers are listed in Table 9-3. This equation is limited to values of $\sigma_g < 2.1$ and $R > 0.9$.

The third problem arises when nonlatex residual particles are present in the aerosol as a result of the impurities and surfactant in the liquid suspension. The nonlatex particles could either distort the size of an individual particle, if they attach to it, or become individual particles with a size different from that of the latex particles in the aerosol. To reduce the impurity in the diluting water, a system that provides deionized and double-distilled water is normally used. To remove the surfactant from the suspension, a procedure of diluting, centrifuging, and discarding the supernate is generally followed.

Vibrating-Orifice and Spinning-Disc (Top) Atomizers

The generators that produce monodisperse droplets can also produce monodisperse aerosols. Two methods are available. The vibrating-orifice atomizer creates a jet of liquid through an orifice and breaks the jet into droplets of a uniform diameter by applying certain disturbing frequencies,(17,60,61) as shown in Figure 9-13. The stability, monodispersity, and diameter of the droplets depend on the diameter of the orifice, the density and surface tension of the liquid, the velocity of the jet, and the disturbing frequency. The advantage of this method is that the diameter of the droplet, d_d (in μm), and the aerosol particle, d_p (in μm), can be determined by the following equations:(17)

$$d_d = 10^4 \left(\frac{Q_l}{10\pi f} \right)^{1/3} \quad (3)$$

$$d_p = C^{1/3}\, d_d \quad (4)$$

where: Q_l = liquid feed rate in cm³/min
f = vibrating frequency in Hz
C = volumetric concentration of the solute in the solution

In the frequency range for stable generation of droplets, the droplet size is about twice the orifice diameter. Therefore, with orifices of 5–30 μm, the droplet sizes range from 10 to 60 μm. The minimum aerosol particle size after evaporation of the solvent is about 1.5 μm because the lowest concentration of aerosol solution, C, is limited by impurity in the solution, which is on the order of 0.001 volume fraction. The output aerosol concentrations are low, about 30 to 400 particles/cm^3, depending on the primary droplet size. In addition, liquid suspension can clog the orifice and may not be used as feeding material. In the case of producing monodisperse solid aerosols (e.g., ammonium fluorescein), the drying process for suspended droplets is crucial to the surface smoothness of the final particles. Inclusion of small amounts of oil can improve sphericity by preventing crystallization. However, density may be affected if the particle dries too fast. The aerosol generated has a narrow size distribution, but the instrument is difficult to operate.

The second method of producing monodisperse droplets is by the spinning-disc (top) atomizer, in which a liquid jet is fed at a constant rate onto the center of a rotating disc (top). The liquid spreads over the disc (top) surface in a thin film, accumulating at the rim until the centrifugal force discharges it, and a droplet is thrown off. Droplet size d_d depends on disc (top) diameter, d_s (in μm), and rotating speed, ω_s (in rpm) as follows:

$$d_d = (W \frac{\gamma}{\rho_l} \omega_s^2 d_s)^{1/2} \quad (5)$$

where: γ = surface tension
ρ_l = density of the liquid
W = constant

The application of this process has been investigated by Walton and Prewett[62] and May[63] using an air-driven, spinning top, and by Whitby *et al.*[64] and Lippmann and Albert[65] using a motor-driven, spinning disc. Unlike a vibrating-orifice atomizer, aqueous suspensions, as well as solutions, can be used. A disadvantage of this method is that undesired satellite droplets are frequently formed and must be removed from the useful aerosol produced by the primary droplets. In addition, the constant W (Equation 4) varies with the instrument and the feed material used, and the droplet size and the final particle size cannot be as easily calculated as with the vibrating-orifice atomizer.

A method for producing monodisperse droplets using electrostatic spray of a semiconductive fluid has recently been described.[66–68] A stable spray can be generated if the applied electrical field exceeds a critical value. The droplet size is smaller than those produced in a vibrating orifice. The method combines the features of high production rate, small droplet size, and easy operation with no clogging of the nozzle. The droplet size is a function of nozzle diameter, liquid feed rate, and surface tension, conductivity, and viscosity of the liquid.[69]

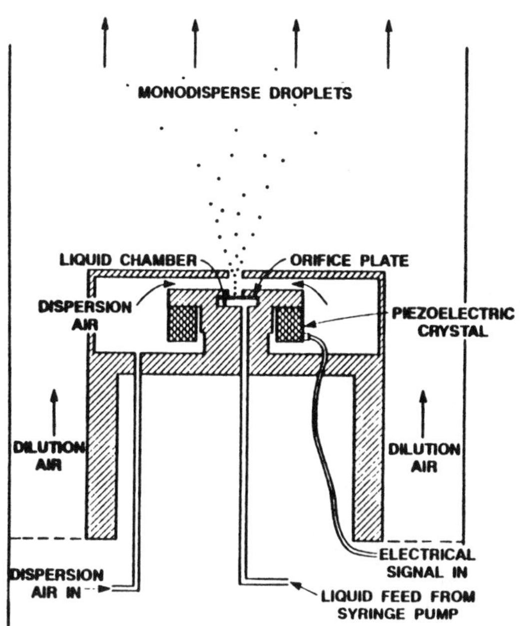

FIGURE 9-13. Schematic of a vibrating-orifice aerosol generator.

Controlled Condensation Techniques

Condensation is also a method that produces monodisperse aerosols for calibration purposes. In this method, the heated vapor of a substance that is normally liquid or solid at room temperature is mixed with the nuclei on which it condenses when it passes in laminar flow through a cooling zone. If the condensation process is diffusion controlled, the surface area of the growing droplet will increase at a constant rate, producing a particle having a diameter, d_t, at time t related to the initial diameter, d_o, of the nucleus, by

$$d_t^2 = d_o^2 + bt \quad (6)$$

where b is a constant, related to the concentration and diffusivity of the vapor and to the temperature. If bt is the same for all particles and much larger than d_o, the diameter of the nucleus has little effect on the final diameter of the particle, so an aerosol containing monodisperse particles is produced. In practice, uniform temperature profile, sufficient vapor concentration, and sufficient residence time in the condensation region are the key controls, and a constant nuclei concentration provides a stable aerosol concentration. Condensation generators are usually for high-boiling-point, low-vapor-pressure liquid droplets, e.g., DOP, triphenylphosphate, and di-octyl sebecate. Solid test aerosols, such as a carnauba paraffin aerosol, can also be generated. Aerosol concentrations are generally in the range of 10^5 to 10^7 particles/cm^3 with narrow size distribution ($\sigma_g < 1.2$).

Sinclair and LaMer[70] described the first condensa-

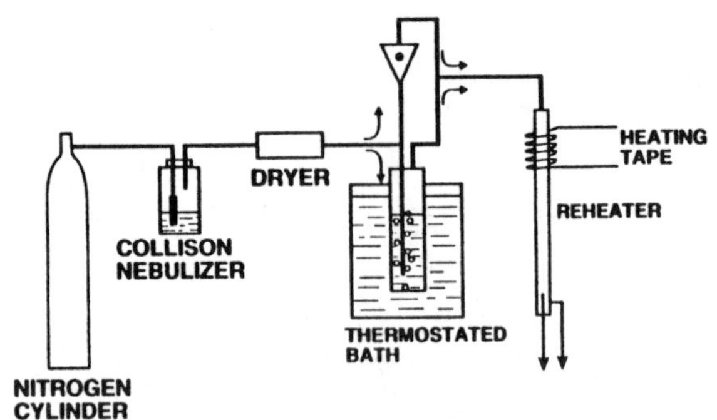

FIGURE 9-14. Schematic of a MAGE generator.

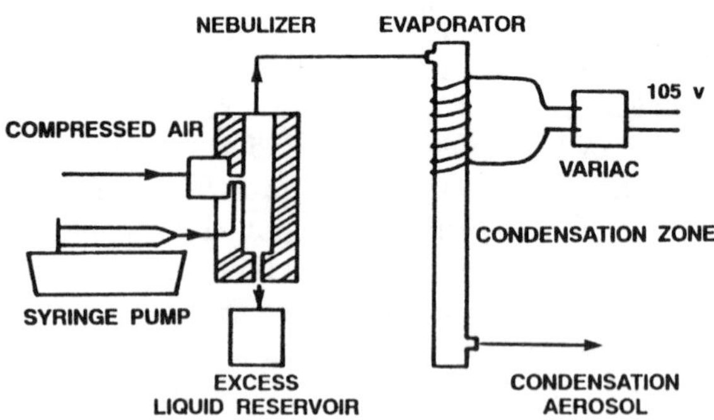

FIGURE 9-15. Schematic of a constant output controlled condensation aerosol generator.

tion liquid aerosol generator based on this principle. Simplifications and modifications of the Sinclair and LaMer generator have been used in the laboratory.(71,72) Figure 9-14 shows a photograph of a modified Sinclair–LaMer generator (MAGE) based on Prodi's design.(72) The size range of particles generated is from 0.2 to 8 μm for liquid droplets and from 0.2 to 2 μm for solid particles (waxes and paraffins). A somewhat different version of the condensation generator as described by Liu and Lee(44) is illustrated in Figure 9-15. A Collison-type nebulizer is used to atomize liquid into polydisperse droplets. An aerosol solution is delivered to the nebulizer by a syringe pump to control the feed rate and to prevent the evaporation of solvent and subsequently the increased concentration of the aerosol solution. The droplets are heated to vaporize in the heat section, and residue nuclei consisting of impurities in the solution are formed. The nuclei number concentration and the vapor pressure are constant, providing a stable environment for condensation in the down flow section of the glass tube. Both the Liu–Lee generator and MAGE are commercially available (Table 9-5).

Condensation generators for ultrafine solid test particles have been designed and used in instrument calibration.(73–76) Figure 9-16 illustrates a basic solid aerosol generator using a tube furnace.(73,76) The solid material is placed in a quartz boat inside the furnace, a stream of nitrogen carries the vapor out of the boat, and the vapor condenses to form particles in the condensation chamber. Test aerosols whose particle is carnauba wax, sodium chloride, or silver are commonly used. The aerosol has a narrow size distribution with a geometric standard deviation between 1.1 and 1.3. More narrow size distributions (with $\sigma_g < 1.1$) can be obtained by classifying the aerosol using an EC as described later in this section. The temperature control in the furnace is essential for the stable generation of aerosols. For generation of metal aerosols of lead, zinc cadmium, and antimony, a high-frequency induction furnace has been used.(77)

TABLE 9-5. Operating Parameters of Monodisperse Aerosol Generators

Generator	Principles	Type of Aerosols	Aerosol Flow Rate (L/min)	Particle Size Range (μm)	Source
Electrostatic classifier (Model 3071)	Electrical mobility	Liquid and solid	2–4	0.005–1	TSI
Constant output generator (Model 3076)	Controlled condensation	Liquid and solid	2–4	0.04–1.3	TSI
MAGE	Controlled condensation	Liquid and solid	1–3	0.2–8	BGI
Spinning-top aerosol generator	Atomization	Liquid and solid	120	1–100	BGI
Vibrating-orifice aerosol generator (Model 3050)	Atomization	Liquid and solid	100	1–40	TSI

Monodisperse Aerosols with Nonspherical Particles

The effects of particle shape on instrument response are important, especially for the sizing instruments in which the measured properties are generally dependent on particle shape. Information concerning the effects of shape on instrument response can be obtained by using monodisperse aerosols of nonspherical particles during calibration. One way of generating these aerosols is to nebulize the liquid suspension containing monodisperse, nonspherical particles. Various techniques have been used to produce monodisperse particles of highly uniform particle size and shape. Matijevic[(78)] produced inorganic and polymer colloid particles of cubic, spindle, and rhombohedral shapes by chemical reactions. Fiber-like particles of a narrow size range were also produced using different methods.[(41,79–82)] The vibrating-orifice and spinning-disc (top) aerosol generators described above can also be used to generate irregularly shaped particles, such as crystalline sodium chloride particles. Although the generators produce spherical droplets, the crystal form of the solid particles becomes the shape of the final aerosol after drying the liquid vapor.

In addition, naturally occurring materials, such as fungal spores, pollens, and bacteria or the fortuitous occurrence of multiplets of spheres, are also frequently used as test aerosols of nonspherical particles.[(83,84)] The aerosols of fungal spores and pollens are commonly generated by using the dry powder dispersion technique described in the previous section.

Size Classification of Polydisperse Aerosols

Although polydisperse aerosols may be used for instrument calibration or to simulate the actual use of equipment under controlled laboratory conditions, they can also be classified according to size in order to provide an aerosol with narrow size range for instrument calibration. For particles smaller than 0.2 μm, Liu and Pui[(23)] developed a differential electrical mobility analyzer to classify aerosol particles of the same electrical mobility. Figure 9-17 shows that the schematic of the EC consists of a bipolar discharger to maintain the aerosol charge distribution, and a concentric mobility analyzer. The polydisperse aerosol is charged and separated in the mobility analyzer, and only particles having the same mobility can exit at the same time. Because most classified particles of submicrometer size are singly charged, the aerosol produced is monodisperse. The particle size of the classified aerosol has a triangular size distribution with the median diameter, d, calculated from the following equation:

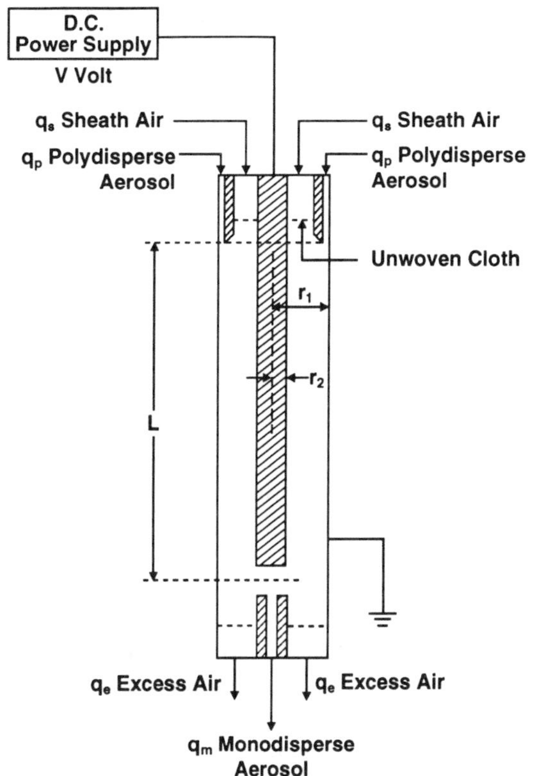

FIGURE 9-17. Schematic of an electrostatic classifier.

$$d = \frac{4ne\Lambda V\, C(d)\; 1 \times 10^7}{3\mu\,(q_s + q_e)} \tag{7}$$

where: n = number of charges
e = elementary charge (1.6×10^{-19} Coulomb)
C = Cunningham slip correction
μ = gas viscosity (g/cm sec)
q_s = sheath flow rate (cm^3/sec)
q_e = excess flow rate (cm^3/sec)
V = applied voltage
$\Lambda = L/\ln(r_2/r_1)$
r_2 and r_1 = outer and inner radii of the mobility analyzer
L = length of the analyzer

The geometric standard deviation of the classified aerosol is related to the flow rates:[(18)]

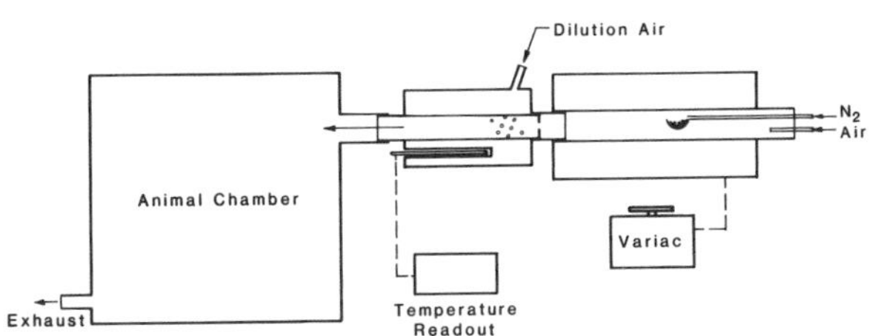

FIGURE 9-16. Schematic of a condensation aerosol generator for solid particles.

TABLE 9-6. Commercial Sources of Monodisperse Latex Test Particles with Fluorescent or Radioactive Tags

Materials	Tags	Size Range (μm)	Source
Polystyrene latex	Green, red, blue	0.025–3	DUK
Polystyrene latex with surface modification	Blue, orange, yellow-green red, dark red	0.02–4	IDC
Polystyrene latex	Yellow-green	0.05–6	POL

$$\sigma_g = \exp\left[\left(\frac{1}{6}\right)^{1/2} \frac{(q_p + q_m)}{(q_p + q_m + q_s + q_e)}\right] \quad (8)$$

where: q_m = monodisperse flow rate
q_p = polydisperse flow rate

This classification technique has been used to produce a submicrometer aerosol standard in calibrating CNCs and diffusion batteries, and in determining particle deposition in human nasal and oral casts.[44,75,76]

For particles greater than 1 μm, the size classifying technique based on aerodynamic property is generally used. Two virtual impactors can be placed in a series to segregate the desired fraction of the input aerosol for use in instrument calibration.[24,85] To classify aerosols in the 0.1- to 1.0-μm range, a technique that involves both the mobility analyzer and a single-stage, microorifice impactor has been used.[25] In addition, latex test spheres can be nebulized and a mobility classifier can be used to remove aggregates and other impurities. In fact, this method is recommended to generate PSL test particles in the size range of 0.03 to 0.1 μm. The above techniques are also used for reducing undesired particles, such as PSL aggregates from an air nebulizer or satellite particles by the spinning-disc generator.

All devices and techniques described above classify aerosol particles when they are still in the airborne state. Other instruments, such as elutriators, spectrometers, cascade impactors, and cascade cyclones, classify particles by means of collecting size-classified particles on a substrate, then resuspending the size-classified particles. For example, a spiral centrifuge collects aerodynamically classified particles on aluminum foil; resuspension of the particles caught on a narrow segment of the foil can be used to produce monodisperse aerosols.[86] The disadvantage of all size-classifying techniques is that only a small quantity of particles is produced.

Test Aerosols with Tagging Materials

For some applications, particle detection is often facilitated by incorporating dyes or radioisotope tags in the particles during their production. For example, test aerosols composed of fluorescent dyes can be analyzed in solutions containing as little as 10^{-10} g/m^3. The radioactivity of the aerosols can be determined by counting the samples with much lower detection limits than electrobalances. Assuming tagged materials are evenly distributed in the aerosol material and therefore are proportional to the mass, the tagged material can be measured by colorimetric, fluorometric, or radioactive counting techniques to determine the particle mass with low detection limits. These techniques are especially useful for calibration of instruments having low flow rates (<1 L/min), such as Mercer impactors or low-pressure impactors. Tagged particles deposited in the inlet section, transport lines, and internal wall of the detector can be washed and measured.[2,87]

Commonly used dye materials include eosin,[2] methylene blue,[1] and ammonium fluorescein. Minute amounts of these chemicals can be dissolved in aqueous or alcohol solutions with oleic acid and DOP. Monodisperse-tagged liquid droplets can be generated by techniques described in the previous sections, including a VOAG, a spinning-top generator, and condensation techniques. Commercial PSL particles that incorporate fluorescent dyes are also available (Table 9-6). Radiolabeling techniques have been used in many forms and radiolabels can usually be detected at extremely low concentrations.[45,88] Radiolabels including ^{99}Tc, ^{51}Cr, and ^{137}Cs have been incorporated into PSL to produce monodisperse test particles. Similarly, several radiolabels have been incorporated into aluminosilicate clay by ion exchange; the clay solution is then nebulized and heat treated at 1150°C to form insoluble spherical particles.[45,89] Ultrafine particles (< 0.2 μm) of metal oxides ($^{67}Ga_2O_3$, $^{144}CeO_2$, and $^{57}Co_3O_4$) have been produced by evaporation, subsequent thermal degradation, and condensation of organic ketone compounds.[73]

Calibration Procedures

This section describes the steps used in a typical calibration practice. It is always useful to describe detailed procedures in a test plan or protocol and then follow through during the test.

Set Up Test Facility

The criteria for selecting a proper test facility for a calibration program have been described in detail in previous sections. The selected test facility may already exist in the laboratory. In this case, it is only necessary to ensure the performance system for the specified procedure. If a new test facility or experimental apparatus is needed, then the system should be designed accordingly, and individual components of the test facility purchased and installed.

Select Test Aerosols

Proper selection of test aerosols is essential to instrument calibration. A variety of test aerosols and their generation methods have been described. For general purposes, standard test aerosols as listed in Table 9-2 provide sufficient choices. The selection is further narrowed by considering the particle sizes, monodisperse versus polydisperse aerosol, and liquid versus solid particles. Sometimes the choice is dictated by the standards specified in the regulation. In other cases, special test aerosols are required for certain classes of instruments. For example, fiber test aerosols should be used to calibrate the response of real-time fiber monitors. Once the test aerosol is selected, appropriate aerosol generator and accessory parts are assembled and become part of the test system.

Test Calibration Systems

After the test system is assembled, the system should be checked for leaks. All meters used to regulate flows in the generator, dilution air, chamber supply, exhaust, and sampler should be calibrated and the results documented. The system should be tested without aerosol generation to determine the stability of the flow, the uniformity of flow in the test chamber, and the turbulence intensity in case a wind tunnel is used. Test runs with aerosols should be made to determine the stability of aerosol concentration at target levels, the particle size distribution, and distribution of aerosol concentration in the test section. The operating conditions can be adjusted and the test system modified during the test run to obtain the desired test conditions.

On-line detection of aerosol size and/or concentration in the calibration system is also recommended to ensure the stable generation of aerosol. For example, an optical counter or an aerodynamic particle sizer can be used to monitor the satellite's generation of a VOAG or spinning-disc generator.

Data Collection, Analysis, and Documentation

A calibration curve that contains the relationship between the instrument's responses and the values of a certain aerosol property is established after calibration. In the case of an instrument that directly indicates a value of the measured parameter, calibration provides an adjustment (or a correction factor) to the indicated value. In addition, resolution and sensitivity of the instrument should be examined and analyzed. The rule of thumb is to conduct the calibration based on all important parameters, assemble all the data, and express those data in a generalized mathematical equation, relating the instrument response to a single parameter.

For data analysis, instrument manufacturers sometimes provide a built-in algorithm whose properties, accuracy, and limitations are often unknown to the user. Unless a user understands the algorithm, development of the analysis should only be based on the raw calibration data, without any manipulation by the built-in algorithm.

All pertinent data, including experimental conditions, aerosol data, and analysis, should be documented carefully. Documentation is especially important if the study is intended for regulatory or compliance purposes. It is likely the information will be examined and scrutinized carefully. Examination of the documents is needed to remove any mistakes before submission to the agency for approval.

Quality Assurance

To obtain high quality test data and to minimize experimental errors, steps should be taken to ensure that the test facility, instruments, and aerosol generator are functioning properly. Integrity of the test system and the instrument itself should be maintained by avoiding possible leakage or blockage of flow. Techniques and criteria of isokinetic sampling and sampling from still air should be followed, especially for aerosol particles greater than 5 μm in aerodynamic diameter. Before reliable data can be obtained, precalibration tests should be carried out to ensure that a stable aerosol can be maintained for a long period of time, that the aerosol concentration and size are consistent, and that the aerosol is uniformly distributed in the test chamber. For each data point, at least three calibrations are required to provide statistically valid information. Also, it is a good practice to calibrate the test standard before the test proceeds. For example, PSL test particles may need to be examined in a microscope for the accuracy of particle size and the impurity.

A quality assurance program should also include written documentation of the protocol, standard operating procedures for each procedure used in the protocol, and careful documentation of the results. After the procedures are finalized, the operator should adhere to the established procedures. If problems occur during the test, the cause should be identified, corrected, and documented before the test is continued. A quality

TABLE 9-7. Commercial Sources

BGI	BGI Incorporated 58 Guinan Street Waltham, MA 02154 (617)891-9380 FAX (617)891-8151	FLU	Fluid Energy Aljet P.O. Box 428-T Plumsteadville, PA 18949 (215)766-0300	POL	Polyscience, Inc. 400-T Valley Rd. Warrington, PA 18976 (215)343-6484
DEV	The DeVilbiss Co. P.O. Box 635 Somerset, PA 15501 (814)443-4881	IDC	Interfacial Dynamics Corp. P.O. Box 279 Portland, OR 97207 (503)256-0076	SON	Sono-Tek 313-A Main Mall Poukeepsie, NY 12601 (914)471-6090
DUK	Duke Scientific Co. 2463 Faber Pl. Palo Alto, CA 94303 (800)334-3883	INT	In Tox Products 115 Quincy, NE Albuquerque, NM 87108 (505)265-1180 (505)265-1181	TSI	TSI Incorporated 500 Cardigan Rd. P.O. Box 64394 St. Paul, MN 55164 (612)483-0900

assurance program is mandatory if the study is under the Good Laboratory Practices Guidelines or other compliance regulation.

Conclusions

Because the accuracy of measuring aerosols depends on the precision of the aerosol instrument, the instrument must be calibrated very carefully. The following comments summarize this chapter and the philosophy of aerosol instrument calibration:

1. The developer or manufacturer of an instrument has the responsibility for providing instrument performance data that include full-scale calibration data covering the whole applicable range (i.e., the particle size for sizing the instrument and the concentration for mass or number concentration monitors), the test aerosol used, and the conditions under which the instrument is tested (flow rates, ambient temperature, and pressure). This calibration should be performed for new instruments and after extensive repair.
2. The user should understand the principles of the instrument operation and be familiar with the calibration data. The decision on when to recalibrate the instrument is based on scientific and regulatory requirements. Frequent checks of the instrument and its flowmeter are minimum requirements, and a single point check is recommended for routine use of any sampling instrument. Full-scale calibration requires substantial effort, appropriate equipment, and facilities that may not be available for every user.
3. Quality assurance is an important aspect of a successful test program. The calibration procedure should be carefully planned and documented. Test runs should be made to ensure that the system is functioning, that the correct procedures are used, and that the aerosol and flow stability are achieved and maintained. Standard operating procedures should be followed during the calibration, and any problems encountered should be resolved and documented. All records, including test runs, data, problems with appropriate comments, instrument identification, barometric pressure, temperature, flow rate, properties of the test aerosol, and the name of the operator, should be documented.
4. Proper test facilities should be used for an aerosol sampler intended for different environments. Instrument chambers with low air flow should be used for calm air sampling conditions, whereas aerosol wind tunnels should be used to simulate sampling in the flow streams or ambient environments.
5. Proper test aerosols should be used. Standard spherical test aerosols such as PSL and others provide data to compare the instrument response with other instruments using the same kind of aerosol. Whenever possible, test aerosols with physicochemical properties similar to the measured aerosol should be used.

References

1. Rao, A.K.; Whitby, K.T.: Non-Ideal Collection Characteristics of Inertial Impactors - II. Cascade Impactors. J. Aerosol Sci. 9:87 (1978).
2. Cheng, Y.S.; Yeh, H.C.: Particle Bounce in Cascade Impactors. Environ. Sci. Technol. 13:1392 (1979).
3. Lippmann, M.: Calibration of Air Sampling Instruments. In: Air Sampling Instruments, pp. 73–109. S.V. Hering, Ed. ACGIH, Cincinnati, OH (1989).
4. Chen, B.T.: Instrument Calibration. In: Aerosol Management: Principles, Techniques, and Applications, pp. 493–520. K. Willeke and P.A. Baron, Eds. Van Nostrand Reinhold, New York (1993).
5. Davies, C.N.: The Aspiration of Heavy Airborne Particles into a Point Sink. Proc. Roy Soc. 279a:413 (1964).
6. Hinds, W.: Aerosol Technology. John Wiley and Sons, New York (1982).

7. Brockmann, J.E.: Sampling and Transport of Aerosols. In: Aerosol Measurement: Principles, Techniques, and Applications, pp. 77-111. K. Willeke and P.A. Baron, Eds. Van Nostrand Reinhold, New York (1993).
8. U.S. Environmental Protection Agency: Ambient Air Monitoring Reference and Equivalent Methods. Code of Federal Regulations, Vol. 40, Part 53 (1987).
9. Ranade, M.B.; Wood, M.C.; Chen, F.L.; et al.: Wind Tunnel Evaluation of PM-10 Samplers. Aerosol Sci. Technol. 13:54 (1990).
10. Code of Federal Regulations: Good Laboratory Practice Regulations. 21 CFR, Part 58 (1984).
11. Code of Federal Regulations: Toxic Substances Control Act Test Guidelines. 40 CFR, Parts 796–798 (1985).
12. Jaenicke, R.; Kanter, H.J.: Direct Condensation Nuclei Counter with Automatic Photographic Recording, and General Problems of Absolute Counters. J. Appl. Meteorology 15:620 (1976).
13. Schönauer, G.: Electron- and Light-Optical Determination of the Flattening Factor and Size of Oil Droplets. Staub-Reinhalt Luft (Eng.) 27(9):7 (1967).
14. Liu, B.Y.H.; Pui, D.Y.H.; Wang, X.Q.: Drop Size Measurement of Liquid Aerosols. Atmos. Environ. 16:563 (1982).
15. Olan-Figueroa, E.; McFarland, A.R.; Ortiz, C.A.: Flattening Coefficients for DOP and Oleic Acid Droplets Deposited on Treated Glass Slides. Am. Ind. Hyg. Assoc. J. 43:395 (1982).
16. Cheng, Y.S.; Chen, B.T.; Yeh, H.C.: Size Measurement of Liquid Aerosols. J. Aerosol Sci. 17:803 (1986).
17. Berglund, R.N.; Liu, B.Y.H.: Generation of Monodisperse Aerosol Standards. Environ. Sci. Technol. 7:147 (1973).
18. Cheng, Y.S.; DeNee, P.B.: Physical Properties of Electrical Mobility Classified Aerosols. J. Colloid Interface Sci. 80:284 (1981).
19. Liu, B.Y.H.; Kim, C.S.: On the Counting Efficiency of Condensation Nuclei Counters. Atmos. Environ. II:1097 (1977).
20. Kanapilly, G.M.; Raabe, O.G.; Newton, G.J.: A New Method for the Generation of Aerosols of Insoluble Particles. J. Aerosol Sci. 1:313 (1970).
21. Chen, B.T., Cheng, Y.S.; Yeh, H.C.: A Study of Density Effect and Droplet Deformation in the TSI Aerodynamic Particle Sizer. Aerosol Sci. Technol. 12:278 (1990).
22. John, W.: Particle Charge Effects. In: Generation of Aerosols and Facilities for Exposure Experiments, pp. 141–151. K. Willeke, Ed. Ann Arbor Science, Ann Arbor, MI (1980).
23. Liu, B.Y.H.; Pui, D.Y.H.: A Submicron Aerosol Standard and the Primary, Absolute Calibration of the Condensation Nuclei Counter. J. Colloid Interface Sci. 47:155 (1974).
24. Chen, B.T.; Yeh, H.C.; Rivero, M.A.: Use of Two Virtual Impactors in Series as an Aerosol Generator. J. Aerosol Sci. 19:137 (1988).
25. Romay-Novas, F.J.; Pui, D.Y.H.: Generation of Monodisperse Aerosols in the 0.1-1.0 μm Diameter Range Using a Mobility Classification-Inertial Impaction Technique. Aerosol Sci. Technol. 9:123 (1988).
26. Barr, E.B.; Hoover, M.D.; Kanapilly, G.M.; et al.: Aerosol Concentrator: Design, Construction, Calibration, and Use. Aerosol Sci. Technol. 2:437 (1983).
27. Yeh, H.C.; Cheng, Y.S.; Carpenter, R.L.: Evaluation of an In-Line Dilutor for Submicron Aerosols. Am. Ind. Hyg. Assoc. J. 44:358 (1983).
28. Marple, V.A.; Rubow, K.L.: An Evaluation of the GCA Respirable Dust Monitor 101-1. Am. Ind. Hyg. Assoc. J. 39:17 (1978).
29. Moss, O.R.: Sampling in Calibration and Exposure Chambers. In: Air Sampling Instruments, 7th ed., pp.157–162. S.V. Hering, Ed. American Conference of Governmental Industrial Hygienists, Cincinnati, OH (1989).
30. Cheng, Y.S.; Barr, E.B.; Benson, J.M.; et al.: Evaluation of a Real-Time Aerosol Monitor (RAM-S) for Inhalation Studies. Fund. Appl. Toxicol. 10:321 (1988).
31. Gibson, H.; Ogden, T.L.: Some Entry Efficiencies for Sharp-Edged Samplers in Calm Air. J. Aerosol Sci. 8:361 (1977).
32. Kuusisto, P.: Evaluation of the Direct Reading Instruments for the Measurement of Aerosols. Am. Ind. Hyg. Assoc. J. 44:863 (1983).
33. Marple, V.A.; Rubow, K.L.: An Aerosol Chamber for Instrument Evaluation and Calibration. Am. Ind. Hyg. Assoc. J. 44:361 (1983).
34. Vincent, J.H.; Mark, D.: Applications of Blunt Sampler Theory to the Definition and Measurement of Inhalable Dust. Am. Occup. Hyg. 26:3 (1982).
35. Fabries, J.F.; Carton, B.; Wrobel, R.: Equipment for the Study of Air Sampling Instruments with Real Time Measurement of the Aerosol Concentration. Saub Reinhalt. 44:405 (1984).
36. Blackford, D.B.; Heighington, K.: The Design of an Aerosol Test Tunnel for Occupational Hygiene Investigations. Atmos. Environ. 20:1605 (1986).
37. Armbruster, L.; Breuer, H.: Investigations into Defining Inhalable Dust. Ann. Occup. Hyg. 26:21 (1982).
38. Chung, I.P.; Dunn-Rankin, D.; Phalen, R.F.; Oldham, M.J.: Low-Cost Wind Tunnel for Aerosol Inhalation Studies. Am. Ind. Hyg. Assoc. 53:232 (1992).
39. Mercer, T.T.: Aerosol Technology in Hazard Evaluation. Academic Press, New York (1973).
40. Raabe, O.G.: The Generation of Fine Particles. In: Fine Particles: Aerosol Generation, Measurement, Sampling, and Analysis, pp. 57–110. B.Y.H. Liu, Ed. Academic Press, New York (1976).
41. Chen, B.T.; Yeh, H.C.; Hobbs, C.H.: Size Classification of Carbon Fiber Aerosols. Aerosol Sci. Technol. 19:109 (1993).
42. Mercer, T.T.; Tillery, M.I.; Chow, H.Y.: Operating Characteristics of Some Compressed Air Nebulizers. Am. Ind. Hyg. Assoc. J. 29:66 (1968).
43. DeFord, H.S.; Clark, M.L.; Moss, O.R.: 1981. A Stabilized Aerosol Generator. Am. Ind. Hyg. Assoc. J. 42:602 (1981).
44. Liu, B.Y.H.; Lee, K.W.: An Aerosol Generator of High Stability. Am. Ind. Hyg. Assoc. J. 36:861 (1975).
45. Newton, G.J., Kanapilly, G.M.; Boecker, B.B.; Raabe, O.G.: Radioactive Labeling of Aerosols: Generation Methods and Characteristics. In: Generation of Aerosols and Facilities for Exposure Experiments, pp. 399–425. K. Willeke, Ed. Ann Arbor Science, Ann Arbor, MI (1980).
46. Moss, O.R.; Cheng, Y.S.: Generation and Characterization of Test Atmospheres: Particles. In: Concepts in Inhalation Toxicology, pp. 87–121. R.O. McClellan and R.F. Henderson, Eds. Hemisphere, New York (1989).
47. Cheng, Y.S.; Marshall, T.C.; Henderson, R.F.; Newton, G.J.: Use of a Jet Mill for Dispensing Dry Powder for Inhalation Studies. Am. Ind. Hyg. Assoc. J. 46:449 (1985).
48. Milliman, E.M.; Chang, D.Y.P.; Moss, O.R.: A Dual Flexible-Brush Dust-Feed Mechanism. Am. Ind. Hyg. Assoc. J. 42:747 (1981).
49. Bernstein, D.M.; Moss, O.; Fleissner, H.; Bretz, R.: A Brush Feed Micronizing Jet Mill Powder Aerosol Generator for Producing a Wide Range of Concentrations of Respirable Particles. In: Aerosols, pp. 721-724. B.Y.H Liu, D.Y.H Pui, and H.J. Fissan, Eds. Elsevier, New York (1984).
50. Timbrell, V.; Hyett, A.W.; Skidmore, J.W.: A Simple Dispenser for Generating Dust Clouds from Standard Reference Samples of Asbestos. Ann Occup. Hyg. 11:273 (1968).
51. Cheng, Y.S.; Barr, E.B.; Yeh, H.C.: A Venturi Disperser as a Dry Powder Generator for Inhalation Studies. Inhal. Toxicol. 1:365 (1989).
52. Lee, K.P.; Kelly, D.P.; Kennedy, G.L.: Pulmonary Response to Inhaled Kelvar Synthetic Fibers in Rats. Toxicol. Appl. Pharmacol. 71:242 (1983).
53. Tanaka, I.; Akiyama, T.: A New Dust Generator for Inhalation Toxicity Studies. Ann. Occup. Hyg. 28:157 (1984).
54. Marple, V.A.; Liu, B.Y.H.; Rubow, K.L.: A Dust Generator for Laboratory Use. Am. Ind. Hyg. Assoc. J. 39:26 (1978).
55. Fuchs, N.A.; Sutugin, A.G.: Generation and Use of Monodisperse Aerosols. In: Aerosol Science, pp. 1–30. C.N. Davies, Ed. Academic Press, New York (1966).

56. Chen, B.T.; Cheng, Y.S.; Yeh, H.C.; et al.: Test of the Size Resolution and Sizing Accuracy of the Lovelace Parallel-Flow Diffusion Battery. Am. Ind. Hyg. Assoc. J. 52:75 (1991).
57. Porstendörfer, J.; Heyder, J.: Size Distribution of Latex Particles. J. Aerosol Sci. 3:141 (1972).
58. Yamada, Y.; Miyamoto, K.; Koizumi, A.: Size Determination of Latex Particles by Electron Microscopy. Aerosol Sci. Technol. 4:227 (1985).
59. Raabe, O.G.: The Dilution of Monodisperse Suspensions for Aerosolization. Am. Ind. Hyg. Assoc. J. 29:439 (1968).
60. Fulwyler, M.J.; Glascock, R.B.; Hiebert, R.D.: Device Which Separates Minute Particles According to Electronically Sensed Volume. Rev. Sci. Instrum. 40:42 (1969).
61. Raabe, O.G.; Newton, G.L.: Development of Techniques for Generating Monodisperse Aerosols with the Fulwyler Droplet Generator. In: Fusion Product Inhalation Program Annual Report (LF-43), pp. 13–1. Lovelace Foundation for Medical Education and Research, Albuquerque, NM (1970).
62. Walton, W.H.; Prewett W.C.: The Production of Sprays and Mists of Uniform Drop Size by Means of Spinning Disc Type Sprayers. Proc. Phys. Soc. B62:341 (1949).
63. May, K.R.: An Improved Spinning Top Homogeneous Spray Apparatus. J. Appl. Phys. 20:932 (1949).
64. Whitby, K.T.; Lundgren, D.A.; Peterson, C.M.: Homogeneous Aerosol Generator. Int. J. Air Wat. Poll. 9:263 (1965).
65. Lippmann, M.; Albert; R.E.: A Compact Electric-Motor Driven Spinning Disc Aerosol Generator. Am. Ind. Hyg. Assoc. J. 28:501 (1967).
66. Hayati, I.; Bailey, A.; Tadros, T.F.: Investigations into the Mechanism of Electrohydrodynamic Spraying of Liquids, I and II. J. Colloid Interface Sci. 117:205, 222 (1987).
67. Fernandez de la Mora, J.; Navascues, J.; Fernandez, F.; Rosell-Llompart, J.: Generation of Submicron Monodisperse Aerosols in Electrosprays. J. Aerosol Sci. 21:S673 (1990).
68. Meesters, G.M.H.; Versoulen, P.H.W.; Marijnissen, J.C.M.; Scarlett, B.: Generation of Micron-sized Droplets from the Tylor Cone. J. Aerosol Sci. 23:37 (1992).
69. Smith, D.P.H.: The Electrohydrodynamic Atomization of Liquids. IEEE Trans. Ind. Appl. 1A-22:527 (1986).
70. Sinclair, D.; LaMer, K.: Light Scattering as a Measure of Particle Size in Aerosols. Chem. Rev. 44:245 (1949).
71. Rapaport, E.; Weinstock, S.E.: A Generator for Homogeneous Aerosols. Experientia 11:363 (1955).
72. Prodi, V.: A Condensation Aerosol Generator for Solid Monodisperse Particles. In: Assessment of Airborne Particles, pp. 169–181. T.T. Mercer, P.E. Morrow, and W. Stöber, Eds. C.C. Thomas Publ., Springfield, IL (1972).
73. Kanapilly, G.M.; Tu, K.W.; Larsen, T.B.; Fagel, G.R.: Controlled Production of Ultrafine Metallic Aerosols by Vaporization of an Organic Chelate of the Metal. J. Colloid Interface Sci. 65:533 (1978).
74. Tu, K.W.: A Condensation Aerosol Generator System for Monodisperse Aerosols of Different Physicochemical Properties. J. Aerosol Sci. 13:363 (1982).
75. Scheibel, H.G.; Porstendörfer, J.: Generation of Monodisperse Ag and NaCl - Aerosols with Particle Diameters Between 2 and 300 nm. J. Aerosol Sci. 14:113 (1983).
76. Cheng, Y.S.; Yamada, Y.; Yeh, H.C.; Su, Y.F.: Size Measurement of Ultrafine Particles (3 to 50 nm) Generated from Electrostatic Classifiers. J. Aerosol Res. 5:44 (1990).
77. Homma, K.; Kawai, K.; Nozaki, K.: Metal-Fume Generation and its Application to Inhalation Experiments. In: Generation of Aerosols, pp. 361–377. K. Willeke, Ed. Ann Arbor Science, Ann Arbor, MI (1980).
78. Matijevic, E.: Production of Monodisperse Colloidal Particles. Ann. Rev. Mater. Sci. 15:483 (1985).
79. Esmen, N.A.; Kahn, R.A.; LaPietra, D.; McGovern, E.D.: Generation of Monodisperse Fibrous Glass Aerosols. Am. Ind. Hyg. Assoc. J. 41:175 (1980).
80. Loo, B.W., Cork, C.P.; Madden, N.W.: A Laser-Based Monodisperse Carbon Fiber Generator. J. Aerosol Sci. 13:241 (1982).
81. Vaughan, N.P.: The Generation of Monodisperse Fibers of Caffeine. J. Aerosol Sci. 21:453 (1990).
82. Hoover, M.D.; Casalnuovo, S.A.; Lipowicz, P.J.; et al.: A Method for Producing Non-Spherical Monodisperse Particles Using Integrated Circuit Fabrication Techniques. J. Aerosol Sci. 21:569 (1990).
83. Corn, M.; Esmen, N.A.: Aerosol Generation. In: Handbook on Aerosols, pp. 9–39. R. Dennis, Ed. Publ. TID-26608. National Technical Information Service, U.S. Dept. of Commerce, Springfield, VA (1976).
84. Adams, A.J.; Wennerstorm, D.E.; Mazunder, M.K.: Use of Bacteria as Model Nonspherical Aerosol Particles. J. Aerosol. Sci. 16:163 (1985).
85. Pilacinski, W.; Ruuskanen, J.; Chen, C.C.; et al.: 1990. Size-Fractionating Aerosol Generator. Aerosol Sci. Technol. 13:450 (1990).
86. Kotrappa, P.; Moss; O.R.: Production of Relatively Monodisperse Aerosols for Inhalation Experiments by Aerosol Centrifugation. Health Phys. 21:531 (1971).
87. Chen, B.T.; Yeh, H.C.; Cheng, Y.S.: A Novel Virtual Impactor: Calibration and Use. J. Aerosol Sci. 16:343 (1985).
88. Spurny, K.R.; Lodge, J.P.: Radioactivity Labelled Aerosols. Atom. Environ. 2:429 (1968).
89. Thomas, R.G.: Retention Kinetics of Inhaled Fused Aluminosilicate Particles. In: Inhaled Particles III, pp. 193–200. Unwin Bros., Surrey, UK (1971).

Chapter 10

The Measurement Process: Precision, Accuracy, and Validity

John G. Watson, Ph.D.[A]; Paul J. Lioy, Ph.D.[B]; Peter K. Mueller[C]

[A]*Desert Research Institute, Reno, Nevada;* [B]*University of Medicine and Dentistry of New Jersey, Robert Wood Johnson Medical School, Piscataway, New Jersey;* [C]*Electric Power Research Institute, Palo Alto, California*

CONTENTS

Introduction

No environmental or occupational measurement is a single number; it is, in reality, the center of an interval. To complete the measurement, the interval about that centerpoint must be defined. The width of this interval is termed the precision of the measurement. The extent to which the true value differs from the centerpoint of this interval is termed the accuracy of the measurement. If this translation is greater than the precision interval, then the particular measurement is inaccurate. Determining and reporting precision, accuracy, and validity are as important as the acquired data in any monitoring program.

An environmental/occupational measurement system must contain provisions for estimating precision and accuracy, as well as the protocol for acquiring time-averaged measurements of the pollutants under study.[1–3] It is the intent of this chapter to examine these aspects of the measurement process in order to provide a framework for use in environmental/occupational studies.

First, the sources of uncertainty affecting industrial/ambient air measurements are presented. These are sampling statistics, interferences, blank levels, and reproducibility. Not all of these uncertainties can be quantified. Second, methods for combining those uncertainties that can be quantified are proposed. Air measurements can be classified into two categories: direct reading and remote analysis. The direct-reading measurement provides immediate response from an instrument at the time and place of the measurement. The remote analysis measurement requires collection of quantities of the pollutant in a container or on a substrate at a known flow rate for a defined period of time for subsequent laboratory analysis. The precision and accuracy calculations for each of these types of samples are different. Third, methods of quantifying these precisions and accuracies are outlined. Finally, criteria are proposed for validating data after they are acquired.

Though the general concepts of "precision" and "accuracy" exist in all branches of science, it is useful to provide definitions for use in the environmental context, along with other closely related definitions. These definitions appear in Table 10-1 and should be referred to for clarification throughout this chapter. These definitions are not universally held, and more work is needed to standardize the methods by which precision and validity are reported for air quality measurements.

TABLE 10-1. Definitions

Accuracy [A]: The degree of correctness with which a measurement system yields the true value of an observable. Specifically, the percent difference between the measured and true value (the "true" value is determined by Standard Reference Materials or the use of two or more independent procedures to measure the same observable).

$$A = \frac{(C_m - C_t) \times 100}{C_t} \quad (1)$$

where: A = accuracy (in percent)
C_m = measured value
C_t = true value

Bias [K]: The ratio of the measured value to the true value

$$K = \frac{C_m}{C_t} \quad (2)$$

K is related to A by

$$A = (K - 1) \times 100 \quad (3)$$

Coefficient of Variation [s_m/C_m]: The ratio of precision of a measurement (s_m) to the value of the measurement (C_m). The coefficient of variation is also called the relative precision. It is expressed as a unitless number or, when multiplied by 100, as a percent.

Dynamic blank: The concentration of a chemical species found on a transfer medium that is involved in all aspects of the sampling process except for the deliberate collection of the chemical species being measured.

Interference: Positive or negative response of the measurement to an observable other than the one being measured.

Lower detectable limit [LDL]: The smallest quantity or concentration of a chemical species for which an analytical method will show a recognizable positive response.

Lower quantifiable limit [LQL]: The smallest quantity or concentration of a chemical species that can be quantified in an environmental sample. Defined here as one standard deviation of the dynamic blank or the LDL of the analytical method, whichever is higher.

Measurement: The amount of the observable quantified at a particular location and time by a measurement method with its associated precision, accuracy, and validity.

Measurement method: The combination of equipment, reagents, and procedures that provide the value of a measurement.

Measurement method validity: The identification of measurement method assumptions, the quantification of effects of deviations from those assumptions, the ascertainment that deviations are within reasonable tolerances for the specific application, and the creation of procedures to quantify and minimize those deviations during a specific application.

Pollutant: The material or contaminant under investigation.

Precision [s_m]: The standard deviation of repeated measurements of the same observable with the same measurement method. Precision can be defined as:

Deviations from the average response to the same measurable quantity

$$s_m = \sqrt{\frac{\sum_{i=1}^{N} (C_i - \overline{C})^2}{N - 1}} \quad (4)$$

where: C_i = i^{th} measurement of observable C

$$\overline{C} = \frac{1}{N} \sum_{i=1}^{N} C_i \quad \text{arithmetic mean of } N \text{ measures} \quad (5)$$

N = total number of measures

Sample blank: The concentration of a chemical species in the clean medium used to transfer the ambient sample to the measurement method.

Sample validity: Identification and flagging of deviations from measurement method assumptions and procedures for individual samples.

Uncertainty: The combination of the uncorrected biases and the precision.

Sources of Measurement Uncertainty

There are many sources of uncertainty in industrial/ambient air measurements. However, the four most common ones are statistical sampling, interferences, variability of blank levels, and reproducibility of the measurement.

In fixed-site monitoring studies, statistical sampling error arises because only a portion of the air is measured at a few locations over finite time periods. The sample is assumed to represent all of the air in the area under study. Typical sample volumes over a 24-hr period range between only 0.2 m^3 and 2000 m^3 of air. For environmental studies, a moderate-sized (30 × 30 km) urban area with a 500-m mixing height will contain nearly 5×10^{11} m^3 of air, with certain portions containing quite different quantities of pollutant concentrations. A factory building may contain from 10^3 to 10^5 m^3 of air, but concentration variability may be even higher than that found in ambient air because of many localized emissions sources. Both fixed-site and personal samples are often taken periodically instead of continuously. If sample averaging times are much longer than those over which changes in pollutant concentrations occur, then the degree to which the sample represents the highest exposures diminishes. The latter point is important in industrial situations where the variation of a particular pollutant may be significant over the course of the working day, and an extended sampling period could mask a hazardous situation.

The interference or amount of bias caused by an interferent on a pollutant concentration can vary with the interferent concentration in the air sample, the concentration of the pollutant under study, or both. To complicate the problem, the same interferent can cause a measurement to exceed the true value of an observable under one set of circumstances and to underestimate the true value under another set of circumstances.

Reproducibility is the extent to which a physical or chemical measurement method yields the same response to the same quantity of a sampled species. This is based on performance of the method over a long period of use. Reproducibility is a function of the instrument rather than of the entire measurement process. For example, the sample being measured may contain interferents, such as elevated blank levels, and could be nonrepresentative of the situation under study, but the measurement instrument will still yield the same response to the same sample within a definable interval.

The numerical value of the blank must be subtracted from the value provided by the measurement instrument. The sample blank, as defined in Table 10-1, is the minimum amount that must be subtracted from the observed concentrations under ideal circumstances. However, a dynamic blank, also defined in Table 10-1, is more representative because it is associated with all possibilities for contamination that might be present in the sampling environment. When blank levels are greater than the concentration of the pollutant being measured, their variability must be much lower than the mean concentrations of the pollutant. Thus, the lower quantifiable limit of the measurement method is dictated by the variability of the dynamic blanks.

Accuracy and Precision Estimation Methods

Methods that estimate the uncertainty introduced by spatial and temporal sampling statistics still require development. The quantification of this uncertainty depends on the denser placement of measurement instruments and more frequent sampling and is best illustrated by examples. As a special substudy with the U.S. Environmental Protection Agency's Inhalable Particulate Matter (PM_{10}) Sampling Network,[4] seven sampling sites were located with nominal 1.0-km separations in an industrial area. Three of these sites were in a core area near the heaviest concentration of industries and four were on the perimeter of these sources. The average concentrations of several particle size fractions for the core, perimeter, and background sites as a function of distance from the center of the neighborhood are illustrated in Figure 10-1. In a typical monitoring network, one sampling site would be chosen to represent the entire area. From these data, the accuracy of using average PM_{10} measurements from a perimeter site to represent the average concentration of PM_{10} at a core site is approximately 20%.

The temporal sampling error is illustrated in Figures 10-2 and 10-3. They show the variation in the estimation of annual arithmetic mean and maximum PM_{10} concentrations for comparison with ambient air quality standards with intervals between successive samples of 3, 6, 12, 24, and 48 days at three sites in Philadelphia. The averages did not vary substantially with sampling frequency, even though the averages are less precise as the number of samples decreases. Differences of up to 50% are evident for estimates of the maximum concentrations. As the comparison of data from three sites in Figure 10-3 shows, a lower sampling frequency does not guarantee an underestimate of a maximum concentration, but it does lower the probability of measuring it. Statistical methods are sometimes used to estimate an expected maximum concentration by assuming the measurements are drawn from a known population.

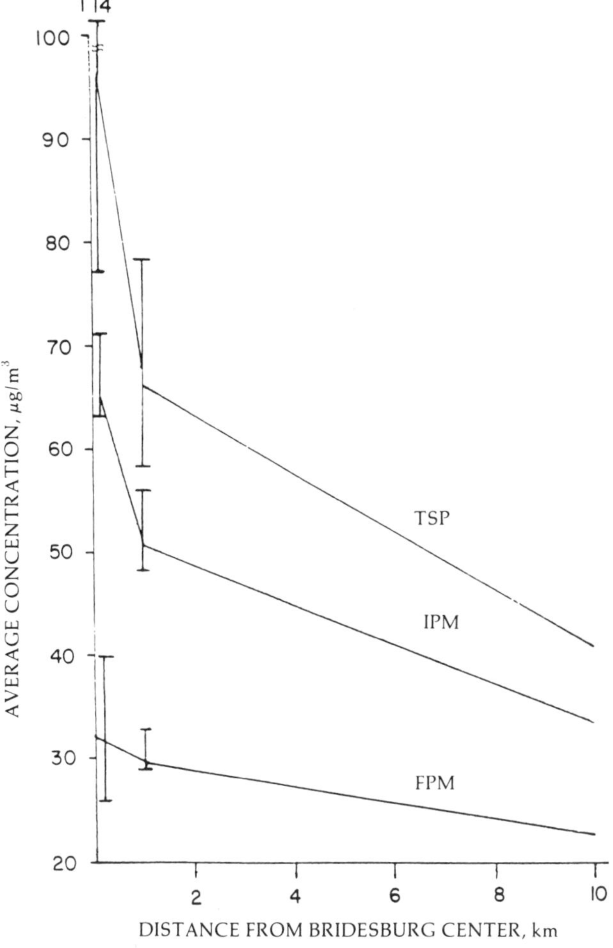

FIGURE 10-1. Average concentrations and concentration ranges versus distance from the Bridesburg industrial area of Philadelphia.[4] TSP = Total Suspended Particulate (<50-μm aerodynamic diameter); IPM = Inhalable Particulate Matter (<15-μm aerodynamic diameter); FPM = Fine Particulate Matter (<2.5-μm aerodynamic diameter). The current ambient air quality standard is for PM_{10} (<10-μm aerodynamic diameter).

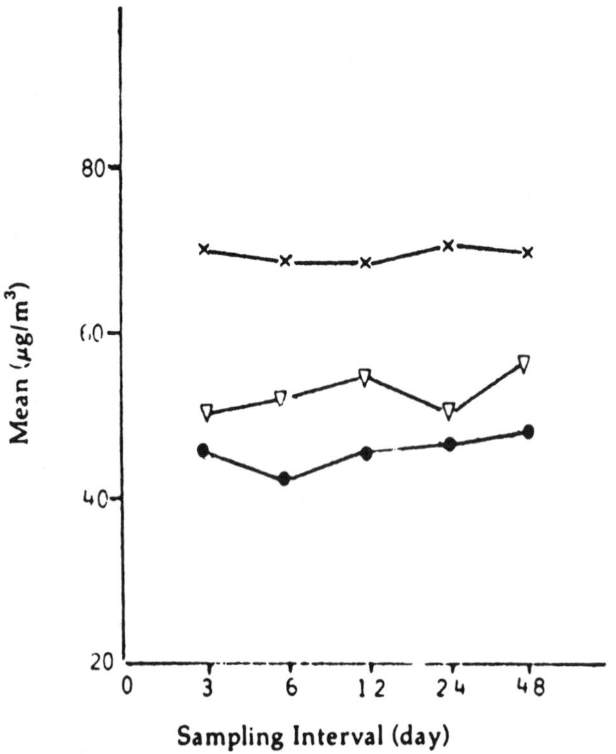

FIGURE 10-2. Annual arithmetic average inhalable particulate concentrations determined for different sampling intervals at three sites in Philadelphia.[4] Note that the average concentration is not very sensitive to sampling frequency in this example.

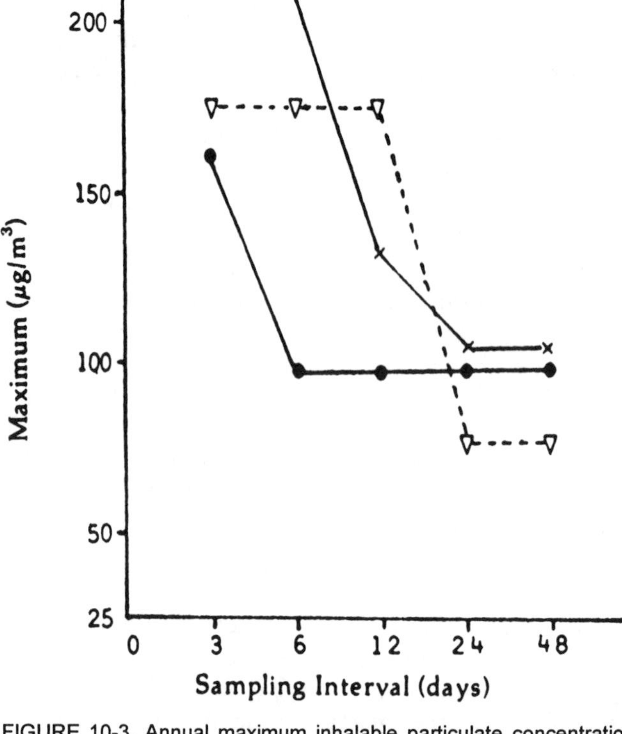

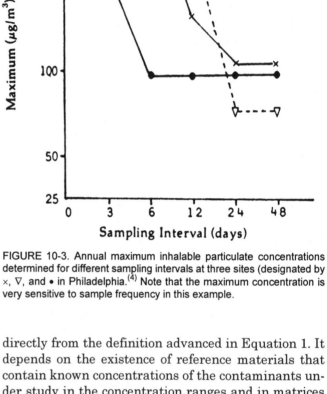

FIGURE 10-3. Annual maximum inhalable particulate concentrations determined for different sampling intervals at three sites (designated by ×, ∇, and • in Philadelphia.[4] Note that the maximum concentration is very sensitive to sample frequency in this example.

Methods to estimate the effects of interferences also need to be developed further. In some cases, interferences are not recognized until after samples have been taken. For most commonly measured contaminants, however, the likely interferences have been identified. Before any surveillance begins, it is necessary to 1) identify potential interferences, 2) quantify their potential effects on the measurements, and 3) minimize the effects on the measurements by improving measurement equipment and procedures.

For example, after years of measuring sulfate concentrations from extracts of ambient total suspended particulate (TSP) samples, it was found that the glass fiber filter medium adsorbs sulfur dioxide gas and converts it into sulfate. The amount of adsorption was subsequently quantified on several filter media,[5–7] and substrates without this interference are now used for sulfate concentration measurements. The variable effects of interferences made it almost impossible to incorporate their uncertainty into the measurement process and minimize their influence. As another example, problems have been identified recently for organic sampling in environmental and occupational settings where the interference depends on the organic substances examined, sample duration, and sample substrate.[8,9]

Estimating the accuracy of a measurement follows directly from the definition advanced in Equation 1. It depends on the existence of reference materials that contain known concentrations of the contaminants under study in the concentration ranges and in matrices similar to those of the contaminant. The measured concentration, C_m, and the known concentration in the reference material, C_t, are then used to calculate the accuracy of the analytical method defined in Equation 1. In practice, C_t also includes some measurement uncertainty.

Fairly simple formulas can be derived for propagating the reproducibility and blank precision to the measurement of contaminant concentrations. The simplest form for propagating errors assumes them to be randomly distributed about the true value according to a normal distribution and uncorrelated with each other. Though these assumptions may not be completely valid for large errors, they are usually met in most practical applications where precisions are on the order of ±10%. When a variable (x) is derived from more than one measurement (a and b), two simple rules can be used to propagate the precisions of the measured values (s_a and s_b) to estimate the precision of the derived value (s_x).[10]

1. For addition and subtraction of the form $x = a + b$ or $x = a - b$:

$$s_x^2 = s_a^2 + s_b^2 \tag{6}$$

2. For multiplication and division of the form $x = ab$ or $x = a/b$:

$$\left(\frac{s_x}{x}\right)^2 = \left(\frac{s_a}{a}\right)^2 = \left(\frac{s_b}{b}\right)^2 \tag{7}$$

These simple rules can be used to derive concentration precisions for air sampling both with a direct-reading device and for sampling on a substrate used in subsequent laboratory analyses.

Direct-reading Instrument Precisions

For a direct-reading monitor which yields a response that is linearly proportional to the ambient concentration, the calibration relationship between the true concentration, C_t, and the measured concentration, C_m, is:

$$C_m = aC_t + b \tag{8}$$

where: a = the proportionality constant (or span)
b = the baseline or blank level

Because C_t is assumed to be the true value, its precision is set equal to zero. When Equations 6 and 7 are applied to Equation 8, the measurement precision, s_m, is:

$$s_m^2 = \frac{s_a^2}{a^2}(C_m - b)^2 + s_b^2 \tag{9}$$

Thus, the precision for a direct-reading measurement, s_m, is seen to be a function of the concentration, C_m, the relative standard deviation of the span (s_a/a), and the absolute standard deviation of the baseline response, s_b. Each of these (C_m, s_a/a, and s_b) must be quantified to estimate the precision of the measurement C_m. These values are determined by periodic performance testing using standard concentrations and scrubbed air. Many direct-reading instruments in common use today automatically provide daily zero and span values that can be used in Equation 9.

Figure 10-4 presents an example of the ratio of concentrations measured by a flame photometric sulfur dioxide analyzer to constant concentrations of sulfur dioxide produced by a test gas generator ($K = C_m/C_t$) over a period of several months. These tracking results can be used to estimate a by rearranging Equation 8 such that

$$a = \frac{C_m - b}{C_t} = K - \frac{b}{C_t} \tag{10}$$

and using Equations 6 and 7 to obtain

$$s_a^2 = s_K^2 + \left(\frac{s_b}{C_t}\right)^2 \tag{11}$$

If the challenge gas concentration is much higher

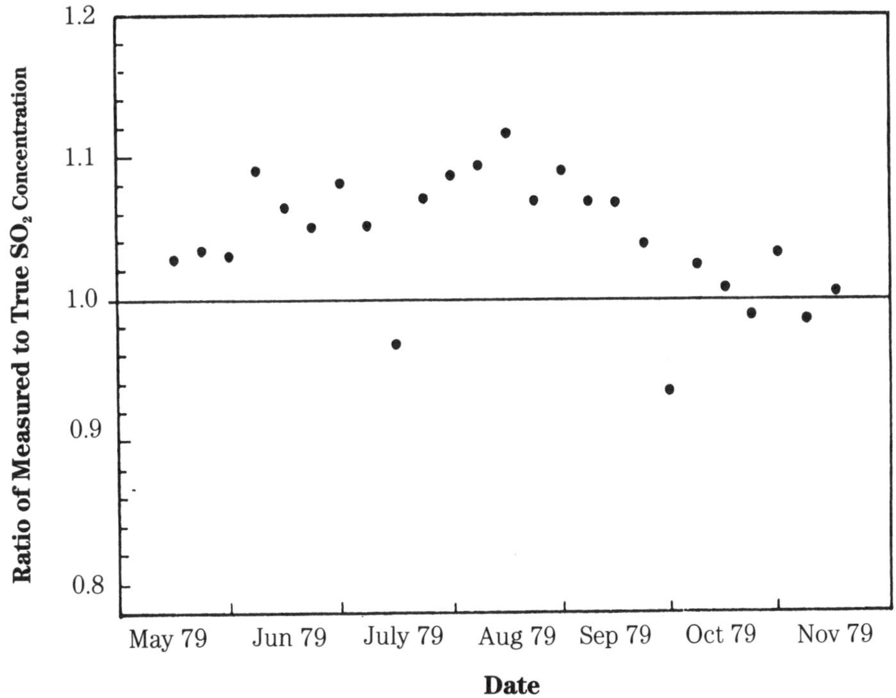

FIGURE 10-4. Typical deviations of sulfur dioxide analyzer responses from a standard test atmosphere of 50 ppb over a 6-month period.[11] Measurement accuracy and precision can be estimated from these deviations.

than the baseline and its variability, $C_t >> b$ and $C_t >> s_b$, which can be true if the test gas concentration is appropriately selected, then,

$$s_a \cong s_K \quad (12)$$

The value of s_K, which is dimensionless, can be calculated from the standard deviation of the points in Figure 10-4, which is equal to 0.0428 for the period of time indicated. The best estimate of K obtained from the average of these points is 1.044. From Equation 3, the average accuracy of this measurement for this time period is 4.4%. To obtain the coefficient of variation:

$$\frac{s_K}{K} = \frac{0.0428}{1.044} = 0.04 \quad (13)$$

The precision of the blank, s_b, is determined by the standard deviation of the instrument response to ambient air scrubbed of sulfur dioxide over the same sampling period. It was found to be 3 ppb in the case represented in Figure 10-4. Putting these values for s_a/a and s_b into Equation 9, the relative precision of the measurement, C_m, can be outlined as a function of concentration for this sampler over the time period. The dependence of this relative precision on concentration is illustrated in Figure 10-5.

This precision estimate exhibits several features:

- Precision depends on the period over which performance tracking is completed. Normally, the period of time would be bounded by sequential recalibrations, though certain events such as an instrument repair, modification, or an unusually large change in bias might divide the period further.
- The relative (%) uncertainty is NOT constant but depends on the measured concentration.
- At measured concentrations less than approximately five times the lower quantifiable limit, the precision of the baseline dominates the measurement precision.
- At measured concentrations greater than five times the lower quantifiable limit, the precision of the instrument span dominates the measurement precision.

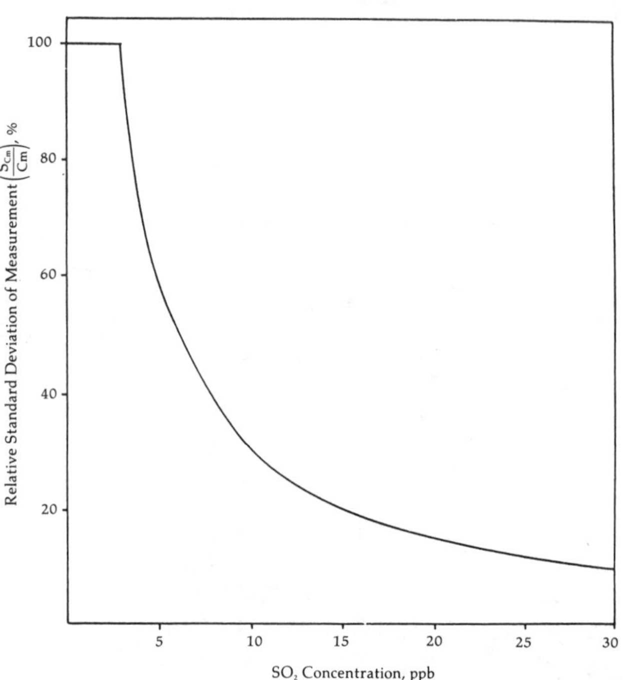

FIGURE 10-5. Coefficient of variation of sulfur dioxide measurements as a function of observed concentration derived from Equation 9 for the same 6-month period represented in Figure 10-4.

Remote Analysis Precisions

For remote analysis sampling which draws a quantity of air of volume V through the substrate, the measured concentration, C_m, is

$$C_m = \frac{M - B}{V} \quad (14)$$

where: M = amount of the contaminant measured on the substrate
B = amount of contaminant on the blank substrate

Using equations 6 and 7, the relative precision of the measurement becomes

$$\frac{s_m}{C_m} = \left[\frac{s_M^2 + s_B^2}{(M - B)^2} + \frac{s_V^2}{V^2}\right]^{1/2} \quad (15)$$

where: s_m = absolute precision of C_m
s_M = absolute precision of M
s_B = absolute precision of B
s_V = absolute precision of V

The precision of the contaminant measurement, s_m, can be estimated from duplicate analyses of the same sample. For N duplicate analyses with results M_{1i} and M_{2i} for the ith pair, s_m can be approximated by the average of the standard deviations of each measured pair:

$$s_m^2 = \frac{1}{2N}\sum_{i=1}^{N}(M_{2i} - M_{1i})^2 \quad (16)$$

The precision of the blank measurement, s_B, can be estimated from the standard deviation of measurements from N dynamic blank substrates using Equation 4, where B_i is the ith blank measurement and B is the average of all B_i.

The precision of the volume measurement, s_V, is calculated as the standard deviation of repeated measurements, V_i, of the same volume using Equation 4. If the volume is calculated from flow rate and duration measurements, Equations 6 and 7 can be used to propagate the precisions of those measurements to s_V.

Accuracy estimates can be made for M and V, separately. This is done using standards of known values for each method and calculating the fractional deviations from these standards using Equation 1.

Data Validation

"Data validation is the process whereby data are filtered and accepted or rejected based on a set of criteria."[12] These criteria should include the following steps:

1. Flagging (and possible correction or removal) of values that were achieved under significant deviations from standard operating procedures.
2. Identifying and correcting mistakes and errors in data transfer.
3. Identifying periods during which baselines or calibrations deviated from tolerable limits, and correction, flagging, or removal of data taken during those periods.
4. Checking of internal consistency of simultaneous measurements with corrections where possible and flags where corrections are not possible.
5. Checking outlier and extreme values to verify whether an error in the measurement process was responsible.
6. Checking consistency of measurements with expectations.
7. Creating validation summaries documenting changes and flagged values.

Missing and invalid values should be replaced with a consistent number (–99 is often used) that is outside of the range of permissible values. A measurement is often of value for interpretive purposes even though it may not pass all validation criteria. Thus, preference is given to flagging a value as "suspect" rather than deleting it. Clearly invalid values should be replaced with the missing value code, however.

Once this validation has been completed, the data may still have information that could be either indicative of scientifically significant episodes or of a measurement error which has not been detected. At this point, the interpreter of the data must use some scientific judgment. If the previous steps have been carried out and documented, the researcher may trace the path of the measurement to establish that a measured error is not the cause. After this is accomplished, the data can then be used for subsequent analyses as indicative of a real event.

Summary and Conclusion

This chapter has presented definitions, procedures, and calculation methods for estimating the accuracy, precision, and validity of measurements in ambient air and in the workplace. No environmental measurement can be considered complete without adding these three attributes to the measured value. These concepts are applicable to each of the measurement methods described in other sections of this volume. Since its first publication in 1983, these concepts have been incorporated into several ambient measurement programs[13,14] which can be examined to illustrate practical applications of the concepts presented here. Sampling systems, data acquisition methods, and operating procedures have been modified to accommodate the additional blank, replicate, and performance test data needed to apply these methods.[15–22] Comparison studies have been conducted to identify and reduce interferences.[23–25] The availability of quantitative accuracy, precision, and validity estimates along with measurements has influenced the formulation of models which use these data to relate ambient concentrations to their emissions sources for suspended particulate measurements.[26–27] There is a need to extend these concepts to all environmental and occupational monitoring programs.

References

1. Mueller, P.K.: Comments on Advances in the Analysis of Air Contaminants. J. Air Pollut. Control Assoc. 30:998 (1980).
2. Hidy, G.M.: Jekyll Island Meeting Report. Environ. Sci. Technol. 19:1032 (1985).
3. Keith, L.H., Ed.: Principles of Environmental Sampling. American Chemical Society, Washington, DC (1988).
4. Watson, J.G.; Chow, J.C.; Shah, J.J.: Analysis of Inhalable Particulate Matter Measurement. EPA-450/4-81-035. U.S. Environmental Protection Agency, Research Triangle Park, NC (1981).
5. Coutant, R.W.: Effect of Environmental Variables on Collection of Atmospheric Sulfate. Environ. Sci. Technol. 11:873 (1977).
6. Meserole, F.B.; Schwitzgebel, K.; Jones, B.F.; et al.: Sulfur Dioxide Interferences in the Measurement of Ambient Particulate Sulfates. Research Project 262. Electric Power Research Institute, Palo Alto, CA (1976).
7. Mueller, P.K.; Hidy, G.M.: The Sulfate Regional Experiment (SURE): Report of Findings, Vol. 1. Report EA-1901. Electric Power Research Institute, Palo Alto, CA (1982).
8. Schwartz, G.P.; Daisey, J.M.; Lioy, P.J.: The Effects of Sampling Duration on the Concentration of Particulate Organics Collected on Glass Fiber Filters. Am. Ind. Hyg. Assoc. J. 42:258 (1981).
9. McDow, S.R.; Huntzicker, J.J.: Vapor Adsorption Artifact in the Sampling of Organic Aerosol: Face Velocity Effects. Atmos. Environ. 24A: 2563 (1990).
10. Bevington, P.R.: Data Reduction and Error Analysis for the Physical Sciences. McGraw–Hill, New York (1969).
11. Mueller, P.K.; Watson, J.G.: Eastern Regional Air Quality Measurements, Vol. 1. Report EA-1914. Electric Power Research Institute, Palo Alto, CA (1982).
12. U.S. Environmental Protection Agency: Quality Assurance Handbook for Air Pollution Measurement Systems, Vol. 1, Principles. EPA 600/9-76-00J. U.S. EPA, Research Triangle Park, NC (1976).

13. Chow, J.C.; Watson, J.G.: Summary of Particulate Data Bases for Receptor Modeling in the United States. Transactions: Receptor Models in Air Resources Management, p. 108. J.G. Watson, Ed. Air & Waste Management Association, Pittsburgh, PA (1989).

14. Watson, J.G.; Chow, J.C.: Data Bases for PM_{10} and $PM_{2.5}$ Chemical Compositions and Source Profiles. Transactions: PM_{10} Standards and Nontraditional Particulate Source Controls, pp. 61–91. J.C. Chow and D.M. Ono, Eds. Air & Waste Management Association, Pittsburgh, PA (1992).

15. Chow, J.C.; Watson, J.G.; Bowen, J.L.; et al.: A Sampling System for Reactive Species in the Western U.S. ACS Symposium Series. E. Winegar, Ed. American Chemical Society, Washington, DC (1993).

16. Eldred, R.A.; Cahill, T.A.; Pitchford, M.; Malm, W.C.: IMPROVE — A New Remote Area Particulate Monitoring System for Visibility Studies. J. Air Pollut. Control Assoc. 54:3 (1988).

17. Fitz, D.; Chan, M.; Cass, G.; et al.: A Multi-Component Size-Classifying Aerosol and Gas Sampler for Ambient Air Monitoring. Presented at 82nd Annual Meeting, Air & Waste Management Association, Anaheim, CA. AWMA, Pittsburgh, PA (1989).

18. Koutrakis, P.; Wolfson, J.M.; Slater, J.L.; et al.: Evaluation of an Annular Denuder/Filter Pack System to Collect Acidic Aerosols and Gases. Environ. Sci. Technol. 22:1463 (1988).

19. Rogers, C.F.; Watson, J.G.; Mathai, C.V.: Design and Testing of a New Size Classifying Isokinetic Sequential Aerosol Sampler (SCISAS). J. Air Pollut. Control Assoc. 39:1569 (1989).

20. Solomon, P.A.; Fall, T.; Salmon, L.; et al.: Chemical Characteristics of PM_{10} Aerosols Collected in the Los Angeles Area. J. Air Pollut. Control Assoc. 39:154 (1989).

21. Thurston, G.D.; Gorczynski, J.E.; Jaques, P.; et al.: An Automated Sequential Sampling System for Particulate Acid Aerosols: Description, Characterization, and Field Sampling Results. J. Exposure Anal. Environ. Epidem. 2:415 (1992).

22. Tombach, I.H.; Allard, D.W.; Drake, R.L.; Lewis, R.C.: Western Regional Air Quality Studies; Visibility and Air Quality Measurements: 1981–1982., Document EA-4903. Electric Power Research Institute, Palo Alto, CA (1987).

23. Hering, S.V.; Lawson, D.R.; Allegrini, I.; et al.: The Nitric Acid Shootout: Field Comparison of Measurement Methods. Atmos. Environ. 22:1519 (1988).

24. Hering, S.V.; Appel, B.R.; Cheng, W.; et al.: Comparison of Sampling Methods for Carbonaceous Aerosols in Ambient Air. Aerosol Sci. Technol. 12:200 (1990).

25. Mathai, C.V.; Watson, J.G.; Rogers, C.F.; et al.: Intercomparison of Ambient Aerosol Samplers Used in Western Visibility and Air Quality Studies. Environ. Sci. Technol. 24:1090 (1990).

26. Pace, T.G.; Watson, J.G.: Protocol for Applying and Validating the CMB Model. EPA 450/4-87-010. U.S. Environmental Protection Agency, Research Triangle Park, NC (1987).

27. Watson, J.G.; Cooper, J.A.; Huntzicker, J.J.: The Effective Variance Weighting for Least Squares Calculations Applied to the Mass Balance Receptor Model. Atmos. Environ. 18:1347 (1984).

Chapter 11

Performance Testing Criteria for Air Sampling Instrumentation

Judson Kenoyer, CIH, CHP[A] and David Leong, Ph.D., CIH[B]

[A]*Science Applications International Corporation, 1845 Terminal Drive, Richland, Washington;*
[B]*Ontario Ministry Labour, 14 Axsmith Crescent, Willowdale, Ontario, Canada*

CONTENTS

Introduction

Air sampling and monitoring instruments are used by industrial hygiene and safety personnel to establish safe working environments and to check the establishment and reliability of exposure control mechanisms in the workplace. This instrumentation includes but is not limited to air movers and pumps, particle size-selective sampling devices, passive dosimeters and adsorption tubes, radioactivity samplers, direct-reading instruments for aerosols, gases, and vapors, detector tubes for gases and vapors, and bioaerosol samplers.

Concern about performance criteria has grown substantially in recent years as more diverse advisory groups and regulatory bodies have become involved in establishing guidelines for air sampling instrument performance. Many different industrial hygiene instrument manufacturers have attempted to establish themselves as the "experts" on different air sampling needs and it is very difficult for the potential users of the instrumentation to be able to determine which instrument can best meet the needs while meeting cost restrictions. The basic requirement is that the worker must be protected from exposure to toxic and hazardous materials by reducing exposure to a level at which health and safety is established. The performance of the instruments used must be accurate, reproducible, and reliable.

Included in this chapter is a synopsis of the First International Symposium on Air Sampling Instrumentation held in 1991. This synopsis provides details of the plenary and technical sessions and summarizes major discussion points and recommendations that came out of the workshops at that symposium. Discussions on other performance criteria that exist and testing of air sampling instruments that is currently being performed are also included in this chapter. Performance testing criteria needs that were identified at the International Symposium and by other instrument users and manufacturers are also noted.

Current Performance Criteria

The Occupational Safety and Health Act and the Clean Air Act Amendments were passed in 1970. The passage of these acts initiated the control of airborne contaminants in the workplace and the environment by

United States government agencies. Reference and recommended methods for air sampling, monitoring, and analyses of specific chemicals, radionuclides, and other hazardous materials and conditions have been established by several different organizations including the U.S. Environmental Protection Agency (U.S. EPA), National Institute for Occupational Safety and Health (NIOSH), Occupational Safety and Health Administration (OSHA), and the American National Standards Institute (ANSI).

The nuclear industry has been thoroughly regulated for decades. Regulations were established to limit occupational exposures and set release limits for airborne radioactive effluents from nuclear facilities. These limits are adhered to by all licensees and facilities operated under the Nuclear Regulatory Commission (NRC) and the Department of Energy (DOE). Standards and guides on calibration of instruments,(1) performance testing of health physics instrumentation,(2) and sampling of airborne radioactive materials(3) have been written to establish minimum requirements to be met by both manufacturers and users of instruments.

In the industrial hygiene field, regulations exist for compliance with the exposure limits for hazardous materials (i.e., chemicals) and conditions, but the guidance for the operation and performance criteria requirements of instrumentation to be used to measure the hazards does not exist at the level that is seen in the nuclear field. Threshold Limit Values for chemical and physical agents have been established by the American Conference of Governmental Industrial Hygienists (ACGIH) and are used by industrial hygienists to establish control measures and personal protection equipment requirements. The American Industrial Hygiene Association (AIHA) has provided some guidance on the use of sampling equipment (e.g., the Cascade Impactor Monograph(4)) and for the use of other equipment (e.g., noise), but, in general, a need exists for more cohesive guidance on the performance criteria for specific types of industrial hygiene instrumentation. Performance criteria and the testing results based on those criteria help users in making scientific as well as cost-effective selection of air sampling instruments, serving their needs for protecting the health of workers.

International Symposium on Air Sampling Instrument Performance

The First International Symposium was held October 29–November 1, 1991, in Research Triangle Park, North Carolina. It was sponsored by the Air Sampling Instruments Committee of ACGIH. During that symposium, users, manufacturers, and regulators discussed air sampling instrument performance and criteria. Details of this symposium were published in *Applied Occupational and Environmental Hygiene*.(5) The following information has been excerpted or summarized from discussions held at that symposium. Table 11-1 summarizes information discussed during the symposium related to performance criteria for air sampling instrumentation.

Plenary Session

The International Standards Organization (ISO)(6) and ACGIH(7) have both proposed quantitative criteria for particle size-selective sampling based on experimental data for the inhalation and regional deposition of airborne particles. The European Standards Commission (CEN) has, over the last few years, come into agreement with these groups. Curves for the inhalable fraction, the thoracic fraction, and the respirable fraction have been developed by all three groups.

In the United States, performance criteria for gas detectors were established in a certification program sponsored by NIOSH in the 1970s. This program has since been discontinued. OSHA proposed regulations for butanone that stated a desired accuracy of ±25% for "above the Permissible Exposure Level (PEL)," ±30% "at or below the PEL and above the action level," and ±50% "at or below the action level." Procedures were defined for determining noncompliance that set the stage for performance criteria for sampling and analytical methods.(8,9) The accuracy criterion was established as "The goal is to assure that a single measurement by a method will come within ±25% of the corresponding 'true' air concentration at least 95% of the time."(10) This concept of accuracy encompasses both bias and precision and is currently being applied to several samplers. NIOSH has published several monitoring methods for instruments after they were evaluated and also a number of technical reports on the performance of field portable instruments.(11–17) The evaluations included portability, reliability, calibration, interference, temperature and humidity effects, battery and sensor life, and warm-up and response time.

The U.S. EPA is responsible for reducing the exposure of the United States population to the 189 hazardous air pollutants identified in the 1990 Clean Air Act Amendments.(18) Over the next few years, voluntary reduction in the release of these air pollutants will be expected, followed by the establishment of engineering-based pollution control requirements. Five emerging issues exist: aerosol acidity, enhanced ozone monitoring, development of simple-to-operate and inexpensive air pollutant monitoring systems, indoor air pollution, and continuous measurement of stack gas flow rate.

Existing performance standards for aerosol instrumentation include the PM_{10} Standard,(19) ACGIH guidelines for workplace sampling, ISO sampling criteria, and the European community performance standards. In the PM_{10} Standard, specifications are included

TABLE 11-1. Existing Performance Criteria for Air Sampling

Type of Instrumentation	Performance Criteria/Guidelines	Regulatory Agency or Organization
Gas Detector Tubes	Accuracy	NIOSH
Portable Field Instruments	Portability, Reliability, Calibration, Interference, Temperature, Humidity, Battery and Sensor Life, Warm-up and Response Time	NIOSH
Aerosol (PM_{10})	Sampling effectiveness, 50% Cut Point, Precision, Flow-rate Stability	U.S. EPA
Aerosol (Workplace Sampling)	Inhalable, Thoracic, and Respirable Fractions; Sampling Efficiency, 50% Cut Point, Sampling Precision	ACGIH ISO
Aerosol (Workplace Sampling)	Inhalable, Thoracic, and Respirable Fractions; Inlet, Fractionator, Particle Collector or Sensor, Air Mover, Controls	CEN
CO, NO_2, SO_2, O_3, Pb, Particles	Reference Test Methods (Standards) with Performance Specifications	U.S. EPA
Passive Samplers	Random Error Limit, Limit of Detection, Limit of Quantitation	NIOSH, OSHA Amer. Chem. Soc.
Flammable Gases	Accuracy, Repeatability, Drift	BSI, CENELEC
Toxic Gases	Selectivity, Overall Uncertainty, Measurement Range, Environmental, Interferences	CEN
SO_2	Rise Time, Fall Time, Ranges of Operation, Lag Time, Flow Rate, Auto-Range Feature, Variable Damping Feature	U.S. EPA
Workplace Air Monitors (Radioactivity)	Electronic (Stability, Response Time, Coefficient of Variation); Radiation Response (Beta-Energy, Accuracy); Interferences (RF, MW); Environmental (Temperature, Humidity); Air Circuit (Flow Rate Accuracy, Aerosol Collection)	ANSI
Personal Sampling Pumps	Interferences	OSHA, ANSI
Respirable Dust Sampler	Entry Efficiency, Penetration Efficiency, Sampling Efficiency	ISO, CEN

for parameters such as sampling effectiveness, 50% cutpoint, precision, and flow rate stability. The basic components of an aerosol sampler are the inlet, fractionator, collector/sensor, air mover, and the controls; the parameters that could affect performance need to be considered in the interpretation of test data. Guidance on these important factors can be found throughout this text and in aerosol instrumentation references.[20,21] The changing needs for aerosol sampling and the new advances in aerosol technology mean a continuing need for new performance standards. Integration of the experience in the fields of environmental and workplace sampling will be helpful because many of the technical problems are similar.

Instruments are employed in a wide range of applications, most of which fall within five major categories: pollution monitoring and control, process monitoring and control, combustion monitoring and control, hazard monitoring, and occupational hygiene. During the past 20–30 years, a large number of instruments have been developed to meet these measurement tasks. More than 1000 instruments manufactured by 240 companies have been identified. For instruments for the measurement of flammable gases, initial standards were developed that related to the risk of the instrument becoming a source of ignition during operation. There are now minimum performance standards relating to parameters such as accuracy, repeatability, and drift. A five-part British Standard[22] was developed that formed the base document for the European Standard.[23] Both general and specific performance requirements are established for different applications. It is much more difficult to establish standards for instruments that are used for the measurement of toxic gases and vapors. There is a large range of toxic substances that may present a range of hazards (e.g., acute, chronic, sensitization) over a wide range of concentrations and affect individuals differently. In Europe, the lead is being taken by the CEN Technical Committee 137.

There are two classes of statistical methods that can be considered in analyzing the field performance of instruments: descriptive and inferential. Descriptive methods involve estimating the level of a summary statistic from a set of data (e.g., uncertainties around a sample result, magnitude of the difference between two instruments reading the same concentration). Inferential methods involve testing hypotheses regarding a system (e.g., Is the response from one sampler consistently different from that of a second sampler? Is the measurement uncertainty greater than a specific requirement?). The user of the instruments must use the available statistical methods to decide which instruments are adequate or best to use for the requirements and restrictions for specific tasks. Field evaluations of instrument performance may take many forms. Statistical considerations in the design and analysis of field evaluation studies will be guided by the purpose of the study.

Technical Sessions

A wide range of work related to instrument performance criteria and instrument responses to those criteria is being performed by manufacturers and users of instruments in the national and international arena today. While much remains to be done, progress has been achieved in the following areas:

- Evaluations of several portable and/or personal types of gas, vapor, and aerosol monitors. Criteria studied include accuracy (either to a known value or to the manufacturers' specification), precision (i.e., reproducibility), and interference.
- A proposed national ambient air quality standard for sulfur dioxide by U.S. EPA. Comparison of available, state-of-the-art instruments to the requirements have been made with regard to rise time, fall time, ranges of operation, lag time, flow rate, auto-range feature, and variable damping feature.
- Comparisons of NIOSH reference sampling methods for specific gases and the determination of lower detection limits for those gases. Newly developed sampling methods are also being compared to NIOSH and OSHA standard methods.
- Evaluations of the performance of aerosol samplers against manufacturer's specifications by many users, including the effects of operating conditions, gas medium, and particle characteristics on instrument response.
- Evaluations of the criteria in an existing ANSI standard on workplace air monitors used for the measurement of airborne radioactivity, as well as the performance of available instrumentation against those criteria. Categories of the criteria included general, electronic, radiation response, interfering response, environmental, and air circuit.
- Evaluations of video exposure monitoring as a means of studying sources of occupational air contaminant exposure. Methods include one in which the measurement of chemical and/or physical agent(s) in the breathing zone with the real-time monitoring instruments are recorded simultaneously with the video recording of the work tasks.
- Documentation of degraded instrument performance due to radio interference. The use of a human exposure standard (ANSI C95.1-1982)[(24)] as a basis for requirements to avoid electromagnetic susceptibility has been recommended. This is a case where there exists a standard for combustible gas detectors,[(25)] but the performance requirements of the standard does not cover the interference problem in adequate detail.
- Evaluation of a respirable dust sampler used in British coal mines against ISO/CEN criteria. The test protocol for the work followed the principles discussed by the ISO and CEN working group CEN/TC137/WG3.[(26)]

Workshops

Eight workshops were held during the Symposium with leading experts in each specific area in attendance. The following topics were discussed: pumps and air movers, particle size-selective samplers, active and passive sorbent samplers, radioactivity samplers, direct-reading instruments for aerosols; direct-reading instruments for gases and vapors, detector tubes for gases and vapors, and bioaerosol samplers. Table 11-2 identifies the themes for each workshop and lists specific recommendations on instrument performance.[(5)]

Other Performance Criteria and Testing

Other performance criteria and testing programs exist that have not been discussed in this chapter; these may be used by manufacturers and users of air sampling instruments nationally and internationally. Many instrument manufacturers will have their instruments "certified" in different countries by appropriate testing programs or services so that their instruments can be available for purchase in those countries. The following examples are included to describe some of these programs.

One air sampling instrument manufacturer has had its instruments through no less than eight testing programs. These programs include: the Underwriters Laboratory Inc. (UL Listing), USA; Mine Safety and Health Administration (MSHA), USA; SIRA Certification Service, England; ISO 9002, International Standards Organization (ISO); Institute for Workers Safety (BIA), Germany; Government Mining Engineer (GME), South Africa; Work Cover Authority (WA), Australia; and National Association of Testing Authorities (NATA), Australia. The UL Listing certifies instruments of different classes of hazards (e.g., Class I [Group A, B, C, D], Class II [Groups E, F, G], and Class III). MSHA performs testing for intrinsic safety for use in specific gas-air mixtures. SIRA Certification Service,

TABLE 11-2. Recommendations Developed in the Symposium Workshops[5]

Workshop #1 on Pumps and Air Movers

1. Standardized performance tests need to be developed for criteria of importance which will be suitable for use by both users and manufacturers of air movers and pumps. Standards are needed for both personal and area sampling pumps and air movers.

   The performance criteria should include flow calibration; effects of temperature, atmospheric pressure, pump load, strong electromagnetic fields, and pump orientation; noise; contaminate emissions; pulsation dampening; tamper resistance; intrinsic safety; x-hour performance test; timing accuracy; drop test; and vibration susceptibility.
2. There needs to be international cooperation for the development of pump and air mover performance standards (e.g., communication with CEN/TC/137 Working Group 2 regarding pump performance standards being developed in Europe).
3. Needed features of new pumps and air movers include a smaller, quieter, self-contained weatherproof package; continuous air monitoring in indoor environments; and, for battery-operated pumps, higher flow rate and longer operating life.

Workshop #2 on Particle Size-Selective Samplers

1. The new CEN/ISO sampling conventions need to be adopted and an implementation plan needs to be developed.

Workshop #3 on Active and Passive Sorbent Samplers

1. International consensus standards need to be developed for the performance evaluation of active and passive sorbent samplers. The standards should be broad enough to encourage rather than inhibit development of innovative methods, new technologies, and new applications.
2. The development of performance standards for semivolatile pollutants has the highest priority. There is a growing interest in and need to sample semivolatile species, such as the polycyclic aromatic hydrocarbons, which are distributed between the vapor and particle phases. Sampling such species so that the original distribution is not changed during the process of sampling is a challenging problem.

Workshop #4 on Radioactivity Samplers

1. Integrated performance standards, which include sampling, siting, hardware, and QA/QC protocols, should be promulgated for both stack and stationary CAMS.
2. There is a need to develop the hardware for a size selective CAM to sample and monitor aerosol classes appropriate to particular workplace situations.

Workshop #5 on Direct-Reading Instruments for Aerosols

1. The development of voluntary consensus standards for two types of instruments is needed: aerosol mass measuring instruments, optical particle counters.
2. The development of an accurate direct-reading portable aerosol mass monitor is also needed.

Workshop #6 on Direct-Reading Instruments for Gases and Vapors

1. The development of uniform international criteria for testing of direct-reading instruments is needed. These should define terms such as limit of detection and limit of quantification and should stress uniform reporting of technical specifications.

Workshop #7 on Detector Tubes for Gases and Vapors

1. ANSI/ISEA-102 1990 should be reviewed and modified to allow approval at other than TLV levels. Ranges above or below the current TLV may be appropriate.
2. Testing performed to certified tubes under SEI should also include other variables:
   - Temperature range: 0°C and 40°C, or limits advertised by the manufacturer
   - Humidity 20 and 80 percent RH; and
   - Accelerated aging tests.
3. The development of an ANSI/ACGIH standard on direct-reading, length-of-stain dosimeters, possibly incorporating these requirements into ANSI/ISEA-102 1990 is needed. Specific criteria should include:
   - Temperature range: 0°C and 40°C, or limits advertised by the manufacturer;
   - Humidity 20 and 80 percent RH; and
   - Accelerated aging tests

Workshop #8 on Bioaerosol Samplers

1. Published reports of bioaerosol sampler performance could be used as the bases to develop test methods and performance criteria for bioaerosol samplers. Applicable performance criteria that have been developed for other aerosol sampling instruments should be included, modifying these criteria, as required, to accommodate the special needs of bioaerosol sampling.

England, is the European equivalent to the American UL Listing for intrinsic safety approval. ISO 9002 is an internationally recognized quality standard that specifies management and production procedures. The other testing programs are used less frequently in the international market.

A standard exists that is used for testing of gas detector tube units. It is ANSI/ISEA 102-1990[27] and is entitled "American National Standard for Gas Detector Tube Units — Short Term Type for Toxic Gases and Vapors in Working Environments." This standard establishes performance requirements for gas detector tube units and components that are used to determine the concentration of toxic gases and vapors in working environments. This standard includes the following major sections: required information, construction and performance requirements, sampling pump requirements, and quality assurance requirements. Required information includes instructions for the user to verify accurate flow rates, absence of leakage, and specific labeling requirements (e.g., contaminant for measurement, expiration dates of tubes). Construction and performance requirements include accuracy of the units, shelf life, and calibration specifics (e.g., correction factors for environmental effects, operating ranges, calibration concentrations). Sampling pump requirements such as limits on air in-leakage, flow rate accuracy, and prevention of backflow are discussed. Quality assurance details that are discussed include sampling plan information, acceptable quality levels, and inspection levels.

An international document, published by the Organisation Internationale De Metrologie Legale (OIML), OIML D 22,[28] provides definitions and guidelines for selecting portable instruments to measure airborne pollutants at hazardous waste sites. This document also provides background and literature references on the application of these instruments. Emphasis is placed on methods and requirements for testing and calibrating instruments. Information is provided for the following types of instruments: compound-specific instruments, chemical detector tubes, total hydrocarbon analyzers, gas chromatographs, infrared analyzers, and dust monitors.

Many manufacturers have the resources needed to test their own units with company-owned equipment and with the use of procedures developed by their own personnel based on requirements found in standards or regulations (e.g., U.S. EPA, DOE, NRC, ANSI, ISO). Testing can be performed by outside services using the similar procedures. One thorough testing program that is operated by a specific instrument manufacturer performs the following tests: calibration gas repeatability, long-term stability, gas-alarm, bounce/transportation, vibration, unpowered storage, linearity, step response time, gas velocity variation, gas saturation, supply voltage variation, temperature, humidity, ambient pressure, poisoning (hydrogen sulfide), cross sensitivity, radio frequency interference (RFI), time-weighted average (TWA), short-term exposure limit (STEL), battery lifetime, and air velocity for internal pumps.

Additional standards are needed to ensure that the quality of air sampling instruments available to the user is good enough to ensure the safety of the worker is not compromised. Accurate gas and particulate concentrations need to be measured with reliable, precise, rugged, sensitive, fast-response instrumentation.

Performance Testing Criteria Needs

The following is a list of performance testing criteria needs that have been identified by instrument users, manufacturers, and regulators:

- Comparison and evaluation of different instrument performance criteria established or proposed by different groups (national and international).
- Establishment of standards for different types of industrial hygiene instrumentation—many types of instruments are not currently covered.
- Integration of the experience in the fields of environmental and workplace sampling; the technical problems are similar.
- Establishment of performance testing programs or laboratories that would ensure uniformity of testing procedures and levels of quality assurance.
- Standards that are broad enough to encourage rather than inhibit the development of innovative methods, new technologies, and new applications.
- Performance criteria that are flexible—As technology changes, the performance criteria will need to be reevaluated for their applicability and may need to be enhanced or changed accordingly.

Conclusions

The current status of performance criteria standards is as follows:

- Performance testing criteria and testing results do exist—but in limited number, areas, and depth.
- There are proposed instrument performance criteria based on experimental data that require approval and acceptance.
- Some performance criteria that currently exist or are proposed by different groups are not consistent when compared to each other or com-

pared to the parameter that is being measured.

- There exists the need for the continuation of the presentation and publication of performance data on all types of industrial hygiene instrumentation. There needs to be direct feedback to the writers and evaluators of the standards that results in timely communication.
- Many instrument users, manufacturers, and regulators believe that performance testing standards need to be established in several areas and that they should be periodically revised to reflect changes in technology.
- The effort to establish performance criteria will require funding that does not exist now. Instrument users and manufacturers expect governmental funding to support this effort.

References

1. American National Standards Institute: American National Standard for Radiation Protection Instrumentation Test and Calibration. ANSI N323-1978. ANSI, New York (1978).
2. American National Standards Institute: American National Standard for Radiation Instrumentation, Performance Specifications for Health Physics Instrumentation - Occupational Airborne Radioactivity Monitoring Instrumentation. ANSI N42.17B-1989. ANSI, New York (1990).
3. American National Standards Institute: American National Standard Guide to Sampling Airborne Radioactive Materials in Nuclear Facilities. ANSI N13.1-1969. ANSI, New York (1969).
4. Lodge, J.P.; Chan, T.L., Eds.: Cascade Impactor Sampling and Data Analysis. American Industrial Hygiene Association, Akron, OH (1986).
5. Cohen, B.S.; McCammon, C.S.; Vincent, J.H., Eds.: Proceeding of The International Symposium on Air Sampling Instrument Performance. Appl. Occup. Environ. Hyg. 8(4):209–424 (1993).
6. International Standards Organisation (ISO): Air Quality - Particle Size Fraction Definitions for Health-Related Sampling. Technical Report ISO/TR/7708-1983 (E). ISO, Geneva (1983).
7. American Conference of Governmental Industrial Hygienists: Particle Size-Selective Sampling in the Workplace. Report of the ACGIH Technical Committee on Air Sampling Procedures. ACGIH, Cincinnati, OH (1985).
8. Leidel, N.A.; Busch, K.A.: Statistical Methods for the Determination of Noncompliance with Occupational Health Standards. DHEW (NIOSH) Pub. No. 75-159; NTIS Pub. No. PB-83-180-414. National Technical Information Service, Springfield, VA (1975).
9. Leidel, N.A.; Busch, K.A.; Lynch, J.R.: Occupational Exposure Sampling Strategy Manual. DHEW (NIOSH) Pub. No. 77-173; NTIS Pub. No. PB-274-792. National Technical Information Service, Springfield, VA (1977).
10. Taylor, D.G.; Kupel, R.E.; Bryant, J.M.: Documentation of the NIOSH Validation Tests. DHEW (NIOSH) Pub. No. 77-185; NTIS Pub. No. PB-274-248. National Technical Information Service, Springfield, VA (1977).
11. Parker, C.D.; Lee, M.B.; Sharpe, J.C.: An Evaluation of Personal Sampling Pumps in Sub-Zero Temperatures. DHEW (NIOSH) Pub. No. 78-117; NTIS Pub. No. PB-279-615. National Technical Information Service, Springfield, VA (1977).
12. Bissette, L.W.; Parker, D.D.: Evaluation of Batteries Used in Sampling Pumps. Final Report. NIOSH Contract 210-75-0080. NTIS Pub. No. PB-83-109-694. National Technical Information Service, Springfield, VA (1975).
13. Tompkins, F.C., Jr.; Becker, J.H.: Evaluation of Portable Direct-Reading H_2S Meters. Report of NIOSH Contract HEW 210-75-0037. DHEW (NIOSH) Pub. No. 77-137. NIOSH, Cincinnati, OH (1976).
14. Parker, C.D.; Strong, R.B.: Evaluation of Portable, Direct-Reading Carbon Monoxide Meters, Part 1. DHEW (NIOSH) Pub. No. 75-106; NTIS Pub. No. PB-273-870. National Technical Information Service, Springfield, VA (1975).
15. Parker, C.D.; Strong, R.B.: Evaluation of Portable, Direct-Reading Sulfur Dioxide Meters, Part 2. DHEW (NIOSH) Pub. No. 75-137; NTIS Pub. No. PB-273-799. National Technical Information Service, Springfield, VA (1977).
16. Willey, M.A.; McCammon, C.S.: Evaluation of Portable, Direct-Reading Hydrocarbon Meters. DHEW (NIOSH) Pub. No. 76-166; NTIS Pub. No. PB-266-439. National Technical Information Service, Springfield, VA (1977).
17. Woodfin, W.J.; Woebkenberg, M.L.: An Evaluation of Portable, Direct-Reading Oxygen Deficiency Monitors. NTIS Pub. No. PB-85-196-442. National Technical Information Service, Springfield, VA (1985).
18. U.S. Congress: Titles I, II, III, and IV of the Clean Air Act as Amended in 1990. Public Law 101-549. Washington, DC (November 15, 1990).
19. U.S. Environmental Protection Agency: Revisions to the National Ambient Air Quality Standards for Particulate Matter. Fed. Reg. 52:24634-24750 (1987).
20. Hinds, W.C.: Aerosol Technology. John Wiley & Sons, New York (1982).
21. Willeke, K.; Baron, P.A.: Aerosol Measurement Principles, Techniques, and Applications. Van Nostrand Reinhold, New York (1993).
22. British Standards Institution: Instruments for the Detection of Combustible Gases, Parts 1 to 5. Document BS6020. BSI, London (1981).
23. European Committee for Electrotechnical Standardisation: Electrical Apparatus for the Detection and Measurement of Combustible Gases. Document EN 50054-58. CENELEC, Brussels (1991).
24. American National Standards Institute/The Institute of Electrical and Electronics Engineers: ANSI/IEEE C95.1-1982, American National Standard Safety Levels with Respect to Human Exposure to Radio Frequency Electromagnetic Fields, 300 kHz to 100 GHz, p. 10. IEEE, New York (1982).
25. American National Standards Institute/Instrument Society of America: ANSI/ISA S12.13 Part 1-1986, American National Standard Performance Requirements, Combustible Gas Detectors, p. 19. ISA, Research Triangle Park, NC (1986).
26. Comite de Normalisation: Test Protocols for Health-Related Aerosol Samplers. CEN/TC137/WG3/N100. CEN, Luxembourg (1991).
27. American National Standards Institute: ANSI/ISEA 102-1990, American National Standard for Gas Detector Tube Units — Short Term Type for Toxic Gases and Vapors in Working Environments. ANSI, New York (1990).
28. Organisation Internationale De Metrologie Legale: OIML International Document D 22, Guide to Portable Instruments for Assessing Airborne Pollutants Arising from Hazardous Wastes. OIML, Paris (1991).

Chapter 12

Air Movers and Samplers

Kenneth L. Rubow, Ph.D.

Senior Research Associate and Manager, Particle Technology Laboratory, University of Minnesota, Minneapolis, Minnesota

CONTENTS

Introduction

Air sampling for airborne contaminants requires a system for moving air, a collection method, and a procedure to determine the quantity of contaminant collected. Because occupational exposure limits and air quality standards frequently are expressed in terms of concentrations, a method of determining the volume of air sampled is also needed.

The four principal components in a sampling train are shown in Figure 12-1. The inlet admits the air sample into the train; the collector(s) separates the gas, vapor, or particles from the air; the flowmeter measures the rate or total quantity of air sampled; and the pump (air mover) provides the suction required to draw an air sample through the train. Inlet sampling considerations are discussed in Chapter 21. Various types of collectors are described in subsequent chapters. Flowmeters are discussed in Chapter 7.

This chapter will describe the air mover portion of the sampling train and air sampling systems that contain three or four components in a convenient package. The chapter consists of two parts. The first part contains a brief description of the different types of air movers and air sampling systems. The second part consists of tables and figures showing detailed information on a wide variety of commercially available air movers and sampling systems.

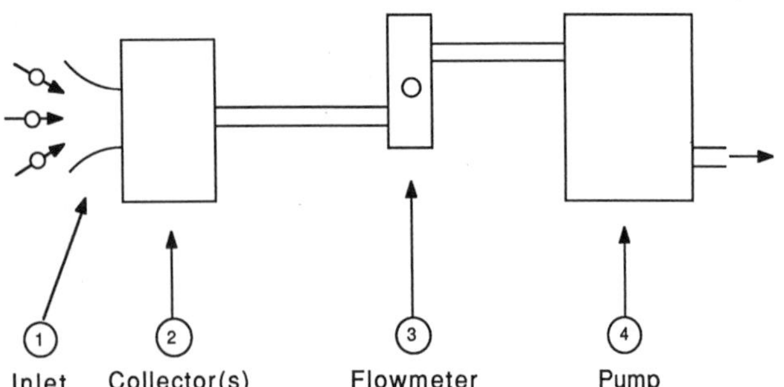

FIGURE 12-1. Principal components of sampling train.

Air Movers

Air movers are classified according to the means by which an air flow is induced. These fall into three basic groups: volumetric displacement, centrifugal force (or acceleration), and momentum transfer. The following sections briefly describe the operating principles and salient features of many types of air movers within each of these three basic classifications. In particular, Tables 12-1 to 12-5 at the end of this chapter list characteristics for five different types of commercially available air movers. These are:

1. Diaphragm pumps
2. Piston pumps
3. Rotary vane pumps
4. Blowers
5. Ejectors

Information presented in these tables includes the source code, pump model number, dimensions, weight, maximum air flow rate, and motor power requirements. The source code can be used in conjunction with Table 12-11 to determine the company name, address, and telephone number.

Volumetric Displacement

One method of producing movement of a given volume of air is to displace it, either by mechanical means, or by use of a second volume of gas. This principle is the basis of operation for a diverse group of air movers.

Air Displacement

One type of air displacement collector is an airtight flask or rigid-walled vessel in which a hard vacuum has been created. When the vessel is opened at the sampling location, a sample, which is often called a grab sample, that is equal in size to the free volume of the vessel is instantaneously collected. The most admirable feature of such a device is its simplicity. Its use is limited mainly by sample size restrictions. Also, care must be taken to prevent loss of vacuum before sampling. For practical purposes, sample size is limited by the portability of the flask, with the upper range of approximately 1 liter. Additional description of this method and a list of commercial sources are provided in Chapter 17.

This procedure is not limited to simple collection of air samples for subsequent gaseous analysis. The evacuated flask may contain an absorbing solution in which the desired component of the grab sample may be concentrated for analysis by wet chemical methods. For example, the U.S. Environmental Protection Agency (U.S. EPA) test method for "Determination of Nitrogen Oxide Emissions from Stationary Sources"[1] uses evacuated flasks containing a dilute sulfuric acid–hydrogen peroxide absorbing solution (U.S. EPA Appendix Method 7; see Table 21-7).

Air displacement samples can also be collected without prior evacuation of the flask by simply displacing the air in the flask with sample air. In this case, the flask should be flushed with at least 5–10 volumes of sample air before being sealed, so that the clean air initially inside is displaced completely.

A related method somewhat overcomes the portability problem and allows collection of much larger samples. The collecting vessel is a plastic bag. If it is mounted within a rigid outer container, it can be filled by creating a slight vacuum in the space around the bag. If it is used without an airtight outer container, it can be filled by directly pumping air into the bag, provided that the material being sampled is not absorbed or altered when passing through the pump. Commercial plastic bags are available in a variety of sizes up to 0.3 m^3 and come equipped with several types of leak-proof valves. A list of commercial sources can be found in Chapter 17.

The sample bag method is particularly useful for contaminants that can be analyzed by infrared spectroscopy or gas chromatography. Different types of plastics have been studied for use in this fashion, with the relatively nonreactive fluorocarbons currently in favor. If the bag is to be used for aerosols, it should be foil-lined and grounded. Unless the interaction of the contaminant of interest with the plastic bag, or the possible permeability of the contaminant through the bag, is known or is at least predictable, such bags should be used only for semiquantitative identification. For example, data on such wall losses have been discussed by Posner and Woodfin.[2]

Liquid Displacement

The evacuated flask normally is prepared in the laboratory and carried to the field. A similar method, which can be prepared in the field but does not require a pump, is liquid displacement. A vessel of any convenient size is filled with a liquid in which the suspected contaminant is insoluble. When the liquid is allowed to escape from the vessel, it is replaced by air from the atmosphere to be sampled. Such an air sample is an integrated sample rather than an instantaneous sample because the mass of fluid requires a finite time to empty. In fact, by employing a large vessel with controlled drainage, this method can be used to move air at low flow rates through a sample collector for extended intervals. Additional discussion of this method can be found in Chapter 17.

Diaphragm Pumps

A diaphragm pump, as shown in Figure 12-2, is a device in which a flexible diaphragm of metal or elastomeric material is moved back and forth. The diaphragm is clamped between the pump head and housing, forming a leak-tight seal between the pump chamber and the crankcase. Through the action of a rod or yoke, air in the chamber is displaced on one side of the diaphragm. By using a suitable arrangement of one-way check valves, a variable vacuum is produced in the chamber on the other side of the diaphragm. Mechanical damping is required for more uniform suction. Diaphragm pumps are fairly simple in construction and are used commonly in personal sampler pumps. Diaphragm pumps are oil-free and available in corrosion-resistant materials. They provide contamination-free pumping. Table 12-1 summarizes the characteristics of some commercially available diaphragm-type air movers.

Piston Pumps

Piston pumps are related to diaphragm pumps in that both use a mechanical reciprocating action to provide the motive force. In the piston pump, the piston oscillates in a cylinder equipped with inlet and outlet valves. Because the piston can displace a greater proportion of the air in the chamber above it, piston pumps can provide greater differential pressure or vacuum. In either case, a surge chamber usually is required to smooth out irregularities in flow. In multiple-piston pumps, these irregularities are small and sometimes can be ignored. One new version of the piston pump is the linear-motor-driven free piston, as illustrated in Figure 12-3. This pump uses an electromagnet and return spring to alternately drive the reciprocating free piston. This design results in a compact structure, less vibration, and quieter operation than the conventional piston pump. It also has an oil-less construction. Table 12-2 summarizes the characteristics of some commercially available piston-type air movers.

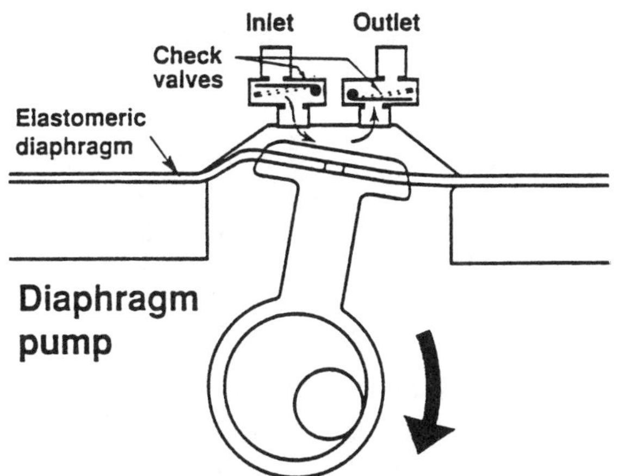

FIGURE 12-2. Schematic diagram of diaphragm pump (KNF Neuberger).

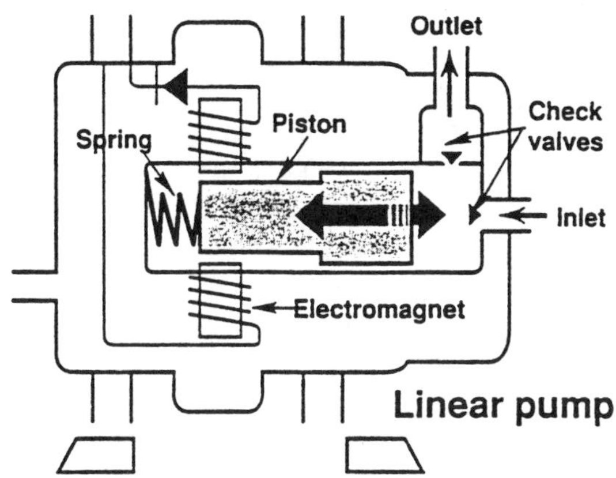

FIGURE 12-3. Schematic diagram of linear-motor-driven free piston pump (KNF Neuberger).

Rotary Vane Pumps

Rotary vane pumps are used extensively as air movers for portable sampling instruments. There are two basic variants, both having the same operating principle. A rotor revolves eccentrically in a cylindrical housing, with multiple blades on the rotor providing the air-moving drive. Centrifugal force (or springs) keeps the outer edges of the blades in contact with the housing. However, because the rotary motion is eccentric, the vanes must be movable to retain constant contact. One common method is to place the vanes in slots in the rotor (see Figure 12-4). This guided or sliding vane type usually operates at fairly high speeds and it is subject to wear on the blade edge that contacts the casing. Such wear may lead to leakage and reduce capacity. Table 12-3 summarizes the characteristics of some commercially available rotary vane pumps.

Rotary vane pumps, as well as piston pumps, usually are available either in oil-less or lubricated models. In some air sampling procedures, concern may arise about generating contaminants with the sampling apparatus itself. Lubricated pumps can introduce oil mists into the sample if the sample passes through the pump, or if the

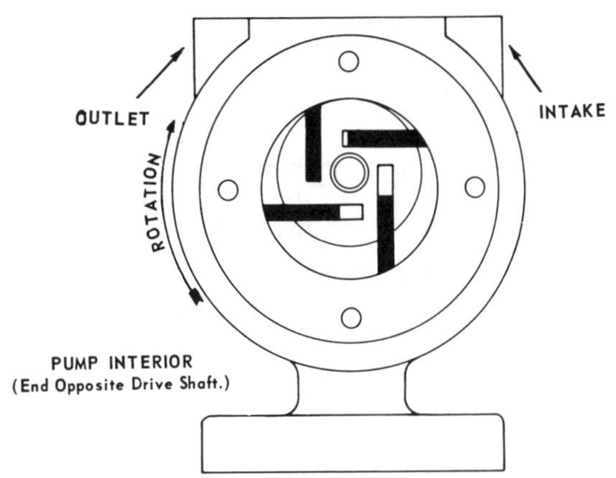

FIGURE 12-4. Schematic diagram showing principle of sliding vane pump operation.

pump exhaust is resampled. Nonlubricated pumps, which frequently use graphite rings or vanes, can produce carbon dust that may also be an undesirable contaminant. The selection of pump must be based, in part, on the specific air sampling intended.

Gear Pumps

The gear pump is another type of positive displacement air mover. Like a vane pump, it usually is valveless and operates on a rotary principle. The typical gear pump has two shafts, each with a gear. The gears mesh on the interior side and contact the semicylindrical casing on the exterior side. The large number of teeth in contact with the outer surface reduces peripheral leakage.

Lobe Pumps

Lobe pumps are similar to gear pumps but use two counter-rotating impellers instead of meshing gears. The impellers can be either a two-lobed, figure-eight-shaped design (see Figure 12-5) or a three-lobed design. As each impeller passes the blower inlet, a volume of gas is trapped, carried through to the blower discharge, and expelled against the discharge pressure. As a result, the volumetric capacity varies little with changes in pressure. Lobe pumps with volumetric capacities from 0.3 to 100 m^3/min are available.

Hand-Operated Air Movers

Hand-operated air movers include manually actuated piston pumps, bellows pumps, and squeeze bulbs. The piston principle has been employed in several hand-operated air movers. The most familiar of these is the hypodermic syringe, which is used in several commercial instruments and in countless homemade systems. A similar air mover is the hand-operated piston. For industrial hygiene purposes, it is usually calibrated carefully to provide an accurate air volume. This type of pump is often used with direct-reading colorimetric indicators as described in Chapter 18.

Squeeze bulbs or small bellows pumps have been used commonly as air movers on commercial air sampling devices, such as the direct-reading indicator tubes described in Chapter 18, and on several models of combustible gas meters, described in Chapter 19. Squeezing the bulb or bellows expels air through a one-way valve; the subsequent self-expansion of the bulb or bellows allows air to be drawn through the detector. With bulbs, the amount of air drawn by a single bulb compression varies according to the efficiency with which the air was expelled from the previous volumetric stroke. This variation may result in serious errors because the calibrations are based on sampling a constant volume of air. Possible sample size variation is less important in combustible gas meters, which indicate the concentration within the sensing zone (i.e., they are not integrating devices).

An example of a squeeze bulb application is found in the U.S. EPA test method for "Gas Analysis for Carbon Dioxide, Oxygen, Excess Air, and Dry Molecular Weight."[(1)] This method offers a choice of grab sampling with a one-way squeeze bulb, or integrated sampling with a leak-free pump (U.S. EPA Appendix Methods 3 and 3A; e.g., see Tables 21-7 and Figure 21-9A).

Centrifugal Force

A second basic method of inducing air movement is to produce kinetic energy by means of centrifugal force, with conversion of the resulting velocity pressure to suction for moving the sampled air. Centrifugal fans

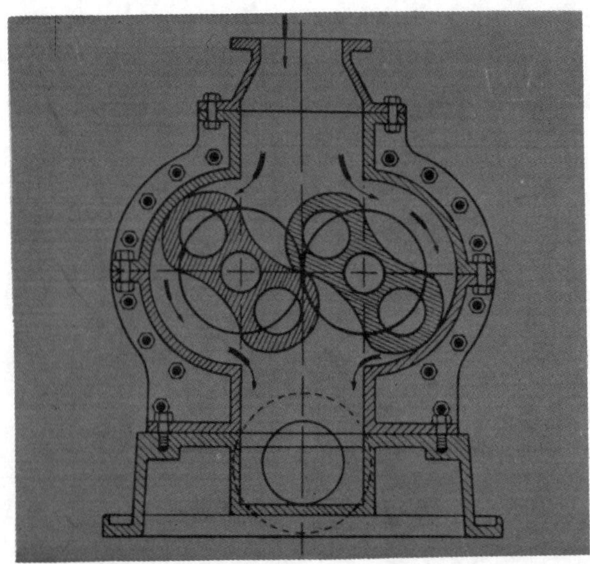

FIGURE 12-5. Schematic diagram showing principle of operation of twin-lobed positive displacement blower.

that use this approach consist of an impeller and stationary casing, the impeller being a rotary device with vanes. There are two major types of centrifugal fans, either radial flow or axial flow, depending on the direction of air flow through the impeller. Table 12-4 summarizes the characteristics of commercially available centrifugal fans.

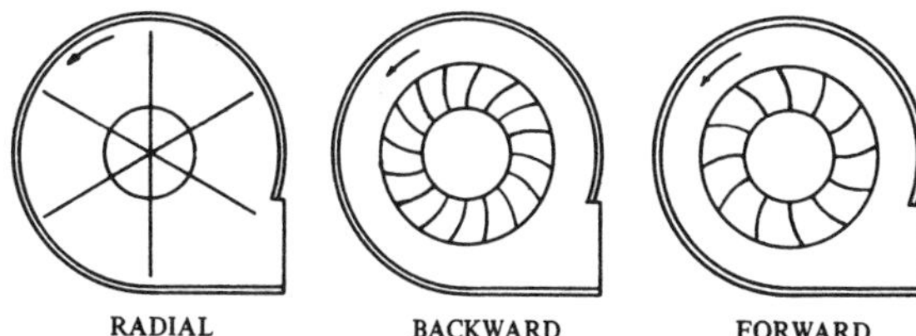

FIGURE 12-6. Curvature of centrifugal fan blades.

Radial-Flow Fans

The term centrifugal fan (or blower), while connoting all types of fans, usually is used in a restrictive sense to indicate just radial-flow fans. These fans are available in three basic types, differentiated by the direction of blade curvature at the delivery edge (see Figure 12-6).

The first of these types is the forward-curved blade fan which has its blade tips curved in the direction of fan rotation. This design usually is more compact, operates at low speeds with less noise than other types, and has a lower initial cost. It is relatively inefficient and not capable of producing high static pressures or high vacuums. These fans are found typically in comfort ventilation systems that have low static pressure or vacuum requirements and where low noise levels are desirable.

The second type is the radial blade fan in which the blades are straight and are aligned along the radii of the fan. This is similar to the old style straight (or paddle-wheel) blade, but the radial blade fan is more compact in design, capable of higher rotational velocity, and slightly more efficient. This type of fan is less prone to clogging than the other types and therefore finds application in systems that handle high particulate mass loads. Unlike the forward-curved fan, radial blade fans operate well in parallel and can produce relatively high static pressures or vacuums.

The third type of centrifugal fan, the backward-curved blade fan, is characterized by blades that curve away from the direction of rotation. Such fans are highly efficient and, because of their high speed capability, are particularly well suited to use with electric motor drives. This type of fan has a distinct advantage over the other two types in that it is difficult to overload the backward-curved fan. Its power requirement peaks at its normal design loading, whereas the power requirements of each of the other types of centrifugal fans continue to increase with increasing flow volume requirements. The disadvantages of this fan design are relatively high noise levels and high susceptibility to clogging.

The backward-curved fan blade is used in several high-volume air samplers. The usual design is to use a 1/2- to 1-horsepower electric motor (AC or DC) to drive a two-stage turbine impeller. (Multiple-staging is required to increase suction.) The exhaust (sampled) air is often used to cool the motor, which imposes a lower flow-rate limit. Some units have separate cooling fans for the motor and therefore can be used with high-resistance filters at lower flow rates. Some representative types of this kind of blower are described in Table 12-4.

Axial-Flow Fans

Axial-flow fans also come in three types: propeller, tube-axial, and vane-axial. These types are named in increasing order of complexity, weight, cost, and static pressure.

The propeller fan is the most common. The fan blades are carried on a small hub in which the motor is often mounted. It can provide high flow volumes and usually operates at or near ambient static pressures. This type of fan is used on some electrostatic precipitator samplers (see Chapter 15), where the flow resistance is both very low and constant.

The tube-axial fan is a propeller fan enclosed in a short cylinder. The fan blades are mounted on a central ring slightly larger than the average propeller fan hub. This unit can operate at moderate static pressures.

The vane-axial fan is a further modification of the tube-axial. It has the same parts, but the cylinder is slightly longer. The extra length accommodates a set of guide vanes that serve to convert the useless tangential velocity component of the discharge into useful static pressure. Vane-axial fans can be either single or multiple stage. In general, vane-axial fans can operate at much higher pressures than tube-axial fans. Because of the high fan speed, the vane-axial fan is sensitive to abrasion of the blades and thus should be used only to move clean air.

Momentum Transfer

A third basic method of inducing air movement is to transfer the momentum of one fluid to another. This process is relatively inefficient, but the equipment involved is very simple and reliable and, in certain cases, particularly well suited for portable sampling units because it does not need electrical power for operation. It has the added advantage of being useful in potentially explosive atmospheres.

A mechanism that utilizes this principle is called an

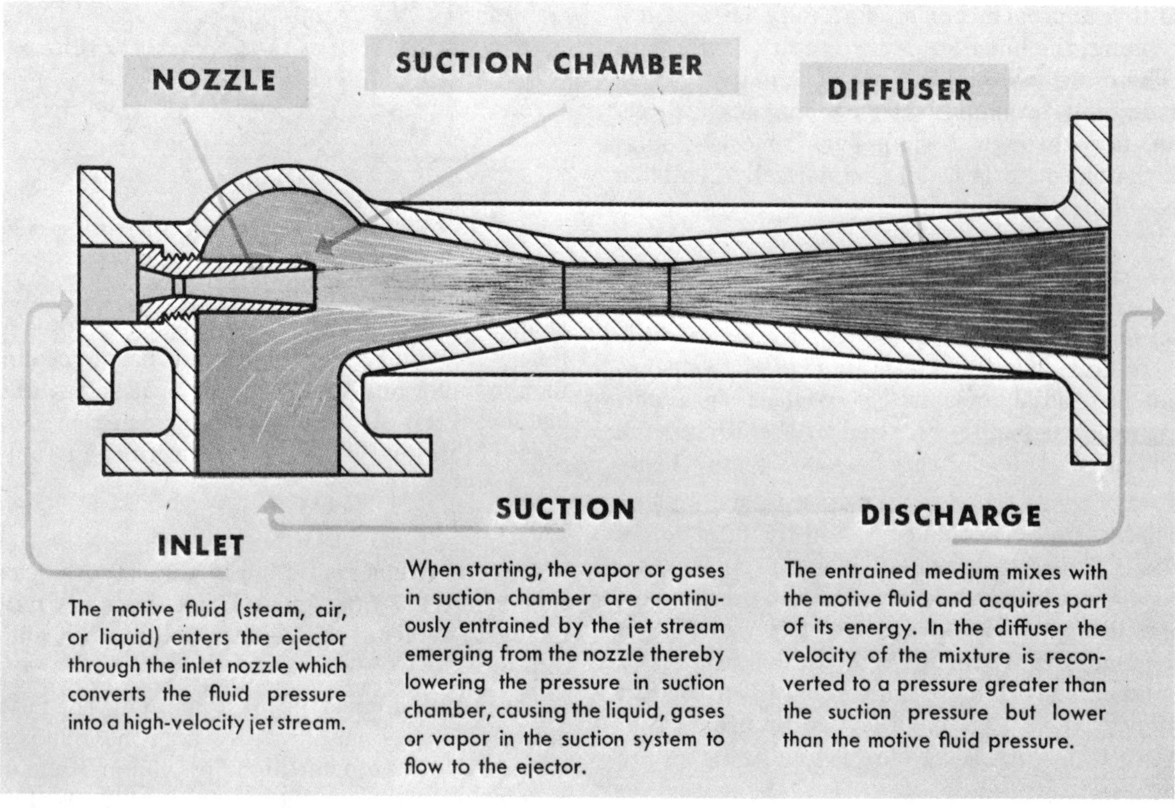

NOZZLE
SUCTION CHAMBER
DIFFUSER
SUCTION
DISCHARGE
INLET
The motive fluid (steam, air, or liquid) enters the ejector through the inlet nozzle which converts the fluid pressure into a high-velocity jet stream.
When starting, the vapor or gases in suction chamber are continuously entrained by the jet stream emerging from the nozzle thereby lowering the pressure in suction chamber, causing the liquid, gases or vapor in the suction system to flow to the ejector.
The entrained medium mixes with the motive fluid and acquires part of its energy. In the diffuser the velocity of the mixture is reconverted to a pressure greater than the suction pressure but lower than the motive fluid pressure.

FIGURE 12-7. Schematic diagram showing principle of ejector operation.

ejector. An ejector consists of a source of high pressure primary fluid, a nozzle, a suction chamber containing a secondary fluid, and a diffuser tube (see Figure 12-7). The primary fluid enters the suction chamber at very high velocity, entraining the available secondary fluid in the chamber and carrying it through the diffuser. It is discharged at a pressure higher than that of the suction chamber. The entrainment of suction chamber secondary fluid reduces the pressure in the chamber and subsequently causes entrainment of the remaining secondary fluid (sampled air).

The driving medium can be steam, high pressure air, water, or any compressible gas. For portable units, a small can of refrigerant can be used to power a compact, low-volume sampler. Characteristics of some small, commercially available ejector air movers are summarized in Table 12-5.

Air Samplers

The previous discussion has been concerned solely with air movers, with minimum attention to the other three components of the sampling train illustrated in Figure 12-1. An air sampler combines all four functions in a convenient package and is widely used in industrial hygiene practice and indoor or ambient air sampling. Many commercial varieties of air samplers are available, employing many of the air moving devices previously discussed. Tables 12-6 through 12-10 list characteristics of several classes of commercial air samplers. Table 12-11 provides a list of the commercial sources for the air movers and samplers.

The listing of samplers presented in Tables 12-6 to 12-10 has been divided into five categories based on the sampling flow rate, source of power, sampler size, and primary application of the sampler. These categories are:

1. Personal sampler: battery powered
2. Low-volume area samplers: battery powered
3. Low-volume area samplers: portable
4. Medium and high volume samplers: portable
5. High volume samplers: with shelters

Personal samplers generally operate at a sampling air flow rate of up to 5 L/min and are intended for personal exposure monitoring. Low-volume area samplers typically operate at flow rates in the 3–100 L/min range. Medium and high volume samplers generally operate at flow rates from 0.1 to 0.3 m^3/min and 0.3 to 3 m^3/min, respectively, and are most often used for ambient air sampling.

Information presented in Tables 12-6 to 12-10 includes the source code, model number, dimensions, weight, air flow-rate range, type of flowmeter, standard sampling attachments (inlets or collection devices), and motor power requirements. The source code can be used in conjunction with Table 12-11 to determine the company name, address, and telephone number.

Many of the samplers listed in Tables 12-6 to 12-10 are designed to be used in conjunction with a variety of sampling inlets or sample collection devices. Several of the commonly used inlets and collection devices associated with these samplers are listed in these tables. For example, personal sampling pumps are used with charcoal and other sorbent tubes, filters, bubblers, cyclone-filter assemblies for respirable dust sampling, and gas collection bags. Medium- and high-flow area samplers are often used with PM_{10} or $PM_{2.5}$ inlets or collection devices. PM_{10} and $PM_{2.5}$ inlets or collection devices remove particulate matter greater than 10 µm or 2.5 µm, respectively. Detailed discussions of these inlets and devices are provided in later chapters.

A variety of air movers (pumps) are used in the samplers listed in Tables 12-6 to 12-10. Diaphragm pumps are generally used in personal sampler pumps. Low-volume area samplers usually use rotary vane, piston, or diaphragm pumps. Blowers are primarily used in medium and high volume samplers.

Flowmeters are frequently incorporated into the design of the samplers listed in Tables 12-6 to 12-10. The most commonly used flowmeters are either a rotameter or a calibrated orifice plate. To achieve reliable results from such instruments, a basic understanding of the limitations of these flow measuring devices is necessary. Procedures for calibrating air sampling flowmeters are discussed in Chapter 7.

A rotameter consists of a float inside a tapered vertical tube; the tube cross section increases in area from bottom to top. The position of the float in the tube is governed by establishing an equilibrium between the weight of the float and the force exerted on the float by the velocity pressure of the fluid or gas flowing through the annular space between the float and the tube wall. With increasing flow, the height of the float and the annular area increases, permitting equilibrium to be established at any flow. Because the position of the float is related to fluid flow, flow rates can be etched directly on the tube after appropriate calibration.

Rotameters are available for a wide range of gas flows. For a given unit, the range of accurate performance is usually about a factor of 10. For example, if the lowest accurate reading is 100 cm^3/min, the highest would be about 1000 cm^3/min. The accuracy of an individual rotameter depends mostly on the quality of construction. For a well-made unit with an individual calibration, accuracy to within ± 2% of full scale is possible. However, the rotameters found on "air samplers" are mass produced and are often far less accurate. The rotameters usually used with samplers are also imprecise because of their short length. It is advisable to initially check their calibration over their entire range against a secondary standard and to rapidly check calibration at one or two points before each use. Because proper operation of a rotameter depends on clear annular space, these gauges are sensitive to accumulation of dirt or water vapor on either the float or tube walls. Periodic cleaning is recommended, usually in conjunction with a recalibration.

Because contamination of rotameter walls is a problem, it is general practice to place the meter downstream of the sampling device. This accomplishes the dual function of minimizing both wall buildup and sampling line losses. This practice, however, will usually introduce another problem. Most sampling mechanisms induce a pressure drop in the system, so the rotameter will operate in a partial vacuum. Because the manufacturer normally calibrates at atmospheric pressure, a significant error can be introduced. For a concise discussion of the problem, the reader is referred to the short note by Craig.[3] The air sampling system flowmeter needs to be calibrated each time it is used (see Chapter 7).

A calibrated orifice plate is a second flow-measuring device commonly used in air samplers, mainly because of simplicity and low cost. A thin metal plate with a carefully machined sharp-edged hole is placed in the air stream. The hole, or orifice, causes a convergence of streamlines downstream, with maximum contraction occurring at the *vena contracta*, the point of lowest pressure. A differential pressure device is then used to measure the pressure drop caused by the orifice. Flow rates can be calculated using orifice equations. However, with all physical parameters designated, the pressure gauge can be empirically calibrated directly in flow units.

Most problems with orifice meters can be associated with careless construction. The upstream edges of the orifice must be clean and sharp, with a 90° corner. The pressure taps must be positioned carefully with no roughness inside the nipple, or burrs or rough edges inside the hole. Three sets of pressure tap positions commonly are used: 1) flange taps are centered "from the nearest face of the orifice plate," 2) *vena contracta* taps have the upstream tap located one pipe diameter from the upstream face and downstream tap at the *vena contracta*, and 3) pipe taps are located 2.5 pipe diameters upstream and 5.0 pipe diameters downstream.

A special type of orifice known as a "critical flow orifice" is popular in air sampling work because it can maintain a moderately constant flow rate despite minor changes in inlet conditions. Flow through a critical orifice reaches a maximum value when sonic flow conditions are achieved in the throat of the orifice. Although increased sampler resistance during a run (e.g., filter buildup) could affect the critical flow rate, the pressure changes normally encountered do not produce major errors in flow rate measurement. A typical example of this type of device is found in the U.S. EPA reference method for the "Determination of Sulfur Dioxide in the Atmosphere,"(4) which offers a choice of several gauges (22, 23, or 27) of hypodermic needle to maintain a range of sample flow rates.

Several manufacturers now offer "constant flow" air samplers. These devices are designed to overcome flow rate variation problems that are inherent in many sampling situations (e.g., with a constant speed pump, an increase in sample media resistance will result in a decrease in flow rate). These samplers feature sophisticated flow rate sensors with feedback mechanisms that permit maintenance of a preset flow for the duration of the sample. A block diagram of this system is shown in Figure 12-8. Although these commercial devices are most commonly used for personal samplers with flow rates up to several liters per minute, the concept is readily applied to high volume samplers.(5)

Selection of an Air Mover or Air Sampler

The choice of an air mover or sampler for a particular application can be influenced by a variety of factors. Among the more important of these are sample volume and sampling rate, applicable governmental standards, power source, sampling location, hazardous environments, and servicing and calibration.

The minimum or maximum amount of air to be sampled is usually dependent on the requirements of the analytical procedure, the anticipated concentration of the contaminant to be sampled, or applicable governmental standards. The minimum amount of sample is dictated by the lower detection limit of the analytical procedure. The maximum amount sampled is often a balance between the capacity of collection medium (e.g., charcoal, impinger solution) and sampling strategy (e.g., short-term versus time-weighted average [TWA] sampling). However, with some sampling systems, the collection period cannot be extended indefinitely because the accumulation of sample can cause changes in the operating characteristics of the system. This is particularly true with filter papers, where increasing resistance can affect flow rates and efficiency, and for the cascade impactor, where sample buildup encourages re-entrainment. Another example is the charcoal tube, where extended sampling may lead to problems with breakthrough. Lastly, standards often require sampling at a certain flow rate, or within a set range (e.g., Asbestos Hazard Emergency Response Act [AHERA] standards for asbestos) and for a certain period of time (e.g., an 8-hour work shift). These requirements set the total sample volume.

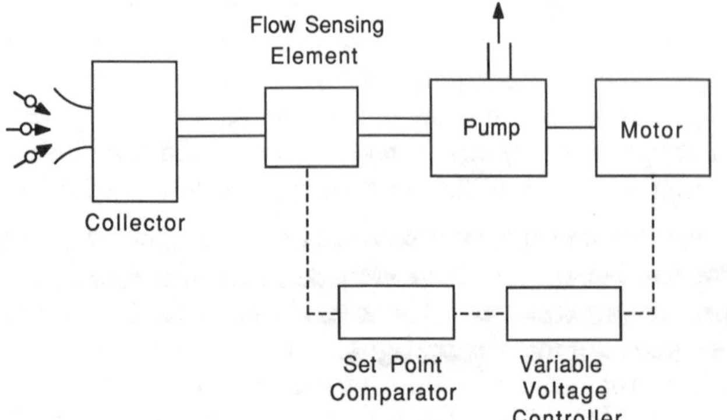

FIGURE 12-8. Block diagram of sampling system with feedback system for flow rate control.

Having defined the sample volume, the next choice is sampling rate. Two factors that can influence this decision are the total sampling time required and the dynamic characteristics of the collector.

It is obvious that total sampling time is important in those cases where, because the required volume is large, only higher sampling rates will accomplish the procedure in a reasonable time. However, given a more moderate volume requirement, it must be decided whether to sample in a relatively instantaneous fashion, or obtain a longer-term, time-averaged sample. For a long-term sample, there is an additional choice of continuous versus intermittent sampling.

The sampling rate can affect both the overall efficiency and the size selectivity of a collecting device. The efficiency of a given collector, whether filter paper, liquid media, granular beds, or cyclone, will usually vary with sampling rate. This variation is seldom linear and must be determined experimentally. Furthermore, the sampling rate often determines what size of particulate material will be removed most efficiently. For those cases where the size distribution of the sample is of critical importance, desirable flow rates usually are established during instrument calibration and must not be altered. A flow controlling device will reduce this problem considerably. Lastly, the sampling flow rate may be specified by an applicable governmental standard. For example, a flow rate of 2 L/min is required for sampling respirable coal mine dust,(6) whereas a flow rate of 1.13 m^3/min (40 CFM) is required for PM_{10} sampling of ambient particulate matter.(7)

A final factor related to sampling rate is the increase in sample media resistance as flow velocity increases. For small, battery-operated samplers, such resistance increases place a practical upper limit on sampling rate.

Proper attention must also be paid to the effect of battery life and sample loading on flow rate because both can lead to decreases in sampling air flow rate. Many samplers are designed with feedback systems to maintain a constant air flow rate by continuously adjusting the pump or a flow control valve. These samplers are called constant flow rate samples. Menard *et al.*[8] described a computerized personal pump test system designed to test the ability of pumps to operate at a desired air flow rate.

Two further factors to consider when selecting an air mover are sampling location and power. These factors tend to interact because the power source is often determined by the location of the sampling device. The choices of sampler location are fairly obvious, ranging from permanent fixed installations, through various degrees of portability and mobility, to the ultimate in lightweight, fully portable devices used for various forms of personal monitoring. For power, the choice usually is between line current, storage battery, hand power, or compressed gas cylinder or cans, such as refrigerant cans (momentum transfer ejectors). The use of portable, gasoline-powered generators is increasing for remote area monitoring, but their use in air sampling must be monitored carefully to ensure that their exhausts do not introduce contamination. The usefulness of air movers and samplers requiring batteries has been increased by the development of longer-lived and more compact cells, many of which are rechargeable.

Hazardous environments may also be a factor when selecting an air mover or sampler. In flammable and explosive atmospheres, only explosion-proof electric devices or those instruments that are inherently explosion-proof (such as ejectors) may be used. The term "intrinsically safe" is often used to describe an electrically powered device that is capable of operating in an explosive atmosphere. Some of the air movers and samplers described in Tables 12-1 to 12-10 are suitable for such use and have been approved by the Mine Safety and Health Administration, Underwriters Laboratories, Inc. (for Class 1 Group D Flammable Atmospheres), National Fire Protection Association, and Factory Mutual Engineering Corporation.

Another type of hazardous environment involves the effect of electromagnetic interference/radio frequency interference (EMI/RFI) on the performance of samplers. In particular, this problem is of concern for sensitive, low power instruments such as personal sampler pumps where EMI/RFI can adversely affect the operating performance of the pump.[9] This degraded performance is called electromagnetic susceptibility. EMI/RFI effects on pumps can be minimized through proper shielding. Several of the newer personal sampler pumps are designed with EMI/RFI shielding.

Other types of hazards may be present. For extremely toxic environments, remotely activated, automatically sequenced devices may be required. For corrosive or high-temperature environments, the materials used in constructing the device may be important. Also, although the original environment may be fairly innocuous, it is possible that the air mover itself could generate a hazardous or annoying condition, such as carbon monoxide from gasoline-powered samplers, or excessive noise. Noise generation can be extremely important when dealing with high volume samplers over extended sampling periods and samplers designed for indoor air sampling.

Another consideration in sampler selection is the degree of difficulty involved with calibration and maintenance. The amount of effort expended in these areas varies with both the sampling apparatus and the degree of precision desired. Naturally, it is desirable that field instruments require a minimum of such care. Battery-powered personal air samplers require constant attention for maintenance, repair, and recharging. Flow calibration is now straightforward with automatic calibration devices.

A concluding comment addresses the current need for instrument performance criteria. A symposium sponsored by ACGIH was held in 1991 to specifically assess both the current state of performance of air sampling field instruments and instrument performance criteria.[10] In particular, one of the eight symposium workshops specifically dealt with the need for performance criteria for pumps and air movers in sampling systems.[11] The recommendations of this workshop covered the areas of standardized performance standards, including international cooperation, user technical education and training, use of generally acceptable terminology, and improvement needs in air samplers (see Chapter 11 for additional discussion).

References

1. Code of Federal Regulations, Title 40, Chapter 1, U.S. Environmental Protection Agency, Part 60. U.S. Government Printing Office, Washington, D.C. (1992).
2. Posner, J.C.; Woodfin, W.J: Sampling with Gas Bags. 1. Loss of Analyte with Time. Appl. Ind. Hyg. 1:163 (1986).
3. Craig, D.K.: The Interpretation of Rotameter Air Flow Readings. Health Physics 21:328–332 (l97l).
4. Code of Federal Regulations, Title 40, Chapter 1, U.S. Environmental Protection Agency, Part 50.5, Appendix A. U.S. Government Printing Office, Washington, D.C. (1992).
5. Bernstein, D.M.: An Electronic Feedback Constant Flow Controller for High Volume Samplers and Air Movers. Am. Ind. Hyg. Assoc. J. 40:835–837 (1979).
6. Code of Federal Regulations, Title 30, Subchapter 0, Coal Mine Safety and Health Administration, Part 70. U.S. Government Printing Office, Washington, D.C. (1992).
7. Code of Federal Regulations, Title 40, Subchapter C, U.S. Environmental Protection Agency, Part 50, Appendix J. U.S. Government Printing Office, Washington, D.C. (1992).
8. Menard, L.; Caron, B.; Lariviere, P.: Computerized Personal Pump Tester and Cycler. Appl. Occup. Environ. Hyg. 8:327–333 (1993).
9. Feldman, R.F.: Degraded Instrument Performance due to Radio Interference: Criteria and Standards. Appl. Occup. Environ. Hyg. 8:351–355 (1993).
10. Cohen, B.S.; McCammon, C.S.; Vincent, J.H.; Eds.: Proceedings of The International Symposium on Air Sampling Instrument Performance. Appl. Occup. Environ. Hyg. 8:223–411 (1993).
11. Rubow, K.L.: Report of Workshop #1 on Pumps and Air Movers. Appl. Occup. Environ. Hyg. 8:397–398 (1993).

TABLE 12-1. Diaphragm Pumps*

Source Code	Figure Number	Item, Model No., or Catalog No.	Dimensions (cm) L	W	H	Wt. (kg)	Maximum Flow (L/min)	Remarks
ADI	12-9	Mini Dia-Vac	19.3	10.7	14.5	3.6	17–35	See Figure 12-9 for pressure volume characteristic for Dia-Vac pumps. Neoprene-, Viton®-, or Teflon®-coated diaphragms; explosion proof and air motor; aluminum, Carpenter 20, and stainless steel body; also available for all pumps.
		Dia-Vac 1310	23.4	17.8	19.3	7.2	25	
		Dia-Vac 1320	25.9	21.6	15.5	8.6	45	
		Dia-Vac 1340	34.3	19.1	15.5	10.9	85	
		Dia-Vac 19310T	23.4	17.8	19.3	8.2	25	
		Dia-Vac 19320T	25.9	21.3	15.5	9.5	45	
		Dia-Vac 19340T	34.3	19.1	15.5	12.7	85	
		Micro-Mini-19310V	12.2	6.2	11.0	1.1	7	
ACI	12-10	Dia-Pump, G3	27.2	14.2	19.1	7.0	22	Neoprene diaphragms standard, but corrosion-resistant materials are available. Model G4 requires separate power; 220 VAC/50 Hz motors available as option. Models G4 and G5A are rated as explosion-proof. See Figure 12-10 for vacuum-flow characteristic.
		G4	11.9	15.2	15.2	2.5	28	
		G4A	39.9	16.5	19.8	16.3	22	
		G5/G5A	37.1	45.7	25.4	13.2	28–50	
ASF	12-11	ASF more than 10 models	—	—	—	—	0.9–43	Selected technical data on ASF diagram pumps in Figure 12-11; 6, 12, and 24 VDC and 115 VAC/60 Hz.
	12-12	WISA 113	11.6	6.2	8.4	0.8	4.2	Only data for selected models are listed. Corrosion-resistant diaphragms available for all pumps. Alternate power modes (220/240 VAC, 50 Hz, and 24 VDC/60 Hz) are also available. Model 115 has plastic case; Model 504 also has steel case.
		125	15.7	6.6	9.0	1.1	4.2	
		203	16.9	7.4	10.5	1.6	4.6	
		303	19.4	10.0	10.6	2.2	5.5	
		504	24.7	15.3	11.3	3.9	21	
ASF		ROMEGA 014	5.4	2.7	4.5	0.05	0.8	2.4, 6, and 12 VDC.
		020	5.8	2.7	4.8	0.08	1.9	
		041	7.4	3.5	4.8	—	2.9	12 VDC.
		044	7.4	3.5	4.8	0.12	2.9	
		074	13.0	5.9	9.2	1.0	9.2	220VAC/50Hz; 110VAC/60Hz; 12 VDC.
		084	9.7	6.0	6.0	0.22	4.0	12 VDC.
		094	9.7	6.0	6.0	0.22	3.9	12 VDC.
BAR		Series 400	17.8	10.0	12.7	2.5	4–23	15 models; 115 VAC/60 Hz, 230 VAC/50 Hz, 12 and 24 VDC; Fluorel®, Nitrile®, and Viton diaphragms; plastic pump head.
		Series 900	24.1	15.9	12.4	3.2	25–31	

TABLE 12-1 (con't.). Diaphragm Pumps*

Source Code	Figure Number	Item, Model No., or Catalog No.	Dimensions (cm) L	W	H	Wt. (kg)	Maximum Flow (L/min)	Remarks
BRA		TD-2A/1A	7.9	3.8	9.1	0.3	3.5	6, 9, 12, 16, and 24 VDC versions; all models have plastic housing with synthetic rubber diaphragm, optional adjustable stroke; all motors are brushless.
		TD-2L/2N/2S/1S	7.7	3.8	8.6	0.3	3.5	
		TD-4X2L/4X2N/4X2S/4X2	11.9	3.8	8.6	0.4	6.0	
		TD-3LL/3L/3LS	7.2	3.8	8.6	0.2	2.0	
		TD-4L/4N/4S/4	8.3	3.8	8.6	0.3	4.0	
		TD-4X23H	11.9	3.8	11.9	0.5	5.0	
		TD-45BD	8.8	3.8	8.6	0.4	3.0	
GST	12-13	MOA series	18.0	10.9	11.9	2.7	11–23	For technical data on Gast diaphragm pumps, see Figure 12-13. Also available with 110 V/50 Hz, 230 VAC/60 Hz, and 220 VAC/50 Hz and 12 and 24 VDC motors.
		MAA series	21.6	10.9	11.9	4.1	11–45	
		DOA series	19.3	13.0	19.8	8.2	27–51	
		DOL series	19.3	13.5	26.7	8.2	31	
		DAA series	30.0	14.0	19.3	12.7	24–100	
GIC	12-14	OEM sampling pumps	—	—	—	—	0.001–14	Available with 1-48 VDC and 120 VAC/60 Hz motors; silicon, neoprene, or Viton diaphragms.
KNF	12-15	More than 30 models	—	—	—	0.1 to 15.9	0.55 to 300	2.3 to 24 VDC and 115 VAC/60 Hz; explosion-proof motor available. All KNF diaphragm pumps are oil-free and available in corrosion-resistant materials.
MBC	12-16	MB-21/41	16.5	8.6	10.9	2.3	5–11	See Figure 12-17 for pressure-volume characteristic; bellows made of 350 stainless; gaskets Teflon or Viton. Following available in high-temperature versions: MB-21/41/118/158/302/601. Following available as explosion proof: MB-21/41/118/158. All except MB-111/151 available in 230 VAC/50 Hz.
		MB-118/158	21.8	10.2	19.1	6.4	18–40	
		MB-111/151	27.9	14.2	22.4	10.9	28–40	
		MB-302	33.3	14.2	22.6	14.1	85	
		MB-601	33.8	33.3	22.9	21.8	140	
		MB-602	33.8	30.5	20.3	15.9	170	
MRM		Model EC500-LC	3.4	2.2	3.3	0.02	1.1	All models 1.5, 4.5, 6, and 9 VDC; chlorobutadine or Viton diaphragms.
		ACI series 100	8.9	5.7	5.7	0.19	3.0	
		ACI series 50	8.3	3.8	5.4	0.16	0.9–1.7	
		ACI series 25	4.9	2.5	3.5	0.07	0.8–1.07	
SPE	12-18	AS-120	7.9	5.6	5.6	0.3	1.5	See Figure 12-18 for pressure-volume characteristic. Models AS-100/120 are 6 VDC; AS-300/350 series operate at 3–15 VDC, but are also available at 110 VAC/60 Hz. Pump bodies are polycarbonate resin.
		AS-300 series	7.9	6.4	5.8	0.2	—	
		AS-350 series	8.4	6.4	7.9	0.2	—	
THO	12-19	14 models available	—	—	—	—	17-175	See Figure 12-19 for specifications.

*Unless otherwise noted, all pumps listed above have aluminum cases and are rated for 115 VAC/60 Hz. Maximum flow is for free air. Where no maximum flow is listed, see cited figure.

TABLE 12-2. Piston Pumps*

Source Code	Item, Model No., or Catalog No.	Dimensions (cm) L	W	H	Wt. (kg)	Maximum Flow (L/min)	Remarks
GST	1VAF-10	29.5	14.2	21.8	7.3	51	All pumps oil-less. Available with 110 VAC/50 Hz, 230 VAC/60 Hz, and 220 VAC/50 Hz motors.
	1VSF-10	31.8	14.8	11.4	8.6	85	
	1VBF-10	31.8	14.8	11.4	8.6	90	
	4VSF-10	38.1	30.3	22.6	15.0	120	
	4VCF-10	38.1	31.2	22.6	15.0	140	
	5VSF-10	52.5	30.3	22.6	24.0	180	
	5VDF-10	52.5	31.2	22.6	24.0	300	
	ROC-R LOA	18.9	10.9	14.8	3.0	24	Rocking piston type; all pumps are oil-less. Available with 115 VAC/60 Hz, 230 VAC/50 Hz, 12 VDC, and 24 VDC motors.
	LAA	24.8	10.9	14.8	5.1	43	
	SOA	21.4	10.2	16.8	4.4	45	
	SAA	24.8	14.3	17.0	5.0	94	
	ROA	22.5	13.5	19.9	5.6	45	
	RAA	30.3	19.8	13.5	8.6	76	
MED	VP 0125	9.2	7.5	9.0	0.7	7	All pumps linear-motor-driven free piston system; 115 VAC/60 Hz and 230 VAC/50 Hz motors.
	VP 0140	9.2	7.5	9.0	0.7	3	
	VP 0435A	16.0	10.4	12.2	2.3	25	
	VP 0625	17.5	11.8	13.8	3.0	40	
	VP 0645	18.9	11.8	13.8	3.2	10	
	VP 0660	21.0	15.0	15.4	5.0	25	
	VP 0935A	19.3	15.0	15.4	4.4	60	
	VP 0945	20.6	15.0	15.4	4.9	12	
	VP 0550x2	28.6	10.6	13.5	4.7	30	
	VP 0660x2	39.6	15.0	15.4	10	50	
	VP 0950x2	37.0	15.0	15.4	9.5	80	
SCI	D-1000	5.1	8.9	10.2	0.4	1	All pump surfaces contacting gas are Teflon reinforced with 15% glass fiber. Model D-1000 has 12 VDC motor. Model D-200 has 6, 12, or 24 VDC motor.
	A-1000	5.1	8.9	10.2	1.0	1	
	D-200	5.1	6.4	7.6	0.1	0.2	
	A-150	—	—	—	0.2	0.15	

TABLE 12-2 (con't.). Piston Pumps*

Source Code	Item, Model No., or Catalog No.	Dimensions (cm) L	W	H	Wt. (kg)	Maximum Flow (L/min)	Remarks
SPE	AS-300 & -301	7.8	3.8	5.7	0.2	4	12 VDC and 115 VAC/60 Hz.
	AS-350 & -351	8.4	3.8	7.8	0.2	8	12 VDC and 115 VAC/60 Hz.
THO	TASKAIR (11 models)	—	—	—	—	38–280	See Figure 12-20 for specifications.
	WOB-L (28 models)	—	—	—	—	10–200	See Figure 12-21 for specifications.
	Linear 5020V	11.1	12.8	14.8	2.2	33	All pumps linear-motor-driven free piston system; 115 VAC/60 Hz motor.
	5030V	16.1	19.6	20.3	4.9	51	
	5040V	16.1	19.6	20.3	5.2	59	
	5060V	16.1	19.6	20.3	5.8	76	
	5070V	16.1	19.6	20.3	6.1	86	

*All pumps 115 VAC/60 Hz unless otherwise specified.

TABLE 12-3. Rotary Vane Pumps*

Source Code	Item, Model No., or Catalog No.	Dimensions (cm) L	W	H	Wt. (kg)	Maximum Flow (L/min)	Remarks
ASF	Brey- (28 models available)	—	—	—	—	1–23	See Figure 12-22 for specifications.
MRM	Model FZ 135	1.5	1.5	3.4	0.01	0.9	1.5, 3, and 4.5 VDC.
GST	Gast 0532 series	10.4	9.0	7.6	2.0	18	All pumps oil-less. Available with 115 VAC 60/50 Hz, 220 VAC 60/50 Hz, and 24 VDC motors.
	0531 series	22.3	8.9	11.1	3.2	17	
	1031 series	22.9	8.9	12.4	3.2	31	
	1531 series	22.8	10.6	12.1	3.6	42	
	0211 series	29.6	16.8	17.9	7.7	31	
	0323 series	33.6	14.3	15.0	14.1	90	
	0523 series	33.6	14.3	15.0	13.6	130	
	0823 series	41.2	16.5	22.6	21.3	230	
	1023 series	41.2	16.5	22.6	23.6	283	
SPE	Model AS-400	6.6	4.2	3.0	0.1	3	6, 12, and 24 VDC.
THO	TASKAIR (10 models)	—	—	—	—	52–600	See Figure 12-23 for specifications.

*All pumps 115 VAC/60 Hz unless otherwise specified.

TABLE 12-4. Centrifugal Blowers

Source Code	Model Number	Dimensions (cm) L[A]	W	H	Wt (kg)	Power Requirements	Maximum Vacuum (cm water)	Maximum Flow (m^3/min)	Discharge	Remarks
ALE	114786	20.0d	—	21.2	—	115VAC/60Hz	186	3.7	Peripheral	This listing is only a portion of the product line.
	114788	20.0d	—	21.2	—	220VAC/60Hz	178	4.1	Peripheral	
	115937	18.2d	—	17.7	—	115VAC/60Hz	280	3.0	Tangential	
	115950	18.2d	—	17.7	—	220VAC/60Hz	245	2.8	Tangential	
	115923	14.7d	—	15.9	—	115VAC/60Hz	255	3.5	Thru-flow	
	116312-00	14.7d	—	14.8	—	220VAC/60Hz	223	2.9	Thru-flow	
	116155-00	15.2d	—	16.5	2.4	24VDC	112	1.9	Peripheral	
	116157-00	14.7d	—	16.7	—	24VDC	112	1.9	Tangential	
	116156-00	15.2d	—	16.8	2.3	36VDC	120	2.0	Peripheral	
	116158-01	14.7d	—	16.8	—	36VDC	120	2.0	Tangential	
BRA	TB1-1	6.6	5.3	5.8	0.2	6-24VDC	0.5	0.4	Tangential	All motors brushless.
	TB1-1.5	7.9	7.4	7.6	0.3	6-24VDC	0.9	0.3	Tangential	
	TBO-2.5	9.6	9.9	10.9	0.4	12-24 VDC	1.1	1.0	Tangential	
	TBL-2.5	9.6	9.9	10.9	0.4	12-24VDC	2.0	1.4	Tangential	
	TB1-2F	—	7.9d	7.0	0.2	12-24 VDC	—	3.4	Axial	
	TB1-3F	—	10.2d	7.3	0.2	12-24VDC	—	4.2	Axial	
CLE	Cadillac F-10	52.1	19.7	18.4	4.5	115VAC/60Hz	—	3.1	Tangential	Self-contained blower.
	HP-33	54.6	23.5	24.8	7.6	115VAC/60Hz	—	5.6	Tangential	Self-contained blower
	G-12	—	—	—	5.9	115VAC/60Hz	—	4.4	Tangential	Self-contained blower.
EGG	46 models available. See Figures 12-24 and 12-25 for specifications.									

[A]d indicates diameter.

TABLE 12-5. Ejectors

Source Code	Item, Model No., or Catalog No.	Dimensions (cm) L	Dimensions (cm) W	Wt. (kg)	Maximum Flow (L/min)	Operating Pressure (kPa [psig])	Remarks
AVE	TD series (25 models available)	15.5 to 50.3	7.6d to 22.6	0.01 to 7.3	65 to 3600	up to 540 [80]	Require compressed air; can handle solids; available in aluminum, brass, 316 stainless steel. See Figure 12-26.
	AV series (31 models available)	"	"	"	4 to 850	up to 540 [80]	Require compressed air; cannot handle solids; available in aluminum, brass, 316 stainless steel.
FOX	Series 250 AJV (more than 8 models available)	22.6 to 280	—	—	up to 28,000	—	Require compressed air; pipe thread or flanged ends; can handle solids; available in aluminum, brass, steel, stainless steel, ceramic, titanium.
	Mini-educator No. 611210 (more than 5 models available)	—	—	—	5 to 90	up to 1000 [150]	Require compressed air; available in brass, Teflon, CPCV, and stainless steel.
GST	VG series (27 models available)	7.1 to 26.9	1.6 to 8.2	0.09 to 6.4	5.7 to 3600	up to 610 [90]	Require compressed air; single and multistage units; available in anodized aluminum and Delrin®.

TABLE 12-6. Personal Samplers: Battery Powered

Source Code	Figure Number	Item, Model No.	Dimensions (cm) L	W	H	Wt. (g)	Rate (cm^3/min)	Pump Type[A]	Flow Meter[B]	Standard Heads[C]	Remarks
AVI		Pulse Pump 111	7.4	4.1	10.2	260	17–330 1500	p	—	6	Pulsing or continuous flow.
AMG		Ametek ALPHA-2	7.5	3.8	13.3	450	2–200	d	—	1	Formerly manufactured by DuPont; Models ALPHA-1, ALPHA-2, ALPHA-LITE, P2500B, P4LC, and P4L are intrinsically safe and electronically controlled constant flow.
		P2500B	10.1	3.8	15.8	740	300–2500	d	—	1	
		ALPHA-1	10.8	5.7	14.9	1060	5–5000	d	—	1	
		ALPHA-LITE	10.8	5.7	12.7	880	5–5000	d	—	1	
		P4LC	10.2	5.8	12.7	970	5–5000	d	—	1	
		P4L	10.2	5.8	12.7	970	500–4000	d	—	1	
		MG-4	10.5	5.1	10.8	630	5–4000	d	r	1	
	12-27	MG-5P	10.5	5.1	13.6	800	5–5000	d	r	1	Programmable.
ASC, ALT	12-28	Sipin SP-13	6.4	3.2	13.0	310	10–200	d	sc	1, 5, 6	All pumps are intrinsically safe.
		SP-13P	6.4	3.2	13.0	310	10–200	d	sc	1, 5, 6	
		SP-15	6.4	3.2	13.0	310	2–200	d	sc	1, 5, 6	
		SP103	6.4	3.2	13.0	340	10–1000	d	sc	1, 2, 5, 6	
BIO	12-29	BIOS AirPro 6000D	9.1	5.6	11.7	940	5–6000	d	e	—	Electronically controlled constant flow; EMI resistant.
BGI	12-30	BGI AFC123	7.4	4.4	11.7	450	1000–2500	d	—	4, 6	All models are electronically controlled constant flow; intrinsically safe.
		BF-1	7.4	4.4	11.8	590	1000–3000	d	—	4, 6	
		BF-1-A	7.4	4.4	11.8	590	200–1000	d	—	4, 6	
BUC, SUP	12-31	BUCK S.S.	10.2	5.1	13.6	680	600–5000	d	e	1, 2, 3	All models are electrically controlled constant flow; intrinsically safe; EMI resistant, programmable.
		I.H.	10.2	5.1	13.6	680	5–5000	d	e	1, 2, 3	
		H.F.	10.2	5.1	18.4	1160	1000–10,000	d	e	1, 2, 3	
CAL		Pulse Pump III	7.6	5.1	12.7	—	17–1500	p	—	6	Pulsing or continuous flow.
CPI, ALT		Pulse Pump GB-7600-00	7.4	4.1	10.2	260	17–300 1500	—	—	6	

TABLE 12-6 (con't.). Personal Samplers: Battery Powered

Source Code	Figure Number	Item, Model No.	Dimensions (cm) L	W	H	Wt. (g)	Rate (cm^3/min)	Pump Type[A]	Flow Meter[B]	Standard Heads[C]	Remarks
GIC		Gilian LFS113	6.4	3.5	11.7	340	1–350	d	—	1, 2, 3, 4, 6	All models are electrically controlled constant flow; intrinsically safe; optional EMI/RFI shielding case; GilAir-3 and -5 are optionally programmable.
		HFS513A	11.7	4.8	13.0	1020	1–5000	d	r	1, 2, 3, 6	
	12-32	GilAir	9.1	5.1	10.0	600	1–3000	d	r	1, 2, 3, 4, 6	
		GilAir-5	10.3	5.1	10.0	640	1–5000	d	r	1, 2, 3, 4, 6	
HIQ		LF-20	7.5	4.0	10.0	380	500–2500	—	—	2	
		LF-45	9.5	5.5	12.0	900	1000–5000	—	r	2	
MSA		Flow-Lite 479680	10.7	5.1	10.7	620	500–3500	d	r	1, 2, 3, 4, 6	All models have electronic flow control; intrinsically safe; optional heavy duty battery pack and programmable pump; all models except Flow-Lite ET are EMI/RFI protected.
	12-33	482700	13.5	5.1	10.7	760	500–3500	d	r	1, 2, 3, 4, 6	
		484107	10.7	5.1	13.0	670	500–3500	d	r	1, 2, 3, 4, 6	
		484108	13.0	5.1	13.5	810	500–3500	d	r	1, 2, 3, 4, 6	
		Flow-Lite ET series (4 models)	10.7	5.1	10.7	620	500–3500	d	r	1, 2, 3, 4, 6	
		Escort	10.3	5.1	9.8	550	500–3000	d	—	1, 2, 3, 4, 6	
		Escort ELF	10.3	5.1	9.8	550	500–3000	d	—	1, 2, 3, 4, 6	
NUC, HIQ		Victoreen Model 08-430	8.9	5.7	10.5	540	5000–7000	—	—	2, 7	
SEN		Model BDX 34LF	10.2	6.0	11.4	620	25–225	d	r	1	Several models intrinsically safe; several models for respirable mine dust sampling; Models 34LF, 44, and 75 have stroke counters; electronically controlled constant flow on Models 44, 55, 530, 74, and 75.
		BDX 44	10.2	6.0	11.4	620	500–3000	d	r	1, 2, 3, 4	
		BDX 55HD	12.7	6.0	11.4	850	500–3000	d	r	1, 2, 3, 4	
		BDX 530	10.2	6.0	11.4	650	500–3000	d	r	1, 2, 3, 4	
	12-34	BDX 74	12.7	6.0	11.4	970	1500–4500	d	r	1, 2, 3, 4	
		BDX 75	12.7	6.0	11.4	970	1500–4500	d	r	1, 2, 3, 4	
SKC	12-35	Model 224-PCXR8	11.9	4.9	13.0	970	1–5000	d	r	1, 2, 3, 4, 5, 6	All models constant flow, intrinsically safe, and EMI/RFI shielded case; Models PCXR7 and PCXR74 computer controlled elapsed time and timed shut down.
		224-PCXR4	11.9	4.9	13.0	970	1–5000	d	r	1, 2, 3, 4, 5, 6	
		224-44XR	11.9	4.9	13.0	970	1–5000	d	r	1, 2, 3, 4, 5, 6	
		222-4	6.4	3.2	13.0	280	20–80	d	—	1	
		222-3	6.4	3.2	13.0	280	50–200	d	—	1	
		AirChek 50 series	7.6	4.4	12.7	510	5–3000	d	—	1, 2, 3, 4, 5, 6	

TABLE 12-6 (con't.). Personal Samplers: Battery Powered

Source Code	Figure Number	Item, Model No.	Dimensions (cm) L	W	H	Wt. (g)	Rate (cm^3/min)	Pump Type[A]	Flow Meter[B]	Standard Heads[C]	Remarks
SPE		Spectrex PAS-1000	7.6	3.6	10.2	280	up to 2000	d	—	1, 2, 3	All models electronically controlled constant flow.
		PAS-2000	10.7	6.1	11.7	—	600–3000	d	—	1, 2, 3	
	12-36	PAS-3000	10.7	6.1	11.7	910	5–3000	d	r	1, 2, 3	
		PAS-500	3.0	2.0	10.9	110	20–200	—	—		Colorimetric, charcoal, and absorbent tubes mount directly onto pump.
STA		Staplex PST-5	13.1	7.1	18.4	1250	500–2000	—	—	2	Both models electronically controlled constant flow.
		PAS-2	10.8	6.3	11.7	910	500–2000	—	r	2	
SUP		Supelco 2-4829	13.6	5.1	10.2	700	5–5000	d	—	1, 2, 3, 4	

[A]Pump type: d = diaphragm.
p = piston.

[B]Flowmeter: sc = stroke counter.
r = rotameter.
e = electronic.

[C]Standard sampling heads: 1 = adsorption tube.
2 = filter.
3 = bubbler.
4 = cyclone-filter assembly
5 = colorimetric tube.
6 = air bag.
7 = activated-charcoal filter.

TABLE 12-7. Low-Volume Area Samplers: Battery Powered

Source Code	Figure Number	Item, Model No.	Dimensions (cm) L[A]	W	H	Wt. (kg)	Rate (L/min)	Flow Meter[B]	Standard Heads[C]	Remarks
AVI		Air Quality Sampler II	61d	—	117	10.9	0.033–0.17	—	3	Sample >500 hrs, multiple sample bags.
		Air Quality Sampler III	61	41	47	11.4	0.033–0.17	—	3	Sample up to 250 hrs, multiple sample bags.
ASC		Model AP-100	29	19	21.6	5.0	3–15	r	1, 4	Sample up to 3 hrs, internal flow controller.
BIO	12-37	BIOS AirPro series	25	31	13	3.0	0.005–1	m	—	Sample >700 hrs; 1–4 parallel samples; constant flow control.
GIC	12-38	AirCon-2	19	13	26	5.4	2–30	r	1, 2, 3, 4	Constant flow control; sampling time — maximum of 2 and 4 hrs; optional programmable.
HIQ		Model LF-800	17	16	9.5	2.5	4–12	—	1	Three-position program timer.
		LFRR	—	—	—	—	5–25	r	1	
MEI		Thunderbolt series IDC	33	21	28	11.8	1–8.5	r	1, 2	Two models with constant flow control; optional shut-off timer.
STA	12-39	Model BN/BNA	22	11	18	4.5	5–17	r	1	Ni-Cad batteries, 1 hr.
		BS/BSA	22	11	18	4.5	5–17	r	1	Ni-Cad batteries, 2 hrs.
SUP		10-liter Vacuum Bag Sampler	55	37	23	8.6	5.0	—	3	Sampling into 10-liter bag.
		1-liter Vacuum Bag Sampler	23.7	20.3	15.2	2.3	1.9	—	3	Sampling into 1-liter bag.
		Automatic Six-Bag Sampler	55	37	23	9.5	—	—	3	Automatic sampling into six bags.

[A]d indicates diameter.

[B]Flowmeter: r = rotameter.
m = mass flowmeter.

[C]Standard sampling heads: 1 = filter.
2 = bubbler.
3 = air bag.
4 = Asbestos Hazard Emergency Response Act (AHERA) asbestos sampling.

TABLE 12-8. Low-Volume Area Samplers: Portable[A]

Source Code	Figure Number	Item, Model No.	Dimensions (cm) L	W	H	Wt. (kg)	Rate (L/min)	Flow Meter[B]	Standard Heads[C]	Remarks
ASI		Model HV-108-5	58.4	50.8	22.9	17.2	0–15	r, o	1, 2	Up to five simultaneous samples; Model HV-108 EXP suitable for use in explosive atmospheres.
		HV-108-SP	45.7	38.1	15.2	9.5	5–25	r, o	—	
		HV-108-ES	33.0	30.5	15.2	5.0	0–27	r, o	—	
		HV-108 EXP	58.4	50.8	22.9	17.2	0–15	r, o	—	
ALG		Model A-100	—	—	152	4.3	3–20	—	1, 2	
		A-200	—	—	152	4.3	4–12	o	1, 2	Choice of critical orifices.
ASC		Model AP-100	27.9	17.8	17.5	5.9	3–15	r	1, 2	Both models have constant flow controller.
		SP-280	48.3	25.4	35.6	13.0	4–28	r	1, 2	
BGI		Model ASB-11	33.0	20.3	17.8	6.8	11–15	o	1, 2	All models available with a choice of critical orifices; Model ASB-11-S designed with sound absorption material.
	12-40	ASB-11-S	45.7	30.5	30.5	13.2	11–15	o	1, 2	
		ASB-111	45.7	30.5	30.5	12.7	15–24	o	1, 2	
DAW		High Volume Sampler	24.1	10.2	11.4	4.1	3–20	r, o	1, 2	Choice of critical orifices.
EIC		Model RAS-1	45.1	17.8	27.9	15.9	0–100	r	1, 2	Both models have constant flow controller.
	12-41	RAS-2	58.0	23.5	33.0	26.3	0–100	r	1, 2	
EPC		Model S0269	—	—	—	4.1	10, 12	o	1, 2	Choice of critical orifices.
		S0270	—	—	—	4.1	0–20	—	1, 2	
GIC	12-38	AirCon-2	19.0	13.3	26.0	5.4	2–30	r	1, 2	Constant flow controller; optional programmable.
GRA		Series 110 (3 versions)	43.2	23.2	40.0	15.4	0–30	r	1	Constant flow controller.
	12-42	PM10 Median Flow Sampler Model SA254M	107	107	161	38.6	110	g	3	PM_{10} inlet; constant flow control; weather-flow recorder.
	12-43	Universal Sampler Model 209087	34.3	31.8	54.6	27	1–50	o	—	Precalibrated orifices for 1, 2, 5, 14, 28, and 50 L/min; records time and volume; 113 L/min (4 cfm) free flow.
HIQ		Series CF971T	29.2	20.3	20.3	4.3	30–170	r	1	47 mm 2 in., 4 in., and 8 in. × 10 in. filter.

TABLE 12-8 (con't.). Low-Volume Area Samplers: Portable[A]

Source Code	Figure Number	Item, Model No.	Dimensions (cm) L	W	H	Wt. (kg)	Rate (L/min)	Flow Meter[B]	Standard Heads[C]	Remarks
		Model LFRR	—	—	—	—	5–25	r	1, 2	Optional elapsed timer.
		MRV-14C	—	—	—	22.2	110	—	1	Golf cart-type stand.
MEI	12-44	Ultra Sampler series 1AC	33.0	20.6	27.9	7.7	1–15	r	1, 2	Six models with constant flow control; optional shut-off timer; programmable.
		series 2AC	33.0	20.6	27.9	7.7	1–18	r	1, 2	
MSP		Micro-Environmental Monitor	24.0	23.0	30.0	3.6	10	g	1, 2, 4, 6	Constant flow control.
NUC	12-45	Low-Volume Air Sampler Model 08-030	—	—	—	3.2	0–30	r	1	220 VAC/50 Hz model available.
PMC		Tool Box Gas Sampler	50.8	24.8	26.7	—	0–6.5	r	5	Constant flow control.
SCH		Model 3-AH	—	—	—	—	10–100	g	—	Flow regulator system for single or multiple sampling points.
SCI		Teflon Sampling Pump	—	—	—	3	0.15	—	—	Programmable up to 7 days for sampling gases; Teflon inner surfaces.
SEC		Asbestos Sampling Pump	26.7	15.2	24.1	7.4	4–22	r	1, 2	
STA, HIQ	12-46	Model VM-3	11.4	14.6	23.4	5	3–25	r	1, 2	220 VAC version available.
STA	12-47	Models LV-1 and LV-2	10.2	10.2	17.8	2.7	15–35	r	1	LV-1 is 115/125 VAC, 50/60 Hz; LV-2 is 220/240 VAC, 50/60 Hz.
		EC-1	32.4	10.0	12.7	4.3	2–16	r	1, 2	

[A]Unless otherwise specified, all power is 115V/60Hz.

[B]Flowmeter: r = rotameter.
o = orifice.
g = pressure gauge.

[C]Standard sampling heads: 1 = filter.
2 = AHERA asbestos sampling.
3 = PM_{10}.
4 = $PM_{2.5}$ or PM_1.
5 = bag sampling.
6 = diffusion denuder.

TABLE 12-9. Medium- and High-Volume Samplers: Portable

Source Code	Fig. No.	Item, Model No.	Dimensions (cm) L	W	H	Wt. (kg)	Standard Flow Rate (m^3/min [cfm])	Speeds/ Stages	Cool Air[A]	Flow Meter[B]	Sampling Head[C]	Notes[D]
GMW		Handi-Vol 2000	25.4	20.3	25.4	6	0.4–0.6 [15–20], 4" filter 0.6–1.7 [20–60], 8" × 10" filter	—	sam	o	1, 2	a
HIQ	12-48	Model CF-990B	35.6	25.3	22.8	15	up to 0.85 [30]	1/2	—	r	1, 2	b, e
		Series CF-1000 (3 versions)	29.2	20.3	20.3	4	0.17–1.7 [6–60]	1/2	—	r	1, 2	a, d
		EPCF-1500 (4 versions)	30.5	25.4	50.8	15	0.03–1.4 [1–50]	1/2	sep	o	1, 2	a
		Series CF-900 (13 versions)	29.2	20.3	20.3	4	0.03–1.7 [1–60]	1/2	sep	r	1, 2	a, d
		Series CF-972T	29.2	20.3	20.3	—	0.14–0.85 [5–30]	—	—	r	1, 2	a, d
		Series CF-973T	29.2	20.3	20.3	—	0.43–1.7 [15–60]	—	—	r	1, 2	a, d
		Model CF-910FT	30.5	30.5	20.3	5	0.09–0.85 [3–30]	1/2	sep	—	1, 2	a, d
		Model CF-24B	29.2	20.3	20.3	5	0.08–0.22 [3–8]	—	—	r	1	b
	12-49	Series CMP23 (4 versions)	—	—	—	20–25	0.11–0.22 [4–8]	—	—	r	—	a, d, e
		Series MRV (5 versions)	—	—	—	22–28	0.14–0.29 [4.8–10.2]	1/1	—	—	1	a, d, e
		Series VS-23 (5 versions)	—	—	—	17–28	0.14–0.29 [4.8–10.2]	—	—	r	1	a, d
MSP		Universal Air Sampler 310	152	76	142	43	0.3 [10.6]	—	—	g	3, 4, 5	a, c, e
NUC		Model 08-600ER	—	—	—	6	0.57 [20]	1/2	—	o	1	a, b
STA, HIQ	12-50	Staplex, TFIA-Series	21.6	19.1	19.1	5	2.0 [70], free air	1/2	—	o	1, 2	a, b, c
WED	12-51	Intermediate Flow Sampler	61	61	208	44	0.11 [4]	—	—	—	3, 4	a, d, e

[A]Cooling air: sam = through sample.
sep = separate.

[B]Flowmeter: g = pressure gauge.
o = orifice.
r = bypass rotameter.

[C]Sampling head: 1 = 4" diameter.
2 = 8" × 10".
3 = PM_{10} inlet.
4 = TSP inlet.
5 = PUF sampler.

[D]Notes:
a = 115VAC/60Hz standard.
b = 12V or 24VDC available.
c = Shelter version available.
d = 250VAC/50Hz.
e = Constant flow control.

TABLE 12-10. High-Volume Samplers: With Shelters

Source Code	Fig. No.	Item, Model No.	Dimensions (cm) L[A]	W	H	Wt. (kg)	Flow Rate (m^3/min [cfm])	Remarks
GRA	12-52	PM-10 High Volume Sampler	71d	—	155	45	1.1 [40]	Features constant flow control; timer, chart recorder, and other options available; PM_{10} and TSP inlet; optional brushless motor.
GRA, GMW	12-52	TSP High Volume Sampler	61	46	132	27	1.1 [40]	
GRA, GMW	12-53	PS-1 PUF	61	46	132	—	0.2–0.3 [7–10]	Pesticide particulate and vapor collection system.
GMW, BGI	12-54	ACCU-Vol IP-10	71d	—	155	43	1.1 [40]	Features constant flow control; timer, chart recorder, and other options available; PM_{10} inlet; optional brushless motor.
HIQ		Models HVP-2000	47	47	132	25	1.1 [40]	Optional features include constant flow control, elapsed timer, and brushless motor; PUF and IP_{10} inlets.
		Models HVP-3000	47	47	132	27	1.1 [40]	
STA		TSP	61	46	132	—	1.1 [40]	Metal or wooden shelters.
WED	12-55	PM-10 Critical Flow High	47	47	220	47	1.1 [40]	Features constant flow control, timer; PM_{10}, TSP, or PUF inlets; optional brushless motor.
		TSP Sampler	61	46	132	29	1.1 [40]	
		PUF Sampler	61	46	132	40	0.2–0.3 [7–10]	

[A]d indicates diameter.

Notes:

1. All meet requirements of U.S. EPA federal reference method (8" × 10" filter) and PM_{10} sampling standard.
2. All 115 VAC/60 Hz; other power options may be available.
3. See Chapter 14 for description of PM_{10} inlets.

TABLE 12-11. Commercial Sources for Air Movers and Samplers

Code	Source
AVI	AeroVironment Inc. 222 East Huntington Drive, Suite 200 Monrovia, CA 91016 (818)357-9983
ACI	Air-Control, Inc. 237 Raleigh Road, Box 1738 Henderson, NC 27536 (919)492-2300
ADI	Air Dimensions Inc. 1015 West Newport Center Drive, Suite 101 Deerfield Beach, FL 33442 (305)428-7333
ASI	Air Systems International, Inc. 821 Juniper Crescent Chesapeake, VA 23320 (804)424-3967
AVE	Air-Vac Engineering Co., Inc. Vacuum Pump Div. 100 Gulf Street Milford, CT 06460 (203)874-2541
ALG	Allegro Industries 6403 E. Alondra Blvd. Paramount, CA 90723 (310)633-4861
ALT	Alltech Associates, Inc. 2051 Waukegan Road Deerfield, IL 60015 (312)948-8600 or (800)255-8324 FAX (708)948-8600
ALE	Ametek/Lamb Electric Div. 627 Lake Street Kent, OH 44240 (216)673-3451
AMG	Ametek/Mansfield & Green Div. 8600 Somerset Dr. Largo, FL 34643 (813)536-7831
ASC	Anatole J. Sipin Co., Inc. 505 Eight Avenue New York, NY 10018 (212)695-5706 FAX (212)695-5916
ASF	ASF, Inc. 2100 Norcross Parkway Norcross, GA 30071 (404)441-3611
BAR	Barnant Co. 28W092 Commercial Ave. Barrington, IL 60010 (708)381-7050
BGI	BGI Incorporated 58 Guinan Street Waltham, MA 02154 (617)891-9380 FAX (617)891-8151
BIO	BIOS International 230 West Parkway, Unit 1 Pompton Plains, NJ 07444-1029 (201)839-6960
BRA	Brailsford & Company, Inc. 670 Milton Road Rye, NY 10580 (914)967-1820
BUC	A.P. Buck, Inc. 3139 S. Orange Avenue Orlando, FL 32806 (407)851-8602
CAL	Calibrated Instruments, Inc. 200 Saw Mill River Road Hawthorne, NY 10532 (914)741-5700 or (800)969-2254 FAX (914)741-5711
CLE	Clements National Company 6650 S. Narragansett Avenue Chicago, IL 60638 (312)767-7900
CPI	Cole-Parmer Instrument Company 7425 North Oak Park Avenue Niles, IL 60714 (708)647-7600 FAX (708)647-9660
DAW	Dawson Associates P.O. Box 846 Lawrenceville, GA 30246 (404)963-0207
EIC	Eberline Instrument Corporation P.O. Box 2108 504 Airport Road Santa Fe, NM 87504 (505)471-3232 FAX (505)473-9221
EGG	EG&G Rotron Industrial Division North Street Saugerties, NY 12477 (914)246-3401
EPC	Envirometrics Inc. Envirometrics Product Co. 1019 Bankton Drive Charleston, SC 29406 (803)740-1700 or (800)255-8740
FMI	Fluid Metering, Inc. P.O. Box 179 29 Orchard Street Oyster Bay, NY 11771 (516)922-6050
FOX	Fox Valve Development Corp. Hamilton Business Park, Unit 6A Franklin Road Dover, NJ 07801 (201)328-3651
GST	Gast Manufacturing Corp. P.O. Box 97 2550 Meadowbrook Rd. Benton Harbor, MI 49023 (616)926-6171
GIC	Gilian Instrument Corporation 35 Fairfield Place West Caldwell, NJ 07006 (201)808-3355 FAX (201)808-6680
GRA	Graseby Andersen Inc. 500 Technology Court Smyrna, GA 30082-5211 (404)319-9999 or (800)241-6898 FAX (404)319-0336
GMW	Graseby GMW General Metal Works, Inc. 145 S. Miami Ave. Village of Cleves, OH 45002 (513)941-2229 FAX (513)941-1977
HIQ	HI-Q Environmental Products Co. 7386 Trade Street San Diego, CA 92121 (619)549-2820 FAX (619)549-9657
KNF	KNF Neuberger, Inc. Two Black Forest Road Trenton, NJ 08691 (609)890-8600
MDA	MDA Scientific, Inc. 405 Barclay Blvd. Lincolnshire, IL 60069 (708)634-2800 or (800)323-2000 FAX (708)634-1371
MED	Medo U.S.A., Inc. 808-A N. Central Avenue Wood Dale, IL 60191 (708)860-0500
MBC	Metal Bellows Corp. 1075 Providence Hwy. Sharon, MA 02067 (617)784-1400

TABLE 12-11 (con't.). Commercial Sources for Air Movers and Samplers

Code	Source
MEI	Midwest Environics, Inc. 10 Oak Glen Court Madison, WI 53717 (608)833-0158
MSA	Mine Safety Appliances Company P.O. Box 426 Pittsburgh, PA 15230 (800)672-2222; Safety Products Division, portable units (800)672-4678; permanently installed units
MRM	MRM International 3905 Whitney Place Duluth, GA 30136 (404)476-4040
MSP	MSP Corporation 1313 Fifth Street SE, Suite 206 Minneapolis, MN 55414 (612)379-3963 FAX (612)379-3965
NUC	Nuclear Associates P.O. Box 349 100 Voice Road Carle Place, NY 11514 (516)741-6360
PMC	Pollution Measurements Corporation 1013 S. Lyman Avenue Oak Park, IL 60304 (708)383-7794
SCH	Schmidt Instrument Co. P.O. Box 111 San Carlos, CA 94070 (415)591-5347
SCI	Science Pump Corporation 1431 Ferry Avenue Camden, NJ 08104 (609)963-7700
SEN	Sensidyne, Inc. 16333 Bay Vista Drive Clearwater, FL 34620 (813)530-3602 or (800)451-9444
SKC	SKC Inc. 863 Valley View Road Eighty Four, PA 15330-9614 (412)941-9701 or (800)752-8472 FAX (412)941-1396
SPE	Spectrex Corporation 3580 Haven Avenue Redwood City, CA 94063 (415)365-6567 or (800)822-3940 FAX (415)365-5845
STA	Staplex Company Air Sampler Div. 777 Fifth Avenue Brooklyn, NY 11232 (718)768-3333
SUP	Supelco, Inc. Supelco Park Bellefonte, PA 16823-0048 (814)359-3441 FAX (814)359-3044
THO	Thomas Industries, Inc. P.O. Box 29 1419 Illinois Avenue Sheboygan, WI 53082 (414)457-4891
WED	Wedding & Associates, Inc. 209 Christman Drive, #2 Fort Collins, CO 80524 (303)221-0678 or (800)367-7610 FAX (303)221-0400

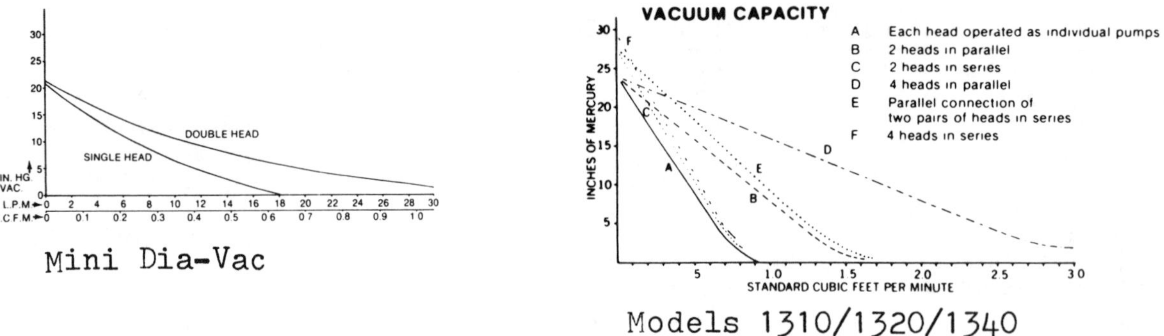

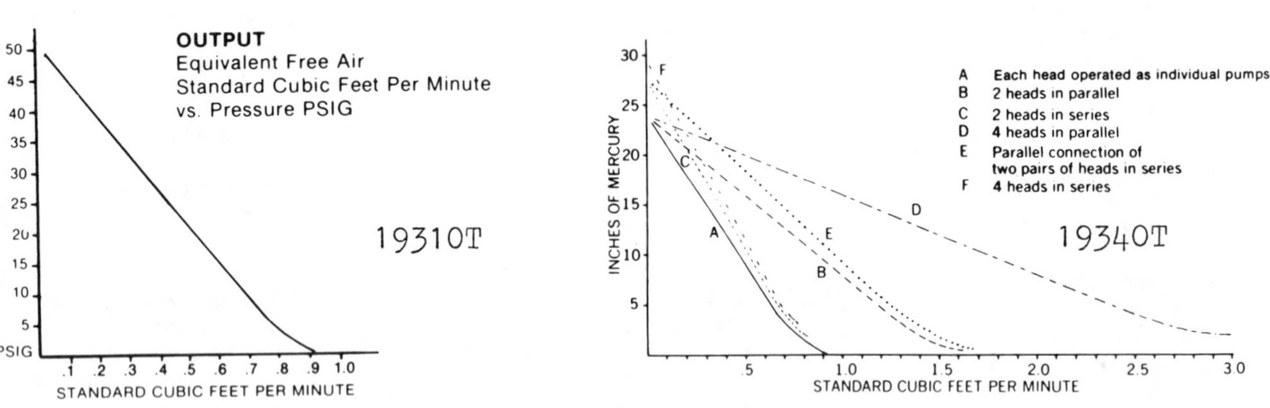

FIGURE 12-9. Operating characteristics for Air Dimensions Dia-Vac diaphragm pumps.

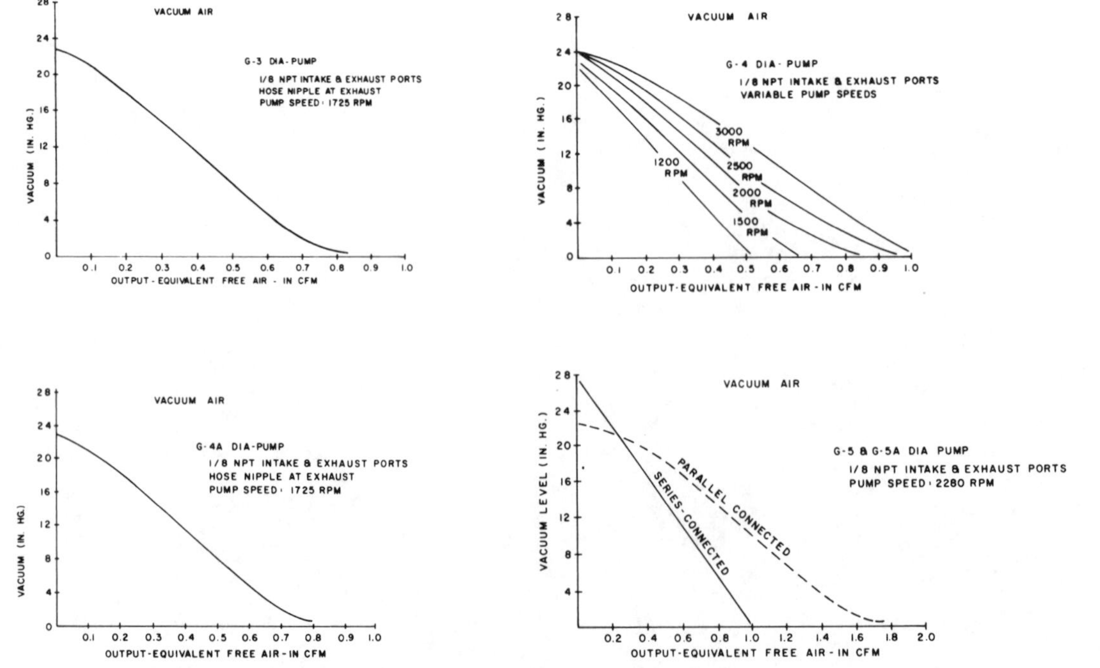

FIGURE 12-10. Vacuum-air flow characteristic for Air-Control Dia-pumps.

MODEL NO.	VOLTAGE	COMPRESSOR PERFORMANCE L/M VS PSIG								MAX PSIG		VACUUM PERFORMANCE L/M VS IN. HG.							MAX VAC IN. HG.	PHYSICAL SPECIFICATIONS	
		0	5	10	15	20	25	30	60	CONT	INT	0	5	10	15	20	25	28		WT.	HxWxL (in mm)
3003	6 VDC	0.9	0.4	0.1	—	—	—	—	—	3	10.5	0.9	0.4	0.1	—	—	—	—	10.5	1.5 oz.	36 x 23 x 42
	12 VDC	0.9	0.4	0.1	—	—	—	—	—	3	10.5	0.9	0.4	0.1	—	—	—	—	10.5	1.5 oz.	36 x 23 x 42
5002	6 VDC	2.2	1.5	0.8	0.1	—	—	—	—	5	16	2.2	1.5	0.6	0.1	—	—	—	15	6.5 oz.	53 x 30 x 82
	12 VDC	2.2	1.5	0.8	0.1	—	—	—	—	5	16	2.2	1.5	0.6	0.1	—	—	—	15	6.5 oz.	53 x 30 x 82
	24 VDC	2.2	1.5	0.8	0.1	—	—	—	—	5	16	2.2	1.5	0.6	0.1	—	—	—	15	6.5 oz.	53 x 30 x 82
	115/60	2.0	1.2	0.6	0.1	—	—	—	—	5	16	2.0	1.2	0.5	—	—	—	—	15	1.3 lb.	53 x 30 x 82
5010	6 VDC	3.7	1.9	0.9	0.1	—	—	—	—	5	16	3.7	2.1	1.1	0.3	—	—	—	17	10 oz.	68 x 40 x 85
	12 VDC	3.7	1.9	0.9	0.1	—	—	—	—	5	16	3.7	2.1	1.1	0.3	—	—	—	17	10 oz.	68 x 40 x 85
	24 VDC	3.7	1.9	0.9	0.1	—	—	—	—	5	16	3.7	2.1	1.1	0.3	—	—	—	17	10 oz.	68 x 40 x 85
7010	6 VDC	6.0	4.5	3.3	2.4	1.5	0.7	0.2	—	22	32	6.0	4.0	2.6	1.5	0.4	—	—	22	1.3 lb.	95 x 61 x 108
	12 VDC	6.0	4.5	3.3	2.4	1.5	0.7	0.2	—	22	32	6.0	4.0	2.6	1.5	0.4	—	—	22	1.3 lb.	95 x 61 x 108
	24 VDC	6.0	4.5	3.3	2.4	1.5	0.7	0.2	—	22	32	6.0	4.0	2.6	1.5	0.4	—	—	22	1.3 lb.	95 x 61 x 108
	115/60	6.0	4.5	3.3	2.4	1.5	0.7	0.2	—	22	32	6.0	4.0	2.6	1.5	0.4	—	—	22	2.1 lb.	95 x 61 x 108
7010Z	12 VDC PARALL.	12.0	9.5	7.2	5.4	3.7	2.0	0.5	—	22	32	12.0	8.0	5.0	2.9	1.0	—	—	22	1.7 lb.	95 x 61 x 158
	12 VDC SERIES	6.0	5.3	4.8	4.2	3.6	3.2	2.7	0.3	22	72	6.0	4.1	2.8	1.8	1.0	0.2	—	27	1.7 lb.	95 x 61 x 158
	115/60 PARALL.	12.0	9.5	7.2	5.4	3.7	2.0	0.5	—	22	32	12.0	8.0	5.0	2.9	1.0	—	—	22	3.3 lb.	95 x 61 x 158
	115/60 SERIES	6.0	5.3	4.8	4.2	3.6	3.2	2.7	0.3	22	72	6.0	4.1	2.8	1.8	1.0	0.2	—	27	3.3 lb.	95 x 61 x 158
7012	12 VDC	9.0	4.0	0.5	—	—	—	—	—	—	12	9.0	5.3	3.1	1.5	0.4	—	—	22	1.1 lb.	78 x 95 x 117
	24 VDC	9.0	4.0	0.5	—	—	—	—	—	—	12	9.0	5.3	3.1	1.5	0.4	—	—	22	1.1 lb.	78 x 95 x 117
7015	12 VDC	12.5	9.8	7.7	5.8	4.0	2.5	1.0	—	22	36	12.5	8.5	5.5	3.1	1.0	—	—	22	2.3 lb.	134 x 86 x 125
	115/60	12.5	9.8	7.7	5.8	4.0	2.5	1.0	—	22	36	12.5	8.5	5.5	3.1	1.0	—	—	22	3.5 lb.	134 x 86 x 125
8025	115/60	13.0	10.0	8.0	6.5	5.5	4.5	3.7	—	36	50	13.0	8.7	6.0	3.5	1.6	—	—	24	7.7 lb.	100 x 115 x 220
8050	115/60 PARALL.	25.0	22.5	20.0	17.5	15	13	12	3.5	36	80	25.0	17.4	12.0	7.5	3.5	—	—	25	9 lb.	100 x 154 x 220
	115/60 SERIES	13.0	12.2	11.4	10.6	9.7	8.8	8.0	5.3	36	85	13.0	8.5	5.8	3.5	2.0	0.7	—	28	9 lb.	100 x 154 x 220
8050Z	115/60 PARALL.	43.0	39.0	36.0	33.0	30.0	27.0	24.0	10.0	36	85	43.0	33.0	23.0	15.0	8.0	—	—	25	28.2 lb.	100 x 154 x 324
	115/60 SERIES	19.0	18.5	18.0	17.5	17.0	16.0	15.0	12.0	36	140	19.0	14.0	10.0	7.0	4.0	0.1	—	28	28.2 lb.	100 x 154 x 324

FIGURE 12-11. Technical data for ASF diaphragm pumps.

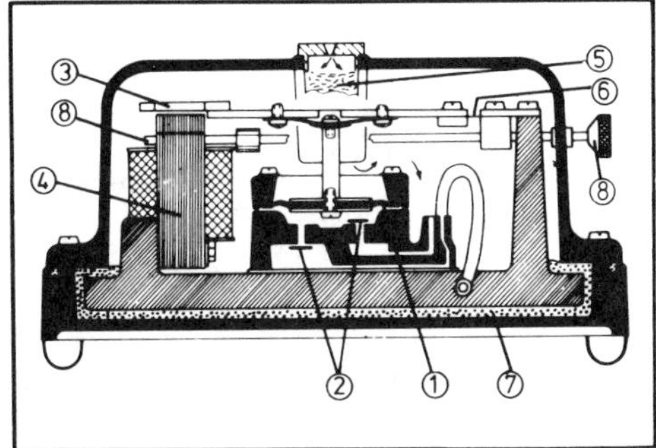

Section through type 3-1.000.010.0
Pressure pump with casing, output adjustable by slider-type magnetic shunt.

1 Diaphragm
2 Valve plates
3 Armature arm
4 Electro-magnet
5 Cotton wool filter
6 Leaf spring
7 Foam bedding
8 Slider-type magnetic shunt

FIGURE 12-12. Schematic diagram of ASF WISA pump.

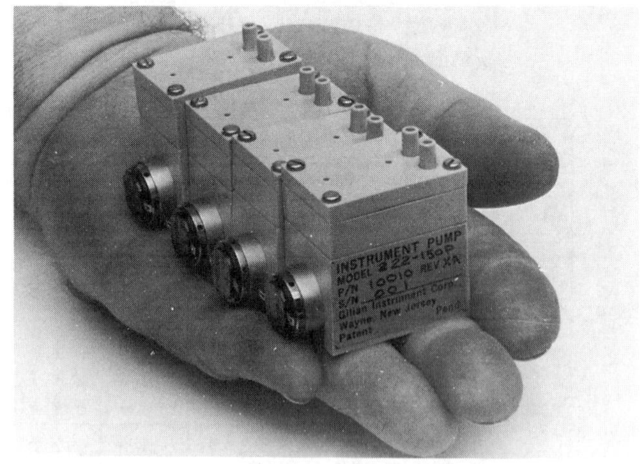

FIGURE 12-14. Gilian OEM air sampling pumps.

Model	HP	RPM		Airflow CFM @ 0" Hg		Airflow m³/h @ 1000 mbar		Maximum Vacuum	
		50 Hz	60 Hz	50 Hz	60 Hz	50 Hz	60 Hz	" Hg	mbar
MOA-V112-AE	1/16	1275	1575	0.40	0.49	0,68	0,83	24.0	200
MOA-V111-CD	1/16	1275	1575	0.40	0.49	0,68	0,83	24.0	200
MOA-V112-FB	1/16	2500	3000	0.60	0.72	1,02	1,22	24.0	200
MOA-V112-FD	1/16	2500	3000	0.60	0.72	1,02	1,22	24.0	200
MOA-V112-HB	1/16	1275	1575	0.40	0.49	0,68	0,83	24.0	200
MOA-V112-HD	1/16	1275	1575	0.40	0.49	0,68	0,83	24.0	200
MOA-V121-CG	1/16	1275	–	0.40	–	0,68	–	24.0	200
MOA-V111-JH	1/16	1800 (D.C.)		0.56	0.56	0,95	0,95	24.0	200
MOA-V111-KH	1/8	3200 (D.C.)		0.80	0.80	1,36	1,36	24.0	200
MOA-V111-JK	1/16	1800 (D.C.)		0.56	0.56	0,95	0,95	24.0	200
MAA-V103-HB	1/16	1275	1575	0.85	1.02	1,45	1,73	24.0	200
MAA-V109-HB	1/16	1275	1575	0.39	0.47	0,66	0,80	28.0	65
MAA-V103-HD	1/16	1275	1575	0.85	1.02	1,45	1,73	24.0	200
MAA-V109-HD	1/16	1275	1575	0.39	0.47	0,66	0,80	28.0	65
MAA-V103-MB	1/8	2500	3000	1.60	1.70	2,72	2,89	24.0	200
MAA-V109-MB	1/8	2500	3000	0.66	0.80	1,12	1,36	28.5	48
DOA-V191-AA	1/8	–	1575	–	1.10	–	1,87	25.5	150
DOA-V113-AC	1/8	–	1575	–	1.10	–	1,87	25.5	150
DOA-V111-AE	1/8	1275	–	0.95	–	1,62	–	25.5	150
DOA-V112-BN	1/8	1275	–	0.95	–	1,62	–	25.5	150
DOA-V110-BL	1/8	1275	1575	0.95	1.10	1,62	1,87	25.5	150
DOA-V113-DB	1/8	1275	1575	0.95	1.10	1,62	1,87	25.5	150
DOA-V119-DD	1/8	1275	1575	0.95	1.10	1,62	1,87	25.5	150
DOA-V112-FB	1/3	2500	3000	1.50	1.80	2,55	3,06	25.5	150
DOA-V114-FD	1/3	2500	3000	1.50	1.80	2,55	3,06	25.5	150
DOA-V113-FG	1/3	2500	–	1.50	–	2,55	–	25.5	150
DOA-V111-JH	1/8	2100 (D.C.)		1.26	1.26	2,14	2,14	25.5	150
DOA-V111-KH	1/6	3200 (D.C.)		1.70	1.70	2,89	2,89	25.5	150
DOA-V111-JK	1/8	2100 (D.C.)		1.26	1.26	2,14	2,14	25.5	150
DAA-V110-EB	1/4	1275	1575	1.80	2.20	3,06	3,74	25.5	150
DAA-V111-EB	1/4	1275	1575	0.85	1.16	1,45	1,97	29.0	31
DAA-V110-ED	1/4	1275	1575	1.80	2.20	3,06	3,74	25.5	150
DAA-V111-ED	1/4	1275	1575	0.85	1.16	1,45	1,97	29.0	31
DAA-V124-EG	1/4	1275	–	1.80	–	3,06	–	25.5	150
DAA-V134-EG	1/4	1275	–	0.85	–	1,45	–	29.0	31
DAA-V110-GB	1/2	2500	3000	3.00	3.60	5,10	6,12	25.5	150
DAA-V111-GB	1/2	2500	3000	1.40	1.95	2,38	3,32	29.0	31
DAA-V110-GD	1/2	2500	3000	3.00	3.60	5,10	6,12	25.5	150
DAA-V111-GD	1/2	2500	3000	1.40	1.95	2,38	3,32	29.0	31
DAA-V112-GG	1/2	2500	–	3.00	–	5,10	–	25.5	150
DAA-V111-GG	1/2	2500	–	1.40	–	2,38	–	29.0	31

FIGURE 12-13. Technical data for Gast diaphragm pumps.

See page 231 for Figure 12-15.

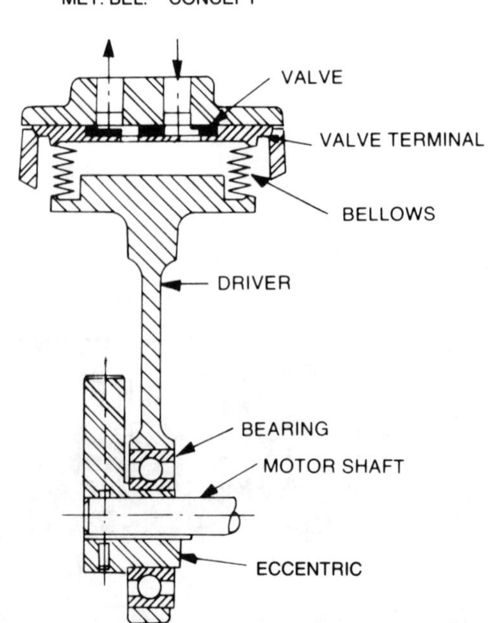

FIGURE 12-16. Schematic diagram of Metal Bellows pump.

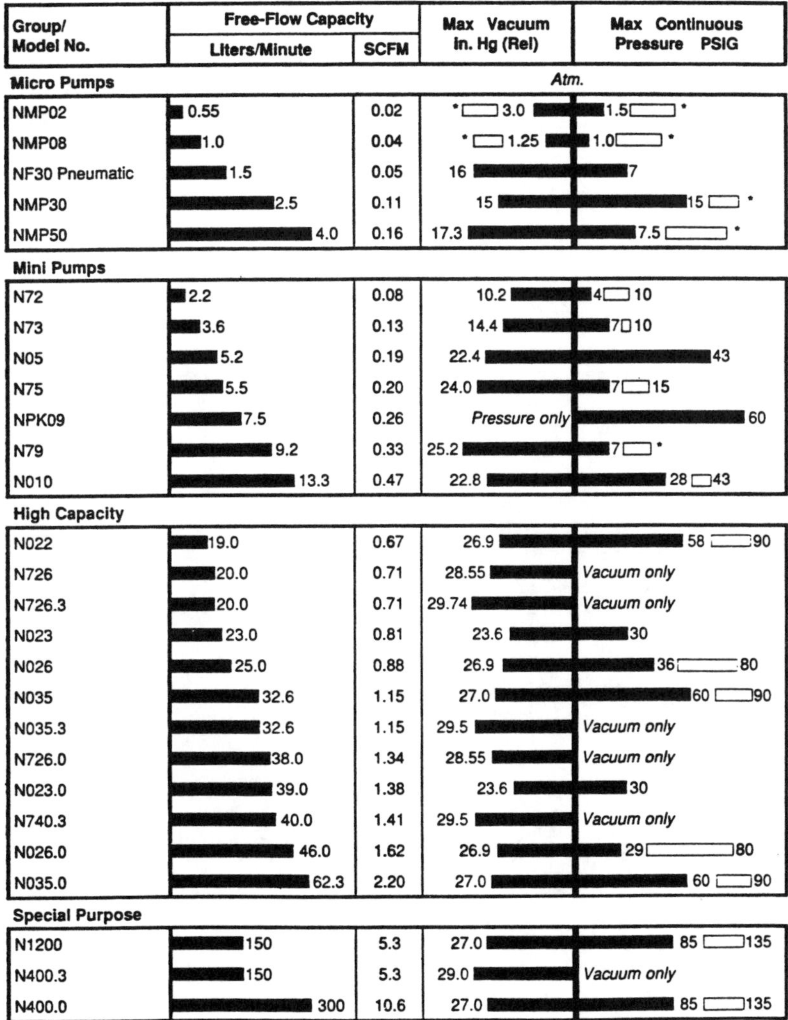

Group/ Model No.	Free-Flow Capacity Liters/Minute	SCFM	Max Vacuum in. Hg (Rel)	Max Continuous Pressure PSIG
Micro Pumps			Atm.	
NMP02	0.55	0.02	* □ 3.0	1.5 □ *
NMP08	1.0	0.04	* □ 1.25	1.0 □ *
NF30 Pneumatic	1.5	0.05	16	7
NMP30	2.5	0.11	15	15 □ *
NMP50	4.0	0.16	17.3	7.5 □ *
Mini Pumps				
N72	2.2	0.08	10.2	4 □ 10
N73	3.6	0.13	14.4	7 □ 10
N05	5.2	0.19	22.4	43
N75	5.5	0.20	24.0	7 □ 15
NPK09	7.5	0.26	*Pressure only*	60
N79	9.2	0.33	25.2	7 □ *
N010	13.3	0.47	22.8	28 □ 43
High Capacity				
N022	19.0	0.67	26.9	58 □ 90
N726	20.0	0.71	28.55	*Vacuum only*
N726.3	20.0	0.71	29.74	*Vacuum only*
N023	23.0	0.81	23.6	30
N026	25.0	0.88	26.9	36 □ 80
N035	32.6	1.15	27.0	60 □ 90
N035.3	32.6	1.15	29.5	*Vacuum only*
N726.0	38.0	1.34	28.55	*Vacuum only*
N023.0	39.0	1.38	23.6	30
N740.3	40.0	1.41	29.5	*Vacuum only*
N026.0	46.0	1.62	26.9	29 □ 80
N035.0	62.3	2.20	27.0	60 □ 90
Special Purpose				
N1200	150	5.3	27.0	85 □ 135
N400.3	150	5.3	29.0	*Vacuum only*
N400.0	300	10.6	27.0	85 □ 135

FIGURE 12-15. Technical data for KNF diaphragm pumps. Standard continuous performance ratings at sea level with an ambient temperature of 70°F (21°C) and nominal electrical supply.

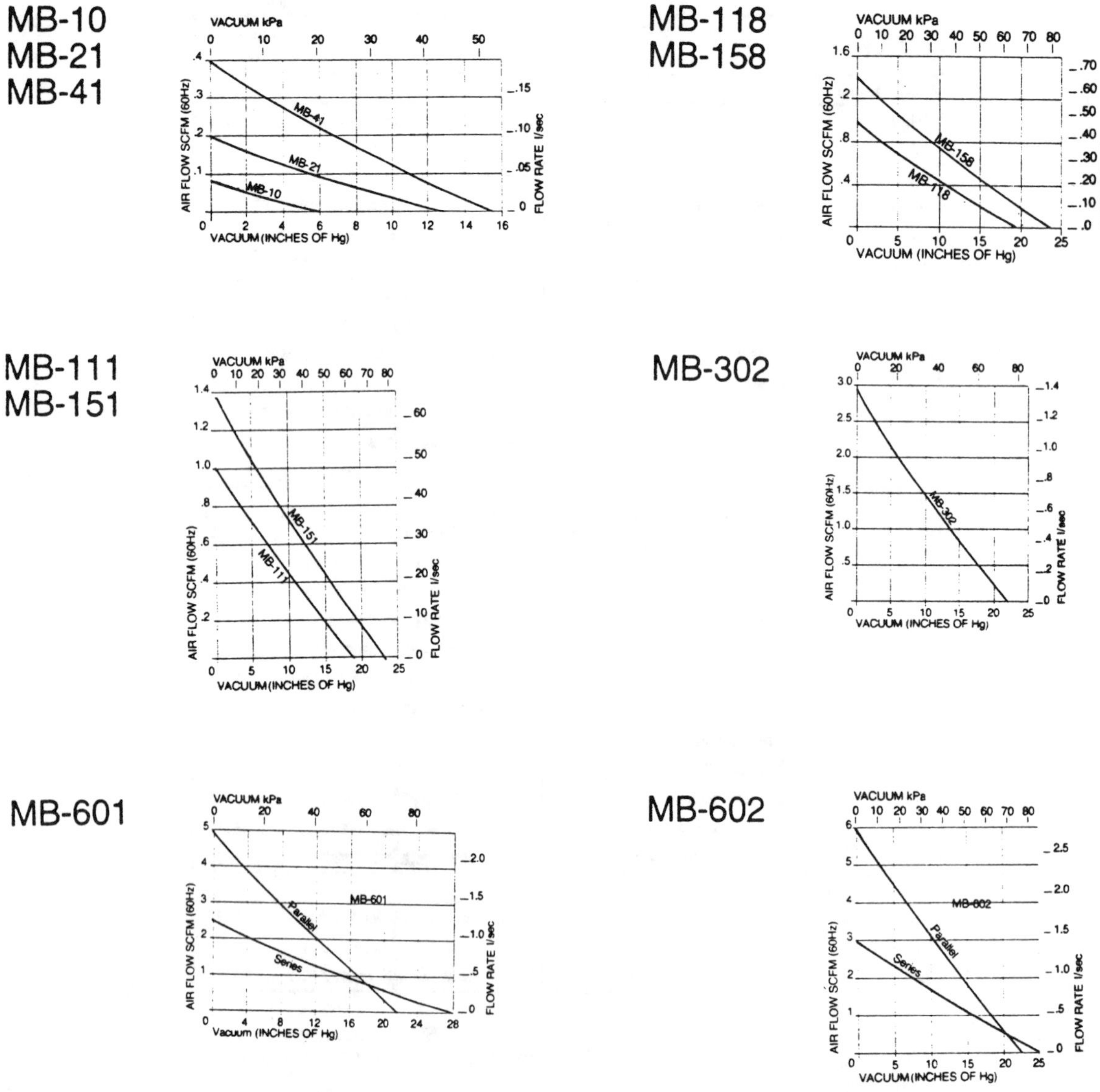

MB-10
MB-21
MB-41

MB-118
MB-158

MB-111
MB-151

MB-302

MB-601

MB-602

FIGURE 12-17. Vacuum-air flow characteristic for Metal Bellows pumps.

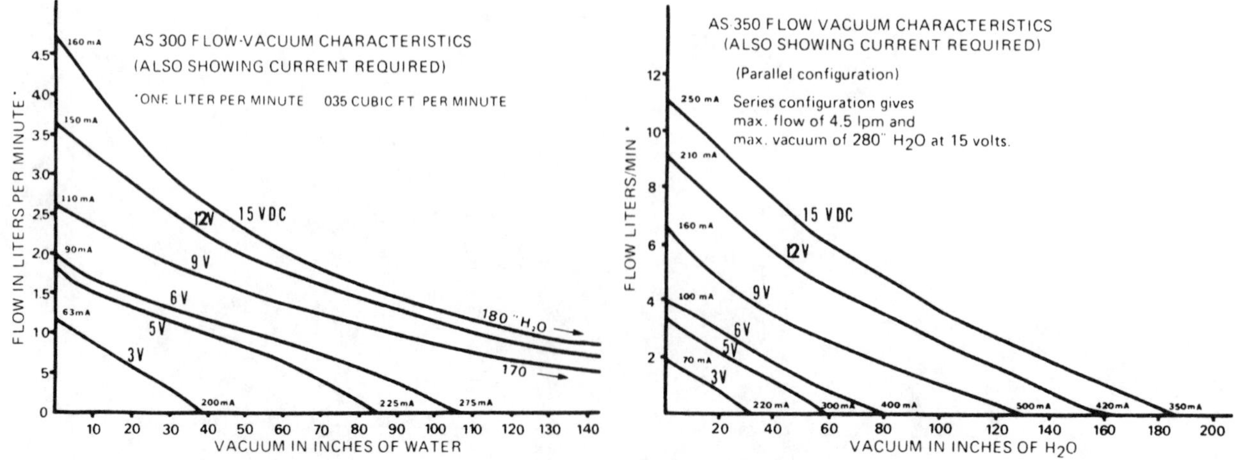

FIGURE 12-18. Vacuum-air flow characteristic for Spectrex Models AS-300 and AS-350.

MODEL NUMBER	HP	kW	VOLTAGE	MOTOR TYPE	PHYSICAL SPECIFICATIONS WT.		H x W x L		VACUUM PERFORMANCE IN. HG. vs. CFM						MM HG. vs. LPM						MAX. VACUUM	
					LBS.	KG.	IN.	CM	0	5	10	15	20	25	0	127	254	381	508	635	IN. HG.	MM HG.
007CDC19	1/32	.023	12VDC	Perm. Magnet	3.6	1.6	5.09 x 3.38 x 6.25	12.9 x 8.5 x 15.8	.65	.48	.34	.21			18.4	13.6	9.6	5.9			23.0	584.2
007BDC19	1/32	.023	12VDC	Perm. Magnet	3.6	1.6	5.04 x 3.35 x 6.16	12.8 x 8.5 x 15.6	1.26	.90	.58	.34			35.7	25.5	16.4	9.6			23.0	584.2
007CA13*	1/30	.024	115/60/1	Shaded Pole	2.5	1.1	5.12 x 3.50 x 6.00	13.0 x 8.8 x 15.2	.61	.38	.23	.11			17.3	10.8	6.5	3.1			20.3	515.6
107CAB18*	1/20	.037	115/60/1	Shaded Pole	5.1	2.3	4.70 x 4.25 x 6.84	11.9 x 10.7 x 17.3	.76	.58	.40	.23	.08		21.5	16.4	11.3	6.5	2.3		23.2	589.3
107CDC20*	1/10	.075	12VDC	Perm. Magnet	4.5	2.0	4.70 x 4.25 x 7.34	11.9 x 10.7 x 18.6	1.20	.86	.62	.41			34.0	24.4	17.6	11.6			22.9	581.7
2107CA20	1/20	.037	115/60/1	Shaded Pole	9.0	4.0	6.78 x 4.75 x 8.00	17.2 x 12.0 x 20.3	1.65	1.15	.77	.47	.17		46.7	32.6	21.8	13.3	4.8		22.4	569.0
2107CEF18	1/20	.037	115/60/1	PSC	7.0	3.1	5.31 x 5.25 x 8.84	13.4 x 13.3 x 22.4	1.50	1.10	.75	.41	.13		42.5	31.2	21.2	11.6	3.7		22.6	574.0
2107VA20	1/20	.037	115/60/1	Shaded Pole	6.3	2.8	4.70 x 4.25 x 8.18	11.9 x 10.7 x 20.7	.85	.65	.49	.33	.20		24.1	18.4	13.9	9.3	5.7		28.2	716.3
905CA18	1/15	.049	115/60/1	Shaded Pole	6.5	2.9	5.88 x 4.75 x 7.84	14.9 x 12.0 x 19.9	1.40	.87	.55	.32	.09		39.6	24.6	15.6	9.1	2.5		22.2	563.9
907CDC18*	1/10	.075	12VDC	Perm. Magnet	6.0	2.7	4.70 x 4.25 x 8.19	11.9 x 10.7 x 20.8	2.18	1.06	.64	.41			61.7	30.0	18.1	11.6			23.2	589.3
917CA18*	1/8	.093	115/60/1	Shaded Pole	11.0	4.9	6.78 x 4.75 x 8.00	17.2 x 12.0 x 20.3	1.49	.89	.64	.36	.16		42.2	25.2	18.1	10.2	4.5		23.8	604.5
727CM39*	1/4	.186	115/60/1	Split Phase	21.0	9.5	8.81 x 5.81 x 11.50	22.3 x 14.7 x 29.2	3.10	1.72	1.27	.87	.48		87.8	48.7	36.0	24.6	13.6		25.7	652.8
2737CM39*	1/2	.372	115/60/1	Split Phase	25.0	11.3	6.56 x 11.12 x 15.34	16.6 x 28.2 x 38.9	6.20	4.30	2.90	1.80	.97		175.6	121.8	82.1	51.0	27.5		25.3	642.6
2737VM39	1/2	.372	115/60/1	Split Phase	25.8	11.7	6.56 x 11.12 x 15.34	16.6 x 28.2 x 38.9	3.10	2.40	1.90	1.40	.89	.34	87.8	68.0	53.8	39.6	25.2	9.6	29.0	736.6

FIGURE 12-19. Technical data for Thomas diaphragm pumps.

MODEL NUMBER	NOM. HP	# OF CYL.	VOLTAGE/ HERTZ/ PHASE	MOTOR TYPE	FRAME	PHYSICAL SPECIFICATIONS		VACUUM PERFORMANCE IN. HG VS. CFM						MAX. VACUUM IN. HG
						WT. (LBS.)	H" x W" x L"	0	5	10	15	20	25	
LGH-1V	1/12	1	115/50/60/1	Split Phase	48	16	8.06x5.65x10.29	1.35	1.09	.83	.57	.31	.05	26.0
TA-1V1	1/12	1	115/50/60/1	Split Phase	48	16	8.06x5.65x10.29	1.35	1.09	.83	.57	.31	.05	26.0
LGH-2V	1/6	1	115/50/60/1	Split Phase	48	20	8.00x5.65x10.88	2.15	1.76	1.37	.98	.59	.20	27.5
TA-2V1	1/6	1	115/50/60/1	Split Phase	48	20	8.00x5.65x10.88	2.15	1.76	1.37	.98	.59	.20	27.5
TA-3V2	1/4	2	115/230/60/1	Capacitor Start	56	33	6.88x10.03x13.80	3.60	2.95	2.29	1.64	.98	.33	27.5
GH-3V1B	1/4	1	115/230/60/1	Capacitor Start	56	33	8.75x10.20x15.31	1.70	1.39	1.08	.77	.46	.15	27.5
GH-3V2B	1/4	2	115/230/50/1	Capacitor Start	56	34	8.75x11.50x15.31	3.10	2.54	1.97	1.41	.85	.28	27.5
GH-4VB	1/3	2	115/230/60/1	Capacitor Start	56	38	8.75x11.50x16.00	3.60	2.95	2.29	1.64	.98	.33	27.5
TA-4V2	1/3	2	115/230/60/1	Capacitor Start	56	37	6.88x10.03x14.03	4.20	3.44	2.67	1.91	1.15	.38	27.5
GH-5VB	1/2	2	115/230/60/1	Split Capacitor	56	41	8.75x12.30x16.19	4.20	3.44	2.67	1.91	1.15	.38	27.5
HP-100V	1	2	115/230/60/1	Capacitor Start, Capacitor Run	56	70	9.22x18.00x19.81	8.00	6.55	5.09	3.64	2.18	.73	27.5

FIGURE 12-20. Technical data for Thomas piston pumps.

MODEL NUMBER	HP	kW	VOLTAGE	MOTOR TYPE	PHYSICAL SPECIFICATIONS WT. LBS.	KG.	H x W x L IN.	CM	VACUUM PERFORMANCE IN. HG. vs. CFM 0	5	10	15	20	25	MM HG. vs. LPM 0	127	254	381	508	635	MAX. VACUUM IN. HG.	MM HG.
014CDC20	1/30	.024	12VDC	Perm. Magnet	2.3	1.0	4.13 x 1.89 x 5.48	10.4 x 4.8 x 13.9	.39	.24	.18	.12	.06		11.0	6.8	5.1	3.4	1.7		25.3	642.6
014CA28	1/16	.046	115/60/1	Shaded Pole	4.7	2.1	5.06 x 4.50 x 5.89	12.8 x 11.4 x 14.9	.46	.37	.28	.19	.09		13.0	10.5	7.9	5.4	2.5		26.0	660.4
010CA26*	1/25	.029	115/60/1	Shaded Pole	3.3	1.4	4.25 x 3.00 x 5.17	10.8 x 7.6 x 13.1	.37	.27	.18	.10	.02		10.5	7.6	5.1	2.8	.6		22.3	566.4
010CDC26	1/25	.029	12VDC	Perm. Magnet	1.7	.7	4.01 x 2.36 x 4.82	10.1 x 5.9 x 12.2	.37	.27	.18	.10	.02		10.5	7.6	5.1	2.8	.6		22.3	566.4
405AE38	1/12	.061	115/60/1	PSC	6.5	2.9	6.00 x 5.25 x 8.75	15.2 x 13.3 x 22.2														
405ADC38*	1/10	.075	12VDC	Perm. Magnet	4.3	1.9	6.50 x 4.00 x 7.27	16.5 x 10.1 x 18.4														
415CDC30	1/10	.075	12VDC	Perm. Magnet	4.8	2.1	5.25 x 4.00 x 7.12	13.3 x 10.1 x 18.0	.92	.75	.54	.34	.20		26.1	21.2	15.3	9.6	5.7		24.6	624.8
215ADC38	1/6	.124	12VDC	Perm. Magnet	3.0	1.3	4.46 x 2.10 x 6.20	11.03 x 5.3 x 15.7														
315CDC50	1/5	.149	12VDC	Perm. Magnet	4.3	1.9	6.30 x 4.00 x 9.31	16.5 x 10.1 x 23.6	1.18	.86	.58	.29			33.4	24.4	16.4	8.2			21.0	533.4
317CDC56	1/5	.149	12VDC	Perm. Magnet	6.5	2.9	6.30 x 4.00 x 8.60	16.0 x 10.1 x 21.8	1.12	.86	.61	.36			31.7	24.4	17.3	10.2			22.0	558.8
607CA22*	1/8	.093	115/60/1	Shaded Pole	11.0	4.9	6.78 x 5.00 x 8.00	17.2 x 12.7 x 20.3	.84	.62	.46	.31	.15		23.8	17.6	13.0	8.8			25.9	657.9
607FA22	1/8	.093	115/60/1	Shaded Pole	25.0	11.3	14.82 x 7.00 x 16.50	37.6 x 17.1 x 41.9	.84	.62	.46	.31	.15		23.8	17.6	13.0	8.8			25.9	657.9
607CA32*	1/7	.105	115/60/1	Shaded Pole	11.0	4.9	6.78 x 5.00 x 8.00	17.2 x 12.7 x 20.3	1.22	.87	.65	.45	.23		34.6	24.6	18.4	12.7	6.5		26.8	680.7
607CE44*	1/3	.248	115/60/1	PSC	14.5	6.5	6.78 x 5.00 x 9.17	17.2 x 12.7 x 23.2	1.60	1.15	.90	.62	.33	.11	45.3	32.6	25.5	17.6	9.3	3.1	27.6	701.0
619CE44*	1/5	.149	115/60/1	PSC	10.0	4.5	6.75 x 5.00 x 6.44	17.1 x 12.7 x 16.3	2.00	1.20	.96	.64	.36		56.6	34.0	27.2	18.1	10.2		26.0	660.4
2607CE22	1/4	.186	115/60/1	PSC	14.8	6.7	6.76 x 6.03 x 11.00	17.1 x 15.3 x 27.9	1.68	1.20	.93	.63	.33		47.6	34.0	26.3	17.8	9.3		26.2	665.5
2608TE22/18	1/3	.248	115/60/1	PSC	17.8	8.0	6.94 x 5.00 x 11.04	17.6 x 12.7 x 28.0														
2608VE44	1/3	.248	115/60/1	PSC	16.6	7.5	6.76 x 6.03 x 11.00	17.1 x 15.3 x 27.9	1.60	1.20	.98	.69	.48	.16	45.3	34.0	27.8	19.5	13.6	4.5	29.0	736.6
2618CE44*	1/3	.248	115/60/1	PSC	14.3	6.4	6.68 x 5.00 x 9.71	16.9 x 12.7 x 24.6	3.15	2.30	1.60	1.10	.64	.18	89.2	65.1	45.3	31.2	18.1	5.1	27.6	701.0
2619CE44*	1/3	.248	115/60/1	PSC	15.9	7.2	6.75 x 5.00 x 9.38	17.1 x 12.7 x 23.8	3.75	2.75	2.15	1.49	.86		106.2	77.9	60.9	42.2	24.4		27.3	693.4
2621CE564	1/3	.248	115/60/1	PSC	16.0	7.2	7.87 x 5.00 x 9.38	19.9 x 12.7 x 23.8	4.80	4.10	3.20	2.30	1.30	.30	135.9	116.1	90.6	65.1	36.8	8.5	27.5	698.5
2750CE50	1/3	.248	115/60/1	PSC	20.0	9.0	9.29 x 5.37 x 10.09	23.5 x 13.6 x 25.6	5.35	4.58	4.36	4.16	3.94	3.74	151.5	129.7	123.5	117.8	111.6	105.9	27.0	558.8
2750BE75	1/3	.248	115/60/1	PSC	20.0	23.5	9.29 x 5.37 x 10.09	23.5 x 13.6 x 25.6	7.05	6.27	4.69	3.17	1.77	.49	199.7	177.6	132.8	89.8	50.1	13.9	27.0	658.8
707CK50	1/4	.186	115/60/1	Capacitor Start	26.0	11.7	10.00 x 6.38 x 10.72	25.4 x 16.2 x 27.2	2.70	1.99	1.54	1.12	.65	.20	76.5	56.4	43.6	31.7	18.4	5.7	27.7	703.6
807CK60	1/3	.248	115/60/1	Capacitor Start	26.0	11.7	10.00 x 6.38 x 10.72	25.4 x 16.2 x 27.2	3.25	2.07	1.60	1.14	.67	.21	92.0	58.6	45.3	32.3	19.0	5.9	27.7	703.6
1007CK72	1/2	.372	115/60/1	Capacitor Start	26.0	11.7	10.00 x 6.38 x 10.72	25.4 x 16.2 x 27.2	4.05	2.49	1.93	1.39	.83	.28	114.7	70.5	54.7	39.4	23.5	7.9	27.9	708.7
1107CK75	3/4	.559	115/60/1	Capacitor Start	26.0	11.7	10.00 x 6.38 x 10.72	25.4 x 16.2 x 27.2	4.25	2.70	2.10	1.40	.86	.29	120.4	76.5	59.5	39.6	24.4	8.2	27.4	696.0
2807CE72*	1	.745	115/60/1	PSC	39.0	17.6	10.03 x 6.54 x 15.71	25.4 x 16.6 x 39.9	6.60	3.60	2.66	1.80	.88		186.9	102.0	75.3	51.0	24.9		25.0	635.0

FIGURE 12-21. Technical data for Thomas WOB-L piston pumps.

Model	Available Voltages		Max. Flow L/M	Maximum Pressure PSI		Maximum Vacuum in. HG		Weight		Dimensions HxWxL (mm)
				INT.	CONT.	INT.	CONT.			
G01-K	6	VDC	1.0	0.3	0.3	0.6	0.6	1	oz	21x21x44
G01	3, 6,12,16	VDC	1.1	1	1	3	1.8	3	oz	26x26x55
G01-4	6,12,16	VDC	1.0	2	1	4.7	1.8	3	oz	26x26x55
G02	3, 6,12,16	VDC	2.6	2	1	3.5	1.8	3	oz	26x26x55
G02-LC	6,12	VDC	3.0	3	1	6	2	4	oz	26x26x71
G02-4	6,12,16	VDC	2.5	3	1	7	1.8	3	oz	26x26x55
GO2-8	6,12	VDC	2.4	7	4	13	9.0	5	oz	26x26x71
GO2-8-LC	6,12	VDC	2.5	6	4	12	9.0	4	oz	26x26x71
GO4	3, 6,12,16	VDC	4.5	1	1	2.4	1.5	3	oz	26x26x61
GO4-LC	6,12	VDC	5.0	2	1	3.0	1.5	4	oz	26x26x77
GO4-4	6,12,16	VDC	4.5	3	1	6	1.5	3	oz	26x26x61
G045	6,12,24	VDC	6	7	4	15	9	5	oz	42x42x84
G045-LC	12	VDC	7	12	4	20	9	8	oz	42x42x89
G045-TP	12,24	VDC	10	7	4	15	9	11	oz	42x42x130
G045-TS	12,24	VDC	5	13	9	27	18	11	oz	42x42x130
W045-U	110V/60*	Hz	9	9		18		12	oz	59x42x93
W045-S	110V/60*	Hz	3.5	5	5	10	10	1.2	lbs	74x60x90
W05	110V/60*	Hz	6	9	6	18	18	3.2	lbs	63x90x119
W08	110V/60*	Hz	15	10	7	21	21	4.6	lbs	105x65x135
G07	12,24	VDC	14	10		21		1.3	lbs	51x51x135
G08	12,24	VDC	14	10	4	21	9	2.0	lbs	62x62x165
G08-TP	12,24	VDC	28	10	4	21	9	3.4	lbs	62x62x210
G08-TS	12,24	VDC	14	12	6	27	18	3.4	lbs	62x62x210
G09	12,24	VDC	20	10	4	21	9	2.0	lbs	50x50x165
TF1	110V/60*	Hz	20	10	10	22	22	9	lbs	156x95x175
TF1E	12,24	VDC	25.6	11	11	23	23	6.5	lbs	101x90x193
	110V/60*	Hz	20	10	10	22	22	8.8	lbs	100x95x175
TF1.5	110V/60*	Hz	23	12	12	23	23	7	lbs	116x105x182
TF1.5-E-LC	110V/60*	Hz	23	12	12	23	23	7.3	lbs	114x110x196

FIGURE 12-22. Technical data for ASF Brey vane pumps.

MODEL NUMBER	NOMINAL HP	VOLTAGE/ HERTZ/ PHASE	MOTOR TYPE	FRAME	PHYSICAL SPECIFICATIONS		VACUUM PERFORMANCE IN. HG VS. CFM						MAX. VACUUM
					WT. (LBS.)	H" x W" x L"	0	5	10	15	20	25	IN. HG
SR-0015-VP	1/10	115/50/60/1	Split Phase		8.5	4.94x4.19x7.62	1.50	1.19	.88	.58	.25	0	24.0
SR-0015-VP	1/10	115/50/60/1	PSC		8.0	4.94x4.19x6.32	1.50	1.14	.88	.56	.25	0	24.0
SR-0030	1/6	115/60/1	PSC		9.3	3.95x3.86x6.85	2.85	2.26	1.66	1.07	.48	0	24.0
TA-0015-V	1/8	115/50/60/1	Split Phase	48	17.0	6.00x5.75x9.00	1.85	1.45	1.05	.64	.24	0	23.0
TA-0030-V	1/6	115/50/60/1	Split Phase	48	20.0	5.75x5.75x10.96	3.00	2.38	1.75	1.13	.50	0	24.0
TA-0040-V	1/4	115/50/60/1	Split Phase	48	24.0	5.81x5.75x9.56	4.00	3.23	2.46	1.69	.92	.15	26.0
TA-0075-V	1/2	115/230/60/1	Capacitor Start	56	42.0	6.75x6.50x13.70	7.20	5.82	4.43	3.05	1.66	.28	26.0
TA-0100-V	3/4	115/230/60/1	Capacitor Start	56	44.0	6.75x6.50x13.95	10.00	8.08	6.15	4.73	2.31	.38	26.0
TA-0170-V	1	115/230/60/1	Capacitor Start	Close Coupled Rotary	71.0	7.50x8.50x21.25	17.00	13.85	10.70	7.56	4.41	1.26	27.0
TA-0210-V	1½	115/230/60/1	Capacitor Start, Capacitor Run	Close Coupled Rotary	84.0	7.50x8.50x21.25	21.00	17.11	13.22	9.33	5.41	1.56	27.0

FIGURE 12-23. Technical data for Thomas TASKAIR vane pumps.

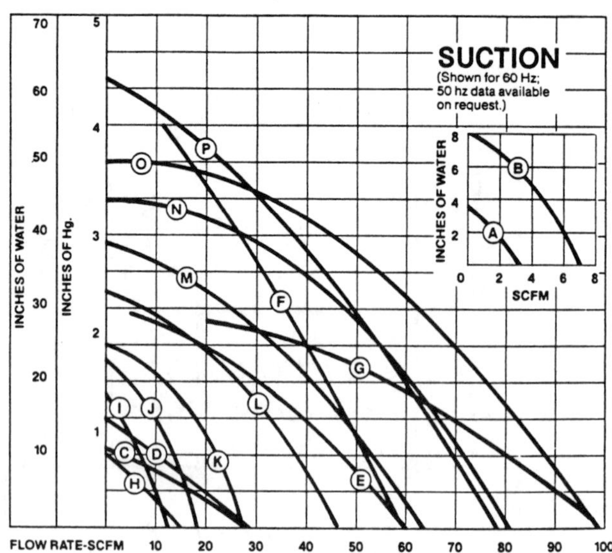

FIGURE 12-25. Vacuum-air flow data for EG&G Rotron blowers. A = Model SE; B = SE-DC; C = SL1P; D = SL1S; E = SL2P; F = SL4P; G = SL5P; H = RDC; I = DR068; J = DR083; K = DR101; L = DR202; M = DR303; N = DR353; O = DR404; P = DR513.

TD DESIGN
Straight-through vacuum passage allows material to pass directly through Vacuum Transducer with no reduction of vacuum flow. Compressed air enters through annular orifice.

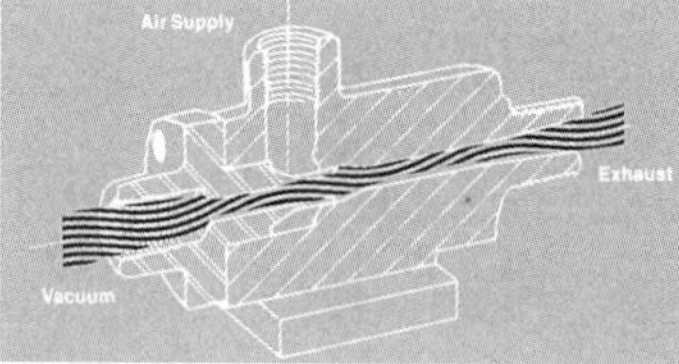

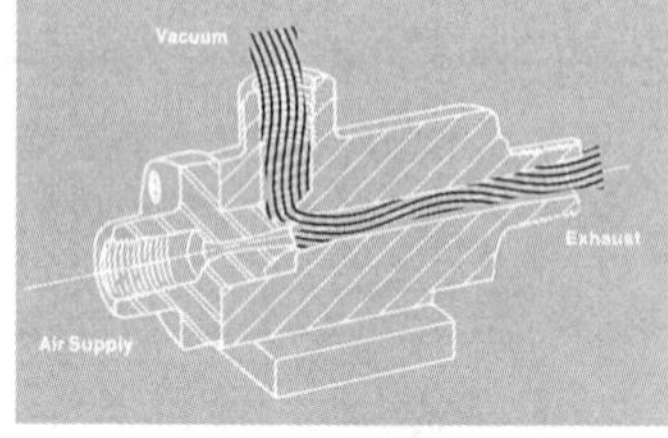

AV DESIGN
Vacuum passage has 90° change of direction. Compressed air flows directly through circular orifice into venturi section. AV design converts compressed air to vacuum more efficiently than TD design. No solid material should pass through Vacuum Transducer.

FIGURE 12-26. Schematic diagram of Air-Vac transducers.

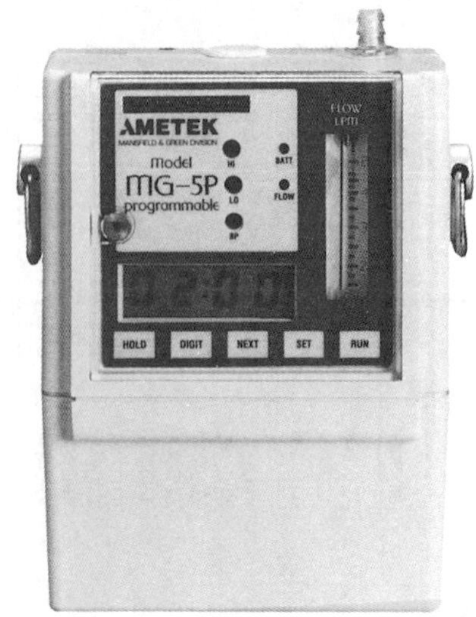

FIGURE 12-27. Ametek MG-5P personal air sampler.

See page 237 for Figure 12-24.

MODELS	MOTOR TYPE[1]	PHASE	VOLTAGES					WEIGHT (lbs.)	HORSEPOWER (see footnotes below)																							PART NUMBER "S" UNIT	PART NUMBER "A" UNIT	MAXIMUM FLOW (SCFM)	MAXIMUM PRESS. (IWG) "S" UNITS[5]	MAXIMUM VAC. (Hg) "S" UNITS[5]	PERFORMANCE CURVE INDEX
			115V, 50hz 115V, 60hz	220V, 50hz 208-230V, 60hz	220V, 50hz 200-230V, 60hz	380V, 50hz 460V, 60hz	380-415V, 50hz 460V, 60hz		1/60	1/16	1/9	1/8	1/6	1/4	1/3	1/2	3/4	1	1½	2	2½	3	4	5	7½	10	15	20	25	30	40						
MINISPIRAL BLOWERS																																					
SE-B21		1	A	F					X																								036258	3.2	3.0	.22	A
SPIRAL BLOWERS																																					
SL1P_	TE[2]	1	S	F				22			X																					036005					
	TE	3			A			22			X																						036007	29	12	.73	B
SL1S_	TE	1	S	F				22					X																			036006					
	TE	3			A			22					X																				036008	29	17	1.0	C
SL2P_	TE	1	S	A				27								X																036000	036013				
	TE	3			A	F	F	23								X																	036020	58	35	2.1	D
SL4P_	TE	1	S	A				43									X															036009	036027				
	TE	3			A	F	F	37									X																036021	61	62	3.7	E
SL5P_	TE	1	S	A				43									X															036010	036261				
	TE	3			A	F	F	37									X																036022	100	33	2.1	F
SL6P_	TE[2]	1	S	F				43							X																	036011		100	62	3.7	E/F
	TE	3			A	F	F	37							X																		036023				
DR XOX BLOWERS																																					
DR068_	TEFC	1		115/230				14		S																						037143					
	TEFC	3		230/460				14		S																						037144		12	17	17	G
DR083_	TEFC	1		115/230				15				S																				036862					
	TEFC	3		230/460				15				S																				037164		18	24	23	H
DR101_	TEFC	1		115/230				27						S	F																	036244					
	TEFC	3		230/460				25						A	F																		036245	28	27	1.8	I
	TEFC	3		575				25						A	F																		036672				
DR202_	TEFC	1		115/230				32							S																	037066					
	TEFC	3		230/460				29							A																		037067	48	33	2.3	J
	TEFC	3		575				29							A																		036373				
DR303_	TEFC	1		115/230				36							F	F	S															036233					
	TEFC	3		208-230/460				31							F	F	A																036234	63	40	3.0	K
	TEFC	3		575				31							F	F	A																036372				
DR353_	TEFC	1		115/230				56								F	S															037147					
	XP	1		115/230				56								F	A																037149	88	48	43	
	TEFC	3		230/460				56								F	S															037148		88	50	45	L
	XP	3		230/460				56								F	A																037150				
	TEFC	3		575				56								F	A																037146				
DR404_	TEFC	1		115/230				75										S	F	F	F	F										037062					
	XP	1		115/230				89										A	F	F													037058				
	TEFC	3		208-230/460				61										S	F	F	F	F	F									037063		98	56	3.6	M
	TEFC	3		575				61										A	F	F	F	F	F										036267				
	XP[3]	3		230/460				76										A		F		F											037059				
DR513_	TEFC	1		115/230				78											S													037209					
	TEFC	3		230/460				78											S													037217		80	75	60	N
DR BLOWERS																																					
DR312_	XP	1		115[4]				36							A																		037048	48	26	1.7	O
DR313_	XP	1		115[4]				45								A																	037047	53	50	3.1	P
DR4_	TEFC	1		115/230				68											S													036104					
	XP	1		115/230				103											A														036108				
	TEFC	3		208-230/460				56											S													036103		100	74	5.9	Q
	TEFC	3		575				56											A														036109				
	XP[3]	3		230/460				79											A														036106				

1. All 3 ph motors are factory tested and certified to operate on 200-230/460 VAC-3 ph-60 Hz and 220-240/380-415 VAC-3 ph-50 Hz. All 1 ph motors are factory tested and certified to operate on 115/230 VAC-1 ph-60 Hz and 220-240 VAC-1 ph-50 Hz.
2. Spiral motors are Rotron manufactured, totally enclosed within the blower body but open to the gas stream.
3. Three phase explosion proof motors are shown as 230/460 volt. They are also available in 575 volt.
4. DR3 – are shown in 115V, 1 phase. They are available by special order in many other voltages.
5. Performance shown for "A" units when no "S" unit is listed.

S. Cataloged, stocked by distributors
A. Cataloged, available from but not stocked by distributors
F. Non-cataloged, available from factory
X. Denotes Spiral blower horsepower. There are no optional horsepowers in Spiral models.

FIGURE 12-24. Technical data for EG&G Rotron blowers.

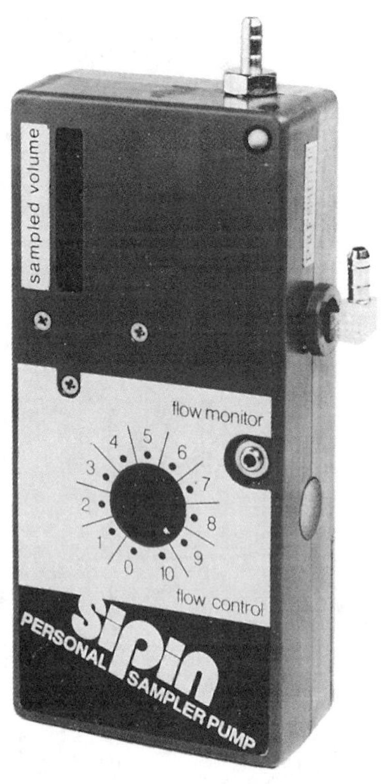

FIGURE 12-28. Sipin SP-13 personal air sampler.

FIGURE 12-30. BGI Personal Sampler AFC 123.

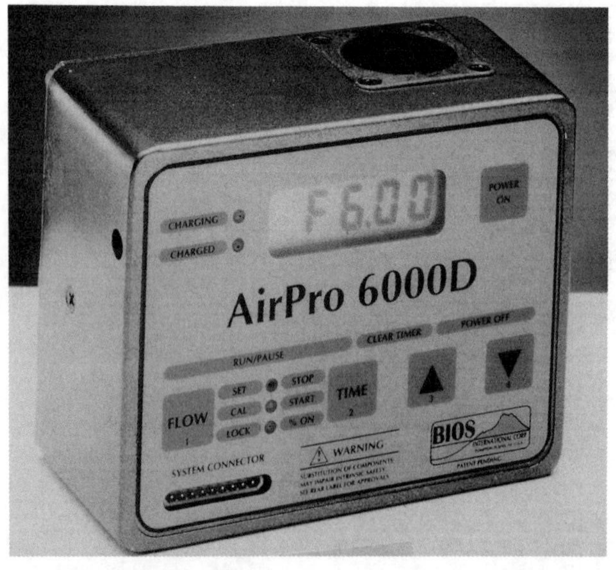

FIGURE 12-29. BIOS AirPro 6000 personal air sampler.

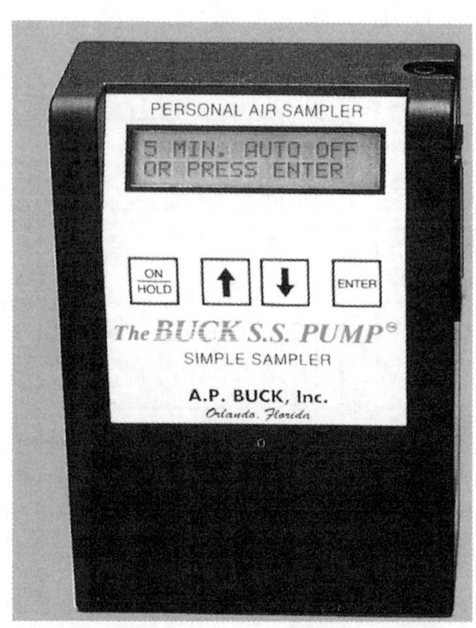

FIGURE 12-31. BUCK Personal Sampler SS.

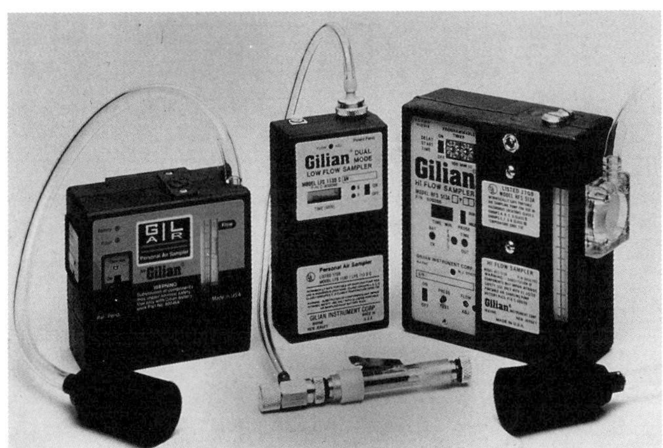

FIGURE 12-32. Gilian GilAir-3 personal air sampler.

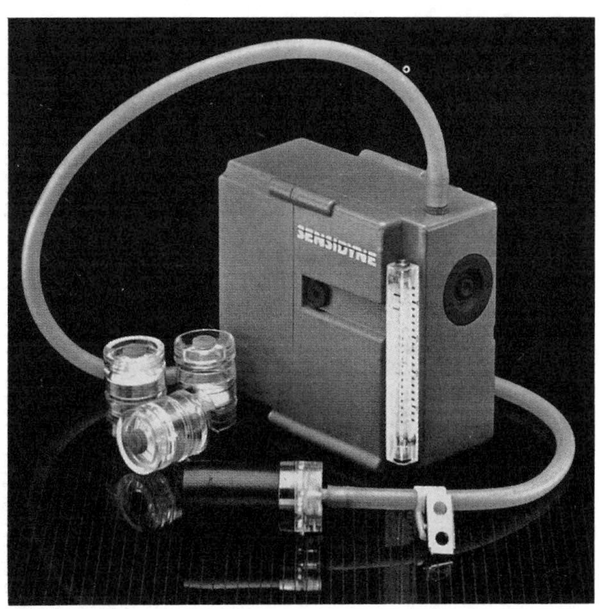

FIGURE 12-34. Sensidyne Model BDX74 personal air sampler and filter attachment.

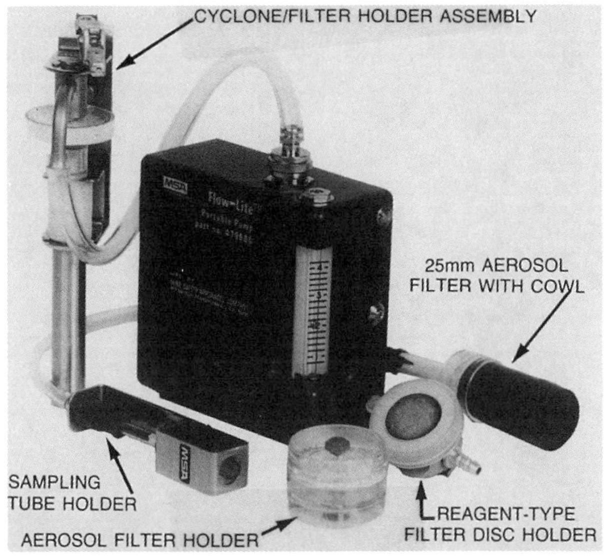

FIGURE 12-33. MSA Flow-Lite personal air sampler with various sampling attachments.

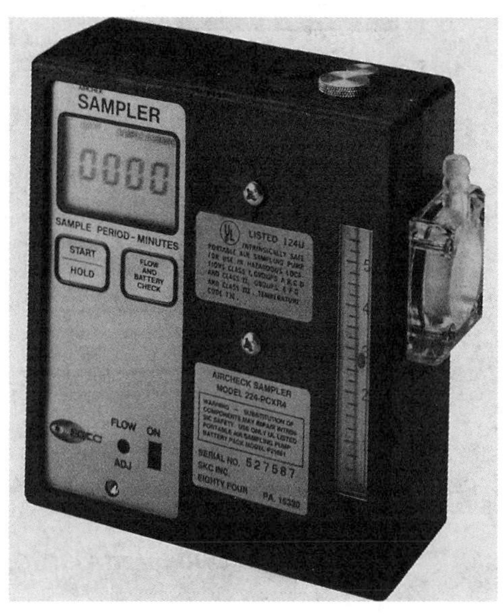

FIGURE 12-35. SKC Personal Sampler.

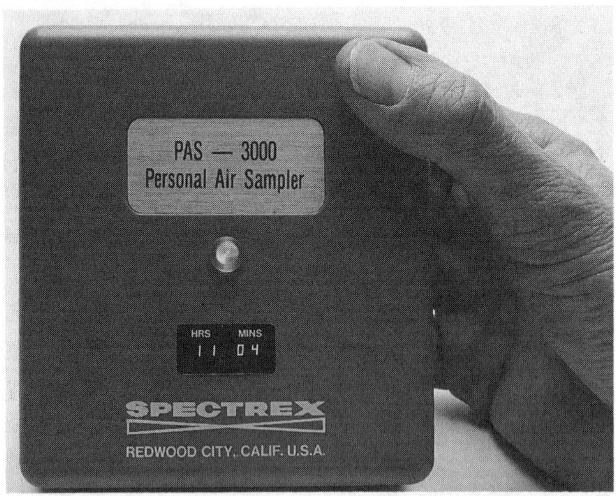

FIGURE 12-36. Spectrex PAS-3000, Model II personal air sampler.

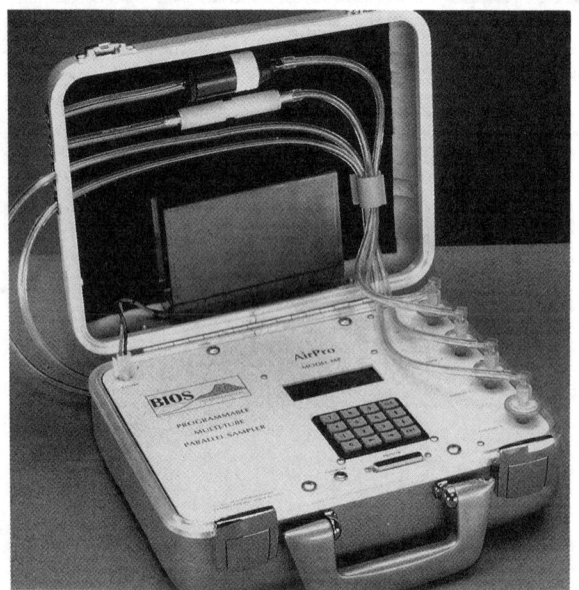

FIGURE 12-37. BIOS AirPro series area sampler.

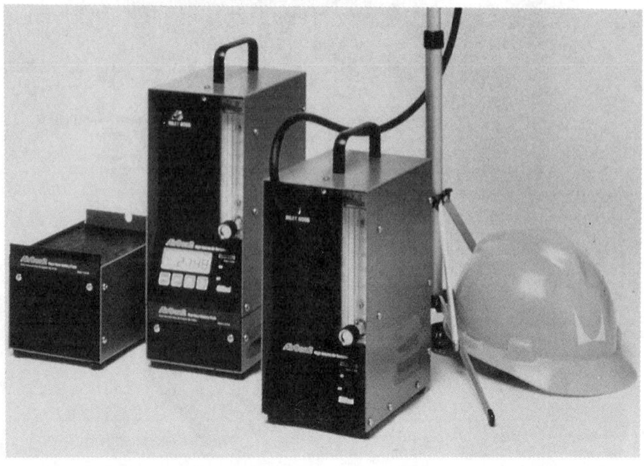

FIGURE 12-38. Gilian AirCon-2 Air Sampling System.

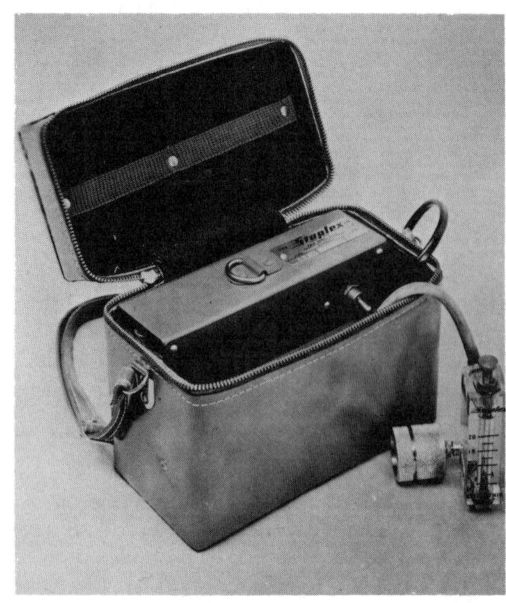

FIGURE 12-39. Staplex Model BN/BS battery-powered, low-volume air sampler.

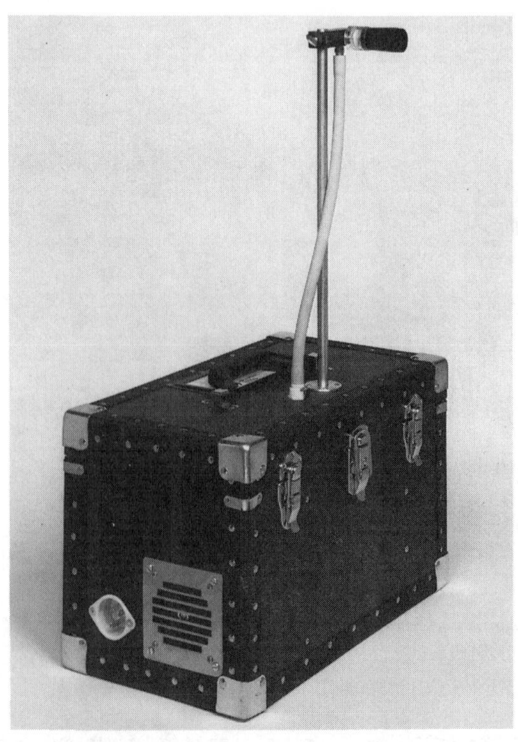

FIGURE 12-40. BGI Model ASB-II-S low-volume air sampler.

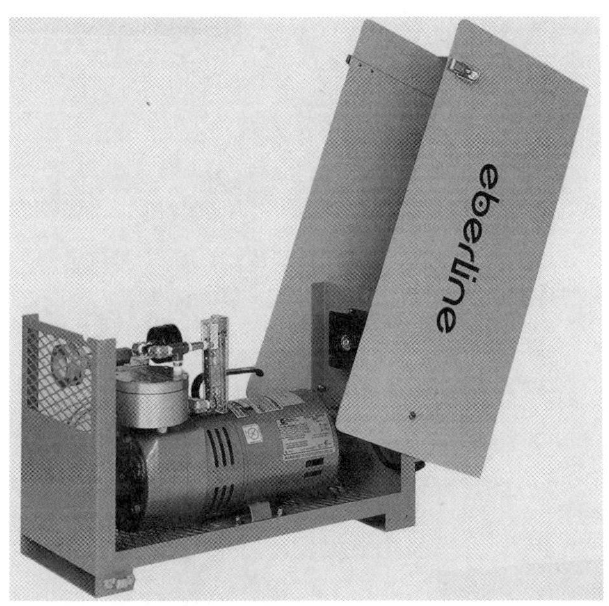

FIGURE 12-41. Eberline Model RAS-2 Environmental Air Sampler.

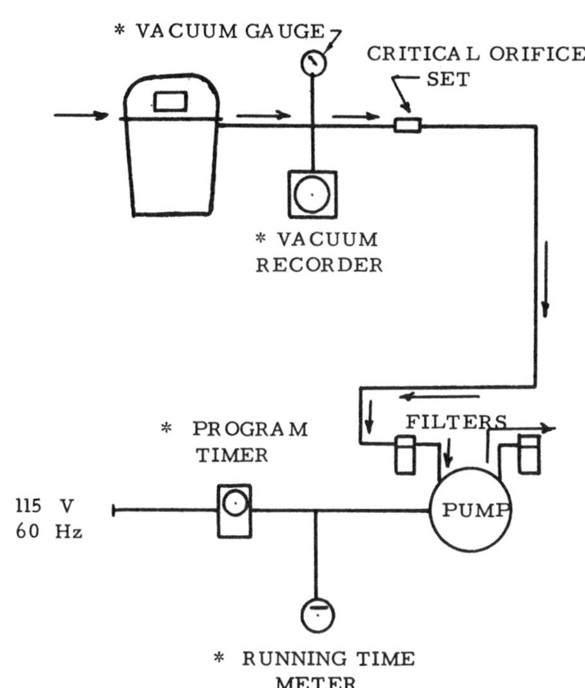

FIGURE 12-43. Flow diagram for Graseby Andersen Universal Sampler.

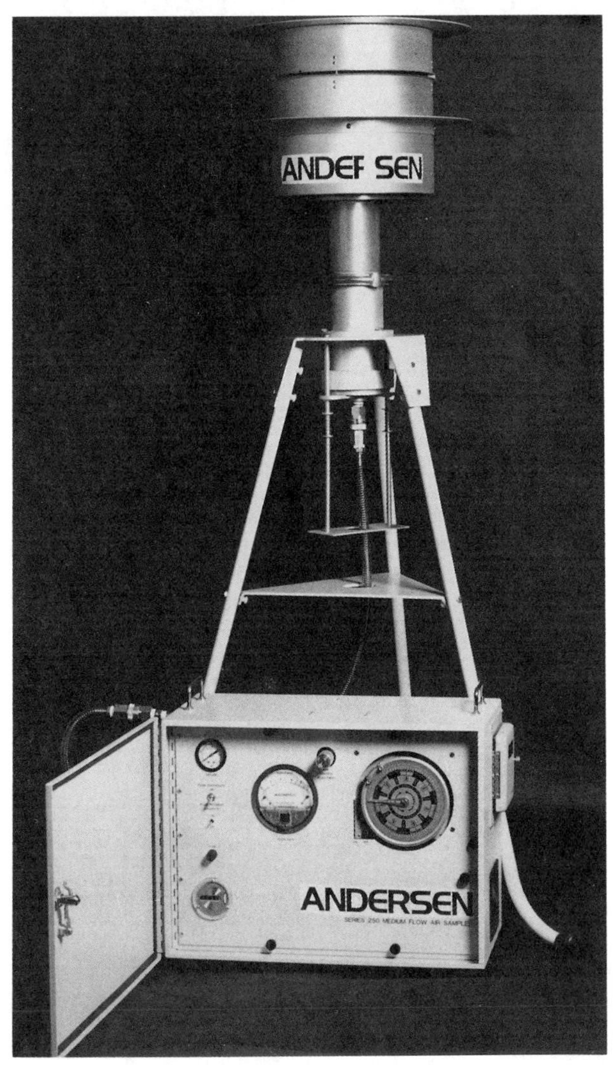

FIGURE 12-42. Graseby Andersen PM10 Medium Flow Sampler.

FIGURE 12-44. Midwest Environics Ultra Sampler.

FIGURE 12-45. Nuclear Associates Low-Volume Air Sampler.

FIGURE 12-47. Staplex Model VM-2 low-volume air sampler.

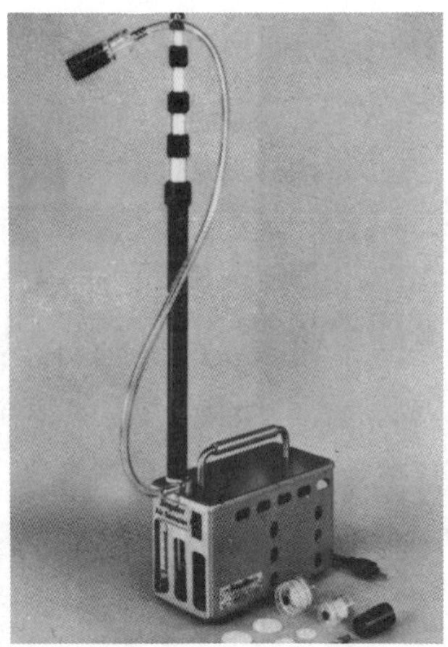

FIGURE 12-46. Staplex Model VM-3 low-volume air sampler.

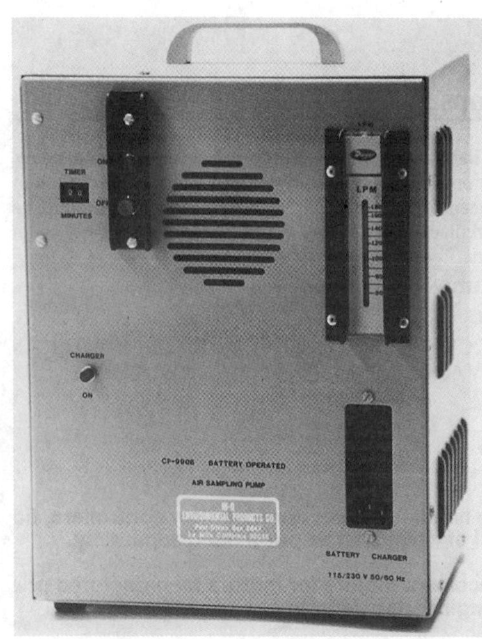

FIGURE 12-48. Hi-Q Model CF-990B sampler.

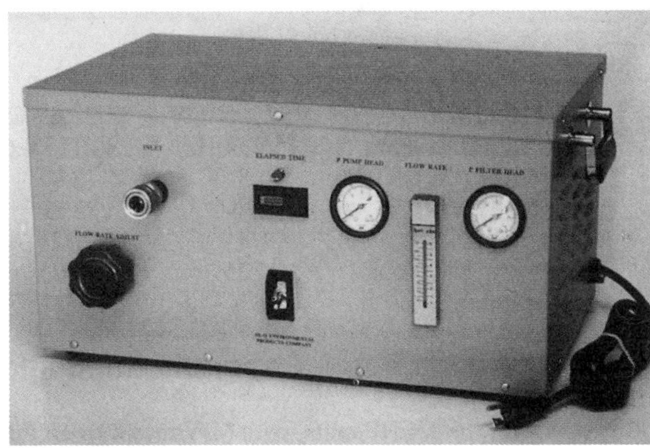

FIGURE 12-49. Hi-Q Model CMP23 sampler.

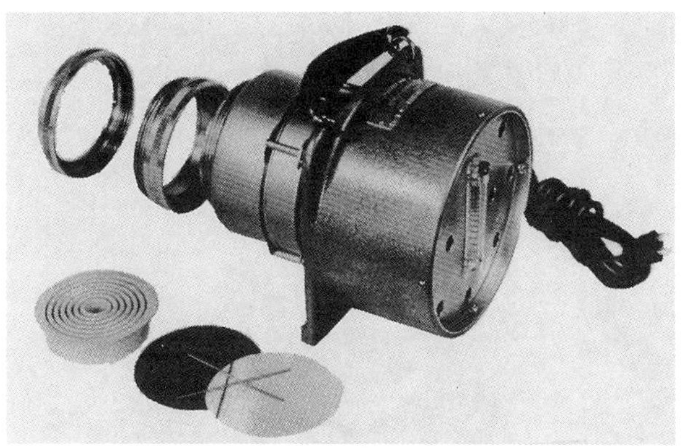

FIGURE 12-50. Staplex TFIA sampler.

FIGURE 12-51. Wedding Intermediate-Volume Sampler.

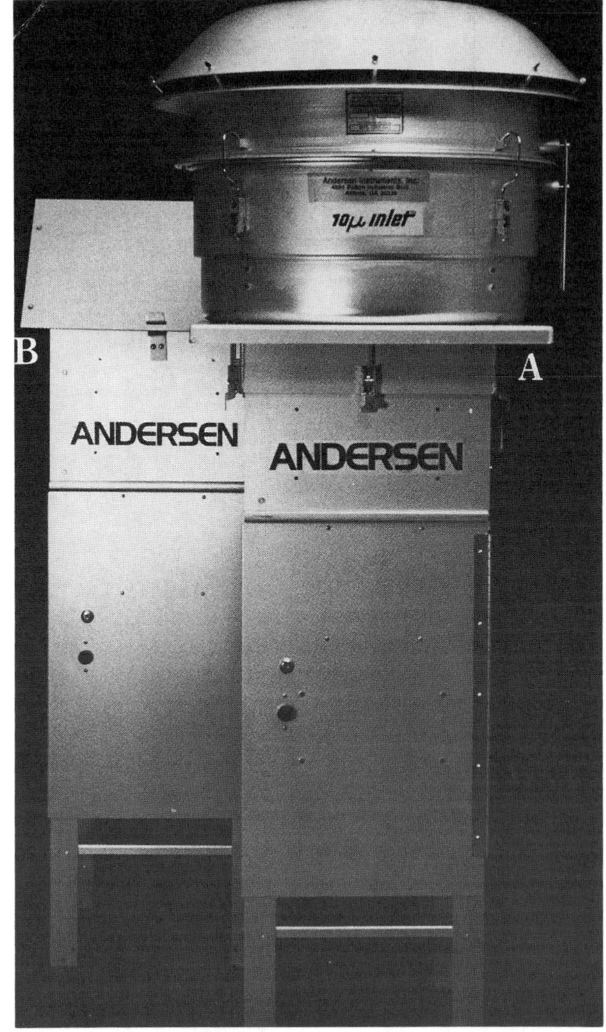

FIGURE 12-52. Graseby Andersen (A) PM-10 High Volume Sampler and (B) TSP High Volume Sampler.

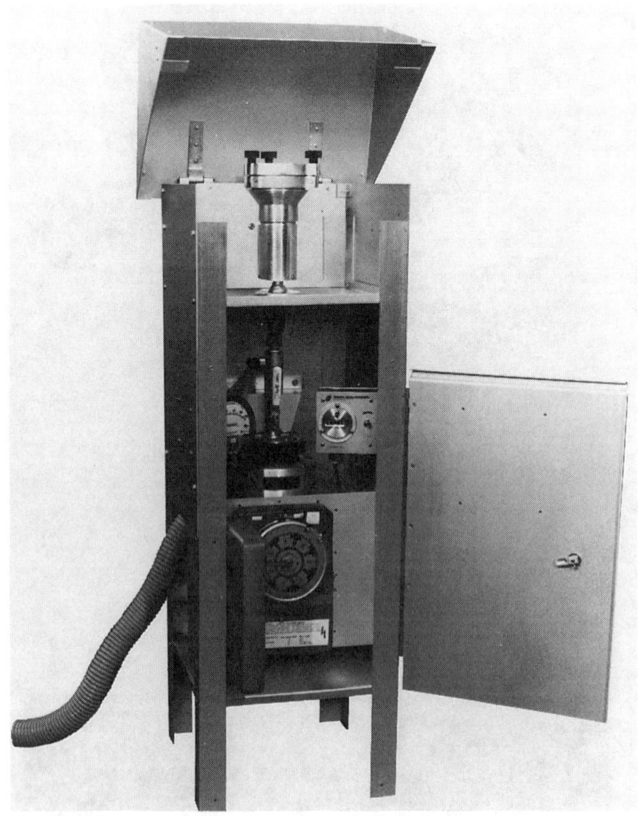

FIGURE 12-53. Graseby Andersen Model PS-1 PUF sampler.

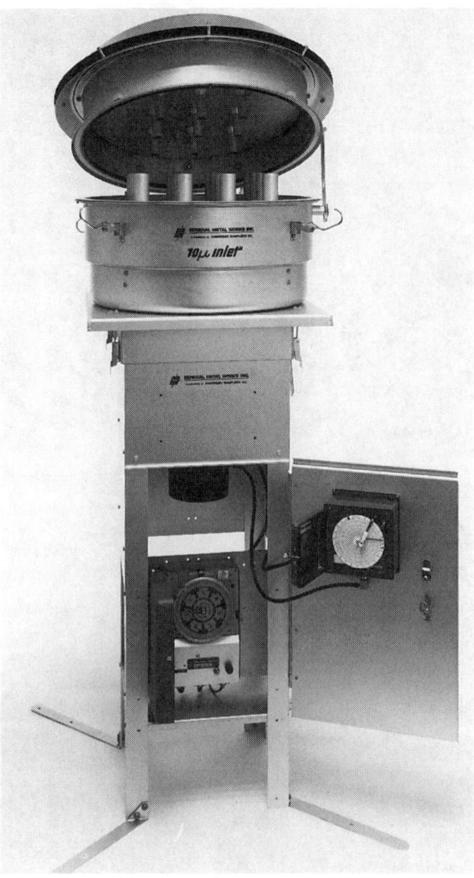

FIGURE 12-54. General Metal Works Model ACCU-Vol IP-10 high volume sampler.

FIGURE 12-55. Wedding Critical Flow High-Volume Sampler.

Chapter 13

Filters and Filter Holders

Morton Lippmann, Ph.D.
Nelson Institute of Environmental Medicine, New York University Medical Center, Tuxedo, New York

CONTENTS

Introduction

Filtration is the most widely used technique for aerosol sampling, primarily because of its low cost and simplicity. The samples obtained usually occupy a relatively small volume and may often be stored for subsequent analysis without deterioration. By appropriate choice of air mover (see Chapter 12), filter medium, and filter size, almost any sample quantity desired can be collected in a given sampling interval.

Figure 13-1 is a schematic representation of the elements of a filter sampling system. The component parts may include all or some of the following: sampling probe, filter holder, filter, pressure sensor, flowmeter, air mover, and a means of regulating the flow. A probe is needed only when sampling large particles from a moving stream, e.g., a duct or stack. For these applications, careful attention must be given to the probe's shape, size, and orientation with respect to the flowing stream in order to obtain representative samples. The factors affecting the entry of large particles into a sampling tube, i.e., particle inertia, gravity, flow convergence, and the inequality of ambient wind and suction velocity, have been critically evaluated by Davies.[1] They are also discussed in detail in Chapter 21. Errors can also arise from particle deposition onto the surfaces of plastic inlet probes due to electrostatic deposition, or to deposition between the probe inlet and the filter due to impaction at the bends and turbulent diffusion.[2]

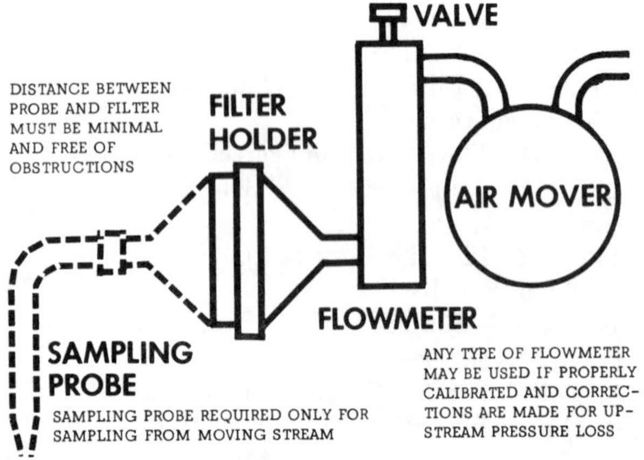

FIGURE 13-1. Elements of a filter sampling system.

The filter should be upstream of everything in the system but the nozzle, so that any dirt in the system, manometer liquid, or pump oil will not be carried accidentally onto it. The filter should be as close as possible to the sampling point, and all sampling lines must be free of contamination and obstructions.

The filter holder, designed for the specific filter size used, must provide a positive seal at the edge. A screen or other mechanical support may be required to prevent rupture or displacement of the filter in service. An in-line filter holder should also include a gradual expansion from the inlet to the filter. With a properly designed holder, the air velocity will be uniform across the cross section of the filter holder. Uniform flow distribution is especially desirable when analyses are to be performed directly on the filter, or where only a portion of the filter will be analyzed, so that the remainder can be archived or used for replicate analyses or analyses by other techniques.

The accurate measurement of either flow rate and sampling time or sample volume is as important as the measurement of sample quantity because aerosol concentration is determined by the ratio of sampled quantity to sampled volume. Unfortunately, air volume measurements are often inaccurate (see Chapter 7). When the volumetric capacity of the air mover is highly pressure dependent, as it is for turbine blowers, ejectors, and some other types of air movers, the flow cannot be metered by any technique that introduces a significant pressure drop itself. This precludes the use of most meters that require the passage of the full volume through them and limits the choice to low resistance flowmeters. Low resistance flowmeters include bypass meters, which measure the flow rate of a small volume fraction of the sampled air, and meters utilizing very sensitive measurements of vane displacement or pressure drop. These types of meters can provide sufficiently accurate measurements, but they often require more careful maintenance and more frequent calibration and adjustment than they are likely to receive in field use.

Most flowmeters are calibrated at atmospheric pressure, and many require pressure corrections when used at other pressures. Such corrections must be based on the static pressure measured at the inlet of the flowmeter. The flowmeter should be downstream of the filter to preclude the possibility of sample losses within it. It will, therefore, be metering air at a pressure below atmospheric, due to the pressure drop across the filter. Furthermore, if the filter resistance increases with loading, as is often the case, the pressure correction will not be a constant factor. Chapter 7 provides a comprehensive discussion of air flow calibration.

If the sampling flow rate is to be controlled by a throttling valve, this valve should be downstream of the flowmeter to avoid adding to the pressure correction for the flowmeter. Flow rate adjustments can be made either with a throttling valve or by speed control of the air mover's motor, and they can be either manual or automatic. Automatic control requires pressure or flow transducers and appropriate feedback and control circuitry.

The discussion that follows is designed to provide the background necessary for the proper selection of filters for particular applications. Filtration theory is outlined, the various kinds of commercial filter media used for air sampling are described, and the criteria that limit the selection for various sampling situations are discussed.

Filtration Theory

Types and Structures of Filters

All filters are porous structures with definable external dimensions such as thickness and cross section normal to fluid flow. They differ considerably in terms of flow pathways, flow rates, and residence times, and these factors are strongly influenced by their structure. One of the oldest and most common filter types for air sampling is the fibrous filter, which is comprised of a mat of cellulose, glass, quartz, asbestos, or plastic fibers in random orientation within the plane of the filter sheet. Another type of filter is the granular bed, in which solid granules are packed into a definable sheet or bed. In granular bed filters used in air sampling, the granules are usually sintered to the point where they form a relatively rigid mechanical structure. Granules of glass and aluminum oxide are frequently sintered in the form of a thimble for high-temperature stack sampling. Thin sintered beds of silver granules are used in disc form for a variety of applications and are generally known as silver membranes.

The term membrane filter was originally applied to discs of a cellulose ester gel having interconnected pores of uniform size. First and Silverman[3] described various applications of such filters for air sampling in 1953. Gel-type membrane filters are now also available in polyvinyl chloride (PVC), nylon, and other plastics. Whereas the method of production is quite different from those used to make fibrous filters or granular beds, the flow pathways of all three types of structures are quite similar in terms of the tortuosity of the air flow pathways. The Nuclepore® filter, a polycarbonate pore filter, is generally considered to be a membrane filter, but it has a radically different structure, i.e., a series of nearly parallel straight-through holes. It is made by exposing a thin sheet (approx. 10 µm) of polycarbonate plastic to a flux of neutrons from a nuclear reactor and then chemically etching the neutron tracks. Simplified versions of the various filter structures are illustrated in Figure 13-2.

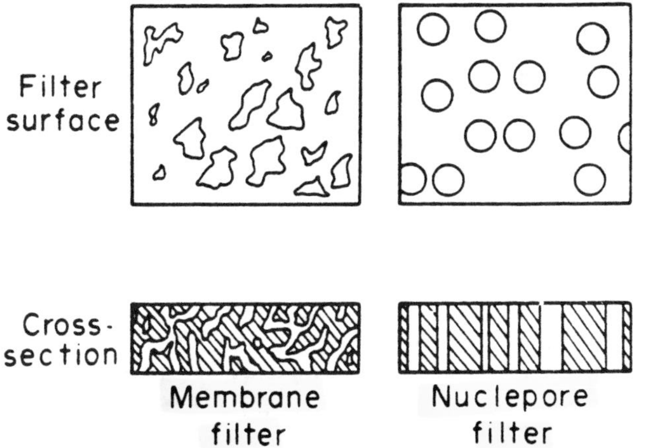

FIGURE 13-2. Surface and section views of porous gel-type membrane filter and Nuclepore (polycarbonate pore) filter.

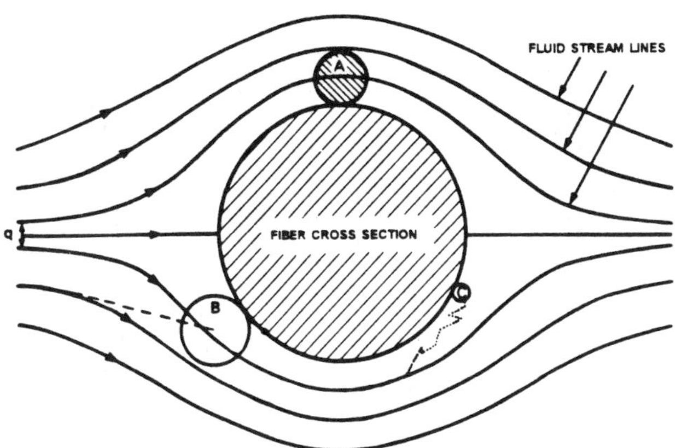

FIGURE 13-3. Flow pattern around a filter fiber and particle capture mechanisms: Particle A – direction interception; Particle B – inertial impaction; Particle C – diffusional deposition.

Flow Fields and Collection Mechanisms

Theoretical models of particle filtration have been developed using simplified flow field and particle motion in the vicinity of a single isolated cylindrical fiber. Extension of the theory to a filter mat depends upon taking proper account of the influence of adjacent fibers on the flow field.[4–6] The fluid motion and particle motion in the vicinity of a cylindrical fiber are illustrated in Figure 13-3. The corresponding flow fields around the pores in a polycarbonate pore filter are illustrated in Figure 13-4.

Filters remove particles from a gas stream by a number of mechanisms. These mechanisms include direct interception, inertial deposition, diffusional deposition, electrical attraction, and gravitational attraction. The mechanisms that predominate in a given case will depend on the flow rate, the structure of the filter, and the nature of the aerosol.

Interception occurs when the radius of a particle moving along a gas streamline is greater than the distance from the streamline to the surface. This mechanism is important only when the ratio of the particle size to the void or pore size of the filter is relatively large.

Inertial collection results from a change in direction of the gas flow. The particles, due to their relatively greater inertia, tend to remain on their original course and strike a surface. Capture is favored by high gas velocities and dense fiber packing. The factors affecting inertial deposition in a jet impactor are discussed at greater length in Chapter 14. The operation of the inertial mechanism in a variety of commercially available fibrous filters was demonstrated experimentally

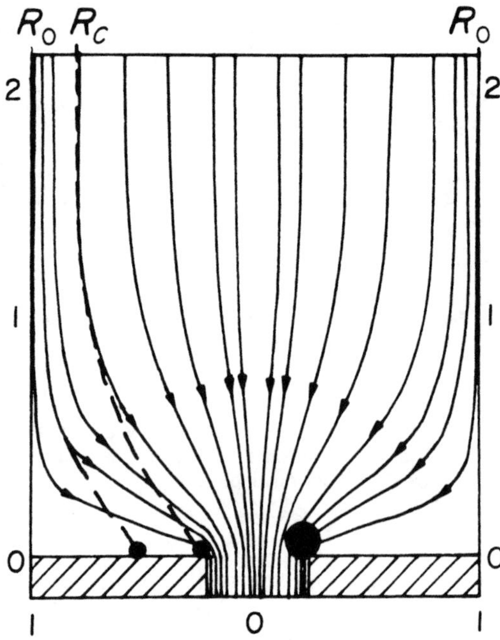

FIGURE 13-4. Streamlines for flow approaching a polycarbonate pore filter with porosity 0.05. The interception, impaction, and diffusion mechanisms are shown.

by Ramskill and Anderson.[7]

Diffusion is most effective for small particles at low flow rates. It depends on the existence of a concentration gradient. Particles diffuse to the surfaces of the fibers, where the concentration is zero. Diffusion is favored by low gas velocities and high concentration gradients. The root-mean-square displacement of the particles, and hence the collection efficiency, increases with decreasing particle size down to about 10 nm. Below this size, there is particle rebound from the filter surface, as discussed by Wang and Kaspar.[8]

Kirsch and Zhulanov[9] tested the performance of high efficiency fibrous filters made of glass and polymeric polydisperse fibers. They found good agreement with the theory proposed earlier by Kirsch, Stechkina, and Fuchs.[6]

Gentry *et al.*[10] studied the diffusional deposition of ultrafine aerosols on polycarbonate pore filters. They found that particles <0.03 µm were collected by diffusion on the upstream surface of the filter and that the efficiency was only slightly higher than the values predicted by theory. On the other hand, for particles of 0.04 to 0.10 µm, the particles were collected primarily around the rims of the pores, and the efficiencies were much higher than those predicted by theory.

Electrical forces may contribute greatly to particle collection efficiency if the filter or the aerosol has a static charge. Lundgren and Whitby[11] showed that image forces, i.e., the forces between a charged particle and its electrical image in a neutral fiber, can strongly influence particle collection. The factors controlling particle deposition on a filter suspended in a uniform electric field and the influence of such a field on the deposition of both charged and uncharged particles were described by Zebel.[12] Unfortunately, the data needed to predict the effect of electrostatic charges on the collection efficiency of sampling filters are seldom available.

Gravitational forces may usually be neglected when considering filter sampling. The settling velocities of airborne particles of hygienic significance are too low, and the horizontal components of the surface areas in the filters are too small, for gravitational attraction to have any significant effect on particle collection efficiency unless the face velocity through the filter is very low, e.g., <5 cm/s.

Minimum Efficiencies and Most Penetrating Particle Sizes

Because a variety of collection mechanisms are involved in filtration, it is not surprising that, for a given aerosol and a given filter, the collection efficiency varies with face velocity and particle size. The efficiency of a given filter for a given particle size could be high at low flows, due primarily to the effects of diffusion. With increasing velocity, it could first fall off and then, with still higher velocities, begin to rise because of increased inertial deposition. This pattern has been observed in several experimental penetration tests[13,14] and is illustrated in Figures 13-5 and 13-6. At very high velocities, the retention could decrease because of re-entrainment. Additional data showing these effects are presented in Table 13-1.

Filter retention by the interception and diffusion mechanisms is also strongly influenced by particle size, as illustrated in Figure 13-7. This figure presents experimental data from Spurny *et al.*[15] for polycarbonate pore (Nuclepore) filters with 5-µm-diameter pores at a face velocity of 5 cm/s. Figure 13-8, from Liu and Lee,[16] shows collection efficiency as a function of particle size for 1-µm Nuclepore filters at three different face velocities. Polycarbonate pore filters have a very different structure than other types of filters, as has been discussed, and exhibit a more extreme size dependence. Rimberg[13] has demonstrated experimentally that for fibrous filters, the size at which maximum penetration occurs increases with decreasing face velocity.

The theoretical basis for predicting the minimum collection efficiency and most penetrating particle sizes for fibrous filters was addressed by Lee and Liu.[17] They developed equations for such predictions, which compared favorably with experimental filter efficiency data. Lee[18] extended his analysis of minimum efficiency and most penetrating particle size to granular bed filters. Predictive theories for deposition in such

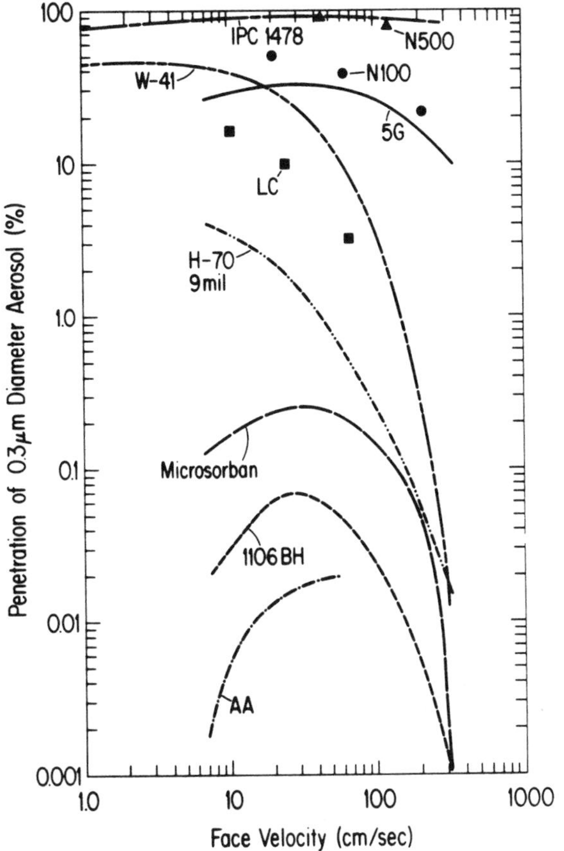

FIGURE 13-5. Effect of face velocity on the penetration of 0.3-μm-diameter particles through various air sampling filter media—based on data reported by Lockhart *et al.*,[14] Rimberg,[13] and Liu and Lee.[16]

filters were also developed by Schmidt *et al.*[19] and Fichman *et al.*[20]

Spurny[21] investigated the collection efficiencies of membrane and polycarbonate pore filters for aerosols of chrysotile asbestos. For Millipore membrane filters with 8-μm pores, the collection efficiency at a face velocity of 3.5 cm/s fell from 100% for fibers >5 μm in length to 75% for fibers of 2 μm in length and to 25% for fibers approximately 0.5 μm in length. For polycarbonate pore filters with pore diameters of 0.2, 0.4, and 0.8 μm, collection efficiencies began to drop for fiber lengths <3 μm and fiber diameters <0.2 μm. For 0.2-μm pores, the efficiencies did not drop below approximately 80%, whereas for 0.8-μm pores, the efficiencies dropped to near zero for fiber lengths below 0.5 μm and diameters below 0.05 μm.

Forces of Adhesion and Re-entrainment

The collection mechanisms discussed above act to arrest the motion of the particles in a gas stream as the gas flows through the voids of a filter. The particles removed from the gas stream are then subject to forces of adhesion. If the forces of adhesion on a particle are greater than the forces that tend to push the particle free, then that particle is "collected" and will be available for analysis. However, the forces exerted on the particle by the flowing gas stream may be greater than the forces of adhesion, resulting in re-entrainment of the particle. At present, it is at least as difficult to

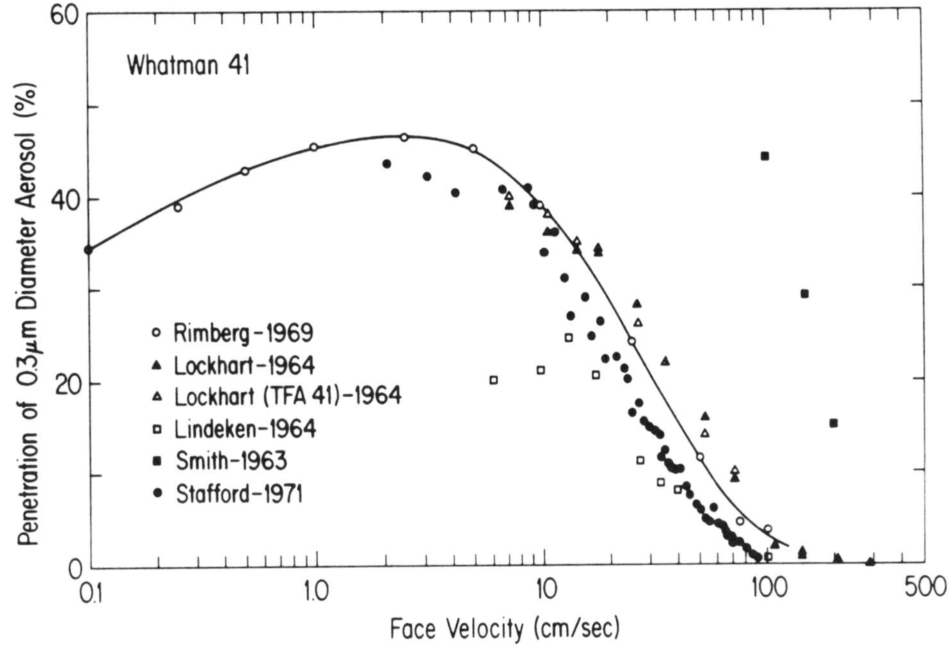

FIGURE 13-6. Effect of face velocity on the penetration of 0.3-μm-diameter particles through Whatman 41 filters—based on data reported by various investigators.

TABLE 13-1. Flow Rate and Collection Efficiency Characteristics of Selected Air Filter Media[A]

Filter Type	Filter	mm Hg Pressure Drop (53)	mm Hg Pressure Drop (106)	mm Hg Pressure Drop (211)	Percent Penetration of 0.3 μm DOP[B] (26.7)	Percent Penetration of 0.3 μm DOP[B] (53)	Percent Penetration of 0.3 μm DOP[B] (106)	Percent Penetration of 0.3 μm DOP[B] (211)	Flow Reduction Due to Loading[C] %/m³/cm²
		Characteristics at Indicated Face Velocities (cm/sec)							
Cellulose	Whatman 1	86	175	350	7	0.95	0.061	0.001	17.9
	41	36	72	146	28	16	2	0.30	5.0
	541	30	61	123	56	40	22	9	10.4
Glass	MSA 1106BH	30	61	120	0.068	0.048	0.022	0.005	0.43
	Gelman A	33	65	129	0.019	0.018	0.011	0.001	0.50
	E	28	57	114	0.036	0.030	0.014	0.004	0.53
	Whatman 934AH	37	74	150	0.010	0.006	0.003	0.001	0.47
	Whatman GF/A	29	60	118	0.018	0.015	0.008	0.001	0.37
Membrane	Millipore AA (0.8 μ)	142	285	570	0.015	0.020	—	—	1.6

[A]Data extracted from NRL Report No. 6054.[14]
[B]DOP = Di(2-ethylhexyl) phthalate.
[C]Normalized to the dust loading in the atmosphere on an "average" summer day (Washington, DC, 1964).

predict forces of adhesion from theoretical considerations as it is to predict the effectiveness of the collection mechanisms. One reason is that it is usually not possible to determine whether particles that penetrate a filter were blown off after collection because of inadequate adhesion, or whether they underwent elastic rebound upon initial contact with the filter surface. This question was theoretically and experimentally investigated by Loffler.[22] He concluded that the measured forces of adhesion were in good agreement with the Van der Waals forces calculated theoretically and that the flow velocity required for blowing collected particles off fibers is much higher than that normally used in air filtration. An increase in particle penetration with increasing velocity will usually be due to increased rebound or to the resuspension of particle flocs.

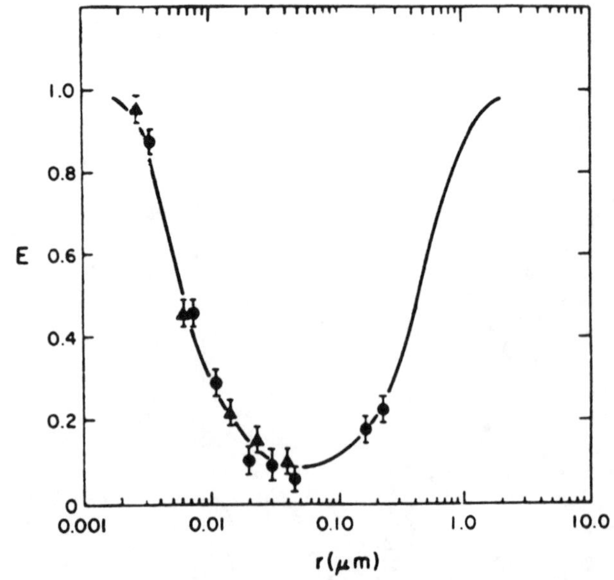

FIGURE 13-7. Effect of particle radius (r) on fraction collected (E) for a Nuclepore filter with 5-μm-diameter pores at a face velocity of 5 cm/s. Experimental data are shown for a selenium aerosol (•) and a pyrophosphoric acid aerosol (s). The line is computed from filtration theory. (Reprinted from *Environ. Sci. Technol.* 3:463, 1969; courtesy American Chemical Society.)

Commercial Filter Media

Filter media of many different types and with many different properties have been designed for, or adapted to, air sampling requirements. For purposes of discussion, they have been divided into groups determined by their composition. Air flow resistance and collection efficiency characteristics of some commonly used filters are tabulated in Table 13-1. (Also see Table 13-I-1 at the end of this chapter which summarizes the physical characteristics of commercially available filter media, based on vendor supplied or approved data.) These

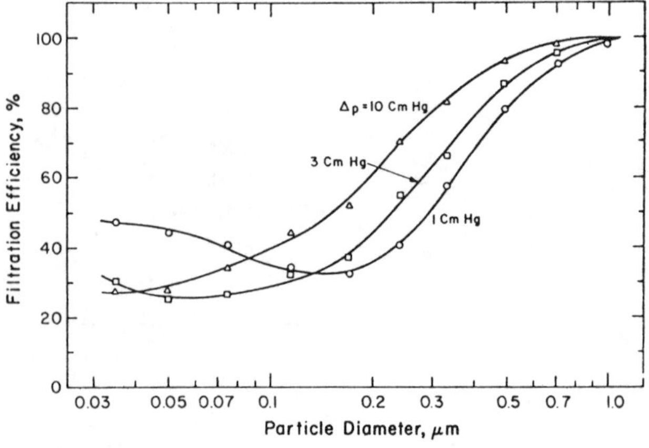

FIGURE 13-8. Efficiency of 1.0-μm polycarbonate pore filter.

media have been subdivided on the basis of their composition and/or structure.

Cellulose Fiber Filters

Most cellulose fiber filters are used widely by analytical chemists for liquid–solid separations. They are made of purified cellulose pulp, are low in ash content, and are usually less than 0.25 mm thick. These filters are relatively inexpensive, are obtainable in an almost unlimited range of sizes, have excellent tensile strength, and show little tendency to fray during handling. Their disadvantages include nonuniformity, resulting in variable flow resistance and collection efficiency, and hygroscopicity, which makes accurate gravimetric determinations either difficult or impossible.

Whatman No. 41 is used for industrial hygiene air sampling. It has the advantages of low cost, high mechanical strength, and high purity typical of these papers and, in addition, has a moderate flow resistance. However, as shown in Figure 13-6, unless used at high face velocity, particle penetration can be significant. Cellulose filter papers also include hardened papers, such as Whatman No. 50, from which collected particles can be removed by washing.

Glass and Quartz Fiber Filters

Glass and quartz fiber filters are, in most cases, more expensive and have poorer mechanical properties than cellulose filters. They also have many advantages, i.e., reduced hygroscopicity, ability to withstand higher temperatures, and higher collection efficiencies at a comparable pressure drop. These properties, combined with the ability to make benzene, water, and nitric acid extracts from particles collected on them, led to the selection of a high-efficiency glass fiber filter as the standard collection medium for high-volume samplers in early air sampling networks. In recent years, quartz fiber filters have replaced glass fiber filters for many applications.

As described by Pate and Tabor,[23] a large number of tests were routinely performed on glass fiber filters. Nondestructive tests, e.g., weighing, gross β-activity, and reflectance, were performed prior to the chemical extractions. Also, portions of the filters were stored untreated for possible use at later times to obtain background data on air concentrations whose need was not anticipated at the time of sample collection.

The types of chemical analyses that can be performed on extracts from the filters are determined by the sensitivity of the analyses and by the magnitude and variability of the extractable filter blank for the particular ion or molecule involved. The filter characteristics are determined by the process variables in at least four production stages, i.e., the production of the glass, the production of glass fiber from the bulk glass, the production of the fiber mat from the glass fiber, and the packaging of the individual filters. For the most widely used filter, for the National Air Sampling Network (NASN), Pate and Tabor[23] described four different types produced sequentially between 1956 and 1962, which differed in softening temperature, chemical composition, and extractability.

One of the determinations, made by NASN, was gross mass of particulate matter by gravimetric analyses. Many other investigators have used the same types of high-volume samplers and filters for routine monitoring and analyzed only for gross mass concentration. The validity of these determinations is suspect. The potential errors arising from inaccurate sample volume determinations, from inadequate temperature and humidity conditioning prior to weighing, and from the limited precision of the weighing procedure are well known; they were discussed by Kramer and Mitchel.[24] An additional potentially serious source of error is the loss of filter fibers drawn through the support screen into the air mover during sample collection. Flash-fired binderfree filters are soft and friable, and the loose fiber content is variable. Some NASN filters returned from the field had lower than tare weights, despite the presence of visible deposit on the filter face. If gross mass concentration analyses are to be performed, other nonhygroscopic filter media, which are both mechanically strong and efficient, should be used, or the filter should include a backing layer to prevent the loss of filter fibers.

All of the preceding discussion applied to glass fiber filters that are virtually 100% efficient for all particle sizes. For some applications, e.g., a filter-pack sampler designed to provide data on particle size distribution, less efficient glass fiber filters may be desirable. Shleien *et al.*[25] described the physical and collection efficiency characteristics of four less-efficient glass fiber filters, produced for gas cleaning and air conditioning applications, which they selected for their filter pack.

Membrane Filters

Filters consisting of porous membranes can be used for many applications where fibrous filters cannot. Organic membranes are produced by the formation of a gel from an organic colloid, with the gel in the form of a thin (approx. 150 μm) sheet with uniform pores. Membrane filters made from cellulose nitrate achieved widespread use for air sampling in the early 1950s.[3] In recent years, membrane filters made of cellulose triacetate, regenerated cellulose, polyvinyl chloride, nylon, polypropylene, polyimide, polysulfone, a copolymer of vinyl chloride and acrylonitrile, Teflon®, and silver have become available. Silver membranes are produced by a different technique and will be discussed separately at the end of this section.

Cellulose nitrate and cellulose triacetate membranes are the most widely used and, as indicated in Table 13-I-1, are available in the widest range of pore sizes. The mass of these filters is very low, and their ash content is usually negligible. Some are completely soluble in organic solvents. Cellulose nitrate filters dissolve in methanol, acetone, and many other organic solvents. Cellulose triacetate, nylon, and PVC filters dissolve in fewer solvents, while filters composed of Teflon and regenerated cellulose do not dissolve in common solvents. The ability to completely dissolve a filter in a solvent permits the concentration of the collected material within a small volume for subsequent chemical and/or physical analyses.

Nylon membrane filters are efficient collectors of nitric acid vapor and are used as back-up collectors in ambient air sampling filter packs to capture nitric acid generated by reactions, on a Teflon primary filter, between strong acid aerosols, i.e., sulfuric acid and ammonium bisulfate, and ammonium nitrate.[26] Such systems are used for accurate determinations of the inorganic ion content of ambient air.

For asbestos and for other mineral and vitreous fibers, fiber count measurements and fiber size analyses are performed by microscopic assays.[27] For occupational health applications, the standard NIOSH 7400 method specifies a 0.8-μm mixed cellulose ester membrane filter, and analysis using a phase-contrast optical microscope. For schools and general occupancy buildings, the U.S. Environmental Protection Agency (U.S. EPA) has recommended use of a 0.45-μm mixed cellulose ester membrane filter and analysis of a filter surface segment transferred directly onto an electron microscope grid. Some investigators use an indirect transfer technique in which a segment of the sampling filter is dissolved and an aliquot is transferred to a new filter. The rationale is to obtain an optimal density of fibers per unit surface on the grid in terms of both sufficient fiber density for efficient surface scanning and avoidance of overlap of fibers and their associated coincidence errors. The disadvantage of the indirect transfer technique is that fiber clumps and bundles are disaggregated, increasing the fiber concentration in an unpredictable way.

Collection efficiency increases with decreasing pore size, but even the large pore size filters have relatively high collection efficiencies for airborne particles much smaller than their pores. Membrane filters do not behave at all like sieves when used for air filtration. As in fibrous filters, particles are removed primarily by impaction and diffusion. Early investigators believed that electrostatic forces played a major role in particle deposition in membrane filters, but experimental studies by Spurny and Pich[28] and Megaw and Wiffen[29] demonstrated that diffusional and inertial deposition account for most of the observed collection and that the contribution of direct interception and electrostatic deposition, if present, is less important.

Membrane filters differ from fibrous filters in that a much greater proportion of the deposit is concentrated at or close to the front surface. Lindeken *et al.*[30] and Lossner[31] measured the penetration depth using test aerosols tagged with alpha emitters. Lindeken *et al.* were interested primarily in the use of the filters for measuring the concentration of α-emitters in air. If the deposit was truly at the surface, there would be no need for correcting for differences in distance from the detector face or for absorption of α-energy in the filter. They found that, on a microscopic scale, the filter surfaces were not smooth. The surface roughness varied among different brands and, for Millipore Company filters, from the front surface to the back. They concluded that the smooth face of an SM Millipore was suitable for their application. Lossner[31] demonstrated the effect of pore size and face velocity on penetration depth for 0.55-μm SiO_2 particles.

The fact that particle collection takes place at or near the surface of the filter accounts for most of the advantages of membrane filters and also some of their disadvantages. The advantages arising from this property are:

1. It is possible to examine solid particles microscopically without going through a transfer step that might change the state or form of the particles. Examination can be by optical microscopy using immersion oil having the same index of refraction as the filter. The oil renders the filter transparent to light rays. Transmission electron microscopy can be performed on a replica of the filter surface produced by vacuum evaporation techniques, whereas scanning electron microscopy can be performed directly on a segment of the filter.
2. Direct measurements of the deposit can be made on the surface without interference caused by absorption in the filter itself. This is advantageous in radiometric counting of dust particles and in soiling index measurements made by reflectance.
3. Autoradiographs of radioactive particles can be produced by a technique whereby photographic emulsion is placed in contact with the membrane filter sample.[32]

The disadvantage arising from surface collection is that the amount of sample that can be collected is limited. When more than a single layer of particles is collected on a membrane filter, the resistance rapidly increases, and there is a tendency for the deposit to slough off the filter.

Silver membranes for air sampling applications are made by sintering uniform metallic silver particles. These membranes possess a structure basically similar to that of the organic membranes previously described. They have a uniform pore size and, for a given pore size, about the same flow characteristics. For filters up to 47 mm in diameter, they are 50 µm thick. The membrane is an integral structure of permanently interconnected particles of pure silver, contains no binding agent or fibers, and is resistant to chemical attack by all fluids that do not attack pure silver. Thermal stability extends from –130° to +370°C (–200° to +700°F).

Richards *et al.*[33] described the use of silver membranes for sampling coal tar pitch volatiles. Other filter media evaluated were not suitable because of the high weight losses of blank filters in the benzene extraction step in the analysis, including 1106BH glass, cellulose acetate membrane, and Whatman 41 cellulose. The weight loss for the silver membrane was negligible. Another application of silver membrane filters is for sampling airborne quartz for X-ray diffraction analysis, as described by Knauber and VonderHeiden.[34] Most instruments satisfying the American Conference of Governmental Industrial Hygienists (ACGIH) criteria for respirable dust samplers operate at low flow rates, and the sample masses on the backup filters are too small for conventional analyses. Using silver membranes, the X-ray diffraction background is very consistent, and quartz determinations can have a lower limit of sensitivity as low as 0.02 mg.

Polycarbonate Pore Filters

Polycarbonate pore filters are similar to membrane filters in that both contain uniform-sized pores in a solid matrix. However, they differ in structure and method of manufacture. They are made by placing polycarbonate sheets approximately 10 µm thick in contact with sheets of uranium into a nuclear reactor. The neutron flux causes ^{235}U fission, and the fission fragments bore holes in the plastic. Subsequent treatment in a caustic etch solution enlarges the holes to a size determined by the temperature and strength of the bath and the time within it. Commercial filters are available with pore diameters between 0.03 and 8 µm.

Polycarbonate pore filters possess many of the attributes erroneously attributed to membrane filters in earlier days. They have a smooth filtering surface, the pores are cylindrical, almost all uniform in diameter, and essentially perpendicular to the filter surface. The filters also are transparent, even without immersion oil.

The structure and air paths through polycarbonate pore filters are so simple that, as demonstrated by Spurny *et al.*,[15] it is possible to predict their particle collection efficiency on the basis of measured dimensions and basic particle collection theory.

Although their pore volume is much lower, polycarbonate pore filters have about the same flow rate–pressure drop relations as membrane filters of comparable pore diameter. However, as shown in Figure 13-7, the filter penetrations at 5 cm/s, reported by Spurny and Lodge, are much greater than those of membrane filters with the same pore sizes. Pore filters have a lower and more uniform weight, and because they are nonhygroscopic, they can be used for sensitive gravimetric analyses. The polycarbonate base is very strong and filter tapes do not require extra mechanical backing. They can be analyzed by light transmittance, or filter segments can be cut from discs or tapes for microscopy.

The very smooth surface makes polycarbonate pore filters good collectors for particles to be analyzed by electron microscopy and X-ray fluorescence analyses. Spurny *et al.*[15] show high resolution electron micrographs made from silicon monoxide replicas of the filter surface. The very smooth surface also permits good resolution of the collected particles by scanning electron microscopy. The very low collection efficiencies of polycarbonate pore filters under certain conditions, as illustrated in Figure 13-7, permit their use in particle classifications that separate aerosols into size-graded fractions. Cahill *et al.*[35] and Parker *et al.*[36] proposed using two Nuclepore filters in series, with the first having a cut-characteristic approximating the ACGIH "respirable" dust criterion (see Chapter 5). Heidam[37] reviewed the use of series polycarbonate pore filters for a variety of applications but cautioned that particle bounce may be a significant source of error. Particle bounce as a means of penetration of such filters was also noted by John *et al.*,[38] Buzzard and Bell,[39] and Spurny.[40] Figure 13-9 from John *et al.*[38] shows that the collection of solid particles was lower than that

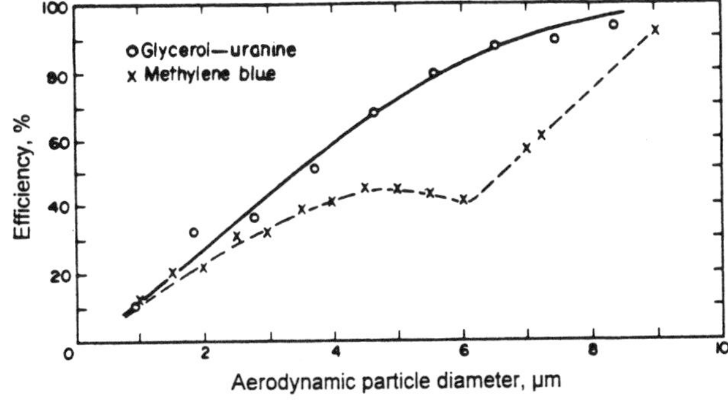

FIGURE 13-9. Measured filtration efficiency of an 8-µm pore size polycarbonate pore filter for methylene blue particles compared to that for glycerol-uranine particles. The flow rate was 5 L/min (face velocity 6 cm/s, based on an exposed area 42 mm in diameter).

for liquid droplets of the same aerodynamic size, and this was attributed to the bouncing of solid particles off the collection surface.

Plastic Foam Filters

Gibson and Vincent[41] described the use of porous filter media to simulate the collection characteristics of the MRE elutriator (see Chapter 5) under a wide range of face velocities. They found that, for particles close to the respirable size, deposition by inertial impaction and gravitational sedimentation compete. As a result, the efficiency remains relatively constant over a substantial range of face velocities.

Filters Occasionally Used for Air Sampling

Respirator Filters

Respirator filters of felt and/or cellulose fiber can be, and have been, used for air sampling. In many of them, the filter is manufactured in a pleated form, which increases the surface area without increasing the overall diameter. Filters of this type have the same advantages and disadvantages as the mixed fiber filters previously discussed. Wake *et al.*[42] described the collection characteristics of 18 respirator filters for radon daughter aerosols.

Thimbles

Filter thimbles, available in glass fiber, paper, and cloth, are sometimes filled with loose cotton packing to reduce clogging. Their advantage is that large samples can be collected. Other thimbles are made from aluminum oxide *(Alundum)* and sintered glass. These rigid filter thimbles are manufactured with a variety of porosities. They have considerably higher resistance to air flow than comparable paper cloth or glass fiber filters, but they can be used for higher temperature sampling.

Filter Selection Criteria

General Considerations

The selection of a particular filter type for a specific application is invariably the result of a compromise among many factors. These factors include cost, availability, collection efficiency, the requirements of the analytical procedures, and the ability of the filter to retain its filtering properties and physical integrity under the ambient sampling conditions. The increasing variety of commercially available filter media sometimes makes the choice seem somewhat difficult, but more importantly, it increases the possibility of a selection that satisfies all important criteria.

Efficiency of Collection

Before discussing experimental efficiency data, it is important that a distinction be made between particle collection efficiency and mass collection efficiency. The former refers to fractions of the total number of particles, while the latter refers to fractions of the total mass of the particles. These efficiencies will be numerically equivalent only when all of the particles are the same size, as in some laboratory investigations of filter efficiency. In almost all other cases, the mass collection efficiency will be significantly larger than the corresponding particle collection efficiency. When sampling for total mass concentration of particulate matter, or for the mass concentration of a component of an aerosol, the efficiency of interest is mass efficiency. Submicrometer particles often contribute only a small fraction of the total mass of an industrial dust, even when they represent the majority of the particles. Therefore, it is not always essential that an air sampling filter have a high efficiency for the smallest particles. Insistence on high efficiency for all size particles may restrict the selection to media with other limitations, such as high flow resistance, high cost, and fragility.

Collection efficiency data for a variety of filter media are given in Table 13-1 for 0.3-μm-diameter di(2-ethylhexyl)phthalate (DOP) droplets at various face velocities.[14] This is a commonly used particle size for a test aerosol because it is close to the size for maximum filter penetration for many commonly used sampling media operating at representative flow rates. On this basis, it is reasonable to assume that penetration of both smaller and larger particles would be lower, i.e., the collection efficiency would be higher. This assumption was confirmed by Stafford and Ettinger,[43] who showed that the collection efficiency of Whatman 41 is lowest for 0.264-μm particles at a face velocity of approximately 15 cm/s. It increases for both larger and smaller particles and is approximately 95% or greater for all sizes at face velocities above 100 cm/s. This information is also shown in Figure 13-5.

Liu and Lee[16] measured the collection efficiencies of Nuclepore and Teflon membrane filters for particles in the 0.03-μm- to 1-μm-diameter range. For Teflon filters with 10-μm pores (Type LC), the collection efficiencies for 0.003- to 0.1-μm particles at low face velocities were in the 60%–65% range; for Type LS filters with 5-μm pores, they were in the 80%–85% range. For higher velocities and/or larger particles, the efficiencies were >99.99% under all conditions tested. For Nuclepore filters, the penetrations were much higher at comparable pore sizes, and reached 100% for small particles with 5- and 8-μm pore filters. The results were consistent with predictions based on interception, impaction, and diffusion collection.

Liu *et al.*[44] summarized the results of collection efficiency measurements at four particle sizes and four face velocities for 76 different air sampling filters. Key results of this extensive body of calibration data are summarized in Table 13-2.

The effect of particle shape on filter penetration was explored by Spurny[21] using aerosols of chrysotile asbestos, as discussed earlier. Collection efficiencies decreased substantially with fiber length for both membrane and polycarbonate pore filters of larger pore size. The orientation of the airborne fibers as they approach the filter pore entrances has an important effect on their ability to penetrate the filter.

Skocypec[45] measured the penetration of condensation nuclei in the 0.002- to 0.007-μm range through most of the commercially available membrane filters at a face velocity of 10 cm/s. Less than 1.0% of the particles penetrated through most of the filters. However, much higher penetrations were observed for some of them. Penetrations of 3% or more were only found for some of the large pore (≥3 μm) filters, Nuclepore filters with ≤0.08-μm or ≥0.6- to 11-μm pores, silver membranes with ≥0.8-μm pores, and Type FG-0.2-μm polytetrafluoroethylene (PTFE) Fluoropore. Some of the large pore membranes, e.g., the cellulose ester filters of Millipore, cellulose triacetate filters of Gelman, and S & S nitrocellulose filters, retained very high efficiencies for these very small particles.

John and Reischl[46] also determined the collection efficiency of various air sampling filters for condensation nuclei. Efficiencies of >99% were found for a variety of Teflon membranes, including the Gelman Teflo filters with 1- to 3-μm and 2- to 4-μm pores, Gelman cellulose acetate with 5-μm pores (GA-1), and glass fiber filters (Gelman A and Spectrograde, MSA 1106BH, and EPA Microquartz). The Gelman Teflo membranes with 3- to 5-μm pores were almost as good, with efficiencies >98%. The Costar Nuclepore (0.8-μm pore) filters had efficiencies of 72%, 72%, and 89% at face velocities of approximately 25, 50, and 150 cm/s, respectively, whereas the efficiencies for Whatman 41 were 64% and 83% at approximately 50 and 150 cm/s, respectively.

Hoover and Newton[47] described the relative radon progeny collection efficiencies for 11 cellulose fiber, glass fiber, and membrane filters used in continuous air monitors for α-emitting radionuclides. Efficiencies above 90% were found for Millipore filters SMWP, AABP, AW19, Fluoropore (3- and 5-μm pores), Gelman A/E, and Whatman EPM 2000.

Lundgren and Gunderson[48] tested the effects of temperature, face velocity, and loading on the particle collection efficiency of glass fiber filters. At room temperatures, they found similar collection efficiencies for Gelman Type A, Gelman Type E, Gelman Spectrograde Type A, MSA 1106B, and the EPA Microquartz filters made of Johns-Manville "Microquartz" fibers by A.D. Little. The EPA filters had a low extractable background and are used for stack gas sampling at temperatures in excess of 500°C. All of the filters had similar pressure drop versus flow rate characteristics and filter masses per unit area, and the high temperature comparisons were limited to the Gelman Type A and "Microquartz" filters.

In all tests, aerosol penetrations of nonvolatile particles were less than about 0.10%. The highest penetrations were for particles approximately 0.1 μm in diameter at the highest face velocity tested, i.e., 51 cm/s. Penetrations dropped significantly with aerosol loadings of only several μg/cm^2.

The effect of pinholes on filter efficiency was examined by punching two 0.75-mm pinholes though the filter mat. Although this action produced higher initial penetrations by up to 30 times, the penetrations were never more than a few percent and fell rapidly with loading. Thus, their effect on sample collection would be essentially negligible.

Particle penetrations decreased with increasing temperature, except when the temperature was sufficient to volatilize the particles or to contribute to mechanical leakage of the filter holder.

Figure 13-5 shows additional data on the penetration of 0.3- to 11-μm-diameter DOP and clearly demonstrates that, for many filters, there is also a face velocity for maximum penetration. These curves were all plotted from the data of Lockhart *et al.*,[14] except for the Whatman 41 and IPC-1478 curves, which were extended to lower flow rates on the basis of the data of Rimberg.[13] The Nuclepore (polycarbonate pore) filter data points at 5 cm/s are from the data of Liu and Lee.[16]

On the basis of the data plotted in Figure 13-5, it can also be seen that the same filter can be inefficient at some face velocities and highly efficient at others. For example, Whatman 41 penetration below 10 cm/s exceeds 40%, while at 100 cm/s, it is only about 4%; at higher flow rates, it is much less than that. This filter is often used in industrial hygiene surveys with both low and high volume samplers. When sampling with a 25-mm filter head at 25 L/min, the face velocity (based on an effective filtration area of 3.68 cm^2) is 113 cm/s. When sampling with a 102-mm (4-in.) filter head at 500 L/min (17.7 cfm), the face velocity (based on effective filtration area of 60 cm^2) is 139 cm/s. On the other hand, when sampling at lower flow rates, as in personal air samplers, Whatman 41 would not be a good choice. With a 25-mm filter head and a flow rate of 2.5 L/min, the face velocity would only be 11.3 cm/s. For such an application, other filters more efficient at this flow rate would be preferred.

TABLE 13-2. List of Filters Tested and Principal Results (from Liu et al.[44])

Filter	Material	Pore Size, μm	Filter Permeability Velocity, cm/sec (ΔP = 1 cm Hg)	Filter Efficiency Range, %*
A. Cellulose Fiber Filter				
Whatman				
No. 1	Cellulose fiber	—	6.1	49 –99.96
No. 2		—	3.8	63 –99.97
No. 3		—	2.9	89.3–99.98
No. 4		—	20.6	33 –99.5
No. 5		—	0.86	93.1–99.99
No. 40		—	3.7	77 –99.99
No. 41		—	16.9	43 –99.5
No. 42		—	0.83	92.0–99.992
B. Glass Fiber Filter				
Gelman				
Type A	Glass fiber	—	11.2	99.92–>99.99
Type A/E		—	15.5	99.6 –>99.99
Spectrograde		—	15.8	99.5 –>99.99
Microquartz		—	14.1	98.5 –>99.99
MSA 1106B		—	15.8	99.5 –>99.99
Pallflex				
2500 QAO	Quartz fiber	—	41	84 – 99.9
E70/2075W		—	36.5	84 – 99.95
T60A20	Teflon-coated glass fiber	—	49.3	55 – 98.8
(another lot)		—	40.6	52 – 99.5
T60A25		—	36.5	65 – 99.3
TX40H12O		—	15.1	92.6 – 99.96
(another lot)		—	9.0	98.9 –>99.99
Reeve Angel 934AH	Glass fiber	—	12.5	98.9 –>99.99
(acid treated)		—	20	95.0
Whatman				
GF/A	Glass fiber	—	14.5	
GF/B		—	5.5	
GF/C		—	12.8	
EPM 1000		—	13.9	
C. Membrane Filter				
Millipore				
MF-VS	Cellulose acetate/nitrate	0.025	0.028	99.999–>99.999
MF-VC		0.1	0.16	99.999–>99.999
MF-PH		0.3	0.86	99.999–>99.999
MF-HA		0.45	1.3	99.999–>99.999
MF-AA		0.8	4.2	99.999–>99.999
MF-RA		1.2	6.2	99.9 –>99.999
MF-SS		3.0	7.5	98.5 –>99.999
MF-SM		5.0	10.0	98.1 –>99.999
MF-SC		8.0	14.1	92.0 –>99.9
Mitex-LS	Teflon	5.0	4.94	–>99.99
Mitex-LC		10.0	7.4	–>99.99
Fluoropore	PTFE-polyethylene reinforced			
FG		0.2	1.31	>99.90–>99.99
FH		0.5	2.32	>99.99–>99.99
FA		0.1	7.3	>99.99–>99.99

TABLE 13-2 (con't.). List of Filters Tested and Principal Results (from Liu et al.[44])

Filter	Material	Pore Size, μm	Filter Permeability Velocity, cm/sec (ΔP = 1 cm Hg)	Filter Efficiency Range, %*
C. Membrane Filter (con't.)				
Gelman Metricel				
GM-6	Cellulose acetate/nitrate	0.45	1.45	>99.8 –>99.99
VM-1	Polyvinyl chloride	0.5	51.0	49 – 98.8
DM-800	PVC/Acrylonitrile	0.8	2.7	99.96–>99.99
Gelman Teflon	Teflon	5.0	56.8	85 – 99.90
Ghia (Gelman)				
S2 37PL 02	Teflon	1.0	12.9	>99.97–>99.99
S2 37PJ 02		2.0	23.4	99.89–>99.99
S2 37PK 02		3.0	24.2	92 – 98.98
S2 37PF 02		10.0		95.4 –>99.99
Selas Flotronics (Poretics)				
FM0.45	Silver	0.45	1.8	93.6 – 99.98
FM0.8		0.8	6.2	90 – 99.96
FM1.2		1.2	9.2	73 – 99.7
FM5.0		5.0	19.0	25 – 99.2
D. Polycarbonate Pore Filter				
Nuclepore (Costar)				
N010	Polycarbonate	0.1	0.602	>99.9 –>99.9
N030		0.3	3.6	93.9 –>99.99
N040		0.4	2.9	78 –>99.99
N060		0.6	2.1	53 – 99.5
N100		1.0	8.8	28 – 98.1
N200		2.0	7.63	9 – 94.1
N300		3.0	12	9 – 90.4
N500		5.0	30.7	6 – 90.7
N800		8.0	21.2	1 – 90.5
N1000		12.0	95	1 – 46
N1200		10.0	161.1	1 – 66
E. Miscellaneous Filter				
MSA Personal Air Sampler		—	12	89 – 99.97

*The range of filter efficiency values given generally corresponds to a particular diameter range of 0.035 to 1 μm, a pressure drop range of 1 to 30 cm Hg, and a face velocity range of 1 to 100 cm/s.

The necessity for caution in interpreting filter efficiency data in the literature is illustrated in Figure 13-6, which shows the data of various authors for the penetration of Whatman 41 by 0.3-μm-diameter particles. The most reliable data appear to be those of Rimberg,[13] Stafford and Ettinger,[42] and Lockhart *et al.*,[14] which are in reasonably good agreement with one another. Lockhart *et al.*'s data are plotted for both Whatman 41 and TFA-41, which is Whatman 41 packaged and sold by the Staplex Company. The differences between the two sets of data are presumably the differences to be expected from randomly selected batches. The Smith and Surprenant[49] data were based on the same techniques as the data of Stafford and Ettinger[43] and of Lockhart *et al.*, i.e., light-scattering measurements of 0.3-μm DOP droplets, and the large discrepancy is inexplicable.

Rimberg[13] measured the penetration of charge-neutralized polystyrene latex spheres using a light scattering photometer. The 0.3-μm points are actually interpolated from the corresponding data for 0.365- and 0.264-μm particles. Lindeken *et al.*[50] used a similar technique except that they did not neutralize the electrical charge on their polystyrene test aerosols. Thus, their data appear to reflect the influence of particle charge on filter penetration.

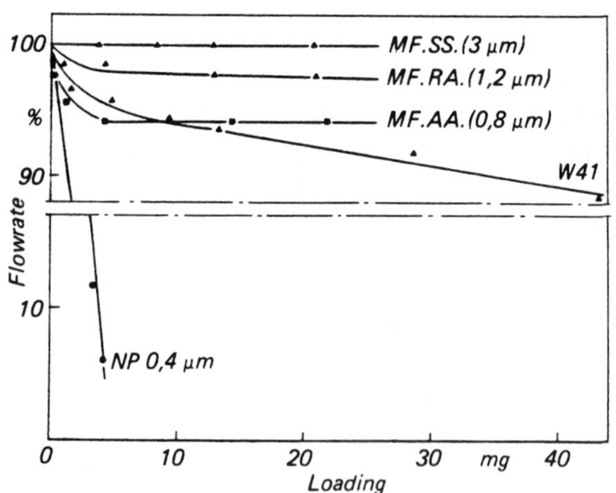

FIGURE 13-10. The effect of dust loading on the flow rate for various filter media.

Stafford and Ettinger[51] also compared the collection efficiencies of Whatman 41 filters for 0.3-µm DOP and latex spheres of similar sizes. The efficiencies were higher for the solid particles, especially at face velocities below 20 cm/s. They also showed that efficiency increased with loading of solid particles but not for liquid DOP droplets. Thus, some of the differences in their efficiency test results could have been due to the increase with loading during the test with the latex.

In interpreting filter efficiency data, it is also important to consider that the test data are usually based on the efficiency of a "clean" filter. For most filters, collection efficiency increases with the accumulation of solid particles on the filter surfaces. The resistance to flow also increases with increasing loading but usually at a much slower rate. A theoretical basis for these phenomena was developed by Davies.[52] A practical implication is that even with reliable published filter efficiency and aerosol size distribution data, it is not possible to know precisely what the collection efficiency of a filter will be for a given sampling interval. The filter efficiency data can only provide an estimate of the minimum collection efficiency. The actual collection efficiency will usually be higher.

Biles and Ellison[53] reported on the increase in collection efficiency for three types of cellulose fiber filters, i.e., Whatman 1, 4, and 451, for collecting lead and "black smoke" from the air of London, England. At a face velocity of 6.5 cm/s, the clean paper efficiencies for lead were 50, 30, and 15%, respectively, and 70, 40, and 30% in terms of the light reflectance measurement for black smoke. As the percent soiling index approached 40%, the collection efficiencies of all three papers approached 100% for both lead and black smoke.

There have been reports in the literature that low concentrations of small atmospheric particles could have large penetration rates through filters such as the Millipore HA or glass fiber filters.[54,55] Because numerous careful investigations have shown such filters to have almost complete collection for all particle sizes and flow rates, as discussed earlier and illustrated in Figure 13-5 and Table 13-2, it appears that such reports are most likely due to background or contamination problems associated with the analysis of the charcoal traps used by the investigators as back-up collectors. Kneip *et al.*[56] investigated the efficiency of Millipore AA and SC membrane filters and Gelman AE glass fiber filters for ambient air lead particles and laboratory-generated dye aerosol particles ≤0.07 µm in diameter at very low loadings and face velocities as low as 1.0 cm/s and found that all efficiencies were >99%.

Requirements of Analytical Procedures

Sample Quantity

In many instances, the limited sensitivity of an analytical method, when combined with a low aerosol concentration, makes it necessary for large volumes of air to be sampled in order to collect sufficient material for an accurate analysis. In addition to the material being studied, background dust and co-contaminants must, unavoidably, also be collected. Therefore, it is highly desirable that the filter medium selected have the capacity to collect and retain large sample masses. Furthermore, it is usually desirable to have the sampling rate nearly uniform over the length of the sampling period. The flow resistance of all filters increases with increased loading, but some do so at much lower rates than others. Table 13-1 shows the rates of resistance increase for a variety of filters when sampling the ambient air outside the Naval Research Laboratory. The loading rate would certainly differ for other aerosols, and these data generally would not be applicable. However, they do indicate the relative loading characteristics of these filters, i.e., those with low values load much more slowly than those with high values. Those filters with the lowest resistance build-up rate are most useful for collecting high-volume samples, especially when using pressure-sensitive, turbine-type blowers as air movers. In general, deep-bed fibrous filters have the lowest rates of resistance pressure increase. The relative rates of loading of some commonly used air sampling filters are illustrated in Figure 13-10.

Sample Configuration

Some analyses require that the sample be collected or mounted in a particular form. For example, microscopic particle size analysis can be performed only when the particles are on a flat surface. This is due to the limited depth of focus of the objective lens. In order to use fibrous filters for collecting samples for size analysis, it must be possible to remove the sample quantitatively and transfer it to a microscope stage without altering it. For such applications, the membrane and polycarbonate pore filters offer significant advantages over other filters. First, the samples can be analyzed directly on the filter surface. Second, because the sample does not have to be transferred, there is a greater likelihood that the sample observed is in the same form as when it was airborne.

Another situation in which the sample configuration may be important to the analysis is the determination of airborne radioactivity. Many radiation detectors such as Geiger–Mueller tubes and scintillation detectors are designed to view a limited surface area, usually a 2.5-cm-diameter circle. Thus, to make efficient use of the detector, the effective filtering area should be limited to a similar size. An additional consideration in radiometric analysis is the depth of penetration of the particles into the filter, especially for alpha and beta emitters.[47] The activity observed by the detector will be affected by the distance of the particles from the detector and by absorption of radiation by intervening filter fibers.

Other characteristics influence the choice of filters when quantitative particulate analysis by X-ray diffraction is desired. Davis and Johnson[57] examined seven filter substrates for both fiber and membrane construction and found that the degree to which the filters were suitable for X-ray diffraction analysis was primarily dependent on 1) interfering background scatter and 2) the mass per unit area of the particulate load collected. They found that Teflon filters were superior when mass loadings were <200 μg/cm^2. On the other hand, when mass loadings were >300 μg/cm^2, quartz and glass fiber filters were more suitable because of their particle retention qualities and their lack of a substrate spectrum in the diffraction pattern.

Sample Recovery from Filter

High collection efficiency is valueless if all of the sample is not available for analysis. For most chemical analyses, it is necessary to either remove the sample from the filter or to destroy the filter. Inorganic particles usually are recovered from cellulose paper filters by low temperature (plasma) ashing, wet ashing (digesting in concentrated acid), or muffling (incinerating) the filter. Samples collected on glass fiber and cellulose–asbestos filters can be recovered only by leaching or dissolving the sample from the filter. Samples can be recovered from membrane filters, polystyrene filters, and soluble granular beds by dissolving the filter in a suitable solvent.

Some of the membrane filters have a limited loading capacity in terms of the ability of the filter to retain the dust after it is collected. The dust retained on the surface may have very poor adhesion to the surface or

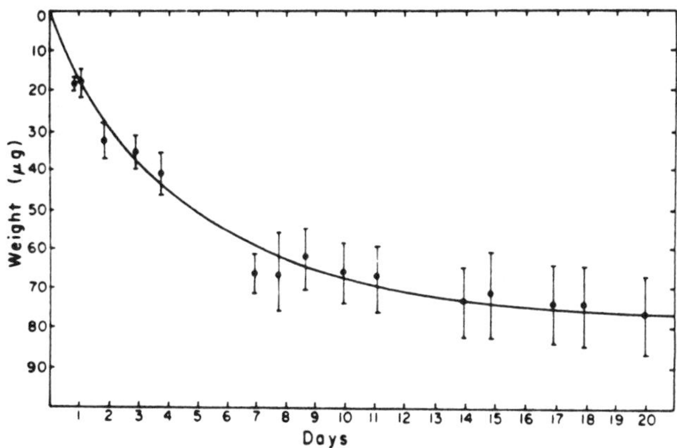

FIGURE 13-11. Microbalance error versus time. Data points represent the mean accumulative mass loss for eight filters. Data are seen to fit a logarithmic curve.

to the dust layer and slough off the surface. The problem is especially severe for polycarbonate pore filters.

Interferences Introduced by Filters

Before selecting a filter for a particular application, the filter's blank count or background level of the material to be analyzed must be determined. All filters contain various elements as major, minor, and trace constituents, and the filter medium of choice for analyzing particular elements must be one with little or no background level for the elements being analyzed. The components of the filter medium itself may introduce undesirable or unacceptable background to the subsequent analyses. If the filter is dissolved or digested, then all of the material in the filter will be mixed with the sample. If it is oxidized, then the residual ash content of the filter will be mixed with the sample. On the other hand, if the sample is extracted from the filter by a solvent, the sample will contain only those components of the filter matrix that are soluble. Finally, if a nondestructive analysis, such as X-ray diffraction, is performed, the contribution of the components of the filter will depend on both the content of the filter, its distribution in space, and the amount of X-ray absorption by the matrix and sample.

Data on the composition and interference levels of some commonly used sampling filters have been presented by Zhang *et al.*,[58] Gelman *et al.*,[59] and Mark.[60] There have also been problems with polycarbonate pore filters used in asbestos sampling because of the presence of such fibers on blank filters.

Polycarbonate pore filters build up an electrical charge that can cause a serious weighing error when they are used in gravimetric analysis. Figure 13-11 shows the change in weight over time due to the decay in charge on the filter observed by Engelbrecht *et al.*[61] The charge effect was attributed to electrostatic force between the charged filter on the weighing pan and the metal case of the electrobalance. Their 30-second exposure to a ^{210}Po source prior to the weighing was not sufficient to fully neutralize the charge on the filter.

Another type of interference is inaccessibility of the sample to a measurement or sensing device. For instance, in determining reflectance of filtered particulate matter, the more the particles penetrate the surface the less they will be visible. In such an application, the sensitivity of measurement on a membrane filter surface would be greater than on a fibrous filter.

Size or Mass of Filter

The mass of the filter itself may be important in gravimetric determinations. In determining the mass of collected aerosol, the mass of the filter should be as small as possible, relative to the mass of the sample. Also, other things being equal, the less the filter weighs and/or the smaller it is, the simpler the sample handling and processing. Collecting the sample on a smaller filter may save a concentrating step in the analysis and make it possible to use smaller analytical equipment and/or glassware.

Limitations Introduced by Ambient Conditions

Temperature

The temperature stability of a filter must be considered when sampling hot gases such as stack effluents. For such applications, combustible materials cannot be used, and a selection must be made from the several types of mineral, glass, or other refractory media. In order to select the appropriate medium, the peak temperature and duration of sampling must be known. Glass fiber filters are widely used for temperatures up to about 500°C.

Moisture Content

For sampling under conditions of high humidity, filter media that are relatively nonhygroscopic must be chosen. Some filters pick up moisture and this may affect their filtering properties. If their efficiency is partially dependent on electrostatic effects, moisture may reduce it. Also, when a filter picks up moisture, it may become mechanically weaker and rupture more easily.

For some airborne dusts, such as suspended particulate matter in the ambient air and coal mine dust, the standards are based on gravimetric analyses without regard to dust composition. Mass concentrations are determined from the gain in weight of the filter during the sampling interval, divided by the sampled volume. Because the filter weighs much more than the sample collected on it, the accuracy of the analysis depends on the stability of the filter's weight. Serious errors can arise if some of the filter's mass is lost due to abrasion during handling between the tare and final filter weighings, or if there is a significant difference in atmospheric water vapor content at the time of analysis.

The highly variable water vapor retention characteristics of cellulose fiber filters usually rule out their selection for use when gravimetric analyses are to be performed.[62] However, even glass fiber and membrane filters, while much less affected by water vapor, may still have enough adsorption to cause problems in gravimetric analyses. Charell and Hawley[63] examined the weight changes at various humidities for cellulose ester, PVC, and polycarbonate membrane filters. They found that all changed their weights reversibly in proportion to the water vapor concentration, that the minimum uptake was seen with polycarbonate and some PVC filters, that other PVC filters took up 6.6 times as much water, and that cellulose ester membranes took up 40–50 times more water vapor. Thus, pre- and postsampling weighings should be done at the same humidity conditions. Mark[60] examined the weight changes associated with changes in humidity for a variety of PVC membranes, some cellulose ester membranes, and a glass fiber filter. The results of his tests are illustrated in Figure 13-12. He also reported that a PVC-type filter developed an electrical charge that repelled particles onto the filter holder during sampling, reducing the apparent collection efficiency. He was able to overcome this source of error by pretreating the filters with a detergent solution.

Artifact Formation

Air sampling filters can collect gases and vapors as well as particles. The intentional collection of vapor phase chemicals by filters is discussed in Chapter 17. When they are collected unintentionally by adsorption or absorption onto filter surfaces, or onto particles collected on those surfaces, their presence in the sample can constitute an artifact. For example, ordinary glass fiber filters are slightly alkaline and collect SO_2 while sampling ambient air. This led to overestimation of the ambient aerosol sulfate concentrations for many years.

As shown by Coutant,[64] Spicer and Schumacher,[65] and Appel *et al.*,[66] artifact particulate matter can be formed by oxidation of acidic gases (e.g., SO_2, NO_2) or by retention of gaseous nitric acid on the surface of alkaline (e.g., glass fiber) filters and other filter types. The effect is a surface-limited reaction and, depending on the concentration of the acidic gas, should be especially significant early in the sampling period. The magnitude of the resulting error depends on such factors as the sampling period, filter composition and pH, and the relative humidity. The magnitude and the significance of artifact mass errors are variable and

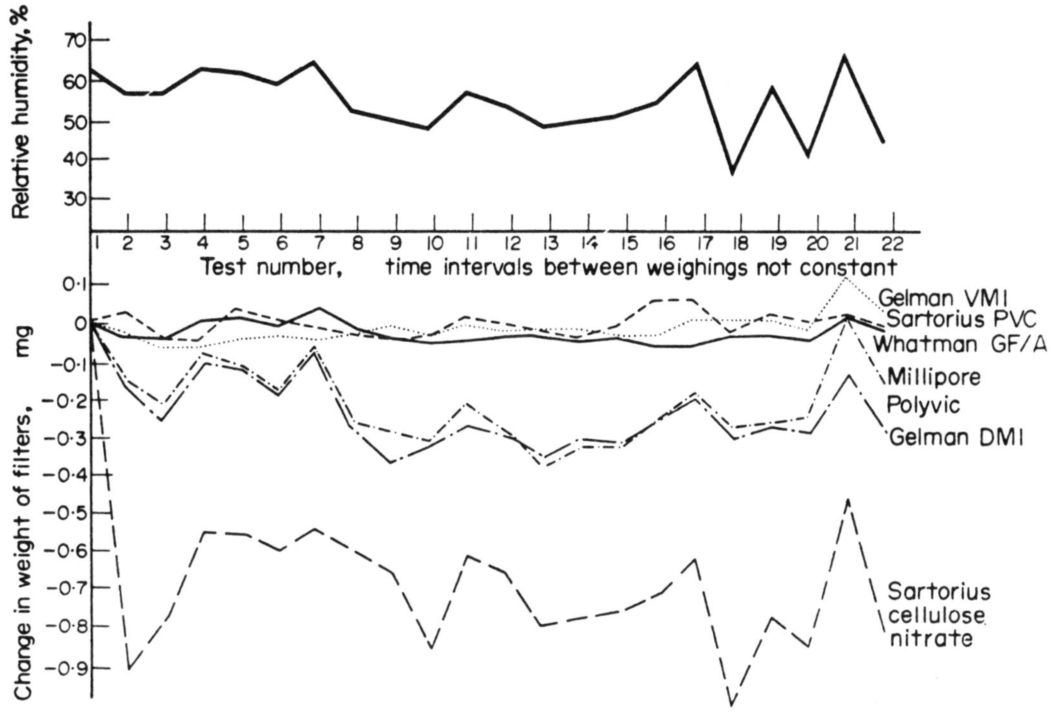

FIGURE 13-12. Variation in weight of filter materials due to absorption of moisture in changing relative humidity.

dependent on local conditions. Excluding the uncertainty associated with the collection and retention of organic particulate matter with appreciable vapor pressure, artifact mass primarily reflects the sum of the sulfates and nitrates formed by filter surface reactions with sulfur dioxide and nitric acid vapors, respectively.

The study by Coutant[64] reported artifact sulfate for 24-hour samples from 0.3 to 3 μg/m^3. Stevens *et al.*[67] found 2.5 μg/m^3 average artifact sulfate sampling at eight sites around St. Louis, Missouri, and Rodes and Evans[68] noted 0.5 μg/m^3 artifact sulfate in West Los Angeles, California.

Artifact sulfate formation can also occur on nylon filters. Chan *et al.*[69] examined the extent of conversion of SO_2 to sulfate on Nylasorb nylon filters used as nitric acid vapor collectors. The percent conversion was found to depend on both the concentration of SO_2 and the relative humidity.

Appel and Tokiwa[70] reported that artifact particulate nitrate on glass fiber filters is limited only by the gaseous nitric acid concentration. Such filters approximated total inorganic nitrate samplers, retaining both particulate nitrate and nitric acid even when the latter was present at very high atmospheric concentrations, e.g., 20 ppb. Nitric acid was found to represent from approximately 25% to 50% of the total inorganic nitrate at Pittsburgh, Pennsylvania, and Lennox and Claremont, California. Based on an estimate of the most probable 24-hour artifact sulfate error, 3.0 μg/m^3, and of the most probable artifact particulate nitrate, 8.2 μg/m^3 in the Los Angeles Basin and 3.8 μg/m^3 elsewhere, typical errors in mass due to sulfate plus nitrate artifacts are estimated at 11.2 μg/m^3 in the Los Angeles Basin and 6.8 μg/m^3 elsewhere.

Nitrate salts can be rapidly lost from inert filters (e.g., Teflon, quartz) by volatilization[68] and by reactions with acidic materials.[71] Sampling artifacts are also of serious concern for organic contaminants in air. Schwartz *et al.*[72] showed that the apparent concentration of extractable organics collected on glass fiber filters varied with the duration of the sampling period. They found that moderately polar organics extracted by dichloromethane were increasingly difficult to recover as the sampling period became progressively longer. This could have been due to volatilization of sampled material during continued sampling or to their oxidation to a form not extracted by the solvent. For more polar organics extracted with cyclohexane, the apparent concentration increased with increasing sampling time, suggesting that the sampled material was behaving as a vapor adsorbent. Similar observations have been made by Appel *et al.*[73] Much more work is needed on the volatility of sampled material during further sampling, on chemical conversions which take place on filter substrates, and on adsorption of vapors by sampled materials before the extent and significance of those factors can be fully established. Increasingly, quartz fiber filters are being used to minimize such problems.

Limitations Introduced by Filter Holder

Filter Size

In order to use any filter, it must be held securely and without leakage in an appropriate filter holder. This limits the diameter of a filter disc to a particular size unless the filter holder is fabricated especially for the filter. Most filter media can be obtained in any desired size, but some, such as respirator filters, are preformed on molds and are available in only one size.

Mechanical Properties of Filters

Some filter holders can only be used with filters of high mechanical strength. A strong filter paper (e.g., Whatman 41) can be used in a simple head without a back-up screen, whereas softer filters (e.g., glass and quartz fiber) or brittle filters (e.g., the membrane filter) require a more elaborate holder with a firm back-up screen or mesh support to prevent rupture.

Materials Used in Filter Holders and Inlets

Experience has shown that nonconductive plastic inlet cowls remove asbestos fibers before they can reach the sampling filter. The use of conductive cowls has reduced, but has not eliminated, this problem.

Availability and Cost

There are great variations in the unit cost of filter media. For example, although cellulose–asbestos and glass cost about twice as much as cellulose filters, membrane filters may cost 10 times as much. For large-scale sampling programs, such price differentials can add up to significant annual cost increments. The less expensive filter should be chosen when the differences in performance are marginal. Ready availability is another factor to be considered. The cellulose and glass filters can be obtained from any chemical supply house, whereas other types may only be available from a limited number of suppliers. Information on the availability of filter holders is presented in Tables 13-I-2 and 13-I-3.

Filter holder characteristics are listed in Table 13-I-2. This table also contains cross references to filter holder illustrations that follow. Both tables provide code letters for instrument manufacturers; complete names and addresses are given in Table 13-I-3.

Summary and Conclusions

The advantages of sampling by filtration have been discussed, filtration theory has been outlined, commercial filter media have been described, and the criteria for selecting appropriate filters for particular applications have been reviewed.

Of all the particle collection techniques, filter sampling is the most versatile. With appropriate filter media, samples can be collected in almost any form, quantity, and state. Sample handling problems are usually minimal, and many analyses can be performed directly on the filter. No single filter medium is appropriate to all problems, but a filter appropriate to any immediate problem can usually be found.

References

1. Davies, C.N.: The Entry of Aerosols into Sampling Tubes and Heads. Br. J. Appl. Phys. Ser. 2, 1:921 (1968).
2. Davies, C.N.: Deposition from Moving Aerosols. In: Aerosol Science, pp. 393–446. C.N. Davies, Ed. Academic Press, London (1966).
3. First, M.W.; Silverman, L.: Air Sampling with Membrane Filters. Arch. Ind. Hyg. Occup. Med. 7:1 (1953).
4. Stenhouse, J.L.T.; Harrop, J.A.; Freshwater, D.C.: The Mechanisms of Particle Capture in Gas Filters. J. Aerosol Sci. 1:41 (1970).
5. Emi, H.; Okuyama, K.; Adachi, M.: The Effect of Neighboring Fibers on the Single Fiber Inertia-Interception Efficiency of Aerosols. J. Chem. Eng. Japan 10: 148 (1977).
6. Kirsch, A.A.; Stechkina, I.B.; Fuchs, N.A.: Efficiency of Aerosol Filters made of Ultrafine Polydisperse Fibers. J. Aerosol Sci. 6:119 (1975).
7. Ramskill, E.A.; Anderson, W.L.: The Inertial Mechanism in the Mechanical Filtration of Aerosols. J. Coll. Sci. 6:416 (1951).
8. Wang, H.C.; Kasper, G.: Filtration Efficiency of Nanometer-Size Aerosol Particles. J. Aerosol Sci. 22:31 (1991).
9. Kirsch, A.A.; Zhulanov, U.V.: Measurement of Aerosol Penetration Through High Efficiency Filters. J. Aerosol Sci. 9:291 (1978).
10. Gentry, J.W.; Spurny, K.R.; Schoermann, J.: Diffusional Deposition of Ultrafine Aerosols on Nuclepore Filters. Atmos. Environ. 16:25 (1982).
11. Lundgren, D.A.; Whitby, K.T.: Effect of Particle Electrostatic Charge on Filtration by Fibrous Filters. I & EC Process Res. Develop. 4:345 (1965).
12. Zebel, G.: Deposition of Aerosol Flowing Past a Cylindrical Fiber in a Uniform Electric Eield. J. Coll. Sci. 20:522 (1965).
13. Rimberg, D.: Penetration of IPC 1478, Whatman 41, and Type 5G Filter Paper as a Function of Particle Size and Velocity. Am. Ind. Hyg. Assoc. J. 30:394 (1969).
14. Lockhart, Jr., L.B.; Patterson, Jr., R.L; Anderson, W.L: Characteristics of Air Filter Used for Monitoring Airborne Radioactivity. NRL Report No. 6054. U.S. Naval Research Laboratory, Washington, DC (March 20, 1964).
15. Spurny, K.R.; Lodge, Jr., J.P.; Frank, E.R.; Sheesley, D.C.: Aerosol Filtration by Means of Nuclepore Filters: Structural and Filtration Properties. Environ. Sci. Technol. 3:453 (1969).
16. Liu, B.Y.H.; Lee, K.W.: Efficiency of Membrane and Nuclepore Filters for Submicrometer Aerosols. Environ. Sci. Technol. 10:345 (1976).
17. Lee, K.W.; Liu, B.Y.H.: On the Minimum Efficiency and the Most Penetrating Particle Size for Fibrous Filters. J. Air Pollut. Control Assoc. 30:377 (1980).
18. Lee, K.W.: Maximum Penetration of Aerosol Particles in Granular Bed Filters. J. Aerosol Sci. 12:79 (1981).
19. Schmidt, E.W.; Gieseke, J.A.; Gelfand, P.; et al.: Filtration Theory for Granular Beds. J. Air Pollut. Control Assoc. 28:143 (1978).
20. Fichman, M.C.; Gutfinger, C.; Pnueli, D.: A Modified Model for the Deposition of Dust in a Granular Bed Filter. Atmos. Environ. 15:1669 (1981).
21. Spurny, K.: On the Filtration of Fibrous Aerosols. J. Aerosol. Sci. 17450 (1986).
22. Loffler, F.: The Adhesion of Dust Particles to Fibrous and Particulate

Surfaces. Staub 28:29 (English trans.) (November 1968).

23. Pate, T.B.; Tabor, E.C.: Analytical Aspects of the Use of Glass Fiber Filters for the Collection and Analysis of Atmospheric Particle Matter. Am. Ind. Hyg. Assoc. J. 23:145 (1962).
24. Kramer, D.N.; Mitchel, P.W.: Evaluation of Filters for High Volume Sampling of Atmospheric Particulates. Am. Ind. Hyg. Assoc. J. 28:224 (1967).
25. Shleien, B.; Cochran, J.A.; Friend, A.G.: Calibration of Glass Fiber Filters for Particle Size Studies. Am. Ind. Hyg. Assoc. J. 27:253 (1966).
26. Koutrakis, P.; Wolfson, J.M.; Spengler, J.D.: An Improved Method for Measuring Aerosol Strong Acidity. Atmos. Environ. 22:157 (1988).
27. Lippmann, M.: Asbestos Exposure Indices. Environ. Res. 46:86 (1988).
28. Spurny, K.; Pich, J.: The Separation of Aerosol Particles by Means of Membrane Filters by Diffusion and Inertial Impaction. Int. J. Air Wat. Pollut. 8:193 (1964).
29. Megaw, W.J.; Wiffen, R.D.: The Efficiency of Membrane Filters. Int. J. Air Wat. Pollut. 7:501 (1963).
30. Lindeken, C.L.; Petrock, F.K.; Phillips, W.A.; Taylor, R.D.: Surface Collection Efficiency of Large-Pore Membrane Filters. Health Phys. 10:495 (1964).
31. Lossner, V.: Die Bestimmung der Eindringtiefe von Aerosolen in Filtern. Staub 24:217 (1964).
32. George, II, L.A.: Electron Microscopy and Autoradiography. Science 133:1423 (May 5, 1961).
33. Richards, R.T.; Donovan, D.T.; Hall, J.R.: A Preliminary Report on the Use of Silver Metal Membrane Filters in Sampling Coal Tar Pitch Volatiles. Am. Ind. Hyg. Assoc. J. 28:590 (1967).
34. Knauber, J.W.; VonderHeiden, F.H.: A Silver Membrane X-Ray Diffraction Technique for Quartz Samples. Presented at American Industrial Hygiene Conference, Denver, CO (May 14, 1969).
35. Cahill, T.A.; Ashbauch, L.L.; Barone, J.B.; et al.: Analysis of Respirable Fractions in Atmospheric Particulates via Sequential Filtration. J. Air Pollut. Control Assoc. 27:675 (1977).
36. Parker, R.D.; Buzzard, G.H.; Dzubay, T.G.; Bell, J.P.: A Two-Stage Respirable Aerosol Sampler Using Nuclepore Filters in Series. Atmos. Environ. 11:617 (1977).
37. Heidam, N.Z.: Review: Aerosol Fractionation by Sequential Filtration with Nuclepore Filters. Atmos. Environ. 15:891 (1981).
38. John W.; Reischl, G.; Goren, S.; Plotkin, D.: Anomalous Filtration of Solid Particles by Nuclepore Filters. Atmos. Environ. 12: 1555 (1978).
39. Buzzard, G.H.; Bell, J.P.: Experimental Filtration Efficiencies of Large Pore Nuclepore Filters. J. Aerosol Sci. 11:435 (1980).
40. Spurny, K.: Discussion: A Two-Stage Respirable Aerosol Sampler Using Nuclepore Filters in Series. Atmos. Environ. 11:1246 (1977).
41. Gibson, H.; Vincent, J.H.: The Penetration of Dust Through Porous Foam Filter Media. Ann. Occup. Hyg. 24:205 (1981).
42. Wake, D.; Brown, R.C.; Trottier, R.A.; Liu, Y.: Measurements of the Efficiency of Respirator Filters and Filtering Facepieces Against Radon Daughter Aerosols. Ann. Occup. Hyg. 36:629 (1992).
43. Stafford, R.G.; Ettinger, H.J.: Filter Efficiency as a Function of Particle Size and Velocity. Atmos. Environ. 6:353 (1972).
44. Liu, B.Y.H.; Pui, D.Y.H.; Rubow, K.L.: Characteristics of Air Sampling Filter Media. In: Aerosols in the Mining and Industrial Work Environment, Vol. 3; Instrumentation, pp. 989–1038, V.A. Marple and B.Y.H. Liu, Eds. Ann Arbor Science, Ann Arbor, MI (1981).
45. Skocypec, W.J.: The Efficiency of Membrane Filters for the Collection of Condensation Nuclei. M.S. Thesis. University of North Carolina, School of Public Health, Chapel Hill, NC (1974).
46. John, W.; Reischl, G.: Measurements of the Filtration Efficiencies of Selected Filter Types. Atmos. Environ. 12:2015 (1978).
47. Hoover, M.D.; Newton, G.J.: Update on Selection and Use of Filter Media in Continuous Air Monitors for Alpha-Emitting Radionuclides. In: 1991–1992 Inhalation Toxicology Research Institute Annual Report, pp. 5–7, LMF-138, ITRI, Albuquerque, NM 87185 (December 1992).
48. Lundgren, D.A.; Gunderson, T.C.: Efficiency and Loading Characteristics of EPA's High-Temperature Quartz Fiber Filter Media. Am. Ind. Hyg. Assoc. J. 36:806 (1975).
49. Smith, W.J.; Surprenant, N.F.: Properties of Various Filtering Media for Atmospheric Dust Sampling. Presented at the American Society for Testing and Materials, Philadelphia, PA (July 1, 1963).
50. Lindeken, C.L.; Morgan, R.L.; Petrock, K.F.: Collection Efficiency of Whatman 41 Filter Paper for Submicron Aerosols. Health Phys. 9:305 (1963).
51. Stafford, R.G.; Ettinger, H.J.: Comparison of Filter Media Against Liquid and Solid Aerosols. Am. Ind. Hyg. Assoc. J.32:319 (1971).
52. Davies, C.N.: The Clogging of Fibrous Aerosol Filters. Aerosol Sci. 1:35 (1970).
53. Biles, B.; Ellison, J. McK.: The Efficiency of Cellulose Fiber Filters with Respect to Lead and Black Smoke in Urban Aerosol. Atmos. Environ. 9:1030 (1975).
54. Robinson, J.W.; Wolcott, D.K.: Simultaneous Determination of Particulate and Molecular Lead in the Atmosphere. Environ. Lett. 6:321 (1974).
55. Skogerboe, R.K.; Dick, D.L; Lamothe, P.J.: Evaluation of Filter Inefficiencies for Particulate Collection Under Low Loading Conditions. Atmos. Environ. 11:243 (1977).
56. Kneip, T.J.; Kleinman, M.T.; Gorczynski, J.; Lippmann, M.: A Study of Filter Penetration by Lead in New York City Air. In: Environmental Lead, pp. 291–308. D.R. Lynam, L.G. Piantanida, and J.F. Cole, Eds. Academic Press, New York (1981).
57. Davis, B.L.; Johnson, L.R.: On the Use of Various Filter Substrates for Quantitative Particulate Analysis by X-ray Diffraction. Atmos. Environ. 16:273 (1982).
58. Zhang, J.; Billiet, S. J.; Dams, R.: Stationary Sampling and Chemical Analysis of Suspended Particulate Matter in a Workplace. Staub-Reinhalt. Luft. 41:381 (1981).
59. Gelman, C.; Mehta, D.V.; Meltzer, T.H.: New Filter Compositions for the Analysis of Airborne Particulate and Trace Metals. Am. Ind. Hyg. Assoc. J. 40:926 (1979).
60. Mark, D.: Problems Associated with the Use of Membrane Filters for Dust Sampling When Compositional Analysis is Required. Ann. Occup. Hyg. 17:35 (1974).
61. Engelbrecht, D.R.; Cahill, T.; Feeney, P.J.: Electrostatic Effects on Gravimetric Analysis of Membrane Filters. J. Air Pollut. Control Assoc. 30:391 (1980).
62. Demuynck, M.: Determination of Irreversible Absorption of Water by Cellulose Filters. Atmos. Environ. 9:623 (1975).
63. Charell, P.R.; Hawley, R.E.: Characteristics of Water Adsorption on Air Sampling Filters. Am. Ind. Hyg. Assoc. J. 42:353 (1981).
64. Coutant, R.W.: Effect of Environmental Variables on Collection of Atmospheric Sulfate. Environ. Sci. Technol. 11:873 (1977).
65. Spicer, C.W.; Schumacher, P.M.: Particulate Nitrate: Laboratory and Field Studies of Major Sampling Interferences. Atmos. Environ. 13:543 (1979).
66. Appel, B.R.; Wall, S.M.; Tokiwa,Y.; Haik, M.: Interference Effects in Sampling Particulate Nitrate in Ambient Air. Atmos. Environ. 13:319 (1979).
67. Stevens, R.F.; Dzubay, T.G.; Russwurm, G.; Rickel, D.: Sampling and Analysis of Atmospheric Sulfates and Related Species. In: Sulfur in the Atmosphere, Proceedings of the International Symposium, United Nations, Dubrovnik, Yugoslavia, September 7–14, 1977. Atmos. Environ. 12:55 (1978).
68. Rodes, C.E.; Evans, G.F.: Summary of LACS Integrated Measurements. EPA-600/4-77-034. U.S. Environmental Protection Agency, Research Triangle Park, NC (June 1977).
69. Chan, W.H.; Orr, D.B.; Chung, D.H.S.: An Evaluation of Artifact SO_4 Formation on Nylon Filters Under Field Conditions. Atmos. Environ. 20:2397 (1986).
70. Appel, B.R.; Tokiwa, Y.: Atmospheric Particulate Nitrate Sampling Errors Due to Reactions with Particulate and Gaseous Strong Acids.

Atmos. Environ. 15:1087 (1981).

71. Harker, A.; Richards, L.; Clark, W.: Effect of Atmospheric SO_2 Photochemistry Upon Observed Nitrate Concentrations. Atmos. Environ. 11:87 (1977).

72. Schwartz, G.P.; Daisey, J.M.; Lioy, P.J.: Effect of Sampling Duration on the Concentration of Particulate Organics Collected on Glass Fiber Filters. Am. Ind. Hyg. Assoc. J. 42:258 (1981).

73. Appel, B.R.; Hoffer, E.M.; Haik, M.; et al.: Characterization of Organic Particulate Matter. Environ. Sci. Technol. 13:98 (1979).

TABLE 13-I-1. Summary of Air Sampling Filter Characteristics

Filter	Void Size (μm)	Fiber Diam. (μm)	Thickness (μm)	Weight/ Area (mg/cm^2)	Ash Content (%)	Max. Oper. Temp. (°C)	Tensile Strength (g/cm)	ΔP100[A] in H_2O	Source
A. Cellulose Fiber Filter Characteristics									
Whatman 1	2+	NA	180	8.7	0.06	150	4700	40.5	WLS
4	4+	NA	210	9.2	0.06	150	NA	11.5	WLS
40	2	NA	210	9.5	0.01	150	4600	54	WLS
41	4+	NA	220	8.5	0.01	150	4600	8.1	WLS
42	>1	NA	200	10.0	0.01	150	NA	NA	WLS
44	>1	NA	180	8.0	0.01	150	NA	NA	WLS
50	1	NA	120	9.7	0.025	150	NA	NA	WLS
541	4+	NA	160	7.8	0.008	150	NA	NA	WLS
S&S 508	NA	NA	NA	NA	NA	NA	NA	NA	SAS
589	NA	NA	NA	NA	NA	NA	NA	NA	SAS
603	NA	NA	NA	NA	NA	120	NA	NA	SAS
B. Glass Fiber Filter Characteristics									
MSA 11064[B]	NA	NA	180-270	6.1	~95	540	625	19.8	MSA
1106BH[C]	NA	NA	180-460	5.8	~100	540	270	19.8	MSA
Gelman									
Type A/B	1	NA	457	NA	NA	500	NA	NA	GS
A/C	1	NA	279	NA	NA	500	NA	NA	GS
A/D	3.1	NA	686	NA	NA	500	NA	NA	GS
Extra Thick	1	NA	1270	NA	NA	135	NA	NA	GS
Millipore									
AP 15[B]	NA	<1	380	8.0	95	500	625	70	MIL
AP 20[B]	NA	<1	330	7.3	95	500	625	16	MIL
AP 40[C]	NA	<1	410	6.9	100	500	450	18	MIL
Whatman									
GF/A[C]	<1	0.5–0.75	250	5.3	NA	540	500	NA	WLS
GF/B[C]	<1	0.5–0.75	680	14.3	NA	540	1000	NA	WLS
GF-C[C]	<1	0.2–0.5	260	5.3	NA	540	500	NA	WLS
934AH[C]	<1	NA	330	6.4	NA	540	180	24.4	WLS
EPM-2000[C]	NA	NA	430	8.0	NA	540	700	NA	WLS
QM-A Quartz	NA	NA	450	8.5	NA	540	250-300	15.3	WLS
H&V									
HD-2021	NA	1.6	500	9.4	95	500	1150	6.6	H&V
HB-5055	NA	0.6	475	9.0	95	500	1200	12.4	H&V
HB-5211	NA	0.6	400	6.0	95	500	980	13.7	H&V
LB-5211 A-O[D]	NA	0.6	400	8.8	65	175	2000	14.0	H&V
HA-8021[C]	NA	0.45	380	7.3	100	500	700	18.8	H&V
HA-8141	NA	0.45	410	7.8	95	500	650	19.4	H&V
HA-8071	NA	0.25	350	6.7	95	500	1000	65.0	H&V
Pallflex									
600A	<0.4	0.4–0.7	230	3	~95	315	1000	6	PFX
2500A	<0.4	0.4–0.7	500	6.5	~96	315	1500	15	PFX
2500QAO-UP[E]	<0.2	0.4–0.7	530	6.5	100	1000	500–900	10–15	PFX
TX40H120WW[F]	<0.3	<0.5	175	5	~85	315	3500	20	PFX
T60A20[F]	<0.4	0.4–0.7	240	4	~80	315	1200	8	PFX
E70[G]	<0.4	0.4–0.8	175	3.5	~35	120–160	650	8	PFX
Costar									
AAA[C]	NA	NA	NA	NA	NA	NA	NA	NA	CC

TABLE 13-I-1 (con't.). Summary of Air Sampling Filter Characteristics

Filter	Composition	Pore Size (μm)	Thick-ness (μm)	Weight/ Area (mg/cm²)	Ash Content (%)	Max. Oper. Temp. (°C)	Tensile Strength (psi)	Refractive Index	ΔP100[A] in H_2O	Source
C. Membrane Filter Characteristics										
Millipore										
SC	Mixed	8.0	130	5.2	<0.001	125	175	1.515	20	MIL
SM	Cellulose esters	5.0	130	2.8	<0.001	125	160	1.495	32	MIL
SS		3.0	150	3.0	<0.001	125	150	1.495	56	MIL
RA[H]		1.2	150	4.2	<0.001	125	300	1.510	75	MIL
AA[H,I]		0.80	150	4.7	<0.001	125	350	1.510	102	MIL
DA[H]		0.65	150	4.8	<0.001	125	400	1.510	112	MIL
HA[H]		0.45	150	4.9	<0.001	125	450	1.510	250	MIL
PH		0.30	150	5.3	<0.001	125	500	1.510	300	MIL
GS		0.22	135	5.5	<0.001	125	700	1.510	450	MIL
VC		0.10	130	5.6	<0.001	125	800	1.500	2290	MIL
VM		0.05	130	5.7	<0.001	125	1000	1.500	3610	MIL
VS		0.025	130	5.8	<0.001	125	1500	1.500	5100	MIL
LC	Teflon	10.0	125	8.0	NA	260	250	NA	125	MIL
LS		5.0	125	8.0	NA	260	150	NA	187	MIL
FA	PTFE-polyethylene	1.0	180	2.2	NA	130	NA	NA	NA	MIL
FH	reinforced	0.5	180	2.2	NA	130	NA	NA	NA	MIL
FG		0.2	180	2.2	NA	130	NA	NA	NA	MIL
Metricel										
GN 450	Mixed	0.45	150	4.0	NA	74	NA	1.51	NA	GS
GN 800	Cellulose esters	0.8	150	4.0	NA	74	NA	1.51	NA	GS
VM	Polyvinyl chloride	5.0	150	1.0	NA	52	NA	1.55	NA	GS
DM-800	PVC/Acrylonitrile	0.8	150	3.0	NA	66	NA	1.51	NA	GS
DM-450		0.45	150	3.0	NA	66	NA	1.51	NA	GS
Nylasorb	Nylon	1.0	NA	NA	NA	NA	NA	NA	NA	GS
Zylon	PTFE	5.0	127	NA	NA	NA	NA	NA	NA	GS
TF	PTFE with poly-	1.0	NA	NA	NA	NA	NA	NA	NA	GS
	propylene support	0.45	NA	NA	NA	NA	NA	NA	NA	GS
		0.20	NA	NA	NA	NA	NA	NA	NA	GS
Teflo	PTFE with poly-	10	NA	NA	NA	NA	NA	NA	NA	GS
	methylpentene	3.0	NA	NA	NA	NA	NA	NA	NA	GS
	support ring	2.0	NA	NA	NA	NA	NA	NA	NA	GS
		1.0	NA	NA	NA	NA	NA	NA	NA	GS
		0.5	NA	NA	NA	NA	NA	NA	NA	GS
Zefluor	PTFE	10	NA	NA	NA	NA	NA	NA	NA	GS
		3.0	NA	NA	NA	NA	NA	NA	NA	GS
		2.0	NA	NA	NA	NA	NA	NA	NA	GS
		1.0	NA	NA	NA	NA	NA	NA	NA	GS
		0.5	NA	NA	NA	NA	NA	NA	NA	GS
		0.2	NA	NA	NA	NA	NA	NA	NA	GS
S&S PTFE	Polytetrafluoro-	0.45	80	NA	NA	NA	NA	NA	NA	SAS
	ethylene	0.2	65	NA	NA	NA	NA	NA	NA	SAS
Silical										
5.0	PVC	5.0	70	NA	NA	NA	NA	NA	27	OSI
2.0		2.0	100	NA	NA	NA	NA	NA	31	OSI
0.8		0.8	80	NA	NA	NA	NA	NA	43	OSI
0.6		0.6	80	NA	NA	NA	NA	NA	54	OSI
0.2		0.2	100	NA	NA	NA	NA	NA	111	OSI
Poretics										
5.0	Silver	5.0	50	NA	NA	800	NA	NA	NA	POR
3.0		3.0	50	NA	NA	800	NA	NA	NA	POR
1.2		1.2	50	NA	NA	800	NA	NA	NA	POR
0.8		0.8	50	NA	NA	400	NA	NA	NA	POR
0.45		0.45	50	NA	NA	400	NA	NA	NA	POR
0.2		0.2	50	NA	NA	400	NA	NA	NA	POR

TABLE 13-I-1 (con't.). Summary of Air Sampling Filter Characteristics

Filter	Composition	Pore Size (μm)	Thick-ness (μm)	Weight/ Area (mg/cm²)	Ash Content (%)	Max. Oper. Temp. (°C)	Tensile Strength (psi)	Refractive Index	ΔP100^A in H_2O	Source
C. Membrane Filter Characteristics (con't.)										
Costar										
MR	Mixed cellulose ester	0.45	NA	NA	NA	NA	NA	NA	NA	CC
		0.8	NA	NA	NA	NA	NA	NA	NA	CC
		1.2	NA	NA	NA	NA	NA	NA	NA	CC
PVC	Polyvinyl chloride	0.8	NA	NA	NA	NA	NA	NA	NA	CC
		5.0	NA	NA	NA	NA	NA	NA	NA	CC
FN	PTFE-polypropylene reinforced	0.45	NA	NA	NA	NA	NA	NA	NA	CC
		1.00	NA	NA	NA	NA	NA	NA	NA	CC
D. Polycarbonate Pore Filter Characteristics										
Nuclepore-Costar										
PC	Polycarbonate	8.0	9.0	1.0	0.04	140	>3,000	1.58 & 1.614	NA	CC
PC, AP		8.0	NA	NA	NA	NA	>3,000	NA	NA	CC
PC		0.40	10.0	0.8	0.04	140	>3,000	1.58 & 1.614	83.0	CC
PC		0.20	10.0	0.9	0.04	140	>3,000	1.58 & 1.614	208.0	CC
Poretics										
	Polycarbonate	8.0	10	1.0	0.01	140	>3,000	1.584+1.625	NA	POR
		5.0	10	1.0	0.01	140	>3,000	1.584+1.625	NA	POR
		3.0	10	1.0	0.01	140	>3,000	1.584+1.625	NA	POR
		2.0	10	1.0	0.01	140	>3,000	1.584+1.625	NA	POR
		1.0	10	1.0	0.01	140	>3,000	1.584+1.625	NA	POR
		0.8	10	1.0	0.01	140	>3,000	1.584+1.625	NA	POR
		0.6	10	1.0	0.01	140	>3,000	1.584+1.625	NA	POR
		0.4	10	1.0	0.01	140	>3,000	1.584+1.625	NA	POR
		0.2	10	1.0	0.01	140	>3,000	1.584+1.625	NA	POR
		0.1	10	1.0	0.01	140	>3,000	1.584+1.625	NA	POR

Designation	Composition	Size	Void Size (μm)	Max. Oper. Temp. (°C)	Source	Remarks
E. Filter Thimble Characteristics						
D1013	Cellulose	43 × 123 mm	NA	120	GRA	Use with D1012 Paper Thimble Holder
D1016	Glass cloth	2-3/16 × 14"	NA	400	GRA	Use with D1015 Glass Cloth Thimble Holder
RA-98	Alundum	NA	Standard	High	GRA	Use with D1021 Alundum Thimble Holder
RA-360	Alundum	NA	Fine	High	GRA	Use with D1021 Alundum Thimble Holder
RA-84	Alundum	NA	Extra Fine	High	GRA	Use with D1021 Alundum Thimble Holder
S&S 603 GV	Glass fiber Heat treated	from 19 × 90 mm to 90 × 200 mm	NA	510	SAS	
Whatman	Cellulose	from 10 × 50 mm to 90 × 200 mm	NA	120	WLS	
	Glass fiber	from 19 × 90 mm to 43 × 123 mm	NA	550	WLS	

^A Pressure drop at face velocity of 100 ft/min (50 cm/s).
^B With organic binder.
^C Without organic binder.
^D Laminated on one side with polyester.
^E Quartz fiber.
^F Contains Teflon.
^G Contains cellulose.
^H Available with or without imprinted grid lines.
^I Available with black color.
NA = Information not available or not applicable.
AP = Apiezon coated.

TABLE 13-I-2. Summary of Filter Holder Characteristics

Figure No.	Catalog No.	Type	Filter Size (mm)	Effective Area (cm^2)	Fittings Supplied with Holder	Weight (g)	Materials of Construction: Body	Gasket	Filter Support	Fittings	Overall Size (cm) (w/o fittings)	Type of Closure	Max Temp (°C)	Source
13-13	1107	Open	25	3.7	1/8" NPT to 1/4" ID hose	NA	Delrin	—	Stainless screen	Nylon	3.5DX2.0	Threaded	85	GS
	1209	Inline	25	NA	1/8" NPT to 1/4" ID hose	NA	Stainless	Viton	Stainless screen	Nylon	NA	Threaded	204	GS
	1219	Open	37	4.9	1/8" NPT to hose barb	NA	Aluminum	NA	Stainless screen	Nylon	4.4DX2.4	Threaded	NA	GS
	1119	Inline	47	9.6	1/4" NPT	NA	Polycarbonate	Silicone	Polysulfonate	Nylon	6.4DX5.6	Threaded	NA	GS
	1220	Open	47	9.6	1/8" NPT to 1/4" ID hose	NA	Aluminum	—	Stainless screen	Nylon	5.4DX2.2	Threaded	NA	GS
	1235	Inline	47	9.6	3/8" NPT to 1/4" ID hose	NA	Aluminum	Viton	Stainless screen	Nylon	5.9DX2.2	Threaded	NA	GS
13-14	2220	Inline	47	9.6	3/8" NPT to 1/4" ID hose	NA	Stainless	Viton	Stainless screen	Nylon	5.9DX5.7	Threaded	204	GS
13-15	26800	Open	47 or 50	NA	Built-in hose barb	NA	Polysulfone	O-Ring	Polysulfone	Polysulfone	NA	Threaded	NA	SAS
		Open	47	NA	NA	NA	NA	NA	NA	NA	NA	Threaded	NA	SRD
		Open	50.0	NA	NA	NA	NA	NA	NA	NA	NA	Threaded	NA	SRD
		Open	102	NA	Built-in 1"D nipple	NA	NA	NA	NA	NA	NA	Threaded	NA	SRD
		Open	Charcoal cartridge	NA	NA	NA	PVC	NA	NA	NA	NA	Threaded	NA	SRD
		Open	47 or 50 & charcoal	NA	NA	NA	PVC	NA	NA	NA	NA	Threaded	NA	SRD
		Inline	47 or 50	NA	NA	NA	Aluminum or stainless	NA	NA	NA	NA	Threaded	NA	SRD
		Inline	Charcoal	NA	NA	NA	Aluminum or stainless	NA	NA	NA	NA	Threaded	NA	SRD
		Inline	47 or 50	NA	NA	NA	Aluminum or stainless	NA	NA	NA	NA	Threaded	NA	SRD
	SH-18	Open	28	4.9	Luer adaptor	42	Aluminum	—	—	—	NA	Threaded	NA	STA
	SH-20	Open	49	18.5	Luer adaptor	43	Aluminum	—	—	—	NA	Threaded	NA	STA
	SH-4	Open	110	69.3	Flanged w/4" threaded locking ring	NA	Aluminum	Neoprene	Stainless cross bar	—	NA	Threaded	NA	STA
	SH-69	Open	152X228	NA	Flanged w/4" threaded locking ring	NA	Stainless	Neoprene	Stainless screen	Aluminum	NA	Lock nuts (4)	NA	STA
	SH-810	Open	203X254	NA	Flanged w/4" threaded locking ring	NA	Stainless	Neoprene	Stainless screen	Aluminum	NA	Lock nuts (4)	NA	STA

TABLE 13-I-2 (con't.). Summary of Filter Holder Characteristics

							Materials of Construction							
Figure No.	Catalog No.	Type	Filter Size (mm)	Effective Area (cm^2)	Fittings Supplied with Holder	Weight (g)	Body	Gasket	Filter Support	Fittings	Overall Size (cm) (w/o fittings)	Type of Closure	Max Temp (^oC)	Source
13-16	SX0001300[A]	Inline	13	0.7	Female Luer inlet, male Luer outlet	7.1	Poly-propylene	Silicone	Polypropylene	—	1.7 DX3.5	Threaded	NA	MIL
	XX3001200	Inline	13	0.81	Female Luer inlet, male Luer outlet	NA	Stainless	Teflon	Stainless screen	—	1.6 DX3.3	Threaded	NA	MIL
	SX0002500[B]	Inline	25	3.34	Female Luer inlet, male Luer outlet	14.2	Poly-propylene	Silicone	Polypropylene	—	3.2 DX1.6	Threaded	NA	MIL
	XX3002500	Inline	25	NA	Female Luer inlet, male Luer outlet	NA	Stainless	Teflon	Stainless screen	—	3.2 DX3.2	Threaded	NA	MIL
13-16	XX3002514	Inline	25	NA	1/4" NPT female inlet, male Luer outlet	NA	Stainless	Teflon	Stainless	—	3.2 DX3.2	Threaded	NA	MIL
13-17	XX5002500	Inline	25	~3	7/16" OD hose connector	340	Aluminum & stainlesss	Teflon	Stainless screen	—	3.8 & 3.0 Hex flatsX12	Threaded	NA	MIL
	M000025A0[C]	Open or inline	25	3.9	Female Luer ports	NA	Styrene	—	Cellulose pad	—	2.8 DX3.8	Press fit	NA	MIL
13-18	MA00037A0[C]	Open or inline	37	9.0	Female Luer ports	21	Polystyrene	—	Cellulose pad	—	4.3 DX3.5	Press fit	NA	MIL
13-19	XX5004700	Inline	47	9.6	7/16" OD hose connector	906	Aluminum & stainless	Teflon	Stainless steel	—	7.0DX17.8	Bayonet lock	NA	MIL
	XX5004720	Open	47	9.6	7/16" OD hose connector	1160	Aluminum & stainless	Teflon	Stainless screen	—	7.0DX17.8 or 10.2	Bayonet lock	NA	MIL
	XX4304700	Inline	47	9.6	1/4" NPT female inlet & outlets w/hose connectors for 1/4" to 3/8" ID tubing	NA	Glass-filled polystyrene	Silicone O-Ring	Polystyrene	—	7.6DX12.0	Bayonet lock	NA	MIL

TABLE 13-I-2 (con't.). Summary of Filter Holder Characteristics

Figure No.	Catalog No.	Type	Filter Size (mm)	Effective Area (cm^2)	Fittings Supplied with Holder	Weight (g)	Materials of Construction: Body	Gasket	Filter Support	Fittings	Overall Size (cm) (w/o fittings)	Type of Closure	Max Temp (°C)	Source
	SX004700	Inline	47	13.8	Female Luer & 1/4" NPT male inlet, Female Luer & hose connector output	43	Polystyrene	Silicone O-Ring	Polystyrene	—	5.72 DX5.4	Threaded	NA	MIL
	420100	Inline	13	0.8	Female Luer inlet, male Luer outlet	NA	NA	NA	NA	NA	NA	NA	NA	CC
	800932	Open or inline	25	3.9	Female Luer ports	NA	NA	NA	NA	NA	NA	NA	NA	CC
	800927	Open or inline	25	3.9	Female Luer ports	NA	NA	NA	NA	NA	NA	NA	NA	CC
	300075[D]	Open or inline	25	3.9	Female Luer ports	NA	NA	NA	NA	NA	NA	NA	NA	CC
13-20	322514[A]	Open or inline	25	3.9	Female Luer ports	NA	NA	NA	NA	NA	NA	NA	NA	CC
13-20	322575[C]	Open or inline	25	3.9	Female Luer ports	NA	NA	NA	NA	NA	NA	NA	NA	CC
	420200	Inline	25	2.4	Polycarbonate	NA	NA	NA	NA	NA	NA	NA	NA	CC
	430200	Open	25	2.4	Polycarbonate	NA	NA	NA	NA	NA	NA	NA	NA	CC
	470200	Universal	25	2.4	Polycarbonate	NA	NA	NA	NA	NA	NA	NA	NA	CC
	425610	Inline	25	3.9	Stainless	NA	NA	NA	NA	NA	NA	NA	NA	CC
	300061	Inline	37	9.1	Stainless female Luer ports	NA	NA	NA	NA	NA	NA	NA	NA	CC
	300064	Open or inline	37	9.1	Stainless female Luer ports	NA	NA	NA	NA	NA	NA	NA	NA	CC
13-20	322564[E]		37	9.1	Stainless female Luer ports	NA	NA	NA	NA	NA	NA	NA	NA	CC
	361864[F]	Open or inline	37	9.1	Stainless female Luer ports	NA	NA	NA	NA	NA	NA	NA	NA	CC
	420400	Inline	47	11.3	Polycarbonate	NA	NA	NA	NA	NA	NA	NA	NA	CC
	430400	Universal	47	11.3	Polycarbonate	NA	NA	NA	NA	NA	NA	NA	NA	CC
	272	Inline	37	7.1	1/4" FPT	500	Stainless	Viton	Stainless screen	—	5.6 DX4.5	Threaded	NA	GRA
	272-LI	Inline	37	7.1	1/4" FPT	500	Stainless	Viton	Stainless screen	—	5.6 DX8.4	Threaded	NA	GRA
	272-AL	Inline	37	7.1	1/4" FPT	200	Aluminum	Viton	Stainless screen	—	5.6 DX4.5	Threaded	NA	GRA

TABLE 13-I-2 (con't.). Summary of Filter Holder Characteristics

Figure No.	Catalog No.	Type	Filter Size (mm)	Effective Area (cm^2)	Fittings Supplied with Holder	Weight (g)	Materials of Construction: Body	Gasket	Filter Support	Fittings	Overall Size (cm) (w/o fittings)	Type of Closure	Max Temp (°C)	Source
13-20	272-O	Open	37	7.1	1.18"DX0.75"L inlet tube, 1/4" FPT outlet	500	Stainless	Viton	Stainless screen	—	5.6 DX5.5	Threaded	NA	GRA
	272ALO	Open	37	7.1	1.18"DX0.75"L inlet tube, 1/4" FPT outlet	200	Aluminum	Viton	Stainless screen	—	6.5 DX5.5	Threaded	NA	GRA
	273	Inline	47	9.6	3/8" FPT	600	Stainless	Viton	Stainless screen	—	6.5 DX5.2	Threaded	NA	GRA
	273-LI	Inline	47	9.6	3/8" FPT	700	Stainless	Viton	Stainless screen	—	6.5 DX8.9	Threaded	NA	GRA
	273-AL	Inline	47	9.6	3/8" FPT	200	Aluminum	Viton	Stainless screen	—	6.5 DX5.2	Threaded	NA	GRA
	273-O	Open	47	9.6	1.38IDX0.75" inlet tube, 3/8" FPT outlet	600	Stainless	Viton	Stainless screen	—	6.5DX6.1	Threaded	NA	GRA
	273AL-O	Open	47	9.6	1.38IDX0.75" inlet tube, 3/8" FPT outlet	200	Aluminum	Viton	Stainless screen	—	6.5DX6.1	Threaded	NA	GRA
	274	Inline	63.5	23	1/2" FPT	700	Stainless	Viton	Stainless screen	—	7.5DX5.9	Threaded	NA	GRA
	275AL	Inline	100	55	1/2" FPT	1500	Aluminum	Viton	Stainless screen	—	13.3DX6.7	Thumb nuts	NA	GRA
	275AL-O	Open	100	55	1/2" FPT	1300	Aluminum	Viton	Stainless screen	—	13.3DX4.6	Thumb nuts	NA	GRA
	GMW3000	Cartridge	203X254	406	Fits into Model FH2100 8X10 filter holder	NA	Aluminum	Viton	Stainless screen	—	31.1X23.8X2.5	Thumb nuts	NA	GMW
	FH-2100	Open	203X254	406	4" locking cap	NA	Aluminum	Rubber	Stainless	—	31.1X23.8X15.2	Wing nuts	NA	GMW
13-21	23505-1	Inline	203X254	406	4" locking cap	NA	Aluminum	Rubber	Stainless	—	31.1X23.8X15.2	Wing nuts	NA	GMW
	RVPH-20[G]	Open	50	NA	3/8" FPT	NA	Aluminum	—	—	—	NA	Threaded	NA	HIQ
	RVPH-25[G]	Open	47	NA	3/8" FPT	NA	Plastic	—	—	—	NA	Threaded	NA	HIQ
	RVPH-40	Open	108	NA	3/8" FPT	NA	Plastic	—	—	—	NA	Bayonet	NA	HIQ
13-22	CFPH-20[G]	Open	50	NA	1.75" DX11.5 TPI	NA	Aluminum	—	—	—	NA	Threaded	NA	HIQ
13-22	CFPH-25[G]	Open	47	NA	1.75" DX22.5 TPI	NA	Aluminum	—	—	—	NA	Threaded	NA	HIQ
13-22	CFPH-40	Open	108	NA	1.75" DX11.5	NA	Plastic	—	—	—	NA	Bayonet	NA	HIQ
13-23	IFH-25	Inline	Cartridge	NA	3/8" FPT	NA	Cast metal	—	—	—	NA	Hinged	NA	HIQ
	91100	Open	37	7.0	1/4" ID hose	NA	Polyacetal resin	Teflon	Stainless screen	—	58X95	Threaded	NA	POR

TABLE 13-I-2 (con't.). Summary of Filter Holder Characteristics

Figure No.	Catalog No.	Type	Filter Size (mm)	Effective Area (cm^2)	Fittings Supplied with Holder	Weight (g)	Materials of Construction: Body	Gasket	Filter Support	Fittings	Overall Size (cm) (w/o fittings)	Type of Closure	Max Temp (°C)	Source
	91150	Open	47	12.5	1/4" ID hose	NA	Polyacetal resin	Teflon	Stainless screen	—	58X95	Threaded	NA	POR
13-24	F-1	Inline	478	12.97	1/4" NPTX3/8" hose barb	306	Aluminum	Silicone	Stainless screen	—	7.0	Threaded	260	BGI
	F-2	Open	47	12.97	1/4" NPTX3/8" hose barb"	243	Aluminum	Silicone	Stainless screen	—	5.0	Threaded	260	BGI
	F-5/2	Inline	47	12.97	1/4" NPTX3/8" hose barb	236	Teflon	Silicone	Teflon coated stainless screen	—	7.0	Threaded	130	BGI
	F-7	Inline	47	12.97	1/4" NPTX3/8" hose barb	534	Stainless	Silicone	Stainless screen	—	5.2	Threaded	400	BGI
13-25	SS-1	Thimble	30X100	70.7	5/8" compression X5/8" tube	595	Stainless	Silicone or fiber	—	—	20.0 LX5.0 D	Threaded	900	BGI
	SS-3	Thimble	30X100	70.7	5/8" compression X5/8" tube	726	Stainless	Silicone or fiber	—	—	21.3 LX5.0 D	Threaded	1500	BGI
	D1021	Thimble	Uses Ra-98, Ra-360, & Ra-84 Alundum thimbles (see Table 13-I-1)	NA	1/2" NPT female sockets	NA	Stainless	Fiber	—	—	NA	Threaded	NA	GRA
	D1015	Thimble	Uses D1016 glass, cloth thimbles (see Table 13-I-1)	NA	1/2" NPT female sockets	NA	Stainless	Special	—	—	7.5 DX48	Lock nuts (4)	400	GRA

[A] Cellulose ester 0.8-µm (ABC) filter in 3-piece cassette for ambient or area monitoring.
[B] Cellulose ester 0.8-µm (ABC) filter in 3-piece conductive cassette with 2-in. extruder cowl.
[C] Gridded 0.4-µm polycarbonate membrane in 2-piece cassette.
[D] Conductive unit (carbon-filled polypropylene).
[E] Cellulose ester 0.8-µm (ABC) filter in 3-piece cassette.
[F] PVC membrane filter, 5.0 µm in 3-piece cassette.
[G] Also available as combination holder for filter paper plus metal cartridge for vapor sampling.

TABLE 13-I-3. Commercial Sources for Filters and Filter Holders

Symbol	Source	Symbol	Source	Symbol	Source
BGI	BGI Incorporated 58 Guinam Street Waltham, MA 02154 (617)891-9380 FAX (617)891-8151	GRA	Graseby Andersen 500 Technology Court Smyrna, GA 30082-5211 (404)319-9999 or (800)241-6898 FAX (404)319-0336	PFX	Pallflex Corporation Kennedy Dr. Putnam, CT 06260
CC	Corning Costar One Alewife Center Cambridge, MA 02140 (617)868-6200 or (800)492-1110 FAX (617)868-2076	H&V	Hollingsworth & Vose Co. P.O. Box 168 West Groton, MA 01472	POR	Poretics Corp. 151 Lindbergh Ave. Livermore, CA 94550-9520
GS	Gelman Sciences 600 South Wagner Rd. Ann Arbor, MI 48106-1448	HIQ	Hi-Q Environmental Products Co. 7386 Trade Street San Diego, CA 92121 (619)549-2820 FAX (619)549-9657	SRD	SAI/RADECO 4161 Campus Point San Diego, CA 92121-9416
GMW	Graseby GMW General Metal Works, Inc. 145 S. Miami Ave. Village of Cleves, OH 45002 (513)941-2229 FAX (513)941-1977	MIL	Millipore Corporation 80 Ashby Road Bedford, MA 01730 (617)533-2125 or (800)645-5476	SAS	Schleicher and Schuell, Inc. 543 Washington St. Keene, NH 03431
		OSI	Omega Specialty Instrument Co. 4 Kidder Road, Unit 5 Chelmsford, MA 01842	STA	Staplex Company 777 Fifth Avenue Brooklyn, NY 11232 (718)768-3333
				WLS	Whatman Lab. Sales P.O. Box 1359 Hillsboro, OR 97123-9981

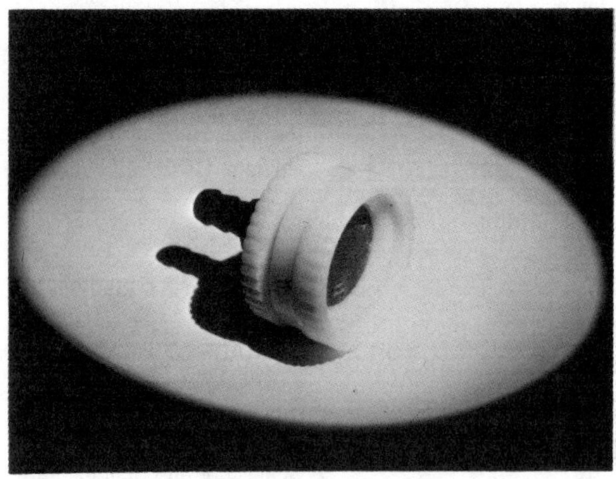

FIGURE 13-13. Gelman #1107 25-mm Delrin open filter holder.

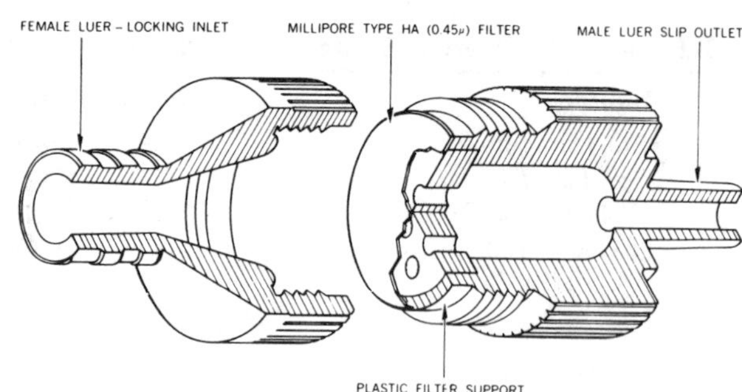

FIGURE 13-16. Schematic of Millipore Corp. Swinnex-13 polypropylene Swinny-type in-line filter unit.

FIGURE 13-14. Gelman #2220 47-mm stainless in-line filter holder.

FIGURE 13-17. Millipore aerosol microanalysis filter holder.

FIGURE 13-15. S&S Aerosol holder, 47 or 50 mm.

FIGURE 13-18. Millipore 37-mm aerosol monitor. At left is a sealed unit, as supplied. The top can be removed with a coin for use as an open filter holder.

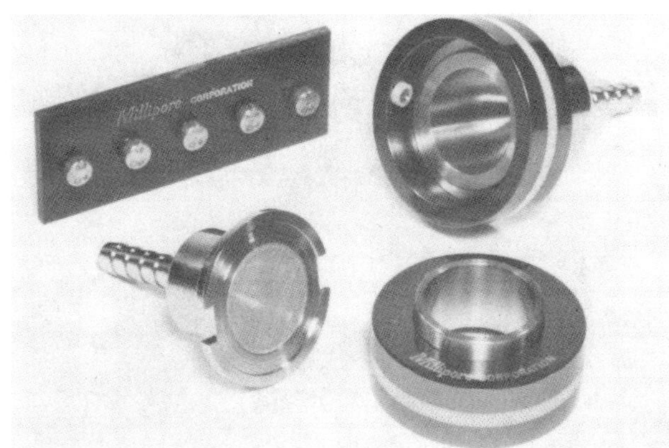

FIGURE 13-19. Millipore aerosol universal filter holder (#XX50 047-20) with a set of limiting orifices. It consists of the front ends of both the open (#XX50 047 10) and standard (#XX50 047 00) holders and an interchangeable base.

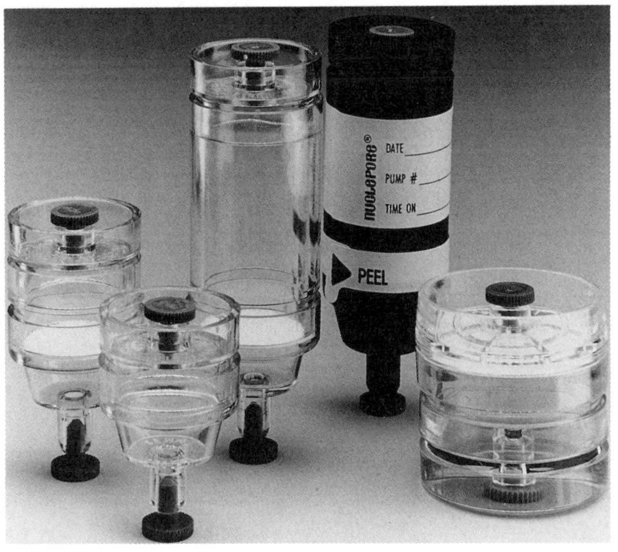

FIGURE 13-20. Costar filter holders. From left: 322314, 322511, 322515, 322575, and 322564.

FIGURE 13-21. General Metal Works #23505-1 8-in. x 10-in. in-line filter holder.

FIGURE 13-22. HI-Q Paper filter open-face holders for high volume samplers for 47-mm-, 2-in.-, and 4-in.-diameter filters.

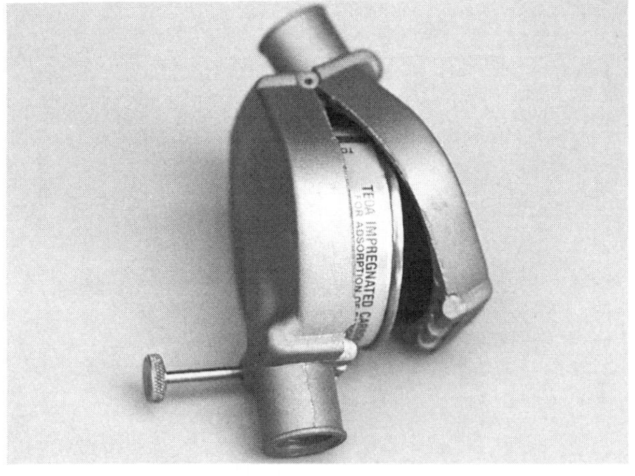

FIGURE 13-23. HI-Q cartridge holder for TCAL type cartridge. TC-12 or 45 cartridge can be used with a spacer.

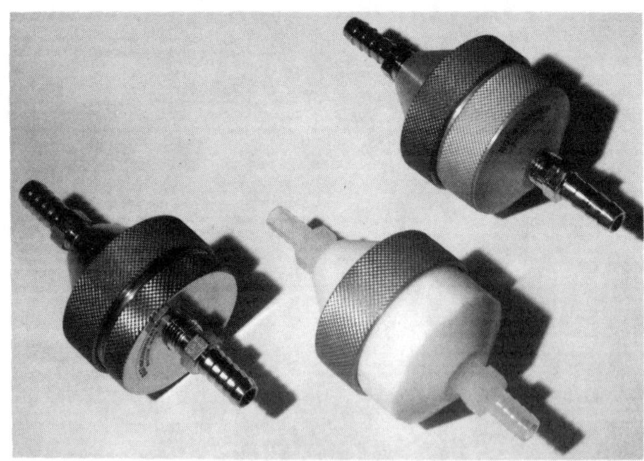

FIGURE 13-24. BGI, Incorporated 47-mm in-line filter holders with stainless steel, Teflon, and aluminum bodies.

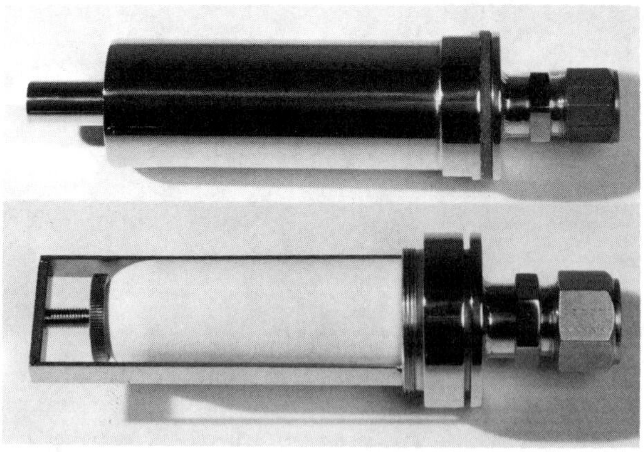

FIGURE 13-25. BGI, Incorporated 30 × 100 Alundum Thimble Adaptor; closed, and with cover sleeve removed.

Chapter 14

Impactors, Cyclones, and Other Inertial and Gravitational Collectors

Susanne V. Hering, Ph.D.

President, Aerosol Dynamics, Inc., 2329 Fourth Street, Berkeley, California

CONTENTS

Overview

Inertial and gravitational collectors include impactors, cyclones, aerosol centrifuges, impingers, and elutriators. In contrast to filters, which generally collect particles of all sizes, these instruments collect particles in characteristic size ranges. They are used for size-selective sampling or size-segregated collection of airborne particles. Size-selective sampling refers to the collection of one specific particle size fraction, such as the collection of respirable particles or particles smaller than a nominal 10 µm (called PM_{10} or American Conference of Governmental Industrial Hygienists—International Standards Organization [ACGIH–ISO] thoracic particles). Size-segregated aerosol collection refers to the physical separation of airborne particles into several size fractions.

Cyclones, elutriators, and single-stage impactors can be used to remove larger particles from the air stream and are commonly followed by a filter for collection of the undersized particles. Some cyclones can be operated to approximate the respirable collection efficiency curve, as discussed in Chapter 5. Other cyclones mimic the thoracic collection efficiency curve. Similarly, elutriators have been used in size-selective sampling to measure respirable or thoracic particle mass. Single-stage impaction heads are used to adapt Hi-Volume samplers for PM_{10} sampling.

Cascade impactors, cascaded cyclones, aerosol centrifuges, and horizontal elutriators can be used to size-fractionate particles with respect to aerodynamic diameter. The multiple stages of a cascade impactor can be analyzed to determine aerosol mass distributions or to assess chemical composition as a function of particle size. Cascaded cyclones have been designed for stack gas sampling in which a robust system is needed to handle the elevated temperatures. Aerosol centrifuges and some horizontal elutriators provide a continuous size spectrum, and they can be used to determine aerodynamic shape factors for irregularly shaped particles. Impingers and impactors are used for collection of bioaerosols. The choice of sampler depends on the application and the analyses to be performed.

The particle separation characteristics of inertial and gravitational collectors depend on particle "aerodynamic diameter," as defined below. The particle collection mechanism pits the particle's aerodynamic resistance against its inertia or an external force. For particles greater than about 0.5 μm, the aerodynamic diameter is generally the quantity of interest because it is the parameter that enters into the equations for particle transport, collection, and respiratory tract deposition. Respirable, thoracic, and inhalable particle sampling, as described in Chapter 5, are based on particle aerodynamic diameter.

This chapter first presents the definition for aerodynamic diameter because this parameter is applicable to all inertial and gravitational collectors. Subsequent sections are devoted to impactors, cyclones, aerosol centrifuges, inertial spectrometers, impingers, and elutriators. Each section gives a basic description of the type of instrument, the theory of operation, its applications, and guidelines for use.

Aerodynamic Diameter

Aerodynamic diameter is defined as the diameter of a smooth, unit density ($\rho_o = 1$ g/cm^3) sphere that has the same settling velocity as the particle. It is dependent on the particle density and particle shape, as well as the particle size. The general expression for the particle aerodynamic diameter, d_a, is:

$$d_a = \left(\frac{\rho\, C}{\rho_o\, C_a}\right)^{1/2} d_p \qquad (1)$$

where: ρ = particle density
ρ_o = 1 g/cm^3
C = Cunningham slip factor (defined below) evaluated for the particle diameter d_p
C_a = Cunningham slip factor evaluated for the particle diameter d_a
d_p = physical diameter for spherical particles and the Stokes diameter (also defined below) for nonspherical particles

The slip factor C is an empirical factor that accounts for the reduction in the drag force on particles due to the "slip" of the gas molecules at the particle surface. It is important for small particles, less than 1 μm in diameter, for which the surrounding air cannot be modeled by a continuous fluid. The slip factor is a function of the ratio between particle diameter and mean free path of the suspending gas; it is given by the following expression:[1]

$$C = 1 + \frac{\lambda}{d_p}\left[2.514 + 0.800 \exp\left(-0.55\,\frac{d_p}{\lambda}\right)\right] \qquad (2)$$

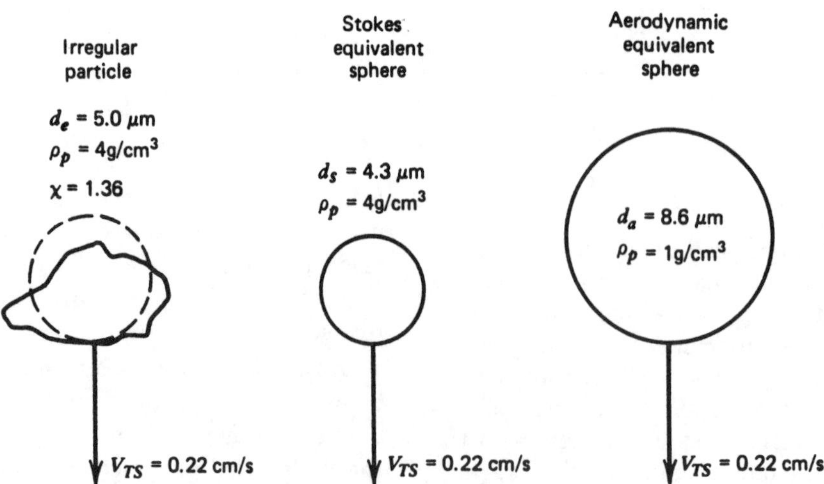

FIGURE 14-1. An irregularly shaped particle and its equivalent Stokes and aerodynamic spheres.[1] Reprinted by permission of John Wiley & Sons, Inc.

where: λ = mean free path of air

At normal atmospheric conditions (i.e., temperature = 20°C, pressure = 1 atmosphere), $\lambda = 0.066$ µm. For large particles ($d_p > 5$ µm), $C = 1$; for smaller particles, $C > 1$.

The particle Stokes diameter d_p is defined as the diameter of a sphere having the same density and settling velocity as the particle. For a smooth, spherically shaped particle, d_p exactly equals the physical diameter of the particle. For irregularly shaped particles, d_p is the diameter that characterizes the aerodynamic drag force on the particle. The relationship between the physical particle size, Stokes, and aerodynamic diameters is illustrated in Figure 14-1.[1] Particles with the same physical size and shape, but different densities, will have the same Stokes diameter but different aerodynamic diameters.

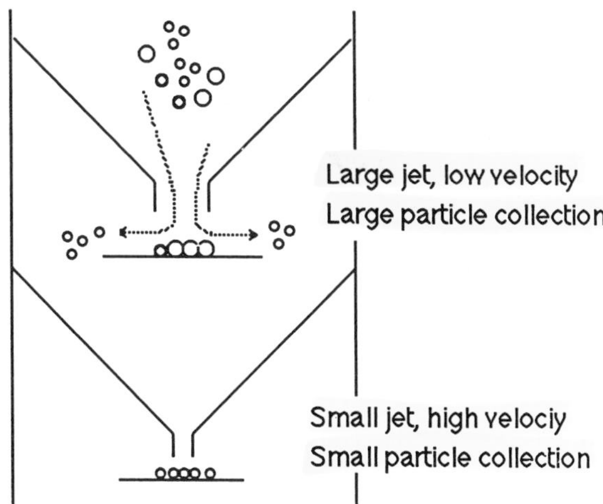

FIGURE 14-2. Schematic of two impactor stages showing large and small particle trajectories.[2]

For two particles of the same physical size but differing densities, the particle with the larger density will have the larger aerodynamic diameter. If the density of a particle is greater than 1 g/cm^3, then its aerodynamic diameter is larger than its Stokes diameter. Conversely, for particles of densities less than 1 g/cm^3, the aerodynamic diameter is smaller than the Stokes diameter.

For particles with diameters much greater than the mean free path, the aerodynamic diameter given by Equation 1 can be approximated by:

$$d_a = \sqrt{\frac{\rho}{\rho_0}}\, d_p \qquad (d_p >> \lambda) \tag{3}$$

In this approximation, the aerodynamic diameter is directly proportional to the square root of the particle density. This expression holds for large particles for which the slip factor equals one. It is often used for particles as small as 0.5 µm, which is acceptable if the particle density is at all close to 1 g/cm^3. For example, a density of 2 g/cm^3 and a Stokes diameter of 0.5 µm gives an aerodynamic diameter calculated from Equation 1 of 0.68 µm. The approximation of Equation 3 gives 0.71 µm, an error of only 4%.

For particles with diameters much smaller than the mean free path, the slip factor C is inversely proportional to particle diameter, which makes the aerodynamic diameter directly proportional to the particle density:

$$d_a = \frac{\rho}{\rho_0} d_p \qquad (d_p << \lambda) \tag{4}$$

This small particle limit is applicable for low-pressure systems, such as low-pressure or inertial devices used in stratospheric sampling.

Impactors

Description and Operational Principle

The term "impactor" encompasses a large category

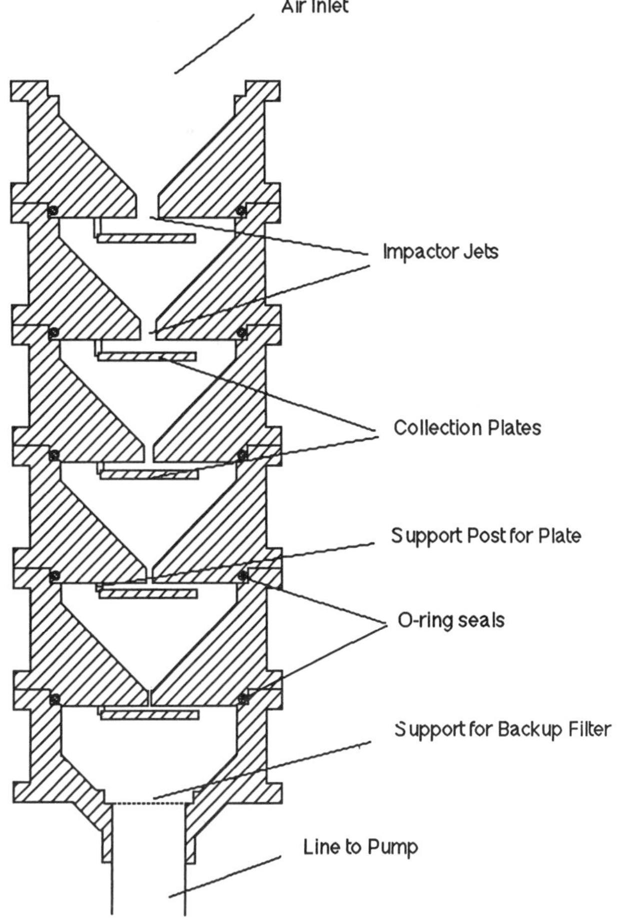

FIGURE 14-3. A single-jet, five-stage cascade impactor.

of aerosol collection instruments in which particle impaction in a nonrotating flow is the primary mechanism of particle capture. Particle impaction refers to the collection of particles that by virtue of their inertia deviate from the air flow streamlines. Impaction occurs when streamlines bend as the air flow bypasses a solid object.

Conventional flat-plate impactors employ a collection surface located internal to the device, as illustrated in Figure 14-2.[2] Particle-laden air passes through the nozzle and impinges on a collection plate oriented perpendicular to the nozzle axis. The air flow is laminar, and particles within the nozzle are accelerated to a nearly uniform velocity. At the nozzle exit, the streamlines of the gas are deflected sharply by the collection plate. Larger particles are propelled across the air streamlines and deposit on the plate. Smaller particles follow the streamlines more closely and remain suspended in the air.

The cascade impactor shown in Figure 14-3 is a multistage device that fractionates the sample by particle size. Air enters at the top, passes through each of the impactor stages, and is exhausted through a back-up filter. Each impactor stage consists of one or more jets followed by a collection plate. Successive stages are designed to collect smaller particles. Those particles that penetrate the last impaction stage are collected by the back-up filter. Air flow is generated by means of a pump and controlled by a valve or critical orifice downstream of the back-up filter.

Particle trajectories in the single-jet cascade impactor are illustrated in Figure 14-2. The minimum size collected by an individual stage depends on the jet diameter and the air stream velocity in the jet. In low-pressure impactors, it also depends on the pressure at which the stage operates. Typically, the collection of smaller particles is achieved by using smaller diameter jets with higher jet velocities. Within limits, particle impaction is insensitive to the spacing between the collection plate and the jet exit, and to the geometry of the stage.

Size-fractionated samples from cascade impactors are used to determine the distribution of aerosol mass or chemical species with respect to particle size. When cascade impactor samples are analyzed chemically, they yield species size distributions as shown in Figure 14-4.[3] Alternatively, the impactor samples can be assayed gravimetrically to provide an aerosol mass distribution. Simultaneous data on particle size and mass or chemical composition are important for assessing health effects and particle transport in the atmosphere or in a room. Cascade impactors were introduced by May in 1945[4] and are widely used. A recent discussion of these instruments, their use, and data analysis procedures is given by Lodge and Chan.[5]

Commercially available impactors are listed in Table 14-I-1 of the "Instrument Descriptions" section at the end of this chapter. The impactor jets may be round or rectangular in cross section. Many use multiple jets per stage to permit larger collection of particles at larger

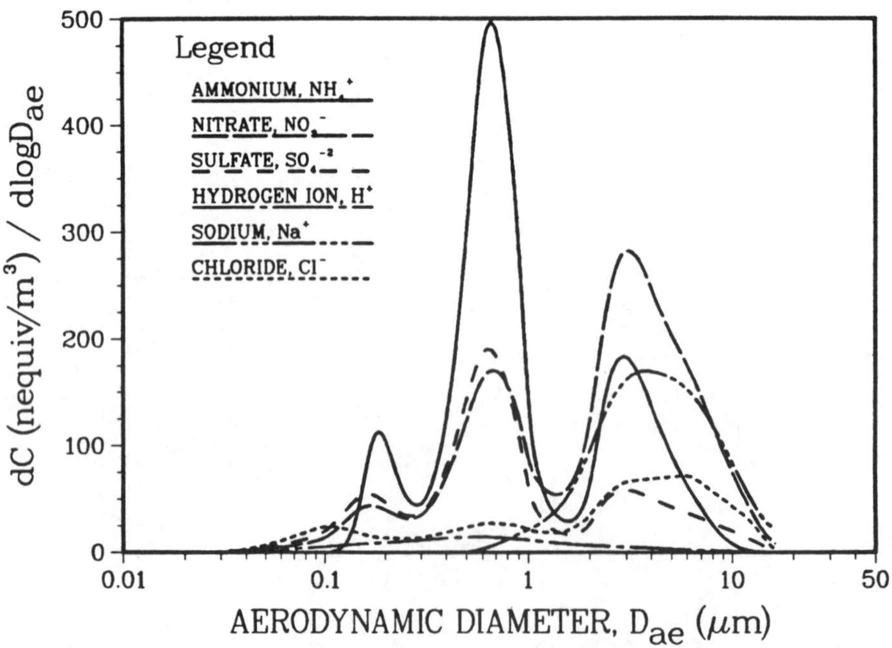

FIGURE 14-4. Inorganic ion particle size distributions collected with the Berner impactor in Claremont, CA.[3] Reprinted by permission of Elsevier Science Publishing Co., Inc.

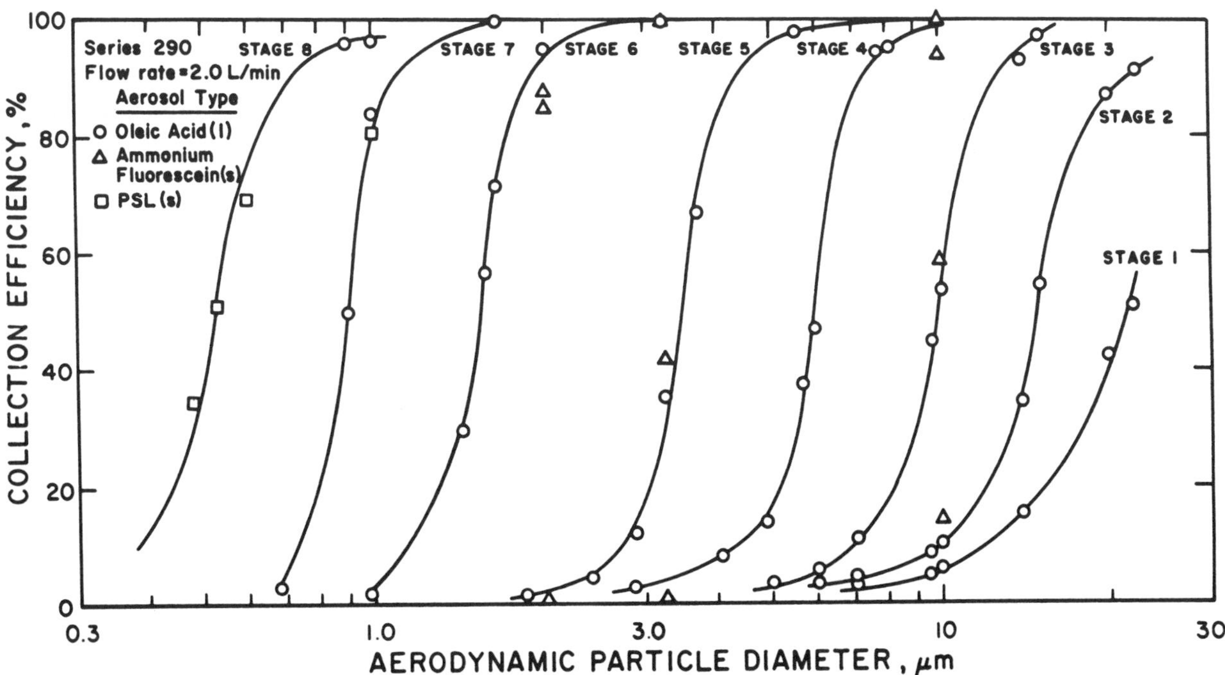

FIGURE 14-5. Collection efficiency curves for the Sierra/Andersen personal sampler.[16] Reprinted with permission, American Industrial Hygiene Association Journal.

flow rates. Large flow rate cascade impactors have been designed for use with Hi-Volume samplers.[6,7] Low flow rate impactors are used for personal and ambient sampling.[8–12] Impactors are also used for stack sampling[13,14] and viable particle sampling,[15] as discussed in Chapters 21 and 23.

The overall size range covered by an impactor depends on its design. Conventional cascade impactors can be designed to collect particles as small as 0.4 μm. Low-pressure and micro-orifice impactors can collect particles as small as 0.05 μm. Some impactors, such as the Andersen microbial sampler, are designed to collect very large particles, as much as 30 μm in diameter. Rotary impactors have been used with high efficiency to sample ambient air particles as large as 250 μm. In these, a rod moving through the ambient air impacts and collects particles larger than the characteristic cut-size for the sampler.

Impactors differ in the nature of the particle collection surface. Most collect particles on a solid plate located immediately downstream of the accelerating jet, as shown in Figure 14-2. However, unless the collection plate is greased, particles may bounce and be re-entrained in the flow. To avoid this problem, the virtual impactor uses a nearly stagnant airflow to transport the size-fractionated sample to a filter. Although it does not have an impaction surface, the air flow streamlines are similar to those in conventional impactors.

Impactor Theory

Impactor performance is characterized by a set of collection efficiency curves such as those shown in Figure 14-5.[16] Each curve shows the efficiency with which a particle entering the stage is collected. The point corresponding to a collection efficiency of 50% is referred to as the cut-size, or cutoff diameter, d_{50}. The curve shape indicates the sharpness of the size-segregation. For an infinitely steep collection efficiency curve, all particles above the cutoff diameter would be collected, and all below that size would pass onto the next stage. In practice, efficiency curves have a finite slope, which gives rise to crossover in particle size between neighboring stages.

Generally, impactors are designed such that the efficiency curves are as steep as possible. This is especially desirable because the most common data reduction methods use only the cutoff diameter to characterize stage performance. More sophisticated inversion methods for data reduction take into account the actual shape of the efficiency curves and produce a smoothed size distribution (e.g., see Figure 14-4).

Impactor theory can be used to predict the cutoff diameter and the shape of the collection efficiency curves. Theory does not account for nonideal effects such as particle rebound from the surface, but it is applicable for sticky particles. The first impactor theories were advanced by Ranz and Wong[17] and Davies and Aylward.[18] Currently used models include those of Marple and Liu[19,20] and Rader and Marple,[21] which use numerical solutions to the fluid dynamics and particle trajectory equations in impactors. Other models of note are those of Mercer and coworkers[22,23] and Ravenhall and Forney.[24] Results from these models are used as guidelines in the design of impactors.[25,26]

In an impactor, whether a particle impacts depends on the drag force on the particle, the particle momentum, and the effective transit time across the plate. Impactor theory combines these parameters into a dimensionless parameter called the Stokes number, given by:

$$St = \frac{\rho \, d_p^2 \, C \, V}{9 \, \mu \, W} \tag{5}$$

where: ρ = particle density
d_p = particle Stokes diameter
C = Cunningham slip factor, as defined in Equation 2
V = mean velocity in the jet
μ = air viscosity
W = jet diameter or width

Physically, the Stokes number is proportional to the ratio of the particle-stopping distance to half the jet diameter. (The stopping distance is the distance traveled by a particle before stopping when injected into still air.) Alternatively, it may be viewed as the ratio of particle relaxation time to the transit time of the air flow through the impaction region. (The relaxation time is the time for a particle initially at rest to accelerate within $1/e$ of the velocity of the air stream, which is 63%, where e is the base of natural logarithms.) The larger the Stokes number, the greater the impaction efficiency.

One of the most important uses of the Stokes number is to predict the cutoff diameter, d_{50}. Impactor stages with similar geometry but varying jet diameters or flow rates will have collection efficiencies that tend to fall on a common curve when plotted as a function of St. The cutoff diameter d_{50} corresponds to a single Stokes number, referred to as the critical Stokes number, St_{50}. The value of St_{50} is approximately the same for different impaction stages, and even for different impactors of similar geometry, and it can be used to predict impactor performance.

It is useful to express the cutoff diameter in terms of the critical Stokes number; the sampler volumetric flow rate, Q; and the number of jets per stage, n. This is accomplished by writing the jet velocity in Equation 5 as the ratio of the flow rate to the jet cross-sectional area. For round jet impactors, the expression is:

$$d_{50}^2 \, C = \frac{9 \, \mu \, \pi \, n \, W^3 \, (St_{50,\,round})}{4 \, \rho \, Q} \tag{6}$$

The Cunningham slip factor, C, depends on the particle diameter and thus has been placed on the left-hand side of the equation. For rectangular jet impactors, with jets of width W and length L, and with n jets (or slots) per stage, the cutoff diameter is given by:

$$d_{50}^2 \, C = \frac{9 \, \mu \, n \, L \, W^2 \, (St_{50,rect.})}{\rho \, Q} \tag{7}$$

For most slotted impactors, the value of $St_{50,rect.}$ is close to 0.59. For round jet impactors, $St_{50,round}$ is about 0.24.

Equations 6 and 7 are used to calculate stage cutoff diameters for impactors operated at different flow rates, or at temperatures and pressures other than the design conditions. Changes in temperature affect μ; changes in pressure affect C. Impactor cutoff diameters decrease with increasing flow rate per jet and decrease with decreasing jet diameter. Because the cutoff diameter is relatively insensitive to the distance between the jet exit and the collection plate, this parameter does not appear in the Stokes number.

The shape of an impactor collection efficiency curve depends on the jet Reynolds number, defined as:

$$Re = \frac{\rho_{air} V W}{\mu} \tag{8}$$

Impactor collection efficiency curves tend to be steeper at higher Reynolds numbers, as shown in the model calculations of Figure 14-6.[19] The performance at $Re = 500$ is much better than at $Re = 100$. For very low Reynolds numbers, below 100, impactors are not very effective, and collection efficiencies may never reach 100%. Once the Reynolds number is above about 200, the impactor will perform well, and the effect of Re on the efficiency curves is relatively small.

The effect of the jet-to-plate spacing on impactor cutoff diameters is shown in Figure 14-7.[19] The jet-to-plate spacing is the distance between the outlet of the impactor nozzle and the impaction plate. Figure 14-7 plots the nondimensional cutoff diameter, expressed in terms of the critical Stokes number, against the ratio of the jet-to-plate spacing, S, to the jet diameter or width, W. For values of S/W between 1 and 5, the impactor stage d_{50} is almost unaffected. At much smaller jet-to-plate spacings, the cut-sizes are smaller and strongly affected by the spacing. At large S, greater than $5W$ or $10W$, depending on the jet Reynolds number, the cut-sizes increase because of the expansion of the jet. The recommended jet-to-plate spacing corresponds to S/W values near 1 for round jet impactors and 1.5 for rectangular jets.

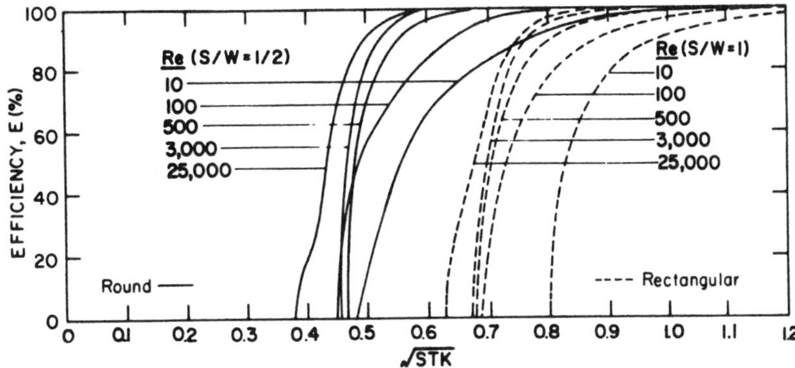

FIGURE 14-6. Model calculations of impactor collection efficiency curves for round and rectangular jet impactors at various jet Reynolds numbers.[19] Reprinted with permission from American Chemical Society.

Particle Bounce

Impactor theory assumes that all particles striking the collection surface adhere to it. In practice, this criterion is not always met. Dry, solid particles may bounce from the surface on impaction and be reentrained in the air stream. If collected on a subsequent stage, the size distribution will be further distorted. This problem is perhaps the greatest limitation in the use of impactors. It was recognized in 1945 by May[4] in the initial development of the impactor and has been raised by many others since.[27–41] Examples of solid particle collection on different impaction surfaces are shown in Figure 14-8.[33]

The theory of particle interactions with surfaces shows there is a critical approach velocity below which the particle will stick on a clean surface, and above which it will bounce.[42–44] This velocity depends on the coefficient of restitution, which is a measure of the particle's tendency to rebound. Cheng and Yeh[45] proposed a criterion for impactor design that would maintain jet velocities below typical critical approach velocities, thereby minimizing particle bounce. However, obtaining the desired cut-sizes at low jet velocities requires small orifices, which often is not a practical option. Generally, case substrate coatings must be used.

Submicrometer as well as supermicrometer particles are subject to particle bounce. Particles as small as 0.2

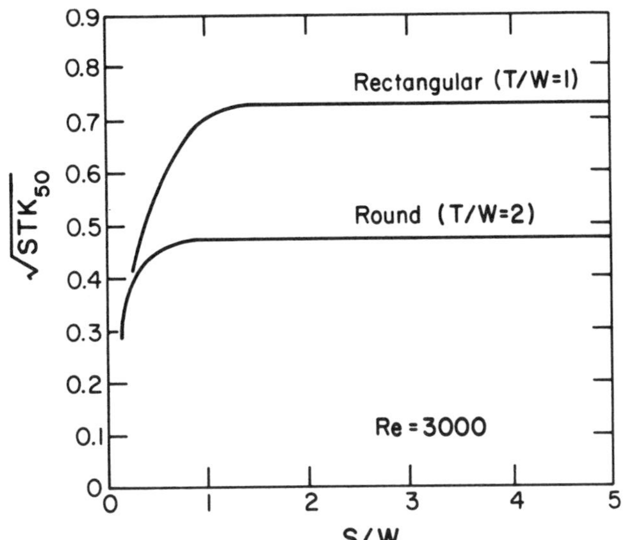

FIGURE 14-7. Impactor 50% cutoff size as a function of the jet-to-plate spacing, S, expressed as a fraction of the jet diameter, W. Curves are shown for round and rectangular jets with a throat length T and diameter or width W.[19] Reprinted with permission from American Chemical Society.

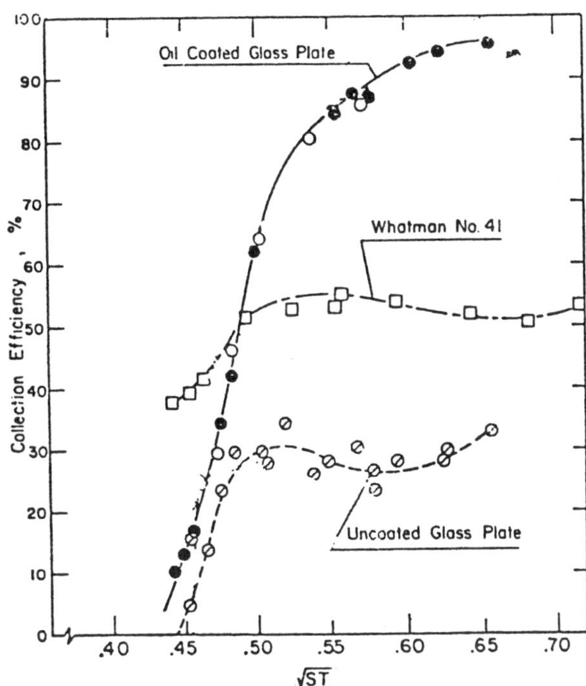

FIGURE 14-8. Collection characteristics of a single jet impactor for solid, polystyrene latex particles with uncoated, coated, and fiber filter impaction surfaces (adapted from Reference 33). Reprinted with kind permission from Pergamon Press, Ltd, Headington Hill Hall, Oxford OX3 0BW, UK.

TABLE 14-1. Adhesive Coatings Used for Impaction Surfaces

	Source*	Author (Ref. No.)
A. Recommended Coatings:		
Apiezon L grease	1.	Wesolowski *et al.*,[31] Lawson,[37] Vanderpool *et al.*,[49] and Pak *et al.*[46]
Dow Corning Antifoam A silicone adhesive	2.	Mercer and Chow[22]
Dow Corning oil (200 & 600 cst)	2.	Rao and Whitby,[32,33] Mercer and Stafford,[23] Vanderpool *et al.*,[49] and Pak *et al.*[46]
Dow Corning silicone grease	2.	Cushing *et al.*,[29] Wesolowski *et al.*,[31] and Vanderpool *et al.*[49]
Flypaper mixture: one part rosin to three parts castor oil	—	May[4]
Halocarbon	3.	Wang and John[3]
One part methylated starch to three parts tricresyl phosphate	—	May[4]
Polyisobutene	—	May[4]
Petroleum jelly (Vaseline)	—	May,[4] Hering *et al.*,[58] Rao and Whitby,[32,33] Lawson,[37] Cushing *et al.*,[29] and Vanderpool *et al.*[49]
Oil-sintered metal	—	Reischl and John[41]
Oil Teflon® membrane filters	—	Turner and Hering[47]
B. Ineffective Coatings:		
Sticky tape		Wesolowski *et al.*[31]
Paraffin		Lawson[37] and Wesolowski *et al.*[37]

*Source: 1. Apiezon Products Ltd., England; available through most scientific supply houses.
2. Dow Corning Co., Midland, Michigan 48686; available through most scientific supply houses.
3. Halocarbon Products Co., 82 Burlews Court, Hackensack, New Jersey 07601.

μm have been observed to bounce from uncoated surfaces. Particles that bounce are often lost to the walls of the impactor.[35,45] Thus, bounce can underestimate mass loadings, as well as distort size distributions. Some have tried to correct for bounce errors in the data analysis. However, bounce-off errors do not affect all types of particles equally. For the same operating conditions, liquid particles adhere, whereas solid particles may not. Therefore, the stage collection efficiency becomes dependent on an unknown and uncontrollable factor, namely the composition of the aerosol being sampled.

To obtain reliable data, it is best to use an adhesive coating on the impaction stage to ensure that all sampled particles will stick. In some cases, the sampled aerosol itself will be sticky and no coating will be needed, but this must be evaluated on a case-by-case basis. In practice, only collection surfaces that show good retention of solid particles are considered "bounce-free."

The effectiveness of different impaction surfaces has been evaluated in several laboratory[28,31–33,35–37] and field[27,30,34,37] studies, as given in Table 14-1. In general, greases and oils are quite effective in reducing particle bounce. It is important that the coating be sufficiently thick and that substrates not be overloaded with particles. A laboratory study of the effect of coating thickness showed that Apiezon L (Apiezon Products Ltd., England; available through most scientific supply houses) coatings less than 0.7 μm thick were not as effective as 9-μm-thick coatings of the same grease for capturing 0.56- and 1-μm latex particles.[46] These same investigators found that for silicone oil, the coating thickness did not have as large an effect on capture efficiencies.

When sampling solid particles, it is important not to overload the substrate. John and coworkers[40,41] found that greased surfaces become ineffective after becoming partially coated with particles. As shown in Figure 14-9, the effect is noticeable at submonolayer loadings, with sticking efficiencies dropping below 50% at less than one monolayer substrate loadings. With half of the grease coating covered with particles, the incoming particle is equally likely to impact on top of a deposited particle as on the greased surface.

To eliminate the effect of substrate loading, Reischl and John[41] used an oil-soaked sintered metal disk. This surface is bounce-free even for high substrate

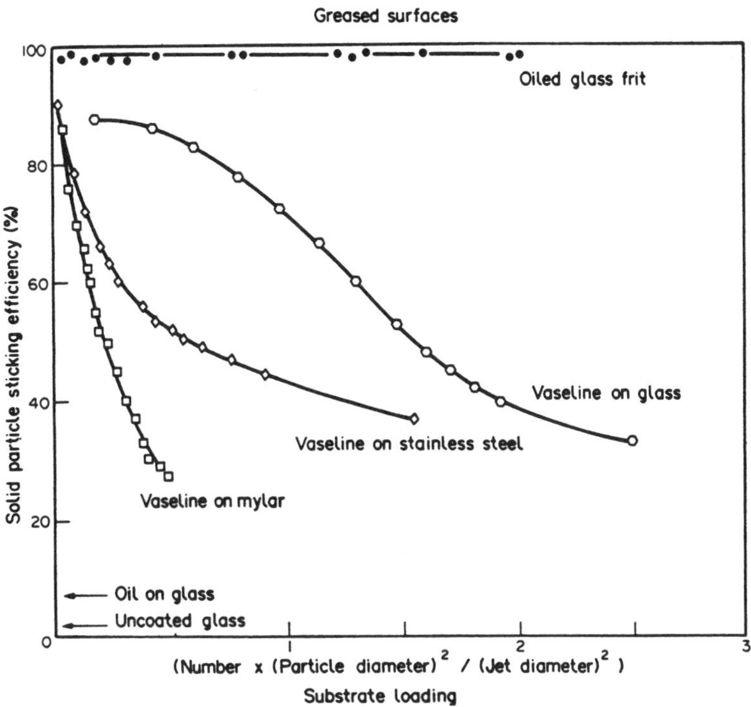

FIGURE 14-9. Dependence of solid particle sticking efficiency on substrate loading for greased and oiled surfaces.[47] Reprinted with kind permission from Pergamon Press, Ltd, Headington Hill Hall, Oxford, OX3 0BW, UK.

loadings. The oil is drawn up onto the depositing particles by capillary action; thus, incoming particles are always presented with an oily surface. The porous metal serves to hold the oil in place under the impactor jet. Sticking efficiencies do not drop even for large accumulations of deposited aerosol. This concept has been used in some commercial devices such as the Wedding PM_{10} particle inlet for Hi-Volume samplers, and it is analogous to the oiled glass frit data shown in Figure 14-9.[47] The disadvantage for some applications is that the surface is not amenable to chemical analysis. Turner and Hering[47] evaluated oil-impregnated membrane filters, which are more readily analyzed chemically, and found that oil-impregnated 10-µm pore size Nuclepore and Teflon filters gave solid particle sticking efficiencies above 90% for substrate loadings up to several monolayers.

Fiber filters are not effective impactor collection substrates for solid particles. Rao and Whitby[33] found that while fiber filters reduce particle bounce, they do not eliminate it (Figure 14-8). Furthermore, the filter has the effect of shifting and flattening the efficiency curve because a fraction of the air stream penetrates the filter mat and is, in effect, filtered. These curves no longer follow impactor theory. The ineffectiveness of filters has been confirmed by several investigators including Dzubay *et al.*,[30] Walsh *et al.*,[34] Willeke,[48] Vanderpool *et al.*,[49] and Newton *et al.*[35]

An alternative approach to eliminating particle bounce is exemplified by the grooved surface[50] once used in the Sierra/Andersen 246 PM_{10} sampler. Grease and oil coatings minimize particle bounce by absorbing the kinetic energy of the incoming particle. The grooved surface uses multiple collisions to dissipate the particle kinetic energy. This design proved effective in laboratory tests with glass beads. It has the disadvantage that the machining requirements render the approach infeasible for smaller cutpoint stages.

Impactor Operation: Guidelines for Use

The mechanical and theoretical simplicity of impactors has made them popular instruments for particle sampling; however, they are easily misused, leading to the generation of erroneous data. Correct operation requires 1) proper preparation and loading of the collection substrates, 2) leak-tight assembly of the instrument, 3) measurement and regulation of the flow rate, 4) appropriate choice of sample time, 5) a suitable inlet system, and 6) a precut device, where appropriate.

Substrate Coatings and Preparation

One of the most critical factors in impactor operation is the preparation of the collection surface. Except for virtual impactors, sampling of solid aerosols requires an adhesive coating to prevent errors from particle bounce. Although many manufacturers supply fibrous filter substrates, these substrates degrade impactor performance and do not eliminate bounce-off, as discussed above.

The choice of the adhesive surface depends on the application. Greases work well for chemical or elemental analyses of nonorganic species. They have also been used for determining the size distributions of specific organic species. The size distributions of polycyclic aromatic hydrocarbon compounds presented in Chapter 6 were collected using Vaseline-coated substrates. Other commonly used adhesive greases are Apiezon L and M, Halocarbon (Halocarbon Products Co., 82 Burlews Court, Hackensack, New Jersey 07601), and Dow silicone (Dow Corning Co., Midland, Michigan 48686). Although these vacuum greases have the advantage that they do not volatilize during sampling, Vaseline has the advantage of lower blank values for sulfur and trace metals.[37] Various types of oils and greases that have been used in impactor applications are listed in Table 14-1.

Analyses for total organic carbon remain a problem because there are no noncarbon greases or oils. To date, these samples are collected on uncoated substrates, which are suspect except in cases such as the sampling of cigarette smoke, where the aerosol particles may be self adhesive. In some cases, investigators have operated parallel, single-stage impactors with different cutpoints and analyzed only the after-filters. The impactor stages can then be coated without interfering with the analyses, provided suitable precautions are taken to prevent any transfer of the grease to the after-filter.

Installation of Collection Substrates

In using any impactor, the operator must be careful to ensure that the impaction stages are installed correctly. Jet-to-plate spacings often equal the diameter of the jet and can be quite small. An improperly installed collection surface that is too close to the jet or, worse yet, one that partially blocks the flow, can sharply affect the cutoff diameter. Impactor cutoffs are significantly affected when jet-to-plate spacings are less than 0.4 jet diameters. It is generally a good idea to inspect each stage before sampling to ensure proper installation.

Flow Rate Regulation

As with most inertial samplers, the particle cut-sizes depend on the sampler flow rate. Thus, proper operation requires a steady flow at a known rate. Simply knowing the sampled volume is not sufficient. Pumps that produce pulsating flows, such as some of the small diaphragm pumps, should not be used for impactor sampling because the cut-sizes will fluctuate. Likewise, a large drop in the flow rate during the course of sampling will affect the sharpness of the size fractionation. It is recommended that the operator measure the flow rate at the beginning and end of sampling. This can be done using a low pressure-drop device such as a rotometer or a dry-test meter placed at the inlet. Rotameter response depends on pressure, and readings will be different if the rotometer is placed downstream of the flow-regulating valve or orifice. If a rotometer is used on the low-pressure side, its pressure must be noted and the appropriate calibration applied.

Sample Duration

With impactors, it is possible to sample for too long a period as well as too short. Minimum sample durations are chosen on the basis of expected particle concentrations, analytical requirements, and substrate blanks. Maximum sample times are limited by the buildup of particle deposits on the collection surface. For sampling solid particles, greases can become ineffective at substrate loadings of a fraction of a monolayer (see Figure 14-9), and particle bounce errors can reappear if sampling times are excessive. If a porous oiled substrate is used, the particle deposit can grow to be quite high, and jet-to-plate distances can decrease enough to lower the particle size cutoff. In some applications, the first impactor stage may become overloaded prior to collection of enough sample on subsequent stages. This problem can be avoided by use of a precutter, as discussed below.

Inlets

If impactor size distributions are to be representative, the sampler placement and inlet configuration must not exclude particles of the size range of interest. This can be quite significant for sampling large particles (greater than about 5 μm). Long stretches of tubing on the impactor inlet can cause unaccounted-for losses. If the impactor inlet is a small tube oriented perpendicular to the air currents in the room or atmosphere being sampled, larger particles will not follow the streamlines into the impactor. The problem is lessened by using a wider inlet with a lower intake velocity, or pointing the probe inlet into the flow. The accurate collection of coarse particles requires isokinetic sampling, as discussed in Chapter 4.

Precutters

In many applications, it is necessary to prevent very large particles from entering the impactor. This is accomplished by means of a precut device such as a cyclone or size-selective inlet. Precutters exclude large particles that would otherwise bounce or overload the first impactor stage and thereby distort the impactor size distribution measurement. They are appropriate for applications that call for size distributions below a specified particle diameter, such as in respirable or thoracic sampling.

Data Reporting

Impactors provide data on aerosol mass or chemical composition in one or more size ranges. To obtain mass or chemical species size distributions, one of several data reduction procedures can be employed. The approaches include 1) histogram and cumulative plots based on stage cutoff diameters, 2) data inversion methods that take into account the shape of the collection efficiency curves, and 3) extraction of mass median diameters and distribution widths.

Histograms, such as those shown in Chapter 6, are a straightforward means of presenting impactor data. In this approach, each impactor stage is characterized by its cutoff diameter, and crossover between neighboring stages is neglected. This is the same as assuming infinitely steep collection efficiency curves. These graphs plot the quantity $\Delta M_i/\Delta \log d_a$ against $\log d_a$, where ΔM_i is the mass collected on the ith stage, d_a is aerodynamic diameter, and $\Delta \log d_a = \log (d_{50,i-1} / d_{50,i})$ is the difference between logarithms of the aerodynamic cutoff diameters, $d_{50,i-1}$ and $d_{50,i}$ for the stage immediately preceding stage i (labeled i–1) and stage i itself. The denominator $\Delta \log d_a$ is a normalizing factor, such that the area under the histogram is proportional to the mass collected. It also accounts for whatever nonuniformity may exist in the spacing of the impactor cut-sizes, so that the shape of the histogram reflects the mass distribution. The data reduction procedures are described in Chapter 6 and will not be repeated here.

The histogram presentations do not account for cross-sensitivity in the impactor calibration curves. They assume infinitely sharp collection efficiencies such that the impactor stage collects all particles at or above the cutoff and no particles below that size. Actual efficiency curves have a finite slope, and particles of equal size will collect on several stages. When the impactor calibration efficiency curves are known, it may be desirable to take them into account in the data reduction. These procedures are known as data inversion methods.

Data inversion techniques have been applied to a variety of problems for which instrument responses are multivalued. There is no unique solution to the inversion problem. Mathematically it is possible to have several mass distributions yielding the same loadings on the impactor stages. The inversion methods that have been developed are constrained to produce physically reasonable solutions. Inversion results are to be considered "best estimates" and will vary somewhat depending on the algorithm used.

One of the more widely used inversion methods for aerosol instruments is that of Twomey.[51] The data of Figure 14-4 were reduced using this method, and they show a smooth curve for the chemical species size distributions. Another method with similar output is that of Wolfenbarger and Seinfeld.[52] Hasan and Dzubay[53] developed an inversion method that assumes a lognormal form for the aerosol size distribution. The accuracy of these methods depends on how well the efficiency curves are known.

Sometimes the investigator is not interested in the details of the aerosol size distribution but simply wishes to extract certain parameters, such as the mass median diameter or the fraction of aerosol in the respirable size range. These calculations are facilitated by presenting the data in terms of a cumulative distribution, as shown in Chapter 6. Cumulative distributions display the percentage of the aerosol in particles with diameters equal to or smaller than the diameter indicated.

Aerosol size distributions can often be approximated by lognormal distributions, which have a Gaussian shape when displayed against the logarithm of the particle diameter. When the cumulative distribution is plotted on a log-probability graph, the result is a straight line. These plots are useful for evaluating whether a distribution is lognormal, and for extracting the median diameter and the geometric standard deviation, which is the measure of the width of the distribution. For lognormal distributions, the mass median and count median diameters are related through the geometric standard deviation. For a detailed treatment of this approach to the analysis of impactor data, refer to Hinds[54] and Chapter 6.

Special Types of Impactors

Micro-orifice and Low-Pressure Cascade Impactors

Traditional impactors do not offer much size resolution for submicrometer particles; typically, their finest cut-size size is around 0.4 μm. Yet for many aerosol applications, it is useful to be able to size-segregate smaller particles. Diesel emissions, welding fumes, cigarette smokes, and photochemically generated smog aerosols typically exhibit mass median diameters between 0.1 and 0.6 μm. When sampling these aerosols with a conventional impactor, 50% or more of the aerosol mass can penetrate the final impactor stage. Although the material can still be collected on a back-up filter, the filter gives no size resolution; as a result, the investigator has no size information on a substantial portion of the sample. Often a lower cutoff diameter of 0.1 μm or less is needed to size-segregate the majority of the aerosol mass.

Two types of impactors have been developed to obtain smaller cutoff diameters: low-pressure impactors and micro-orifice impactors. Both instruments can provide size cut-points as small as 0.05 µm. Low-pressure impactors were introduced more than 30 years ago,[55] and a variety of these samplers are in use today. Examples are the ambient impactors of Berner[3,56,57] and Hering *et al.*,[58,59] and the in-stack sampler of Vanderpool *et al.*[60] Micro-orifice impactors have been developed more recently at the University of Minnesota.[61,62] Commercially available low-pressure and micro-orifice impactors are listed in Table 14-I-1 of the "Instrument Descriptions" section.

Low-pressure and micro-orifice impactors use two different approaches to achieve their small particle-size cutpoints. Low-pressure impactors resemble ordinary impactors but operate at reduced pressures of 5–40 kPa (0.05–0.4 atm). They take advantage of the decreased aerodynamic drag on particles that occurs when the mean free path in the air is as large or larger than the particle diameter. Micro-orifice impactors operate closer to atmospheric pressure (0.8–0.9 atm), but employ very small orifices (40–200 µm in diameter). The streamlines of the air impinging on the impaction plate have correspondingly smaller radii of curvature; the air is accelerated more quickly, making it more difficult for the particles to follow. The basic operating principles for both types of impactors are evident from the particle Stokes number, defined in Equation 5 above. To collect small particles, the quantity (W/CV) must be small. Low-pressure impactors operate at large values of the slip factor C; micro-orifice impactors operate at small jet diameters W. Both types of impactors use relatively high jet velocities ($V > 100$ m/s) for the particle cutpoints of 0.1 µm and lower.

The pressure drops in an impactor can lead to a change in the size of particles during sampling. The magnitude of the change depends on the chemical nature of the aerosol, namely its volatility and hygroscopicity, on the ambient relative humidity, and on the operating pressures and geometry of the impactor. Theory and data for particle size changes in a low-pressure impactor are presented by Biswas and Flagan.[63] Effects of relative humidity on sizing of sulfuric acid aerosols in a micro-orifice impactor are given by Fang *et al.*[64]

Virtual Impactors

Virtual impactors do not have a collection plate. Instead, an axial probe is placed below the impactor jet. Only a small fraction of the flow passes through the probe; the majority of the flow bends around the tip of the probe to pass onto the next stage. The streamlines above the probe tip resemble those of a conventional impactor, and the particles are separated by size into the two air streams. One is the minor flow, which passes through the probe; the other is the major flow, which bypasses the probe. The minor flow through the probe carries with it all of the large particles from the total sample flow plus the small particles from the minor flow. The major air flow that bypasses the probe contains smaller particles only. Particles are collected by filtration of the two air streams.

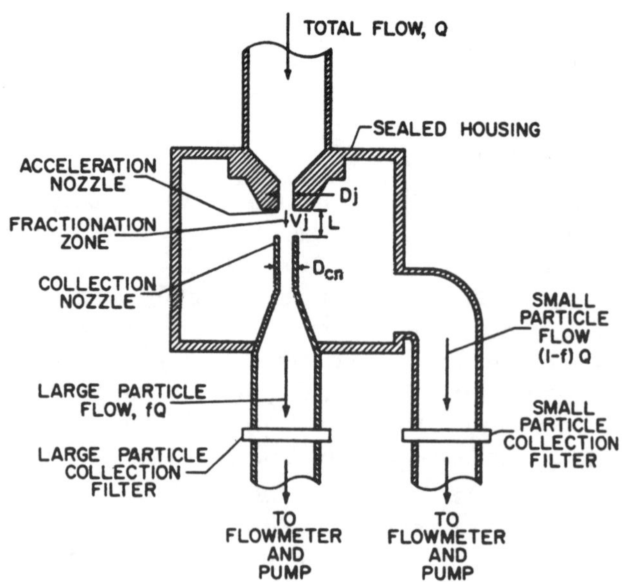

FIGURE 14-10. Dichotomous sampler, showing the fine particle (2.5-m cutpoint) virtual impaction stage.[72] Reprinted with permission from American Chemical Society.

A major advantage of virtual impactors is that they are not subject to errors resulting from particle bounce or re-entrainment, and grease coatings are not required. Aerosols may be collected on whatever filter medium is best suited for the analyses to be performed. A limitation is that unless they are carefully designed and constructed, they are subject to significant wall losses for liquid particles near the cutpoint size.[65,66] Experimentally determined criteria for minimizing these losses are given by Loo and Cork.[67]

The first type of virtual impactor was the "aerosol centripeter" introduced by Hounam and Sherwood.[68] The most widely used virtual impactor is the dichotomous sampler shown in Figure 14-10. This instrument was introduced by Conner[69] and developed by Dzubay and Stevens[70] and Loo *et al.*[71] It operates at a sample rate of 16.7 L/min, or 1 m^3/hr with aerosol collection onto two 37-mm filters. The commercially available instrument provides a fine particle cut at 2.5 µm, although earlier versions had a 3.5-µm cut. The unit is generally operated with a PM_{10} inlet as described in Chapter 5, and it is most frequently used for ambient air monitoring. Calibration curves are given by McFarland *et al.*[72] and John and Wall.[65]

Although not commercially available at the time of this writing, several other virtual impactors have been developed. Solomon *et al.*[73] have developed a high-volume virtual dichotomous sampler that operates at 500 L/min and employs 100-mm-diameter filters. This sampler has the advantage of providing larger sample volumes, permitting analyses of trace species, or facilitating collection in cases of low airborne concentrations. Chen and coworkers[74,75] have developed a virtual impactor that uses a particle-free air stream to eliminate the fine particle collection in the minor (coarse) particle flow. Novick and Alvarez[76] have designed a three-stage virtual impactor. Noone *et al.*[77] have developed a counterflow virtual impactor for separately sampling cloud droplets and interstitial aerosol. Theoretical analyses of virtual impactors are given by Forney[78,79] and Marple and Chien.[80]

Collection efficiency curves for the virtual impaction stage of the dichotomous sampler are shown in Figure 14-11.[72] For particle sizes below the cutoff diameter, collection efficiencies reach a minimum value equal to the fraction of the total flow passing through the receiving probe. The cutoff diameter decreases as the fraction of the flow through the receiving probe is increased. Wall losses are most significant at the cutoff diameter. A critical factor in minimizing wall losses is the radius of curvature at the inlet of the receiving probe. John and Wall[65] found that alignment of the jet and receiving probe is critical and that deviations of more than 0.05 mm in concentricity can increase wall losses and affect the cutpoint.

Impactors for Coarse Particle Sampling

Several types of impactors have been designed for collection of particles in the 10- to 100-μm size range. They are used for collecting fogs, cloudwater, and coarse airborne particles. One of the first large particle collectors is the WRAC.[49] It uses four parallel impactors with rectangular slots. Each samples at 55 scfm, using a standard Hi-Volume blower. Particles are collected on greased metal foils. Two independent calibrations give equal cutpoints for liquid and solid particles of 9, 18, 34, and 48 ± 1 μm.[49] Collection efficiencies on ungreased plates or fiber filters are 7% because of bounce.

Rotary impactors are another type of coarse particle collector. These samplers collect particles on a rapidly rotating rod or tube that moves through the air much like a large propellor. There are no jets and no accelerated air streams. Instead, the relative motion is achieved by rotation of the collection surfaces. Air streamlines bend around the collection surface, and particles too large to follow are intercepted.

The Noll rotary impactor,[81, 82] designed for atmospheric coarse particle sampling, has four stages with size cuts from 6 to 29 μm. Collection surfaces are external and greased to prevent particle bounce. Deposits are analyzed gravimetrically and microscopically. Air sampling rates are inferred from the rotational speed and collection surface cross-sectional area. Recently, Regtuit *et al.*[83] developed a tunnel impactor that uses a tube pointing into the wind with four parallel impactors mounted inside. The tube is suspended to give a well-defined sampling rate. Calibration data show cutpoints between 10 and 60 μm.

A rotating coarse particle sampler developed at the University of Minnesota[84] uses internal collection surfaces and a rotating L-shaped sampling probe that is aspirated at a speed equal to the speed of the probe tip. Particles are deposited at the elbow inside the probe. Comparative tests with open-faced filters and sedimentation plates indicate greater than 90% collection efficiencies for particle diameters between 40 and 250 μm.

As with conventional impactors, sampler collection efficiencies can be calculated from the particle Stokes number and flow Reynolds number. The size fraction collected is dependent on particle aerodynamic diameter, instrument geometry, and rotational speed. For a rotating rod, narrower widths and higher rod velocities give smaller cutoff diameters. Some collectors use a slot in the leading edge of the rotating rod. Examples are the fog water collectors of Mack and Pillie,[85] Kramer and Schultz,[86] and Jacob *et al.*,[87] and the large-particle sampler of Tomic and Lilienfeld as reported by McFarland *et al.*[88] The performance of these collectors also depends on Stokes numbers, as has been modeled by Lesnic and coworkers.[89]

Precutters

Single-stage impactors are often used as inlets for size-selective sampling. Examples include PM_{10} inlets

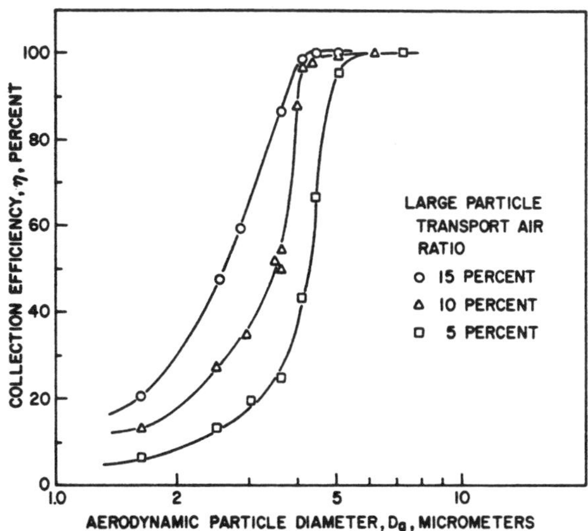

FIGURE 14-11. Virtual impaction efficiencies for large particle transport air rations of 5%, 10%, and 15%.[72] Reprinted with permission from American Chemical Society.

used in Hi-Volume and dichotomous samplers[90–92] and the indoor air sampling impactor.[93] Some personal samplers for PM_{10} and $PM_{2.5}$ measurements also use a single-stage impactor.

Diffusion denuder systems, as discussed in Chapter 20, also use either a cyclone or a single-stage impactor that is precut to remove particles above 2 or 3 µm. One example is the glass impactor[94] used in the Harvard annular denuder system.[95] This impactor was especially designed to pass nitric acid.

Real-Time Impactor Sensors

Some impactors have been equipped with real-time sensors on each collection plate for providing direct-reading size distribution. The QCM uses quartz crystal impaction surfaces, which detect the mass of deposited aerosol.[96–98] Tropp *et al.*[99] and Keskinen *et al.*[100] have designed "electrical" impactors that use a charger and impactor in series. Deposited particles are detected by the electrical current. These impactors are described in more detail in Chapter 16.

Inertial Spectrometer

The inertial spectrometer illustrated in Figure 14-12 was developed by Prodi and coworkers.[101,102] With this device, particles are separated by size in a laminar air flow and then collected by filtration. Aerosol is injected into a clean air flow in a rectangular channel immediately upstream of a 90° bend. Particles are separated aerodynamically in the bend and then collected on a membrane filter. The position of particle deposition on the filter corresponds to aerodynamic size. Aerosol sample rates are < 0.1 L/min. Total flow rates, including the sheath air, are 3–10 L/min.

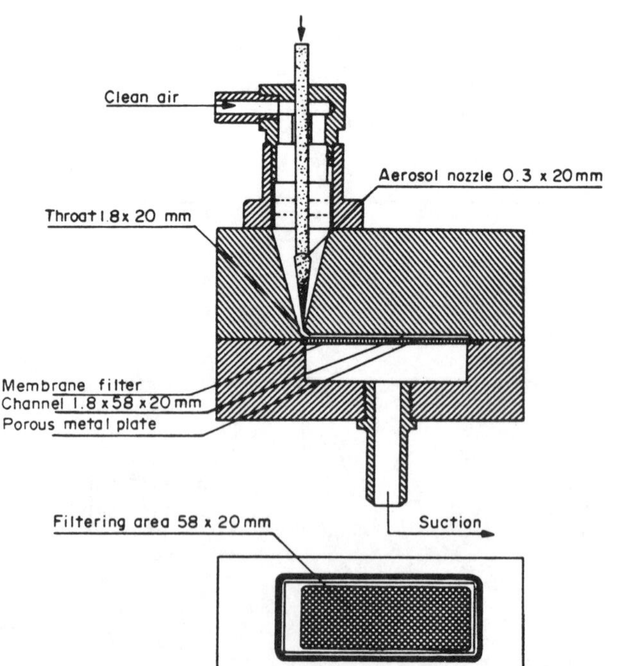

FIGURE 14-12. Cross section of the inertial spectrometer showing aerosol and clean air flows, and the membrane filter collection surface.[101] Reprinted with kind permission from Pergamon Press, Ltd, Headington Hill Hall, Oxford OX3 0BW, UK.

The instrument provides aerodynamic separation for particles in the 1- to 10-µm size range. Particles outside this range are collected, but not separated by size. Unlike conventional impactors, the inertial spectrometer uses filtration for particle collection and is not susceptible to particle bounce sampling errors. The basic theory of operation for this instrument is given by Prodi *et al.*[101] and Belosi and Prodi[102] and has been modified by Aharonson and Dinar[103] to include gravitational effects. As with other inertial instruments, the sizing by the inertial spectrometer is dependent on the aerodynamic diameter of the particle. Applications include the measurement of fibrous particles.[104] Calibration data under various operating conditions are given by Mitchell and Nichols.[105]

Impingers

Impingers operate much like an impactor, except that the sampled air stream jet is immersed in water at the bottom of a flask. The sampled air stream is accelerated in the impinger orifice to velocities of 60 m/s or greater. The air stream exits underneath the liquid surface immediately above an impaction plate or at a specified distance above the bottom of the collection flask. Particles impinge on the plate or flask bottom, stop, and are subsequently retained by the liquid.

Impingers were developed in 1922[106] and until 1984 were recommended by ACGIH for dust counting. "Dust counting" is the determination of the particle number concentration (i.e., millions of particles per cubic foot of air) for particles such as graphite, mica, and mineral wool fibers. The actual number concentration of insoluble particles collected by an impinger is determined by microscopic examination of an aliquot of the sample using a dust-counting cell to immobilize the liquid in a 0.1-mm layer between two glass surfaces. Dust concentrations measured in this way have been correlated with the incidence and severity of respiratory disease in trades such as mining, quarrying, smelting, and the manufacture of metallic and mineral (stone or clay) products. ACGIH also used such dust concentration measurements to set more than a dozen threshold limit values (TLVs™) for occupational exposure. These TLVs have since been converted from particle number concentrations to respirable mass concentrations, and impinger sampling for particles has been largely replaced by respirable mass sampling, as described in Chapter 5.

Although developed for dust counting, impingers are now also used for the collection of gases, vapors, acid mists, and viable aerosols. They are used for sampling toxic organic vapors such as formaldehyde, as described in Chapter 17. They are also used to collect moisture and condensible materials in the U.S. EPA Method 5 particulate stack sampling train, as described in Chapter 20. The use of impingers for viable particles, such as bacteria, is described in Chapter 23. For vapor sampling, modifications of the impinger include a spill-proof design and/or use of a fritted glass in place of the orifice.

Dust counting impingers include the Greenburg–Smith impinger,[106–108] which uses a 2.3-mm-diameter jet located 5 mm above an attached impinging plate. It is designed to operate at a flow rate of 28 L/min (1 cfm) with a jet velocity of 100 m/s and collects particles greater than 1 μm in diameter. The Hatch modification[109,110] of this impinger uses the flat bottom of the collection bottle for the impinging surface; however, it has the same size jet, flow rate, and performance characteristics as the standard Greenburg–Smith impinger.[111] The midget impinger[112,113] was developed as a more portable instrument. It uses a smaller jet (1 mm in diameter) and operates at 2.8 L/min. It has a lower jet velocity of 60 m/s and can be operated with a smaller pump. The midget impinger is also used for vapor sampling, and it is available in spill-proof designs or with fritted glass in place of the orifice (see Chapter 17).

The all-glass impingers, such as the AGI-4 (All Glass Impinger, 4 mm) and AGI-30, are used for sampling microbial aerosols. Both operate at 8.5–12.5 L/min, corresponding to 70% to 100% of sonic velocity at the jet exit. The AGI-4 uses a submerged jet located 4 mm above the bottom of the collection bottle. The exit of the AGI-30 is 30 mm above the bottom of the collection bottle and is generally operated such that the level of the collection liquid is a few millimeters below the jet exit. Although not as efficient a collector as the AGI-4, the AGI-30 is gentler and bacterial cells are not as likely to be shattered or damaged during collection. Impingers for bioaerosol collection are described in Chapter 23.

Cyclone Samplers

Cyclone samplers use a vortical flow inside a cylindrical or conical chamber. A typical "reverse flow" cyclone is illustrated in Figure 14-13.[114] Air is introduced tangentially near the top, creating a double vortex flow within the cyclone body. The flow spirals down the outer portion of the chamber and then reverses and spirals up the inner core to the exit tube. Particles having sufficient inertia are unable to follow the air streamlines, and they impact onto the cyclone walls. The particles are either retained on the cyclone walls, or they migrate to the bottom of the cyclone cone. The work of Ranz[115] shows that a wall flow in the boundary layer plays an important role in transporting the particles along the walls to the collection cup at the bottom.

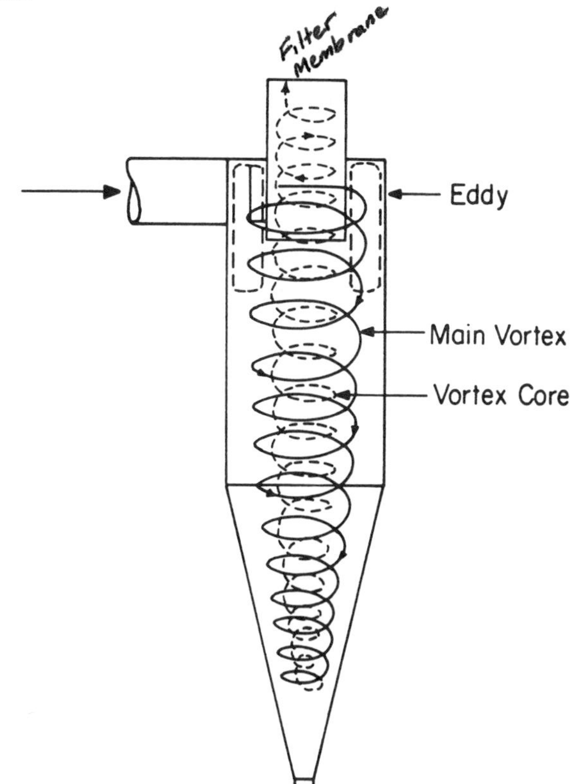

FIGURE 14-13. Flow patterns in a cyclone collector.[114] Reprinted with permission, University Presses of Florida.

Historically, cyclones have mostly been used for removing particles from process streams. These gas-cleaning cyclones are generally quite large, 0.2–3 m in diameter, and are designed to handle flows of several cubic meters per second. Air sampling cyclones are much smaller, typically 1–5 cm in diameter, operating at flows as small as a few liters per minute. Since the 1950s, these miniature cyclones have been used for particle sampling in the workplace and in ambient air. One of the most common applications is respirable particle sampling, wherein the cyclone is operated upstream of a filter. The cyclone is used to remove the larger, nonrespirable particles such that the material collected on the filter is representative of that which penetrates into the nonciliated deep lung spaces of humans. There has been considerable research on the development and calibration of cyclones to mimic the ACGIH respirable curve, as described in Chapter 5.

Cyclones are also used in ambient air sampling to separate the coarse mode aerosols from the fine mode, less than 2.5 μm. This division is very useful because the mass distribution of particulate matter in ambient air is often bimodal. The coarse particle mode, corresponding to particles greater than about 2.5 μm, is composed of soil dusts and particles produced by mechanical processes such as abrasion. The fine particle mode, below 2.5 μm diameter, is mostly secondary aerosol, consisting of particles produced in the atmosphere from gaseous precursors, by combustion effluents, and by photochemical reactions. The particles in these two modes are distinct chemically, and cyclones can be very useful in separating them.

Usually cyclones are used to provide a particle precut to another aerosol collector such as a filter or an impactor. Often the material collected in the cyclone itself is not assayed. An exception is the cyclone cascade developed by Smith *et al.*,[116] with five cyclones arranged in series much like a cascade impactor. This system was designed for collection in high-temperature process streams, as described in Chapter 20.

Cyclones have several advantages in air sampling, including their relatively low cost of construction and ease of operation. They have no moving parts, and they are easily maintained. Unlike impactors, they are not subject to errors caused by particle bounce or re-entrainment, and they do not require special coatings. They are especially suited to applications requiring the removal of coarse aerosols prior to sample collection. One disadvantage is the absence of an adequate theoretical description. The flow pattern inside cyclones is complex and not easily modeled. Thus, it is not easy to predict cyclone performance without reference to empirical correlations.

Cyclones: Theory of Operation

Cyclones are characterized by a collection efficiency curve much like that described for impactors in the preceding section. Again, the particle size collected with a 50% efficiency is referred to as the cutpoint of the cyclone, or d_{50}. As with impactors, the collection efficiency depends on the particle aerodynamic diameter. The two points of interest in cyclone design are 1) how the cyclone cutpoint depends on the cyclone dimensions, gas viscosities, and flow rate and 2) the shape of the collection efficiency versus particle size curve.

Over the years, many different theories have been proposed to predict cyclone behavior. These theories all present somewhat different expressions for the dependence of cyclone cutpoints on the cyclone dimensions, flow rate, gas viscosity, and temperature. Some conventional theories include as a parameter the effective number of turns the air flow makes within the cyclone, which is largely unknown. Summaries and comparison with experimental data are given by Chan and Lippmann,[117] Leith and coworkers,[118–121] and DeOtte.[122]

At present there is no generally accepted fundamental relationship to describe cyclone performance. The flow inside cyclones is often turbulent and not easily modeled. Furthermore, most of the aforementioned theories were developed for the large cyclones used in air cleaning and do not accurately describe the behavior of the small cyclones used for aerosol sampling. Specifically, for small cyclones, the experimentally determined dependence of cutpoint on flow rate and temperature is not in agreement with theory.[116,123]

Types of Cyclones

Commercially available cyclones are listed in Table 14-I-2 of the "Instrument Descriptions" section. These include the 10 mm, or "Dorr–Oliver" cyclone, often used for personal sampling of respirable particles.[124] This is a reverse-flow cyclone, as depicted in Figure 14-13. The HASL cyclone has a similar reverse-flow configuration but is somewhat larger. It has been used in ambient air sampling networks.[125] The SRI cyclones were designed as a five-stage cascade cyclone system for stack-sampling.[116,126] The AIHL cyclone[127] follows the design of the midsize SRI cyclone and has been used in several ambient sampling studies. Stairmand cyclones refer to the general class of reverse-flow cyclones. A large Stairmand cyclone has been designed for sampling cotton dust, as a substitute for the cotton dust elutriator.[128] A different approach is an aerial flow cyclone, which uses a helical spiral in the entrance tube to introduce the cyclonic flow.[129]

Empirical Correlations for Predicting Cyclone Performance

The characteristics of cyclone performance are perhaps best illustrated by experimental data. The effect of flow rate is illustrated in Figure 14-14, which shows collection efficiency curves for the AIHL cyclone for six different flows ranging from 8.4 to 26.6 L/min. These data, taken from John and Reischl,[127] are for a short cone cyclone with a body diameter of 3.66 cm. As is readily apparent, the cyclone cutpoint decreases with increasing flow rate. The shape of the collection efficiency curve appears steeper at the higher flow rates. However, when plotted as a function of the normalized particle diameter, $(d_p - d_{50})/d_{50}$, a common collection efficiency curve describes the behavior at all flow rates. This is shown in Figure 14-15.

The dependence of cyclone cutpoint on flow rate for many of the commonly used air sampling cyclones is shown in Figure 14-16. These data are well described by the relation:

$$d_{50} = K\,Q^{n} \tag{9}$$

where: d_{50} = cutpoint
Q = flow rate
n and K = empirically determined constants

The values of K and n vary for different cyclones.

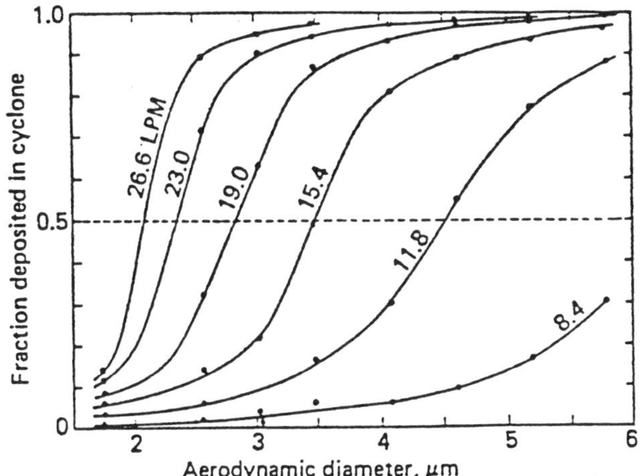

FIGURE 14-14. Fraction of solid particles deposited in the AIHL cyclone as a function of aerodynamic diameter. The curves are labeled with the flow rate.[127] Reprinted with permission, Air & Waste Management Association.

Several investigators[116,117,124,127,130,131] have correlated cyclone cutpoints with flow rate according to this relation. Resulting values of K and n are given in Table 14-I-2 of the "Instrument Descriptions" section.

Two points are significant with regard to the variation of cyclone cutpoint with flow rate. First, the value of the exponent n falls within the range from –0.6 to –2. This is in disagreement with most cyclone theories, which predict an inverse square root dependence of cutpoint on flow, or $n = -0.5$. Second, the performance of the 10-mm Dorr–Oliver cyclone is not described by a single curve. This effect is attributed to different flow regimes within the cyclone, as described below.

The effect of cyclone body size is illustrated in Figure 14-17.[123] Cyclones II through IV are similar in design, with dimensions as shown. The efficiency curves correspond to a flow rate of 28.3 L/min at a temperature of 25°C. As expected, the smaller cyclones give smaller cutpoints.

Several correlations have been advanced to predict cyclone peformance as a function of cyclone body size and flow rate. Saltzman[132] correlated cutpoints of many different cyclones to body diameter and the Reynolds number in the outlet flow (see Equation 8 for definition of Reynolds number). More recently, Moore and McFarland[133] developed a correlation for Stairmand-type cyclones based on Reynolds numbers calculated from inlet velocity and cyclone body diameter. Leith and coworkers[120,121] used flow visualization methods to better understand and model cyclone performance. Kim and Lee's systematic experimental evaluation of nine different cyclones at three flow rates provides qualitative guidelines for understanding cyclone performance.[134] These studies are of special interest in the design of new cyclones.

The effect of temperature on cyclone performance is of interest for sampling stack gases and high temperature streams. Air viscosity increases with temperature, which in turn increases the cyclone cutpoint. The data presented in Figure 14-18[116] show that cutpoint increases in direct proportion to the increase in the gas viscosity. This contrasts with cyclone theories which predict a square root dependence of cutpoint on air viscosity. It becomes evident that even for a fixed geometry, cyclone performance is not solely dependent on particle Stokes number.

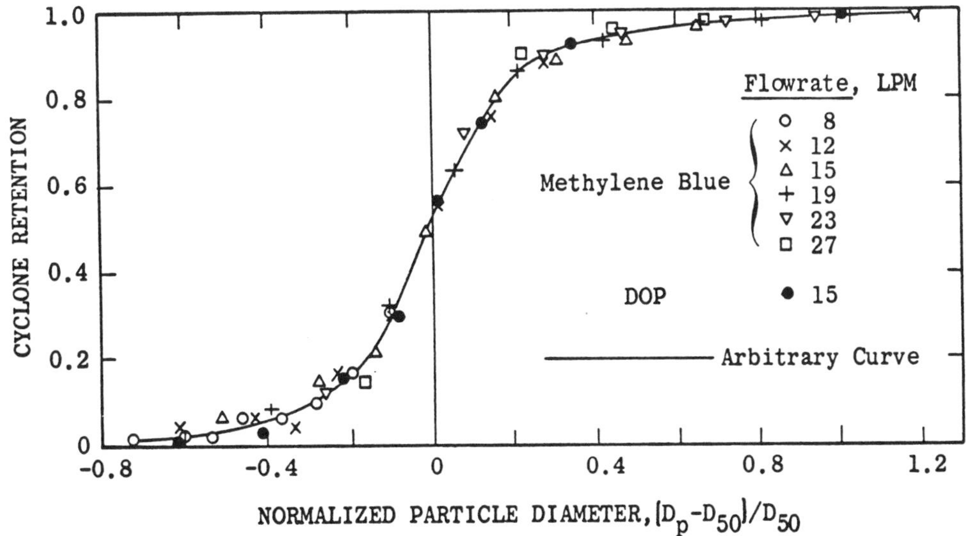

FIGURE 14-15. Particle deposition in the AIHL cyclone taken at various flow rates versus the normalized particle diameter. Methylene blue data points refer to solid particle collection, DOP points are for liquid particle collection.[127] Reprinted with permission, Air & Waste Management Association.

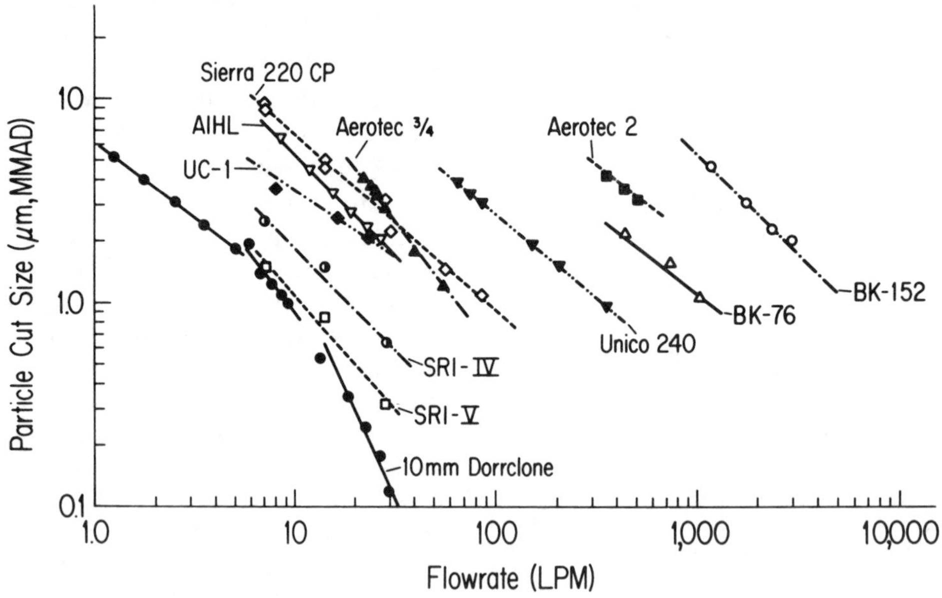

FIGURE 14-16. Aerodynamic diameter cutpoint as a function of flow rate for various cyclones.[123]

Flow Instabilities in Small, Long-Cone Cyclones

Saltzman and Hochstrasser[135] found unstable pressure drops across long-cone cyclones at low flow rates. When starting at low flow rates, the pressure drop across the cyclone would increase with increasing flow and then would suddenly decrease by about 25%. Further increases in flow rate would once again give proportional increases in the pressure drop. The value of the flow rate at which the sudden change occurred was variable. They attribute the phenomenon to an unstable, transitional flow within the cyclone. Their data indicate that for long-cone cyclones operated at low flow rates, the exit flow in the cyclone is laminar. The sudden reduction in pressure drop as the flow increases occurs when the exit flow becomes turbulent.

Under transitional flow conditions, the flow does not correspond to the double vortex shown in Figure 14-13; instead, only the main outer vortex remains. The descending flow bypasses the lower portion of the cone and ascends through the exit tube under laminar con-

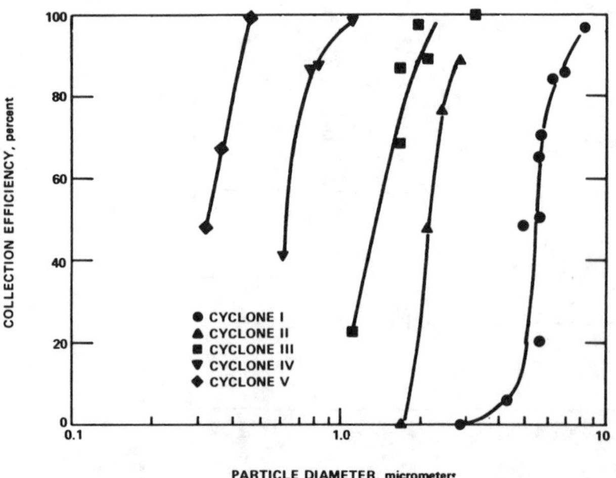

FIGURE 14-17. Collection efficiency curves for cyclones of different size but similar proportions and design. Body diameters for Cyclones I–V are 4.47, 3.66, 3.11, 2.54 and 1.52 cm, respectively.[116] Reprinted with permission from American Chemical Society.

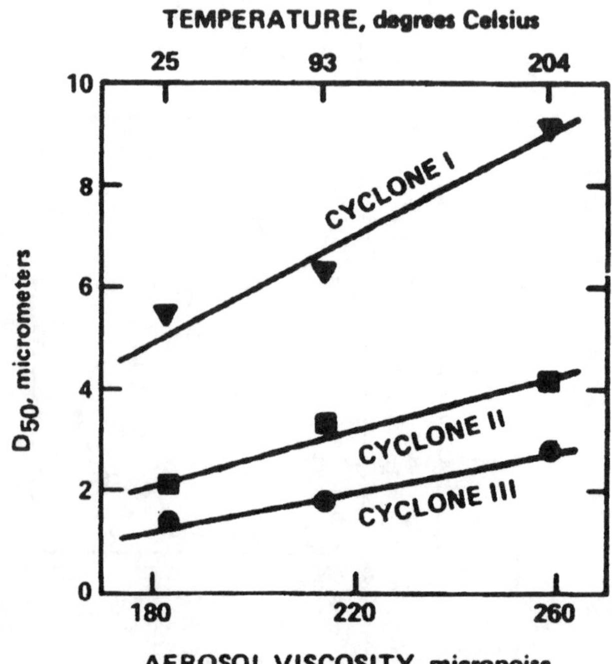

FIGURE 14-18. Change in cyclone cutpoint diameter as a function of temperature.[116] Reprinted with permission from American Chemical Society.

ditions. The stagnation region at the bottom of the cyclone cone was verified by means of a static pressure probe placed at the cyclone bottom. The orderly flow reversal is also substantiated by the appearance of a ring deposit along the wall of the cyclone cone. This unstable, transitional flow is not observed for short cone cyclones such as SRI or AIHL cyclones.

For the 10-mm Dorr–Oliver, it was noted that the plot of cutpoint versus flow rate does not give the simple power law dependence observed for other cyclones (Figure 14-16). Lippmann and Chan[123] and collaborators have attributed this to laminar flow conditions below 5 L/min and turbulent flow at the higher flows. Saltzman[135] also noted that the shape of the collection efficiency curves for the 10-mm cyclone differs significantly for flows above and below 5 L/min, with the sharpness of the cutpoint greatly reduced at the higher flows.

Comparison of Solid and Liquid Particle Collection Efficiencies

Unlike impactors, cyclones are not easily subject to errors due to particle bounce. This is substantiated by John and Reischl,[127] who calibrated their AIHL cyclone with both liquid and solid particles. Very little difference in the overall cyclone collection efficiency was observed. This can be seen in Figure 14-15 by comparing the collection efficiencies for the solid methylene blue particles with those obtained from the liquid dioctyl phthalate (DOP) particles. These data demonstrate that particle bounce does not significantly affect overall cyclone collection efficiencies. However, John and Reischl did observe that the region of the cyclone in which the particles deposited was quite different for the two aerosol types. Liquid particles tended to remain on the walls of the cyclone and were collected within the cyclone body. In contrast, the solid methylene blue particles tended to collect in the cup at the bottom of the cyclone cone. The heavier the solid particle-loading within the cyclone, the greater the proportion deposited in the cup.

Sources of Sampling Errors for Cyclones

Cyclones are one of the easier types of aerosol sampling instruments to use properly; nonetheless, some words of warning are appropriate. First, a constant flow rate is needed to ensure a constant cutpoint. Diaphragm pumps used in conjunction with personal samplers produce a fluctuating flow, which degrades the cyclone cutpoint. These oscillations are not necessarily eliminated by the commonly used pulsation dampers. Berry[136] found that pulsations produced by some pumps can change the penetration through a personal cyclone by 10%; use of a damper reduced the error to less than 3%.

For nylon and other nonconducting plastic cyclones, the particle collection efficiency can be influenced by electrostatic effects,[137] leading to retention of small particles. If the cyclone carries a net charge, particles of the same charge will be repelled. Briant and Moss[138] demonstrated that particles of like charge can be repelled by the electric field surrounding the cyclone and thus are not sampled efficiently. Obviously this effect is more pronounced when sampling charged aerosols. Electrostatic effects can bias the collection of net neutral aerosols because "neutral aerosols" contain many charged particles. This artifact could be eliminated by using metal or electrically conducting plastic for the construction of cyclones.

Although cyclones are designed to collect large particles, they can also be a sink for reactive gases. This is of concern in gaseous sampling systems that employ a cyclone upstream of the gaseous collection. Often this arrangement is used for diffusional collection systems such as the annular denuder, the transition flow reactor, or the denuder difference method described in Chapter 19. Appel *et al.*[139] studied the penetration of nitric acid through several types of Teflon and Teflon-coated cyclones and found that losses were as high as 40%–70% for freshly cleaned cyclones, but were small for those preconditioned by operation in ambient air.

Aerosol Centrifuges

Description

Aerosol centrifuges refer to a class of aerosol samplers that spin at high rotational speeds in order to subject particles to large centrifugal forces. One example is the spiral centrifuge[140–142] shown in Figure 14-19. This sampler consists of a spiral duct that is 180 cm long and 1 cm wide (except for the first semicircle, which is 1.73 cm at the center). During operation, it spins at a typical rate of 3000 revolutions per minute. Aerosol and particle-free sheath air are introduced at the center, with the aerosol flow confined along the inner wall of the spiral. The air flow exits at the outer end of the spiral.

Typical particle trajectories in the rotating, curved duct are illustrated in Figure 14-20.[143] The particles are driven across the sheath air flow to the outer wall of the duct by centrifugal force. Particles with large aerodynamic diameters deposit first, near the flow entrance. Smaller particles are collected in the outer, larger-diameter portion of the spiral. Generally, particles are collected on a foil that lines the outer wall of the channel. The foil is removed after collection. The linear distance along the foil at which the particle deposits is directly related to its aerodynamic diameter.

The reason for spinning the sampler is to subject the particles to a much greater centrifugal force than can

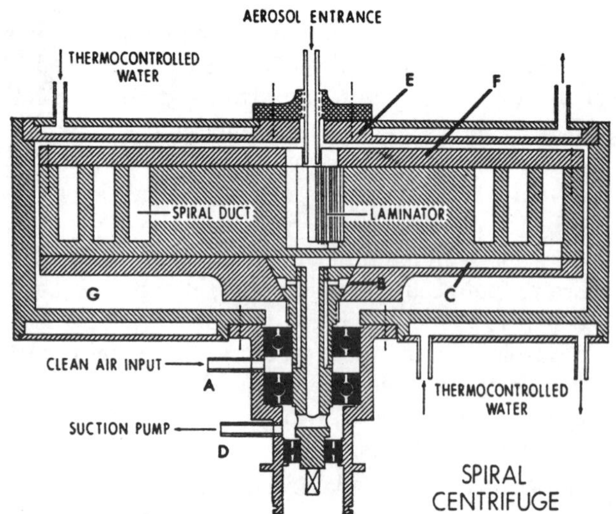

FIGURE 14-19. View of the rotor and vertical cross section of the Stoeber spiral duct centrifuge.(140) Reprinted with permission from American Chemical Society.

be accomplished by air flow alone. Because of viscosity, the air in the duct rotates with the sampler. Consider a rotating duct like that in Figure 14-20, with a cross-sectional area A and a volumetric flow rate Q. From the rotating frame of reference of the sampler, the mean air stream velocity is Q/A, but from the surrounding inertial reference frame (i.e., as viewed from the table on which the sampler sits), the mean air stream velocity is $Q/A + 2\pi Rf$, where R is the mean radius of curvature of the duct and f is the rotational frequency. In most cases, $2\pi Rf >> Q/A$, and the centrifugal force on the particles is dominated by the spinning of the duct.

Calibration curves for the spiral duct centrifuge are shown in Figure 14-21, which gives the particle aerodynamic diameter as a function of the deposition distance from the aerosol entrance. The instrument calibration depends on the speed of rotation, the total flow rate, and the geometry of the duct. The resolution of the instrument depends on the ratio of sample to sheath air flow rates. The data of Figure 14-21[140] were collected for aerosol flows ranging between 0.6% and 15% of the total flow. Some of the first aerosol centrifuges, such as the Goetz spectrometer,[144,145] were designed to operate without sheath air; but for these instruments, the deposition pattern represents a cumulative distribution, which is generally not as desirable.

Another geometry used for aerosol centrifuges is the conifuge,[146,147] shown in Figure 14-22. In this device, the aerosol is introduced into the annular space between two coaxial cones that spin together. The net flow is a descending spiral of increasing radius. Clean sheath air makes up the outer portion of the flow, so that the aerosol is initially confined next to the inner cone. Centrifugal force transports the particles across the clean air sheath to the outer wall, and particles deposit along the inner surface of the outer cover. As the air flow moves down the annulus, the centrifugal force increases, enabling the collection of smaller particles.

Different types of aerosol centrifuges are summarized in Table 14-I-3. At one time, both the Lovelace[148] and Stoeber[140–142] spiral centrifuges were manufactured, but currently none are available commercially. Conventional centrifuges such as those described here employ low sampling rates. An exception is the high-volume drum centrifuge,[149] which employs particle deposition on the inner surface of a porous, rotating drum. This sampler was designed to collect large amounts of aerosol for trace analyses.

Principle of Operation

An annular centrifuge duct with a constant radius of curvature is used to illustrate the theory of operation of the aerosol centrifuge (Figure 14-20). Centrifuges of this design are reported by Tillery[150] and Hochrainer.[151,152] Although centrifuges such as those shown in Figures 14-19 and 14-22 use ducts of varying curvature, the principle is the same.

In the radial direction, particles are subject to a centrifugal force:

$$F_{r,centr} = \frac{m}{R}\,(\,2\pi Rf + U\,)^2 \qquad \textbf{(12)}$$

and to an aerodynamic resistance:

$$F_{r,aero} = \frac{3\pi\mu}{C}\,\frac{dR}{dt}\,d_p \qquad \textbf{(13)}$$

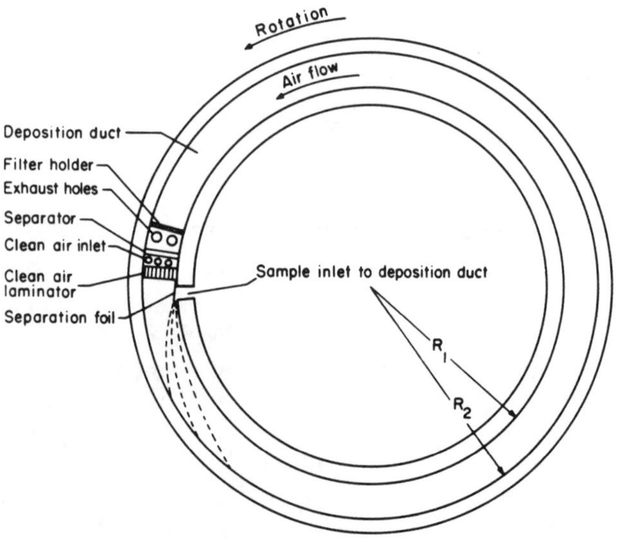

FIGURE 14-20. Top view of a cyclindrical duct aerosol centrifuge, with particle trajectories shown by dashed lines.(150) Reprinted with permission, American Industrial Hygiene Association Journal.

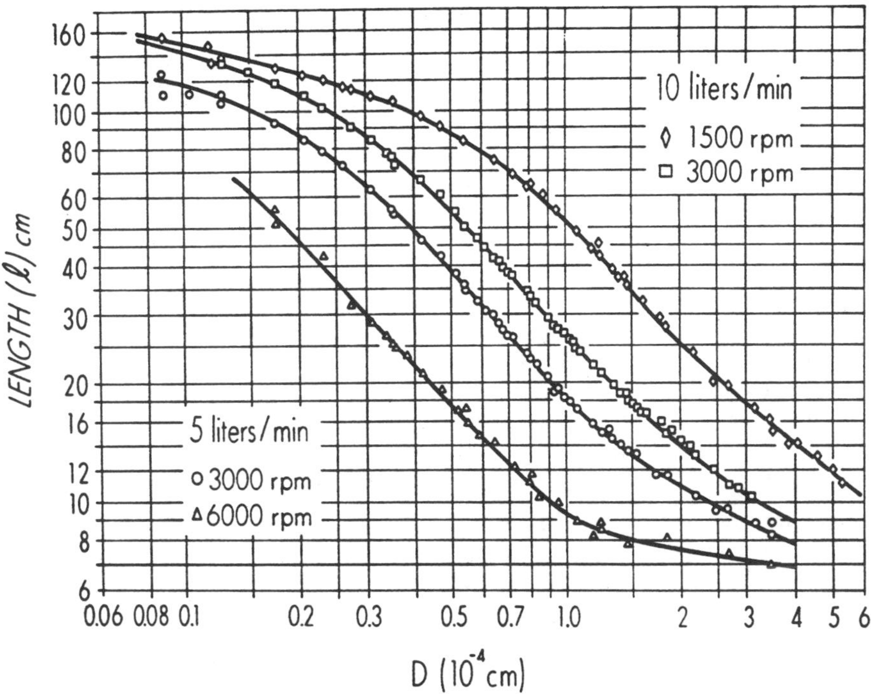

FIGURE 14-21. Calibration curves for the Stoeber spiral duct centrifuge at different rotation rates and at different total flow rates. Total flow refers to both aerosol sample flow plus the particle-free sheath air flow.[140] Reprinted with permission from American Chemical Society.

where: m = particle mass
R = particle radial position
f = frequency of rotation
U = fluid velocity due to the volumetric flow
dR/dt = particle velocity in the radial direction

(As before, C = Cunningham slip factor and μ = gas viscosity.) Note that the radial component of the fluid velocity is zero.

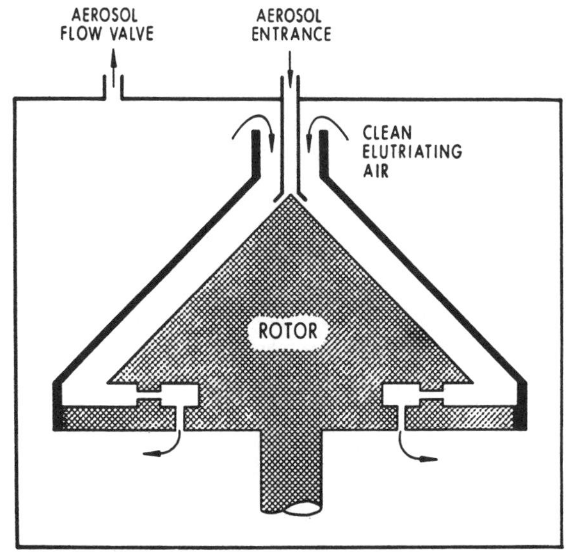

FIGURE 14-22. Schematic of the conifuge.[146] Reprinted with permission from American Chemical Society.

In expression 12 for centrifugal force, the fluid velocity U is usually neglected because it is small by comparison to the tangential velocity due to the spinning of the duct. With this approximation, the equation for the radial particle velocity becomes:

$$\frac{dR}{dt} = \frac{2\pi^2 R f^2 \rho d_p^{\,2} C}{9\mu} \tag{14}$$

where $|F_{r,centr}| = |F_{r,aero}|$ (i.e., the magnitude of the centrifugal and aerodynamic resistance forces is equal).

The quantity of interest in the aerosol centrifuge is the farthest distance along the outer channel wall at which particles of a specified diameter will deposit, L_d. This is found by evaluating the transit time, t, for the particle to travel across the entire duct from the inner radius, R_1, to the outer radius, R_2. Integration of Equation 14 gives:

$$t = \ln\left(\frac{R_2}{R_1}\right)\frac{9\mu}{2\pi^2 f^2 \rho d_p^{\,2} C} \tag{15}$$

Because particles must traverse the entire width of the channel, the distance they travel down the channel prior to capture depends only on the average duct velocity. The average velocity is just the ratio of the total volumetric flow to the duct cross-sectional area, $Q/[h(R_2 - R_1)]$, where Q is the sum of the aerosol sample and sheath air flows, and h is the height of the duct. This gives an expression for the deposition distance, L_d:

$$L_d = \frac{Q}{h(R_2 - R_1)} t = \left(\frac{\ln\left(\frac{R_2}{R_1}\right)}{h\,(R_2 - R_1)} \right) \left(\frac{9\mu\, Q}{2\,\pi^2 f^2 \rho d_p{}^2 C} \right) \quad (16)$$

The first term is a geometric factor, depending on the dimensions of the centrifuge duct. The second term gives the dependence on the operational parameters, Q = total volumetric flow rate in the duct and f = rotational frequency.

The resolution of the centrifuge depends on the ratio of the aerosol sample flow rate S to the total flow rate Q. When the aerosol flow rate is very small by comparison to the total flow Q, then all of the particles will have to cross the entire duct radius, R_2–R_1, to be collected, and the deposition distance is given by Equation 16. However, when the aerosol flow is a significant portion of the total flow, then some of the particles will start at a position closer to the outer duct wall, and they will not have to travel as far to be collected. As a result, there will be a range of deposition distances.

In the case where the duct width (R_2–R_1) is small compared to the radius, R_1, the radial velocity of the particle across the duct is essentially constant, and the difference between the maximum and minimum deposition distances for a particles of uniform aerodynamic diameter is given by:

$$\frac{\Delta L_d}{L_d} = \frac{S}{Q} \quad (17)$$

where: S = aerosol sample flow
Q = sum of the sample and sheath flows

Applications

Aerosol centrifuges can provide exceptionally high particle-size resolution, but they generally operate at relatively low sample flow rates. One of their major applications has been to measure aerodynamic shape factors for particle clusters. They have also been used to measure densities for spherical particles by comparing the aerodynamic sizing provided by the centrifuge with microscopically determined geometric diameters. In some inhalation exposure applications, centrifuges have been used to preselect a narrow particle size range for subsequent resuspension as a nearly monodisperse aerosol.

In principle, centrifuge deposits can be analyzed chemically to provide species size distributions similar to those obtained with impactors. However, their application in this field has been limited. Limitations are the relatively low sample rates, usually less than 1 L/min, and the large deposit area, which makes chemical analyses difficult. Larger flow rates lead to secondary flow patterns in the duct because of Coriolis effects, and this can disrupt the centrifuge sizing capability. For particles with diameters greater than a few micrometers, most centrifuges are subject to inlet losses. But in contrast to impactors, particle bounce is not a problem because centrifugal force holds the particles tightly to the collection surface.

Elutriators

Elutriators use gravitational settling in a laminar flow to separate particles by aerodynamic diameter. They provide segregation for particles greater than 3 μm. Common applications are respirable and thoracic sampling, as discussed in Chapter 5. Examples include the Occupational Safety and Health Administration (OSHA)-recommended cotton dust sampler,[153,154] which is a vertical elutriator, and the Hexhlet[155] and MRE[156] dust samplers, which are horizontal elutriators used for respirable sampling. Horizontal elutriators can also be operated as spectrometers to measure distributions of particle size.

In still air, particle sedimentation is characterized by a terminal settling velocity, which is reached when the aerodynamic resistance exactly balances the gravitational force. The terminal settling velocity depends on aerodynamic diameter, and is given by:

$$V_{TS} = \frac{\rho d_p{}^2 g C}{18\mu} = \frac{\rho_o d_a{}^2 g C_a}{18\mu} \quad (18)$$

Settling velocities for aerosols are relatively small. A 10-μm aerodynamic diameter particle has a settling velocity of 0.305 cm/s; for 1 μm, it is only 0.0035 cm/s.

Vertical Elutriators

The vertical elutriator consists of a vertical duct through which air flows slowly upward. Particles whose sedimentation velocity is greater than the duct velocity cannot follow the air flow and settle out. In laminar flow with a known velocity profile, particle penetration characteristics can be calculated. The sharpness of the cutpoint is reduced by the parabolic distribution of velocities in the duct; nonetheless, it is an effective method for removing large particles.

The OSHA-required sampler for cotton dust sampling is a vertical elutriator. It has been used in epidemiological studies to establish correlation between dust and the prevalence of byssinosis among cotton mill workers. The device is 15 cm in diameter and 70 cm high. Air enters a 2.7-cm-diameter conical inlet at the bottom, and a 37-mm filter is mounted at the top. At the recommended flow rate of 7.4 L/min, the average upward velocity in the main section equals the terminal settling velocity for a 15-μm aerodynamic diameter particle. However, the actual performance of this sampler is more complicated.

Calibration data for the cotton dust sampler are shown in Figure 14-23, as is the predicted performance. Although calculations based on flat and parabolic velocity profiles show 50% penetration at diameters of 10 and 15 μm, the calibration data show 50% penetration for 20-μm particles.[154] The discrepancies are due to the conical inlet at the bottom of the sampler, which causes a jet of air to travel up along the centerline at a velocity sufficient for the 30-μm-diameter particles to reach the filter. It also induces a recirculation pattern along the walls within the main duct.[153] Another problem is that the velocity at the 2.7-cm inlet is large enough to draw very large particles, as much as 95 μm in diameter, into the sampler. These particles then become trapped and can act as a floating filter for the upward moving air stream.

Horizontal Elutriators

The principle of the horizontal elutriators is illustrated by the MRE Gravimetric Dust Sampler[156] shown in Figure 14-24. Air travels slowly through a set of closely spaced parallel plates oriented horizontally. All particles whose settling velocity is greater than the ratio of the plate separation to transit time will be trapped. Smaller particles will be trapped at less than 100% efficiency. Particles that penetrate are collected by filtration.

One of the advantages of the horizontal elutriator is that its performance is predicted easily from basic principles. Consider an elutriator containing a total of n horizontal channels, each with a rectangular cross-sectional area, A, a separation distance, h, and length,

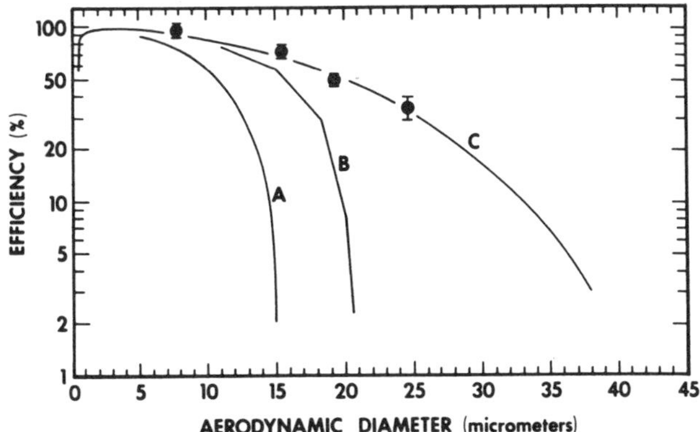

FIGURE 14-23. Comparison of theoretical and experimental collection efficiencies for the cotton dust elutriator. A — theory for laminar plug flow; B — theory for a parabolic velocity profile; C — theory for separated flow.[154] Reprinted with permission, American Industrial Hygiene Association Journal.

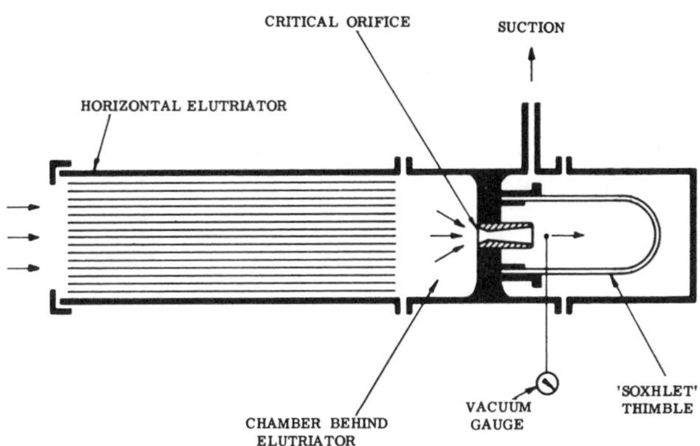

FIGURE 14-24. Schematic of the Hexhlet horizontal elutriator. Air flow enters from the left, passes through the set of parallel plates, and the remaining aerosol is collected on the "thimble" filter.

L. The 50% penetration efficiency will occur at

$$\rho\, C\, d_p^2 = \frac{hQ}{2nAL}\left(\frac{18\mu}{g}\right) \tag{19}$$

where: Q = volumetric flow rate
g = gravitational constant

This corresponds to the settling velocity of a particle that enters along the centerline between the plates and just reaches the bottom plate at the exit of the elutriation section.

More generally, the penetration, P, for particles with a settling velocity V_{TS} is given by:

$$P = 1 - \frac{V_{TS}F}{Q} \quad \text{for } V_{TS} < Q/F$$
$$= 0 \quad \text{for } V_{TS} > Q/F \tag{20}$$

where: F = horizontal area for collection[157]

This relation also holds for elutriators of variable cross-sectional area and plate separation, provided the flow is laminar and the particle trajectories are not affected by inertia.

In practice, there can be discrepancies between the theory and the performance. If the air stream velocity is too high, or if the device has not been cleaned, dust that has settled can be re-entrained and transported to the collection filter. This difficulty was observed in the original Hexhlet elutriator and corrected by reducing the flow rate and increasing the plate spacing. When flow velocities are very low, elutriator performance will be sensitive to thermal convection. If not operated in a fixed, horizontal orientation, its effective cutoff diameter will increase. In some older commercial units, discrepancies in elutriator performance have been traced to nonuniformity in plate spacings.

Horizontal elutriators can also be used as aerosol spectrometers by employing particle-free sheath air as the main carrier gas. Only a single channel consisting of two parallel plates is used. Aerosol is introduced as a thin stream along the upper plate. Particles of different sizes settle at different speeds, and they deposit at different positions along the bottom plate. The resolution with respect to particle size depends on the ratio of aerosol flow to sheath air flow. The principle is very much the same as for the aerosol centrifuge spectrometers, except that particles are drawn across the air flow by gravitational force rather than centrifugal force.

Summary

This chapter has presented the operating principles for impactors, inertial spectrometers, impingers, cyclones, aerosol centrifuges, and elutriators. Some of these instruments are used to provide precuts to other aerosol collection devices; others are used to provide size-segregated aerosol samples. All distinguish particles according to aerodynamic diameter, which is the parameter characterizing respiratory deposition for supermicrometer-sized particles. Without the physical separation of particles by size provided by these aerosol samplers, it would be difficult to determine the distribution of mass or chemical species with respect to particle diameter. Because adverse effects from airborne particles depend on both parameters, the simultaneous size and composition information obtained with these samplers is exceptionally valuable.

References

1. Hinds, W.C.: Aerosol Technology: Properties, Behavior and Measurement of Airborne Particles. p. 50. J. Wiley, New York, NY (1982).
2. Mitchell, R.I.; Pilcher, J.M.: Improved Cascade Impactor for Measuring Aerosol Particles Sizes in Air Pollutants, Commercial Aerosols and Cigarette Smoke. Industrial and Engineering Chemistry 51:1039–1042 (1959).
3. Wang, H.C.; John, W.: Characteristics of the Berner Impactor for Sampling Inorganic Ions. Aerosol Sci. Technol. 8:157–172 (1988).
4. May, K.R.: The Cascade Impactor: An Instrument for Sampling Coarse Aerosols. J. Scient. Instrum. 22:187–195 (1945).
5. Lodge, J.P.; Chan,T.L.; Eds.: Cascade Impactor Sampling and Data Analysis. Am. Ind. Hyg. Assoc., Akron, Ohio (1986).
6. Knuth, R.H.: Calibration of a Modified Sierra Model 235 Cascade Impactor, Report EML-360. Environmental Measurements Laboratory, New York (1979). Available from National Technical Information Service, Springfield, VA.
7. Burton, R.; Howard, J.N.; Penley, R.L.; et al.: Field Evaluation of the High-Volume Particle Fractionating Cascade Impactor. J. Air Pollut. Contr. Assoc. 23:277–281 (1973).
8. Mercer, T.T.; Tillery, M.I.; Newton, G.J.: A Multi-Stage, Low Flow-Rate Cascade Impactor. J. Aerosol Sci. 1:9–15 (1970).
9. Lippmann, M.: Review of Cascade Impactor for Particle Size Analysis and a New Calibration for the Casella Cascade Impactor. Am. Ind. Hyg. Assoc. J. 20:406–416 (1959).
10. Soole, B.W.: Concerning the Calibration Constants of Cascade Impactors, with Special Reference to the Casella MK-2. J. Aerosol Sci. 2:1–14 (1971).
11. Marple, V.A.; McCormack, J.E.: Personal Sampling Impactors with Respirable Aerosol Penetration Characteristics. Am. Ind. Hyg. Assoc. J. 44:916–922 (1983).
12. Rader, D.J.; Mondy, L.A.; Brockmann, J.E.; et al.: Stage Response Calibration of the Mark III and Marple Personal Cascade Impactors. Aerosol Sci. and Technol. 14:365–379 (1991).
13. Pilat, M.J.; Ensor, D.S.; Bosch, J.C.: Source Test Cascade Impactor. Atmos. Environ. 4:671–679 (1970).
14. Pilat, M.J.; Ensor, D.S.; Bosch, J.C.: Cascade Impactor for Sizing Particles in Emission Sources. Am. Ind. Hyg. Assoc. J. 32:508–511 (1971).
15. Andersen, A.A.: A New Sampler for the Collection, Sizing and Enumeration of Viable Airborne Particles. J. Bacteriol. 76:471–484 (1958).
16. Rubow, K.L.; Marple, V.A.; Olin, J.; McCawley, M.A.: A Personal Cascade Impactor: Design, Evaluation and Calibration. Am. Ind. Hyg. Assoc. J. 48:532–538 (1987).
17. Ranz, W.E.; Wong, J.B.: Impaction of Dust and Smoke Particles on Surface and Body Collectors. Industrial Engineering Chemistry, 44:1371–1381 (1952).
18. Davies, C.N.; Aylward, M.: The Trajectories of Heavy Solid Particles in a Two-Dimensional Jet of Ideal Fluid Impinging Normally Upon a Plate. Proc. Phys. Soc. B 64:889–911 (1951).
19. Marple, V.A.; Liu, B.Y.H.: Characteristics of Laminar Jet Impactors. Environ. Sci. Technol. 8:648–654 (1974).
20. Marple, V.A.; Liu, B.Y.H.: On Fluid Flow and Aerosol Impaction in Inertial Impactors. J. Colloid and Interface Sci. 53:31–34 (1975).
21. Rader, D.J.; Marple, V.A.: Effect of Ultra-Stokesian Drag and Particle Interception on Impaction Characteristics. Aerosol Sci. Technol. 4:141–156 (1985).
22. Mercer, T.T.; Chow, H.Y.: Impaction from Rectangular Jets. J. Colloid and Interface Sci. 27:75–83 (1968).
23. Mercer, T.T.; Stafford, R.G.: Impaction from Round Jets. Ann. Occup. Hyg. 12:41–48 (1969).
24. Ravenhall, D.G.; Forney, L.J.: Aerosol Impactors: Calculation of Optimum Geometries. J. Phys. E: Sci. Instrum. 13:87–91 (1980).
25. Marple, V.A.; Willeke, K.: Impactor Design. Atmos. Environ. 10:891–896 (1976).
26. Marple, V.A.; Rubow, K.L.: Theory and Design Guidelines. In: Cascade Impactor Sampling and Data Analysis, pp. 79–102. J.P. Lodge, Jr. and T.L. Chan, Eds. Am. Ind. Hyg. Assoc. Akron, OH (1986).
27. Hinds, W.C.; Liu, W.V.; Froines, J.R.: Particle Bounce in a Personal Cascade Impactor: A Field Evaluation. Am. Ind. Hyg. Assoc. J. 46:517–523 (1985).
28. Rao, A.K.; Whitby, K.T.: Non-Ideal Collection Characteristics of Inertial Impactors II: Cascade Impactors. J. Aerosol Sci. 9:87–100 (1978).
29. Cushing, K.M.; McCain, J.D.; Smith,W.B.: Experimental Determination of Sizing Parameters and Wall Losses of Five Source-Test Cascade Impactors. Environ. Sci. Technol. 13:726–731 (1979).
30. Dzubay, T.H.; Hines, L.E.; Stevens, R.K.: Particle Bounce in Cascade Impactors. Environ. Sci. Technol. 13:1392–1395 (1976).
31. Wesolowski, J.J.; John, W.; Devor, W.; et al.: Collection Surfaces of Cascade Impactors. In: X-Ray Fluorescence Analysis of Environmental Samples. p. 121. T. Dzubay, Ed. Ann Arbor Science Publishers, Ann Arbor, MI (1977).
32. Rao, A.K.; Whitby, K.R.: Nonideal Collection Characteristics of Single-Stage and Cascade Impactors. Am. Ind. Hyg. Assoc. J. 38:174–179 (1977).
33. Rao, A.K.; Whitby, K.R.: Nonideal Collection Characteristics of Inertial Impactors I: Single-Stage Impactors and Solid Particles. J. Aerosol Sci. 9:77–86 (1978).
34. Walsh, P.R.; Rahn, K.A.; Duce, R.A.: Erroneous Elemental Mass-Size Functions from a High-Volume Cascade Impactor. Atmos. Environ. 12:1793–1795 (1978).
35. Newton, G.J.; Cheng, Y.S.; Barr, E.B.; Yeh, H.C.: Effects of Collection Substrates on Peformance and Wall Losses in Cascade Impactors. J. Aerosol Sci. 21:467–470 (1990).
36. Ellenbecker, M.J.; Leith, D.; Price, J.M.: J. Air Pollut. Control Assoc. 30:1244–1227 (1980).

37. Lawson, D.R.: Impaction Surface Coatings Intercomparison and Measurements with Cascade Impactors. Atmos. Environ. 14:195–199 (1980).
38. Boesch, P.: Practical Comparison of Three Cascade Impactors. J. Aerosol Sci. 14:325–330 (1983).
39. Aylor, D.E.; Ferrandino, F.J.: Rebound of Pollen and Spores During Deposition on Cylinders by Inertial Impaction. Atmos. Environ. 19:803–806 (1985).
40. Wang, H.-C.; John, W.: Comparative Bounce Properties of Particle Materials. Aerosol Sci. Technol. 7:285–299 (1987).
41. Reischl, G.P.; John, W.: The Collection Efficiency of Impaction Surfaces. Staub Reinhalt. Luft 38:55 (1978).
42. Wall, S.; John W.; Wang, H.-C.: Measurements of Kinetic Energy Loss for Particles Impacting Surfaces. Aerosol Sci. Technol. 12:926–946 (1990).
43. Xu, M.; Willeke, K.: Right-Angle Impaction and Rebound of Particles. J. Aerosol Sci. 24:19–30 (1993).
44. Tsai, C.-J.; Pui, D.Y.H.; Liu, B.Y.H.: Capture and Rebound of Small Particles upon Impact with Solid Surfaces. Aerosol Sci. Technol. 12:497–507 (1990).
45. Cheng, Y.S.; Yeh, H.C.: Particle Bounce in Cascade Impactors. Environ. Sci. Technol. 13:1392–1395 (1979).
46. Pak, S.S.; Liu, B.Y.H.; Rubow, K.L.: Effect of Coating Thickness on Particle Bounce in Inertial Impactors. Aerosol Sci. Technol. 16:141–150 (1992).
47. Turner, J.R.; Hering, S.V.: Greased and Oiled Substrates as Bounce-Free Impaction Surfaces. J. Aerosol Sci. 18:215–224 (1987).
48. Willeke, K.: Performance of the Slotted Impactor. Am. Ind. Hyg. Assoc. J. 36:6883–691 (1975).
49. Vanderpool, R.W.; Lundgren, D.A.; Marple, V.A.; Rubow, K.L.: Cocalibration of Four Large-Particle Impactors. Aerosol Sci. Technol. 7:177–185 (1987).
50. Liu, B.Y.H.; Pui, D.Y.H.; Wang, X.Q.; Lewis,C.W.: Sampling Carbon Fiber Aerosols. Aerosol Sci. Technol. 2:499–511 (1983).
51. Twomey, S.J.: Comparison of Constrained Linear Inversion and Iterative Nonlinear Algorithm Applied to Indirect Estimation of Particle Size Distributions. Comput. Phys. 18:188–200 (1975).
52. Wolfenbarger, J.K.; Seinfeld, J.H.: Estimating the Variance in Solutions to the Aerosol Data Inversion Problem. Aerosol Sci. Technol. 14:348–357 (1991).
53. Hasan, H.; Dzubay, T.G.: Size Distributions of Species in Fine Particles in Denver Using a Micro-Orifice Impactor. Aerosol Sci. Technol. 6:29–40 (1987).
54. Hinds, W.C.: Data Analysis. In: Cascade Impactor Sampling and Data Analysis, Chapter 3. J.P. Lodge, Jr. and T.L. Chan, Eds. Am. Ind. Hyg. Assoc., Akron, OH (1986).
55. Stern, S.C.; Zeller, H.W.; Schekman, A.I.: Collection Efficiency of Jet Impactors at Reduced Pressures. I&EC Fundamentals 1:273–277 (1962).
56. Berner, A.; Luerzer, C.; Pohl, F.; et al.: The Size Distribution of the Urban Aerosol in Vienna. Sci. Tot. Environ. 13:245–261 (1979).
57. Hillamo, R.E.; Kauppinen, E.I.: On the Performance of the Berner Low-Pressure Impactor. Aerosol Sci. Technol. 14:33–47 (1991).
58. Hering, S.V.; Flagan, R.C.; Friedlander, S.K.: Design and Evaluation of a New Low-Pressure Impactor 1. Environ. Sci. Technol. 12:667–673 (1978).
59. Hering, S.V.; Friedlander, S.K.; Collins, J.J.; Richards, L.W.: Design and Evaluation of a New Low-Pressure Impactor 2. Environ. Sci. Technol. 13:184–188 (1979).
60. Vanderpool, R.W.; Lundgren, D.A.; Kerch, P.E.: Design and Calibration of an In-Stack Low-Pressure Impactor. Aerosol Sci. Technol. 12:215–224 (1990).
61. Kuhlmey, G.A.; Liu, B.Y.H.; Marple, V.A.: Micro-orifice Impactor for Submicron Aerosol Size Classification. Am. Ind. Hyg. Assoc. J. 42:790–795 (1981).
62. Marple, V.A.; Rubow, K.L.; Behm, S.M.: A Microorifice Uniform Deposit Impactor (MOUDI): Description, Calibration, and Use. Aerosol Sci. Technol. 14:434–446 (1991).
63. Biswas, P.; Flagan, R.C.: High-Velocity Inertial Impactors. Environ. Sci. Technol. 18:611–616 (1984).
64. Fang, C.P.; McMurry, P.H.; Marple, V.A.; Rubow, K.L.: Effect of Flow-Induced Relative Humidity Changes on Size Cuts for Sulfuric Acid Droplets in the Microorifice Uniform Deposit Impactor (MOUDI). Aerosol Sci. Technol. 14:266–277 (1991).
65. John, W.; Wall, S.M.: Aerosol Testing Techniques for Size-Selective Samplers. J. Aerosol Sci. 14:713–727 (1983).
66. Chen, B.T.; Yeh, H.C.; Cheng, Y.S.: A Novel Virtual Impactor: Calibration and Use. J. Aerosol Sci. 16:343–354 (1985).
67. Loo, B.W.; Cork, C.P.: Development of High-Efficiency Virtual Impactors. Aerosol Sci. Technol. 9:167–176 (1988).
68. Hounam, R.F.; Sherwood, R.J.: The Cascade Centripeter: A Device for Determining the Concentration and Size Distribution of Aerosols. Am. Ind. Hyg. Assoc. J. 26:122–131 (1965).
69. Conner, W.D.: An Inertial-Type Particle Separator for Collecting Large Samples. J. Air Pollut. Control Assoc. 16: 35–38 (1966).
70. Dzubay, T.G.; Stevens, R.D.: Ambient Air Analysis with Dichotomous Sampler and X-ray Fluorescence Spectrometer. Environ. Sci. Technol. 9:663–668 (1975).
71. Loo, B.W.; Jaklevic, J.M.; Goulding, F.S.: Dichotomous Virtual Impactors for Large Scale Monitoring of Airborne Particulate Matter. In: Fine Particles, Aerosol Generation, Measurement, Sampling and Analysis, pp. 311–350. B.Y.H. Liu, Ed. Academic Press, New York (1976).
72. McFarland, A.R.; Ortiz, C.A.; Bertch, R.W.: Particle Collection Characteristics of a Single-Stage Dichotomous Sampler. Environ. Sci. Technol. 12:679–682 (1978).
73. Solomon, P.A.; Moyers, J.L.; Fletcher, R.A.: High-Volume Dichotomous Virtual Impactor for the Fractionation and Collection of Particles According to Aerodynamic Size. Aerosol Sci. Technol. 2:455–465 (1983).
74. Chen, B.T.; Yeh, H.C.; Cheng, Y.S.: Performance of a Modified Virtual Impactor. Aerosol Sci. Technol. 5:369–376 (1986).
75. Chen, B.T.; Yeh, H.C.: An Improved Virtual Impactor: Design and Performance. J. Aerosol Sci. 18:203–214 (1987).
76. Novick, V.J.; Alvarez, J.L.: Design of a Multistage Virtual Impactor. Aerosol Sci. Technol. 6:63–70 (1987).
77. Noone, K.J.; Ogren, J.A.; Heintzenberg, J.; et al.: Design and Calibration of a Counterflow Virtual Impactor for Sampling of Atmospheric Fog and Cloud Droplets. Aerosol Sci. Technol. 8:235–244 (1988).
78. Forney, L.J.: Aerosol Fractionator for Large-Scale Sampling. Rev. Sci. Instrum. 47:1264–1269 (1976).
79. Forney, L.J.; Ravenhall, D.G.; Lee, S.S.: Experimental and Theoretical Study of a Two-Dimensional Virtual Impactor. Environ. Sci. Technol. 16:492–497 (1982).
80. Marple, V.A.; Chien, C.M.: Virtual Impactors: A Theoretical Study. Environ. Sci. Technol. 14:976–985 (1980).
81. Noll, K.E.; Pontius, A.; Frey, R.; Gould, M.: Comparison of the Coarse Particles at an Urban and Non-Urban Site. Atmos. Environ. 19:1931–1943 (1985).
82. Noll, K.E.: A Rotary Inertial Impactor for Sampling Giant Particles in the Atmosphere. Atmos. Environ. 4:9–19 (1970).
83. Regtuit, H.E.; de Ruiter, C.J.; Vrins, E.L.M.; et al.: The Tunnel Impactor. A Multiple Inertial Impactor for Coarse Aerosol. J. Aerosol Sci. 21:919–933 (1990).
84. Hameed, R.; McMurry, P.H.; Whitby, K.T.: A New Rotating Coarse Particle Sampler. Aerosol Sci. Technol. 2:69–78 (1983).
85. Mack, E.; Pillie, R.: Fog Water Collector. U.S. Patent 3889532.
86. Kramer, M.; Schultz, L.: Collection Efficiency of the Mainz-Rotating-Arm-Collector. J. Aerosol Sci. 21(Suppl. 1):653–656 (1990).
87. Jacob, D.; Wang, R.-F. T.; Flagan, R.C.: Fogwater Collector Design and Characterization. Environ. Sci. Technol. 18:827–833 (1984).

88. McFarland, A.R.; Ortiz, C.A.; Cermak, J.E.; et al.: Wind Tunnel Evaluation of a Rotating-Element Large-Particle Sampler. Aerosol Sci. Technol. 12:422–430 (1990).
89. Lesnic, D.; Elliott, L.; Ingham, D.B.: A Mathematical Model for Predicting the Collection Efficiency of the Rotating Arm Collector. J. Aerosol Sci. 24:163–180 (1993).
90. McFarland, A.R.; Ortiz, C.A.; Bertch, Jr., R.W.: A 10 μm Cutpoint Size-Selective Inlet for Hi-Vol Samplers. J. Air Pollut. Contr. Assoc. 34:544 (1984).
91. McFarland, A.R.; Ortiz, C.A.; Bertch, Jr., R.W.: Particle Collection Characteristics of a Single-Stage Dichotomous Sampler. Environ. Sci. Technol. 12:679 (1978).
92. Wedding, J.B.; Weigand, M.A.: The Wedding Ambient Aerosol Sampling Inlet (D_{50} = 10 μm) for the High-Volume Samplers. Atmos. Environ. 19:535 (1985).
93. Georghlou, P.; Blagden, E.; Snow, D.E.; et al.: Mutagenicity of Indoor Air Containing Environmental Tobacco Smoke: Evaluation of a Portable PM_{10} Impactor Sampler. Environ. Sci. Technol. 25:1496–1500 (1991).
94. Koutrakis, P.; Wolfson, J.M.; Brauer, M.; Spengler, J.D.: Design of a Glass Impactor for an Annular Denuder/Filter Pack System. Aerosol Sci. Technol. 12:607–612 (1990).
95. Koutrakis, P.; Fasano, A.M.; Slater, J.L.; et al.: Design of a Personal Annular Denuder Sampler to Measure Atmospheric Aerosols and Gases. Atmos. Environ. 23:2767–2773 (1989).
96. Fairchild, C.I.; Wheat, L.D.: Calibration and Evaluation of a Real-Time Cascade Impactor. Am. Ind. Hyg. Assoc. J. 45:205–211 (1984).
98. Horton, K.D.; Ball, M.H.E.; Mitchell, J.P.: The Calibration of a California Measurements PC-2 Quartz Crystal Cascade Impactor (QCM). J. Aerosol Sci. 23:505–524 (1992).
99. Tropp, R.J.; Kuhn, P.J.; Brock, J.R.: A New Method for Measuring Particle Size Distributions of Aerosols. Rev. Sci. Instrum. 51:516–520 (1980).
100. Keskinen, J.; Pietarinen, K.; Lehtimaki, M.: Electrical Low-Pressure Impactor. J. Aerosol Sci. 23:353–360 (1992).
101. Prodi, V.; Melandri, C.; Tarroni, G.; et al.: An Inertial Spectrometer for Aerosol Particles. J. Aerosol Sci. 10:411–419 (1979).
102. Belosi, F.; Prodi, V.: Particle Deposition Within the Inertial Spectrometer. J. Aerosol Sci. 18:37–42 (1987).
103. Aharonson, E.F.; Dinar, N.: The Effect of Gravity on Deposition Distances in an Inertial Particle Spectrometer. J. Aerosol Sci. 18:193–202 (1987).
104. Prodi, V.; De Zaiacomo, T.: Fibre Collection and Measurement with the Inertial Spectrometer. J. Aerosol Sci. 13:49–58 (1982).
105. Mitchell, J.P.; Nichols, A.L.: Experimental Assessment and Calibration of an Inertial Spectrometer. Aerosol Sci. Technol. 9:15–28 (1988).
106. Greenburg, L.; Smith, G.W.: A New Instrument for Sampling Aerial Dust. Bureau of Mines R.I. 2392. U.S. Dept. of the Interior, Washington, D.C. (1922).
107. Katz, S.H.; Smith, G.W.; Meyers, W.M.; et al.: Cooperative Tests of Instruments for Determining Atmospheric Dusts. pp. 41–55. Public Health Bulletin #44, Washington, D.C. (1925).
108. Greenburg, L.; Bloomfield, J.J.: The Impinger Dust Sampling Apparatus as Used by the United States Public Health Service. Pub. Health Reports 47:654 (1932).
109. Hatch, T.; Warren, H.; Drinker, P.: Modified Form of the Greenburg–Smith Impinger for Field Use With a Study of Its Operating Characteristics. J. Ind. Hyg. 14:301 (1932).
110. Hatch, T.; Pool, C.L.: Quantitation of Impinger Samples by Dark Field Microscopy. J. Ind. Hyg. 16:177 (1934).
111. DallaValle, J.M.: Note on Comparative Tests Made With the Hatch and Greenburg–Smith Impingers. Pub. Health Reports 42:1114 (1937).
112. Schrenk, H.H.; Feicht, F.L.: Bureau of Mines Midget Impinger. Bureau of Mines I.C. 7076. U.S. Dept. of the Interior, Washington, D.C. (1939).
113. Littlefield, J.B.; Schrenk, H.H.: Bureau of Mines Midget Impinger for Dust Sampling. Bureau of Mines R.I. 3360. U.S. Dept. of the Interior, Washington, D.C. (1937).
114. Ayer, H.E.; Hochstrasser, J.M.: Cyclone Discussion. In: Aerosol Measurement, pp. 70–79. D.A. Lundgren, F.S. Harris, W.H. Marlow, et al., Eds. University Presses of Florida, Gainesville, FL (1979).
115. Ranz, W.E.: Wall Flows in a Cyclone Separator: A Description of Internal Phenomena. Aerosol Sci. Technol. 4:417–432 (1985).
116. Smith, W.B.; Wilson, Jr., R.R.; Harris, D.B.: A Five-Stage Cyclone System for *in situ* Sampling. Environ. Sci. Technol. 13: 1387–1392 (1979).
117. Chan, T.L.; Lippmann, M.: Particle Collection Efficiencies of Air Sampling Cyclones: An Empirical Theory. Environ. Sci. Technol. 11:377–382 (1977).
118. Leith, D.; Mehta, D.: Cyclone Performance and Design. Atmos. Environ. 7:527–549 (1973).
119. Dirgo, J.; Leith, D.: Cyclone Collection Efficiency: Comparison of Experimental Results with Theoretical Predictions. Aerosol Sci. Technol. 4:401–415 (1985).
120. Iozia, D.L.; Leith, D.: Effect of Cyclone Dimensions on Gas Flow Pattern and Collection Efficiency. Aerosol Sci. Technol. 10:491–500 (1989).
121. Kessler, M.; Leith, D.: Flow Measurement and Efficiency Modeling of Cyclones for Particle Collection. Aerosol Sci. Technol. 15:8–18 (1991).
122. DeOtte, Jr., R.E.: A Model for the Prediction of the Collection Efficiency Characteristics of a Small, Cylindrical Aerosol Sampling Cyclone. Aerosol Sci. Technol. 12:1055–1066 (1990).
123. Lippmann, M.; Chan, T.L.: Cyclone Sampler Performance. Staub-Reinhalt. Luft 39:7–11 (1979).
124. Blachman, M.W.; Lippmann, M.: Performance Characteristics of the Mulitcyclone Aerosol Sampler. Am. Ind. Hyg. Assoc. J. 35:311–326 (1974).
125. Chow, J.C.; Watson, J.G.; Bowen, J.L.; et al.: A Sampling System for Reactive Species in the Western United States. In: Sampling and Analysis of Airborne Pollutants. E.D. Winegar and L.H. Kei, Eds. Lewis Publishers, Boca Raton, FL (1993).
126. Dekeyser, E.; Dams, R.: *In situ* Comparison of a Multistage Series Cyclone System and a Cascade Impactor for In-Stack Dust Sampling. Environ. Sci. Technol. 22:1034–1037 (1988).
127. John, W.; Reischl, G.: A Cyclone for Size-Selective Sampling of Ambient Air. J. Air Pollut. Control Assoc. 30:872–876 (1980).
128. McFarland, A.R.; Hickman, P.D.; Parnell, Jr., C.B.: A New Cotton Dust Sampler for PM_{10} Aerosol. Am. Ind. Hyg. Assoc. J. 48(3):293–297 (1987).
129. Vaughan, N.P.: Construction and Testing of an Axial Flow Cyclone Preseparator. J. Aerosol Sci. 19:295–305 (1988).
130. Baxter, T.E.; Lane, D.D.; Asce, A.M.; et al.: J. Environ. Eng. 112:468–478 (1986).
131. Beeckmans, J.M.; Kim, C.J.: Analysis of the Efficiency of Reverse Flow Cyclones. Canadian J. Chem. Eng. 55:640–643 (1977).
132. Saltzman, B.E.: Generalized Performance Characteristics of Miniature Cyclones for Atmospheric Particulate Sampling. Am. Ind. Hyg. Assoc. J. 45:671–680 (1984).
133. Moore, M.E.; McFarland, A.R.: Design of Stairmand-Type Sampling Cyclones. Am. Ind. Hyg. Assoc. J. 51(3):151–159 (1990).
134. Kim, J.C.; Lee, K.W.: Experimental Study of Particle Collection by Small Cyclones. Aerosol Sci. Technol. 12:1003–1015 (1990).
135. Saltzman, B.E.; Hochstrasser, J.M.: Design and Performance of Miniature Cyclones for Respirable Aerosol Sampling. Environ. Sci. Technol. 7:418–424 (1983).
136. Berry, R.D.: The Effect of Flow Pulsations on the Performance of Cyclone Pesonal Respirable Dust Samplers. J. Aerosol Sci. 22:887–899 (1991).
137. Almich B.P.; Carson, G.A.: Some Effects of Charging on 10-mm

Nylon Cyclone Performance. Am. Ind. Hyg. Assoc. J. 35:603–612 (1974).
138. Briant, J.K.; Moss, O.R.: The Influence of Electrostatic Charge on the Performance of 10-mm Nylon Cyclones. Am. Ind. Hyg. Assoc. J. 45:440–445 (1984).
139. Appel, B.R.; Povard, V.; Kothny, E.L.: Loss of Nitric Acid Within Inlet Devices for Atmospheric Sampling. Atmos. Environ. 22:2535–2540 (1988).
140. Stoeber, W.; Flachsbart, H.: Size-Separating Precipitation in a Spinning Spiral Duct. Environ. Sci. Technol. 3:1280–1296 (1969).
141. Stoeber, W.: Design Performance and Applications of Spiral Duct Aerosol Centrifuges. In: Fine Particles, Aerosol Generation, Measurement, Sampling and Analysis, pp. 351–398. B.Y.H. Liu, Ed. Academic Press, New York (1976).
142. Hoover, M.D.; Morawietz, G.; Stoeber, W.: Optimizing Resolution and Sampling Rate in Spinning Duct Aerosol Centrifuges. Am. Ind. Hyg. Assoc. J. 44:131–134 (1983).
143. Tillery, M.I.; Aerosol Centrifuges. In: Aerosol Measurement, pp. 3–23. D.A. Lundgren, F.S. Harris, W.H. Marlow, et al., Eds. University Presses of Florida, Gainesville, FL (1979).
144. Goetz, A.; Stevenson, H.J.R.; Preining, O.: The Design and Performance of the Aerosol Spectrometer. J. Air Pollution Control Assoc. 10:378 (1960).
145. Gerber, H.E.: The Goetz Aerosol Spectrometer. In: Aerosol Measurement, pp. 36–55. D.A. Lundgren, F.S. Harris, W.H. Marlow, et al., Eds. University Presses of Florida, Gainesville, FL (1979).
146. Stoeber, W.; Flachsbart, H.: Aerosol Size Spectrometry With a Ring Slit Conifuge. Environ. Sci. Technol. 3:641–651 (1969).
147. Hochrainer, D.; Brown, P.M.: Sizing of Aerosol Particles by Centrifugation. Environ. Sci. Technol. 3:830–835 (1969).
148. Kotrappa, P.; Light, M.E.: Design and Performance of the Lovelace Aerosol Separator. Rev. Sci. Instrum. 43:1106–1112 (1972).
149. Holländer, W.; Morawietz, G.; Pohlmann, G.; et al.: Very High-Volume Aerosols Sampling With a Novel Drum Centrifuge. Aerosol Sci. Technol. 7:67–77 (1987).
150. Tillery, M.I.: A Concentric Aerosol Spectrometer. Am. Ind. Hyg. Assoc. J. 35:62–74 (1974).
151. Hochrainer, D.: A New Centrifuge to Measure the Aerodynamic Diameter of Aerosol Particles in Submicron Range. J. Coll. Interface Sci. 36:191–194 (1971).
152. Hochrainer, D.; Stoeber, W.: A Stoeber-rotor With Recirculation of Particle-Free Air. Am. Ind. Hyg. Assoc. J. 39:754–757 (1978).
153. Claassen, B.J.: Effects of Separated Flow on Cotton Dust Sampling With a Vertical Elutriator. Am. Ind. Hyg. Assoc. J. 40:933–941 (1979).
154. Robert, K.Q.: Cotton Dust Sampling Efficiency of the Vertical Elutriator. Am. Ind. Hyg. Assoc. J. 40:535–541 (1979).
155. Wright, B.M.: A Size-Selecting Sampler for Airborne Dust. Brit. J. Industr. Med. 11:284–288 (1954).
156. Dunmore, J.H.; Hamilton, R.J.; Smith, D.S.G.: An Instrument for the Sampling of Respirable Dust for Subsequent Gravimetric Assessment. J. Sci. Instrum. 41:669 (1964).
157. Mercer, T.T.: Aerosol Technology in Hazard Evaluation. Academic Press, New York (1973).
158. Newton, G.J.; Raabe, O.G.; Mokler, B.V.: Cascade Impactor Design and Performance. J. Aerosol Sci. 8:339 (1977).
159. Marple, V.; Rubow, K.; Turner, W.; et al.: Low Flow Rate Sharp Cut Impactors for Indoor Air Sampling: Design and Calibration. J. Air Poll. Cont. Assoc. 37:1303–1307 (1987).

INSTRUMENT 14-1. May/R.E. cascade impactor with access door open and intake adaptor in place, showing mask slide, filter support, and critical orifice.

Instrument Descriptions

Cascade Impactors for Ambient Particle Sampling

14-1. May/R.E. Cascade Impactor

BGI Incorporated

This is a seven-stage impactor based on the design of May.[4] Particles are collected on standard 3-in. × 1-in. microscope slides that are inserted into the impactor from the front of the instrument. The slides may be removed without dismantling the impactor through a door located along the side. A constant flow of 5 L/min is maintained by a critical orifice located in the suction hose nipple. Fifty-percent efficiency cutpoint diameters for the impactor are 32, 16, 8, 4, 2, 1, and 0.5 µm. A 47-mm-diameter filter holder with an electro-etched filter support is located at the bottom of the last stage. The impactor is constructed of aluminum block and is held together by removable tie rods. Dimensions: 120 mm high × 82 mm × 87 mm.

14-2. Sierra/Marple Series 210 Ambient Cascade Impactor

Graseby Andersen Samplers, Inc.

This is a radial slot cascade impactor for ambient sampling. It is equipped with a cyclone preseparator and uses 47-mm-diameter, slotted impaction substrates. A built-in, 47-mm-diameter after-filter follows the impactor stages. Nominal cutpoints at the designed flow rate of 7 L/min are 0.16, 0.32, 0.53, 0.95, 1.7, 2.65, 4.4, 11, and 18 µm. Cutpoints are listed by the manufacturer at six additional flow rates of 0.3, 1, 3, 10, 14, and 21 L/min. Ten stages are available; however, stages with smaller nozzles cannot be operated at the higher flow rates. For example, at 7 L/min, only nine stages are operable. The impactor and impactor stages are made of 316 stainless steel. Dimensions: 6.4 cm diameter × 28 cm high (2.5 in. × 11 in.). Weight: 2 kg (4.5 lb).

INSTRUMENT 14-2. Sierra/Marple Series 210 ambient cascade impactor.

14-3. Sierra/Marple Series 260 Ambient Cascade Impactor

Graseby Andersen Samplers, Inc.

This impactor has interchangeable nozzles that screw into the impaction stages. A set of six single, round, jet impactor nozzles and four rectangular nozzles give size cuts between 0.5 and 20 µm. Impactor flow rates may be varied from 0.3 to 20 L/min. Size cuts depend on flow rate and which impactor nozzles are used. Impactor nozzles are located off axis so that the location of the deposit can be varied by rotating stages relative to each other during collection. Impaction substrates are 18-mm diameter disks. Construction: aluminum. Size: 5 cm diameter × 40 cm high. Weight: 1.4 kg.

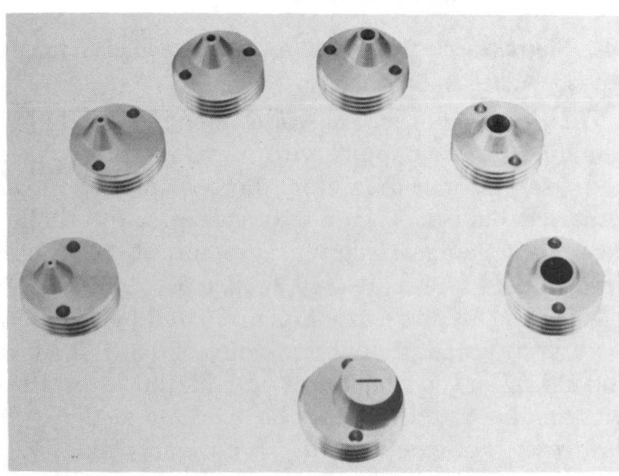

INSTRUMENT 14-3. Interchangeable nozzles for the Sierra/Marple cascade impactor.

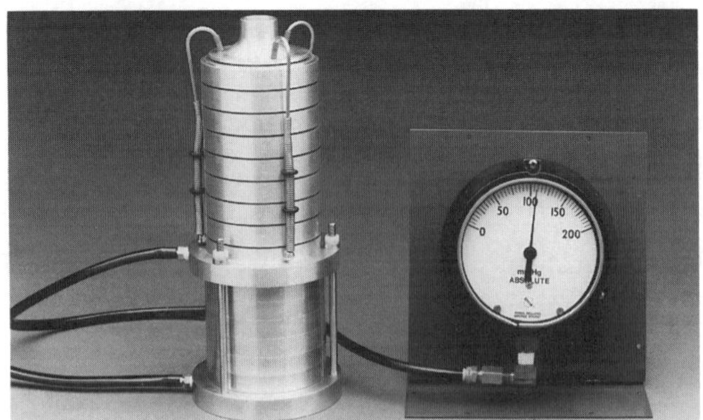

INSTRUMENT 14-4. Andersen low pressure impactor.

14-4. Andersen Low Pressure Impactor

Graseby Andersen Samplers, Inc.

This is a 13-stage, multijet impactor that operates at a fixed flow rate of 3 std L/min. The first eight stages are the same as those from the Andersen One ACFM ambient cascade impactor and provide size cuts at 35, 21.7, 15.7, 10.5, 6.6, 3.3, 2.0, and 1.4 µm. The last five stages operate at low pressure (≤ 0.15 atm) to provide size cuts at 0.90, 0.52, 0.23, 0.11, and 0.08 µm. The low pressure enables the capture of these smaller particles (see text). A critical orifice separates the low pressure and atmospheric pressure stages and controls the flow rate. An adapter kit is available for modifying Andersen One ACFM impactors. The complete kit includes a high-pressure vacuum pump and absolute pressure gauge.

14-5. Andersen One ACFM Ambient Cascade Impactor

Graseby Andersen Samplers, Inc., Graseby GMW

This multijet cascade impactor has eight aluminum stages and a back-up filter holder, held together by

INSTRUMENT 14-5. Andersen One ACFM ambient cascade impactor.

INSTRUMENT 14-6. Flow sensor ambient cascade impactor.

three spring clamps and gasketed with O-ring seals. The first two stages contain 96 circular orifices each arranged in a radial pattern. The next five stages have 400 orifices each; the last stage has 201 orifices. Cutpoints at a sampling rate of 28 L/min (1 cfm) range from 10 to 0.4 μm. Each stage has a removable, 8.2-cm- (3.25 in.-) diameter stainless steel or glass collection plate. An impactor preseparator is optional. The sampler is furnished as a complete system with a vacuum pump and carrying case. Dimensions: 11 cm diameter × 20 cm high (4.25 in. × 7.75 in.). Weight: 1.7 kg (3.75 lb).

14-6. Flow Sensor Ambient Cascade Impactor

Graseby Andersen Samplers, Inc.

This is a seven-stage, multijet cascade impactor with a preimpactor stage and a back-up filter holder. It is based on the design of Andersen (A.A., Sampler for Respiratory Health Hazard Assessment. Am. Ind. Hyg. Assoc. J. 27; 1966). Cutpoints at a sampling rate of 28 L/min (1 cfm) are 6, 4.6, 3.3, 2.2, 1.1, 0.7, and 0.4 μm. The sampler is furnished as a complete system with a flow controller, vacuum pump, and carrying case. Construction is of aluminum with O-ring seals. Dimensions of the impactor case: 15 cm × 15 cm × 30 cm high (6 in. × 6 in. × 12 in.). Impactor weight: 5.3 kg (7.5 lb); pump weight: 14 kg (31 lb).

14-7. Berner Impactor

Hauke KG

The Berner impactor is a multijet, reduced pressure impactor that provides size cuts below 0.1 μm at a sampling rate of 30 L/min. Several models are available. The lower stages operate at pressures of 0.3 to 0.8 atmospheres. Acceleration nozzles on each stage are arranged in a circle. Experimentally determined cut-

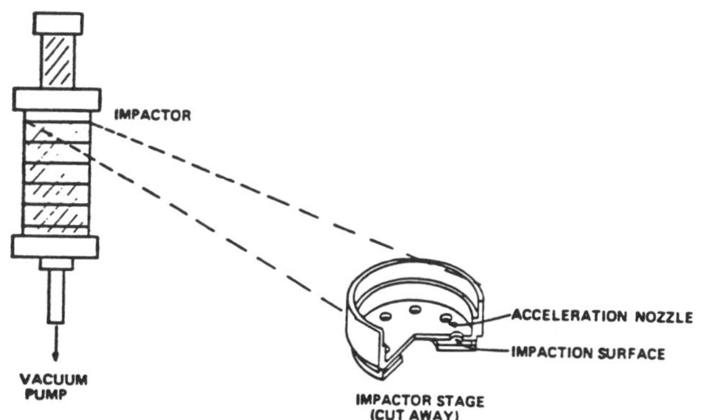

INSTRUMENT P-8. Berner impactor.

points for the Model 30/.06 are 0.082, 0.13, 0.21, 0.43, 0.96, 2.1, 4.2, and 8.6 μm (Wang and John[3]).

14-8. Mercer Seven-Stage Cascade Impactors

In-Tox Products

These are seven-stage, round-jet cascade impactors based on the design of Mercer *et al.*[8] Four models are available with flow rates from 0.1 to 5 L/min using one to four jets per stage. Effective cutpoint diameters are as follows: 3.1, 2.1, 1.6, 1.0, 0.85, 0.58, and 0.33 μm for the 0.1 L/min impactor; 4.5, 3.0, 2.1, 1.5, 1.0, 0.71, and 0.32 μm for the 1 L/min impactor; 5.0, 4.0, 3.0, 1.8, 1.0, 0.4, and 0.25 μm for the 2 L/min model; and 5.0, 3.4, 2.3, 1.5, 1.0, 0.7, and 0.5 μm for the 5 L/min model. Collection substrates are 22 mm in diameter, and the stages are sealed in O-rings. The impactors are made of brass (stainless steel versions are available upon request) and are 4.5 cm in diameter, 10 cm high, and weigh 0.9 kg (2 lb).

14-9. Multijet Cascade Impactors

In-Tox Products

These seven-stage cascade impactors are available in four models with flow rates of 10, 15, 20, and 28 L/min. They are similar in construction to the Mercer seven-

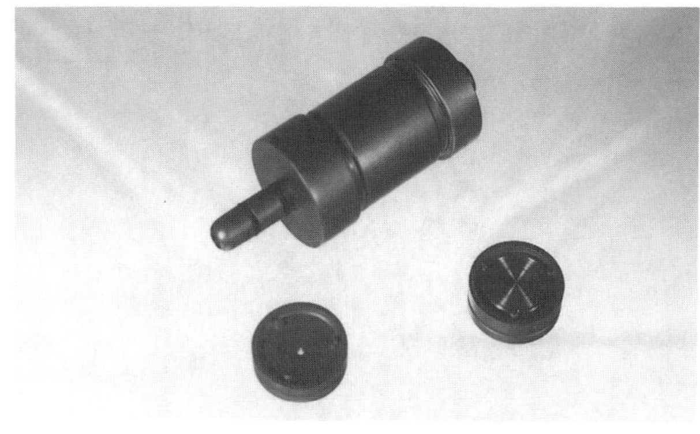

INSTRUMENT 14-8. Mercer seven-stage cascade impactor.

INSTRUMENT 14-9. In-Tox multijet cascade impactor.

stage impactor described above. The stages have round jets, 37-mm-diameter collection substrates, and are sealed with O-rings. The impactors are made of brass (stainless steel available upon request) and are 7 cm in diameter, 15 cm high, and weigh 2 kg (4.4 lb). The effective cutpoint diameters are as follows: 8.0, 5.0, 3.2, 2.0, 1.3, 0.8, and 0.5 for the 10 L/min, 15 L/min, and 20 L/min models; and 9.25, 5.7, 3.6, 2.2, 1.4, 0.8, and 0.5 for the 28 L/min model.

14-10. MOUDI (Model 100)
MSP Corporation

The MOUDI (*M*icro-orifice *u*niform *d*eposit *i*mpactor) is an eight-stage cascade impactor with round jets. Stages may be rotated to provide a uniform deposit on the collection stage. The lower four impactor stages use chemically etched, micro-orifice impaction plates, which have 900 to 2000 jets per stage and jet diameters of 0.0048 to 0.0139 cm. Cutpoints at the nominal flow rate of 30 L/min are 10, 5.62, 3.16, 1.78, 1.0, 0.56, 0.316, 0.178, 0.10, and 0.056 μm in aerodynamic diameter. The total pressure drop across the impactor is 0.3 atmospheres. The MOUDI is constructed of hard-coated aluminum with stainless steel micro-orifice plates. Dimensions: 13 cm diameter × 28 cm high (5 in. × 11 in.). Weight: 5 kg (11 lb), plus 6 kg (13 lb) for the rotating unit.

INSTRUMENT 14-10. Model 100 MOUDI.

INSTRUMENT 14-11. URG portable size-selective impactor inlet with PUF.

14-11. Portable Size Selective-Impactor Inlet with PUF
URG Corporation

The operating principle for this instrument is based on separating fine particles from coarse particles by impaction of the latter on an oiled coarse plate. The purpose of the size-selective inlet is to collect only respirable (deep lung penetrating) particles and vapors. Analysis can be done of particles collected on the filter paper. Pesticides, semivolatile, and condensable organic PAHs are collected on the polyurethane foam (PUF).

The portable size-selective impactor inlet with PUF operates at 4 L/min and has a 2.5-μm size impactor inlet. The impactor is made of Teflon-coated stainless steel. It can be removed for cleaning and a removal tool is provided. The unit is 160 mm long with a 35-mm OD. The PUF cartridge located inside the housing unit is 3 in. × 3/4 in. A housing unit surrounds the PUF and provides a protective encasement for both the PUF and the impactor, as well as for the stainless steel support screen for the filter paper. The unit attaches to a pump with tubing of suitable material.

14-12. Hi-Volume Fractionating Sampler (Model 65-800)
Graseby Andersen Samplers, Inc.

This is a multijet cascade impactor designed to mount on a Hi-Volume sampler. The impactor segregates particles by aerodynamic diameter on each of the stages, with the smallest particles collected by the Hi-Volume filter. The impaction stages use round impaction jets

INSTRUMENT 14-12. Andersen Hi-Volume fractionator.

arranged in a circular pattern. Two versions of the impactor, with four or two stages, respectively, are designed for operation at 566 L/min (20 cfm). A third version has one stage for operation at 1132 L/min (40 cfm). For operation at 566 L/min, the size cuts for the four-stage impactor are 1.1, 2.0, 3.3, and 7 μm; for the two-stage version, the size cuts are 1.1 and 7.0 μm. At 1132 L/min, the single-stage version of the impactor has a cutpoint at 3.5 μm. Dimensions: 30 cm diameter × 13 cm high (12 in. × 5 in.). Weight: 8.6 kg (19 lb).

INSTRUMENT 14-13. General Metal Works Series 230 high-volume cascade impactor.

14-13. High-Volume Cascade Impactors (Series 230)
Graseby Anderson Samplers, Inc., Graseby GMW

This is a rectangular-jet cascade impactor designed to mount on a Hi-Volume sampler. Collection substrates are 14.3 cm × 13.7 cm and must be slotted to allow air flow to the next stage. The Model 235 is designed for a nominal flow rate of 1.13 m^3/min (40 cfm) and has five stages with cutpoints at 7.2, 3.0, 1.5, 0.95, and 0.49 μm. The Model 236 is designed for a flow rate of 0.566 m^3/min (20 cfm) and has six stages with particle cutpoints at 10.2, 4.2, 2.1, 1.4, 0.73, and 0.41 μm in aerodynamic diameter. Single-stage versions of the impactors with 1.13 m^3/min (40 cfm) cutpoints at 3.5 μm (respirable) and 2.5 μm (fine) are available. Stages are made of aluminum. Dimensions: 23 cm × 30 cm × 5 cm high (9.25 in. × 12 in. × 2 in.). Weight: 2.5 kg (5.5 lb).

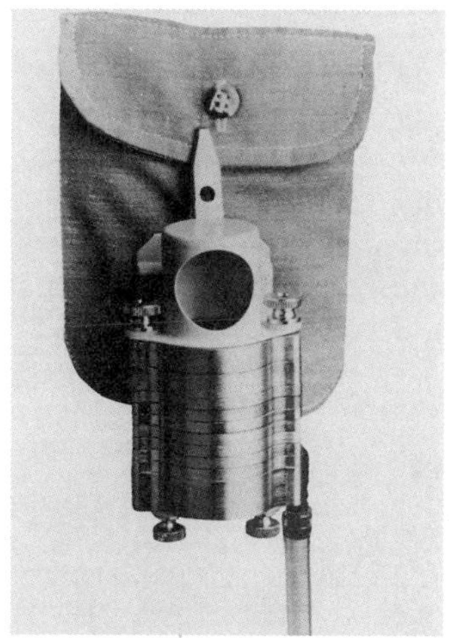

INSTRUMENT 14-14. Marple personal sampler, Series 290.

Personal Sampling Impactors

14-14. Marple Personal Samplers (Series 290)
Graseby Andersen Samplers, Inc., Graseby GMW

This impactor is designed to be worn on the lapel of a worker for personal monitoring in the workplace. It has a radial slot jet design, 34-mm-diameter collection substrates, and a 34-mm-diameter PVC back-up filter. The design sample flow rate is 2 L/min. An inlet cowl excludes extraneous debris. The three models available are of four, six, and eight stages, respectively. For the eight-stage model, cutpoints are 0.6, 1, 2, 3.5, 6, 10, 15, and 20 μm; for six stages, the cutpoints are 0.6, 1, 2, 3.5, 6, and 10 μm; and for four stages, the cutpoints are at 3.5, 10, 15, and 20 μm. The impactors are machined from aluminum, and the impactor stages are nickel plated. The Andersen and GMW instruments were identical. Dimensions for both: 5.7 cm wide and 7.2–8.6 cm high. Weight: 170 to 200 g (6–7 oz), depending on the model.

14-15. Personal Environmental Monitoring Impactor
MSP Corporation

This is a single-stage impactor with ten circular jets that provides a cutpoint at either 2.5 μm or 10 μm. Four models are available with flow rates of 4 L/min or 10 L/min at each cutpoint. The impaction surface is an

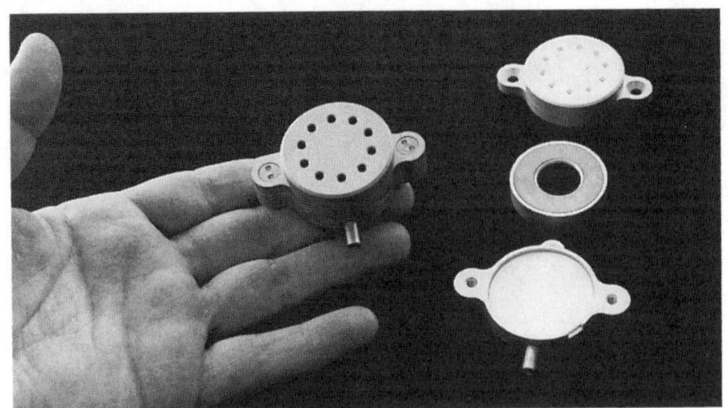

INSTRUMENT 14-15. MSP personal environmental monitor.

oil-soaked, porous, stainless steel plate. Samples are collected on 37-mm or 47-mm after-filters. The impactor is constructed of aluminum. Dimensions: 2.5 cm high × 6 to 9 cm diameter (1 in. × 2.5–3.5 in.). Weight: 55 g (2 oz.).

Virtual Impactors

14-16. Cascade Centripeter

BGI Incorporated

This instrument is a type of multistage virtual impactor based on the design of Hounam and Sherwood.[68] The air stream passes through a series of orifices of diminishing diameter. Successively finer fractions of the aerosol are collected by sharp-edged nozzles located immediately downstream of each orifice. Particles are deposited on filters located behind the receiver nozzles. A final filter collects particles that escape removal by the three centripeter stages. The sampler flow rate is 30 L/min and corresponding cut-points are at 1.2, 4, and 14 μm. Dimensions: 3.8 cm diameter × 18 cm high (1.5 in. × 7 in.).

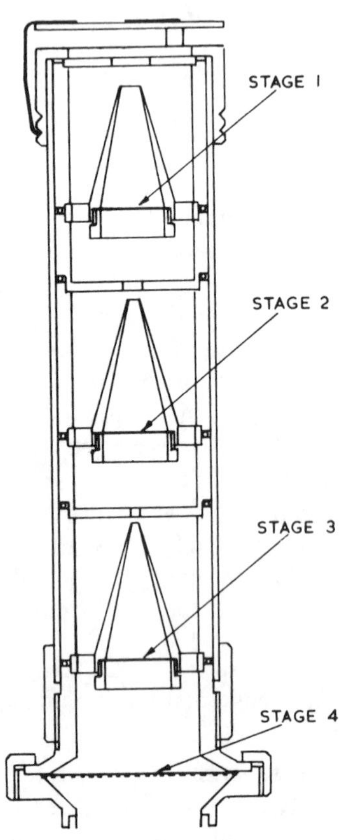

INSTRUMENT 14-16. Schematic diagram of cascade centripeter.

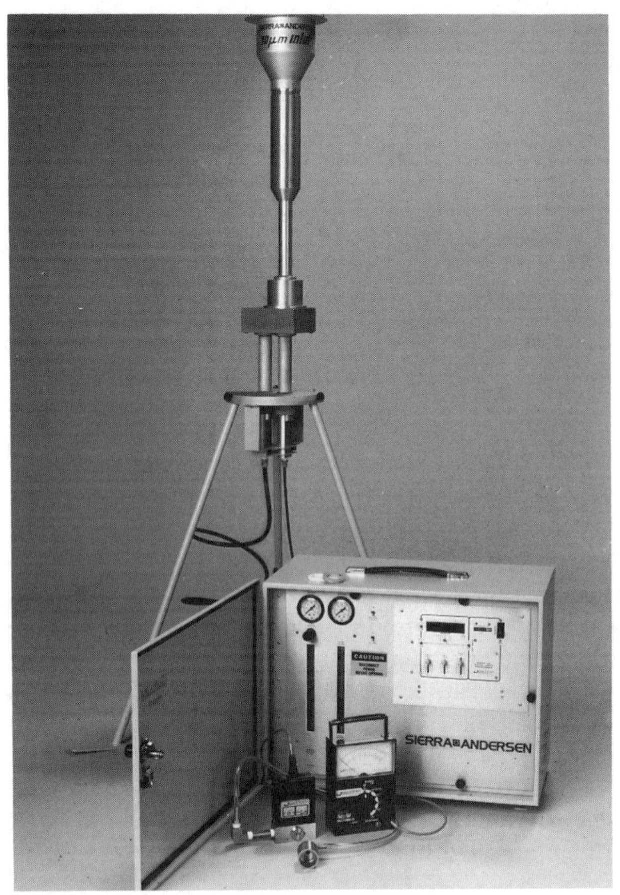

INSTRUMENT 14-17. Series 241, PM_{10} manual dichotomous sampler.

14-17. PM-10 Manual Dichotomous Sampler (Series 241)

Graseby Andersen Samplers, Inc., Graseby GMW

The dichotomous sampler has a PM_{10} inlet to provide a precut at 10 μm, followed by a virtual impaction stage that provides a second particle size cut at 2.5 μm. The inlet is based on the design of McFarland; the virtual impactor is based on the design of Loo.[71] It samples at 16.7 L/min (1 m^3/hr) and provides samples in two particle size fractions: coarse (2.5 to 10 μm) and fine (<2.5 μm). Samples are collected on 37-mm filters. Air flow is regulated by a flow controller. The sampling module is made of aluminum, measures 162 cm high × 76 cm diameter (64 in. × 30 in.), and weighs 9 kg (20 lb). The control module measures 41 cm high × 56 cm wide × 28

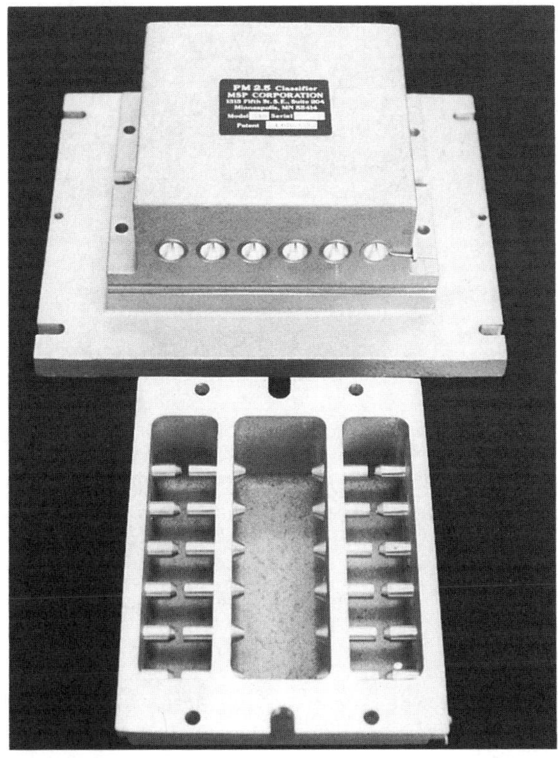

INSTRUMENT 14-18. Model 340 high-volume virtual impactor.

cm diameter (16 in. × 22 in. × 11 in.) and weighs 27 kg (60 lb).

14-18. High Volume Virtual Impactor (Model 340)
MSP Corporation

The high-volume virtual impactor operates at 1130 L/min (40 cfm) and has a multijet 2.5-µm cutpoint virtual impaction stage with a 5% minor flow. Coarse (> 2.5 µm) and fine (< 2.5 µm) particles are collected on 20-cm × 25-cm (8-in. × 10-in.) filters. The virtual impactor fits inside either the Andersen or Wedding PM_{10} high-volume sampler inlets. Construction is of aluminum. Dimensions: 15 cm high × 25 cm × 30 cm (5 in. × 9.5 in. × 12 in.). Weight: 5 kg (11 lb).

14-19. Microcontaminant Particle Sampler
MSP Corporation

The microcontaminant particle sampler uses a 1-µm cut virtual impactor at 30 L/min to concentrate supermicrometer particles into a 1.5-L/min stream that passes though a two-stage impactor followed by a final 25-mm filter. The first impactor stage collects particles on a scanning electron microscope (SEM) stud. Particles that bounce from this ungreased SEM stud are collected on a greased SEM stud in the second impaction stage. The fine fraction from the virtual impaction stage is collected on a 37-mm filter. Construction is of aluminum. Dimensions: 15 cm high × 11 cm diameter (5.8 in. × 4.2 in.). Weight: 1.4 kg (3 lb).

INSTRUMENT 14-19. Microcontaminant particle sampler.

Source Test Impactors

14-20. Series 220 In-Stack Cascade Impactor
Graseby Andersen Samplers, Inc.

This is a multijet, radial slot cascade impactor with six, eight, or ten impaction stages, a built-in 47-mm holder for the after-filter, and an optional cyclone preseparator. At the nominal flow rate of 7 actual L/min, the impactor stage cutpoints are 0.16, 0.32, 0.53, 0.95, 1.7, 2.65, 4.4, 11, and 18 µm aerodynamic diameter. Isokinetic sampling nozzles are available. Impactor construction: nickle-plated aluminum or 316 stainless steel. Dimensions: 6.3 cm diameter × 28 cm high (25 in. × 11 in.). Weight: 2 to 4 kg (4 to 9 lb).

INSTRUMENT 14-20. Andersen in-stack cascade impactor, Model 226.

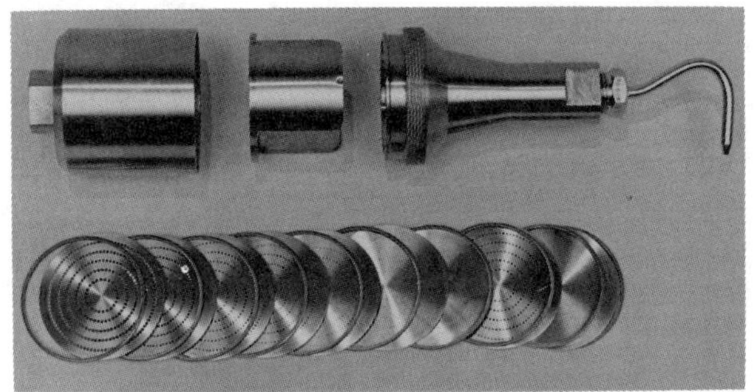

INSTRUMENT 14-21. Andersen stack head sampler.

INSTRUMENT 14-23. Andersen impactor preseparator, Model 50-160.

14-21. Andersen Mark III and Mark IV Stack Sampling Heads

Graseby Andersen Samplers, Inc.

These are nine-stage, multijet cascade impactors designed to adapt to stack sampling trains. Jets are round and arranged in concentric circles. Nominal flow rates are 2.8 to 21 actual L/min (0.1 to 0.75 acfm). At the 21-L/min flow rate, aerodynamic diameter cutpoints are 10.9, 6.8, 4.6, 3.2, 2.0, 1.0, 0.61, and 0.41 μm. The impactor is made of stainless steel and can be operated at 800°C. The Mark III is available with a stainless steel cyclone preseparator. The Mark IV uses an external right angle inlet nozzle preseparator. The entire assembly will fit through a 7.6-cm- (3-in.-) diameter port. Dimensions: 7 cm diameter × 25 cm long (2.8 in. × 10 in.).

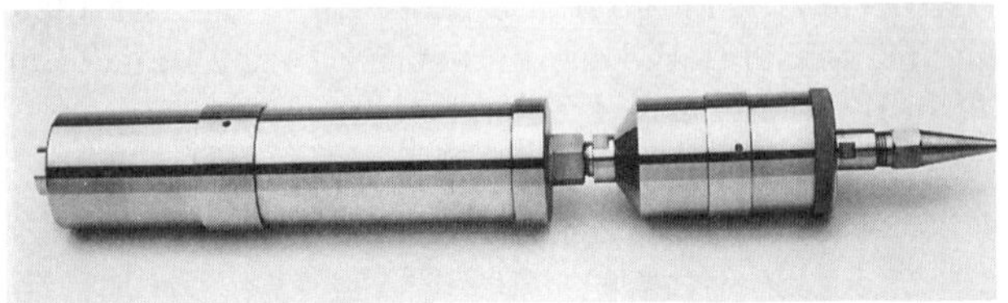

INSTRUMENT 14-22. Andersen high capacity stack sampler, Model 70-900.

14-22. High Capacity Stack Sampler (Model 70-900)

Graseby Andersen Samplers, Inc.

The high-capacity stack sampler has two impaction stages followed by a cyclone and back-up filter thimble. At the recommended flow rate of 14 actual L/min (0.5 acfm) and 25°C, the cutpoints are 10.8, 5.8, and 1.5 μm. A preimpactor with a 12-μm cutpoint is available. The assembled unit fits through a 7.6-cm- (3-in.-) diameter sampling port. Units are made of stainless steel.

14-23. Impactor Preseparator (Model 50-160)

Graseby Andersen Samplers, Inc.

The impactor preseparator is designed for stack sampling under conditions of high particulate loadings. It is a single-stage, high capacity impactor that screws directly into the inlet of the high capacity or Mark III stack samplers. It has a 10-μm cutpoint at 25°C and 21 L/min, is made of stainless steel, and fits through a 7.6-cm- (3 in.-) diameter sampling port.

14-24. High Temperature, High Pressure Cascade Impactor

In-Tox Products

This seven-stage cascade impactor is designed for process stream sampling and has been tested at pressures of 10 atmospheres (140 psig) and 540°C (1000°F). It is made of stainless steel and uses gold wire seals. Collection substrates are constructed of 313 stainless steel shim stock and are 0.13 mm (0.005 in.) thick and 47 mm in diameter. At room temperature and a flow rate of 16 L/min, the 50% efficiency cutpoint diameters are 8.8, 6.4, 4.5, 2.5, 1.9, 1.3, and 0.62 μm. The impactor is 11 cm in diameter, 20 cm long, and weighs approximately 4 kg.

14-25. Pilat UW Source Test Cascade Impactor

Pollution Control Systems Corporation

There are six cascade impactor models available, the Mark 3, 4, 5, 8, 10, and 20. The Mark 3 and the Mark 5 have 7 and 11 impactor stages plus back-up filters, respectively, with D_{50} cut diameters between 0.2 and 20 μm. The Mark 8 is a three-jet stage plus back-up filter for high particulate concentrations and has cut diameters at 10.8, 5.8, and 1.5 μm. The Mark 4, 10, and 20 models are low-pressure cascade impactors. The Mark 4 is designed to be located downstream of a Mark

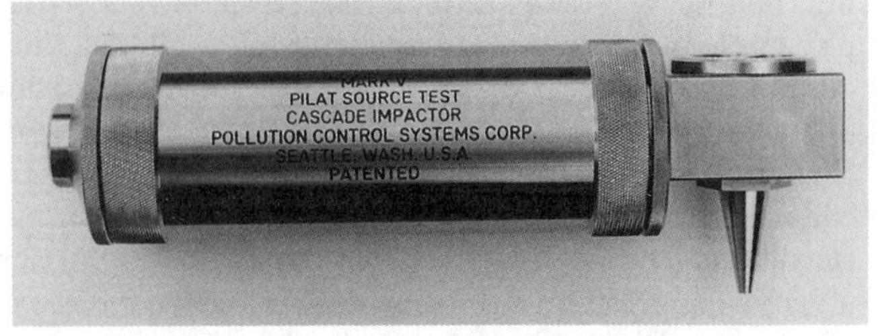

INSTRUMENT 14-25. UW source test cascade impactor.

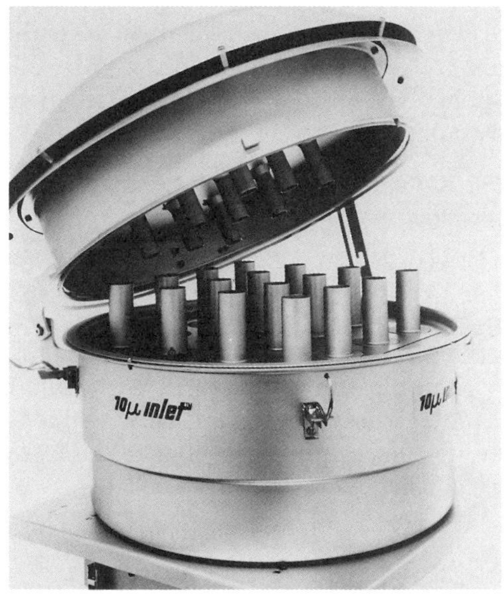

INSTRUMENT 14-26. General Metal Works PM-10 size-selective hi-volume inlet.

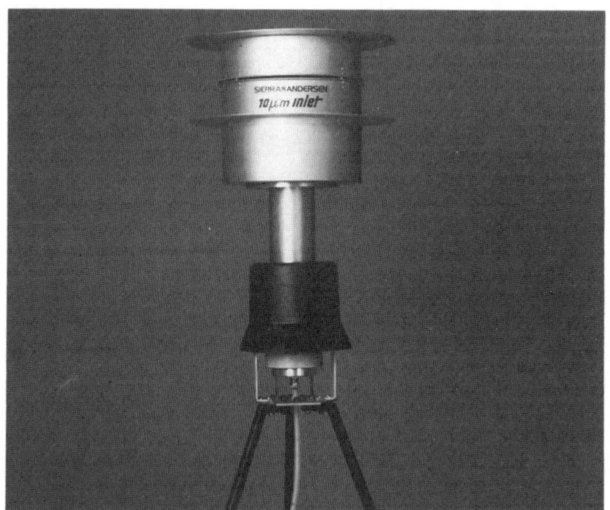

INSTRUMENT 14-27. General Metal Works Series 245 PM-10 medium flow air sampler.

3 or 5 impactor with a sampling flow of about 0.5 cfm (14 L/min). The Mark 20 has 14 jet stages and a back-up filter, operates at 2.0 cfm (56 L/min), has cut diameters between 0.02 and 20 µm, and is designed for sampling downstream of particle control equipment. The Mark 10 has 27 jet stages and a back-up filter, operates at 0.2 cfm (5.6 L/min), has cut diameters between 0.02 and 20 µm, and is designed for sampling upstream of particle control equipment. The impactors have stainless steel sampling nozzles and can be used inside a stack to temperatures as high as 800°C.

PM_{10} Inlets

14-26. PM-10 Size Selective Hi-Volume Inlet

General Metal Works, Inc.
Graseby Andersen Samplers, Inc.

The Hi-Volume sampler PM_{10} inlet removes particles greater than 10 µm at sampling rates of 1.1 m^3/min (40 cfm); it can be mounted on a high-volume sampler to provide PM_{10} sampling. This inlet was designed by McFarland[90] to give a consistent size precut, independent of wind speed and coarse particle loading. The inlet is made of aluminum, weighs 16 kg (35 lb), and measures 70 cm (28 in.) in diameter.

14-27. PM-10 Medium Flow Samplers (Series 254)

General Metal Works, Inc.
Graseby Andersen Samplers, Inc.

The medium flow samplers operate at 112 L/min (4 cfm) and are equipped with a PM_{10} inlet to remove particles greater than 10 µm. Particles are collected onto 102-mm filters and flow rates are regulated by a flow controller. The inlet is based on a design of McFarland.[90] The sampling module is made of aluminum, measures 134 cm high × 110 cm diameter (53 in. × 40 in.), and weighs 11 kg (25 lb). The control module measures 51 cm high × 74 cm wide × 46 cm diameter (20 in. × 29 in. × 18 in.) and weighs 44 kg (96 lb).

14-28. Andersen Dichot Inlet

General Metal Works, Inc.
Graseby Andersen Samplers, Inc.

The Andersen Dichot inlet is based on the design of McFarland.[90] It removes particles greater than 10 µm at sampling rates of 16.7 L/min (1 m^3/hr). It is designed to give a consistent size precut, independent of wind speed and coarse particle loading. The inlet is made of aluminum.

14-29. Wedding PM_{10} Inlet

Wedding & Associates, Inc.

This PM_{10} inlet provides a 10-µm cutpoint for instru-

INSTRUMENT 14-28. Dichot inlet by General Metal Works.

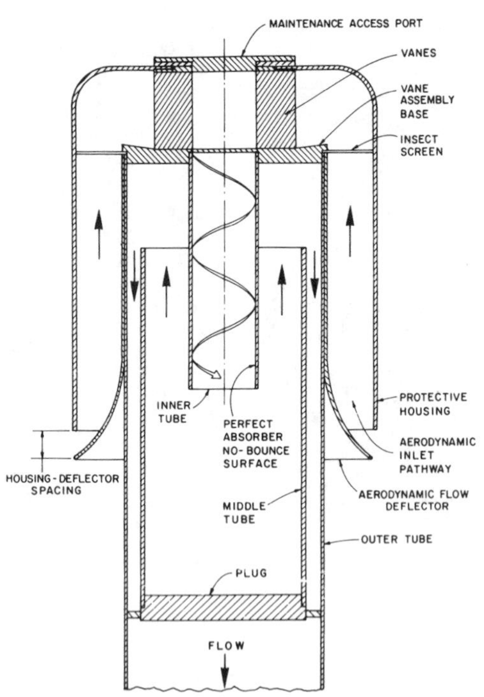

INSTRUMENT 14-29. Schematic of the Wedding PM_{10} inlet.

ments with flow rates of 1.13 m^3/min (40 cfm) to conform with U.S. Environmental Protection Agency (EPA) air quality sampling methods. The inlet uses a cyclonic separation method that allows efficient sampling of the PM_{10} particle size fraction. It operates in any wind orientation or speed. The inlet is fabricated of aluminum and weighs 29.5 kg (65 lb). PM_{10} inlets are also manufactured for flow rates of 18.9 L/min and 113 L/min (4 cfm).

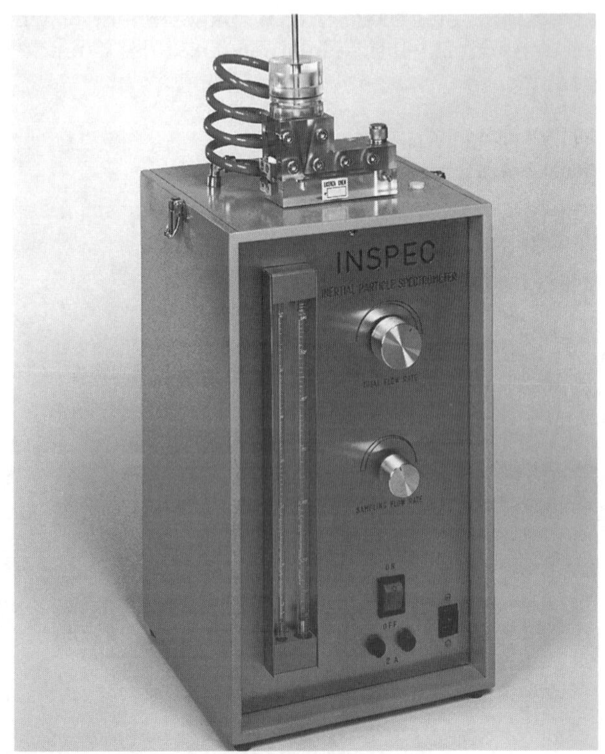

INSTRUMENT 14-30. INSPEC inertial particle spectrometer.

14-30. INSPEC Aerosol Spectrometer

BGI Incorporated

The aerosol spectrometer aerodynamically separates particles from 1 to 10 µm, as described in this chapter. Particles are collected on a single membrane filter wherein the position of deposition depends on particle diameter. The filter may be sectioned for analysis of mass or radioactivity, or it may be examined microscopically. The maximum aerosol sample rates are 0.1 L/min. No substrate coatings are needed.

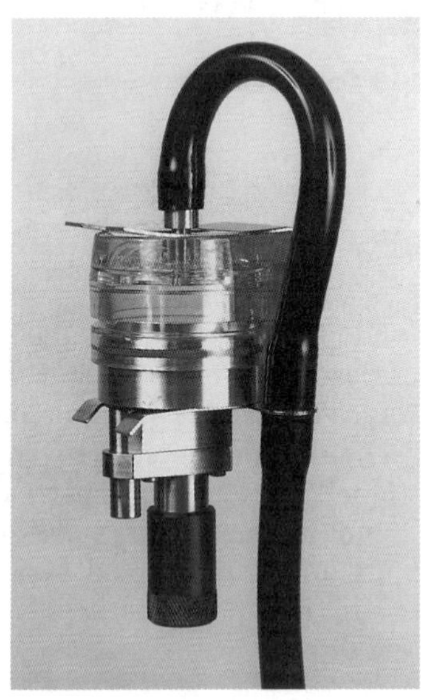

INSTRUMENT 14-31. BGI-4 respirable dust cyclone.

14-31. Respirable Dust Cyclone

BGI Incorporated

The BGI-4 respirable dust cyclone is a new unit designed to match a respirable curve with a 50% cutpoint at 4 µm at a sample flow rate of 2.3 L/min. The cyclone is all-metal construction with a black oxide finish. Aerosol samples are collected by a 37-mm disposable plastic filter cassette that presses over an O-ring seal at the cyclone outlet. The cassette is secured by a spring steel lapel clip.

Cyclones

14-32. Cyclade (Series 280)

Graseby Andersen Samplers, Inc.

The cyclade consists of a train of two to six cyclones (depending on model) followed by a 64-mm back-up

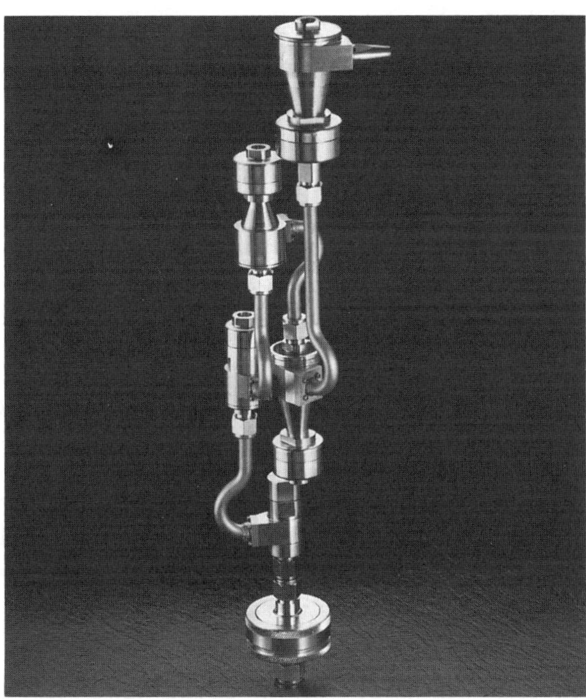

INSTRUMENT 14-32. Andersen Series 280 Cyclade.

filter. The cyclones are designed for stack sampling and are based on the design of Smith *et al.*[116] For stack temperatures of 150°C and a flow rate of 28 actual L/min, cutpoints for the model containing five cyclones are 0.57, 1.1, 2.7, 3.5, and 7.5 µm. Isokinetic sampling nozzles are available. Cyclones and the filter holder are made of 316 stainless steel with C-ring seals. All units will fit through a 20-cm- (4-in.-) diameter sampling port. Length: 36 to 74 cm (14–29 in.), depending on the model. Weight: 3 to 6 kg (7–12 lb).

INSTRUMENT 14-33. In-Tox cyclone system.

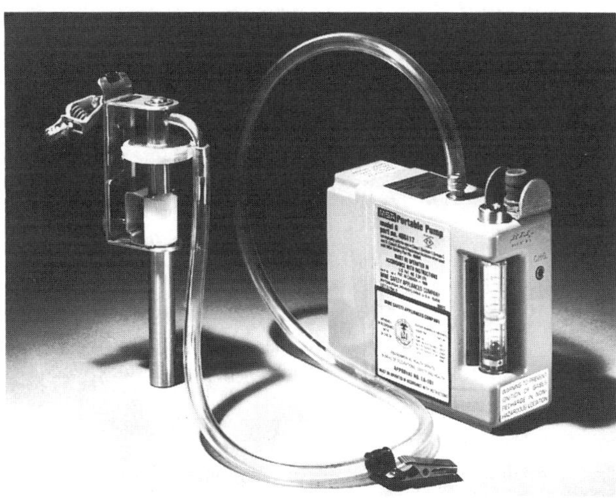

INSTRUMENT 14-34. MSA cyclone respirable dust sampler.

14-33. Cyclone Sampling Train
In-Tox Products

The cyclone train consists of five cyclones based on the design of Smith *et al.*,[116] with cutpoints of 0.32, 0.65, 1.4, 2.1, and 5.4 at a sampling rate of 28 L/min (1 cfm). The laboratory model cyclones are made of brass. The stack sampling train uses a folded configuration that can pass through a 10-cm- (4-in.-) diameter sampling port; it is constructed of stainless steel with Neoprene O-ring seals. Cyclones may be purchased individually. Sizes of individual cyclones range from 4 cm × 8 cm for the smallest to 5 cm × 13 cm for the largest.

14-34. Cyclone Respirable Dust Sampler
Mine Safety Appliances Company

The MSA gravimetric dust sampler uses a 10-mm cyclone followed by a 37-mm filter. The cyclone provides a respirable 3.5-µm precut at a flow rate of 2 L/min. The cyclone is used with a battery-powered pump capable of 8 hours of continuous operation.

14-35. Respirable Cyclones
Sensidyne, Inc.

Sensidyne manufactures three cyclones. Model 240

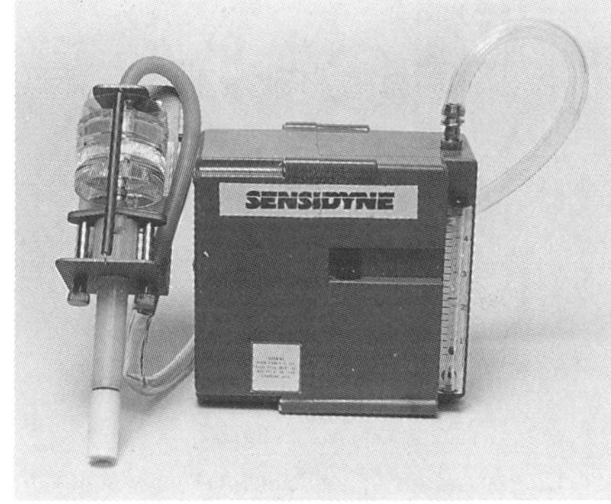

INSTRUMENT 14-35. Sensidyne Model BDX99R personal cyclone.

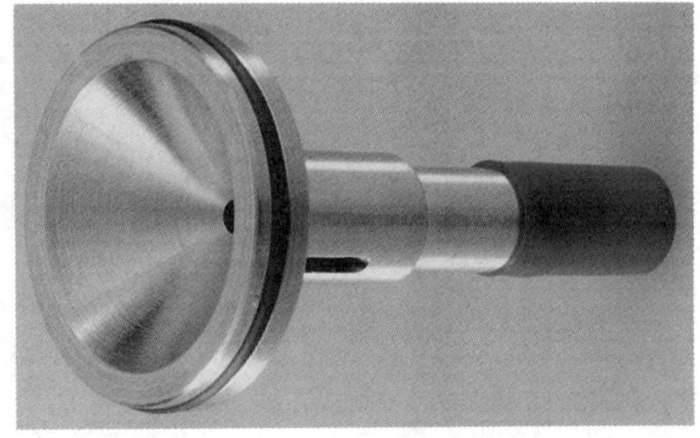

INSTRUMENT 14-36. SKC cyclone for personal filter cassette.

is a 2.5-cm- (internal) diameter, stainless steel cyclone that provides a respirable cut at 240 L/min. Model 18 provides a respirable cut at 9 L/min. Model BDX99R is a lapel-mounted, 10-mm nylon cyclone designed for personal monitoring at 1.7 L/min. Dimensions: Model 240 is 5 cm in diameter × 16.5 cm, Model 18 is 2.5 cm in diameter × 7.6 cm, and Model BDX99R is 1.9 cm in diameter × 10 cm. All three cyclones were formerly manufactured by Bendix.

14-36. Cyclone for Personal Filter Cassette
SKC, Inc.

The SKC cyclone is used for personal sampling of respirable particles. It is specifically designed to be operated with a 37-mm filter cassette holder. The stated cutpoint is 5 μm at a flow rate of 1.9 L/min. The cyclone is made of aluminum to eliminate static charge buildup.

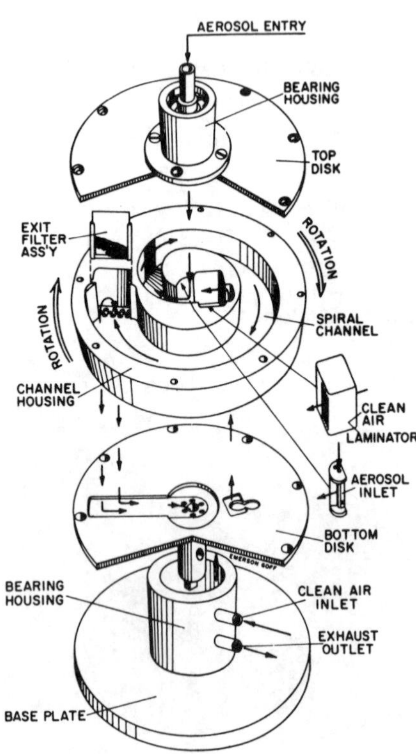

INSTRUMENT 14-37. Schematic of the LAPS aerosol centrifuge. Reprinted from *Aerosol Measurement* with permission, University Presses of Florida.

Aerosol Centrifuges

14-37. LAPS Aerosol Centrifuge
In-Tox Products

The LAPS (*L*ovelace *A*erosol *P*article *S*eparator) is an aerosol centrifuge with an expanding spiral duct. It is based on the design of Kotrappa and Light.[148] Particles are size segregated by aerodynamic diameter and deposited along a 3-cm × 46-cm foil that is mounted along the outside wall of the flow channel. For operation at 4500 rpm, with an aerosol flow rate of 0.4 L/min and a total flow rate of 5 L/min, particles between 0.4 and 4 μm are collected. The LAPS is 18 cm in diameter and weighs 15 kg (including motor).

INSTRUMENT 14-38. Casella Hexhlet. The casing that fits over the soxhlet filter thimble is removed and stands at the right of the picture.

Elutriators

14-38. Hexhlet
Casella London, Ltd.

The Hexhlet is a horizontal elutriator followed by a filter thimble for the collection of respirable particles (less than 3.5 μm in aerodynamic diameter). A schematic of the Hexhlet horizontal elutriator is found in Figure 14-24. The sampling rate is 50 L/min. A 42.5-mm-diameter filter can be used in place of the filter thimble. Construction is of aluminum. Dimensions: 17 cm × 17 cm × 50 cm (6.5 in. × 6.5 in. × 20 in.). Weight: 5 kg (11 lb).

14-39. Gravimetric Dust Sampler
Casella London, Ltd.

This is a horizontal elutriator followed by a filter. At a sampling rate of 2.5 L/min, the elutriator provides a respirable precut at 3.5 μm in aerodynamic diameter. The unit contains a diaphragm pump, a flowmeter, and

INSTRUMENT 14-39. Gravimetric Dust Sampler, Type 113A.

an elapsed time counter; it is housed in a stainless steel case. Dimensions: 17 cm × 23 cm × 11 cm (7 in. × 9 in. × 4.5 in.). Weight: 4 kg (9 lb).

14-40. Cotton Dust Sampler

General Metal Works, Inc.
Graseby Andersen Samplers, Inc.

The cotton dust sampler is a vertical elutriator designed for the sampling of particles below 15 µm. The air flow moves upward through the elutriator and particles that penetrate are collected on a 37-mm filter mounted at the elutriator exit. Construction is of aluminum. Weight: 10 kg (22 lb).

Impingers for Particle and Vapor Collection

14-41. Greenburg–Smith Impinger

Ace Glass

This impinger follows the design of the original Greenburg–Smith impinger for the collection of dusts. It is an all-glass impinger with a ground glass joint and a 500-ml capacity. One version of the impinger uses an attached impingement disk, while the other uses the bottom of the flask as the impingement plate. Nominal sampling rate is 28 L/min (1 cfm).

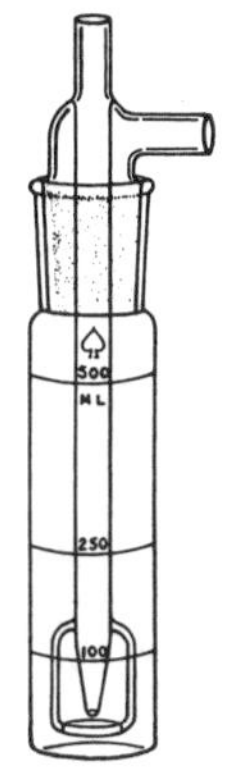

INSTRUMENT 14-41. Greenburg–Smith impinger.

INSTRUMENT 14-42. MSA Monitaire Sampler, Model S, with MSA midget impinger.

14-42. Midget Impinger

Mine Safety Appliances Company

The MSA midget impinger can be used for both particle and dust collection. It is an all-glass impinger with a ground glass joint. The collection volume is 25 ml. It can be operated at 2.8 L/min with a battery-powered pump.

14-43. Midget and Micro Impingers

SKC, Inc.

The SKC standard midget impinger is a two-piece, 25-ml capacity, Pyrex™ glass impinger graduated in 5-ml increments. The two pieces are joined by a ground glass joint. It can be fitted with a fritted top for vapor collection. A miniature version of this impinger is the micro-impinger, which is one-tenth the size of the standard midget impinger.

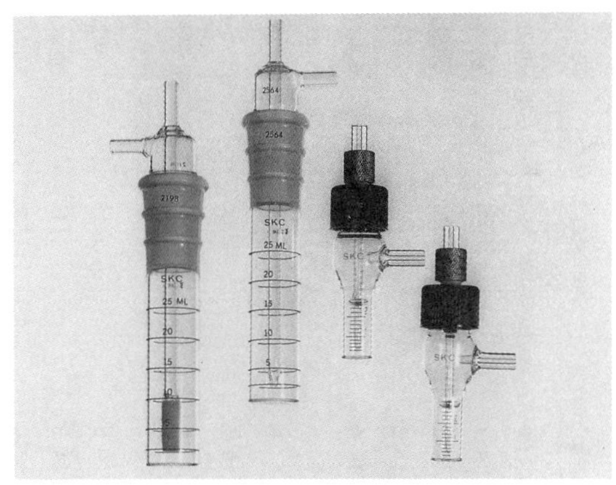

INSTRUMENT 14-43. SKC midget and micro-impingers.

TABLE 14-I-1. Commercially Available Impactors

Description	Manufacturer[A]	Sampler Name	Flow Rate (L/min)	No. of Stages	Cutpoints (Range, μm)	Reference Author (Ref. No.)	Comments[B]
Cascade Impactors for Ambient Air Sampling							
14-1	BGI	May/R.E.	5	7	0.5–32	May[4]	
14-2	GRA	Sierra/Marple Model 210	7	10	0.16–18		1
14-3	GRA	Sierra/Marple Model 260	0.3–20	6	0.5–20		2
14-4	GRA	Low pressure impactor	3	12	0.08–35		3
14-5	GRA, GMW	One ACFM ambient impactor	28	8	0.4–10	Rao and Whitby[33]	
14-6	GRA	Flow sensor ambient impactor	28	7	0.4–6		
14-7	HAU	Berner impactor	30	9	0.063–16.7	Wang and John[3]	
14-8	ITP	Mercer 7-stage impactor (02-100)	0.1	7	0.33–3.1	Mercer *et al.*[8]	4
14-8	ITP	Mercer 7-stage impactor (02-130)	1	7	0.32–4.5	Mercer *et al.*[8]	
14-8	ITP	Mercer 7-stage impactor (02-150)	2	7	0.25–5.0	Mercer *et al.*[8]	
14-8	ITP	Mercer 7-stage impactor (02-170)	5	7	0.5–5.0	Mercer *et al.*[8]	
14-9	ITP	Multijet CI (02-200)	10	7	0.5–8	Newton *et al.*[158]	
14-9	ITP	Multijet CI (02-220)	15	7	0.5–8	Newton *et al.*[158]	
14-9	ITP	Multijet CI (02-240)	20	7	0.5–8	Newton *et al.*[158]	
14-9	ITP	Multijet CI (02-260)	28	7	0.5–9	Newton *et al.*[158]	
14-10	MSP	MOUDI (micro-orifice impactor)	30	10	0.56–10	Kuhlmey *et al.*[61]	5
14-11	URG	Portable size selective impactor	4	1	2.5	Marple *et al.*[159]	
16-5-1	CMI	Quartz crystal microbalance, PC-2	0.25	10	0.5–25	Fairchild and Wheat[96]	7
Impactors for Ambient HiVol Samplers							
14-12	GRA	HiVol impactor, Series 65-800	1130	1	3.5	Burton *et al.*[7]	8
14-12	GRA	HiVol impactor, Series 65-800	565	4	1.1–7.0	Burton *et al.*[7]	8
14-13	GRA, GMW	HiVol impactor, Series 230	1130	4	0.49–7.2	Willeke,[48] Knuth[6]	9
14-13	GRA, GMW	HiVol impactor, Series 230	565	6	0.41–10		9
Personal Samplers							
14-14	GRA, GMW	Marple personal sampler (Model 290)	2	8	0.5–20	Rubow *et al.*,[16] Hinds[27]	1
14-14	SKC	Marple personal sampler	2	8	0.5–20	Rubow *et al.*,[16] Hinds[27]	1
14-15	MSP	Personal environmental monitor	4 or 10	1	2.5		
14-15	MSP	Personal environmental monitor	4 or 10	1	10		
Virtual Impactors							
14-16	BGI	Cascade centripeter	30	3	1.2, 4, 14	Hounam and Sherwood[68]	
14-17	GRA, GMW	Dichotomous sampler	16.7	1	2.5	Loo,[71] McFarland *et al.*[72]	

TABLE 14-I-1 (con't.). Commercially Available Impactors

Description	Manufacturer[A]	Sampler Name	Flow Rate (L/min)	No. of Stages	Cutpoints (Range, μm)	Reference Author (Ref. No.)	Comments[B]
14-18	MSP	High volume virtual impactor	1130	1	2.5		
14-19	MSP	Microcontaminant particle sampler	30	1	1		
Source Test Impactors							
14-20	GRA	In-stack air sampler, Series 220	7	9	0.16–18		
14-21	GRA	Stack sampling head (Mark III, IV)	3–21	8	0.4–11		1
14-22	GRA	High capacity stack sampler	14	3	1.5–11		
14-23	GRA	Impactor preseparator	1	21	10		
14-24	ITP	High temp., high pres. impactor	16	7	0.62–8.8		
14-25	PCS	UW source test cascade impactor	28	10	0.2–20	Pilat *et al.*(13)	
14-25	PCS	UW high capacity source test impactor	28	3	1.5–11	Pilat *et al.*(13)	
14-25	PCS	UW low pressure source test impactor	28	14	0.05–20	Pilat *et al.*(13)	
PM_{10} Inlets							
14-26	GRA, GMW	Hi-Volume PM-10 inlet	1130	1	10	McFarland *et al.*(90)	
14-27	GRA, GMW	Medium flow PM-10 inlet	112	1	10	McFarland *et al.*(90)	
14-28	GRA, GMW	Dichotomous sampler inlet	16.7	1	10	McFarland *et al.*(72)	
14-29	WED	Hi-Volume PM_{10} inlet	1130	1	10	Wedding and Weigand(92)	
Viable and Biological Impaction Samplers							
23-2a(iii)	GRA	Single stage bioaerosol sampler	28	1	0.65	Andersen(15)	10
23-2b	GRA	Microbial air sampler	28	2	0.65, 3.5	Andersen(15)	10
23-2c	GRA	Particle fractionating viable sampler	28	6	0.65–7	Andersen(15)	10
23-1b	BGI	Casella Bacteria Sampler MK II	30	1	Not stated	Soole(10)	11
23-1b	BGI	Casella Bacteria Sampler MK II	700	1	Not stated	Soole(10)	11
23-1c	NBS	Slit-to-agar biological sampler	50	1	Not stated		11
23-7a(i)	BMC	Spore trap	10	1	Not stated		11
23-2a(ii)	SSI	SAS portable sampler	90,180	1	Not stated		

[A]See Table 14-I-5 for explanation of manufacturers codes.

[B]Comments:

1 Radial slot design.
2 Circular jets, interchangeable nozzles.
3 Four low-pressure stages.
4 One round jet per stage.
5 Micro-orifice plates of 2000 jets on bottom stages.

Comments (con't.)

6 Two low-pressure stages added to 1 CI.
7 Uses quartz crystal collection surfaces for continuous mass measurement.
8 Fits on Hi-Volume, round jets.
9 Fits on Hi-Volume, rectangular jets.
10 Collection directly onto agar plates.
11 Slot impactor with rotating turntable for agar plates.

TABLE 14-I-2. Cyclones and Their Performance Characteristics

Description	Manufacturer	Cyclone Name	Flow Rate Range (L/min)	d_{50} Range (μm)	Internal Dimensions Body (cm)	Internal Dimensions Outlet (cm)	Coefficients $d_{50} = KQ^n$ K[A]	n	Correlations by Saltzman (see text) Kd × 10^4	Reference Author (Ref. No.)
14-31	BGI	Respirable	2.3	4.0	—	—	—	—	—	
14-34	MSA	10-mm cyclone	0.9–5	1.8–7.0	1	0.25	6.17	–0.75	4.043	Blachman & Lippmann(124)
14-35	SEN	(also called	5.8–9.2	1.0–1.8			16.10	–1.25		Blachman & Lippmann(124)
14-36	SKC	Dorr–Oliver)	18.5–29.6	0.1–1.0			178.52	–2.13		Blachman & Lippmann(124)
14-32, 14-33	GRA, ITP	SRI V	7–28	0.3–2.0	1.52	0.36	14.0	–1.11	1.927	Smith *et al.*(116)
14-32, 14-33	GRA, ITP	SRI IV	7–28	0.5–3.0	2.54	0.59	17.6	–0.98	1.429	Smith *et al.*(116)
14-35	SEN	1/2" HASL	8–10	2–5	3.11	0.50	—	—	2.462	—
14-32, 14-33	GRA, ITP	SRI III	14–28	1.4–2.4	3.66	0.83	22.7	–0.84	1.648	Smith *et al.*(116)
	—	AIHL	8–27	2.0–7.0	3.66	1.05	52.48	–0.99	1.718	John and Reischl.(127)
14-32, 14-33	GRA, ITP	SRI II	14–28	2.1–3.5	4.13	1.05	22.2	–0.70	1.747	Smith *et al.*(116)
	—	Aerotec 3/4	22–55	1.0–5.0	4.47	0.75	214.17	–1.29	2.567	Chan and Lippmann(117)
14-32, 14-33	GRA, ITP	SRI I	14–28	5.4–8.4	5.08	1.50	44.6	–0.63	2.402	Smith *et al.*(116)
14-35	SEN	1" HASL	65–350	1.0–5.0	7.6	1.09	123.68	–0.83	4.461	Chan and Lippmann(117)
	—	BK 76	400–1100	1.0–3.0		3.8	221.48	–0.77	3.421	Beeckmans and Kim(131)

[A]Units of K are (μm $(L/min)^{-n}$).

TABLE 14-I-3. Aerosol Centrifuges

Description	Manufacturer	Sampler	Duct Length (cm)	Aerosol Flow (L/min)	Total Flow (L/min)	Rotational Speed (rpm)	Particle Size Rar. (mm)	Reference Author (Ref. No.)	Com-ments
Spiral Duct Centrifuges									
		Stöber spiral centrifuge	180	0.05–2	5–19	1500–6000	0.08–6	Stöber and Flachsbart(140)	
		Stöber small rotor	60	0.05–	1–2	3000	0.15–2	Hochrainer and Stöber(136)	
14-37	ITP	LAPS centrifuge	46	0.2–0.5	5–10	1500–4500	0.3–4	Kotrappa and Light(148)	
		Goetz spectrometer	30	1–5	—	6000–18000	0.05–1	Goetz *et al.*(144) and Gerber(145)	1
Cylindrical Duct Centrifuges									
–		Concentric spectrometer	40	0.05–0.5	1–5	2000–6000	0.3–4	Tillery(150)	
		Constant radius centrifuge	30	0.03	0.5	10000	0.2–1	Hochrainer(151)	
High Flow Rate Centrifuges									
–		Drum centrifuge	—	5000–20000	—	1000–3000	>0.5	Holländer *et al.*(149)	2
Conifuges and Annular Duct Centrifuges									
–		Ring slit conifuge	19	0.1–1	5–14	1500–9000	0.1–4	Stöber and Flachsbart(146)	
		Cylindrical centrifuge	3	0.01	0.6	3600–10000	0.5–2	Hochrainer and Brown(147)	

1 Total and aerosol flows are equal. Instrument yields a cumulative distribution.
2 Designed for large-scale particle collection without size resolution. Particles are deposited on a 0.1-m^2 surface. Total and aerosol flows are equal.

TABLE 14-I-4. Impingers for Particle Collection

Description	Manufacturer	Sampler Name	Material	Sample Rate (L/min)	Capacity (mL)	Impingement Distance (mm)
Impingers for Particle and Vapor Collection						
14-41	AGI	Greenburg–Smith	Glass	28	500	5
14-42	MSA	Midget	Glass	2.8	25	5
14-43	SKC	Midget	Glass	2.8	25	5
14-43	SKC	Micro	Glass	0.3	3	5
Impingers for Viable and Biological Particle Sampling						
23-4a	AGI	AGI-4	Glass	12	125	4
23-4a	AGI	AGI-30	Glass	12	125	30

Impingers for vapor collection are described in Chapter 17.

TABLE 14-I-5. List of Instrument Manufacturers

Code	Manufacturer
ACE	Ace Glass Incorporated P.O. Box 688 1430 Northwest Blvd. Vineland, NJ 08360 (609)692-3333 (800)223-4524
BGI	BGI Incorporated 58 Guinan Street Waltham, MA 02154 (617)891-9380 FAX (617)891-8151
CMI	California Measurements, Inc. 150 E. Montecito Avenue Sierra Madre, CA 91024-1934 (818)355-3361 FAX (813)355-5320
CLL	Casella London Limited Regent House Britannia Walk London N1 7ND, England 01-253-8581
GMW	Graseby GMW 145 South Miami Avenue Village of Cleves, OH 45002 (513)941-2229 or (800)543-7412
GRA	Graseby Andersen 500 Technology Ct. Smyrna, GA 30082-5211 (404)319-9999 or (800)241-6898 FAX (404)319-0336
HAU	Hauke KG P.O. Box 63 A-4810 Gmunden, Austria (076) 12 41 33
ITP	In-Tox Products 115 Quincy, NE Albuquerque, NM 87108 (505)265-1180 FAX (505)265-1181
MSP	MSP Corporation 1313 Fifth Street, SE Suite 206 Minneapolis, MN 55414 (612)379-3963
MSA	Mine Safety Appliances Co. 121 Gamma Drive Pittsburgh, PA 15238-2937 or P.O. Box 426 Pittsburth, PA 15230-0426 (412)967-3000 or (800)672-2222
NBS	New Brunswick Scientific Co., Inc. P.O. Box 4005 44 Talmadge Rd. Edison, NJ 08818-4005 (908)287-1200 or (800)631-5417
PCS	Pollution Control Systems Corp. P.O. Box 15570 Seattle, WA 98115 (206)523-7220
QCM	QCM, Inc. 2825 Laguna Canyon Rd. Laguna Beach, CA 92651 or P.O. Box 277 Laguna Beach, CA 92652 (714)497-5748
SEN	Sensidyne, Inc. 16333 Bay Vista Drive Clearwater, FL 34620 (813)530-3602 or (800)451-9444
SSI	Spiral Biotech, Inc. 7830 Old Georgetown Road Bethesda, MD 20814 (301)657-1620
WED	Wedding & Associates 209 Christman Drive, #2 Fort Collins, CO 80524 (303)221-0678 or (800)367-7610
URG	URG Corporation 116 Merritt Mill Rd. P.O. Box 368 Carrboro, NC 27510 (919)942-2753

Chapter 15

Electrostatic and Thermal Precipitators

David L. Swift, Ph.D.[A] and Morton Lippmann, Ph.D.[B]

[A]*The Johns Hopkins University, Environmental Health Engineering, Room 6010, 615 N. Wolfe Street, Baltimore, Maryland;* [B]*NYU Medical Center, Dept. of Environmental Medicine, Longmeadow Rd., Tuxedo, New York*

CONTENTS

Electrostatic Precipitators

Introduction

Electrostatic precipitation uses electrostatic forces to separate the particles from the gas in which they are suspended. Because electrostatic force is exerted directly on the particles instead of on the whole gas volume, relatively less energy is required to precipitate the particles or to move the gas stream through the collector compared to other collectors. For inertial collectors (e.g., impactors, impingers, cyclones, scrubbers, and filters), most of the energy is used to drive the gas through the collector, and high collection efficiency is associated with a large pressure drop.

Electrostatic augmentation of fibrous (Jodeit and Loffler[(1)]) and granular filters (Shapiro, Gutfinger and Laufer[(2)]) has been actively developed during recent years for both small- and large-volume air cleaning applications where they provide higher efficiency at lower pressure drop. Electret-impregnated (e.g., resin wool) fibrous filters are commonly used in air-purifying respiratory protective devices for particulate matter (Kanaoka *et al.*[(3)]). Neither of these commercial developments has been applied to air sampling methods, although there is no technical reason why they could not be so used.

Electrostatic precipitator samplers have two significant advantages over filter samplers: 1) the sampling rate is not affected by mass loading and 2) the sample is in a readily recoverable form. In "conventional" elec-

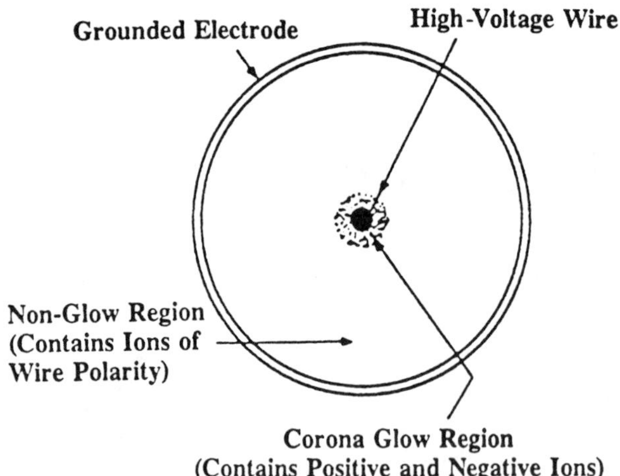

FIGURE 15-1. Axial view of high voltage corona discharge (adapted from White[4]).

trostatic precipitator samplers, the particles are collected on a large surface, similar to an electrostatic precipitator, following charging. The surface may be covered by a paper or a liquid film depending on the subsequent analysis.

A second class of electrostatic samplers is the electron microscope grid sampler, which collects small samples for particle size distribution analyses. These instruments can collect representative samples rapidly and they do not introduce the potential sample losses and alterations that often take place when transferring membrane filter samples to electron microscope grids.

Principles of Electrostatic Precipitation

General Considerations

The collection of a particle by electrostatic precipitation involves two separate and distinct operations. First, the particle must acquire electric charges, and second, the charged particle must be accelerated toward an electrode of opposite polarity by an electric field.

Particles can acquire electric charges by several mechanisms, including friction with solid matter, ionization in flames, and absorption of energy from ionizing radiation. Radioactive isotope sources such as tritium and polonium have been used for particle charging in some laboratory instruments. However, for speed, efficiency, and controllability of the charging process, none of these mechanisms can compare favorably with the high-voltage corona discharge.

A corona is usually established at high voltage around a fine wire that is located within a coaxial cylinder or between parallel plates at ground potential. The electric field near the surface of the wire accelerates free electrons that ionize the gas molecules, resulting in the characteristic corona glow. Within the glow region along the wire, equal numbers of both negative and positive charge carriers are found. However, beyond the narrow confines of the glow region, the space between the electrodes is occupied almost entirely by ions of the same polarity as the wire. A schematic diagram of corona discharge is shown in Figure 15-1. The mechanisms for charging particles through interaction with these ions is described later in this section. A somewhat less controllable corona can be maintained between a point electrode at high voltage and a grounded plane surface. Several sampling instruments which use such electrodes are discussed below.

The attraction of the charged particles toward a collection electrode of opposite polarity is a function of the number of charges acquired, the electric field strength, and the viscous drag of the air. In a single-stage or Cottrell-type precipitator, both charging and precipitation take place within the same region. A two-stage precipitator consists of a corona section for particle charging and a separate noncorona section, usually with a lower interelectrode potential and closer spacing, for precipitating the charged particles.

Characteristics of Corona Discharge

Unipolar corona is a stable gas discharge between a small radius electrode, e.g., a fine wire or point, and a receiving electrode, e.g., a cylinder or plate. In positive corona (where the wire is positively charged), free primary electrons are drawn to the positive electrode, creating electron-positive ion pairs by impact ionization. In a wire-cylinder configuration, the glow region occupies much less than 1.0% of the cross section, and the remainder of the cross section is occupied by positive ions, aerosol particles, and neutral air molecules. In this region, the unipolar positive ions are moving toward the receiving electrode. They interact with the particles, charging them positively, so that they can then be accelerated toward the receiving electrode(s).

Positive corona along a wire is manifested by a smooth uniform glow, as opposed to negative corona, which appears as a series of localized glow points or brushes and which, on a clean wire, appears to dance along the wire surface. The glow points are spread more or less uniformly along the wire and increase in number with increasing voltage and current.

Negative corona is similar to positive in that the glow region is also composed of a mixture of positive ions, negative ions, and free electrons occupying a similar small fraction of the cross section. The negative ions in this zone, and those that fill the unipolar remainder of the cross section, are formed by electron attachment to neutral air molecules. In this case, particles are charged negatively and then accelerated toward the receiving electrode(s).

Negative corona is initiated at lower applied voltages than positive and yields a higher corona current at any given applied voltage. It is often assumed that negative corona is therefore more efficient for collecting particles; however, this is so only if conditions require voltage and corona current beyond the breakdown for positive corona. Brown, Hosey, and Jones[5] reported no measurable differences in collection efficiency among four samplers collecting simultaneous samples of lead oxide and zinc oxide. All were operated at the same flow rate and voltage, with one instrument using positive corona and the remainder using negative.

The voltage-current relations characteristic of corona discharge are illustrated in Figure 15-2. The actual numerical values of voltage and current in a given electrode system would depend on the dimensions and geometries of the electrodes.

It can be seen that no current flows until a minimum voltage level is reached, which is that required to begin ionizing air molecules. Beyond this point, current increases rapidly with increasing voltage. As the voltage is increased still further, either of two limiting conditions will be reached. At normal atmospheric pressures, the practical limitation is usually sparkover or spark discharge. This occurs when the field concentration at a localized point on one of the electrodes becomes too great. A large concentration of charge carriers at this point creates a shortened electrical path, and the entire flow of current tends to dump into it. During the duration of such a spark discharge, the corona current disappears. When the breakdown is caused by a temporary occurrence, such as the passage of a large conducting particle or a fluctuation in the ambient humidity, the breakdown may be temporary and the normal corona can return. On the other hand, when the breakdown at a given voltage is inherent in the electrode design, the breakdown would become continuous and normal corona could only be obtained by lowering the applied voltage. If the electrode design is conservative and there is no sparkover breakdown, such as at point A on Figure 15-2, the second limitation on corona current will be reached. This occurs when the potential gradient is high enough to cause a generalized ionization of the air between the electrodes. This is illustrated by the area above point B in Figure 15-2. Here, the glow region, containing both negative and positive air ions, is no longer confined to the vicinity of the corona wire, but rather fills the entire air gap. There is no longer a large region filled with unipolar ions and thus particles can no longer be given unipolar charges.

One practical consideration that can be deduced from Figure 15-2 is that a small change in applied voltage makes a large difference in the magnitude of the corona current. For submicrometer particles, where the efficiency is strongly dependent on the ion density in the charging zone, it is important to maximize the corona current in order to obtain maximum collection efficiency.

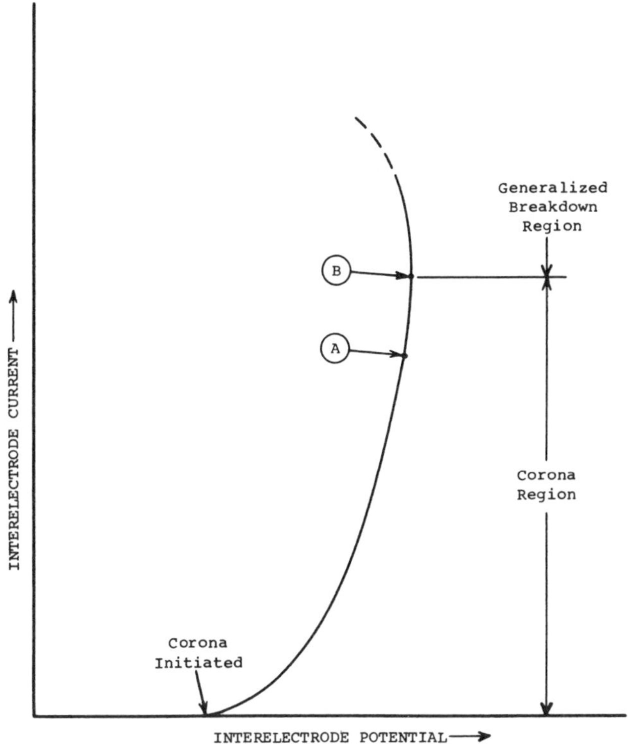

FIGURE 15-2. Typical corona discharge characteristics.

Precipitator samplers have been designed using high voltage alternating current. Drinker, Thomson, and Fitchet[6] found that for the small dimensions of their apparatus, it functioned as well with AC as with DC. This was possible because the time required for a particle to become charged was small compared to the inverse of the AC frequency. Also, charged particles migrating toward the corona wire at the time the polarity changes will be neutralized and rapidly recharged with the opposite polarity and will then be driven further toward the collection surface. An electron microscope grid sampler of Billings and Silverman[7] also uses high voltage AC.

One disadvantage of corona charging is that ozone is produced by the corona discharge. White[4] reports that the discharge air from a high-voltage, single-stage industrial precipitator of the Cottrell type may contain several parts per million of ozone. The two-stage precipitators used in homes and offices generate much less ozone because they operate at lower voltages and use positive instead of negative corona.

Ohkubo *et al.*[8] measured ozone production rates and typical room concentrations for positive and negative corona discharge in a wire and plate geometry at similar high voltages (10–18 kV). They reported that the

TABLE 15-1. Number of Charges on a Particle after Time *t* for Field and Diffusion Charging*

Particle Diameter μm	Field Charging Time, sec 0.01	0.1	1.0	∞	Diffusion Charging Time, sec 0.01	0.1	1.0	10
0.2	0.7	2.0	2.4	2.5	3	7	11	15
2.0	72	200	244	250	70	110	150	190
20.0	7200	2×10^4	2.4×10^4	2.5×10^4	1100	1500	1900	2300

*From Lowe and Lucas.[11]

ozone production rate was 10 times greater for negative corona. In a typical indoor room, positive corona precipitation did not raise the ozone level above background (outdoor) levels (0.02 ppm), whereas a steady state ozone concentration of 0.10 ppm was measured with negative corona. Modest wire heating was found to decrease the ozone production rate for the negative corona significantly. Similarly, for a point-to-plane geometry, Brandvold *et al.*[9] reported that negative corona produced 7.2 times more ozone than positive corona and that ozone production rates for both cases increased linearly with current.

Particle Charging

The charging of fine particles in a corona discharge can take place by several different mechanisms. Two of the mechanisms have been defined theoretically and confirmed experimentally at normal atmospheric pressures. One is known as field charging or bombardment charging. It depends on the interaction of the ions moving with the electric field and the particles passing through the field. For this mechanism, the maximum or saturation number of electron charges, n_s, that can be acquired by a particle is given by White[4] in the expression:

$$n_s = \left(1 + 2\,\frac{\varepsilon-1}{\varepsilon+2}\right)\frac{E_o a^2}{e} \tag{1}$$

where: n_s = maximum number of charges/particle
ε = dielectric constant of particle
E_o = electric field, volt/cm
a = particle radius, cm
e = charge per electron, 1.6×10^{-19} coulombs

The actual number of charges, $n(t)$, acquired in time t will be:

$$n(t) = n_s\left(\frac{\pi N_o eKt}{\pi N_o eKt + 1}\right) \tag{2}$$

where: $n(t)$ = number of charges/particle in time t
N_o = ion density in charging zone, ions/cm^3
K = ion mobility, cm^2/volt•sec
t = time, seconds

According to White,[4] a typical value for N_o is 5×10^8 ions/cm^3, whereas an appropriate value of K for negative gas ions is 2.2 cm^2/volt•sec.

The above equations are for unipolar charging of particles. Jantunen and Reist[10] presented equations for field charging of particles in bipolar ion fields. They showed that for equal numbers of positive and negative ions, the charging time can be reduced 90% for an increase of 60% of the field strength. For aerosol sampling instruments, bipolar ionic charging by irradiation offers advantages in that charging is more rapid and separation by field forces occurs for a greater time within the instrument.

The second mechanism is known as diffusion or thermal charging. In this mechanism, the ions come in contact with the particles by virtue of the Brownian movement of the particles. White's[4] equation for the number of charges acquired by diffusion charging in time t, $n(t)$, of an initially uncharged particle is:

$$n(t) = \frac{akT}{e^2}\ln\left(1 + \frac{\pi a v_{rms} N_o e^2 t}{kT}\right) \tag{3}$$

where: $n(t)$ = number of charges/particle in time t
k = Boltzmann constant, 1.38×10^{-16} erg/°K
T = absolute temperature, °K
v_{rms} = root-mean-square velocity of ions, cm/sec

Table 15-1 shows a comparison of the charges for various particle sizes and charging periods calculated according to Equations 2 and 3 at identical space charges (according to Lowe and Lucas[11]). For particles <1 μm, charging by diffusion is seen to predominate; above 1 μm, ion bombardment is the predominant method. In the latter case, 80% of the maximum charge is already reached within 0.1 seconds. Neither the diffusion charging nor the field charging equations adequately account for the observed charging of particles on the order of 0.1-μm diameter and smaller where the predicted number of charges per particle approaches unity. They fail because they do not take into account the mechanisms whereby the particle acquires its initial charges. Assumptions made in the development of the diffusion charging equation limit its validity to relatively low charging rates and do not take into account the effect of the electric field.

It has been demonstrated that an enhanced rate of diffusion charging of up to 10 fold can be realized with free electrons rather than ions (O'Hara *et al.*[12]). Enhanced precipitation in sampling instruments can, in principle, be realized by providing high free electron concentrations (such as by an electron beam precharger) and in precipitator devices either at high temperature or low concentration of electronegative gases (e.g., CO_2, O_2, or H_2O).

Equation 3 does not hold strictly for the transition or free molecular particle size regime which, for normal atmospheric pressure, is below particle diameters of 0.2 µm. Diffusion charging of particles in the range of 0.004–0.050 µm was measured by Pui, Fruin, and McMurry[13] and found to fit the theoretical predictions of Fuchs[14] for particles above 0.010 µm and that of Marlow and Brock[15] for particles in the range of 0.004–0.010 µm. The recent review of Yeh[16] contains a more complete discussion of both field and diffusion charging.

Collection of Charged Particles

The separation force acting on a charged particle is given by Coulomb's Law, which states that the force is proportional to the product of the particle charge and the strength of the collecting field. The Coulomb force is opposed by inertial and viscous forces. For small particles, the inertial forces are usually negligible, and the viscous or retarding force can be approximated from Stokes' Law. The migration velocity of the particle can be calculated by balancing the Stokes and Coulomb forces. For streamline flow, relatively simple calculations could be made of collection efficiency. However, purely streamline flow is seldom achieved in electrostatic precipitators. By assuming completely turbulent flow, collection efficiency can be calculated by probability theory. This leads to an exponential type formula for the probability of capturing a given charged particle and, by extension to the case of a large number of particles which do not interact, it leads to precipitator efficiency. It follows that 100% collection efficiency is approached only as an asymptotic limit.

Collection of Aerosol Samples

Factors Affecting Collection Efficiency

The collection efficiency of any precipitator sampler is dependent on many variables. These include the operating parameters, e.g., current, voltage, and flow rate; the particle parameters, e.g., particle size, shape, dielectric properties, and mass loading; and the carrier gas parameters, e.g., humidity, ambient pressure, temperature, and composition. Collection efficiency is aided by high charging currents, high voltage gradients, and low flow rates. For particles >0.5-µm diameter, the charging, and hence the collection efficiency, is strongly dependent on the potential gradient in the charging field, whereas for smaller particles, the charging current, i.e., the number of air ion charge carriers, is more significant. The flow rate affects performance in several ways. In most instruments, it exerts a drag force vector normal to the electrical force vector. In addition, the tendency of collected particles to be re-entrained or eroded from the collection surface by the air stream is strongly dependent on the linear air velocity.

In general, large particles are more easily re-entrained than smaller ones. The adhesion of the collected particles to the collection surface is affected by the kind of dust layer formed by the particles. Particles that form loose, light flocs are more readily re-entrained than those that form dense deposits. The role of adhesion in electrostatic precipitation has been discussed by Penney.[17] He shows that the electrostatic forces which drive the dust particles to the collection surface in general do not hold the dust onto the surface. The electrostatic force frequently reverses and tends to pull the dust off so that adhesion is of primary importance, particularly in the two-stage precipitator. Penney also shows that most small particles exhibit a significant dipole characteristic which imparts relatively high adhesive qualities to electrostatically deposited dust.

High voltage sparking in precipitators results in localized re-entrainment. The spark creates a "crater" in the dust layer on the ground electrode, resuspending the displaced dust. Thus, the rate of sparking should be held to minimum. Corona current acts to retard re-entrainment caused by the scouring action of the air stream, because the flow of current through the dust layer serves to increase the forces holding the particles to the surface. Thus, re-entrainment tends to occur more readily in the noncorona zones of a precipitator.

For effective precipitation, the particles should have some electrical conductivity. Nonconductive particles precipitated on the collection electrode within the corona zone can form an insulating barrier that will reduce the corona current. However, the electrical conductivity of particles is not necessarily the same as that of the parent material. For most dusts and fumes of mineral origin in the temperature range below 200°F, the humidity of the air influences the particle conductivity. Water vapor is absorbed on the surface, and the resultant surface conductivity aids precipitation. On the other hand, very high humidity can have an adverse effect on precipitator performance, because electrical breakdown takes place at lower voltages in humid atmospheres.

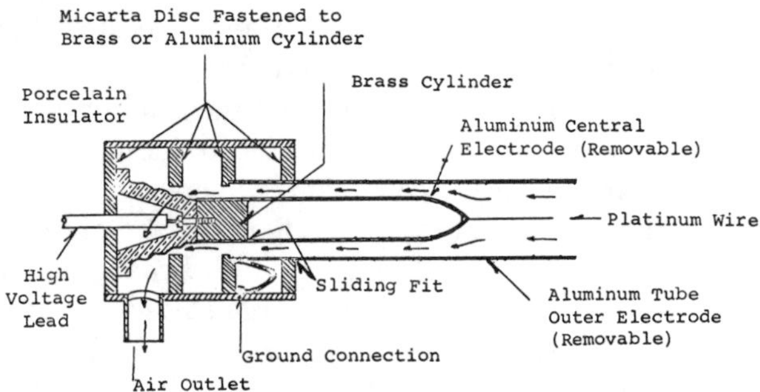

FIGURE 15-3. Sampling head design of Barnes and Penney[18] electrostatic precipitator sampler.

Precautions in Sampling

To obtain the maximum collection efficiency in a precipitator sampler, the voltage should be maintained as high as possible throughout the sampling interval. The maximum voltage which should be used is that at which high voltage sparkovers are minimal, e.g., up to an average of 1 to 2 sparks per minute. More frequent sparking can reduce overall collection efficiency in two ways: 1) the corona current and electric field are interrupted for the duration of the spark, and 2) the spark can dislodge collected dust, as previously discussed. On the other hand, operation at voltages low enough so that sparking never occurs can result in an unnecessarily low collection efficiency. Not only is the voltage lower at a lower setting, but the charging current may be much lower, as can be seen in Figure 15-2. For particles <0.5 μm in diameter, the charging efficiency is strongly dependent on the corona current. A visual examination of the collected sample can often provide a useful indication of the collection efficiency. When the sampling efficiency approaches 100%, there should be no significant deposit on the last few centimeters of the collector. Also, there should be no significant deposit on the corona wire or axial rod. Collection on these surfaces is indicative of dust re-entrained from the collection tube surface.

Specific Applications of Electrostatic Samplers

Mass Concentration Analysis

The development of electrostatic precipitator samplers for airborne dust occurred simultaneously with the development of commercial air cleaning precipitators. Early laboratory designs used the Cottrell principle of negative direct-current corona discharge or high-voltage alternating current. Air was passed axially through a cylindrical tube; a central wire was maintained at a high voltage with respect to the grounded tube. A corona discharge from the wire provided charges and the particles drifted to the tube surface.

A commercial field instrument following the design of Barnes and Penney[18] was manufactured for many years using a negative corona central electrode; a diagram of the sampling head is shown in Figure 15-3. The instrument operated at 85 L/min with high voltage adjustable from 8000–15,000 volts. Area samples for gravimetric or particulate analysis could be obtained with the instrument.

Although electrostatic samplers of this type are no longer commercially available, a paper by Steen[19] describes an "isokinetic sampler" employing electrostatic collection for gravimetric or other particulate analysis. This instrument has a specially designed nozzle and Venturi screen to provide for isokinetic flow through the sampler at the air velocity outside the sampler. The tube is 15 cm long and has a 2.5-cm i.d.; it has an axially mounted wire electrode that is maintained at 12 kV AC. The front 1.0 cm of this electrode is 1.0 mm in diameter for corona discharge, whereas the remainder is 2.5 mm. Particles drift outward radially and are collected on the outer tube.

High-volume samplers with rates up to 10,000 L/min have been designed for gravimetric analysis; in these devices, the air enters the instrument from above through a conical mouth and flows radially under a circular plate on which a ring of corona discharge needles are mounted. Particles drift toward a lower rotating plate on which a thin film of liquid is maintained (see Figure 15-4). Decker *et al.*[20] report that such a device can concentration particulate matter from 10,000 L into 10 ml of a collecting fluid for gravimetric or other analysis.

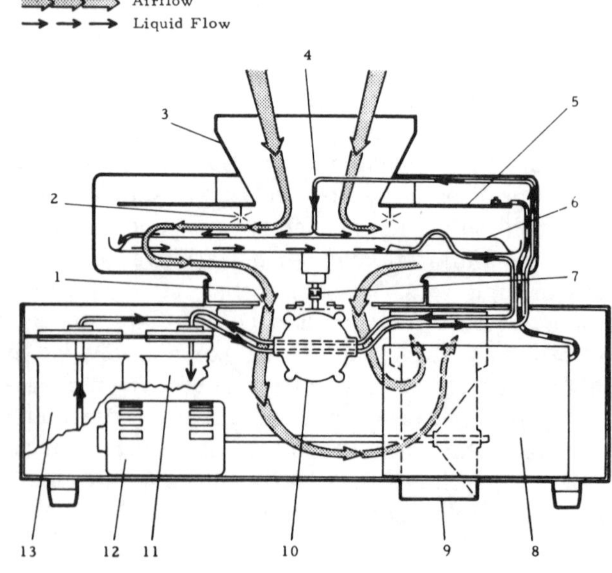

FIGURE 15-4. Diagram of high-volume electrostatic collector.

Sampling for Radioactive Aerosols

Radioactive aerosols can, in general, be sampled similarly to other aerosols (see Chapter 22). All of the aforementioned samplers can be used for radioactive aerosols, with the possible limitation that radioactive particles may influence charging by the emanation of α or β radiation. Present commercially available samplers for radioactive aerosols employ filters for particle collection. Instruments employing electrostatic collection for such aerosols were described by Wilkening[21] and Bergstedt;[22] likewise, a method for radioactive analysis of the aerosol collected in a conventional annular precipitator (Figure 15-3) was described by Thomas.[23]

Sampling for Particle Size Analysis

The distance that a particle will travel in the axial direction in an electrostatic precipitator before it reaches a grounded collection surface is dependent on many variables. In addition to particle size, these include the linear air velocity in the tube, the radial position at which the particle enters, the dielectric properties of the particle, the ion density, and the voltage gradient. Furthermore, all of these factors are interrelated in a complex way. Thus, the variation in the size of the deposited particles along the length of a simple coaxial precipitator is hardly surprising.

In the charging zone, the ion density and linear air velocity vary with radial position. A particle entering near the wall is subjected to different charging conditions and drag forces than one that enters near the axis. Variations in particle size of deposited dust as a function of length were described by Drinker, Thomson, and Fitchet,[6] who used celluloid foil as a liner that could be examined under a microscope. Such variations were documented by Fraser,[24] who extended his analysis to submicron particles. He placed electron microscope grids along the length of a collecting slide in the Hosey and Jones[25] sampler and analyzed the sample collected on each.

A number of electron microscope grid samplers based on electrostatic precipitation have been designed in which a single electron microscope grid of 3 mm diameter is the entire grounded collection surface. Although the samples collected by these instruments are very small in terms of numbers and mass of particles, they are very dense in terms of numbers of particles per unit area of collection surface.

Most of these devices utilize a point-to-plane electrode configuration, with a needle point as the corona-emitting electrode and the electron microscope grid, backed and supported by a metal bar, as the grounded collection electrode. Samplers of this type are described by Billings and Silverman.[7] The flow rate through such samplers ranges from 50 to 1000 cm^3/min. The interelectrode spacing is 0.5–1.0 cm and the interelectrode potential is 10–15 kV AC. The sampler described by Morrow and Mercer[26](Figure 15-5) is constructed of polymethyl methacrylate (e.g., Lucite®), except for the electrodes, and is usually operated at a sampling rate of 70 cm^3/min. The interelectrode spacing is 1.0 cm and the interelectrode potential is 7 kV DC with negative corona. Based on geometric considerations alone, the samplers would not be expected to collect all of the aerosol passing through them (Cheng, Yeh, and Kanapilly[27]).

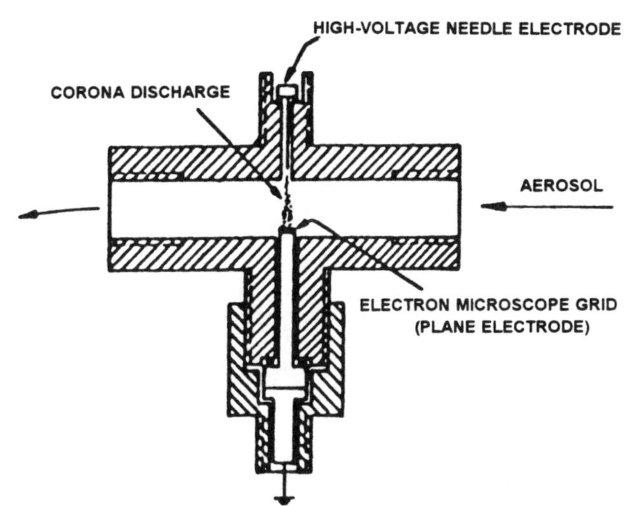

FIGURE 15-5. Diagram of point-to-plane electrostatic precipitator from Cheng, Yeh, and Kanapilly.[27]

However, with this type of instrument, the overall collection efficiency is much less important than the ability to collect representative samples for size distribution analyses. Such ability can be and has been demonstrated by comparing the electrostatically collected grid samples with simultaneous thermal precipitator samples. Such a comparison was made by Arnold, Morrow, and Stöber[28] using a Walkenhorst thermal precipitator[29] as the reference instrument. Several rock dusts were used, and the only difference revealed between the two samplers was some evidence that more large particles, both aggregate and single particles of diameter >1.0 μm, were sampled by the electrostatic precipitator than by the thermal device. Similar comparisons were reported by Morrow and Mercer[26] and are illustrated in Table 15-2.

An electrostatic precipitator, electron microscope grid sampler without an ionizing corona field was described by Mercer, Tillery, and Flores.[30] In this instrument, the source of unipolar air ions for charging the particles is a tritium source. This permits the use of lower applied voltages (+2100 volts in this case) and avoids the possibility of undesirable high-voltage discharges that can destroy the collection surface film of an electron microscope grid.

The sampling flow rate is 5 cm^3/min, corresponding

TABLE 15-2. Comparison of Particle Size Analysis by Electrical and Thermal Precipitators[A]

		Electrical Ppt.		Thermal Ppt.	
Experiment	Aerosol	CMD[B]	GSD[C]	CMD	GSD
1	UO_2	0.39	2.25	0.39	2.34
2	UO_2	0.36	1.80	0.35	1.82
3	Fe_2O_3	0.15	1.89	0.16	1.87
4	CrO	0.07	1.40	0.06	1.42

[A]From Morrow and Mercer.(26)
[B]CMD = count median diameter, µm.
[C]GSD = geometric standard deviation.

to a linear velocity of 4–5 cm/sec. The entire sample is deposited on a small area of a single electron microscope grid. Within this area, there is a marked segregation of particles with respect to size, so that it is necessary to obtain a series of electron micrographs of each sample. Size distributions so obtained were found to be in good agreement with distributions measured on micrographs of simultaneously collected thermal precipitator samples.

In the two-stage sampler described by Liu, Whitby, and Yu,(31) the separate charging and precipitation zones allow for optimization of each. Furthermore, because the precipitation region does not have to carry current, it can utilize nonconducting particle collection surfaces such as glass slides and polymer-coated electron microscope grids. Particles of all sizes are uniformly distributed over the collection surface by the periodic application of 4200 volts to the precipitating region, with the overall collection efficiency varying from 60% for 0.28-µm-diameter particles to 80% for 3.2-µm particles.

Summary

Operation of electrostatic precipitator samplers for aerosols is based on the well-established principles of charged particle drift in electric fields; these principles are also employed in the design of large-scale particle scrubbing devices. A number of devices that employ electrostatic collection have been designed and used in the past, some of which are still used in specific instances for particle collection. A major advantage of such devices is the absence of high impact collection velocities which may fracture or deform particles. Specific instances where such samplers offer distinct advantages should be known by persons carrying out sampling tasks.

Thermal Precipitators

Operation

A thermal precipitator removes particles from an aerosol by passing it through a relatively narrow channel having a significant temperature gradient perpendicular to the direction of flow. The movement of a particle in the direction of decreasing temperature, called its thermophoretic velocity, causes the particle to deposit on a collecting surface appropriate to the type of subsequent evaluation.

Figure 15-6 shows a cutaway view of a thermal precipitator.(32) In this device, air is drawn through the slit at 6 cm³/min. A nichrome wire, 0.254 mm in diameter, is centered in the 0.5-mm gap between the glass cover slips and is heated to approximately 120°C. The glass slips are held in place and kept at ambient temperature by contact with brass cylinders. As the aerosol passes through the slit, the particles are deposited as two strips on the cover slips opposite the heated wire. Examination of the cover slips with an optical microscope yields information about the size distribution and/or particle concentration of the aerosol.

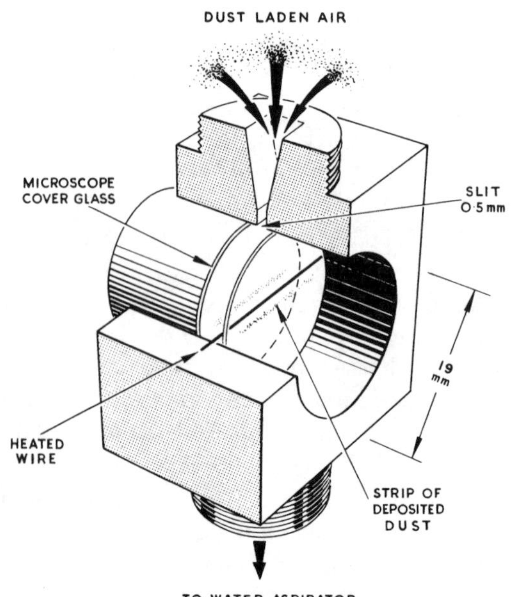

FIGURE 15-6. Sampling head of thermal precipitator from Watson(32) (Crown Copyright, by permission of Controller of H.M. Stationery Office, London).

Theory of Thermophoresis

The theory of thermophoretic motion of aerosol particles is discussed in detail by Waldmann and Schmitt.[33] For a particle whose diameter, d_p, is small with respect to the gas mean free path, λ ($\lambda_{air} = 0.066$ µm at 1 atm, 20°C), a free molecular theory has been developed, and experiments performed in this regime are in good agreement with the theory. The thermophoretic velocity for a spherical particle in this regime is:

$$V_{th} = \frac{-0.55\eta\nabla T}{\rho_g T} \quad (4)$$

where: η = gas viscosity (1.81×10^{-4} poise for air, 20°C)
ρ_g = gas density (1.2×10^{-3} g/cm^3 for air, 1 atm, 20°C)
T = gas temperature, °K
∇T = temperature gradient, dT/dx, for direction x

V is proportional to the temperature gradient and is independent of the particle size. For air at 1 atm and 20°C, this condition holds for a particle diameter <0.01 µm.

For particles that are large with respect to the mean free path ($d_p > 1$ µm), a simplified theoretical treatment was initially given by Epstein,[34] whose solution included the temperature gradient within the particle:

$$V_{th} = \frac{2K_g}{5P(2K_g + K_p)}\nabla T \quad (5)$$

where: K_p = particle thermal conductivity, cal/cm•sec•°K
K_g = air thermal conductivity, 5.6×10^{-5} cal/cm•sec•°K
P = gas pressure, dyne/cm^2

Thermal conductivity for particles varies widely, from a value of about 0.2 cal/cm•sec•°K for metallic iron to 2×10^{-4} for asbestos. The expression above was found to be in good agreement with experimentally measured velocities for particles of low thermal conductivity, but the predicted values for more conductive aerosol particles were low by more than an order of magnitude when compared to experiments of Schadt and Cadle.[35]

A more rigorous treatment of thermophoretic motion was given by Brock.[36] Brock's equation for the transition regime (0.01 µm < d_p < 1 µm) demonstrates particle diameter dependence. The predicted values have been compared to experimentally measured values by Waldmann and Schmitt[33] and Springer[37] and were found to be in good agreement. For particles in the transition regime, typical values of the thermal velocity per unit temperature gradient range from 1×10^{-4} to 2×10^{-4} cm^2/°K·sec. For d_p < 0.01 µm, the value increases to 2.5×10^{-4}. It can thus be seen that to achieve a reasonable thermal velocity, a rather steep temperature gradient is required.

Because the thermophoretic velocity of particles of diameter <0.01 µm is somewhat greater than that of larger particles, aerosols composed of a range of sizes will be differentially deposited in collection devices that employ temperature gradients. In a collector in which the aerosol flow through the temperature gradient, the smaller particles will be collected first and larger particles further downstream. This was demonstrated experimentally by Fuchs.[38]

Thermophoretic theory usually has dealt with a steady-state temperature gradient, whereas in a thermal precipitator, a particle's temporal experience corresponds to the application of a nonsteady gradient. The implication of this for collection has been considered by Reed and Morrison,[39] who showed that for particles less than 10 µm, the relaxation time was short enough to use the steady-state velocity approximation.

Precipitation Efficiency and Deposition Pattern

Provided that a sufficient thermal gradient is established in the sampling region (typically 10^4 °K/cm), thermal precipitators collect essentially all particles from 5 to 0.005 µm and probably smaller. The lower limit of collection has not been determined experimentally, but the theory suggests that the collection efficiency should remain high down to sizes approaching molecular dimensions. For particles larger than 5 µm, the thermal force is adequate for collection, but upstream sampling difficulties due to gravitational and inertial effects in sampling devices may interfere (Prewett and Walton[40] and Watson[41]).

The deposition pattern of a submicron platinum oxide aerosol in a thermal precipitator was described by Polydorova;[42] it was shown that the spatial distribution of the particles on the collection surface in a direction parallel to flow was approximately Gaussian, the deviations being less than 4% at any location. Therefore, if the total volume of aerosol sampled is known accurately, the aerosol concentration can be determined by extrapolation of the spatial distribution curve.

Sampling and Ambient Conditions

Because of the low sampling rates used for most thermal precipitators, inertial effects for particles ≤5 µm in diameter are negligible except under conditions of rather high wind speeds. The sampling efficiency for particles ≤5 µm in diameter has been found to be unaffected for ambient air speeds less than 6 m/sec (Hodkinson *et al.*[43]); this condition is usually satisfied when sampling indoors. The general problem of aerosol sampling has been discussed by Vincent.[44] For a more complete discussion of this issue, see Chapter 4.

Advantages and Disadvantages of Thermal Precipitators

The very high efficiency of collection of submicron particles is one of the great advantages of the thermal precipitators over other collectors, such as liquid impingers or cascade impactors. The degree of charge on the particle appears to have little effect on the collection efficiency in a thermal precipitator. The low velocity of precipitation ensures that shattering or breakup of agglomerated particles does not occur during sampling.

Particles may be collected on a number of different surfaces according to the type of analysis desired; the sample may be evaluated by optical microscopy, electron microscopy, photometry, microscopic spot scanning, colony counting of viable airborne microbes, or radioactivity.

For some applications, the low sampling rate of thermal precipitators (ranging from 7 to 1000 cm^3/min) is unsuitable. Sample evaluation may be very laborious compared to some of the direct-reading instruments for aerosol size or concentration determination. Many relatively volatile aerosols could not be collected in a thermal precipitator. By itself, the standard thermal precipitator has rather poor size selection characteristics; it should not be used when several distinct size fractions of an aerosol are to be separated. However, a sizing instrument using thermophoresis for the collection of transition regime particles has been proposed by Matteson and Keng.[45]

Precautions in the Use of Thermal Precipitators

Volatile aerosol particles should not be sampled in a thermal precipitator because of the likelihood of evaporation in the vicinity of the heated surface. If nonvolatile liquid aerosols are being collected, it is usually necessary to treat the collecting surface with a nonwetting agent or a fluorocarbon to prevent the drops from spreading. Even with these precautions, it is necessary to know the drop diameter to lens diameter ratio (which is a function of the liquid surface tension) for size evaluation (Bexon and Ogden[46]).

If too large a sample is taken, there will be significant particle overlap; this cannot be tolerated if particle size or concentration measurements are to be made. For the thermal precipitator, Davies[47] has established the conditions, given the particle diameter and concentration, for limiting this overlap error to 5% (Figure 15-7). If the aerosol size and concentration cannot be estimated beforehand, several samples of the same aerosol with volumes in a geometric progression should be taken to determine the true concentration or size distribution (Roach[48]).

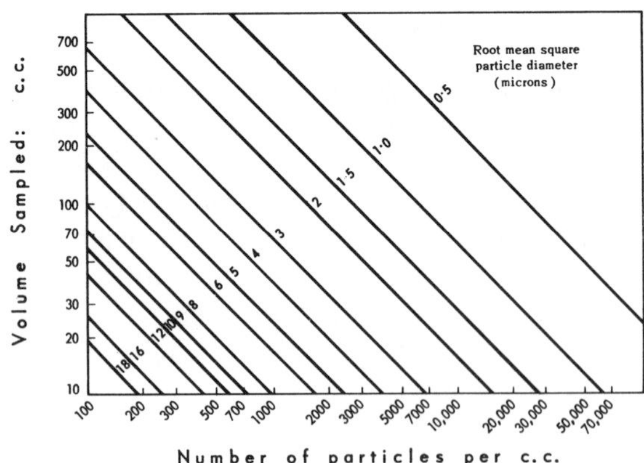

FIGURE 15-7. Maximum air volume sample of Watson thermal precipitator to keep particle overlap error <5% (from *Dust is Dangerous,*[47] by permission of Farber & Farber, London).

Evaluation of Sample

Optical microscopic evaluation of thermal precipitator samples is generally performed with an eyepiece graticule at overall magnification of 500 X or 1000 X. The particles are sized visually by comparison with a graded series of circles on the graticule. In the graticule designed by May,[49] there is a $\sqrt{2}$ geometric progression of circle size; this is convenient for most aerosols that have some sort of geometric size distribution, often a lognormal distribution. In a subsequent paper, May[50] describes a modified graticule; one extra size is added, the open circles are made slightly wider to avoid ambiguity over the line width, and the counting areas are placed closer to the sizing circles (Figure 15-8).

Sampling aerosols for electron microscope evaluation has been done with thermal precipitators. Grids with polymer or carbon films may be placed in a suitable depression in the brass plug of the thermal precipitator. However, this method is not suitable for concentration determination because it has been shown that the particles preferentially deposit near the grid bars (Cartwright[51] and Billings *et al.*[52]). A thermal precipitator that has a moving collecting surface, giving an even deposit, is preferred for electron microscope evaluation. A substrate film can be placed directly onto the collecting surface. After collection, the film can be shadowed and floated off the surface for mounting on an electron microscope grid.

Oil droplet aerosols may be sampled on substrates treated to prevent spreading (see above) and shadowed for volumetric measurement, but during the vacuum operations, the droplets must be kept on a liquid nitrogen cold stage to prevent evaporation (Schonauer[53]).

Summary

Thermal precipitators are useful aerosol sampling devices, particularly when high collection efficiency of

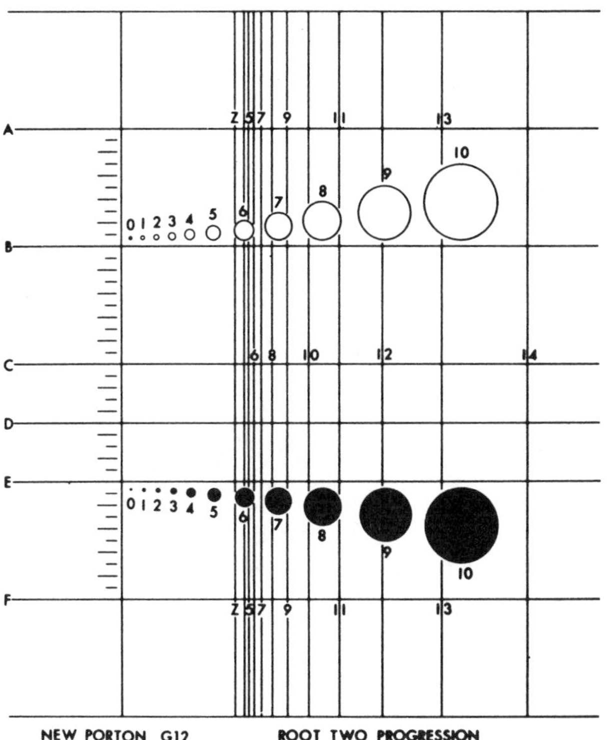

FIGURE 15-8. Porton microscope eyepiece graticule from May[50] (courtesy of Graticules, Ltd., Tonbridge, Kent, UK).

submicron particles is required. Their rather low sampling rate compared to other samplers is a disadvantage for many situations, such as rapid sequential sampling of aerosols. There are many applications for thermal precipitators provided that the user understands the limitations of the particular instrument.

References

1. Jodeit, H.; Loffler, F.: The Influence of Electrostatic Force Upon Particle Collection in Fibrous Filters. J. Aerosol Sci. 15(3):311 (1984).
2. Shapiro, M.; Gutfinger, C.; Laufer, G.: Electrostatic Mechanisms of Aerosol Collection by Granular Filters: A Review. J. Aerosol Sci. 19(6):651 (1988).
3. Kanaoka, C.; Emi, H.; Otani, Y.; Iiyama, T.: Effect of Charging State of Particles on Electret Filtration. Aerosol Sci. & Tech. 7(1): 1 (1987).
4. White, H.J.: Industrial Electrostatic Precipitation. Addison-Wesley Publishing Co., Reading, MA (1963).
5. Brown, J.K.; Hosey, A.D.; Jones, H.H.: A Lightweight Power Supply for an Electrostatic Precipitator. AMA Arch. Ind. Hyg. Occup. Med. 3:198 (1951).
6. Drinker, P.; Thomson, R.M.; Fitchet, S.M.: Atmospheric Particulate Matter, II. The Use of Electric Precipitation for Quantitative Determinations and Microscopy. J. Ind. Hyg. 5(5):162 (1923).
7. Billings, C.E.; Silverman, L.: Aerosol Sampling for Electron Microscopy. J. Air. Pollut. Control Assoc. 12(12):586 (1962).
8. Ohkubo, T.; Hamasaki, S.; Nomoto, Y.; et al.: The Effect of Corona Wire Heating on the Downstream Ozone Concentration Profiles in an Air Cleaning Wire Duct Electrostatic Precipitator. IEEE Trans. on Ind. Appl. 26: 542 (1990).
9. Brandvold, D.K.; Martinez, P.; Dogruel, D.: Polarity Dependence of N_2O Formation from Corona Discharge. Atmos. Env. 23(9):1881 (1989).
10. Jantunen, M.J.; Reist, P.C.: General Field Charging Theory for Aerosol Particle Charging and Neutralization in Unipolar and Bipolar Ion Fields. J. Aerosol Sci. 14(2):127 (1983).
11. Lowe, H.T.; Lucas, D.H.: The Physics of Electrostatic Precipitation. Br. J. Appl. Phys. 24, Supp. 2:40 (1953).
12. O'Hara, D.B.; Clements, J.S.; Finney, W.C.; Davis, R.H.: Aerosol Particle Charging by Free Electrons. J. Aerosol Sci. 20(3):313 (1989).
13. Pui, D.Y.H.; Fruin, S.; McMurry, P.H.: Unipolar Diffusion Charging of Ultrafine Aerosols. Aerosol Sci. & Tech. 8(2):173 (1988).
14. Fuchs, N.A.: On the Stationary Charge Distribution on Aerosol Particles in a Bipolar Ionic Atmosphere. Geofis. Pura Appl. 56:185 (1963).
15. Marlow, W.H.; Brock, J.R.: Unipolar Charging of Small Aerosol Particles. J. Coll. Int. Sci. 50(1):32 (1975).
16. Yeh, H-C.: Electrical Techniques. In: Aerosol Measurement: Principles, Techniques, and Applications. K. Willeke and P.A. Baron, Eds. Van Nostrand Reinhold, New York (1993).
17. Penney, G.W.: Role of Adhesion in Electrostatic Precipitation. AMA Arch. Environ. Health 4(3):301 (1962).
18. Barnes, E.C.; Penny, G.W.: An Electrostatic Dust Weight Sampler. J. Ind. Hyg. Toxicol. 20(3):259 (1938).
19. Steen, B.: A New, Simple Isokinetic Sampler for the Determination of Particle Flux. Atmos. Environ. 11:623 (1977).
20. Decker, H.M.; Buchanan, L.M.; Frisque, D.E.: Advances in Large-Volume Air Sampling. Contamination Cont. 8:13 (1969).
21. Wilkening, M.H.: A Monitor for Natural Atmospheric Radioactivity. Nucleonics 10(6):36 (1962).
22. Bergstedt, B.A.: Application of the Electrostatic Precipitator to the Measurement of Radioactive Aerosols. J. Sci. Instr. 33:142 (1956).
23. Thomas, R.D.: Simplified Air-Sampling Method. Nucleonics. 17:134 (1959).
24. Fraser, D.A.: The Collection of Submicron Particles by Electrostatic Precipitation. Am. Ind. Hyg. Assoc. J. 17(1):73 (1956).
25. Hosey, A.D.; Jones, H.H.: Portable Electrostatic Operating from 110 Volts A-C or 6 Volts D-C. AMA Arch. Ind. Hyg. Occup. Med. 7:49 (1953).
26. Morrow, P.E.; Mercer, T.T.: A Point-to-Plane Electrostatic Precipitator for Particle Size Sampling. Am. Ind. Hyg. Assoc. J. 25(1):8 (1964).
27. Cheng, Y-S.; Yeh, H-C.; Kanapilly, G.M.: Collection Efficiencies of a Point-to-Plane Electrostatic Precipitator. Amer. Ind. Hyg. Assoc. J. 42(8):605 (1981).
28. Arnold, M.; Morrow, P.E.; Stöber, W.: Vergleichende Untersuchung über die Bestimming der Korngrosssenverteilung fester Stauber mit Hilfe eines Hochspannungs-abscheiders und des Elektronenmikroskops. Koll. Z. Polymere 181(1):59 (1962).
29. Walkenhorst, W.: Elektronenmikroskopische Untersuchungen von Stauben, Methoden und Ergebnisse. Beitr Z. Silikose Forschung. 18:2 (1952).
30. Mercer, T.T.; Tillery, M.L.: Flores, M.A.: An Electrostatic Precipitator for the Collection of Aerosol Samples for Particle Size Analysis. LF-7. Lovelace Foundation for Med. Res. and Ed., Albuquerque, NM (1963).
31. Liu, B.Y.H.; Whitby, K.T.; Yu, H.S.: Electrostatic Aerosol Sampler for Light and Electron Microscopy. Rev. Sci. Inst. 38:100 (January 1967).
32. Watson, H.H.: The Thermal Precipitator. Trans. Ins. Mining Metallurgy 46:176 (1936).
33. Waldmann, L.; Schmitt, K.H.: Thermophoresis and Diffusiophoresis of Aerosols. In: Aerosol Science, Chap. VI. C.N. Davis, Ed. Academic Press, London (1966).
34. Epstein, P.: On the Theory of Radiometer. Z. Phys. 54:537 (1929).
35. Schadt, C.F.; Cadle, R.D.: Thermal Forces on Aerosol Particles. J. Phys. Chem. 65:1689 (1961).
36. Brock, J.: Theory of Thermal Forces Acting on Aerosol Particles. J.

Coll. Sci. 17:768 (1962).

37. Springer, G.S.: Thermal Forces on Particles in the Transition Regime. J. Coll. Inte. Sci. 34:215 (1970).
38. Fuchs, N.A.: The Mechanics of Aerosols, p. 66. Pergamon Press, Oxford (1964).
39. Reed, L.D.; Morrison, F.A.: Motion of an Aerosol Particle in an Unsteady Temperature Gradient. J. Coll. Inter. Sci. 42:358 (1973).
40. Prewett, W.G.; Walton, W.H.: The Efficiency of the Thermal Precipitator for Sampling Large Particles of Unit Density. Tech. Paper 63. Chemical Defense Experimental Establishment, Porton, England (1948).
41. Watson, H.H.: The Sampling Efficiency of the Thermal Precipitator. Br. J. Appl. Physics 2:78 (1958).
42. Polydorova, M.: Determining the Concentration of Ultrafine Aerosol Particles by Means of the Thermal Precipitator. Staub 27:448 (1967).
43. Hodkinson, R.; Critchlow, A.; Stanley, N.: Effect of Ambient Airspeed on Efficiency of Thermal Precipitator. J. Sci. Instr. 37:182 (1960).
44. Vincent, J.H.: Aerosol Sampling: Science and Practice. John Wiley & Sons, New York (1989).
45. Matteson, M.J.; Keng, E.Y.H.: Aerosol Size Determination in the Submicron Range by Thermophoresis. J. Aerosol Sci. 3:45 (1972).
46. Bexon, R.; Ogden, T.L.: The Focal Length Method of Measuring Deposited Liquid Droplets. J. Aerosol Sci. 5:509 (1974).
47. Davies, C.N.: Dust is Dangerous. Farber and Farber, London (1954).
48. Roach, S.A.: Counting Errors Due to Overlapping Particles in Thermal Precipitator Samples. Br. J. Ind. Med. 15:250 (1958).
49. May, K.R.: The Cascade Impactor: An Instrument for Sampling Coarse Aerosols. J. Sci. Instr. 22:187 (1945).
50. May, K.R.: A New Graticule for Particle Counting and Sizing. J. Sci. Instr. 42:500 (1965).
51. Cartwright, J.: The Electron Microscopy of Airborne Dusts. Br. J. Appl. Phys. Suppl. 3:109 (1954).
52. Billings, C.E.; Megaw, W.J.; Wiffen, R.D.: Sampling Submicron Particles for Electron Microscopy. Nature 189:336 (1961).
53. Schonauer, G.: Particle Size Analysis of Paraffin Aerosols by Electron Microscopy. Staub 25:24 (in English) (1965).

Instrument Descriptions

15-1 Point-to-Plane Electrostatic Precipitator

In-Tox Products

This instrument is the commercial version of the point-to-plane electrostatic precipitator described by Morrow and Mercer.[27] This device is useful for collecting aerosol samples for electromicroscopic examination. Samples are drawn into a 3/8-in. diameter cylindrical channel at a chosen volumetric rate between 50 cm^3/min and 1.0 L/min for a period of 1–5 min. A sharp needle near one side of the channel serves as a high voltage electrode, producing a corona discharge with an electrical potential near 7000 volts DC. In opposition to this needle, on the other side of the channel, a carbon-substrated electron-microscope grid is mounted on a metal post which serves as the other electrode. Aerosols drawn through this device are unipolarly charged and collected at random on the grid by action of the electric field forces.

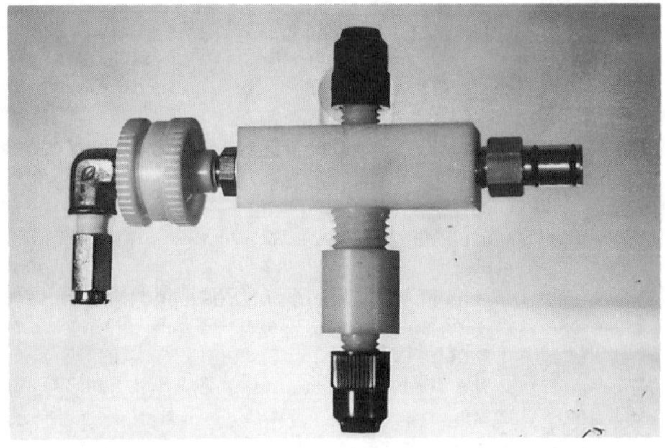

INSTRUMENT 15-1a. Point-to-plane electrostatic precipitator.

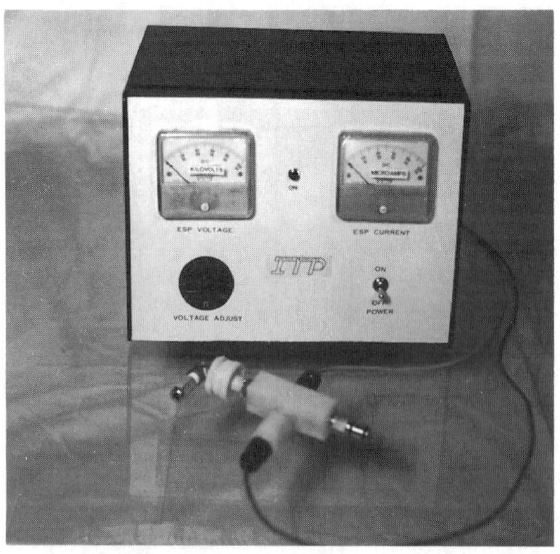

INSTRUMENT 15-1b. Power supply for point-to-plane precipitator (approximate height, 25 cm).

This point-to-plane electrostatic precipitator is constructed of Delrin plastic with a channel threaded at each end so that one end can be used to connect to the sample probe and the other end can be connected to a back-up filter holder and vacuum line. The body of the unit is 12 cm long. High-voltage electrodes are reversible so that the corona discharge can be either positive or negative as desired by the user.

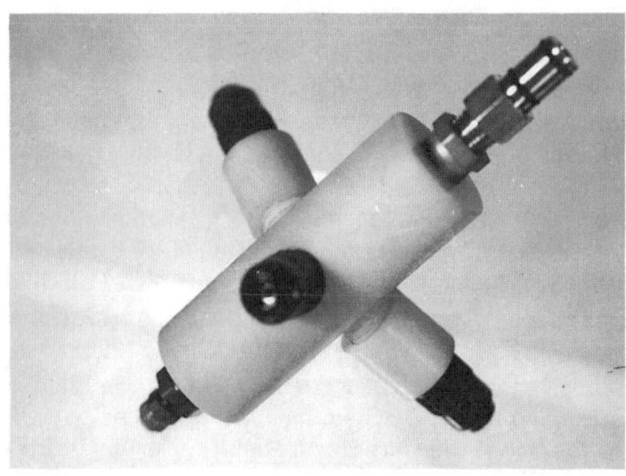

INSTRUMENT 15-2. Combination point-to-plane electrostatic precipitator.

The precipitator is available separately or with a solid-state power supply to provide the necessary 7000 DC high voltage at the normal operational current of 5 microamperes. No flowmetering equipment or vacuum pump is included; provision for these must be made by the user.

15-2 Combination Point-to-Plane Electrostatic Precipitator
In-Tox Products

This instrument is similar to the point-to-plane electrostatic precipitator (ESP), except that two particulate samples (one for transmission, one for scanning electron microscopy) can be collected simultaneously. A single needle provides corona discharge for both collectors. Flow and current characteristics are similar to the point-to-plane ESP. The power supply is portable and operates on 100 VAC, 60 cycle; high-voltage DC up to 5 kV is produced.

15-3 Concentric Electrostatic Precipitator
In-Tox Products

This particle collector is cylindrical in design with an axially mounted needle at the inlet end for charging. Particles drift to a cylindrical foil collector within a 3/4-in.-diameter brass inner cylinder. The total length of the precipitator is 12 in., with a working length of 9 in. The outer cylinder is 2 in. in diameter, constructed of methacrylate plastic. The power supply is the same as for the combination point-to-plane electrostatic precipitator.

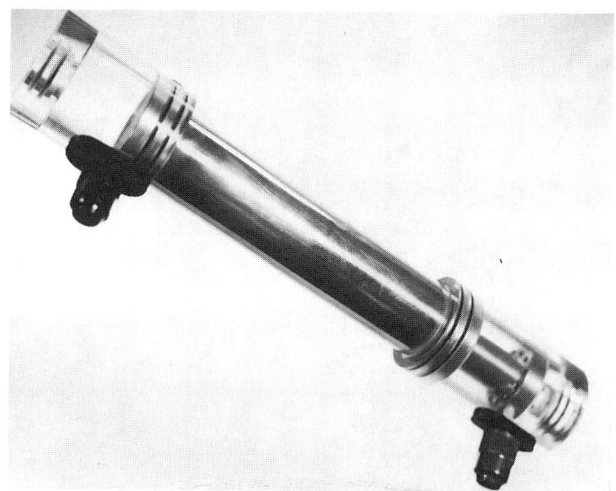

INSTRUMENT 15-3. Concentric electrostatic precipitator.

TABLE 15-I-1. List of Instrument Manufacturers

ITP	In-Tox Products 115 Quincy, NE Albuquerque, NM 87108 (505)265-1180 FAX (505)265-1181

Chapter 16

Direct-Reading Instruments For Airborne Particles

David Y. H. Pui, Ph.D.[A] and David L. Swift, Ph.D.[B]

[A]*Mechanical Engineering Department, University of Minnesota, 111 Church Street, S.E., Minneapolis, Minnesota;* [B]*The Johns Hopkins University, School of Hygiene and Public Health, Baltimore, Maryland*

CONTENTS

Introduction

Aerosol sampling instruments described in previous chapters are used to collect particles for subsequent microscopic, gravimetric, or chemical analyses. Instruments considered in this section are more complex. Sampling and analysis are carried out within the instrument and the property of interest can be obtained immediately. Instruments of this type are called direct-reading instruments.

Recent development of direct-reading instruments capable of real-time measurement is largely the result of the availability of modern electronic components such as laser illumination sources, high-sensitivity photometer or electrometer detectors, operational amplifiers, miniature power supplies, and microprocessors. Direct-reading instruments for real-time aerosol measurements are available to cover particles in the size range of 0.002 to 50 µm. These instruments have fast time response and can follow rapid changes in both particle size and concentration. Good counting statistics can also be obtained because repeated measurements can be performed in a short time. However, these instruments usually rely on indirect sensing techniques and more calibration efforts are usually required. Figure 16-1 summarizes the principal direct-reading instruments used in aerosol studies, their measuring ranges, and the monodisperse aerosol generators used for their calibration. A comprehensive review of the topic has been given in two recent papers by Pui and Liu[1] and Liu and Pui.[2] A state-of-the-art review of several types of direct-reading instruments is contained in the book by Willeke and Baron.[3] The monodisperse aerosol generators have been described in a previous chapter (Chapter 9) by Cheng and Chen.

It must be noted that different aerosol properties are measured by different direct-reading instruments. Although many instruments provide data in particle

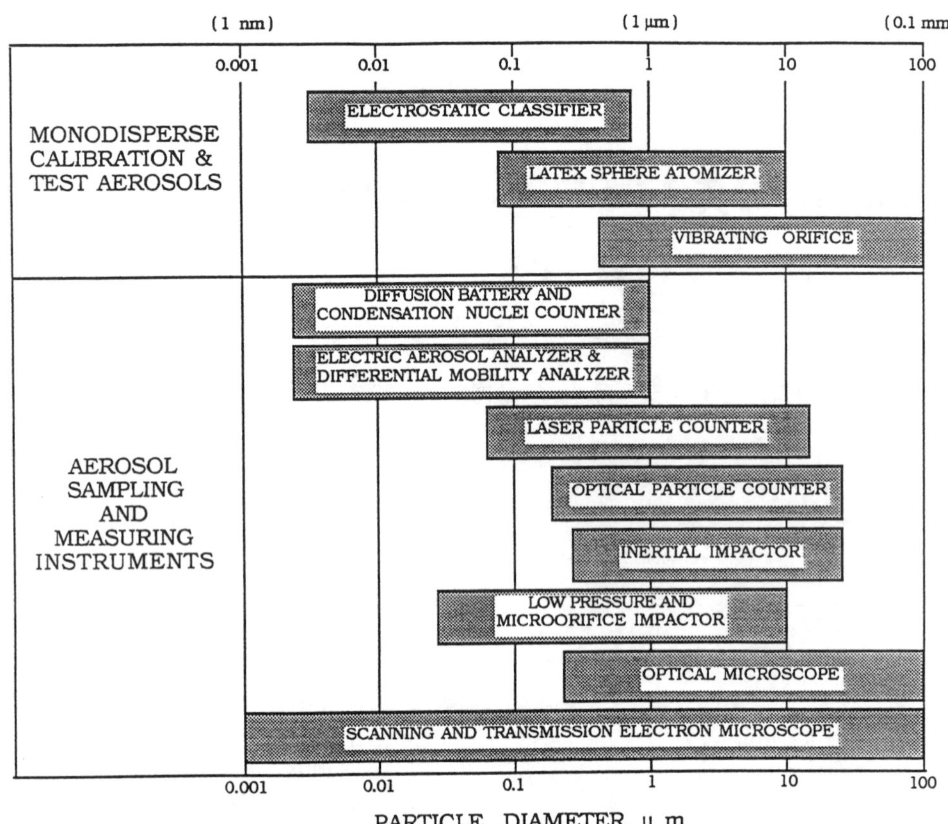

FIGURE 16-1. Measuring range of principal aerosol instruments and their calibration standards.

"size," this "size" is derived from one of many possible particle properties such as its gravimetric, optical, aerodynamic, mechanical, or force field mobility behavior. Thus, these instruments or the particle sizes may not be directly compared without some correction of the data to account for these differences. Other aerosol properties determined by direct-reading instruments include aerosol number concentration, aerosol mass concentration, size distribution, opacity, and chemical composition.

The sensitivity of these instruments is generally limited by one of two factors: 1) the random property fluctuations of the accompanying gas molecules or 2) the noise level of the electronic circuit that converts the property measured to an electronic signal. Accuracy is dependent on the relationship between signals in the sensing zone and the aerosol property. Although this relationship is often based on first principles, it is more common to establish an empirical relationship using a "well-calibrated" aerosol system. The danger of this approach is that the real aerosol measured may have a different, unknown relationship between signals and the aerosol property so that an inaccurate "particle size" may be indicated.

The user of direct-reading instruments must also beware of comparing properties of the same aerosol determined by several direct-reading instruments, particularly those using different principles, because this comparison is likely to give contradictory information. It is important to know what property is changed in the sensing zone and how this is assumed to be related to an aerosol property.

Integral Concentration Measurement

Integral concentration detectors are those that can be used to measure some integral parameters of an aerosol over its entire size distribution, such as the total number or mass concentration, or total light scattering or extinction coefficients. Several of the more widely used instruments are described below. These include the condensation nucleus counter for number concentration determinations, and the beta gauge and quartz-crystal microbalance used for mass concentration measurement and other miscellaneous techniques based on light scattering, contact, or diffusion charging.

Condensation Nucleus Counter

The condensation nucleus counter (CNC), or condensation particle counter (CPC), is widely used to measure particles in the diameter range of approximately 0.002

to 1.0 μm. The instrument operates by saturating the carrier air stream with a vapor and producing a supersaturation either by adiabatic expansion or direct contact cooling to cause vapor condensation on the particles. The particles then grow to a size where they can be detected optically by light scattering. Recent advances include the development of a continuous flow, direct-contact-type CNC[4–6] and the mixing of a hot vapor stream and a cool aerosol stream to achieve supersaturation.[7]

A schematic diagram of a commercially available, continuous-flow CNC is shown in Figure 16-2.[8] In this instrument, butyl alcohol is used as the working fluid and air is saturated with this vapor in a saturator kept at 35°C. The subsequent cooling of this alcohol-vapor laden air stream in a thermoelectrically cooled condenser tube kept at 10°C produces the required supersaturation for vapor condensation on the particles. Particles emerging from the condenser tube at a size of approximately 12 μm are then detected optically by light scattering. For low particle concentrations, the individual particles are counted. Above a particle concentration of 1000 particles/cm^3, the total light scattering from the droplet cloud is detected in a "photometric mode" to measure the total particle concentration. The concentration range of the instrument is from less than 0.01 particles/cm^3 to more than 10^6 particles/cm^3.

Detailed calibration studies of the CNC have shown that below a particle size of 0.05 μm the response of the instrument begins to drop off as a function of particle size.[8–16] The counting efficiency decrease can be attributed to particle loss in the flow passages in the instrument due to diffusion and the lack of 100% activation due to inhomogeneous vapor concentration distribution in the condenser.[17–18] By introducing a clean sheath of air around the aerosol stream in the CNC, Stolzenburg and McMurry[12] were able to increase the counting efficiency of the instrument to over 70% at a particle size of 0.003 μm. Figure 16-3 shows the details of such a sheath air CNC. Wilson *et al.*,[19] using a similar design, have developed a low pressure CNC for stratospheric aerosol measurements. Niessner and Helsper[20] have shown that by changing the supersaturation ratios in steps, the dependence of particle size on critical supersaturation for vapor condensation can be used for size distribution measurement.

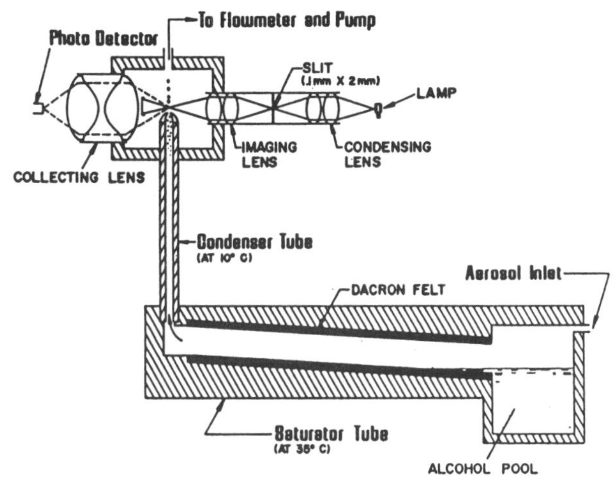

FIGURE 16-2. Schematic diagram of the condensation nucleus (particle) counter.[8]

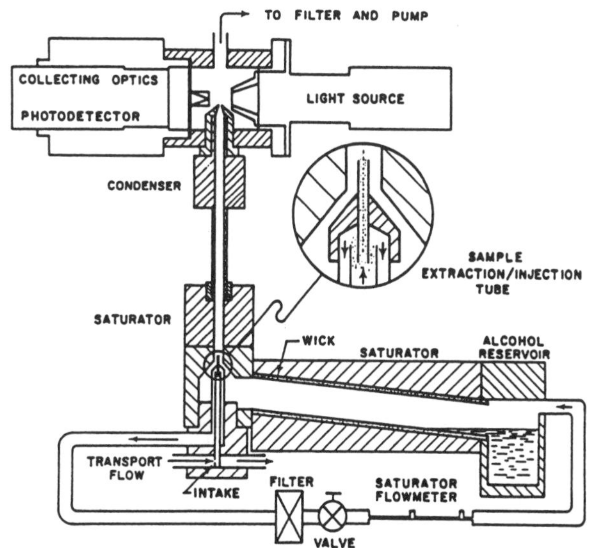

FIGURE 16-3. Schematic diagram of the sheath-air ultrafine aerosol condensation particle counter.[12]

Quartz-crystal Microbalance and Vibrating Mass Sensors

Several sensors for near real-time mass concentration measurements have been developed in recent years. By depositing the particles on a quartz crystal, the natural vibrating frequency of the crystal can be affected and used as a measure of the deposited particle mass. Particle deposition can be achieved either by electrostatic precipitation[21,22] or by inertial impaction.[23] The sensitivity of the quartz crystal microbalance is approximately 5×10^{-9} g, corresponding to a frequency shift of 1 Hz for a 10 MHz AT-cut quartz crystal. Figure 16-4 shows the schematic diagram of a battery operable piezoelectric microbalance for respirable aerosol detection.[24] The instrument incorporates a respirable impactor at the inlet to remove the nonrespirable particles, allowing the respirable particles to be deposited by electrostatic precipitation on the quartz crystal for measurement. The instrument can measure particle concentrations in the range of approximately 0.05–5.5 mg/m^3. Recent advances in the vibrating mass sensing technique include the use of a low frequency vibrating mass in the form of a tapered

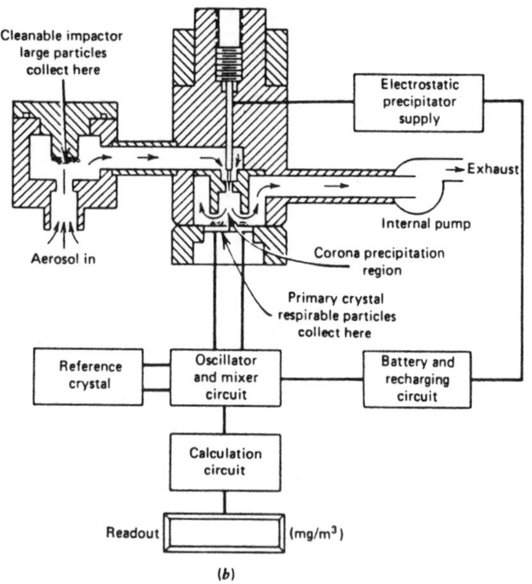

FIGURE 16-4. Schematic diagram of the respirable piezoelectric microbalance (piezobalance).[24]

element[25] coupled to a filter collector. This design extends the measurement range or the technique to mass concentration levels in the g/m^3 range. The application of the technique to particle measurement in high temperature and high pressure gas streams of the pressurized fluidized bed combustor has been reported by Wang.[26]

Beta-attenuation Mass Sensor

Instruments based on the attenuation of beta radiation through collected particle mass on a surface have been developed for respirable dust measurement in mining applications and for atmospheric studies.[27,28] The particles can be deposited either by impaction or filtration. A two-stage continuous atmospheric mass monitor based on the beta attenuation principle has been constructed.[29] The specific instrument uses a ^{14}C beta source and a solid-state, silicon surface-barrier detector to measure the attenuated beta radiation. The particles are separated into two size fractions by impaction and filtration using a rotating tape.

Light-scattering Photometers and Nephelometers

For atmospheric studies, the total light scattering coefficient of the airborne particles is important as it is related to atmospheric visibility or visual range. Measurement of the total light scattering coefficient is usually made with a photometer or integrating nephelometer. For aerosols that differ only in concentration and with the same size distribution, the integral light scattering measurement can be converted to mass concentration. Examples of such a correlation between total scattering and atmospheric mass concentration are given by Waggoner and Charlson.[30]

In the integrating nephelometer, shown schematically in Figure 16-5, the particles are illuminated in a sensing volume of approximately 1.0 L and scattered light from the particles reaches the photoreceptor at angles from 8° to 170° off axis. This simplifies the complex angular scattering relationship by summing the scattering over nearly the entire range of angles. Although the instrument was originally used to measure visual range, it has found applications in studies of the urban and rural atmospheric aerosol. In some cases, the scattering was shown to be well correlated with the atmospheric mass concentration.[30,31] The instrument is simple in construction and has been used in automobiles and aircraft for mapping the concentration of particles in the 0.1- to 1.0-μm range. These particles are chiefly responsible for degraded urban visibility. Some caution must be exercised when using the nephelometer in an environment with sooty particles because the scattering will be attenuated due to light absorption. In this case, the apparent concentration will be lower than expected.

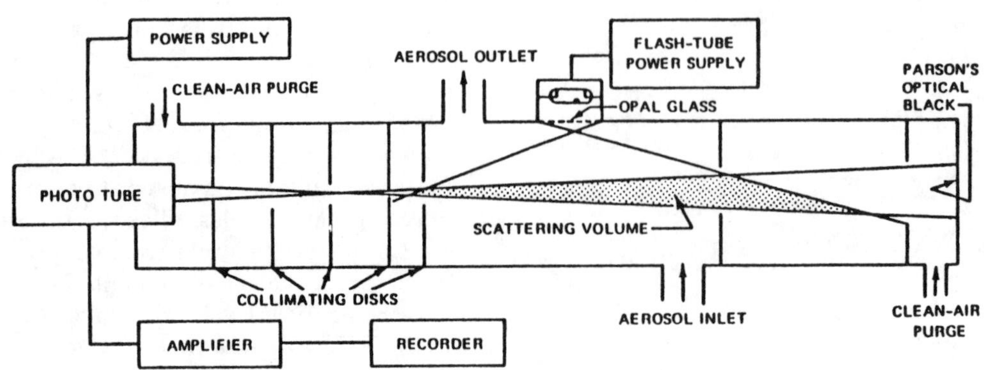

FIGURE 16-5. Schematic diagram of an integrating nephelometer.

Forward-scattering photometers, which employ a laser or incandescent light source and optics similar to dark field microscopy, have been commercially produced. A narrow cone of light converges on the aerosol cloud, but it is prevented from falling directly on the photoreceptor by a dark stop; only light scattered in the near forward direction falls on the receptor. The readout of these instruments is in mass or number concentration, but the calibration may change with composition and size distribution of the particles. Based on the solutions to Maxwell's equations, forward scattering photometers are, however, less sensitive to changes in refractive index than are photometers at other commonly used sensing angles such as 30°, 45°, or 90°.

A forward-scattering photometer (45°–95°), which is a passive personal monitor for airborne particles, has been designed using microelectronics.[(32)] This instrument displays current particle mass concentration for time intervals as small as 10 seconds and calculates time-weighted averages (TWAs) for up to a full shift for display or readout.

A multiparticle, light-scattering instrument that employs a long path and particle back-scattering is LIDAR.[(33)] A powerful pulsed laser is used, and the temporal analysis of back-scattering light indicates the spatial distribution of particles. This type of instrument has been used to map smoke plume opacity in the vicinity of the stack. Unless the size distribution and composition of the particles are known, only a qualitative comparison of aerosol concentration at different locations can be made.

For aerosols composed of specific cations, such as Na, detection of aerosol mass can be achieved by thermal excitation in a H_2 flame. One such instrument[(34)] has been used for laboratory filter testing. The number and size of particles is determined in a similar fashion to the conventional single particle counter, using a photomultiplier and a multichannel pulse height analyzer.

Light-attenuating Photometers

Transmissometers and other light-attenuating photometers are based on the simple extinction of light by particles. In order to get a measurable change in extinction (>5%), the sensing volume must contain a large number of particles. This means that there must be either a high concentration of particles or a long path length. Smoke stack transmissometers are used because of the high particle concentration within the stack. If the mass or number concentration is to be derived directly from theory, it is necessary to design such an instrument to exclude scattered light in the near forward direction, particularly for particles >1.0 μm in diameter. In practice, this is not done, and the calibrations of these transmissometers are empirical, either based on gravimetric or opacity (Ringelmann) comparisons. This procedure is acceptable if the stack particles consist of known and reproducible characteristics (refractive index, chemical composition, and absorption of light), but if these properties are different from the calibration aerosol, the results can only be qualitatively correct. Conner and Hodkinson[(35)] showed that oil and carbon plumes of similar mass concentration and particle size gave significantly different instack transmittance. In transmissometry, the source of light and the photoelectric receptor (usually a photomultiplier or photodiode) are coaxial, and the presence of particles attenuates the light reaching the receptor.

Direct-reading instruments that measure "soiling index" or "coefficient of haze" (COHs) detect changes in the reflectivity or transmission of a filter paper after a fixed volume of air has passed through the filter. This index is highly dependent on particle size, opacity, and composition; thus, it is not considered a scientifically established analytical technique for particle mass concentration.

Electrical Detection Methods

Concentration of aerosols can also be measured by imparting a charge to the particles and measuring the resulting charge with an electrometer. Liu and Lee[(36)] used unipolar diffusion charging and electrometer detection to measure the particle charge for aerosol concentration measurement, and John[(37)] used contact electrification, or impact charging for the same purpose. In general, these techniques can be used for precise concentration measurements only if the charging characteristics of the particles are constant and the size distributions of the aerosol being measured are similar in shape.

Ion interception by particles has been used by laboratory investigators to determine the number concentration and mean radius of aerosol systems.[(38)] In this type of instrument, bipolar ions are produced by a ^{60}Co source on an axial wire in a cylindrical chamber. As particles pass through the chamber, the ions are intercepted, and the current is attenuated and compared to a parallel chamber from which all particles are excluded by filtration. No commercial instrument using this principle is presently available.

Similar to the behavior of certain gases, aerosol particles passing through a H_2 flame alter the dielectric properties of the flame region. This alteration is the basis for a laboratory instrument described by Altpeter *et al.*[(39)] as an aerosol flame ionization detector. With appropriate dilution, the aerosol particles pass through the flame one by one, and for a given substance, the integrated response is simply related to the particle diameter. Response is significantly dependent on the

TABLE 16-1. Major Automatic Integral Concentration Detectors for Aerosol Measurement

Detector	Flow Rate (L/min)	Size Range (μm)	Lower Concentration Limit	References
1. Number Concentration Measurement				
Condensation nucleus (particle) counter, (CNC or CPC)	0.3–1.0	0.01–2.0	<0.001/cm^3	8
Condensation nuclei counter, ultrafine (UCNC or UCPC)	0.03–0.3	0.003–1.0	<0.001/cm^3	9, 10
Optical particle counter, white light and laser	0.1–28	<0.1–20	0.001/cm^3	40–42
Cloud condensation nuclei counter	1–5	0.08–1	1/cm^3	43, 44
Ice nuclei counter	10	—	0.01/cm^3	45
2. Mass Concentration Measurement				
Quartz-crystal microbalance	1–5	0.01–20 electrostatic 0.3–20 impactor	0.01 mg/m^3	23, 24
Vibrating sensor	1–5	0.01–20 filtration	<1 mg/m^3	25, 26
Beta-attenuation sensor	1–12	0.01–20 filtration 0.3–20 impactor	0.01 mg/m^3	27, 29
Photometer, nephelometer, etc.	1–100	0.1–2	0.01 mg/m^3	30
Electrical aerosol detector	0.5–20	0.01–2	5/cm^3 at 1 μm 5000/cm^3 at 0.01 μm	36, 46

particle composition. Particle sizes suitable for detection in this device are similar to optical counters, i.e., 0.5 to 10.0 μm.

Table 16-1 summarizes some of the principal integral concentration detectors and their characteristics.

Size Distribution Measurement

Any of the integral concentration measuring techniques described above can be used with an appropriate particle size classification device to measure the size distribution of aerosols. Examples include the use of the CNC with a diffusion battery, and an impactor with a quartz crystal microbalance for size distribution measurement. In this section, these and other approaches to size distribution measurement are described.

Optical Particle Counter

The optical particle counter (OPC) is widely used for size distribution measurement both in the indoor and outdoor environments. Figure 16-6 shows the operating principle of the optical particle counter.[47] Single, individual particles are carried by an air stream through an illuminated viewing volume in the instrument and cause light to be scattered to a photodetector. The photodetector generates a voltage pulse in response to each particle passing through the viewing volume. The pulse amplitude is then taken as a measure of particle size. The pulse is then counted and processed electronically to yield a pulse-height histogram, which is then converted to a histogram for particle size distribution using an appropriate calibration curve. Many commercial counters using an incandescent light source have been developed for particle size distribution measurement in the range of 0.3 μm to approximately 10 μm.

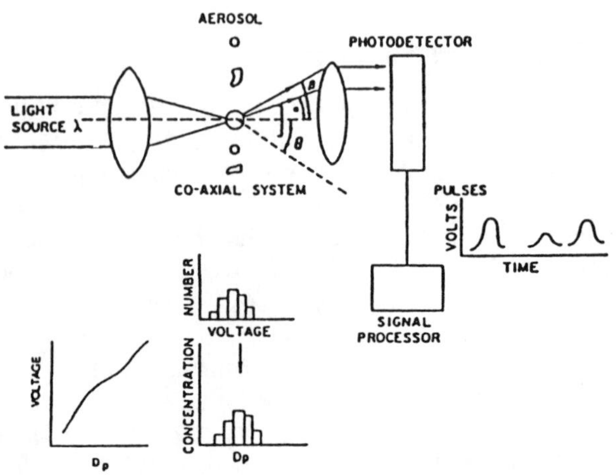

FIGURE 16-6. Operating principle of the optical particle counter.[47]

Recent advances include the use of laser illumination to achieve lower detection limits down to 0.05 μm.

Optical counters differ widely in their design and performance characteristics. Figure 16-7 shows the optical systems used in three commercial OPCs. The PMS counter uses the "active scattering" principle, in which the particles are passed through the resonant cavity of a helium-neon laser. The Hiac/Royco instrument uses a helium-neon laser and an external scattering volume. In contrast, the TSI instrument uses a solid-state laser to obtain a small, lightweight portable sensor. Table 16-2 gives a selected list of optical particle counters available commercially.(47) They can be differentiated by the light source (laser, laser diode, or white light) they use, the sampling flow rate of the instrument, the number of channels of data the instrument provides, and other distinguishing characteristics such as portability and ability to be interfaced with computers. In general, an instrument using a laser source, particularly for the active scattering type, can detect smaller particles than a corresponding instrument using an incandescent light source because of the higher illuminating intensity of the laser. The lower detection limit of the white light and laser diode counters is usually around 0.3 μm, whereas active scattering laser counters can detect particles as small as 0.1 μm and below. A higher flow rate instrument can count more particles in a given time period than an instrument of a lower sampling flow rate. The latter property is important for particle counting in low concentration environments, such as in cleanrooms. A lower flow rate instrument has higher resolution and can detect smaller particles than the high flow counter. A sampling flow rate of 1 cfm is usually considered high and a flow rate of 0.01 cfm is usually considered low.

The OPC response, which gives a functional relationship between the pulse height and the particle size, depends on both the instrument properties and the particle properties. The former includes optical design, illumination source, and electronics gain, and the latter includes particle size and shape, refractive index, and orientation of nonspherical particles with the incident beam. The relative response of the OPC as a function of particle size can be calculated by means of the theory of electromagnetic scattering developed by Mie. The calculation for some white light counters has been reported by Cook and Kerker.(48) Recent studies have concentrated on laser particle counters.(49)

For an OPC with an axisymmetric scattering geometry ($\theta = 0°$, see Figure 16-6) and near forward direction and narrow angle ($\alpha < \beta < 30°$), the simple geometry provides strong signals but with higher background noises. It is also susceptible to strong multivalued response, i.e., different particle sizes giving the same pulse height. The geometry is relatively insensitive to variations in real and imaginary parts of refractive index. Figure 16-8 gives the response of a near forward, light-scattering instrument (PMS-ASAS-300X; 4-22°).(49) For the wide angle counter, e.g., Climet CI-7300 (15–150°), the response is more sensitive to changes in both real and imaginary part of refractive index, but much less prone to multivalued response, particularly for white light illumination. Figure 16-9 shows the calculated response of the Climet CI-7300 counter.(48)

To determine the absolute voltage-size response of the OPCs, as well as other instrument characteristics, such as resolution, count coincidence, response to irregular particles, and inlet efficiency, experimental studies are generally required. Liu *et al.*(50) reported on the evaluation of several commercially available white light counters using monodisperse spherical particles. Wen and Kasper(51) and Liu and Szymanski(52) evaluated the counting efficiencies of several commercial OPCs. A novel technique to determine the OPC response to irregular coal dust particles has been developed by Liu *et al.*(53) Marple and Rubow(54) made use of inertial impactors to obtain aerodynamic particle size calibration of the OPCs. Recent works mostly involve the evaluation of laser OPCs.(55–61) Comprehensive discussions on the principle and application of the OPC may be found in the papers by Willeke and Liu,(40) Knollenberg and Luehr,(41) and Gebhart *et al.*(42)

Particle Relaxation Size Analyzers

In addition to direct light-scattering measurement (described above), light scattering can also be used in combination with other measurement principles to extend the measurement capabilities of the light-scattering technique. An example of this is the combination of vapor condensation with light scattering for sub- 0.1-μm particle measurement(8) discussed earlier in the "Condensation Nucleus Counter" section. Another example is the use of light scattering with an oscillating electric field for the measurement of airborne fibers, including asbestos.(62)

A further example is the use of an accelerating nozzle in combination with light-scattering measurement. Figure 16-10 shows the schematic diagram of a commercially available aerodynamic particle sizer (APS) described by Agarwal *et al.*(63) In this instrument, the particles are accelerated through a small nozzle to different speeds. The larger the particle size, the lower the speed of the particle due to particle inertia. The particle velocity at the nozzle exit is then measured to provide a measure of particle size. This principle enables the "aerodynamic size" of the particles, in the size range from 0.5 to 30 μm, to be measured; this measurement is related to the settling speed of the aerosol and to particle deposition in the lung. Calibration studies on the APS have been reported by Chen *et al.*(64) and Baron.(65)

a

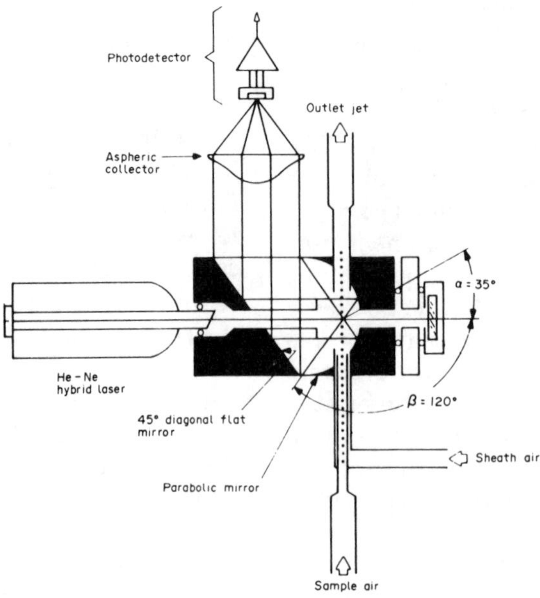

b

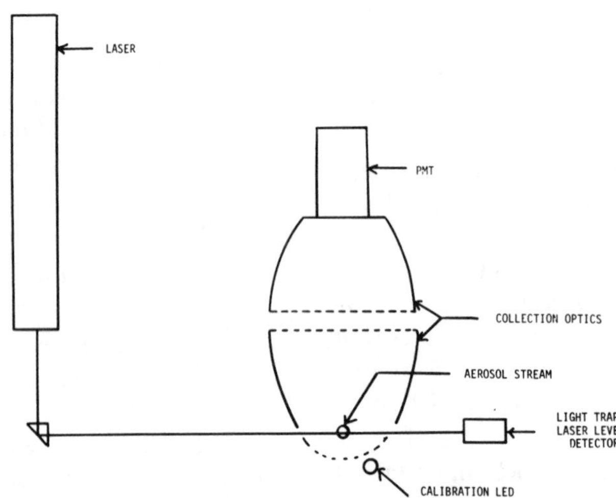

c

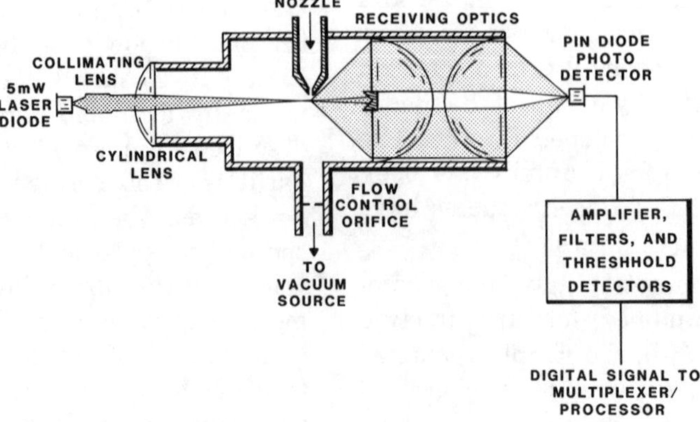

FIGURE 16-7. Schematic diagram of three commercial laser optical particle counters with (a) active scattering, (b) external scattering, (c) solid-state laser.

TABLE 16-2. Selected Optical Particle Counters[47]

Manufacturer	Model No.	Flow rate (cfm)	Size Range (μm)	No. of Size Channels	Illumination Source
Climet Instruments Co.	CI-208C	0.25 or 1	0.3–>20	16	White light
1320 W. Colton Ave.	CI-226	0.25 or 1	0.3–>20	16	White light
Redlands, CA 92374	CI-7500	1.0	0.19–>5.0	6	Laser
	CI-7400	0.1	0.1–>0.5	6	Laser
	CI-7300	1.0	0.3–>10	6	White light
	CI-3100	0.1	0.3–>5	5	Laser
Hiac/Royco	5300	1.0	0.5–>15	6	White light
141 Jefferson Drive	5120	1.0	0.2–>5	6	Laser
Menlo Park, CA 94025	5200	0.1	0.1–>2	6	Laser
	4130	1.0	0.3–>10	6	Laser
	5100	1.0	0.25–>10	6	Laser
	5000	0.01–0.05	0.3–>10	6	White light
Kratel SA	Partoscope				
CH-1222 Geneve-'Vesenaz					
64 Ch. de St. Maurice					
Switzerland					
Met One	205	1.0	0.16–>10	6	Laser
481 California Ave.	200	1.0	0.3–>10	6	White light
Grants Pass, OR 97526	207	0.1	0.5–>5	5	Laser
Particle Measuring Systems, Inc.	LPC-101	0.1	0.1–>1.0	4	Laser
5475 Airport Blvd.	LPC-525	1.0	0.2–>5.0	5	Laser
Boulder, CO 80301-2339	LPC-555	1.0	0.3–>5.0	4	Laser
	LAS-X	0.01	0.09–3.0	16	Laser
	HS-LAS	0.1	0.05–1.0	16	Laser
	uLPC-110	1.0	0.1–5.0	5	Laser
Status (Faley Int. Corp.)	4000	1.0	0.3–>5.0	5	White light
P.O. Box 669	5000	0.0177	0.3–>5.0	5	White light
El Toro, CA 92630-0669	2100	0.01	0.5–>5.0	2	White light
	2100P	0.01	0.5–>5.0	2	White light
TSI, Incorporated	3755	0.1	0.5–>5.0	2	Laser
500 Cardigan Road	3753	0.1	0.3–>5.0	2	Laser
P.O. Box 64394					
St. Paul, MN 55164					

A second commercial aerodynamic sizing instrument, the Aerosizer, operates under the same time-of-flight principle as the APS. One significant difference is that particles are accelerated at sonic flow through a critical orifice in the Aerosizer while they are subjected to a moderate acceleration at subsonic flow in the APS. The instrument is capable of measuring particles in a wider size range, 0.5 to 200 μm and higher concentration up to 1100 particles/cm^3, than the APS. Cheng *et al.*[66] calibrated two Aerosizers using uniform-sized, spherical, polystyrene latex particles and glass beads and with nonspherical natrojarosite particles.

An instrument that employs the laser Doppler velocimetry (LDV) principle for size determination is the "Spart" (single particle aerosol relaxation time) analyzer.[67] In this instrument, the particle is subjected to sinusoidal force by an acoustic transducer at 27 kHz. The motion of the particle, detected by the LDV optics, lags behind the force sine wave by an amount which depends primarily on the particle aerodynamic diameter. The range of aerodynamic diameter measurable with acceptable sensitivity and resolution is stated to be 0.2–10.0 μm.

In-situ Sensing Optical Techniques

The optical techniques described above involve extracting aerosol from the environment and transporting it to a sensing zone for measurement. *In-situ* techniques, often optically based, are noninvasive and measure aerosol in its natural state without extractive sampling. The noninvasive measurement is accom-

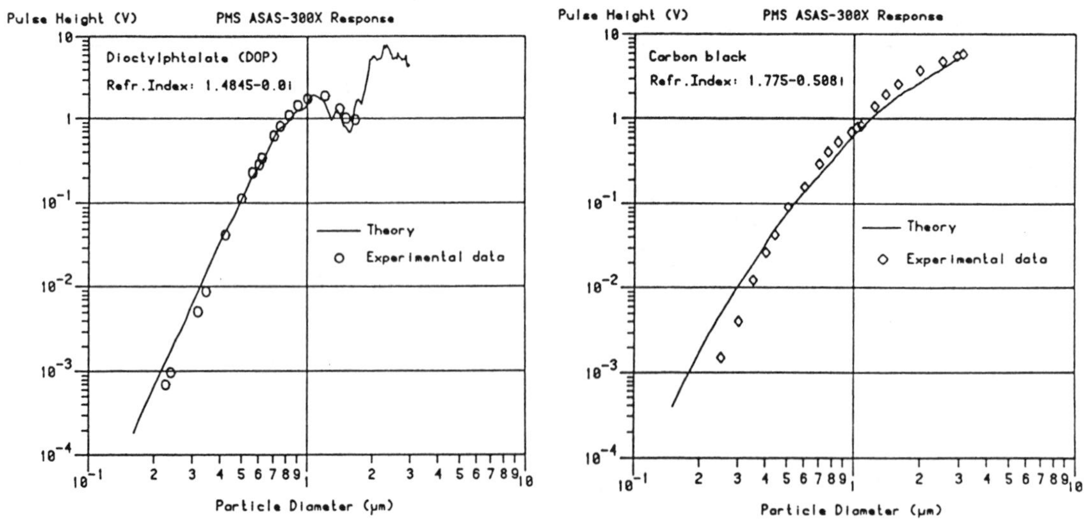

FIGURE 16-8. Theoretical and experimental responses for a near-forward, light-scattering sensor.[49]

plished by locating the sensing volume external to the instrument, thereby eliminating the need for extractive sampling. The techniques are most suitable for measuring aerosols in hostile environments of extreme pressure and temperature ranges, and in reactive or corrosive environments. The techniques have received significant interest over the last decade and were summarized in a recent review paper by Rader and O'Hern.[68] They classified the techniques into the following major categories: single-particle counters of intensity based, phase based, or imaging; and ensemble techniques of particle field imaging, Fraunhofer diffraction, or dynamic light scattering. To determine the particle size, the single-particle counters measure the scattering behavior of an individual particle as it passes through a well-defined sensing zone, whereas the ensemble techniques analyze the collective scattering of a large number of particles. They can be used to measure individual particle sizes from about 0.25 to above 1000 μm, concentrations as high as 10^6 particles/cm^3, and speeds in the km/s range. With the ensemble techniques, particle mean diameters as low as 0.01 μm can be measured.

An example of a single-particle counter based on the phase Doppler principle is shown in Figure 16-11.[68] The principles of a phase Doppler particle analyzer

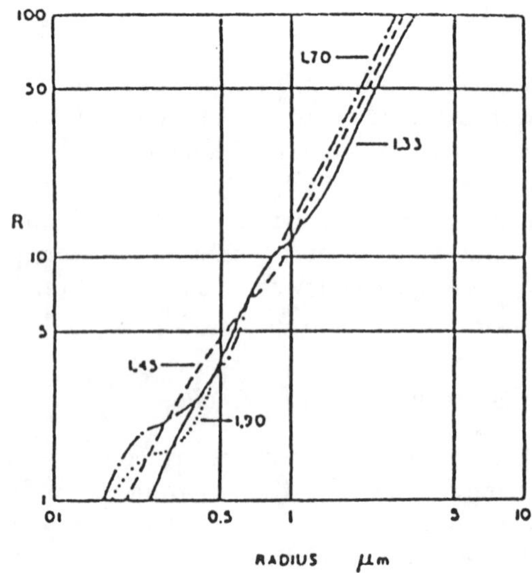

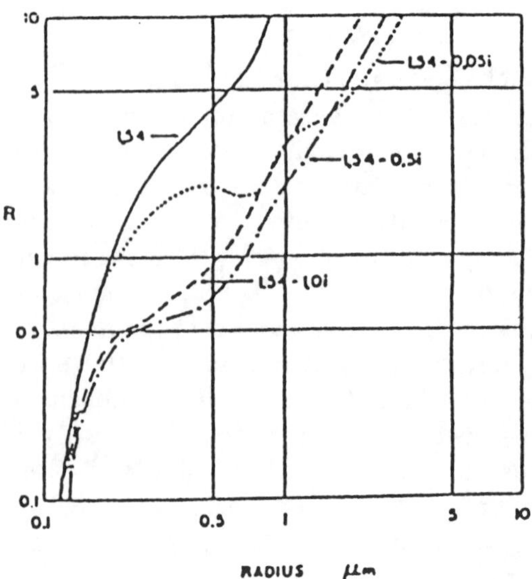

FIGURE 16-9. Theoretical response curves for a wide angle sensor.[48]

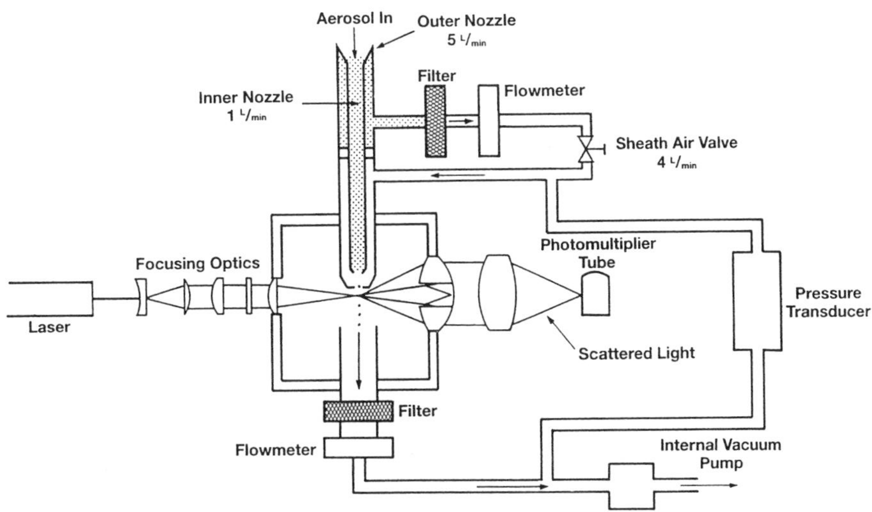

FIGURE 16-10. Schematic diagram of the aerodynamic particle sizer.[63]

(PDPA) were described in the paper by Bachalo and Houser.[69] The system consists of a laser and transmitting optics, and a receiver optics package with multiple photodetectors to measure the spatial and temporal frequency of the Doppler-shifted light scattered by individual particles passing through the measuring volume. The spatial frequency gives a measure of the particle diameter and refractive index; the temporal frequency gives a measure of the particle velocity. A commercial instrument gives the specifications of either one or two velocity component measurements in addition to particle size, particle diameter range of 1–8000 μm and a dynamic range of 35:1, and a velocity range from 1 to 200 m/s. The maximum measurable number concentration is $10^6/cm^3$, which is based on the number of particles passing through a calculated size-dependent measurement volume.

Electrical Aerosol Analyzer

The high electric mobility of submicron particles in an electric field makes it possible to separate and classify electrically charged aerosol particles. If the electric mobility is a monotonic function of the particle size, size classification or size distribution measurement can be made on the basis of the particle electrical mobility.

A widely used instrument for size distribution measurement using the electrical mobility technique is the electrical aerosol analyzer (EAA) originally developed by Whitby[70] and further improved by Liu and Pui.[46] Figure 16-12 is a schematic diagram of the Liu-Pui version of the EAA. The aerosol to be measured is first sampled into the aerosol charger, where it is exposed to unipolar positive ions and becomes electrically charged. The charged aerosol then enters the mobility analyzer, which functions as a low-pass filter to precipitate the high mobility particles while allowing the low mobility particles to pass through. The "cut-off" mobility of the analyzer is determined by the applied voltage on the analyzer. By varying this voltage and measuring the corresponding current carried by the charged particles with the electrometer current sensor, a voltage-current curve is generated. This voltage-current curve can be further analyzed to yield the desired particle-size distribution curve. With the availability of a microcomputer-based data acquisition system, sophisticated data reduction software (e.g., Kapadia[71] and Helsper *et al.*[72]) can be used in near real time to obtain the size distribution of aerosols.

Differential Mobility Particle Sizer

A recent development in the electrical measurement technique includes replacing the integral type of mobility analyzer with a differential type. The differential

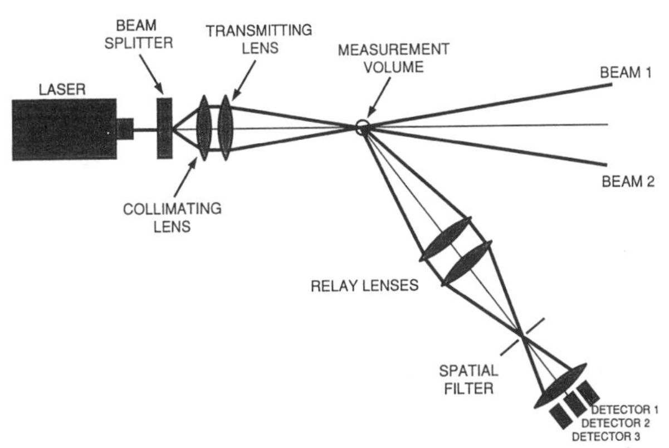

FIGURE 16-11. Schematic diagram of a phase Doppler particle analyzer.[68]

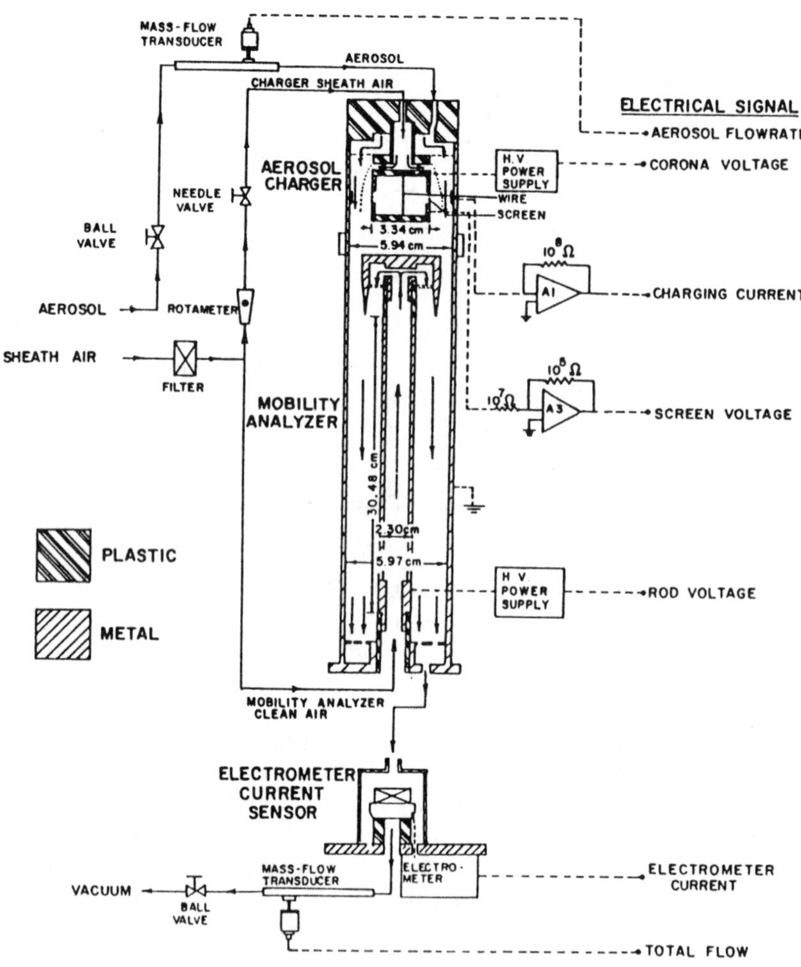

FIGURE 16-12. Schematic diagram of the electrical aerosol analyzer.[46]

mobility analyzer (DMA) described by Liu and Pui[73] and Knutson and Whitby[74] allows high resolution particle sizing using the mobility classification technique. The resolution is further increased using a bipolar charger rather than a unipolar charger. The bipolar charging-differential mobility analysis method for size distribution measurement was first proposed by Knutson.[75] Although the technique is capable of high resolution sizing, the measurement sensitivity decreases due to the smaller current flow to the electrometer. With the introduction of the high sensitivity, single particle counting CNC, accurate size distribution measurement with the DMA becomes possible. A commercial differential mobility particle sizer (DMPS), presented schematically in Figure 16-13, shows the neutralizer (bipolar charger), the DMA, and the CNC.[76] A microcomputer is used to control the instrument for automatic data acquisition and reduction. The general acceptance of the DMPS is due, in part, to the data reduction procedure developed by Fissan *et al.*,[77] who also proposed the use of an impactor to remove the coarse particles that tend to interfere with particle measurement in the sub-0.1-µm range. Work by Hoppel[78] and Reischl[79] further enhanced the DMPS technique. A significant improvement of the accuracy of the technique has been provided by Kousaka *et al.*,[80] who reported the particle loss data within the DMA and the applicable theory for bipolar charging.

Recent advances include the development by Reischl and colleagues of a high resolution DMA with low particle loss in the nanometer particle size range.[81] Wang and Flagan[82] made use of a scanning electric field, in place of changing the electric field in discrete steps in the traditional technique, to speed up the cycle time of the mobility analyzer considerably. Using an exponential ramp in the field strength, the particles are classified in the time-varying electric field while maintaining a one-to-one correspondence between the time a particle enters the classifier and the time it leaves. The method is capable of completing 100 mobility measurements within 30 seconds.

By arranging two DMAs in series and inserting a

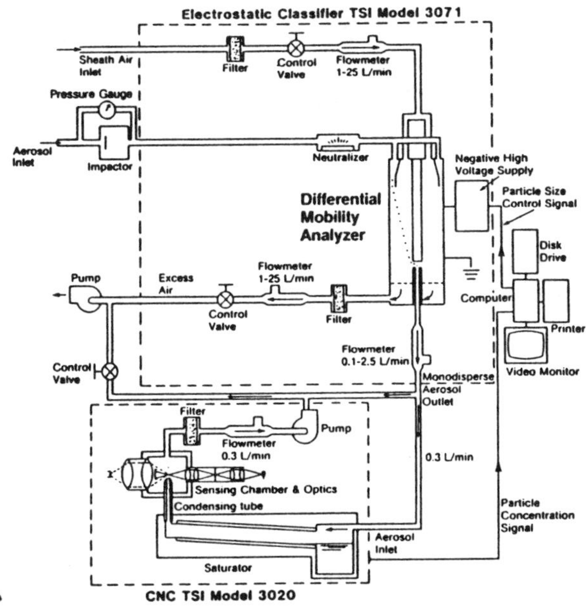

FIGURE 16-13. Schematic diagram of the differential mobility particle sizer.[76]

particle conditioner in between, it is possible to make use of the high resolution capability of the DMA to detect small changes in particle size caused by the conditioner. Liu *et al.*[83] used a humidifier to effect particle size change for sulfuric acid aerosol detection. Rader and McMurry[84] made further refinement in the technique and applied the technique for precise droplet growth and evaporation studies.

Diffusion Batteries

Because the rate of diffusion of aerosol particles to a solid surface is a function of particle size, particle loss in a diffusion collector can be used for size distribution measurement. The technique has been used for many years for size distribution measurements of small particles below 0.1 μm.[85] A simple diffusion battery design consists of a single capillary tube, or a capillary tube bundle through which the aerosol is passed. A CNC is then used to measure the upstream and downstream aerosol concentration. The aerosol penetration through the diffusion collector can then be taken as a measure of particle size. By arranging a number of these diffusion collectors in series, the size distribution of the aerosol can be measured. More detailed information of diffusion devices is given in Chapter 19.

Several novel diffusion batteries have been developed by Sinclair (see the review paper by Sinclair[86]), who used metal disks containing uniform parallel holes of a finite length—the so-called collimated hole structure—and layers of fine stainless steel screens as diffusion collectors. A commercial version of the device is shown in Figure 16-14. Detailed study of the wire screens as diffusion collectors has been reported.[87–89] Various sophisticated data reduction techniques based on Simplex and other minimization techniques for the diffusion battery have also been reported. The CNC/dif-

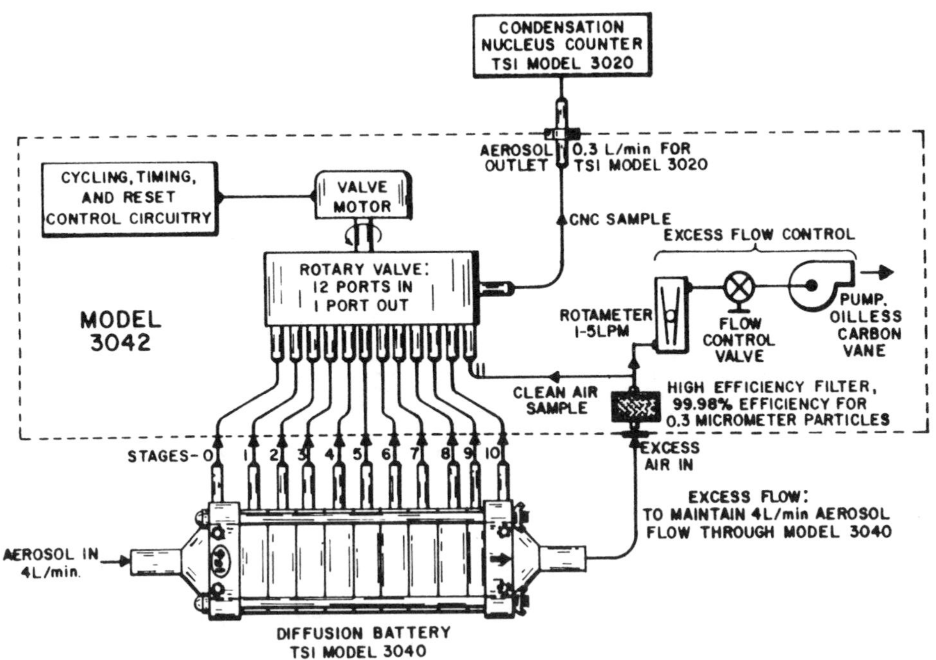

FIGURE 16-14. Schematic diagram of the automatic diffusion battery.

TABLE 16-3. Major Automatic Size Distribution Measuring Techniques for Aerosol Measurement

Method or Instrument	Flow Rate (L/min)	Size Range (μm)	No. Channels	References
1. Optical Particle Counter				
White light counter	0.3–28	0.3–20	2–16	48, 50
Laser counter	1.4–28	<0.1–10	2–6	49, 51, 55–61
Fiber monitor	2–5	0.2 diameter 2–20 length	2–6	62
Laser interferometer	—	0.5–200	2–10	68
Aerodynamic particle sizer	1–5	0.5–30	up to 600	63
Laser settling velocimeter	—	10–20	2–6	68
Ultramicroscope sedimentation	—	0.2–20	2–20	96
2. Electrical Aerosol Analyzer				
Electrical aerosol analyzer	4	0.006–0.6	2–12	46, 70
Differential mobility particle sizer	1–3	0.005–1.0	2–64	76–80
3. Diffusion Batteries	4–6	0.005–0.2	2–11	85–88
4. Other Techniques				
Quartz crystal impactor	2–6	0.3–20	2–8	23, 93
Quartz crystal centrifuge	5–10	0.06–10	2–20	94
Hot-wire anemometer	2–5	1–600	2–15	97
Acoustic sizer	—	5–80	2–8	98

fusion battery (CNC/DB) technique of aerosol size distribution measurement is now widely accepted.

The diffusion battery has also been used as a particle separator for size-selective particle sampling. Lundgren and Rangaraj(90) used it for in-stack particle sampling. George(91) and Sinclair *et al.*(92) made use of the screen diffusion batteries to measure the submicron radioactive aerosols. One of the requirements for accurate diffusion battery measurement is that the counting efficiency of the CNC should be well characterized. Recent development in this area (see the "Condensation Nucleus Counter" section) has further improved the accuracy of the technique.

In addition to the principal techniques described above, other combinations of integral sensors with particle classifiers are possible. One notable example is the use of the quartz-crystal microbalance as the collecting surface of a cascade impactor to obtain a near-real-time measurement of aerosol mass distribution measurement. Two commercial quartz-crystal sensors equipped with cascade impactors have been developed.(23,93) Recently, Stober *et al.*(94) also mounted the sensors in a spiral aerosol centrifuge to measure aerosol mass distribution. Fissan and Marple(95) incorporated a quartz crystal sensor in the micro-orifice impactor for mass distribution measurement down to 0.05 μm.

Table 16-3 summarizes the major size distribution measuring techniques for direct-reading, near-real-time measurement of aerosols.

Summary

Considerable advances have been made in recent years in the development of direct-reading instruments for analyzing airborne particles. Instruments are now available to measure aerosol number concentration up to 10^6 particles/cm^3, mass concentration up to 1000 mg/m^3, and size distribution over a particle size range of 0.003 μm to over 100 μm. Advances in instrumentation in the field is such that many of the measurement problems that were considered too difficult only 10 years ago can now be performed routinely with good experimental accuracy.

With a wide array of available commercial instruments, it is necessary for the practitioners to understand well the operating principles of the instruments and the aerosol system under study. Some of the criteria for selecting an appropriate instrument include the particle size range of interest, the system parameters to be studied (e.g., mass or number concentration versus particle size distribution, aerodynamic property versus light scattering property), and the cost and compactness of the instrument.

Figure 16-15 shows a flowchart for selecting a direct-reading instrument for analyzing airborne particles. The first step is to decide whether to perform an integral concentration measurement or a complete size distribution measurement. In principle, the integral concentration, i.e., mass concentration or number con-

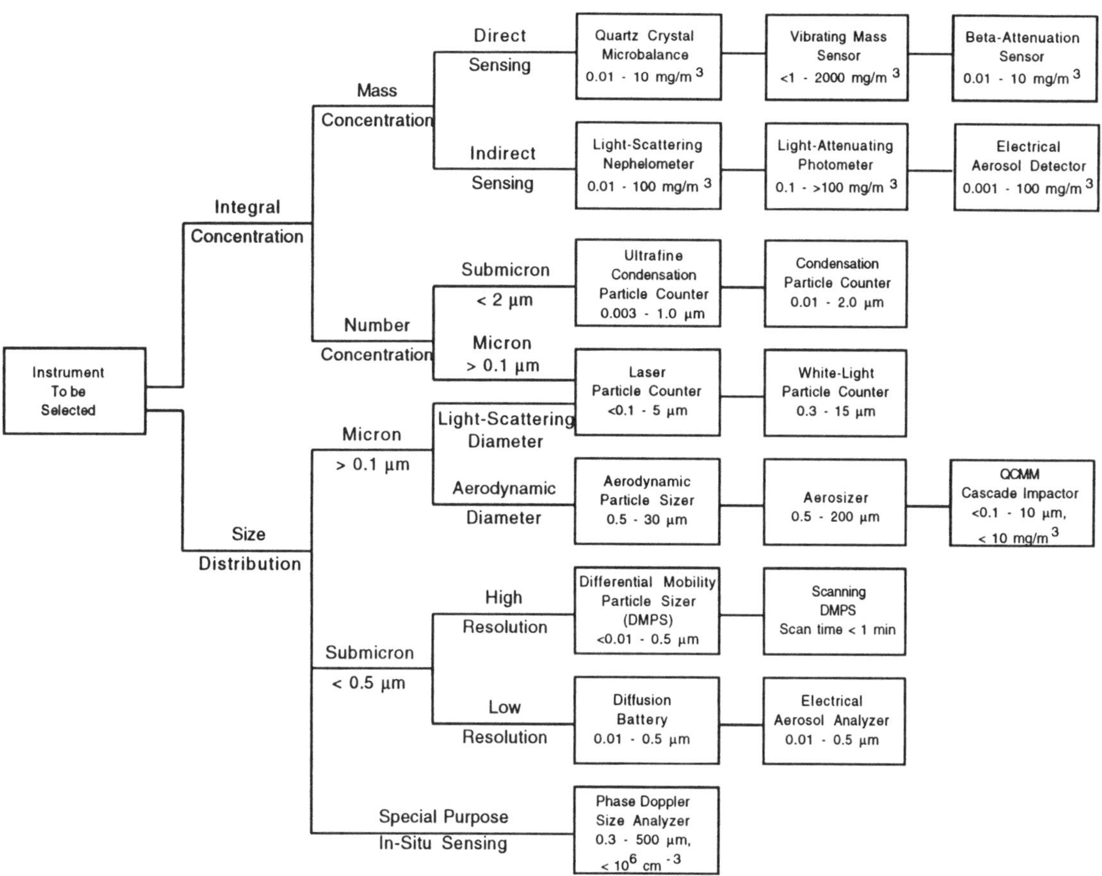

FIGURE 16-15. Flowchart for selecting a direct-reading instrument for analyzing airborne particles.

centration, can be obtained by integrating the size distribution over the appropriate size range. However, there are many compact, inexpensive instruments available for integral concentration measurement compared to the more sophisticated, expensive instruments for size distribution measurement. Considerable cost savings can be realized if an integral concentration detector is deemed appropriate for the application.

For mass concentration measurement, as required in many industrial hygiene applications, the particles may be directly captured on a surface for measurement by the quartz-crystal sensing technique or by the beta-attenuation sensing technique. These techniques generally require longer sampling time and frequent cleaning of the surface. A quicker method would be to measure indirectly the light-scattering intensity of the aerosol and to infer its mass concentration through calibration. The accuracy of the technique depends on the measured aerosols having nearly the same size distribution and differing only in concentration. For number concentration measurement, as required in many cleanroom applications, two classes of instruments may be used depending on the size range of interest. For particle diameter less than 2 µm, several condensation particle counters may be used. For particle diameter larger than 0.1 µm, a large array of white light or laser optical particle counters may be used.

For size distribution measurement, the instruments are divided into two major classes depending on their measuring size ranges. For particles larger than 0.1 µm, the optical particle counters or the particle relaxation size analyzers may be used. The latter is capable of measuring the aerodynamic particle size, which is important for deposition studies in respiratory system. For submicron aerosols, the high-resolution, differential mobility particle sizer or the low-resolution diffusion battery and the electrical aerosol analyzer may be used. A number of special purpose instruments are also available for difficult applications. For example, the phase Doppler size analyzer measures aerosol in its natural state without extractive sampling. The noninvasive measurement is accomplished by locating the sensing volume external to the instrument, thereby eliminating the need for extractive sampling. The technique is most suitable for measuring aerosols in hostile environments of extreme pressure and temperature ranges, and in reactive or corrosive environments. The cost of such a system, however, will be many times that of an integral concentration detector.

References

1. Pui, D.Y.H.; Liu, B.Y.H.: Advances in Instrumentation for Atmospheric Aerosol Measurement. Physica Scripta 37:252–269 (1988).
2. Liu, B.Y.H.; Pui, D.Y.H.: Aerosols. Encyclopedia of Applied Physics 1:415–441 (1991).
3. Willeke, K.; Baron, P.A.: Aerosol Measurement - Principles, Techniques, and Applications. Van Nostrand Reinhold, New York (1993).
4. Bricard, J.; Delattre, P.; Madelaine, G.; Pourprix, M.: Detection of Ultra-fine Particles by Means of a Continuous Flux Condensation Nuclei Counter. In: Fine Particles. B. Y. H. Liu, Ed. Academic Press, New York (1976).
5. Sinclair, D.; Hoopes, G.S.: A Continuous Flow Condensation Nucleus Counter. J. Aerosol Sci. 6:1 (1975).
6. Sinclair, D.; Yue, P.C.: Continuous Flow Condensation Nucleus Counter, II. Aerosol Sci. Technol. 1:217 (1982).
7. Kousaka, Y.; Niida, T.; Okyuama, K.; Tanaka, H.: Development of a Mixing Type Condensation Nucleus Counter. J. Aerosol Sci. 13: 231 (1982).
8. Agarwal, J.K.; Sem, G.J.: Continuous Flow, Single-Particle-Counting Condensation Nucleus Counter. J. Aerosol Sci. 11:343 (1980).
9. Liu, B.Y.H.; Kim, C.S.: Atmos. Environ. 11:1097 (1977).
10. Zhang, Z.Q.; Liu, B.Y.H.: Dependence of the Performance of TSI 3020 Condensation Nucleus Counter on Pressure, Flow Rate and Temperature. Aerosol Sci. Technol. 13:493 (1990).
11. Su, Y.F.; Cheng, Y.S.; Newton, G.J.; Yeh, H.C: Counting Efficiency of the TSI Model 3020 Condensation Nucleus Counter. Aerosol Sci. Technol. 12:1050 (1991).
12. Stolzenburg, M.R.; McMurry, P.H.: An Ultrafine Aerosol Condensation Nucleus Counter. Aerosol Sci. Technol. 14:48 (1991).
13. McDermott, W.T.; Ockovic, R.C.; Stolzenburg, M.R.: Counting Efficiency of an Improved 30A Condensation Nucleus Counter. Aerosol Sci. Technol. 14:278 (1991).
14. Keston, J.; Reineking, A.; Porstendorfer, I.: Calibration of a TSI Model 3025 Ultrafine Condensation Nucleus Counter. Aerosol Sci. Technol. 15:107 (1991).
15. Sinclair, D.: Atmos. Environ. 16:955 (1982).
16. Noone, K.J.; Hansson, H.C.: Calibration of the TSI 3760 Condensation Nucleus Counter for Nonstandard Operating Conditions. Aerosol Sci. Technol. 13:478 (1990).
17. Engilmez, N.; Davies, C.N.: J. Aerosol Sci. 15:177 (1984).
18. Brockmann, J.E., Ph.D.: Thesis: Coagulation and Deposition of Ultrafine Aerosols in Turbulent Pipe Flow. Department of Mechanical Engineering, University of Minnesota, Minneapolis, MN (1981).
19. Wilson, J.C.; Hyun, J.H.; Blackshear, E.D.: The Function and Response of an Improved Stratospheric Condensation Nucleus Counter. J. Geophys. Res. 88:6781 (1983).
20. Niessner, R.; Helsper, C.; Roenicke, G.: Application of a Multistep Condensation Nuclei Counter as a Detector for Particle Surface Composition. In: Aerosols. B.Y.H. Liu, D.Y.H. Pui, and H. Fissan, Eds. Elsevier Sci. Publ., New York (1984).
21. Lundgren, D.A.; Carter, L.D.; Daley, P.S.: Aerosol Mass Measurement using Piezoelectric Crystal Sensors. In: Fine Particles. B.Y.H. Liu, Ed. Academic Press, New York (1976).
22. Sem, G.J.; Tsurubayashi, K.: A New Mass Sensor for Respirable Dust Measurement. J. Am. Ind. Hyg. Assoc. 36:791 (1975).
23. Chuan, R.L.: Rapid Measurement of Particulate Size Distribution in the Atmosphere. In: Fine Particles. B.Y.H. Liu, Ed. Academic Press, New York (1976).
24. Sem, G.J.; Tsurubayashi, K.; Homma, K.: Performance of the Piezoelectric Microbalance Respirable Aerosol Sensor. J. Am. Ind. Hyg. Assoc. 38:580 (1977).
25. Patashnick, H.; Rupprecht, G.: A New Real-Time Aerosol Mass Monitoring Instrument: The TEOM. In: Proceedings: Advances in Particle Sampling and Measurement. EPA-600/9-80-004, p. 264. W.B. Smilh, Ed. U.S. Environmental Protection Agency, Research Triangle Park, NC (1980).
26. Wang, J.C.F.: A Real-Time Particle Monitor for Mass and Size Fraction Measurements in a Pressurized Fluidized-Bed Combustor Exhaust. Aerosol Sci. Technol. 4:301 (1985).
27. Lilienfeld, P.: Design and Operation of Dust Measuring Instrumentation Based on the Beta-Radiation Method. Staub 35:458 (1975).
28. Jaklevic, J.M.; Galli, R.C.; Goulding, F.S.; Loo, B.W.: A Beta-Gauge Method Applied to Aerosol Samples. Environ. Sci. Technol. 15:680 (1981).
29. Macias, E.S.; Husar, R.B.: Atmospheric Particulate Mass Measurement with Beta Attenuation Mass Monitor. Environ. Sci. Technol. 60:904 (1976).
30. Waggoner, A.P.; Charlson, R.J.: Measurement of Aerosol Optical Parameters. In: Fine Particles. B.Y.H. Liu, Ed. Academic Press, New York (1976).
31. Butcher, S.S.; Charlson, R.J.: An Introduction to Air Chemistry. Academic Press, New York (1972).
32. Lilienfeld, P.: Current Mine Dust Monitoring Instrument Development. In: Aerosols in the Mining and Industrial Work Environment. V.A. Marple and B.Y.H. Liu, Eds. Ann Arbor Science, Ann Arbor, MI (1982).
33. Cook, C.S.; et al.: Remote Measurement of Smoke Plume Transmittance using LIDAR. Appl. Optics 11 (1972).
34. Binek, B.; et al.: Using the Scintillation Spectrometer for Aerosols in Research and Industry. Staub 27:1 (in English) (September 1967).
35. Conner, W.O.; Hodkinson, J.R.: Optical Properties and Visual Effects of Smoke Stack Plumes. EPA AP-30. U.S. Environmental Protection Agency, Washington, DC (1972).
36. Liu, B.Y.H.; Lee, K.W.: An Aerosol Generator of High Stability. Am. Ind. Hyg. Assoc. J. 36:861 (1975).
37. John, W.: Contact Electrification Applied to Particulate Matter Monitoring. In: Fine Particles. B.Y.H. Liu, Ed. Academic Press, New York (1976).
38. Mohnen, V.A.; Holtz, P.: The SUNY-ASRC Aerosol Detector. J. Air Pollut. Control Assoc. 18:667 (1968).
39. Altpeter, L.L.; Pilney, J.P.; Rust, L.W.; et al.: Recent Developments Regarding the Use of Flame Ionization Detector as an Aerosol Monitor. In: Fine Particles. B.Y.H. Liu, Ed. Academic Press, New York (1976).
40. Willeke, K.; Liu, B.Y.H.: Single Particle Optical Counter: Principle and Application. In: Fine Particles. B.Y.H. Liu, Ed. Academic Press, New York (1976).
41. Knollenberg, R.C.; Luehr, R.: Open Cavity Laser "Active" Scattering Particle Spectrometry from 0.05 to 5 microns. In: Fine Particles, p. 669. B.Y.H. Liu, Ed. Academic Press, New York (1976).
42. Gebhan, J.; Heyder, J.; Rolh, C.; Stahlhofen, W.: Optical Aerosol Size Spectrometry Below and Above the Wavelength of Light — A Comparison. In: Fine Particles, p. 793. B.Y.H. Liu, Ed. Academic Press, New York (1976).
43. Radke, L.F.; Turner, F.M.: J. Appl. Meteorol. 11:407 (1972).
44. Alofs, D.J.; Trueblood, M.B.; White, D.R.; Behr, V.L.J.: Appl. Meteorol. 18:1106 (1979).
45. Hobbs, P.V.J.: Appl. Meteorol. 9:828 (1970).
46. Liu, B.Y.H.; Pui, D.Y.H.: On the Performance of the Electrical Aerosol Analyzer. J. Aerosol Sci. 6:249 (1975).
47. Szymanski, W.W.: Lecture Notes on Optical Particle Counter. Minnesota Short Course on Aerosol and Particle Measurement, Minneapolis, MN (1993).
48. Cooke, D.D.; Kerker, M.: Response Calculations for Light Scattering Aerosol Particle Counters. Applied Optics 14:734 (1975).
49. Liu, B.Y.H.; Szymanski, W.W.; Pui, D.Y.H.: Response of Laser Optical Particle Counter to Transparent and Light Absorbing Particles. ASHRAE Transactions V.92, Pt. 1 (1986).

50. Liu, B.Y.H.; Berglund, R.N.; Agarwal, J.K.: Experimental Studies of Optical Particle Counters. Atmos. Environ. 8:717 (1974).
51. Wen, H.Y.; Kasper, G.: Counting Efficiencies of Six Commercial Particle Counters. J. Aerosol Sci. 17:947–961.
52. Liu, B.Y.H.; Szymanski, W.W.: Counting Efficiency, Lower Detection Limit and Noise Levels of Optical Particle Counters. In: Proceedings of the 33rd Annual Technical Meeting, Institute of Environmental Sciences, San Jose, CA (1987).
53. Liu, B.Y.H.; Marple, V.A.; Whitby, K.T.; Barsic, N.J.: Size Distribution Measurement of Airborne Coal Dust by Optical Particle Counters. Am. Ind. Hyg. Assoc. J. 8:443 (1974).
54. Marple, V.A.; Rubow, K.L.: Aerodynamic Particle Size Calibration of Optical Particle Counters. J. Aerosol Sci. 7:425 (1976).
55. Hinds, W.C.; Kraske, G.: Performance of PMS Model LAS-X Optical Particle Counter. J. Aerosol Sci. 17:67(1986).
56. Kim, Y.J.; Boatman, J.F.: Size Calibration Corrections for the Active Scattering Aerosol Spectrometer Probe (ASASP-100X). Aerosol Sci. Technol. 12:665 (1990).
57. van der Meulen, A.; van Elzakker, B.G.: Size Resolution of Laser Optical Particle Counters. Aerosol Sci. Technol. 5:313 (1986).
58. Yamada, Y.; Miyamoto, K.; Koizumi A.: Size Measurements of Latex Particles by Laser Aerosol Spectrometer. Aerosol Sci. Technol. 5:377 (1986).
59. Garvey, D.M.; Pinnick, R.G.: Response Characteristics of the Particle Measuring Systems Active Scattering Aerosol Spectrometer Probe (ASASP-X). Aerosol Sci. Technol. 2:477–488 (1983).
60. Chen, B.T.; Cheng, Y.S.; Yeh, H.C.: Experimental Responses of Two Optical Particle Counters. J. Aerosol Sci. 15:457 (1984).
61. Szymanski, W.W.; Liu, B.Y.H.: On the Sizing Accuracy of Laser Optical Particle Counters. Part. Charact 3:1 (1986).
62. Lilienfeld, P.: Light Scattering from Oscillating Fibers at Normal Incidence. J. Aerosol Sci. 18:389 (1987).
63. Agarwal, J.K.; Remiaz, R.J.; Quant, F.J.; Sem, G.J.: Real-Time Aerodynamic Particle Size Analyzer. J. Aerosol Sci. 13:222 (1982).
64. Chen, B.T.; Cheng, Y.S.; Yeh, H.C.: Performance of a TSI Aerodynamic Particle Sizer. Aerosol Sci. Technol. 4:89 (1985).
65. Baron, P.A.: Calibration and Use of the Aerodynamic Particle Sizer (APS-3300). Aerosol Sci. Technol. 5:55 (1986).
66. Cheng, Y.S.; Barr, E.B.; Marshall, I.A.; Mitchell, J.P.: Calibration and Performance of an API Aerosizer. J. Aerosol Sci. 24:501 (1993).
67. Mazumder, M.K.; Kirsch, K.J.: Single Particle Aerodynamic Relaxation Time Analyzer. Rev. Sci. Instrum. 48:622 (1977).
68. Rader, D.J.; O'Hern, T.J.: Optical Direct-Reading Techniques: In Situ Sensing. In: Aerosol Measurement — Principles, Techniques, and Applications. K. Willeke and P.A. Baron, Eds. Van Nostrand Reinhold, New York (1993).
69. Bachalo, W.D.; Houser, M.J.: Phase Doppler Spray Analyzer for Simultaneous Measurements of Drop Size and Velocity Distribution. Opt. Eng. 23:583–590 (1984).
70. Whitby, K.T.; Clark, W.E.: Electrical Aerosol Particle Counting and Size Distribution Measuring System for the 0.015 to 1 μm Size Range. Tellus 18:573 (1966).
71. Kapadia, A., Ph.D.: Thesis: Data Reduction Techniques for Aerosol Size Distribution Measuring Instruments. University of Minnesota, Minneapolis, MN (1980).
72. Helsper, C.; Fissan, H.; Kapadia, A; Liu, B.Y.H.: Data Inversion by Simplex Minimization for the Electrical Aerosol Analyzer. Aerosol Sci.Technol. 1:135 (1982).
73. Liu, B.Y.H.; Pui, D.Y.H.: A Submicron Aerosol Standard and the Primary, Absolute Calibration of the Condensation Nucleus Counter. J. Colloid Interface Sci. 47:155 (1974).
74. Knutson, E.O.; Whitby, K.T.: Aerosol Classification by Electrical Mobility: Apparatus, Theory and Applications. J. Aerosol Sci. 6:443 (1975).
75. Knutson, E.O.: Extended Electric Mobility Method for Measuring Aerosol Particle Size and Concentration. In: Fine Particles. B.Y.H. Liu, Ed. Academic Press, New York (1976).
76. Keady, P.B.; Quant, F.R.; Sem, G.J.: TSI Quarterly 9, 3 (1983).
77. Fissan, H.J.; Helsper, C.; Thielen, J.H.: Determination of Particle Size Distributions by Means of an Electrostatic Classifier. J. Aerosol Sci. 14:354 (1983).
78. Hoppel, W.A.: Determination of the Aerosol Size Distribution from the Mobility Distribution of the Charged Fraction of Aerosols. J. Aerosol Sci. 9:41 (1978).
79. Reischl, G.P.: Measurement of Ambient Aerosols by the Differential Mobility Analyzer Method: Concepts and Realization Criteria for the Size Range between 2 and 500 nm. Aerosol Sci. Technol. 14:5 (1991).
80. Kousaka, Y.; Okuyama, K.; Adachi, M.: Determination of Particle Size Distributions of Ultrafine Aerosols using a Differential Mobility Analyzer. Aerosol Sci. Technol. 4:209 (1985).
81. Winklmayr, W.; Reischl, G.P.; Lindner, A.O.; Berner, A.: A New Electromobility Analyzer for the Measurement of Aerosol Size Distributions in the Size Range from 1 to 1000 nm. J. Aerosol Sci. 22:289 (1991).
82. Wang, S.C.; Flagan, R.C.: Scanning Electrical Mobility Spectrometer. Aerosol Sci. Technol. 13:230 (1990).
83. Liu, B.Y.H.; Pui, D.Y.H.; Whitby, K.T.; et al.: The Aerosol Mobility Chromatograph: A New Detector for Sulfuric Acid Aerosols. Atmos. Environ. 12:99 (1978).
84. Rader, D.J.; McMurry, P.H.: Application of the Tandem Differential Mobility Analyzer to Studies of Droplet Growth or Evaporation. J. Aerosol Sci. 17:771 (1986).
85. Pollak, L.W.; Metnieks, A.L.: Geofisica Pura e Applicata 37:183 (1957).
86. Sinclair, D.: Measurement of Nanometer Aerosols. Aerosol Sci. Technol. 5:187 (1986).
87. Yeh, H.C.; Cheng, Y.S.; Orman, M.M.: Evaluation of Various Types of Wire Screens as Diffusion Battery Cells. J. Colloid Interface Sci. 86:12 (1982).
88. Scheibel, H.G.; Porstendörfer, J.: Penetration Measurements for Tube and Screen-Type Diffusion Batteries in the Ultrafine Particle Size Range. J. Aerosol Sci. 15:673 (1984).
89. Cheng, Y.S.; Keating, J.A.; Kanapilly, G.M.: Theory and Calibration of a Screen-type Diffusion Battery. J. Aerosol Sci. 11:549 (1980).
90. Lundgren, D.A.; Rangaraj, C.N.: ESL-TR-81-04, Defense Technical Information Center, VA (1981).
91. George, A.C.: Health Phys. 23:390 (1972).
92. Sinclair, D.; George, A.C.; Knutson, E.O.: In: Airborne Radioactivity, p. 103. American Nuclear Society, La Grange Park, IL (1978).
93. Wallace, D.; Chuan, R.: A Cascade Impaction Instrument using Quartz Crystal Microbalance Sensing Elements for "Real-Time" Particle Size Distribution Studies. Special Publication 464, p. 199. U.S. National Bureau of Standards, Washington, DC (1977).
94. Stober, W.; Monig, F.J.; Flachsbart, H.; Schwarzer, N.: Mass Distribution Measurements with an Aerosol Centrifuge with Quartz Sensors as Mass Detectors. J. Aerosol Sci. 10:194 (1980).
95. Marple, V.A.; Rubow, K.L.; Ananth, G.; Fissan, H.: Microorifice Uniform Deposit Impactor. J. Aerosol Sci. 17:489 (1986).
96. Yoshida, T.; Kousaka, Y.; Okuyama, K.: Aerosol Science for Engineers. Power Co., Tokyo (1979).
97. Magnus, D.E.; Mahler, D.S.: In: Proceedings: Advances in Particle Sampling and Measurement (Daytona Beach, Florida), p. 320, U.S. Environmental Protection Agency, NC (1979).
98. Coover, S.R.; Reist, P.C.: Environ. Sci. Technol. 14:951 (1980).

Instrument Descriptions

Commercial sources for instruments presented in this section are listed in Table 16-I-1, which is located at the end of this chapter.

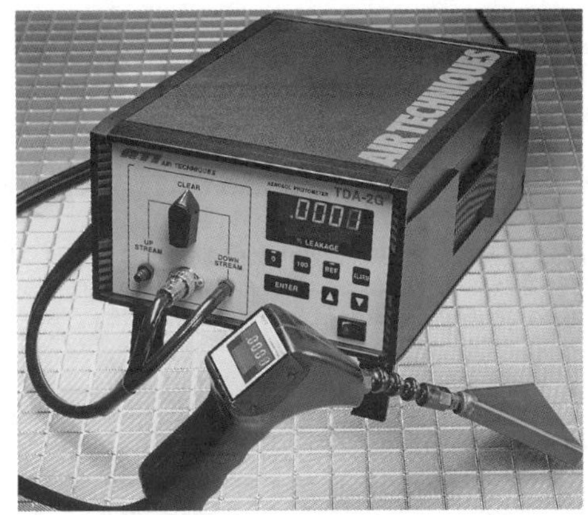

INSTRUMENT 16-1-1. ATI particulate detection apparatus.

1. Light-scattering Photometers

16-1-1. Particulate Detection Apparatus

Air Techniques, Div. of Hamilton Associates, Inc.

The ATI 2E Series particulate detectors are portable, forward-scattering photometers primarily intended for onsite integrity testing (leakage detection) of HEPA filters and other similar test applications. They can be used where the high sensitivity of forward-scattering optics is advantageous for detection and measurement of particles. Filter testing and other applications can be performed with di-2-ethylhexyl-phthalate (DEHP, formerly DOP) aerosols or other liquid or solid particle aerosols. The instrument yields a percent penetration as the ratio of the downstream to upstream aerosol concentration, as indicated by the degree of scattered light.

Sampling at 28.3 L min^{-1} (1 ft^3 min^{-1}) is provided by a vacuum pump, the only moving part of the apparatus, with either a handlemeter probe or a short length of tubing. The instrument is contained in an aluminum case 51 × 43 × 20 cm and weighs 16 kg; it operates on 115 VAC, 50/60 Hz, but can be adapted to other electrical service.

In 1994, ATI introduced the TDA-2G model which has similar operating parameters but is one-third the size and one-half the weight of the 2E series; this reduction is accomplished by microprocessor control and signal handling.

16-1-2. Aerosol Photometer

The Virtis Co., Inc.

This series of instruments measures near-forward scattered light from particles by means of an axisymmetric optical arrangement. A 28.3 L min^{-1} (1 ft^3 min^{-1}) sample is drawn through the sensing zone by a vacuum pump. Particles can be collected on a downstream filter if desired.

The lower sensitivity of the most sensitive model, measured with standard DEHP aerosol, is stated to be 10^{-4} μg L^{-1}. Linear or logarithmic scale models are available; in the linear model, the upper level of linear response is 100 μg L^{-1}.

A hand-grip meter probe permits remote sampling; the instrument is available in either a rack-mounted or suitcase enclosure. The suitcase model measures 53 × 43 × 20 cm and weighs 23 kg. It operates on 115 VAC, 60 Hz., requires 1000 watts, and has a regulated power supply for the light source.

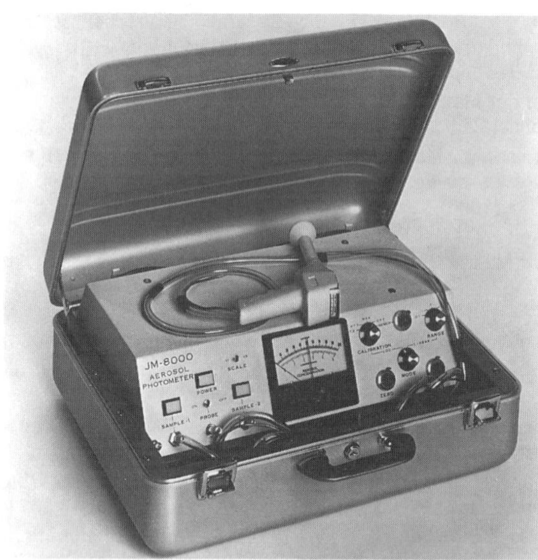

INSTRUMENT 16-1-2. Virtis aerosol photometer.

16-1-3. Integrating Nephelometer

Belfort Instruments

The Model 1590 series integrating nephelometer is designed to measure total light scattering of airborne particles. This measurement is presented as the light-scattering coefficient, b_{scat}, and the visual range. Air is sampled at 100 L min^{-1} through a 10-cm diameter, 112-cm-long cylindrical tube. The particles are illuminated by a quartz halogen lamp and scattered light at angles ranging from 8–179° is detected by a photomultiplier (PM) tube. Zero, span, and linearity are established by particle-free measurement of several gases.

The instrument can be used in automobiles or aircraft for visibility traverses and can operate from –10 to 50°C at relative humidities ranging from 0% to 95%. The instrument consists of an optical assembly that measures 100 × 25 × 15 cm, and a blower box measuring 24 × 21 × 30 cm. The total weight of the two units is 20 kg. An optional air sampling heater is available. The instrument operates on 105–125 VAC, 50 Hz. The minimum visual range detectable is 0.4 km.

16-1-4. Integrating Nephelometers

TSI Incorporated

Series 3500 integrating nephelometers are designed for monitoring visual range and particle air quality in ground-based and airborne studies. For 30 sec averaging times, the instruments measure b_{scat} values as small as 10^{-7} m^{-1}. Model 3551 measures scattering at a single wave length. Model 3553 includes three wave length detectors to determine the wave length dependence aerosol scattering properties. Model 3561 has one wave length scattering plus the capability to measure total- and back-scattering properties continuously. Model 3563 has three wave length detectors and provides for continuous measurement of total- and backscattering aerosol properties.

The instruments consist of a sensor module and a separate power module. The sensor measures 110 × 30 × 25 cm and weighs 18 kg. The power module measures 30 × 15 × 10 cm and weighs 5 kg; it requires maximum 175 watts and runs on 115/230 VAC, 60/50 Hz.

16-1-5. Respirable Dust Measuring Instrument

Hund GmbH

The TM Digital μP and TM Data are hand-held instruments for real-time measurement of respirable aerosol mass concentration. They employ an infrared source (940 nm) and detector for scattered light at 70° from forward. The particle diameter-particle mass relationship for this angle scattering is such that the instruments respond according to the ACGIH definition of respirable dust. They have no air mover; particles enter the detection zone by natural air movement.

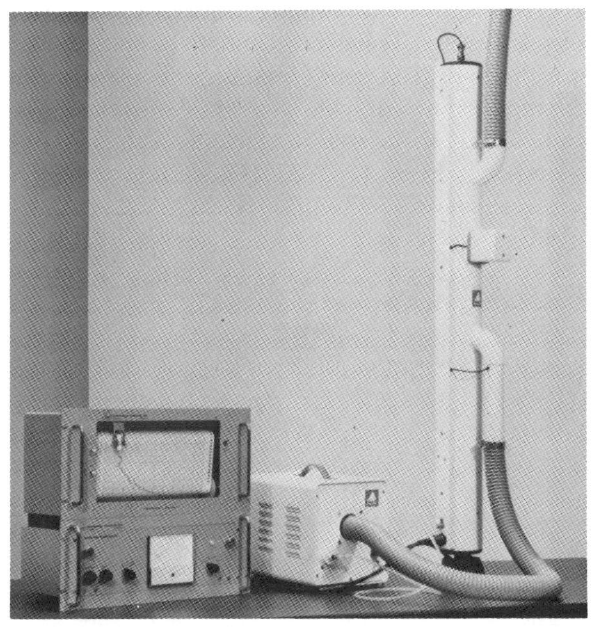

INSTRUMENT 16-1-3. Belfort integrating nephelometer.

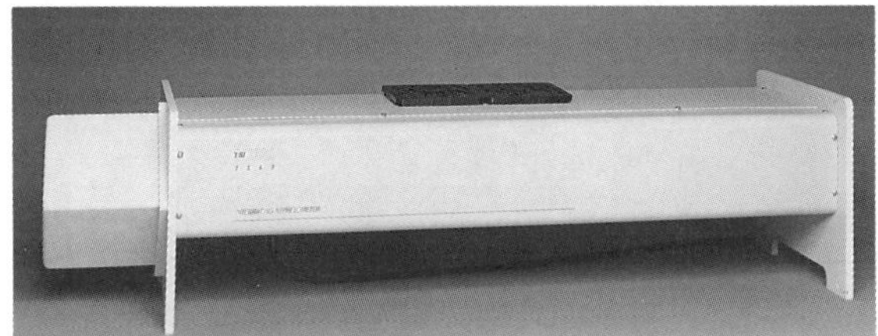

INSTRUMENT 16-1-4. TSI integrating nephelometer.

The instruments display dust concentration (range, 0–100 mg m^{-3}) every second and can store and average concentrations for up to 8 hrs; they are intrinsically safe for use in mines. TM Data permits longer time period averaging and storage of data. Both instruments measure 19 × 10 × 5 cm, weigh 1 kg, and are powered by rechargeable Ni-Cd batteries.

Model FMA-TMS 1 is a stationary respirable dust measuring instrument. It employs the same measuring principle but is stationary and has an integral air mover which draws air into the sensor at velocities up to 7 m sec^{-1}. The instrument consists of a probe unit and a control/data storage unit. The probe measures 25 × 27 × 27 cm; the control unit measures 25 × 60 × 30 cm. The combined weight of the units is 28 kg.

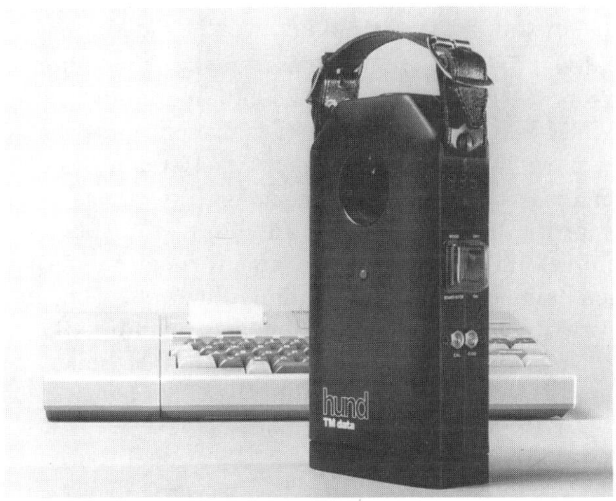

INSTRUMENT 16-1-5. Hund digital μP dust monitor.

16-1-6. Fine Dust Measuring Instruments

Hund GmbH

These instruments employ forward scattering of IR light (880 nm) from dust in the sensing zone with the intention of detecting the mass concentration of aerosols in the diameter range of 0.2–10 μm. Model TM-M is a portable, hand-held instrument intended to measure dust mass concentration in a local area without an air mover; air moves through the sensing zone either by natural convection or in a directed flow situation.

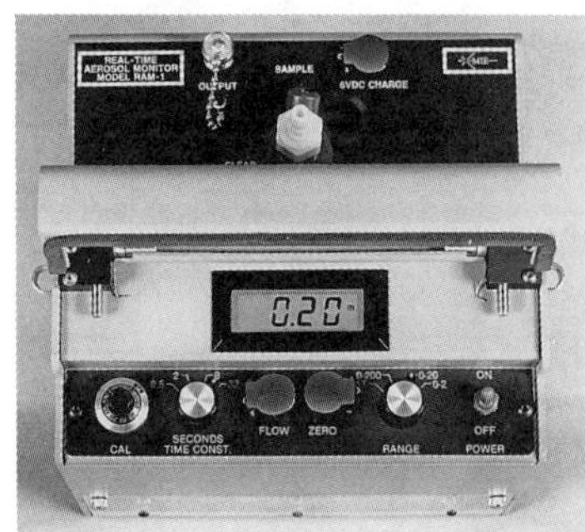

INSTRUMENT 16-1-7. MIE RAM-1 dust monitor.

The instrument has two measuring ranges, 0–1.0 mg m^{-3} and 0–10.0 mg m^{-3}, and a detectable concentration of 5 µg m^{-3}. The instrument measures 20 × 7.5 × 15 cm and weighs 1.2 kg.

Model TM-SE employs the same optical sensing geometry as TM-M (forward scattering at 70°), but is designed as a stationary instrument for insertion into a flowing dusty air stream. Its detection limit is similar to TM-M. The measuring ranges are 0–2.0 mg m^{-3} and 0–20.0 mg m^{-3}. Auxiliary sheath air flow is provided to retain dust-free optics by a pump. The sensor unit measures 68 × 23 × 17 cm, and its support measures 30 × 20 × 8 cm; these weigh 5.7 kg. The control unit measures 32 × 20 × 20 cm and weighs 6.5 kg.

Model TM-E is a fine dust stationary photometer that measures scattered light at 25–50° (more forward than the TM-SE) to indicate aerosol mass concentration over the particle diameter range of 0.2–10.0 µm. Its detection limit is 5 µg m^{-3}, and the measuring ranges include upper limits of 0.1, 0.25, 1, and 5 mg m^{-3}. The aerosol sample and sheath air are drawn through the measuring chamber by a pump (sample flow rate, 1 m^3 hr^{-1}). The instrument consists of a measuring unit (46 × 19 × 42 cm, weight 14 kg) that contains the measuring chamber and a pump assembly (46 × 32 × 42 cm, weight 30 kg). Both units are rack mountable.

16-1-7. Real-Time Aerosol Monitor

MIE, Inc.

The RAM-1 is a portable, forward-scattering (45–95°) photometer for field measurement of particulate concentration. An air sample is continuously drawn through the sensing zone at 2 L min^{-1} in which particles at concentrations ranging from 0.001–200 mg m^{-3} are detected.

The instrument is battery powered (6 V) and will run for 8 hrs. It is contained in a 20-cm-square metal box and weighs 4 kg. In addition to the digital display, an analog signal output is available for chart recording, remote readout, or process control input. With an included cyclone, the instrument can be used to detect only respirable dust. An intrinsically safe version (RAM-1-2G) is available, as well as a fixed-point version (RAM-S).

16-1-8. Miniature Real-Time Aerosol Monitor

MIE, Inc.

The MINIRAM is a portable, battery-operated dust photometer intended for personal sampling. It can be worn on the waist or lapel or be hand held. It provides an LCD output of instantaneous or average dust concentration. Data from up to seven 8-hr shifts can be stored in RAM. The instrument measures 10 × 10 × 5 cm, weighs 0.5 kg, and runs for 16 hrs on rechargeable batteries.

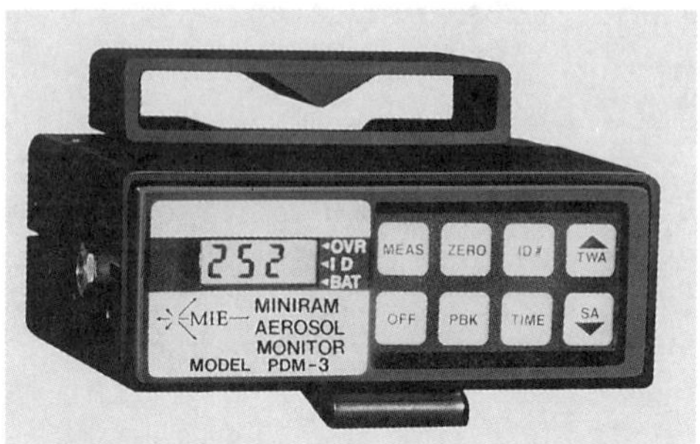

INSTRUMENT 16-1-8. MIE MINIRAM dust monitor.

16-1-9. Industrial Dust Sensor

MIE, Inc.

Model IDS-10 is a fixed-point photometric sensor available with interchangeable sensing chambers for either passive, extractive, or high pressure (up to 150 psig) in-line sampling. It operates over the ranges of 0.01–100 mg m^{-3} or 0.1–1000 mg m^{-3}. An analog output linear with aerosol concentration can be obtained either as a voltage or a current (4–20 mA). The sealed enclosure can be nitrogen purged for explosive environments. The instrument has a selectable alarm level and can be powered by 115 VAC, 60 Hz or a 10–20 VDC source. It measures 23 × 18 × 16 cm and weighs 4 kg.

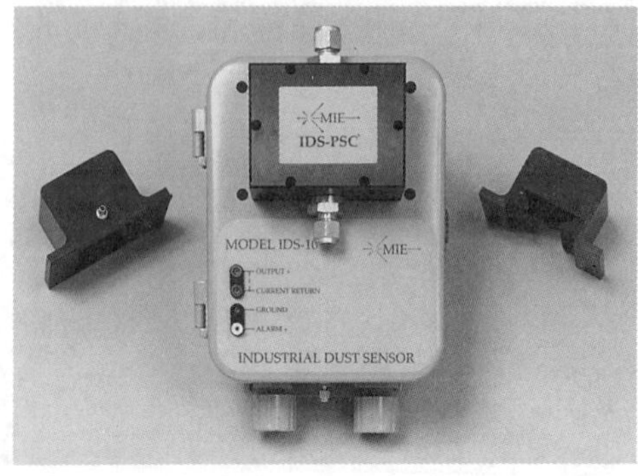

INSTRUMENT 16-1-9. MIE IDS-10 industrial dust sensor.

16-1-10. Portable Dust Monitor
Negretti Ltd.

OSIRIS is a portable instrument for measuring respirable dust by forward light scattering and subsequent collection of the sampled dust on a filter. It has a horizontal elutriator preseparator that conforms to the BMRC respirability convention. Air is sampled through the elutriator at 0.62 L min^{-1} and passes through a sensing zone illuminated by a laser source. Scattered light in the near-forward direction is detected by a photodiode. The light-scattering intensity expressed as an aerosol concentration is displayed on an LCD panel. Additionally, averages of dust levels up to a full 8-hr workshift can be computed and stored in memory for subsequent analysis.

The instrument is powered by rechargeable Ni-Cd batteries that provide up to 30 hrs of continuous operation. The instrument can be hand carried or mounted for area measurement; it measures 41 × 11 × 15 cm and weighs 7 kg.

16-1-11. Aerosol Measuring Photometer
Casella London, Ltd.
U.S. Distributor: BGI, Inc.

Model AMS-950 is a hand-held, forward-scattering aerosol photometer employing an infrared source and photodiode. It has two measuring ranges, 0.01–20 mg m^{-3} and 0.1–200 mg m^{-3} dust concentration; each instrument is factory calibrated using AC fine test dust. Particle concentration can be displayed for 1- or 10-sec averaging times and stored for up to 10 hrs on fully charged Ni-Cd rechargeable batteries. The control unit measures 10 × 20 × 4 cm, the cylindrical probe measures 3.5 cm (diameter) × 36 cm (length) and the entire instrument weighs 1 kg. No air mover is needed to move particles through the cylindrical sensing zone in the probe.

The instrument can be used with an accessory gravimetric filter dust collector and a respirable dust cyclone preseparator if desired.

INSTRUMENT 16-1-11. Casella AMS dust photometer.

INSTRUMENT 16-1-13. ESC particulate monitor.

16-1-12. Hand-Held Aerosol Monitor
ppm Enterprises, Inc.

Model 1005 Aerosol Monitor is a portable, battery-powered instrument that measures dust concentration by forward scattering of LED light in the sensing zone. The instrument has no air mover, relying on convective air flow or movement of the instrument through still air. The measurement sensitivity is stated to be 1 μg m^{-3} with three concentration ranges of 2, 20, and 200 mg m^{-3} maximum. The hand-held version operates on rechargeable batteries for 10 hrs and weighs 1 kg. An alternative Model 1060 has the sampling head separate from the control/data logger unit. A field gravimetric calibration kit is available to provide calibration for a specific aerosol composition.

16-1-13. Particulate Monitor
Environmental Systems Corp.

Model P-5A is a back-scattering stack monitor that employs an LED source to illuminate a cylindrical sensing zone, 1 cm in diameter and 12 cm long. The range of particle concentrations detectable by the instrument is $1–10^4$ mg m^{-3} (measurement sensitivity 1 mg m^{-3}). The instrument mounts onto a standard 4-in. pipe. The instrument measures 170 × 32 × 46 cm and weighs 41 kg. It operates on 115 VAC, 60 Hz, with option for 220 VAC, 50 Hz.

16-1-14. Dust Monitor
Grimm Labortechnik GmbH & Co.

Series 1.100 light-scattering, particle measuring instruments can be employed either in a photometric or single particle detecting mode. Aerosol is drawn into the instrument at 1.2 L min^{-1} by either a "total" or isokinetic sampler head, through an optional cyclone to remove nonrespirable particles and into the measuring cell. Light from a laser diode illuminates the particle(s) and scattered light from 60–120° is measured by a photodetector. The aerosol is then collected on a filter for gravimetric and/or chemical analysis. Single particle detection is used for particle concentrations up to 5 × 105 p L^{-1}. Particles are accumulated in four channels which have average diameters of 1.0, 2.0, 5.0, and 10.0 μm. The instrument is portable with batteries or can be run on 110/220 VAC; it measures 23 × 6 × 11 cm and

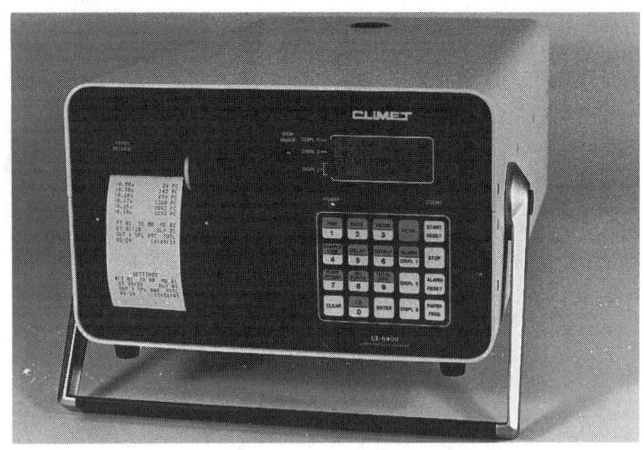

INSTRUMENT 16-2-1. Climet CI-7200 particle counter.

weighs 3 kg. Dust concentration can be displayed each 5 sec and can be stored for downloading onto a PC data storage card.

16-1-15. Laser Photometer
TSI Incorporated

Model 8587 laser photometer is intended for filter testing, respirator fit testing, and general dust monitoring. The instrument detects particles >0.1-µm diameter and measures aerosol concentrations from 0.001–1000 mg m^{-3}. A 30-mW laser diode illuminates particles in the sensing zone and a photodiode detector measures scattered light 45° off axis. Two separate sample ports allow mass concentration comparisons. Sheath air flow is provided to prevent dust degradation of the optics. The photometer has microprocessor-driven, automatic gain selection and a fast purge mode; operation and data storage can be PC linked. The instrument measures 42 × 32 × 13 cm and weighs 7 kg.

2. Light-scattering Single Particle Counters

16-2-1. Laser Diode Particle Counter
Climet Instruments Co.

Series 7000 particle counters employ an elliptical mirror to collect scattered light from a single particle illuminated by a laser diode over the angular range of 15–150°. A particle concentration up to 14 p cm^{-3} can be measured without coincidence errors for particles in the size range 0.3–10.0 µm. Model CI-7350 counts particles in six size ranges from 0.3–10.0 µm, whereas Model CI-7200 counts in six ranges from 0.5–25.0 µm in diameter. Both instruments sample air at 28.3 L min^{-1}, measure 22 × 31 × 49 cm, weigh 18.2 kg, and operate on 120/240 VAC, 50/60 Hz.

16-2-2. Portable Laser Diode Particle Counter
Climet Instruments Co.

Models CI-4102 and CI-4202 employ the same optical detection arrangement as the 7000 series, but are small, lightweight, and battery powered for portable use. They can be powered by 110/240 VAC, 50/60 Hz, as well as by a rechargeable battery for up to 4 hrs continuous use. The self-contained instruments sample air at 2.8 L min^{-1} and can store up to 200 sets of particle size information. These models measure 10 × 15 × 28 cm and weigh 5 kg.

Model CI-500 is a battery-operated instrument employing the same particle detection system and provides for six channels of size information from 0.3- to 25.0-µm particle diameter. Its air sampling rate is 28.3 L min^{-1}. It measures 20 × 20 × 35 cm and weighs 10.7 kg.

16-2-3. Laser Airborne Particle Counter
Met One, Inc.

These light-scattering particle counter/sizing instruments employ a He-Ne open cavity laser to illuminate a single particle in the sensing zone and detect the forward scattering from the particle for size discrimination. Particles are counted in up to six size ranges. Models are available with a lower size limit of detection ranging from 0.10 to 0.5 µm and sampling flows of either 28.3 or 56.6 L min^{-1}.

The instruments operate on 115 VAC, 60 Hz (220 VAC, 50 Hz optional) and require 110 watts. Model A2120 measures 34 × 20 × 57 cm and weighs 19 kg. Other instruments have similar specifications, but vary in sample rate, limit of detectable particle diameter, and number of size channels.

16-2-4. Portable Airborne Particle Counter
Met One, Inc.

Two types of particle counters are represented in this instrument description: 1) portable instruments which are smaller versions of the fixed location counters described above, and 2) hand-held miniature particle meter/counters. Both instrument types employ the same light-scattering geometry but the light source for 1) is a He-Ne laser while 2) employs a laser diode source.

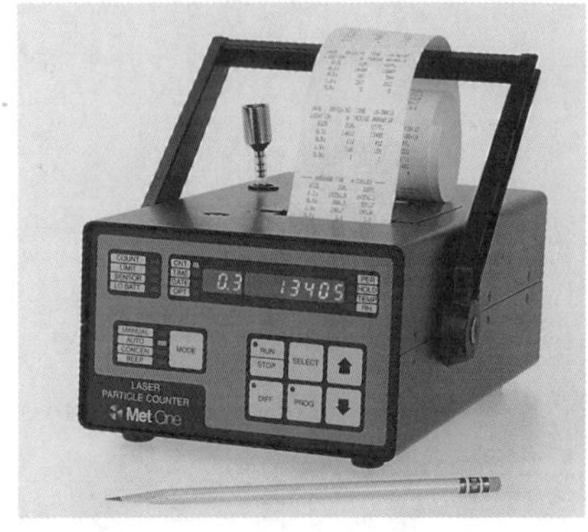

INSTRUMENT 16-2-3. Met One laser particle counter.

Models A237, typical of first type, have lower size sensitivity of 0.1–0.5 μm and count particles in two to six size ranges. They have minimal coincidence errors at particle concentration < 70 p cm^{-3}. The instruments measure 17 × 12 × 30 cm and weigh 3.1 kg. They are normally powered by rechargeable Ni-Cd batteries which provide 5 watts and operate up to 4 hrs continuously. Optional power by 115/220 VAC, 60/50 Hz is available.

Model 227 is a hand-held instrument which has two size channels, the lower limit of 0.3/0.5 μm and a factory-set particle diameter. The air sampling rate is 2.3 L min^{-1}. The instrument can store up to 200 samples and sampling times range upward from 1 sec. The instrument measures 10 × 16 × 6 cm and weighs 1 kg.

A remote particle counter module, Model R4700, consists only of a sensing zone, laser diode source, and detector, and can be connected to a counter module or PC by a 15 pin connector. The remote module measures 9.4 × 6 × 3.8 cm and weighs 0.3 kg.

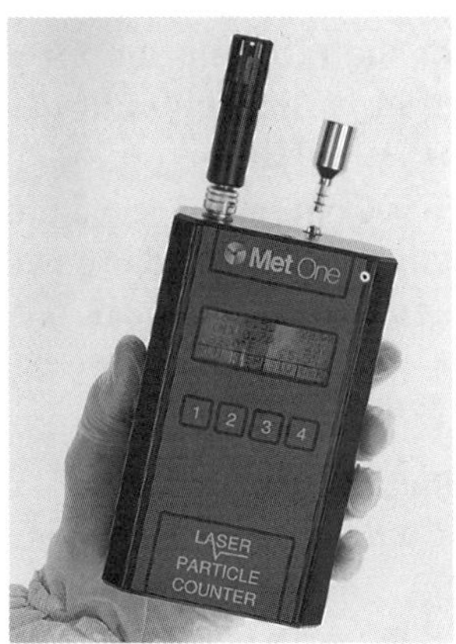

INSTRUMENT 16-2-4a. Met One hand-held particle counter.

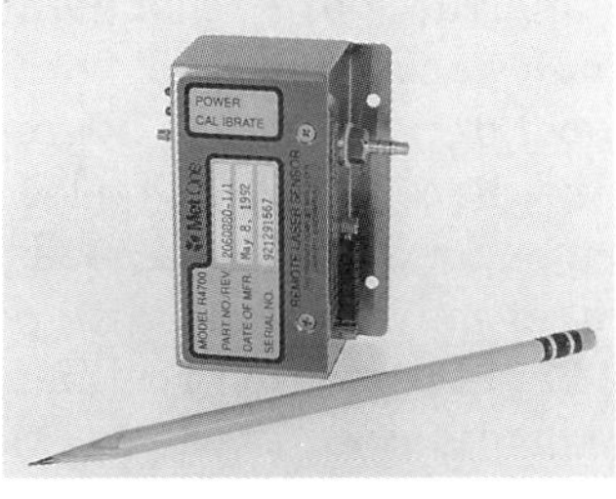

INSTRUMENT 16-2-4b. Met One remote particle counter.

16-2-5. Laser Fiber Monitor

MIE, Inc.

Model FM-7400 is a field instrument for detection and counting of airborne fibers. Air is sampled at 2 L min^{-1} into a cylindrical sensing cell illuminated by a 3-mW He-Ne laser. Particles are subjected to a rotating electric field (3400 v cm^{-1}) at 400 Hz. Fibers are detected by their variable scattering in the field by a photodetector. The concentration range of detection is 10^{-4} to 25 fibers cm^{-3}; the minimal detectable fiber diameter is 0.2 μm. Fiber length distribution is measured from 2 to 30 μm. The instrument is contained in a suitcase; it measures 50 × 35 × 20 cm and weighs 12 kg. It can operate on standard 110 VAC, 60 Hz power or by a 12-VDC battery pack. With an optional virtual impactor, the instrument can be restricted to counting respirable fibers. Analog, digital, and alarm outputs are provided.

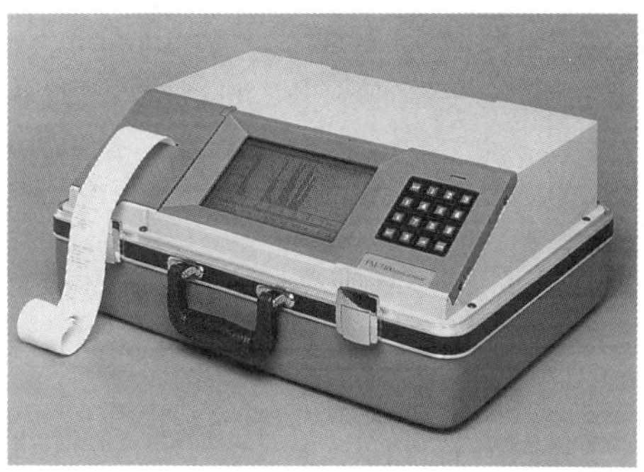

INSTRUMENT 16-2-5. MIE FM-7400 laser fiber monitor.

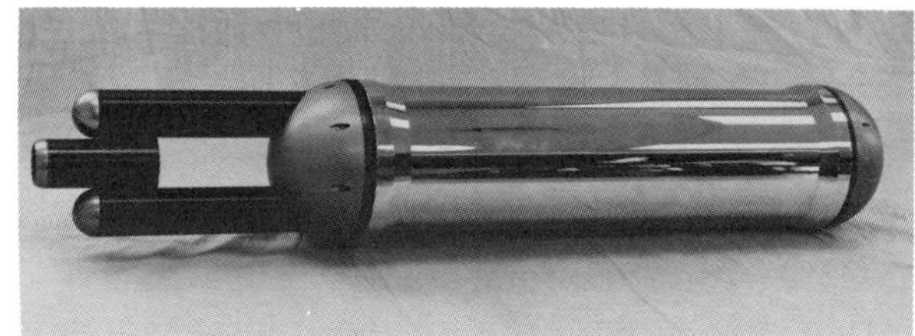

INSTRUMENT 16-2-6. PMS aircraft-mountable probe.

16-2-6. Particle Sizing Aircraft-Mountable Probes

Particle Measuring Systems, Inc.

This group of 15 aerosol measuring probes is designed to collect atmospheric particles of various diameters and shapes and measure their size characteristics one by one as they pass through a laser-illuminated sensing zone. Particles in the diameter range from 0.10–95 μm can be measured by forward light scattering, whereas particles of diameter 10–9,300 μm can be measured by optical array imaging. No single instrument in the group covers the entire size range; the sizing ranges include an instrument with a diameter range of 0.10–3.0 μm for fine particles and an instrument with a diameter range of 150–9,300 μm for precipitation particles. The former instrument has 15 size channels plus oversize; the latter has 62 size channels. Probes for measuring cloud droplets and precipitation droplets have optical arrays capable of two dimensional particle size analysis in accordance with their nonspherical shape.

All probes are contained in an 18-cm-diameter, 79-cm-long cylinder with hemispherical end caps; the particle sensing probe or sampler protrudes from the forward hemisphere into undisturbed air. The probe requires 120 watts of 115 VAC power for the electronics, with additional heating and deicing provided at 28 VDC; it weighs 20 kg.

16-2-7. Particle Sizing Ground-Based Probes

Particle Measuring Systems, Inc.

This series of 10 ground-based probes employs similar optical means for particle detection and sizing to the aircraft probes; because the probes are not moving through the particle cloud, a sample of particles must be pumped through the sensing zone where laser illumination produces forward scattering or (for optical array instruments) the particles move by natural convection through the laser illuminated beam.

Seven of the probes employ light scattering in which the particles interact either actively in the laser beam or passively with the emitted laser light. The most sensitive instrument detects particles down to a diameter of 0.045 μm and counts particles in 31 diameter channels up to 0.90 μm (plus oversize). Four of these instruments are housed in a sampling and sizing module which measures 18 × 36 × 64 cm and weighs 20 kg. They operate on 115/220 VAC, 60/50 Hz and have a carry handle for transport.

The other three light-scattering instruments are laboratory *in-situ* instruments in which particles are drawn by an aspirator fan into an external sampling horn to produce a small wind tunnel through the sensing zone. These instruments weigh 23 kg and measure 18 × 24 × 97 cm. These instruments cover similar diameter ranges as the aircraft probes and count particles in either 15 or 32 diameter channels.

Three instruments are optical array probes for larger particles, ranging from 70 to 4,300 μm in diameter and from 200 to 12,400 μm in 62 size channels. Both one- and two-dimensional particle size instruments are included in this group. These instruments are similar in size, weight, and power requirement to the laboratory *in-situ* scattering instruments.

16-2-8. Particle Size Analyzer HC

Polytec PI, GmbH

Model HC is a 90° scattering spectrometer for particle diameters from 0.5 to 40 μm. The sensing volume detects single particles for particle concentrations up to 10^5 p cm^{-3} without significant coincidence error. The instrument's optical head employs a halogen light source and a photomultiplier detector counts and sizes particle pulses into 256 channels.

The instrument consists of a control-display module and a measuring optical head. The measuring head measures 19 × 56 × 10 cm, weighs 16 kg, and operates on 110/220 VAC, 60/50 Hz. The control module incorporates a portable PC with internal data acquisition hardware and an external compact power supply.

INSTRUMENT 16-2-9. Galai CIS-1 particle analyzer.

16-2-9. Particle Size and Shape Analyzers

Galai Instruments, Inc.

Both Model CIS-1 and CIS-100 are *in-situ* particle measuring instruments which are capable of determining particle dimensionality and shape by the principle of single particle shadowing. As particles pass through a rotating 1.0-μm focused beam, a particle shadows the beam; the resulting illumination falls on a PIN photodiode that provides a signal which is analyzed for size and shape by signal processing software. A 2-mW He-Ne laser provides the illumination for particles whose size can range from 0.5 to 6000 μm at concentrations (for 1.0-μm diameter particles) up to 10^9 p cm^{-3}.

The Model CIS-100 detector optical module measures 66 × 28 × 18 cm, weighs 14 kg, and is powered by 115/230 VAC, 60/50 Hz, requiring 100 watts. The output of the unit is PC compatible where size and shape analysis is performed with provided software.

16-2-10. Aerosol Particle Analyzer

Wyatt Technology Corp.

Model DAWN-A is a multiangle instrument for particle analysis in a moving aerosol. A particle is illuminated by a laser beam within a spherical scattering chamber, 4-cm i.d. The spherical chamber contains 72 small and 2 large apertures for light-scattering detection. The large apertures are permanently fitted with optical fiber bundles at 25° and 155° with respect to the forward direction. Fourteen optical fibers with collimating optics may be placed into any selected apertures, the remaining apertures being sealed. The collimating optics on each fiber may be fitted with polarizing analyzers. Scattered light from the 14 collimated fibers and the 2 fiber bundles is conducted to PM detectors for rapid light measurement of scattering at the selected positions.

Signals from the PMs are analyzed to derive particle size and refractive index (for spherical particles) or for size and shape (for nonspherical particles). The instrument minimum data rate is 200 p sec^{-1}. Typical particles measured range in diameter from 0.2 to 4.0 μm. The detection limit is claimed to be 0.1 μm or less, depending on the laser source used.

16-2-11. Laser Air Particle Counter
Malvern Instruments, Inc.

The Model 300A AutoCounter is intended for use in cleanroom monitoring and other applications where high particle concentrations do not result in coincidence errors (<40 p cm^{-3}). A particle in the sensing zone is illuminated by a 45-mW solid state laser; the light scattered over a wide angle is collected and processed to yield a particle count which is placed in one of eight size channels. Two particle diameter ranges, 0.3–10.0 μm and 0.5–25.0 μm, are available as options. Air is sampled at 28.3 L min^{-1}. Software for size analysis provides an interface between the instrument and a PC or other data logger. The instrument measures 42 × 56 × 19 cm, weighs 15 kg, and is powered by 115/230 VAC, 60/50 Hz.

16-2-12. Laser Diffraction Particle Analyzer
Malvern Instruments, Inc.

Mastersizer X is a series of instruments in which a He-Ne laser beam is expanded to illuminate a field several mm in diameter containing a number of particles. Scattered light from these particles is collected by a circular array of sensors which are scanned to obtain angular intensity information used to derive size distribution information.

16-2-13. Particle Counter Sizer Velocimeter
Insitec Measurement Systems

Model PCSV is a group of single particle, forward-scattering instruments designed for a variety of applications including aerosol process streams. A 5-mW He-Ne laser beam is split and focused to form a non-uniformly illuminated sensing zone. Particle sizing is by near-forward scattering, whereas particle velocity is indicated by the width of the particle scattering intensity as it passes through the sensing zone. A deconvolution process is required to obtain these two particle properties. Particle diameters in the size range 0.2–200 μm are measurable at concentrations <10^7 p cm^{-3} (for submicronic particles). Particle velocities from 0.1 to 400 m sec^{-1} are measurable. The instrument comes in several forms, each of which includes a sensing module, a signal processing module, a PM tube power supply, and motor and flow controls.

INSTRUMENT 16-2-11. Malvern 300A air particle counter.

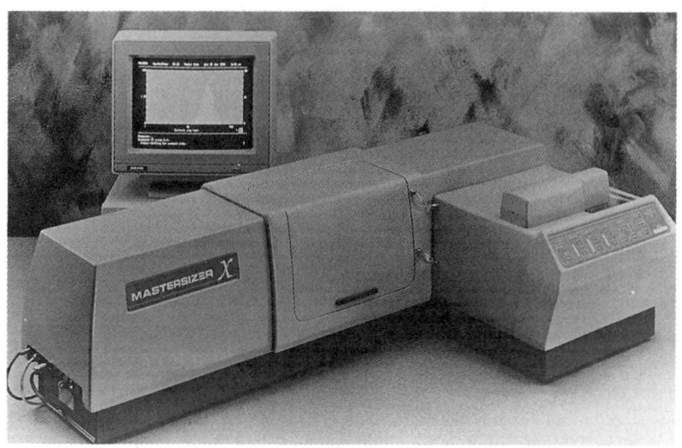

INSTRUMENT 16-2-12. Malvern Mastersizer X particle analyzer.

3. Light-attenuating Photometers

16-3-1. Opacity Monitor
Bailey Controls

Type UC opacity monitor is a single pass, stack particulate monitor in which the transmitter and receiver units are mounted in opposition on the duct/stack walls but are maintained in independent alignment by a standard 2 1/2-in. metal pipe which extends across the duct and supports the two units. The optics are maintained dust free by an air pump which provides clean air for both transmitter and receiver units.

Opacity measurements employ solid-state electronics that provide for electronic chopping and autocalibration.

16-3-2. Visible Emission Monitor
Datatest

Model 1000 monitor comes in two versions, a single pass transmissometer, 1000 MPS, and a double pass instrument, 1000 MPD. Both instruments employ a tungsten/halogen light source. The light is collimated to pass through 5-cm apertures in the stack containing the particulates. A stack path length <57 m is acceptable for the instrument optics. The double pass version is supplied with a retroreflector and a beam splitter to measure the light attenuation. Air purge is supplied to minimize optical dust degradation. A single silicon cell detector measures both the illuminating beam intensity and that of the attenuated light with the aid of a mechanical chopper.

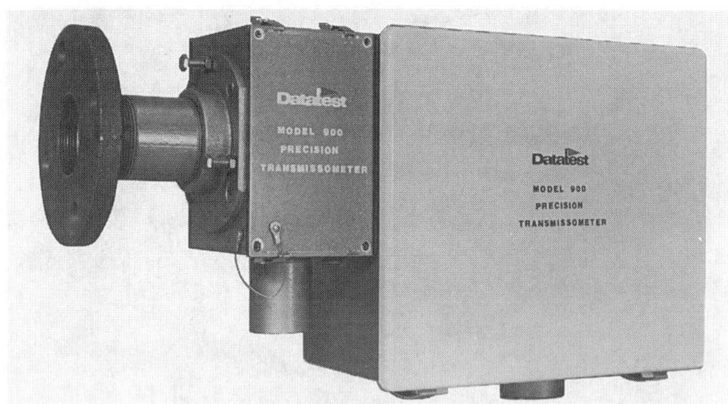

INSTRUMENT 16-3-2. Datatest visible emission monitor.

The single pass model splits the source light into two beams, one of which passes through the stack, while the other is transmitted via a fiber optic cable to the receiver, the silicon cell detector. The instrument employs a microprocessor control unit that runs periodic checks of system parameters and controls printer function and averaging time.

The transmitter/receiver units measure 50 × 20 × 15 cm and weigh 10.5 kg. The retroreflector measures 30 × 20 × 15 cm and weighs 7 kg. The control unit and lamp power supply weigh 5.9 and 11.4 kg respectively. The system is powered by 115 VAC, 60 Hz supply.

16-3-3. Opacity Monitor

Lear Siegler Measurement Controls Corp.

Model LS541 is a double pass stack transmissometer in which a collimated light beam passes through a beam splitter to form a measurement and reference beam. The measurement beam can pass through a stack of up to 22 m to a retroreflector for return to the receiver detector in the main module. Light chopping provides for simultaneous measurement of the reference and attenuated beam intensity from which the opacity is determined.

The instrument consists of a transmitter/receiver unit, a reflector, a control unit, and air purge blowers integral to the two operating units. The transmitter/receiver is housed in a weather cover which measures 76 × 57 × 58 cm and weighs 45 kg. The control unit measures 17 × 48 × 25 cm; reflector units vary in size depending on the separation distance through the stack. The system can be operated on 115/230 VAC, 50/60 Hz.

16-3-4. Transmissometer/Opacity Monitor

Rosemont Analytical Inc.

Model OPM2000 is a double pass stack transmissometer consisting of a transceiver, reflector, and control unit. It provides for both instantaneous and averaged stack opacity measurements and, in common with most stack transmissometers, provides an internal heater to allow operation down to –40°C. Electronic chopping of the beam source is provided to separate the incident from the reflected beam intensity, from which opacity is determined. The control unit records and controls the operation of the instrument through simple keyboard menu choices.

16-3-5. Opacity Monitor

United Sciences Inc.

Model 500C is a double pass transmissometer employing an LED source which is electronically modulated. Beam splitting is used to control fluctuations in the source and transmitted light intensity and a value of the opacity, zero and span is provided each second. The transceiver and reflector units are of similar size and weight to other transmissometers, and a signal processing card is located in the tranceiver. A remote microprocessor records data and controls instrument function. The instrument may be configured to serve as 1) a U.S. EPA compliance opacity monitor, 2) a noncompliance stack opacity monitor, 3) a backscatter dust analyzer, or 4) a long path extinction correlation device for monitoring dust levels in the work place.

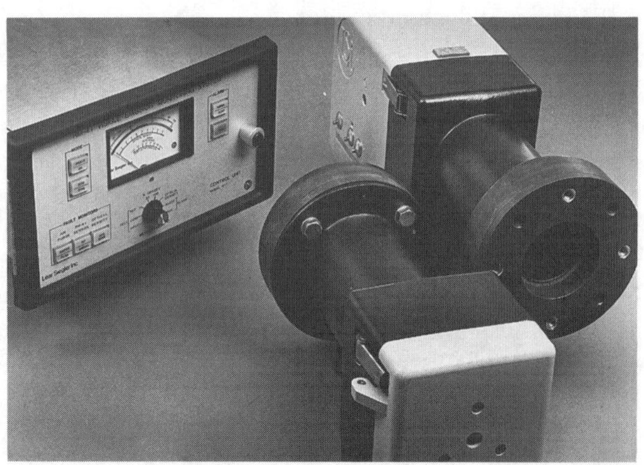

INSTRUMENT 16-3-3. Lear Siegler LS541 opacity monitor.

INSTRUMENT 16-3-5. United Sciences opacity monitor.

4. Condensation Nucleus Counters

16-4-1. Condensation Nucleus Counter
Met One

Models CNC 1100 and 1104 are continuous flow instruments in which ultrafine particles are grown in size by n-butyl alcohol vapor condensation and counted by a laser-based, light-scattering detector. Model 1100 has a sampling flow rate of 1.4 L min^{-1} and comes in two versions: (1) 50% counting efficiency (CE) at 5-nm diameter and (2) 50% CE at 10-nm diameter. The upper particle diameter limit is 1.0 μm. The instruments employ a laser diode light source and coincidence error is < 5% for concentrations < 200 p cm^{-3}. The instrument consists of a saturating chamber, condenser, and particle counter plus associated cooler, flow sensor, and pump; these are contained in a single module that measures 24 × 18 × 39 cm and weighs 8 kg.

Model 1104 draws air through the instrument at 2.8 L min^{-1}. It has four versions, two having identical CE cutoff as the Model 1100 and two additional having 50% CE at 14 and 20 nm, respectively. With a full charge of alcohol, the Model 1100 will run continuously for 7 days; the Model 1104 will run for 4 days. An optional automatic fluid refill will extend these times to 3 months. The minimum sample averaging time is 10 sec for both models. Data storage for 100 records is provided, as is an RS-232C output connection.

The instrument measures 24 × 18 × 39 cm, weighs 8 kg, and requires 150 watts at 115 VAC, 50/60 Hz, with optional 230 VAC.

16-4-2. Condensation Particle Counter
TSI Incorporated

This group of three CPCs, designed for research applications, are all continuous flow instruments employing n-butyl alcohol as the condensing vapor. The saturation section of the instrument (at 35°C) is followed by a 10°C condensation tube (by cooling) and a particle counting zone utilizing light scattering. All particles, regardless of their initial size, grow to a diameter of 10–12 μm.

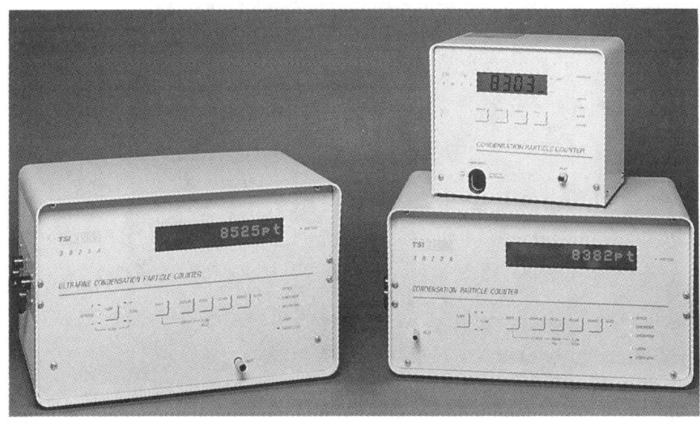

INSTRUMENT 16-4-2. TSI condensation particle counters.

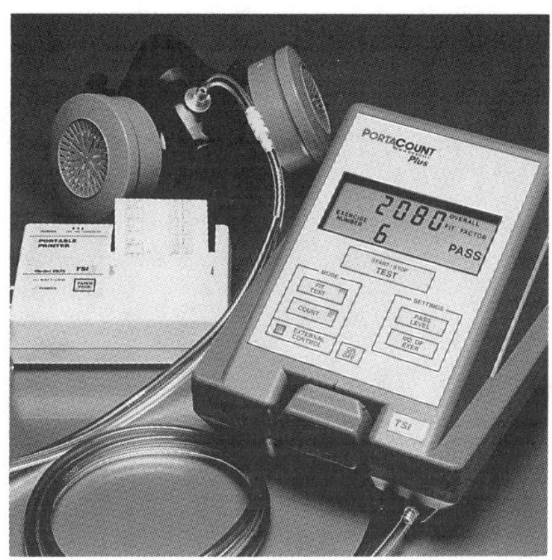

INSTRUMENT 16-4-3. TSI PortaCount respirator fit tester.

Model 3022A detects particles in the diameter range 7 nm–3 μm over the particle concentration range 0–9.99 × 10^6 p cm^{-3}. Below 10^4 p cm^{-3}, the counter operates in a single particle counting mode, while at higher concentrations, the counter operates in a photometer mode. The instrument is contained in a single module measuring 24 × 38 × 20 cm and weighing 12.5 kg.

Model 3025A detects and counts particles down to a diameter of 3 nm with an upper concentration limit of 105 p cm^{-3}. It operates in a single particle counting mode only. The aerosol flow path is maintained near the centerline of the condenser. This model operates at a flow rate of 30 cm^3 min^{-1}, measures 24 × 38 × 25 cm, and weighs 12.5 kg.

Model 3010 has a lower diameter limit of 10 nm and an upper particle concentration limit of 10^4 p cm^{-3}. Its sampling flow rate is 1.0 L min^{-1}; dimensions of the instrument are 19 × 22 × 19 cm and it weighs 5.5 kg. The above instruments all operate on 115/230 VAC, 50/60 Hz.

16-4-3. PortaCount Plus Respirator Fit Tester
TSI Incorporated

Model 8020 is a portable, battery-powered CNC designed for respirator fit testing, using ambient aerosol as the "challenge." The instrument has a dual sampling host system with internal switching valve for alternate in-mask and ambient concentration sampling. For fit testing, a probed mask or respirator sampling adapter is required. Model 8020 employs the same condensation-counting principle as the above instruments (16.4.2), except that isopropanol is used as the condensing vapor. The operating concentration range is 10^{-1}–10^5 p cm^{-3}. The instrument measures 24 × 19 × 14 cm and weighs 1.5 kg. It can operate either on batteries or an AC adapter.

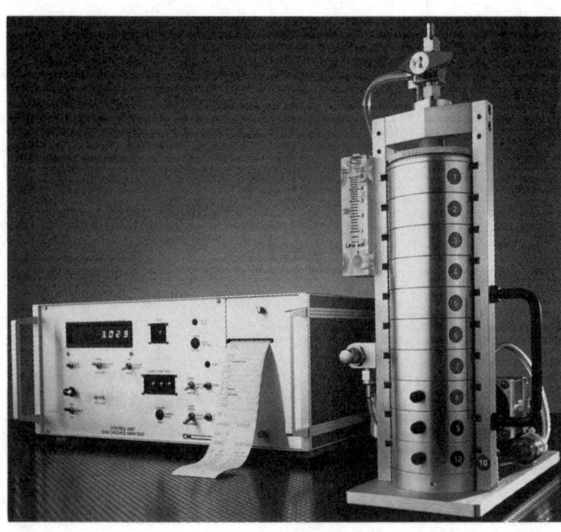

INSTRUMENT 16-5-1. Cal. Measurements PC-2 air particle analyzer.

5. Resonant Oscillation Aerosol Mass Instruments

16-5-1. Air Particle Analyzer

California Measurements, Inc.

Model PC-2 is a 10-stage cascade impactor in which each stage impaction plate contains a piezoelectric quartz crystal microbalance (QCM). Each QCM acts as a mass sensor; as particulate mass is added, the resonant frequency changes in a predictable manner, making the instrument a real-time indicator of aerodynamic mass distribution. The stages of the impactor have 50% aerodynamic diameter cutoffs in a geometric progression ranging from 25 to 0.05 μm. The stated mass concentration range of the instrument is from 5 to 50,000 μg m^{-3}. Correction for ambient conditions is provided by mounting a reference crystal beneath each sensing crystal where no particle can reach the crystal surface. The sensing crystals may be remove after an experimental measurement and mounted directly in an SEM or other type of particle characterizing instrument for particle shape and chemistry analyses.

The instrument flow rate is 240 cm^3 min^{-1}. Sampling times range from 1 to 2 sec (for high concentration) to 15 min for the minimum concentration. The instrument output is in the form of a tape containing the mass collected for each stage during the sampling period. The instrument consists of an impactor stack and a control unit. The stack measures 41 × 29 × 11.5 cm and weighs 5 kg, whereas the control unit measures 43 × 30.5 × 19 cm and weighs 10 kg. The instrument requires 50 watts and operates on 120 VAC, 50/60 Hz (240 VAC, 50 Hz version available).

16-5-2. Ambient Particle Monitor

Rupprecht & Patashnick Co., Inc.

TEOM Series 1400A monitor employs the method of *T*apered *E*lement *O*scillating *M*icrobalance to determine the aerosol mass collected on the head of a sensing tapered element which is part of a resonant oscillating system. The resonant frequency of a TEOM is in the range of 100–1000 Hz, rather than MHz levels used for QCMs. The instrument can be fitted with a particle preselector conforming to the PM_{10}, $PM_{2.5}$, or TSP (total suspended particulate) definition of airborne particulate mass. The main flow of the instrument can be selected from 0.5 to 5.0 L min^{-1}; however, auxiliary flow rate for PM_{10} and TSP ranges from 2.0 to 20.0 L min^{-1}. The range of measurable mass concentrations is stated to be from 5 μg m^{-3} to several g m^{-3}. The mass concentration resolution at a sampling rate of 3 L min^{-1} for 10 min averaging is ± 5 μg m^{-3}. For applications where particle chemistry is desired, the flow through the preselector is split, with a known fraction of the particulate sample passing to a parallel series of collecting filters for subsequent analysis (denoted the ACCU system).

The basic instrument consists of two modules: (1) the sensor module with a heated cylindrical air inlet unit and (2) the control unit. The sensor unit base measures 38 × 21 × 33 cm from which the air inlet (13 cm diameter and 70 cm length) extends; the entire module weighs 14 kg. The control unit measures 44 × 33 × 22 cm (rack mountable) and weighs 12 kg. The ACCU system is contained in an enclosure measuring 76 × 61 × 21 cm which weighs 41 kg. For outdoor ambient monitoring, the sensor and control module are contained in a single weatherproof enclosure which provides temperature control. The system requires 2400 watts and is run on either 120 or 240 VAC, 50/60 Hz.

16-5-3. Aerosol Mass Monitor

TSI Incorporated

Model 8510 Piezobalance Aerosol Mass Monitor measures aerosol mass by the frequency change of an oscillating quartz crystal upon which aerosols are deposited by electrostatic precipitation. Particles entering the instrument pass through an inertial stage that removes the nonrespirable fraction. The air sampling

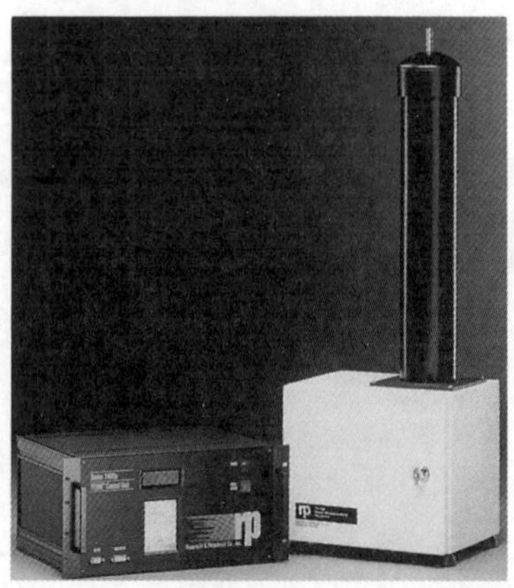

INSTRUMENT 16-5-2. Rupprecht & Patashnick 1400A particle monitor.

rate is 1.0 L min^{-1}. Particle mass concentration of 10 μg m^{-3} can be made with ±10% accuracy with a 2-min sampling time. The instrument is a portable, hand-held, battery-powered unit designed for survey purposes. It measures 31 × 13 × 17 cm and weighs 4.5 kg.

6. Laser Doppler Particle Analyzers

16-6-1. Phase Doppler Particle Analyzer

Aerometrics, Inc.

The phase doppler particle analyzer (PDPA) consists of a laser-based optical transmitter, an optical receiver, an electronic signal processor, and a PC system with software for data acquisition, analysis, and display. The principle used is that of light-scattering interferometry; a single particle passing through the fringes of the sensing zone yields velocity information while the phase relationship between different detectors yields particle size information. Model PDPA-100 uses a He-Ne laser and measures a single velocity component. Model PDPA-200 uses an argon-ion laser to simultaneously measure two velocity components.

The maximum particle concentration is stated to be 10^6 p cm^{-3} for submicronic particles. Particles of diameter 0.5–10,000 μm are measurable, with particle distributions up to 50 size classes. Particle velocity up to 200 m sec^{-1} is measurable and is also distributed into 50 velocity classes. The maximum data rate is 120,000 samples sec^{-1}. Because the instrument is an *in-situ* device, no sample pumping is required; the particles move through the sensing zone by their own convective velocity.

The optical transmitter measures 62 × 22 × 22 cm and weighs 14 kg. The signal processor measures 43 × 32 × 10 cm and weighs 2.3 kg. The system operates on 115 VAC, 60 Hz.

16-6-2. Particle Dynamics Analyzer

Dantec Measuring Technology, Inc.

The PDA system is a laser-based, phase doppler instrument for the simultaneous measurement of particle diameter and velocity by the processes described above. For single velocity component measurement, a 15-mW He-Ne laser is the beam source, whereas for two component velocity measurement, a 2-W argon-ion laser is employed. The instrument contains a built-in laser diode for electronic calibration of the receiver optics; for dynamic calibration, monodisperse aerosols of known diameter are used. The particle diameter range of the instrument is 0.5–10,000 μm. Velocities up to 500 m sec^{-1} are measurable with 1% accuracy.

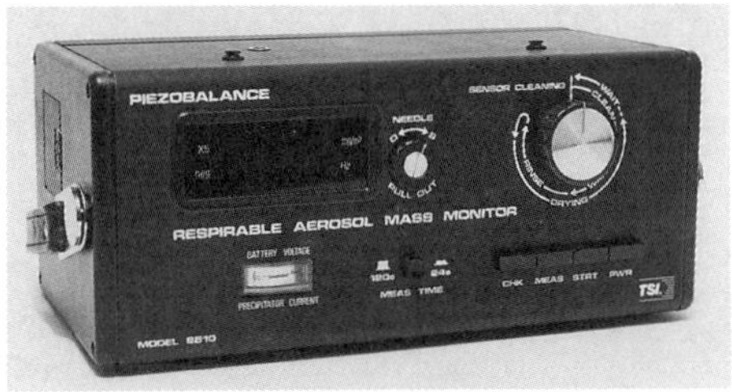

INSTRUMENT 16-5-3. TSI 8510 piezobalance aerosol mass monitor.

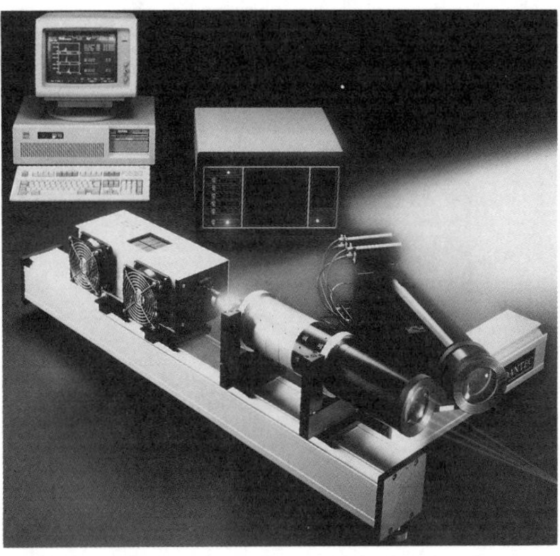
INSTRUMENT 16-6-2. Dantec PDA particle dynamics analyzer.

16-6-3. Airborne Particle Sensor

Titan Spectron

This instrument measures the diameter, velocity, and concentration of particles *in situ* as they pass through a sensing zone illuminated by solid-state laser diodes. These diodes produce light at 800 nm. Avalanche photodetectors are the optical sensors; their cylindrical housing measures 10 cm in diameter and 30 cm long. The stated range of measurable particle diameters is 0.3–10 μm.

16-6-4. Adaptive Phase/Doppler Velocimeter

TSI Incorporated

Model APV provides *in-situ* simultaneous measurement of particle diameter and velocity. These two measurements provide an estimate of local particle concentration and volume flux of the particulate medium.

Illumination of the sensing zone is achieved by a laser beam through a fiberoptic probe. Optical sensors are aligned on the sensing zone to permit the measurement of particle characteristics; the signals from these sensors are processed digitally and analyzed by a software package which displays particle diameter, velocity, and other flow parameters in real time. Geometric and Mie-scattering techniques are employed in a simulation package, SIMAP, which is included with the instrument system. Spherical particles of diameters from 0.5 to 1,000 μm are measured accurately. Particle ve-

INSTRUMENT 16-7-1. Amherst Aerosizer Mach 2.

locities up to 200 m sec^{-1} are likewise accurately measured.

7. *Particle Relaxation Size Analyzers*

16-7-1. Aerosizer

Amherst Process Instruments, Inc.

Model MACH 2 is a time-of-flight instrument for measuring the aerodynamic diameter of single particles as they pass through two laser beams. The illuminating laser beams are split from a 5-mW He-Ne laser and are spaced 1 mm apart downstream from an expansion orifice through which the aerosol is accelerated to supersonic velocity. The time a particle takes to adjust to this rapid gas velocity change is dependent on its aerodynamic diameter.

The aerosol sampling flow rate of the instrument is 2 L min^{-1} with a sheath air flow rate of 5.3 L min^{-1}. The data acquisition rate of the instrument is stated to be 10^5 Hz. Particle with diameters from 0.2 to 700 μm are measurable accurately.

The instrument consists of a sensor unit, vacuum pump, and PC for the acquisition, digital processing, and display of the particle size data. The sensor unit measures 46 × 25 × 20 cm and weighs 10 kg. It operates on 115 VAC, 60 Hz.

16-7-2. Aerodynamic Particle Sizer Spectrometer

TSI Incorporated

Model APS measures the aerodynamic diameter of particles as they pass through a pair of laser beams in the vicinity of a high velocity jet. Each particle produces a pair of pulses from which particle velocity in the defined jet flow determines the aerodynamic diameter. A high resolution size distribution over the diameter range of 0.5–30 μm is obtained after sampling a suitable number of particles. The aerosol flow rate through the jet is controlled at 1.0 L min^{-1}, whereas the total flow rate (augmented by the sheath flow) is 5.0 L min^{-1}.

The entire instrument, including sampling inlet, jet nozzle, laser, controlling electronics, and pumps, is enclosed in a single module measuring 46 × 44 × 23 cm and weighing 22.7 kg. The signal processing, storage, and display of size distributions is performed in an accompanying PC. The instrument requires 200 watts and is powered by 115/220 VAC, 50/60 Hz.

8. *Electric Mobility Aerosol Analyzers*

16-8-1. Electrical Mobility Spectrometer

Hauke GmbH & Co. KG.

EMS VIE-08 is a differential mobility size analyzer that provides particle size measurements over the diameter range of 1 nm to 1 μm in two versions: (1) Model DMA 3/150, which in one instrument covers two size ranges, 1–40 nm and 3–150 nm, and (2) Model DMA 10/1000, whose larger size range covers 3–1000 nm. Both models have variably adjustable aerosol flow rates from 1 to 15 L min^{-1} and sheath air flow rates from 10 to 50 L min^{-1}. Particles larger than the stated size range can be removed with preimpactors, either single or multiple stage.

The instrument can measure a size distribution with 44 channels of data in approximately 1 min. Particle number concentration at a particular size interval is measured by the differential charge collected by a downstream electrometer, FCE-08, whose lower limit of charge detection, 10^{-16} A, corresponds to a number concentration of approximately 10 p cm^{-3}. The upper limit of particle concentration is stated to be 3.5×10^4 p cm^{-3}. For an alternative electrometer, FCE-08/E, the particle concentration range is $100–3.5 \times 10^6$ p cm^{-3}. The operating software for the instrument uses Microsoft® Windows™ graphical user interface.

16-8-2. Electrical Aerosol Analyzer

TSI Incorporated

Model EAA30 employs the principle of electric mobility of charged submicrometer particles to obtain size distributions for particle diameters ranging from 0.01 to 1.0 μm. The aerosol number counts, obtained from the charge collected by an electrometer, are classified

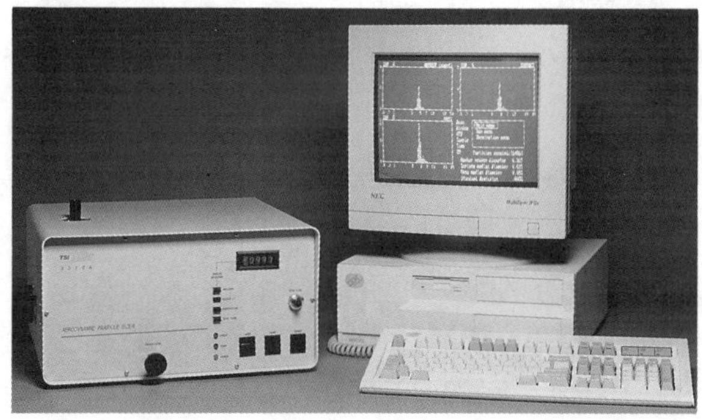

INSTRUMENT 16-7-2. TSI APS aerodynamic particle sizer.

into one of eight channels. A complete size distribution over this range is normally obtained in 2 min or less. Prior to classification, the particles pass through a unipolar charging section where they obtain a charge giving them a unique mobility.

Aerosols flow through the measuring system at 4 L min^{-1}. The instrument consists of a flow module and a control module; the flow module measures 36 × 20 × 63 cm and weighs 20 kg, whereas the control module measures 25 × 20 × 9 cm and weighs 4 kg. The instrument requires 30 watts and is powered by 115/230 VAC, 50/60 Hz.

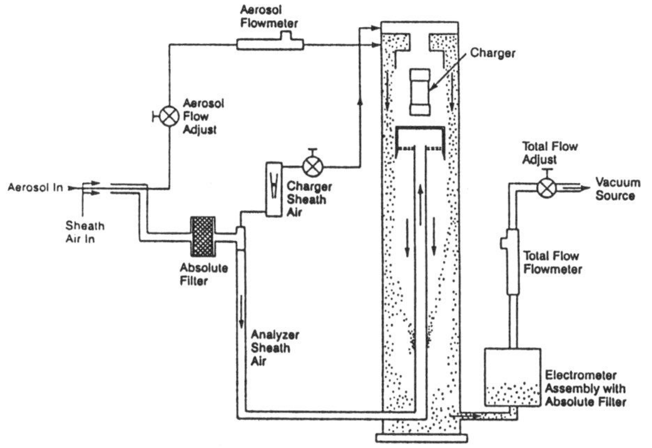

INSTRUMENT 16-8-2. TSI electrical aerosol analyzer schematic.

16-8-3. Scanning Mobility Particle Sizer

TSI Incorporated

Model 3934 SMPS provides high-resolution size distributions for particles in the diameter range from 5 nm to 1.0 μm. An aerosol sample is first drawn through an inertial impactor to remove large particles outside the measuring range. The aerosol then passes through an electrostatic classifier (Model 3071A), which consists of a bipolar charging section and a classifying section. The particles are separated by electrical mobility in the classifier, and a narrow range of particle diameter (by mobility) is selected and passes through an open slit for counting.

The particles that penetrate the classifier enter a CPC where particle concentration at a given size is measured. By automatically changing the electrical field in the classifier, the instrument counts particles in 1 of 147 different channels to construct a size distribution. Three different configurations, each with a different CPC (see above), can be used to obtain size information in a particular diameter range. The instrument is powered at 100/115/220/240 VAC, 50/60 Hz.

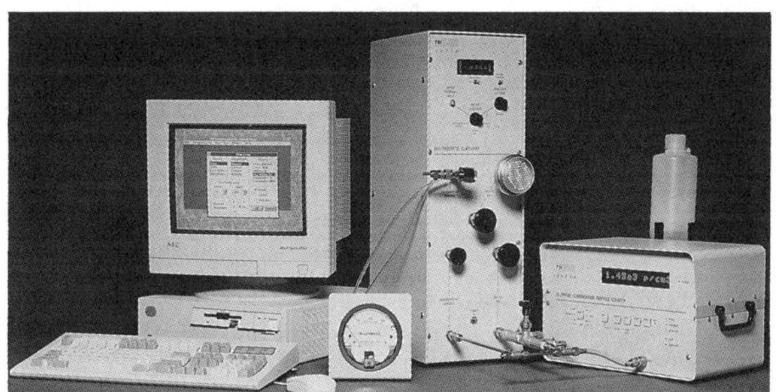

INSTRUMENT 16-8-3. TSI 3943 scanning mobility particle sizer.

9. Beta Gauge Particle Sampler

16-9-1. Beta Gauge Automated Particle Sampler

Wedding & Associates, Inc.

This instrument is similar to ambient outdoor particulate samplers that use a PM_{10} or TSP inlet configuration (see Chapter 5), except that the particulate collected on the filter is continuously measured by the attenuation of beta radiation. Thus, the temporal accumulation of particulate mass can be recorded to detect spikes and other time trends of concentration. Although the ^{14}C source of beta radiation (<100 μCi) is located beneath the filter collector, the measuring counter is mounted above the filter, requiring the radiation to pass through the particulate matter where it is attenuated. The attenuation of beta radiation at this energy level is relatively independent of the atomic composition of the particles, and is thus an appropriate measure of total particulate mass that reaches the filter.

The sample flow rate of the instrument is 18.9 L min^{-1} and the range of detectable mass concentration is from 2 to 50,000 μg m^{-3}. The collector and control module are housed in a weatherproof cabinet for most applications; the cabinet measures 44 × 51 × 31 cm and weighs 16 kg.

TABLE 16-I-1. Commercial Sources

Aerometrics
550 Del Ray Avenue
Sunnyvale, CA 94086
(408)738-6688
FAX (408)738-6871

Air Techniques
11403 Cronridge Drive
Owings Mills, MD 21117
(410)363-9696
FAX (410)363-9695

Amherst Proces Instruments
Mountain Farms Tech. Park
Hadley, MA 01035
(413)586-2744
FAX (413)585-0536

Bailey Controls
29801 Euclid Ave.
Wycliffe, OH 44092
(216)585-8500
FAX (216)585-8756

Belfort Instrument Co.
727 S. Wolfe St.
Baltimore, MD 21231
(410)342-2626
FAX (410)342-7028

BGI Incorporated
58 Guinan St.
Waltham, MA 02154
(617)891-9380
FAX (617)891-8151

California Measurements
150 E. Montecito Ave.
Sierra Madre, CA 91024-1934
(818)355-3361
FAX (818)355-5320

Climet Instruments Co.
1320 W. Colton Ave.
Redlands, CA 92374
(909)793-2788
FAX (909)793-1738

Dantec Measure. Tech. Inc.
777 Corporate Drive
Mahway, NJ 07430
(201)512-0037
FAX (201)512-0120

Datatest
6850 Hibbs Lane
Levittown, PA
(215)943-0668
FAX (215-547-7973

Environmental Systems Corp
200 Tech Center Dr.
Knoxville, TN 37912
(615)688-7900
FAX (615)687-8977

Galai Instruments, Inc.
577 Main St.
Islip, NY 11751
(516)581-8500
FAX (516)581-8573

Greenfield Instruments
P.O. Box 971
Amherst, MA 01004
(413)548-9648
FAX (413)772-6729

Grimm Lobortechnik GmbH
Dorfstrasse 9
D-83404 Ainring, Germany
49-86-545780
FAX 49-86-5457810

Hauke GmbH & Co. KG
Cumberlandstrasse 46-50
A-4810 Gmunden, Austria
43-7612-4133
FAX 43-7612-413385

Hund GmbH
Postfach 63
D-6330 Wetzlar 21, Germany
49-6441-20040
FAX 49-6441-200444

Insitec Measurement Syst.
2110 Omega Rd., Suite D
San Ramon, CA 94583
(510)837-1330
FAX (510)837-3864

Lear Siegler Corp.
74 Inverness Dr. East
Englewood, CO 80112
(303)792-3300
FAX (303)799-4853

Malvern Instruments Inc.
10 Southville Rd.
Southborough, MA 01772
(508)480-0200
FAX (508)460-9692

Met One, Inc.
481 California Ave.
Grants Pass, OR 97526
(503)479-1248
FAX (503)479-3057

MIE, Inc.
1 Federal St. #2
Billerica, MA 01821
(508)663-7900
FAX (508)663-4890

Particle Measuring Systems, Inc.
5475 Airport Blvd.
Boulder, CO 80301-2339
(303)443-7100
FAX (303)449-6870

Polytec PI,GmbH
Polytec Platz 5-7
P.O. Box 1140
W-7517 Waldbronn, Germany
FAX 49-72-436994

ppm Enterprises, Inc.
11428 Kingston Pike
Knoxville, TN 37922
(615)966-8796
FAX (615)675-4795

Rosemount Analytical Inc.
1201 N. Main St.
Orrville, OH 44667
(216)682-9010 or (800)628-1200
FAX (216)682-4447

Rupprecht & Patashnick Co.
25 Corporate Circle
Albany, NY 12203
(518)452-0065
FAX (518)452-0067

Titan-Spectron
1582 Parkway Loop, Suite B
Tustin, CA 92680
(714)566-9060
FAX (714)566-9055

United Sciences Inc.
5310 N. Pioneer Rd.
Gibsonia, PA 15044
(412)443-8610
FAX (412)443-1025

The Virtis Company, Inc.
815 Route 208
Gardiner, NY 12525
(914)255-5000
FAX (914)255-5338

Wedding & Associates, Inc.
209 Christman Drive, #2
Fort Collins, CO 80524
(303)221-0678
FAX (303)221-0400

Chapter 17

Gas and Vapor Sample Collectors

Richard H. Brown, Ph.D.[A] and Lee E. Monteith[B]

[A]*Health and Safety Laboratory, Health and Safety Executive, Sheffield, England;* [B]*Department of Environmental Health, University of Washington, Seattle, Washington*

CONTENTS

List of Symbols

A = cross-sectional area of diffusion path (cm^2)
C = mass concentration of analyte in air (mg/m^3)
C_{corr} = C, corrected to standard temperature and pressure
C' = the volume fraction of the analyte in air in ppm (v/v)
C_e = external concentration being sampled (g/cm^3)
C_o = concentration at the interface of the sorbent (g/cm^3)
$\mathcal{D}$ = coefficient of diffusion (cm^2/sec)
DE = desorption efficiency corresponding to m_1
E = percent error in sample collection efficiency
E_s = sampling efficiency
J = diffusive flux (g/cm^2-sec)

L = length of diffusion path (cm)
MW = molecular mass of the analyte of interest (g/mol)
N = number of bottle volumes swept out
P = actual pressure of air sampled (kPa)
Q = mass uptake (g)
T = absolute temperature of air sampled (°K)
U = sampling rate (ng/ppm-min)
V = volume of air sample (L)
m = mass of analyte in sample (μg)
m_1 = mass of analyte on first tube section (μg)
m_2 = mass of analyte on backup tube section (if used) (μg)
m_{blank} = mass of analyte in blank (μg)
t = sampling time (seconds)
t' = sampling time (min)

Introduction

This chapter discusses the collection and analysis of gases and vapors commonly found in the industrial or workplace environment. It is limited to descriptions of sampling methods for subsequent laboratory analysis. It does not, therefore, include any discussions of direct-reading instruments, colorimetric indicators, tape samplers, or other "on-the-spot" testing devices.

Nature of Industrial Gases and Vapors

The terms "gases" and "vapors" are frequently used interchangeably; however, they are not identical. The majority of gases of interest to the industrial hygienist are elements (e.g., chlorine) or inorganic compounds (e.g., hydrogen cyanide, ammonia, arsine, and carbon monoxide). Vapors of industrial importance are mainly organic substances such as methyl ethyl ketone, benzene, acetone, toluene, and toluene diisocyanate, although some inorganic substances (e.g., mercury) are also encountered.

While it is true that, at ordinary temperature and pressure, gases and vapors will both diffuse rapidly and form true solutions in air, they differ in other respects. Gases are generally understood to be noncondensible at room temperature, whereas vapors are derived from volatile liquids. Therefore, under ordinary conditions, gases remain in the gaseous state even when present at high concentrations. Vapors, on the other hand, may condense at high concentrations and coexist in both gas and aerosol forms. However, unless an aerosol is deliberately produced (as in a spray operation), atmospheric concentrations of vapor pollutants rarely reach saturation conditions; gases and vapors can then be considered similar and the same devices used to collect them.

In this discussion, the word "gas" (or "gaseous") will refer to both gas and vapor, unless it is explicitly stated to mean only gas.

Sampling Procedures

There are two basic methods for collecting gaseous samples. In one, called grab sampling, an actual sample of air is taken in a flask, bottle, bag, or other suitable container; in the other, called continuous or integrated sampling, gases or vapors are removed from the air and concentrated by passage through an absorbing or adsorbing medium.

The first method usually involves the collection of instantaneous or short-term samples, usually within a few seconds or a minute, but similar methods can be used for sampling over longer periods. This type of sampling is acceptable when peak concentrations are sought or when concentrations are relatively constant. Grab samples were once used only for gross components of gases, such as methane, carbon monoxide, or oxygen, where the analysis was frequently performed volumetrically. The introduction of highly sensitive laboratory instruments, however, makes this technique limited only by the detection limit of the analytical methods available.

An important feature of grab samples is that their collection efficiency is normally 100%. However, it must be remembered that sample decay does occur for various reasons, such as reaction or adsorption on the inner surfaces of the collector, and grab sampling must be used with this clearly in mind.

Grab sampling is of questionable value when 1) the contaminant or contaminant concentration varies with time, 2) the concentration of atmospheric contaminants is low (unless, as stated above, a highly sensitive detector is used so that the mass of analyte collected is above the limit of detection), or 3) a time-weighted average exposure is desired. In such circumstances, continuous or integrated sampling is used instead. The gas or vapor in these cases is extracted from air and concentrated by 1) solution in an absorbing liquid, 2) reaction with an absorbing solution (or reagent therein), or 3) collection onto a solid adsorbent. Collection efficiency of active sampling devices used for these sampling procedures is frequently less than 100%; therefore, individual efficiency percentages must be determined for each case. Later in this chapter (and in Chapters 18 and 20), another technique, passive (or diffusive) sampling, is discussed.

Selection of Sampling Devices

The first step in the selection of a sampling device and analytical procedure is to search the available literature. Primary sources are the compendia of methods recommended by the regulatory authorities or governmental agencies in the United States, i.e., the *NIOSH Manual of Analytical Methods*[1] and the *OSHA Analytical Methods Manual*.[2] Recommended methods from other countries, such as the United Kingdom,[3] Germany,[4] or Sweden,[5] might also be consulted. Secondary sources are published literature references in, for example, the "American Industrial Hygiene Association Journal," "Applied Occuational and Environmental Hygiene," or books such as the *Intersociety Committee's Methods for Air Sampling and Analysis.*[6]

If a published procedure is not available, one can be devised from theoretical considerations. However, its suitability must be established experimentally before application. Important criteria for selecting sampling devices are solubility, volatility, and reactivity of the contaminant; the adsorptivity, reactivity, and permeability of the collection device; and the sensitivity of the analytical method.

Generally speaking, nonreactive and nonabsorbing gaseous substances may be collected as grab samples. Water-soluble gases and vapors and those that react rapidly with absorbing solutions can be collected in simple gas washing bottles. Volatile and less soluble gaseous substances and those that react slowly with absorbing solutions require more liquid contact. For these substances, more elaborate sampling devices may be required, such as gas washing bottles of the spiral type or fritted bubblers. Insoluble and nonreactive gases and vapors are collected by adsorption onto activated charcoal, silica gel, or other suitable adsorbent. Frequently, for a given contaminant, there may be several choices of sampling equipment.

Grab Samplers (Short-term Samplers — Seconds or Minutes)

Evacuated Flasks

These are containers of varying capacity and configurations. In each case, the internal pressure of the container is reduced, either to near zero (<1 millibar) or to a known absolute pressure. These containers are generally removed to a laboratory for analysis, although it is possible to achieve field readability if the proper equipment and direct-reading instrument are available. Some examples of evacuated flasks are heavy-walled containers, separation flasks, and various commercial devices. These are described at the end of this chapter.

"Passivated" Canisters

Stainless steel containers that have been specially treated to reduce adsorption effects have been used for collecting trace organic gases, especially the less reactive hydrocarbons and halocarbons.[7] More recently,[8] the U.S. Environmental Protection Agency (U.S. EPA) has used passivated canisters for ambient air analysis alongside adsorbent tubes.

Gas or Liquid Displacement Containers

Any ordinary, sealable container can be used as a displacement sampler. Original air is replaced by test air by pumping or aspirating through the container with a double-acting rubber bulb aspirator or a battery- or electrically operated vacuum pump. The volume of air swept out should be 10–15 times the container volume to achieve a sample collection efficiency of more than 99%. This is mathematically expressed by:[9]

$$N = \ln(100/E) \tag{1}$$

where: N = number of bottle volumes swept out
E = percent error in sample collection efficiency.

An alternative method for sampling with these containers is to fill them with water and allow the water to drain out slowly in the test area. The liquid becomes replaced by test air. Obviously, this procedure is not suitable for collecting water-soluble gases.

For soluble and reactive gases, an absorbent or reagent solution may be introduced into the gas displacement sampler. The usual procedure is to fill the sampler with test air and then add the absorbent. When dealing with partially or totally evacuated flasks, the reagent solution or absorbent is added before they are put under reduced pressure. In both cases, after the sample has been taken, the container is rotated to ensure an even distribution of the reagent on the inside surface of the sampler. This may take a few minutes or overnight, and so the equilibration time must be determined experimentally.

Flexible Plastic Containers

Bags are used to collect air samples and prepare known concentrations that can range from parts per billion to more than 10% by volume in air. The bags are commercially available in sizes up to 250 L. However, 5- to 15-L bags are the most useful to industrial hygienists.

These bags are constructed from a number of materials, including polyester, polyvinylidene chloride, Teflon®, aluminized Mylar®, or other fluorocarbons. Bags have the advantages of being light, nonbreakable, inexpensive to ship, and simple to use. However, they should be used with caution because storage stabilities for gases, memory effects from previous samples, permeability, precision, and accuracy of sampling systems vary considerably.

Plastic bags should be tested before they are used. Such testing should be done under ambient conditions that approximate those of the sampling environment. Some general recommendations are available in the published literature[6,10–12] for the use of such bags for air sampling. A good review of specific applications up to 1967 is Schuette;[13] other specific applications are given in References 14 to 20. Posner and Woodfin[20] made a useful systematic study of five bag types and six organic vapors; they conclude that Tedlar® bags are best for short-term sampling, whereas aluminized Mylar bags are better for long-term storage prior to analysis. Storage properties, decay curves, and other factors, however, will vary considerably from those reported for a given gas or vapor because sampling conditions are rarely identical. Each bag, therefore, should be evaluated for the specific gas or gas mixture for which it will be used.

Continuous Active Samplers (Long-term Samplers — Hours or Days)

Absorbers

The absorption theory of gases and vapors from air by solution, as developed by Elkins *et al.*,[21] assumes that gases and vapors behave like perfect gases and dissolve to give a perfect solution. The concentration of the vapor in solution is increased during air sampling until an equilibrium is established with the concentration of vapor in the air. Absorption is never complete, however, because the vapor pressure of the material is not reduced to zero but is only lowered by the solvent effect of the absorbing liquid. Some vapor will escape with continued sampling, but it is replaced. Continued sampling will not increase the concentration of vapor in solution once equilibrium is established.

According to formulas developed by Elkins *et al.*,[21] and verified by Gage[22] in his experiments with ethylene oxide, the efficiency of vapor collection depends on 1) the volume of air sampled, 2) the volume of the absorbing liquid, and 3) the volatility of the contaminant being collected. Efficiency of collection, therefore, can be increased by cooling the sampling solution (reducing the volatility of the contaminant), increasing the solution volume by adding two or more bubblers in series, or altering the design of the sampling device. Sampling rate and concentration of the vapor in air are not primary factors that determine collection efficiency.

Absorption of gases and vapors by chemical reaction depends on the size of the air bubbles produced in the bubbler, the interaction of contaminant with reagent molecules, the rapidity of the reaction, and a sufficient excess of reagent solution. If the reaction is rapid and a sufficient excess of reagent is maintained in the liquid, complete retention of the contaminant is achieved regardless of the volume of air sampled. If the reaction is slow and the sampling rate is not low enough, collection efficiency will decrease.

Four basic absorbers used for the collection of gases and vapors are 1) simple gas washing bottles, 2) spiral and helical absorbers, 3) fritted bubblers, and 4) glass bead columns. Sampling and absorbent capacities of these absorbers are found in Reference 6. Their function is to provide sufficient contact between the contaminant in the air and the absorbing liquid.

Petri, Dreschsel, and midget impingers are examples of simple gas washing bottles. They function by applying a suction to an outlet tube, which causes sample air to be drawn through an inlet tube into the lower portion of the liquids contained in these absorbers. They are suitable for collecting nonreactive gases and vapors that are highly soluble in the absorbing liquid. The absorption of methanol and butanol in water, esters in alcohol, and organic chlorides in butyl alcohol are examples. They are also used for collecting gases and vapors that react rapidly with a reagent in the sampling media. High collection efficiency is achieved, for example, when toluene diisocyanate is hydrolyzed to toluene diamine in Marcali[23] solution. Hydrogen sulfide reaction with cadmium sulfate and ammonia neutralized by dilute sulfuric acid are other examples.

Several methods for testing the efficiency of an absorbing device are available: 1) by series testing where enough samplers are arranged in series so that the last sampler does not recover any of the test gas or vapor, 2) by sampling from a dynamic standard atmosphere or from a gas-tight chamber or tank containing a known gas or vapor concentration, 3) by comparing results obtained with a device known to be accurate, and 4) by introducing a known amount of gas or vapor into a sampling train containing the absorber being tested.

Cold Traps

Cold traps are used for collecting materials in liquid or solid form primarily for identification purposes. Vapor is separated from air by passing it through a coil immersed in a cooling system, i.e., dry ice and acetone, liquid air, or liquid nitrogen. These devices are employed when it is difficult to collect samples efficiently by other techniques. Water is extracted along with organic materials and two-phase systems result.

Sampling Bags

Bags (as used for grab sampling) can also be used for collecting integrated air samples. Samples can be collected for 8 hrs, at specific times during the day, or over a period of several days. The bags may be mounted on workers as personal samplers or may be located in designated areas.

Solid Adsorbents

Activated Charcoal

Charcoal is an amorphous form of carbon formed by partially burning wood, nutshells, animal bones, and other carbonaceous materials. A wide variety of charcoals are available; some are more suitable for liquid purification, some for decolorization, and others for air purification and air sampling.

Ordinary charcoal becomes activated charcoal by heating it with steam to 800–900°C. During this treatment, a porous, submicroscopic internal structure is formed that gives it an extensive internal surface area, as large as 1000 m^2 per gram of charcoal. This greatly enhances its adsorption capacity.

Activated charcoal is an excellent adsorbent for most organic vapors. During the 1930s and 1940s, it was used in the then well-known activated charcoal apparatus[(24)] for the collection and analysis of solvent vapor. The quantity of vapor in the air sample was determined by a gain in weight of the charcoal tube. Lack of specificity, accuracy, and sensitivity of the analysis and the difficult task of equilibrating the charcoal tube, however, discouraged use.

Renewed interest in activated charcoal as an adsorbent for sampling organic vapors appeared in the 1960s.[(25–27)] The ease with which carbon disulfide extracts organic vapors from activated charcoal and the capability of microanalysis by gas chromatography are the reasons for its current popularity. Today, air sampling procedures using activated charcoal are widely used by industrial hygienists[(28–31)] and form the basis of the majority of the official analytical methods for organic materials recommended by the National Institute for Occupational Safety and Health (NIOSH) and the Occupational Safety and Health Administration (OSHA).[(1,2)]

Analytical information on selected NIOSH procedures is given in Table 17-1. In general, the NIOSH procedures use a 100-mg charcoal tube (with 50-mg back-up), but very volatile analytes may require a larger tube. The NIOSH study showed that the charcoal tube method is generally adequate for hydrocarbons, halogenated hydrocarbons, esters, ethers, alcohols, ketones, and glycol ethers that are commonly used as industrial solvents. Compounds with low vapor pressure and reactive compounds (e.g., amines, phenols, nitrocompounds, aldehydes, and anhydrides) generally have low desorption efficiencies from charcoal and require alternative sorbents such as silica gel or porous polymers for collection, or alternative reagent systems for recovery.

Inorganic compounds, such as ozone, nitrogen dioxide, chlorine, hydrogen sulfide, and sulfur dioxide, react chemically with activated charcoal and cannot be collected for analysis by this method.

Even for substances recommended for sampling on charcoal, this sorbent may not always be ideal. Reference to Table 17-1 will indicate that carbon disulfide is the recommended desorption solvent for nonpolar compounds, whereas a variety of desorption cocktails are required for the more polar compounds. Difficulties arise, therefore, when sampling mixtures of polar and nonpolar compounds because each will give poor recoveries with the other's desorption solvent. Several alternative more universal, solvents have been investigated,[(32–34)] but none of these has achieved wide recognition. In such circumstances, it may be necessary to take two samples and desorb each one with a different solvent.

Sample Collection

The adsorption capacity of a sampler, i.e., the volume of air that can be collected without loss of contaminant, depends on the sampling rate, the quantity of sorbent, the sorbent surface area, the density of active sites and bulk density, the volatility of the contaminant, and the concentration of contaminant in the workroom air. For many organic vapors, a sample volume of 10 L (1.0 L/min) can be collected without significant loss in NIOSH-recommended tubes. A breakthrough of more than 20% in the back-up section indicates that some of the sample was lost. Optimum sample volumes are found in NIOSH procedures.[(1)]

The sample volume for gases and highly volatile solvents must necessarily be smaller. A 3% breakthrough was found to occur on NIOSH-recommended tubes at 0.2 L/min for 15 min in an environment containing 5 ppm of vinyl chloride. Losses occurred before 5 L of the sample was collected in a 200-ppm vinyl chloride environment at a sampling rate of 0.05 L/min.[(31)]

It is always best to refer to an established procedure for proper sampling rates and air sample volumes. In the absence of such information, breakthrough experiments must be performed before field sampling is attempted. Normally, these experiments are conducted using dynamic standard atmospheres prepared at twice the exposure limit (TLV) and 80% relative humidity to give a suitable margin of safety to the measured breakthrough volume. See Chapter 8 for the preparation of known concentrations.

After the procedure has been validated, field sampling may be performed. Immediately before sampling, the ends of the charcoal tube are broken, rubber or Tygon® tubing is connected to the back-up end of the charcoal tube, and air is drawn through the sampling train with a calibrated battery or electrically driven suction pump. A personal or area sample may be collected. The duration of the sampling may be several minutes or up to 8 hrs, depending on the information desired. When sampling is completed, plastic caps or masking tape (but not rubber caps) are placed on the ends of the tube.

TABLE 17-1. Collection and Analysis of Gases and Vapors (solvent desorption)

Method Name	Test Compounds	Sorbent*	Desorption Solvent	NIOSH Method No.
Alcohols I	t-Butyl alcohol Isopropyl alcohol Ethanol	C	99:1 CS_2:2-butanol	1400
Alcohols II	n-Butyl alcohol Isobutyl alcohol sec-Butyl alcohol n-Propyl alcohol	C	99:1 CS_2:2-propanol	1404
Alcohols III	Allyl alcohol Isoamyl alcohol Methyl isobutyl carbinol Cyclohexanol Diacetone alcohol	C	99:5 CS_2:2-propanol	1402
Alcohols IV	2-Butoxyethanol 2-Ethoxyethanol 2-Methoxyethanol	C	99:5 CH_2Cl_2:methanol	1403
Amines, aromatic	Aniline o-Toluidine 2,4-Xylidine N,N,-Dimethyl-p-toluidine N,N,-Dimethylaniline	S	95% ethanol	2002
Aminoethanol compounds	2-Aminoethanol 2-Dibutylaminoethanol 2-Diethylaminoethanol	S	80% ethanol	2007
Esters I	n-Amyl acetate n-Butyl acetate 2-Ethoxyethyl acetate Ethyl acrylate Methyl isoamyl acetate n-Propyl acetate, etc.	C	CS_2	1450
Hydrocarbons BP 36-126°	Benzene, Toluene Pentane thro' Octane Cyclohexane Cyclohexene	C	CS_2	1500
Hydrocarbons aromatic	Benzene Cumene Naphthalene, etc.	C	CS_2	1501
Hydrocarbons halogenated	Chloroform Tetrachloroethylene p-Dichlorobenzene Bromoform, etc.	C	CS_2	1003
Ketones I	Acetone Cyclohexanone Diisobutyl ketone 2-Hexanone Methyl isobutyl ketone 2-Pentanone	C	CS_2	1300
Ketones II	Camphor Ethyl butyl ketone Mesityl oxide 5-Methyl-3-heptanone Methyl n-amyl ketone	C	99:1 CS_2:methanol	1301
Naphthas	Kerosine Petroleum ether Rubber solvent Stoddard solvent, etc.	C	CS_2	1550
Nitrobenzenes	Nitrobenzene Nitrotoluene 4-Chloronitrotoluene	S	Methanol	2005
Nitroglycerine and ethylene glycol dinitrate		T	Ethanol	2507

TABLE 17-1 (con't.). Collection and Analysis of Gases and Vapors (solvent desorption)

Pentachloroethane	R	Hexane	2517
Tetrabromoethane	S	Tetrahydrofuran	2003
Vinyl chloride	C	CS_2	1007

*C = charcoal.
S = silica gel.
T = Tenax.
R = Porapak R.

For each new batch of charcoal tubes, an analysis blank must be prepared to determine the aging, collection efficiency, and recovery characteristics for a given contaminant. This may be achieved by introducing a known amount of the contaminant into a freshly opened charcoal tube, passing clean air through it to simulate sampling conditions, and carrying through its analysis with the field samples. Another charcoal tube, not used to sample, is opened in the field and used as a field blank.

The first step in the analytical procedure is to remove the contaminant from the charcoal. An early drawback to using charcoal for air sampling was the difficulty in recovering samples for analysis. Steam distillation was only partially effective. Extraction with carbon disulfide has been found, in many instances, to be quite satisfactory, although for the more volatile vapors, thermal desorption may also be used (see below).

The most frequently used liquid desorbant is carbon disulfide. Unfortunately, carbon disulfide does not always completely remove the sample from charcoal. Recovery varies for each contaminant and batch of charcoal used. The extent of individual recoveries must be determined experimentally and a correction for desorption efficiency applied to the analytical result.(25) Over a narrow range of analyte concentrations, as used in the NIOSH validations,(35) this desorption efficiency is essentially constant, but it may vary widely over larger concentration ranges, particularly for polar compounds.(36) Desorption efficiency can also be affected by the presence of water vapor and other contaminants.(37) NIOSH(1) recommends that methods be used only where the desorption efficiency is greater than 75%; ideally, it should be greater than 90%.

The practical desorption step in charcoal analysis is also critical because, upon the addition of carbon disulfide to charcoal, the initial heat of reaction may drive off the more volatile components of the sample. This can be minimized by adding charcoal slowly to precooled carbon disulfide. Another technique is to transfer the charcoal sample to vials lined with Teflon septum caps and to introduce the carbon disulfide with an injection needle. The sealed vial will prevent the loss of any volatilized sample. Headspace analysis is also possible.

It should be emphasized that carbon disulfide is a highly toxic solvent that produces serious effects on the cardiovascular and nervous systems. Care should be exercised in handling the solvent, and the analytical procedure should be performed in a well-ventilated area.

Several quality assurance schemes have been developed that apply to the charcoal tube method. One of these is the Proficiency Analytical Testing (PAT) Program(38) and the Laboratory Accreditation Program of the American Industrial Hygiene Association (AIHA).(39) Another is the Health and Safety Executive (HSE) Workplace Analysis Scheme for Proficiency (WASP). Details of these programs may be obtained from The Laboratory Accreditation Coordinator, AIHA, 2700 Prosperity Ave., Suite 250, Fairfax, Virginia 22031, and the WASP Coordinator, Occupational Medicine and Hygiene Laboratory, Health and Safety Executive, Broad Lane, Sheffield, S3 7HQ, United Kingdom.

Silica Gel

Silica gel is an amorphous form of silica derived from the interaction of sodium silicate and sulfuric acid. It has several advantages over activated charcoal for sampling gases and vapors: 1) polar contaminants are more easily removed from the adsorbent by a variety of common solvents, 2) the extractant does not usually interfere with wet chemical or instrumental analyses 3) amines and some inorganic substances for which charcoal is unsuitable can be collected, and 4) the use of highly toxic carbon disulfide is avoided.

One disadvantage of silica gel is that it will adsorb water. Silica gel is electrically polar, and polar substances are preferentially attracted to active sites on its surface. Water is highly polar and is tenaciously held. If enough moisture is present in the air or if sampling is continued long enough, water will displace organic solvents (which are relatively nonpolar in comparison) from the silica gel surface. With water vapor at the head of the list, compounds in descending order of polarizability are alcohols, aldehydes, ketones, esters, aromatic hydrocarbons, olefins, and paraffins. It is obvious, therefore, that the volume of moisturized air that can be effectively passed over silica gel is limited.

In spite of this limitation, silica gel has proven to be an effective adsorbent for collecting many gases and vapors. Even under conditions of 90% humidity, relatively high concentrations of benzene, toluene, and trichloroethylene are quantitatively adsorbed on 10 g of silica gel from air samples collected at the rate of 2.5 L/min for periods of at least 20 min or longer.[40,41] Under normal conditions, hydrocarbon mixtures of 2–5 carbon paraffins, low molecular weight sulfur compounds (H_2S, SO_2, mercaptans), and olefins concentrate on silica gel at dry ice-acetone temperature if the sample volume does not exceed 10 L.[42] Significant losses of ethylene, methane, ethane, and other light hydrocarbons occur if the sampling volume is extended to 30 L.

More recent usage, however, has concentrated on smaller sample tubes (in similar sizes to the NIOSH range of charcoal tubes) operated at room temperature. NIOSH recommends such tubes for a variety of more polar chemicals such as amines, phenols, amides, and inorganic acids (Table 17-1).

Many of the same considerations apply to silica gel tubes as to the charcoal tubes; the sampling capacity and desorption efficiency for the compound of interest should be determined before use, or a reliable, officially established method should be used. A variety of desorption solvents will be needed for desorbing specific compounds with high efficiency; polar desorption solvents, such as water or methanol, are commonly applied.

Thermal Desorption

Because of the high toxicity and flammability of carbon disulfide and the labor-intensive nature of the solvent desorption procedure, a useful alternative is to desorb the collected analyte thermally.[43–45] Except in a few cases, this is not practical with charcoal as adsorbent because the temperature needed for desorption (e.g., 300°C) would result in some decomposition of the analytes. Carbon molecular sieves or, more frequently, porous polymer adsorbents (in particular Tenax®, Porapak Q® and Chromosorb 106®) are used instead.[46–48] Of these, Tenax has the lowest thermal desorption blank (typically less than 0.1 g/g of adsorbent, when properly conditioned) but only modest adsorption capacity compared with carbon.

The thermal desorption procedure typically uses larger tubes than the NIOSH method; usually 200–500 mg of sorbent are used, depending on type. Desorption can be made fully automatic, and analysis is usually carried out by gas chromatography. Some desorbers also allow automatic selection of sample tubes from a multiple-sample carousel. The whole sample can be transferred to the gas chromatograph, resulting in greatly increased sensitivity compared with the solvent desorption method. Alternatively, some desorbers allow the desorbed sample to be held in a reservoir from which aliquots are withdrawn for analysis, but then the concentrating advantage is reduced.

Thermal desorption has been adopted as a (nonexclusive) recommended method in the United Kingdom,[3] Germany,[4] and the Netherlands,[49] but it is less widely accepted in the United States. NIOSH[1] has relatively few methods based on thermal desorption (compared to those which use solvent desorption). U.S. EPA[50] has a number of methods based on thermal desorption and mass spectrometry.

The main disadvantage of thermal desorption directly with an analyzer is that it is essentially a "one-shot" technique; normally, the whole sample is analyzed. This is why many such methods are linked to mass spectrometry. However, with capillary chromatography, it is usually possible to split the desorbed sample before analysis and, if desired, the vented split can be collected and reanalyzed.[51] Alternatively, the desorbate can be split between two capillary columns of differing polarity.[52]

Desorption efficiency is usually 100% for the majority of common solvents and similar compounds in a boiling range of approximately 50 to 250°C. Thus, the analysis of complex mixtures is easier than for charcoal or silica gel solvent desorption methods. However, if a wide boiling range is to be covered, more than one sorbent may be required. Thus, gasoline may be monitored by a Chromosorb 106 tube and carbon tube in series.[53] Extensive lists of recommended sampling volumes and minimum desorption temperatures for Tenax and other sorbents are given in Brown and Purnell[45] and the United Kingdom Health and Safety Executive Method MDHS 72.[54]

Coated Sorbents

Many highly reactive compounds are unsuitable for sampling directly onto sorbents, either because they are unstable or cannot be recovered efficiently. In addition, some compounds may be analyzed more easily, or with greater sensitivity, by derivatizing them first, which can sometimes be achieved during the sampling stage. Methods have been developed that use coated sorbents, either sorbent tubes or coated filters. Table 17-2 lists a number of such methods.

Wet Chemistry and Spectrophotometric Methods

Several gases and vapors may be analyzed by wet chemical methods or by ultraviolet spectrophotometry. There are two primary compendia of methods, the AIHA Analytical Chemistry Committee[55] and the Intersociety Committee.[6] Other useful sources are Han-

TABLE 17-2. Collection and Analysis of Gases and Vapors (coated sorbents)

Test Compounds	Sorbent	Matrix*	Method No.
Acetaldehyde	2-(Hydroxymethyl) piperidine on Supelpak 20N	T	NIOSH 2538
Acrolein	2-(Hydroxymethyl) piperidine on Supelpak 20N	T	NIOSH 2501
Arsenic trioxide	Sodium carbonate	F	NIOSH 7901
Butylamine	Sulfuric acid	T	NIOSH S138
Diisocyanates	1-(2-Pyridyl) piperazine	F	OSHA 42 OSHA 47
Formaldehyde	N-benzylethanolamine on Supelpak 20F	T	NIOSH 2502
Methylene dianiline	Sulfuric acid	F	NIOSH 5029

*T = sorbent tube.
F = filter.

sen,[56] Jacobs,[57–58] the *Methods for the Detection of Toxic Substances in Air* series,[59] Ruch,[60,61] Thomas,[62] and Feigl.[63] Spectrophotometric methods have now been replaced largely by direct-reading instruments or detector tubes (Chapter 18) or by high-performance liquid chromatography (HPLC) or other instrumental techniques.

Sampling Train

Except for grab samplers (described above) and diffusive samplers (described below), sampling devices are used in conjunction with a sampling pump and air metering device. To avoid contaminating the metering device and pump, these are usually placed downstream of the sampler during the sampling period. However, because many samplers introduce back-pressure, the sampling train should be precalibrated by the use of an external flowmeter upstream of the sampling head. The sampling train should also be calibrated after sampling, and preferably should be calibrated periodically during sampling. Air movers are described in Chapter 12 and calibration in Chapter 8.

Calculations

The collected sample is analyzed, either directly if it is a gas phase or impinger sample, or after desorption if it is collected on a solid sorbent, using appropriate gas or liquid standard solutions to calibrate the analytical instrument. Gas phase samples give a result directly in ppm (v/v), but other types of samples will give a mass of analyte per collected sample, or a concentration, which can be converted to a mass by multiplying by the sample volume.

The mass concentration of the analyte in the air sample is then calculated using the following equations:

Impinger

$$C = (m - m_{blank})/(E_s \times V) \quad (2)$$

where: C = mass concentration of analyte in air (mg/m^3)
m = mass of analyte in sample (µg)
E_S = sampling efficiency
m_{blank} = mass of analyte in blank (µg)
V = volume of air sample (L).

Absorbent Tube

$$C = (m_1 + m_2 - m_{blank})/(DE \times V) \quad (3)$$

where: m_1 = mass of analyte on first tube section (µg)
m_2 = mass of analyte on back-up tube section (if used) (µg)
DE = desorption efficiency corresponding to m_1.

Note: If it is desired to express concentrations reduced to specified conditions, e.g., 25°C and 101 kPa, then,

$$C_{corr} = C(101/P)\,(T/298) \quad (4)$$

where: P = actual pressure of air sampled (kPa)
T = absolute temperature of air sampled (°K).

Volume Fraction

The volume fraction of the analyte in air, in ppm (v/v), is

$$C' = C_{corr}\,(24.5/MW) \quad (5)$$

where: MW = molecular mass of the analyte of interest (g/mol).

Diffusive Samplers

Overview

A diffusive sampler is a device that is capable of taking samples of gas or vapor pollutants from the atmosphere at a rate controlled by a physical process, such as diffusion through a static air layer or permeation through a membrane, but does not involve the active movement of the air through the sampler.[64] It should be noted that in the United States, the adjective "passive" is preferred in describing these samplers and should be regarded as synonymous with "diffusive."

This type of diffusive sampler should not be confused with the annular or aerosol denuders, which not only rely on diffusion to collect the gas or vapors but also upon the air in question being simultaneously drawn through the annular inlet into the sampler. Aerosol particles have diffusion coefficients too low to be collected on the annular inlet and are trapped on a back-up filter. More information on denuders can be found in Chapter 20.

Diffusive sampling in the occupational environment dates back at least to the 1930s when qualitative devices were described, but the first serious attempt to apply science to quantitative diffusive sampling was in 1973 when Palmes described a tube-form sampler for sulfur dioxide.[65] Since then, a wide variety of samplers have been described, some relying on diffusion through an air gap, some relying on permeation through a membrane, and some using both techniques for the rate-controlling process in sampling.[65–68] Many of these devices are commercially available.

The theoretical basis for diffusive sampling is now well established.[64] Diffusion and permeation processes can both be described in derivations of Fick's first law of diffusion (Equation 6). These processes result in expressions relating the mass uptake by the sampler to the concentration gradient, the time of exposure, and the sampler area exposed to the pollutant atmosphere.[69] Expressions have also been derived for the application of Fick's law to diffusive sampling in the "real" world, e.g., taking into account nonsteady-state sampling; the effects of fluctuating concentrations, sorbent saturation, wind velocity, and turbulence at the sampler surface; temperature; and pressure.[70–71] Except for sorbent saturation, which may lead to reduced (although sometimes predictable) uptake rates, these modifications to the basic Fick's law expression do not lead to significant errors for well-designed samplers. Such samplers may be regarded as truly integrating devices with accuracies similar to those of active samplers.

A variety of diffusive samplers have been described[72] and only a selection of the major types manufactured can be described here. Diffusive equivalents to the more familiar pumped methods exist for nearly all types; the main exception being the direct collection of gas samples, where the nearest equivalent is an evacuated canister. Thus, the diffusive equivalent of an impinger is a liquid-filled badge such as the Pro-Tek™ inorganic monitor or the SKC badge; the diffusive equivalent of the charcoal tube is the charcoal badge such as the 3M OVM or the SKC Passive Sampler; and the diffusive equivalent of the thermal desorption method is the Perkin-Elmer tube or the SKC thermal desorption badge. There are also diffusive devices based on reagent-impregnated solid supports, but these are mostly direct reading and are dealt with in Chapter 19.

In general, the regulatory authorities have been reluctant to accept diffusive monitoring methods, except in the United Kingdom and the Netherlands where several such methods have been adopted as nonexclusive recommended methods.[3,49] However, the Luxembourg Symposium[64] concluded that:

- The theoretical basis for diffusive sampling has been confirmed by laboratory and field trials.
- Active and diffusive sampling are complementary approaches, having areas of applicability that may overlap. Each has its role in a strategy for monitoring worker exposure.
- In general, there seems to be no significant difference between the accuracy and precision of diffusive sampling and those of other monitoring systems such as active pumped sampling.
- It was agreed that, as a general principle, any method is acceptable by regulatory authorities and hygienists if used by experts within its defined limitations. This applies equally to diffusive samplers.

The symposium also concluded that validation of all sampling systems is essential both in the laboratory and in the field. It also recommended that an established evaluation protocol such as those of NIOSH,[73] HSE,[74] or the European Committee for Standardization (CEN)[75] be followed.

Calibration

The basic expression of Fick's Law is

$$J = \mathcal{D}(C_e - C_o)/L \tag{6}$$

and

$$Q = (\mathcal{D}A)t(C_e - C_o)/L \tag{7}$$

where:
J = diffusive flux (g/cm^2-sec)
$\mathcal{D}$ = coefficient of diffusion (cm^2/sec)
A = cross-sectional area of diffusion path (cm^2)
L = length of diffusion path (cm)
C_e = external concentration being sampled (g/cm^3)
C_o = concentration at the interface of the sorbent (g/cm^3)
Q = mass uptake (g)
t = sampling time (sec).

It is apparent from an inspection of these equations that the expression $\mathcal{D}A/L$ has units of cm^3/sec and therefore represents what can be considered as a "sampling rate" of the diffusive sampler when compared to a pumped sampling system. This simple use of the sampling rate concept has been of considerable value to users of the devices and is often expressed in the dimensionally equivalent units of ml/min. Knowledge of the geometry of the sampler (which will be fixed for any given sampler type) permits the calculation of the sampling rate provided the diffusion coefficient is known. A number of manufacturers have published tables of sampling rates calculated in this way, most of whom have used the same source of published diffusion coefficients.[76] Diffusion coefficients that are not in this list can be calculated theoretically.[77] Representative sampling rates, supplied by Pro-Tek and by the 3M Company, range from 20 to 45 cm^3/min (see Table 17-1).

Environmental Factors Affecting Monitor Performance[64,71–73]

Temperature and Pressure

From Maxwell's equation, the diffusion coefficient, $\mathcal{D}$, is a function of absolute temperature, T, and pressure,

$$\mathcal{D} = f(T^{3/2}, P^{-1}) \tag{8}$$

But from the general gas law;

$$PV = nRT \tag{9}$$

$$C = n/V = P/RT$$

Substituting Equations 8 and 9 in Equation 7, we get:

$$Q = f(P/T, T^{3/2}/P) = f(T)^{1/2} \tag{10}$$

Thus, Q is independent of pressure, P, but dependent on the square root of absolute temperature, T. In practice, the temperature dependence of the sampling rate at ambient temperature levels (about 0.2% per °C) may be ignored. However, temperature may adversely affect the absorption and adsorption capacity of a sorbent.

Humidity

High humidity can affect charcoal adsorption adversely, resulting in a reduction in saturation capacity for charcoal badges. If the sampler becomes saturated, C_o in Equation 6 is no longer zero, and the sampling rate becomes nonlinear. Porous polymers used for thermal desorption are relatively unaffected by humidity.

Transients

Simple derivations of Fick's Law assume steady-state conditions, but in the practical use of such samplers, the ambient concentrations of pollutants are likely to vary widely. The question then arises whether a diffusive sampler will give a truly integrated response or will miss short-lived transients before they have had a chance to diffuse into the sampler. The problem has been discussed theoretically[70,78,79] and practically.[80,81] Generally, transients do not present a significant problem provided the total sampling time is well in excess of the time constant of the sampler, i.e., the time a molecule takes to diffuse into the sampler under steady-state conditions. The time constant of most commercial samplers is between 1 and 10 seconds.

Sorbent Factors

All diffusive samplers rely on sorbents having a high affinity for the contaminant being sampled, i.e., $C_o = 0$ in Equation 6, and uptake is linearly proportional to concentration and time of exposure. Useful checks on sorbent suitability are a back-diffusion test given in Bartley[82] and the measurement of adsorption isotherms.[83]

Face Velocity

Diffusive samplers also rely on the external concentration, i.e., C_e in Equation 6, being maintained at the sampler surface. In the absence of sufficient air movement across the face of the sampler, transport of pollutant to the surface may itself be limited by diffusion and the effective sampling rate will be reduced. At the other extreme, very high air velocities may induce turbulence within the sampler body if the draught shield is inadequate; the effective diffusion path length will be reduced and the sampling rate increased. The magnitude of these effects will vary with the geometry and design of particular samplers, although for the majority of modern samplers, sampling rates are reasonably constant within the range of air velocities likely to be encountered in workplace personal monitoring. Samplers with a large surface area (badge types) should not be used in static positions where air velocities may be below their critical values for this type of sampler (about 0.2 m/s).

Calculations

The method of calculation of atmospheric concentrations is essentially the same as for pumped samplers, i.e., the collected sample is analyzed and the total weight of analyte on the sampler is determined. Then, as before,

$$C = (m_1 + m_2 - m_{blank})/(DE \times V) \tag{3}$$

(m_2 and DE are ignored for liquid sorbent badges)

V, the total sample volume, is calculated from the effective sampling rate (L/min) and the time of exposure (min).

This calculation gives C in mg/m^3; strictly speaking, an appropriate sampling rate for the ambient temperature and pressure should be made because Equation 9 assumes C is in ppm.

Alternatively, sampling rates can be expressed in units such as ng/ppm-min (dimensionally equivalent to cm^3/min), when C' is calculated directly in ppm:

$$C' = m_1 + m_2 - m_{blank}/(DE \times U \times t') \times 100 \quad (11)$$

where: U = sampling rate (ng/ppm-min)
t' = sampling time (min)

Note: m_2 is relevant only to samplers with a back-up section, and an additional multiplication factor may be needed to account for differing diffusion path lengths to primary and back-up sections.

Types of Monitors

Diffusive samplers are available for both organic and inorganic species. Most organic monitors use activated charcoal as the collection medium. Both diffusion and permeation devices are available. As a general rule, organic badges can be used to monitor any compound that can be sampled by pumped charcoal tube methods. Each monitor has a unique design, and the operation characteristics will be discussed in detail in the following section. Most of these require gas chromatographic analysis for determination of the contaminant concentration.

Diffusion monitors for inorganic gases and vapors are far more diverse in design and more chemispecific than the more generally absorbing organic monitors. There are also many direct-reading, passive monitors for inorganic contaminants (see Chapter 18).

Accuracy of Diffusive Monitoring

The overall accuracy of diffusive monitors has been studied extensively.(64) Most of the devices available commercially meet NIOSH and OSHA standards. NIOSH recommends that monitors produce results of +25% for 95% of the samples tested in the range of 0.5 to 2.0 times the environmental standard. OSHA's accuracy requirement varies from ±25% to ±50%, depending on the individual standard.

Field and laboratory test results on several commercially available badges are found in the literature. Brown,(84) for example, examined the Perkin-Elmer tube for acrylonitrile, benzene, butadiene, carbon disulfide, and styrene and found the sampler to be at least as accurate as the equivalent pumped method. Laboratory precision was, on the average, 10% for the diffusive sampler. Field precision was 12% for the diffusive sampler and 13% for the pumped sampler.

Kennedy(85) evaluated a range of inorganic samplers, including 3M, DuPont, MSA, REAL, and SKC samplers, and found they generally met NIOSH criteria.

A European interlaboratory comparison(86) of the 3M badge exposed to butanol, pentanal, trichloroethane, octane, butyl acetate, 3-heptanone, xylene, α-pinene, and decane generally displayed good agreement with the charcoal tube. Exceptions were butanol and pentanal, where the diffusive samplers read low. Again, excluding butanol and pentanal, overall laboratory precision varied between 9% (xylene) and 13% (heptanone). The contribution of interlaboratory error was less than half of these values.

Lautenberger *et al.*(87) measured acrylonitrile, benzene, carbon tetrachloride, acetone, and toluene with DuPont's Pro-Tek G-AA Organic Vapor Air Monitoring Badges. In comparative testing, the badge demonstrated an overall accuracy at least equivalent to the charcoal method.

Kring *et al.*(88) tested the DuPont Passive Colorimetric Air Monitoring Badge System for ammonia, sulfur dioxide, and nitrogen dioxide and found it met both NIOSH and OSHA accuracy requirements.

Seventy-eight pairs of side-by-side charcoal and 3M passive monitor samples were taken in the field and analyzed for 22 organic chemicals.

The study(89) indicated that the monitor assayed concentrations of 20 of these chemicals equally as well as charcoal tubes, on the basis of linear regression analysis. The results differed significantly for methylcyclohexane and n-octane.

Interpretation of Results

Once the analyses are completed, interpretation of results must be made. Federal laws require that exposure to gases and vapors shall not exceed OSHA Permissible Exposure Limits published in 29 CFR 1910.1000 *et seq*. A comparison with these standards will establish whether there is compliance with the law.

This mechanistic approach to the problem should be modified to include a better understanding of the Threshold Limit Values (TLVs) or standards. For this purpose, the American Conference of Governmental Industrial Hygienists TLV/Biological Exposure Indices (TLV/BEI) Committees publish a companion volume to its TLV/BEI booklet(90) called *Documentation of the Threshold Limit Values and Biological Exposure Indices*.(91) NIOSH-recommended exposure limits have also been published under the title of *NIOSH's Recommendations for Occupational Safety and Health Standards*.(92) Other sources of similar information are the AIHA Hygienic Guides and the American National Standards Institute documents. On the other hand, measurements may be taken for reasons other than demonstrating compliance, e.g., an epidemiological survey or assessing the effectiveness of control measures, and an appropriate interpretation of results must be made.

References

1. National Institute for Occupational Safety and Health: NIOSH Manual of Analytical Methods, 2nd ed. DHEW (NIOSH) Pub. No. 75-121 (1975); 3rd ed. DHEW (NIOSH) Pub. No. 84-100 (1984, revised 1990); 4th ed. DHHS (NIOSH) Pub. No. 94-113 (1994).
2. Occupational Safety and Health Administration: OSHA Analytical Methods Manual. OSHA Analytical Laboratories, Salt Lake City, UT. Available from ACGIH, Cincinnati, OH (1985); (Supplements 1991, 1993).
3. Health and Safety Executive: Methods for the Determination of Hazardous Substances. HSE Occupational Medicine and Hygiene Laboratory, Sheffield, UK (in series, 1981-93).
4. Deutsche Forschungsgemeinschaft: Analytische Methoden zur Prufung Gesundheitsschadlicher Arbeitsstoffe. DFG. Verlag Chemie, Weinheim, FRG (1985).
5. Arbetarskyddsverket: Principer och Methoder for Provtagning och Analys av Amnen Upptagna pa Listan over Hygieniska Gransvarden. Arbete och Halsa. Vetenskaplig Skriftserie 1987:17. Solna, Sweden (1987).
6. Intersociety Committee: Methods of Air Sampling and Analysis, 3rd ed. Lewis Publishers, Inc., Chelsea, MI (1988).
7. Denyszyn, R.B.; Harden, J.M.; Hardison, D.L.; et al.: Analytical Facilities for the Analysis of Trace Organic Volatiles in Ambient Air. National Bureau of Standards Special Publication 519 (issued April 1979).
8. Varns, J.L.; Mulik, J.D.; Williams, D.: Passive Sampling Devices and Canisters: Their Comparison in Measuring Air Toxics During a Field Study. Proceedings of the 1990 EPA/A&WMA International Symposium, Measurement of Toxic and Related Air Pollutants, 219-223.
9. Testing Efficiency of Air Aspiration in Collection of Air Samples in Bottles. Tennessee Industrial Hygiene News, p. 4-4 (1962).
10. Nelson, G.O.: Controlled Test Atmospheres, Principles and Techniques. Ann Arbor Science Publishers, Ann Arbor, MI (1971).
11. Pellizzari, E.D.; Gutknecht, W.F.; Cooper, S.; Hardison, D.: Evaluation of Sampling Methods for Gaseous Atmospheric Samples. EPA 600/3-84-062. U.S. Environmental Protection Agency, Research Triangle Park, NC (1984).
12. Apol, A.G.; Cook, W.A.; Lawrence, E.F.: Plastic Bags for Calibration of Air Sampling Devices - Determination of Precision of the Method. Am. Ind. Hyg. Assoc. J. 27:149 (1966).
13. Schuette, F.J.: Plastic Bags for Collection of Gas Samples. Atmos. Environ. 1:515 (1967).
14. Levine, S.P.; Hebel, K.G.; Bolton, Jr., J.; Kupel, R.E.: Industrial Analytical Chemists and OSHA Regulations for Vinyl Chloride. Anal. Chem. 47:1075A (1975).
15. Seila, R.L.; Lonneman, W.A.; Meeks, S.A.: Evaluation of Polyvinyl Fluoride as a Container Material for Air Pollution Studies. J. Environ. Sci. Health All. 11:121 (1976).
16. Scheil, G.W.: Standardization of Stationary Source Method for Vinyl Chloride. EPA 600/4-77-026. U.S. Environmental Protection Agency, Research Triangle Park, NC (1977).
17. Rothwell, R.; Mitchell, A.D.: Plastic Bags for Sampling of C2–C6 Hydrocarbons. Clean Air 7:35 (1977).
18. Knoll, J.E.; Penney, W.H.; Midgett, M.R.: The Use of Tedlar Bags to Contain Gaseous Benzene Samples at Source Level Concentrations. EPA 600/4-78-057. U.S. Environmental Protection Agency, Research Triangle Park, NC (1978).
19. Knoll, J.E.; Smith, M.A.; Midgett, M.R.: Evaluation of Emission Test Methods for Halogenated Hydrocarbons. EPA 600/4-79-025. U.S. Environmental Protection Agency, Research Triangle Park, NC (1979).
20. Posner, J.C.; Woodfin, W.J.: Sampling with Gas Bags; 1: Losses of Analyte with Time. Appl. Ind. Hyg. 1:163 (1986).
21. Elkins, H.B.; Hobby, A.; Fuller, J.E.: The Determination of Atmospheric Contamination; I: Organic Halogen Compounds. J. Ind. Hyg. 19:474 (1937).
22. Gage, J.C.: The Efficiency of Absorbers in Industrial Hygiene Air Analysis. Analyst 85:196 (1960).
23. Marcali, K.: Microdetermination of Toluene Diisocyanates in the Atmosphere. Anal. Chem. 29:552 (1957).
24. Elkins, H.B.: The Chemistry of Industrial Toxicology, 2nd ed. John Wiley & Sons, Inc., New York (1959).
25. Otterson, E.J.; Guy, C.U.: A Method of Atmospheric Solvent Vapor Sampling on Activated Charcoal in Connection with Gas Chromatography. In: Transactions of the 26th Annual Meeting,Philadelphia, PA, p. 37. American Conference of Governmental Industrial Hygienists, Cincinnati, OH (1964).
26. Fraust, C.L.; Hermann, E.R.: The Adsorption of Aliphatic Acetate Vapors onto Activated Carbon. Am. Ind. Hyg. Assoc. J. 30:494 (1969).
27. Reid, F.H.; Halpin, W.R.: Determination of Halogenated and Aromatic Hydrocarbons in Air by Charcoal Tube and Gas Chromatography. Am. Ind. Hyg. Assoc. J. 29:390 (1968).
28. White, L.D.; Taylor, D.G.; Mauer, P.A.; Kupel, R.E: A Convenient Optimized Method for the Analysis of Selected Solvent Vapors in the Industrial Atmosphere. Am. Ind. Hyg. Assoc. J. 31:225 (1970).
29. Fraust, C.L.: The Use of Activated Carbon for Sampling Industrial Environs. Am. Ind. Hyg. Assoc. J. 36:278 (1975).
30. Severs, L.W.; Skory, L.K.: Monitoring Personnel Exposure to Vinyl Chloride, Vinylidene Chloride and Methyl Chloride in an Industrial Work Environment. Am. Ind. Hyg. Assoc. J. 36:669 (1975).
31. Reckner, L.R.; Sacher, J.: Charcoal Sampling Tubes for Several Organic Solvents. DHEW (NIOSH) Pub. No. 75-184 (June 1975).
32. Langvardt, P.W.; Melcher, R.G.: Simultaneous Determination of Polar and Non-polar Solvents in Air Using a Two-phase Desorption from Charcoal. Am. Ind. Hyg. Assoc. J. 40:1006 (1979).
33. Johansen, I.; Wendelboe, F.: Dimethylformamide and Carbon Disulphide Desorption Efficiencies for Organic Vapours on Gas-sampling Charcoal Tube: Analyses with a Gas Chromatographic Backflush Technique. J. Chromatogr. 217:317 (1981).
34. Posner, J.C.: Comments on "Phase Equilibrium Method for Determination of Desorption Efficiencies" and Some Extensions for Use in Methods Development. Am. Ind. Hyg. Assoc J. 41:63 (1980).
35. National Institute for Occupational Safety and Health: Documentation of the NIOSH Validation Tests. DHEW (NIOSH) Publ. No. 77-185 (1977).
36. Posner, J.C.; Okenfuss, J.R.: Desorption of Organic Analytes from Activated Carbon; I: Factors Affecting the Process. Am. Ind. Hyg. Assoc J. 42:643 (1981).
37. Rudling, J.: Organic Solvent Vapor Analysis of Workplace Air. Arbete och Halsa. Vetenskaplig Skriftserie 1987:11. Arbetarskyddsverket, Solna, Sweden (1987).
38. National Institute for Occupational Safety and Health: NIOSH Proficiency Analytical Testing (PAT) Program. DHEW (NIOSH) Pub. No. 77-173 (1977).
39. American Industrial Hygiene Association: Laboratory Accreditation. AIHA, Akron, Ohio (1985).
40. Elkins, H.B.; Pagnotto, L.D.; Comproni, E.M.: The Ultraviolet Spectrophotometric Determination of Benzene in Air Samples Adsorbed on Silica Gel. Anal. Chem. 34:1797 (1962).
41. Van Mourik, J.H.C.: Experiences with Silica Gel as Absorbent. Am. Ind. Hyg. Assoc. J. 26:498 (1965).
42. Altshuller, A.P.; Bellar, T.A.; Clemons, C.A.: Concentration of Hydrocarbons on Silica Gel Prior to Gas Chromatographic Analysis. Am. Ind. Hyg. Assoc. J. 23:164 (1962).
43. Zlatkis, A.; Lichtenstein, H.A.; Tishbee, A.: Concentration and Analysis of Volatile Organics in Gases and Biological Fluids with a New Solid Absorbent. Chromatographia 6:67 (1973).
44. Pellizzari, E.D.; Bunch, J.E.; Carpenter, B.H.; Sawicki, E.: Collection and Analysis of Trace Organic Vapor Pollutants in Ambient Atmospheres. Environ. Sci. Technol. 9:552 (1975).

45. Brown, R.H.; Purnell, C.J.: Collection and Analysis of Trace Organic Vapour Pollutants in Ambient Atmospheres. The Performance of a Tenax-GC Adsorbent Tube. J. Chromatogr. 178:79 (1979).
46. Bertoni, G.; Bruner, F.; Liberti, A.; Perrino, C.: Some Critical Parameters in Collection Recovery and Gas Chromatographic Analysis of Organic Pollutants in Ambient Air using Light Adsorbents. J. Chromatogr. 203:263 (1981).
47. Ciccioli, P.; Cecinato, A.; Brancaleoni, E.; Frattoni, M.: Use of Carbon Adsorption Traps Combined with High Resolution Gas Chromatography — Mass Spectrometry for the Analysis of Polar and Non-polar C4–C14 Hydrocarbons Involved in Photochemical Smog Formation. J. High Res. Chromatogr. 15:75 (1992).
48. Rothweiler, H.: Active Sampling of VOC in Non-industrial Buildings. In: Diffusive Sampling: An Alternative Approach to Workplace Air Monitoring. A. Berlin, R.H. Brown, and K.J. Saunders, Eds. CEC Pub. No. 10555EN, Brussels-Luxembourg (1987).
49. Nederlands Normalissatie-Instituut: Methods in NVN Series (Luchtkwaliteit; Werkplekatmosfeer). NNI, Delft, The Netherlands (in series, 1986-92).
50. U.S. Environmental Protection Agency: EPA Compendium of Methods for the Determination of Toxic Organic Compounds in Ambient Air. U.S. EPA, Washington, DC (1984).
51. Kristensson, J.: Diffusive Sampling and Gas Chromatographic Analysis of Volatile Compounds. Ph.D. Thesis. University of Stockholm, Sweden (1987).
52. Wright, M.D.: A Dual-capillary Column System for Automated Analysis of Workplace Contaminants by Thermal Desorption - Gas Chromatography. Anal. Proc. 24:309 (1987).
53. CONCAWE: Method for Monitoring Gasoline Vapour in Air. CONCAWE Report 8/86. Den Haag, The Netherlands (1986).
54. Health and Safety Executive: Methods for the Determination of Hazardous Substances. Volatile Organic Compounds in Air. MDHS 72. HSE Occupational Medicine and Hygiene Laboratory, Sheffield, UK (1992).
55. Analytical Chemistry Committee: Analytical Abstracts. American Industrial Hygiene Association, Akron, OH (1965).
56. Hanson, N.W.; Reilly, D.A.; Stagg, H.E.: The Determination of Toxic Substances in Air. Heffer, Cambridge, UK (1965).
57. Jacobs, M.B.: The Analytical Chemistry of Industrial Poisons, Hazards and Solvents, 2nd ed. Interscience Publishers, Inc., New York (1949).
58. Jacobs, M.B.: The Analytical Toxicology of Industrial Inorganic Poisons. Interscience Publishers, Inc., New York (1967).
59. Health and Safety Executive: Methods for the Detection of Toxic Substances in Air. HM Factory Inspectorate. HMSO, London, UK (in series, 1943-77).
60. Ruch, W.E.: Chemical Detection of Gaseous Pollutants. Ann Arbor Science Publishers, Ann Arbor, MI (1966).
61. Ruch, W.E.: Quantitative Analysis of Gaseous Pollutants. Ann Arbor Science Publishers, Ann Arbor, MI (1970).
62. Thomas, L.C.; Chamberlain, G.J.: Colorimetric Chemical Analytical Methods, 8th ed. The Tintometer Ltd., Salisbury, UK (1974).
63. Feigl, F.: Spot Tests, 4th ed. Elsevier Publ. Co., London, UK (1954).
64. Berlin, A.; Brown, R.H.; Saunders, K.J., Eds.: Diffusive Sampling: An Alternative Approach to Workplace Air Monitoring. CEC Pub. No. 10555EN. Commission of the European Communities, Brussels-Luxenbourg (1987).
65. Palmes, E.D.; Gunnison, A.F.: Personal Monitoring Device for Gaseous Contaminants. Am. Ind. Hyg. Assoc. J. 34:78 (1973).
66. Jost, W.: Diffusion in Solids, Liquids and Gases, pp. 42–45. Academic Press, New York (1960).
67. Tompkins, F.C.; et al.: A New Personal Dosimeter for the Monitoring of Industrial Pollutants. Am. Ind. Hyg. Assoc. J. 38:371 (1977).
68. Bamberger, R.L.; et al.: A New Personal Sampler for Organic Vapors. Am. Ind. Hyg. Assoc. J. 39:701 (1978).
69. Moore, G.: Diffusive Sampling — A Review of Theoretical Aspects and the State-of-the-Art. In: Diffusive Sampling: An Alternative Approach to Workplace Air Monitoring. A. Berlin, R.H. Brown, and K.J. Saunders, Eds. CEC Pub. No. 10555EN, Brussels-Luxembourg (1987).
70. Bartley, D.L.; Doemeny, W.; Taylor, D.G.: Diffusive Monitoring of Fluctuating Concentrations. Am. Ind. Hyg. Assoc. J. 44:241 (1983).
71. Pozzoli, L.; Cottica, D.: An Overview of the Effects of Temperature, Pressure, Humidity, Storage and Face Velocity. In: Diffusive Sampling: An Alternative Approach to Workplace Air Monitoring. A. Berlin, R.H. Brown, and K.J. Saunders, Eds. CEC Pub. No. 10555EN. Commission of European Communities, Brussels-Luxembourg (1987).
72. Squirrell, D.C.M.: Diffusive Sampling — An Overview. In: Diffusive Sampling: An Alternative Approach to Workplace Air Monitoring. A. Berlin, R.H. Brown, and K.J. Saunders, Eds. CEC Pub. No. 10555EN. Commission of European Communities, Brussels-Luxembourg (1987).
73. Kennedy, E.R.; Hull, R.D.; Crable, J.V.; Teass, A.W.: Protocol for the Evaluation of Passive Monitors. In: Diffusive Sampling: An Alternative Approach to Workplace Air Monitoring. A. Berlin, R.H. Brown, and K.J. Saunders, Eds. CEC Pub. No. 10555EN. Commission of European Communities, Brussels-Luxembourg (1987).
74. Health and Safety Executive: Methods for the Determination of Hazardous Substances. Protocol for Assessing the Performance of a Diffusive Sampler. MDHS 27. HSE Occupational Medicine and Hygiene Laboratory, Sheffield, UK (1987).
75. European Committee for Standardization. Workplace Atmospheres — Requirements and Test Methods for Diffusive Samplers for the Determination of Gases and Vapours. PrEN 838:1992.
76. Lugg, G.A.: Diffusion Coefficients of Some Organic and Other Vapors in Air. Anal. Chem. 40:1072 (1968).
77. Pannwitz, K-H.: Diffusion Coefficients. Drager Rev. 52-1 (1984).
78. Underhill, D.W.: Unbiased Passive Sampling. Am Ind. Hyg. Assoc. J. 44:237 (1983).
79. Hearl, F.J.; Manning, M.P.: Transient Response of Diffusion Dosimeters. Am. Ind. Hyg. Assoc. J. 41:778 (1980).
80. Feigley, C.E.; Chastain, J.B.: An Experimental Comparison of Three Diffusion Samplers Exposed to Concentration Profiles of Organic Vapors. Am Ind. Hyg. Assoc. J. 43:227 (1982).
81. Einfeld, W.: Diffusional Sampler Performance Under Transient Exposure Conditions. Am. Ind. Hyg. Assoc. J. 44:29 (1983).
82. Barley, D.L.; Deye, G.J.; Woebkenberg, M.L.: Diffusive Monitor Test: Peformance Under Transient Conditions. Appl. Ind. Hyg. 2(3):119 (1987).
83. Van den Hoed, N.; Halmans, M.T.H.: Sampling and Thermal Desorption Efficiency of Tube-type Diffusive Samplers: Selection and Performance of Adsorbents. Am. Ind. Hyg. Assoc. J. 48:364 (1987).
84. Brown, R.H.: Applications of the HSE Diffusive Sampler Protocol. In: Diffusive Sampling: An Alternative Approach to Workplace Air Monitoring. A. Berlin, R.H. Brown, and K.J. Saunders, Eds. CEC Pub. No. 10555EN. Commission of European Communities, Brussels-Luxembourg (1987).
85. Kennedy, E.R.; Cassinelli, M.E.; Hull, R.D.: Verification of Passive Monitor Performance. Applications. In: Diffusive Sampling: An Alternative Approach to Workplace Air Monitoring. A. Berlin, R.H. Brown, and K.J. Saunders, Eds. CEC Pub. No. 10555EN. Commission of European Communities, Brussels-Luxembourg (1987).
86. DeBortoli, M.; Molhave, L.; Ullrich, D.: European Interlaboratory Comparison of Passive Samplers for Organic Vapour Monitoring in Indoor Air. In: Diffusive Sampling: An Alternative Approach to Workplace Air Monitoring. A. Berlin, R.H. Brown, and K.J. Saunders, Eds. CEC Pub. No. 10555EN. Commission of European Communities, Brussels-Luxembourg (1987).
87. Lautenberger, W.J.; Kring, E.V.; Morello, J.A.: A New Personal Badge Monitor for Organic Vapors. Am. Ind. Hyg. Assoc. J. 41:737 (1980).
88. Kring, E.V.; et al.: A New Passive Colorimetric Air Monitoring Badge System for Ammonia, Sulfur Dioxide and Nitrogen Dioxide. Am. Ind.

Hyg. Assoc. J. 42:373 (1981).

89. Hickey, J.L.S.; Bishop, C.C.: Field Comparison of Charcoal Tubes and Passive Monitors with Mixed Vapors. Am. Ind. Hyg. Assoc. J. 42:264 (1981).
90. American Conference of Governmental Industrial Hygienists: 1993–1994 Threshold Limit Values for Chemical Substances and Physical Agents and Biological Exposure Indices. ACGIH, Cincinnati, OH (1993).
91. American Conference of Governmental Industrial Hygienists: Documentation of Threshold Limit Values and Biological Exposure Indices, 6th ed. ACGIH, Cincinnati, OH (1991).
92. NIOSH's Recommendations for Occupational Safety and Health Standards. MMWR 37:5 (1988).

Instrument Descriptions

After reviewing the fundamentals of the gas- and vapor-collecting devices discussed in the preceding section, it is important for readers to be able to find out what is currently available and to be aware of the changes that have occurred since the 7th edition of the ASI. New models of bubblers and impingers, sorbent tubes, and adsorbent badges have appeared. Some manufacturers' lines have changed and more has been published about some of the collecting devices.

The instrument descriptions in this chapter are grouped into two major categories: 1) gas and vapor collectors and 2) passive samplers and monitors. Instrument manufacturers' names, addresses, and telephone numbers are grouped in Tables 17-I-5 and 17-I-6. All tables appear at the end of the section.

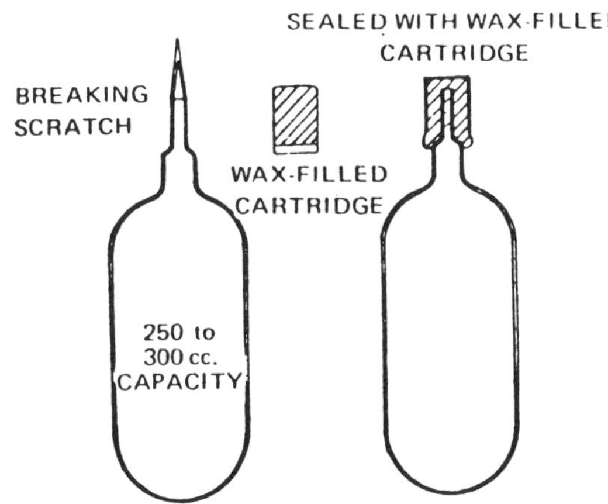

INSTRUMENT 17-1a. Glass Sampling Vacuum Flasks.

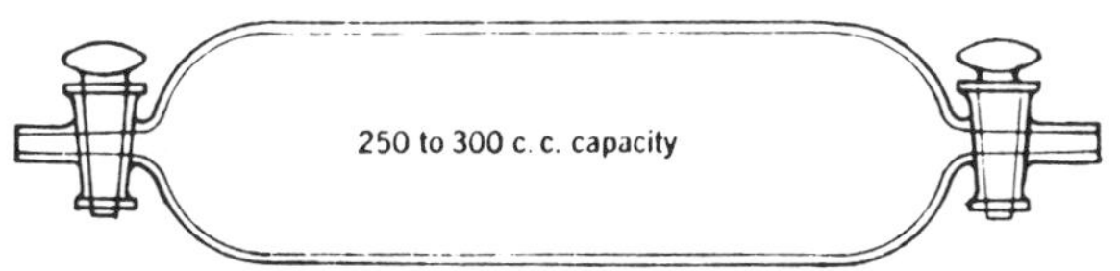

INSTRUMENT 17-1b. Gas or Liquid Displacement Type Sampling Bottle.

Gas and Vapor Collectors

Grab Samplers

17-1. Evacuated Flasks

Ace Glass; Alltech Associates, Inc.; Cole-Parmer; Graseby-Andersen; PMC; SKC Inc.; Supelco, Inc.; Whitey Co.

The evacuated flasks are usually heavy-walled containers of 200- to 1000-ml capacity. By means of a heavy-duty vacuum pump, the internal pressure is reduced (nominally) to zero. Instrument 17-1a illustrates one such container. The neck of the container is drawn to a tip and sealed by heating during the final stages of evacuation. The sample is taken by breaking the sealed end. The barometric pressure and air temperature at the sampling site are noted. After sampling, the flask is resealed with a ball of wax, masking tape, rubber septum cap, or other suitable sealant and sent to the laboratory for analysis.

Instrument 17-1b illustrates a separatory flask fitted with glass-stoppered cocks on each end. Alltech Associates supplies 125-, 250-, and 500-ml gas sampling bulbs with septum ports. These tubes are suitable for partial evacuation. Evacuation is achieved by drawing a vacuum through one stem while the other is kept closed, then closing the open stem before the vacuum is turned off. These containers are available in glass, plastic, and metal.

Cole-Parmer distributes polypropylene bulbs that store 250 cm^3 of gas samples at 25 psi maximum pressure. They have a 4-mm bore stopcock and Teflon plug on one end. The stopcock accepts 1/2- to 3/8-in. i.d. tubing. Bulbs are 3 1/4 in. long and are 2 in. in diameter.

Cole-Parmer also distributes a gas washing bottle that consists of a 250-cm^3 polypropylene graduated cylinder with extended base, a vinyl stopper with 1/4-in. o.d. tubes, and a removable gas dispersion fitting with 70-μm porosity polyethylene disc. Pressure capacity is 0.5 psig.

Alltech Associates also provides gas sampling bulbs with a choice of stopcocks and septum ports.

PMC, Graseby-Andersen, and SKC have heavy-metal gas sampling spheres, which have been called Summa Canisters. They are pictured in Instrument 17-1c and are used as preevacuated stainless steel vessels that have been specially passivated for minimum interaction with sample analytes. They were designed to meet U.S. EPA TO-14 specifications for environmental sampling of volatile organic compounds; however, they find many applications for industrial hygiene sampling.

The Whitey Co. distributes a line of stainless steel and alloy sample cylinders, from 10 cm^3 to 1 gal in size, fitted with Nupro/Whitey™ valves and Swagelok™ connections.

INSTRUMENT 17-1c. Passivated Canister Sampler (Graseby Andersen).

Except for these and the heavy-walled glass containers illustrated in Instrument 17-1a, no attempt has been made to reduce the pressure to zero in other containers. Therefore, the degree of evacuation must be known and is determined from the manometer pressure or vacuum gauge. The sampling information, along with the barometric pressure and temperature at the sampling site, is used to calculate the actual volume of air or gas collected.

17-2. Gas/Liquid Displacement Flasks

General Supply Houses (see Table 17-5)

Many kinds of ordinary, sealable containers can be used as gas/liquid displacement flasks. Numerous commercial firms sell suitable displacement flasks. A user's selection criteria should include the required volume of sample to be taken, reactivity of the analyte of interest, and the practicality of using such a device (i.e., no pump is necessary with liquid displacement, but something must be done with the drained fluid). The major limitation is the solubility of the analyte in the displacement liquid. With bulb displacement (see Instruments 17-2a through 17-2c), the equivalent of three or more collector volumes must be flushed through the container to ensure 99% of the contents is pure sample. See Instruments 17-2a through 17-2d.

17-3. Flexible Plastic Containers (Sampling Bags)

Alltech Associates, Inc.; Anspec Company, Inc.; BGI; Calibrated Instruments, Inc.; Cole-Parmer; Edlon Products Inc.; Plastic Film Enterprises; PMC; Anitole J. Sipin Co.; SKC Inc.; Supelco, Inc.

Sampling bags are widely used, are available from a number of manufacturers and distributors, made of a variety of materials, and come in a selection of sizes (from less than 1 to 250 L). The materials include polyester (e.g., aluminized Scotch Pak™, Scotch Pak™, and Mylar™); polyvinylidene chloride (e.g., Saran™); five-layer, high-density polyethylene (e.g., Cali-5-Bond™); and the fluorocarbons (e.g., Chemtron™, Kel F™, Aclor™, Kynar™, Tedlar™, Crinkle Tedlar™, and Teflon™). Instrument 17-3a illustrates a Teflon bag from Edlon Products, Inc. In addition to the less reactive materials, bags that are black or opaque are now available for the collection of light-sensitive gases and vapors. A crinkle surface bag was developed by Plastic Film Enterprises to facilitate filling, flushing, and complete evacuation of the sample bags. An array of valve types has been employed and is available from the

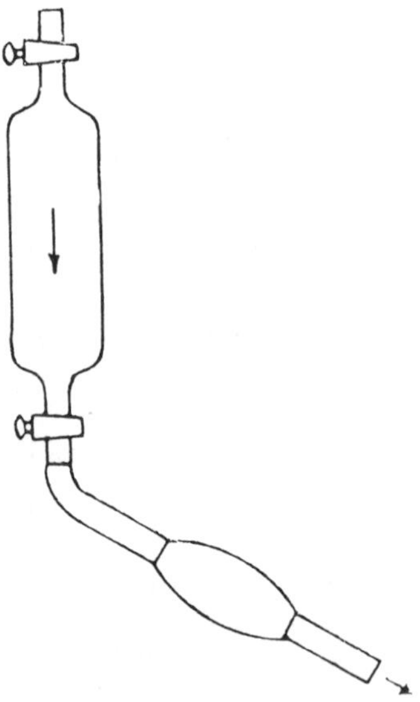

INSTRUMENT 17-2a. Filling container with rubber bulb hand aspirator.

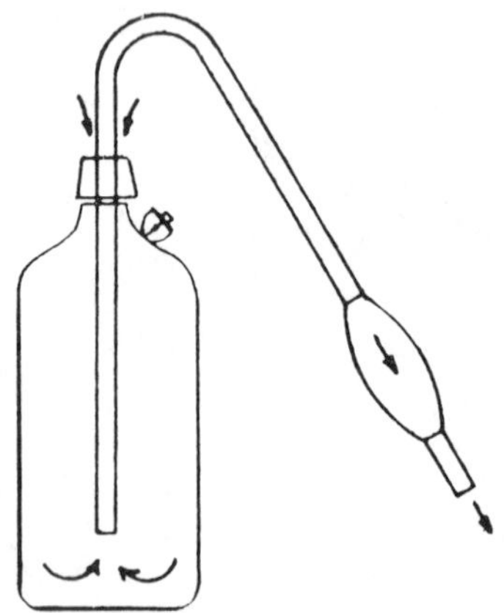

INSTRUMENT 17-2b. Filling bottle with rubber bulb hand aspirator.

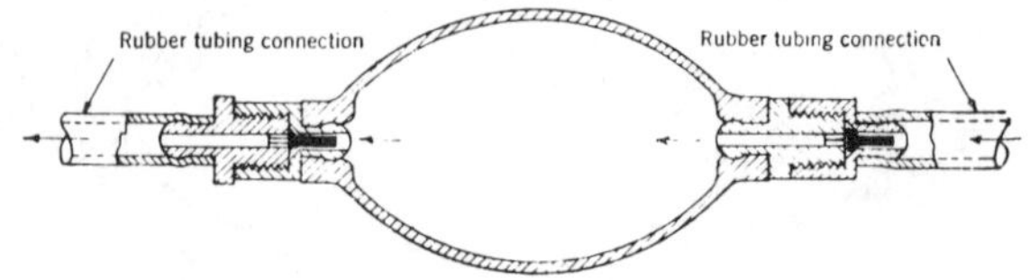

INSTRUMENT 17-2c. Rubber bulb hand aspirator.

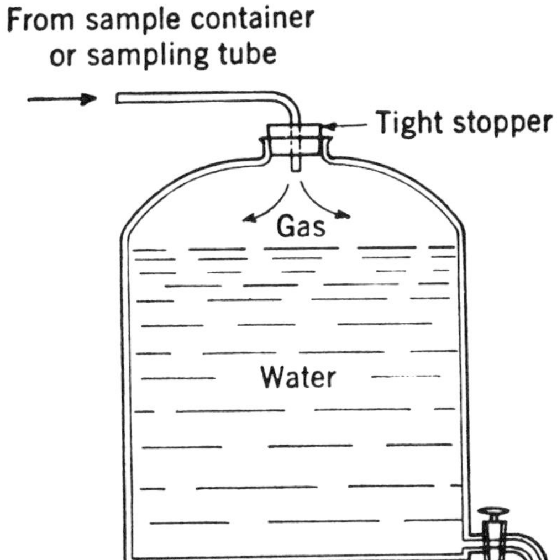

INSTRUMENT 17-2d. Aspirator bottle.

different manufacturers. In addition to the familiar rectangular shape, sampling bags are designed in other shapes to improve sampling techniques, minimize dead volume problems, and relieve stresses around fittings (see Illustration 17-3b).

All bags should be leak tested, cleaned with pure compressed air, and conditioned before use. Three pump and cleaning cycles should be sufficient, unless condensable materials have deposited in the bag. The conditioning is first performed in the laboratory using test atmospheres; it is then repeated in the field before use by filling and emptying a bag several times at the sampling rate that will be used for taking the sample. Gas/vapor storage stability and decay curves for these devices must be determined. Advantages are their low cost, convenient handling, and ease of use. Bags can be selected with appropriate valves, as well as with septum ports for injecting measured gas or liquid volumes for dilution to standard concentrations. Calibrated Instruments makes syringe systems for filling bags.

Cole-Parmer markets Teflon and Tedlar bags from 0.5 to 85.7 L with on/off and septum valves for tubing connections and hypodermic needles, respectively. Tedlar bags come in dust-proof and light-free types for carbon monoxide, sulfur dioxide, hydrogen sulfide, radon, and mercaptans. Bags are 2 mils thick and can be used in cleanroom applications. Tedlar bags are double seamed and Teflon bags are single seamed. The Teflon bags meet National Aeronautics and Space Administration Specification Level 1 and are 5 mils thick.

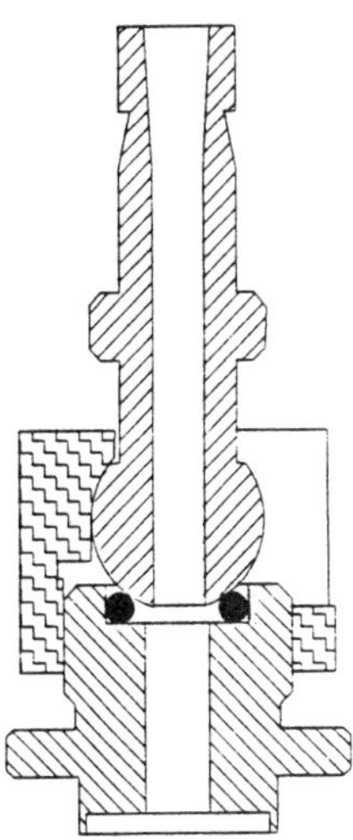

INSTRUMENT 17-3b. Valves for Plastic Sampling Bags (BGI).

BGI also markets Tedlar and Teflon sampling bags of 2 and 5 mil thickness, respectively, in a variety of sizes fitted with new patented valve and septum hardware. Bag filling pumps and sets of critical orifi (as shown in Instrument 17-3c) are available.

SKC Inc. has 2-mil-thick Tedlar bags with septum fittings, two types of valve fittings in dual stainless steel or single inert polypropylene fittings, and hose/valve fittings and replaceable septum units (as shown in Instrument 17-3b).

17-4. Hypodermic Syringes

General Supply Houses (see Table 17-I-6)

Syringes with volumes from 10 to 50 ml have been found satisfactory for air sampling. Suitable syringes

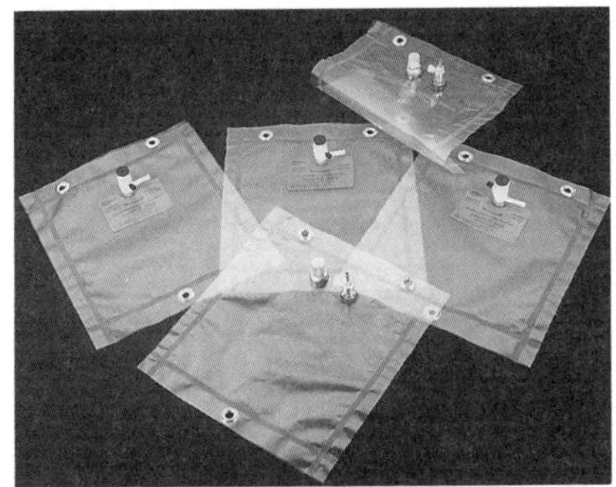

INSTRUMENT 17-3a. Plastic Gas Sampling Bags.

INSTRUMENT 17-3c. Bag Filling Pump (BGI).

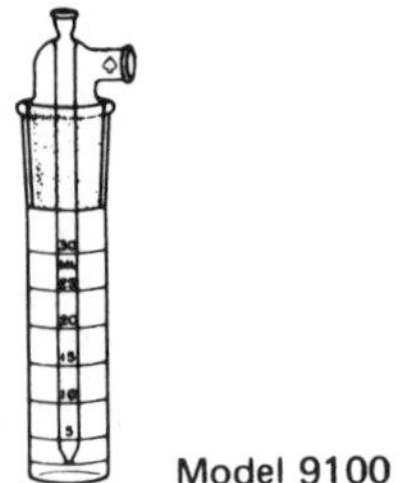

INSTRUMENT 17-5a. Midget Impingers (Ace Glass, Inc.)

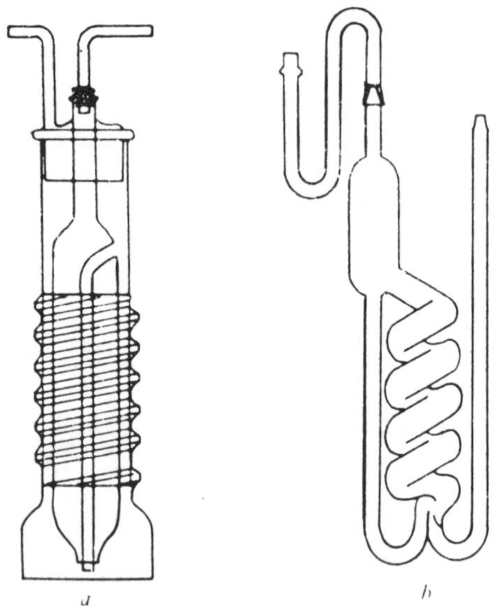

INSTRUMENT 17-5b. Spiral and Helical Absorbers.

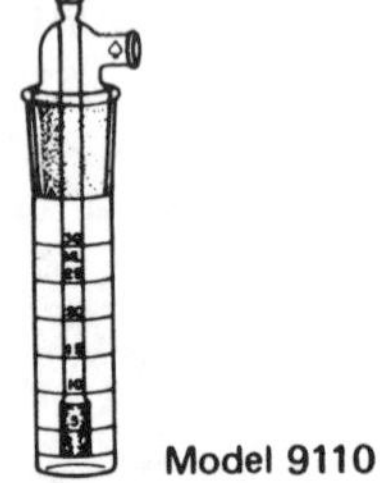

INSTRUMENT 17-5c. Midget Gas Bubbler (Coarse Frit) (Ace Glass, Inc.)

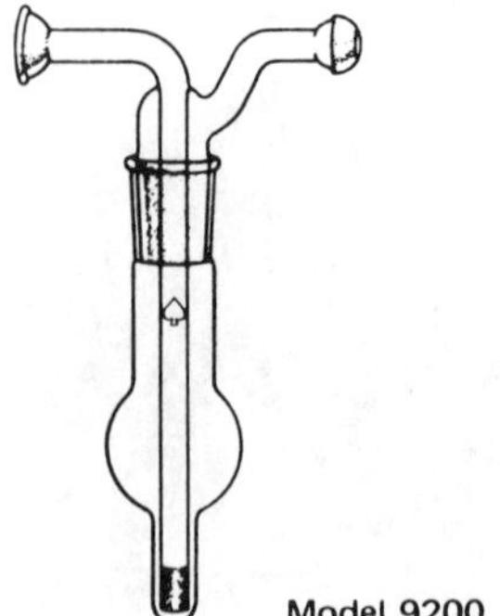

INSTRUMENT 17-5d. Nitrogen Dioxide Gas Bubbler (Ace Glass, Inc.)

should be gas tight. They are available in glass and disposable plastic. Gas and vapor storage and decay curves for these devices must be determined. Advantages are their low cost, convenience, and ease of use. Large-volume acrylic syringes from 0.5 to 2.0 L, made by Hamilton, are available for special purposes from general supply houses.

Continuous Active Samplers

17-5. Bubblers and Gas Washing Bottles

Ace Glass, Inc.; Cole-Parmer; Corning Glass Works; Scientific Glass and Instruments Company; SKC Inc.; Supelco, Inc.

The midget impinger is the most widely used in this group and is illustrated in Instrument 17-5a. It is designed for impacting particles at a flow rate of 2.8 L/min; however, for industrial hygiene use as a bubbler, it is generally used with 10 to 20 ml of absorbing solution and a flow rate of about 1.0 L/min. No more than 20 ml of absorbing solution should be added to the impinger flask. Air sampling is performed by connecting a personal pump or other source of suction to the outlet tube. The impinger is either hand-held or attached to the worker's clothing. Care must be taken that the impinger does not tilt, which could result in a loss of absorbing solution or reagent. Too much reagent solution or excessive flow rate will also lead to loss of sample. Spill-proof impingers have been designed to minimize this problem and are commercially available (e.g., SKC, Supelco). In-line traps are suggested to prevent carryover of liquids into the sample pumps.

Friedrichs and Milligan gas washing bottles are examples of spiral and helical absorbers (Instrument 17-5b). They may be used for collecting gaseous substances that are only moderately soluble or are slow reacting with reagents in the collection media. The spiral or helical structures provide for higher collection efficiency by allowing longer residence time of the contaminant within the tube. Slower acting and less soluble substances are permitted more time to react with the absorbing solution.

Gases and vapors that are sparingly soluble in the collecting medium may be sampled in fritted bubblers (Instruments 17-5c and 17-5d). They contain sintered or fritted glass, or multiperforated plates at the inlet tube. Air drawn into these devices is broken up into very small bubbles, and the heavy froth that develops increases the contact of gas and liquid.

Frits come in various sizes and grades, usually designated as fine, medium, coarse, and extra coarse. A coarse frit is usually best for gases and vapors that are appreciably soluble or reactive. A medium porosity frit may be used for gases and vapors that are difficult collect, but the sampling rate must be adjusted to maintain a flow of discrete bubbles. For highly volatile gaseous substances that are extremely difficult to collect, a frit of fine porosity may be required to break the air into extremely small bubbles and ensure adequate collection efficiency. Air flow, however, must be controlled to avoid the formation of large bubbles by the coalescence of small bubbles. There is little value, for example, in using fine porosity frit and using increased air flow because a population of larger bubbles is produced. The finer the frit, however, the higher the pressure drop, which might require more powerful vacuum pumps. Selection of the proper frit should be made with all of these factors in mind. The collection efficiency of the sampling equipment must be determined for the specific contaminants involved. Generally, lower flow rates are used with fritted bubblers than with impingers of the same liquid capacity.

SKC markets Pyrex-brand glass bubble tubes designed for collecting airborne chemicals and permitting contact with the collecting liquid. A bubbler tube may be mounted on an air sampling pump or worn in a holster. Six types are available. The Standard Midget has a 25-ml capacity with 5-ml graduations. The Midget Fritted Tip Impinger is modified with a fritted glass tip for better contact between the sampling air and the liquid, and is required by many NIOSH and OSHA procedures. The Ozone Impinger follows NIOSH requirements for a Teflon sleeve for ozone sampling. The Spill-Resistant Midget Impinger has been designed to prevent a liquid spill if tipped or inverted. The Micro Impinger is a one-tenth scale miniature of the Standard Midget.

Supelco has a similar line of impingers and bubblers that are available with either conventional ground glass joints or convenient Teflon microconnectors.

17-6. Packed Glass-Bead Columns

General Supply Houses (See Table 17-I-6)

Packed glass-bead columns (Instrument 17-6) are used for special situations where a concentrated solution is needed. Glass pearl beads are wetted with the absorbing solution and provide a large surface area for the collection of sample. It is of historical interest to note that the absorption of benzene and other aromatic hydrocarbon vapors in nitrating acid has been performed with this type of absorber. It is especially useful when a viscous absorbing liquid is required. The rate of sampling is necessarily low, 0.25 to 0.5 L/min of air.

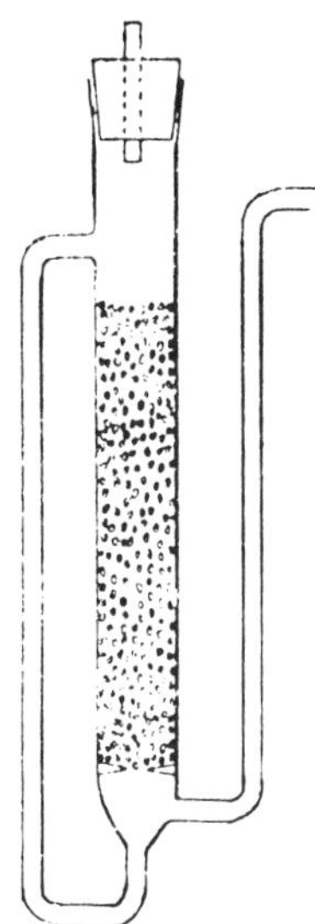

INSTRUMENT 17-6. Packed Glass-Bead Columns.

17-7. Cold Traps

General Supply Houses (see Table 17-I-6)

Cold traps (Instrument 17-7) are generally component assemblies constructed on an as-needed basis. The cold trap usually consists of a U-shaped glass or copper section that is filled with the adsorbent collection medium. The U-shaped section is immersed in liquid nitrogen, dry ice baths, or other cold mixtures to effect the trapping. The adsorbent used is a function of the contaminant needing collection (e.g., activated carbon is used for organics). Vacuum and reduced-pressure cold trapping utilize impinger-shaped traps that can be evacuated and the sample condensed on the inside of the outer wall. These traps can be used with or without adsorbent, depending on the flow rate through the trap. Faster flow or a higher sampling rate require a more torturous path to efficiently trap the vapors.

17-8. Plastic Sampling Bag Systems

Alltech Associates, Inc.; Anspec Company, Inc.; BGI, International; Calibrated Instruments, Inc.; Edlon Products Inc.; Plastic Film Enterprises; PMC; Anatole J.Sipin Co., Inc.; SKC, Inc.; Supelco, Inc.

These bags are similar to those used and described in Section 17-3. The difference between the sections is that these bags are a part of a system used to obtain time-integrated air samples. Air collection systems are available from Calibrated Instruments, Inc., and consist of a five-layer, nonpermeable, high-density polyethylene bag (i.e., Cali-5-Bond) available in sizes ranging from 100 ml to 200 L and a battery-operated air pump with an on-off cycle timer. Sipin provides a similar sampling system that includes a battery-operated air pump (without the timer), a pump belt case, and a protective carrying case for a gas collection bag. This small, day-hike backpack can be worn by a worker for a complete shift, as necessary.

Bags can also be filled by displacing air or water from an airtight container that holds the sampling bag. As the fluids flow out, the bag is distended and the sample is drawn into the bag to fill the container (as illustrated in 17-8a, PMC Drum Sampler). The advantage is that reactive analytes do not pass through a pump. A variety of bag materials are available depending on the reactivity of the analytes. In addition to the less reactive

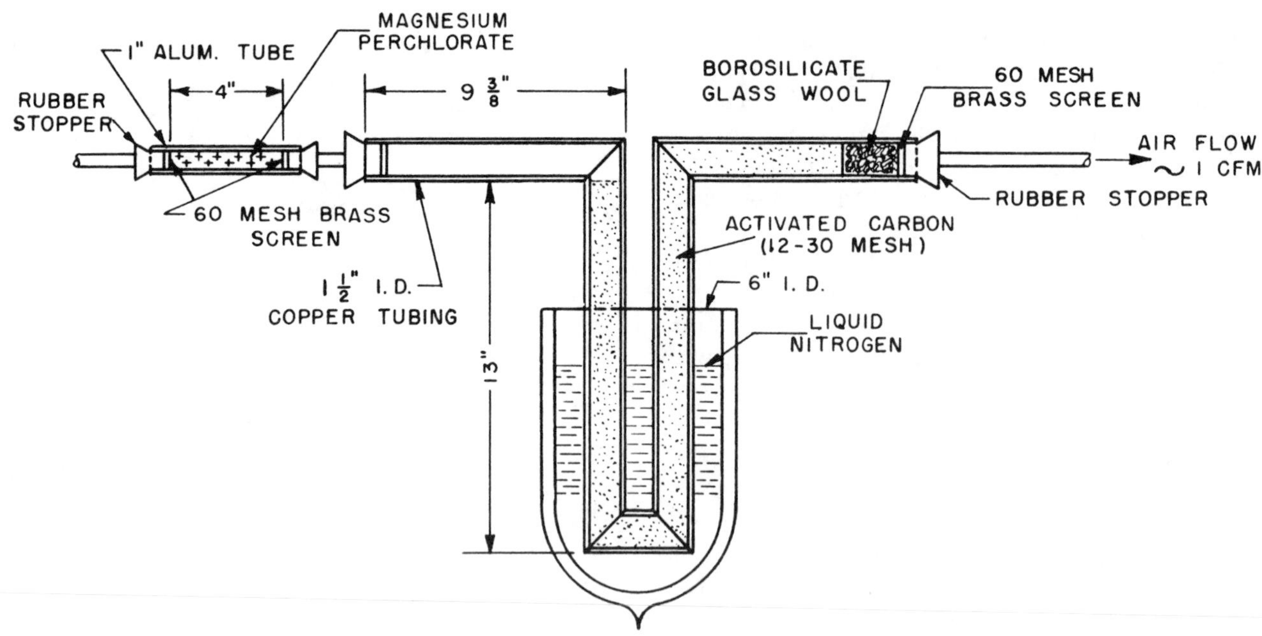

INSTRUMENT 17-7. Cold Trap.

materials, bags that are black or opaque are now available for the collection of light-sensitive gases and vapors.

Vacuum bag samplers by Supelco include a 10-L bag sampler that allows capture of a discrete air sample in the bag without having the air sample pass through a vacuum pump first. This portable vacuum chamber-base sampler provides fast zero–cross-contamination sampling of refinery stack gases and volatile organic compound (VOC) vent gases. Powered by a 12-V DC battery, the bag sampler fills or empties a 10-L bag in 2 min by applying pressure or a vacuum to the outside of the sample bag. The automatic shut-off switch prevents the sample bag from overfilling. Pumping controllers meet the U.S. EPA requirement for taking a 10-L stack sample in 15 min. The sampler includes a battery, charger, flow controller, and pump timer (see Instrument 17-8b). A 1-L size is also available, as well as an automatic, six 1-L-bag sampler that collects multiple air samples.

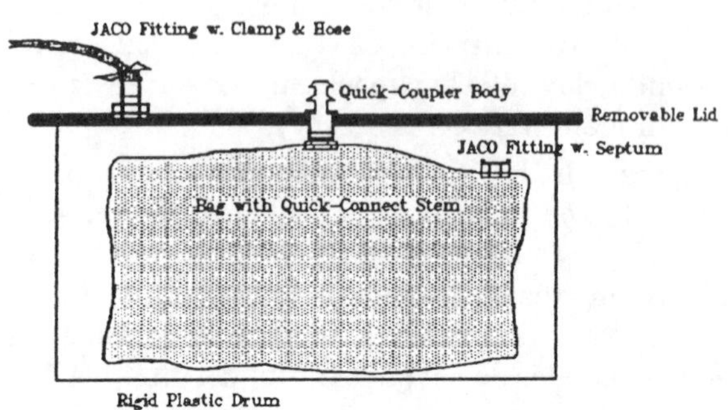

INSTRUMENT 17-8a. Drum Sampler for Bag Filling (PMC).

17-9. Solid Adsorbents, Active Sampling

Barneby Cheney Company; Columbia Scientific Industries; Fisher Scientific Company; Perkin-Elmer Corp.,Pittsburgh; SKC Inc.; Supelco, Inc.; Westvaco, Inc.; Witco

Several types of charcoal are commercially available for both active and passive sampling. Adsorption is used in the field of air quality monitoring as a means of collecting and concentrating airborne contaminants for analysis. The large number of chemical vapors that may be encountered at varying concentrations ensures that no one adsorbent material can effectively collect all contaminants under all conditions. The choice of the adsorbent is designed to maximize collection efficiency

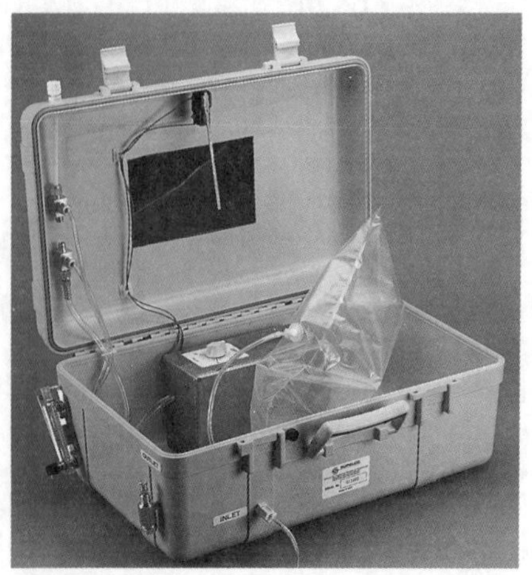

INSTRUMENT 17-8b. Vacuum Bag Sampler (Supelco).

while retaining low selectivity, and forms a critical part of an air sampling program. The products used most frequently for air sampling are derived from coconut shells and lignite (Darco and Muchar). The mesh sizes employed vary considerably. NIOSH recommends 20/40 mesh coconut shell charcoal. Severs and Skory[30] found Pittsburgh PCB 12/30 mesh most suitable for sampling vinyl chloride, vinylidene chloride, and methyl chloride. The final choice for a specific application should be made only after performance tests have been made. Other solid adsorbents are available and are more desirable for polar and reactive analytes. Coated adsorbents are also available for specific analytes as described in the NIOSH Manual of Analytical Methods (3rd and 4th editions).

SKC maintains a large selection of sorbent materials, including the widely used Lot 120 coconut charcoal and the Anasorb Series of sorbents. These and other sorbents are available in regular SKC sorbent devices. The existing sorbent devices can be packed with alternate sorbents by special order. Also, sorbents can be purchased in limited bulk quantities for use in the customer's apparatus. SKC carries the Series 226 sorbent sample tubes. The sorbent sample tubes collect airborne contaminants typically by adsorption of the contaminant onto a solid sorbent surface. Approximately 40 different sorbents are available. Some are chemically coated or treated to facilitate their collection properties. An air sampling pump is used to draw air through the tube at rates from 0 to 1500 ml/min, although flow rates between 20 and 200 ml/min are more typical for long-term, low-flow sampling. Tubes are constructed according to validated OSHA, NIOSH, or U.S. EPA analytical methods for sampling individual chemicals or classes of chemicals in air. These standard methods specify the design and makeup of the tubes, the sampling procedure, and the details of chemical analysis. Most tubes contain a primary sorbent section and a back-up bed that is used to indicate breakthrough. SKC stocks over 130 different sorbent tubes to collect over 1000 different airborne chemicals. See Table 17-I-3 for examples and Instrument 17-9a.

INSTRUMENT 17-9a. Solid Adsorbent Tubes (SKC, Inc.).

INSTRUMENT 17-9b. VOC Monitor (Spectrex).

The standard tube for low-flow, time-weighted average (TWA) sampling contains 150 mg of adsorbent in 100- and 50-mg sections. Large tubes are also available that contain 600 mg of charcoal; 400 mg in the front section and 200 mg in the back section. Jumbo tubes contain 800 mg and 200 mg. The larger tubes allow higher flows for larger total capacities or higher air volumes for collecting very low concentrations. Other sizes of tubes can be ordered or prepared in the laboratory for special applications.

Sampling tubes need not always be made of glass. Many in use are constructed of stainless steel. One such unit, described by Severs and Skory,[30] measures 5.5 × 0.25 in. o.d. × 0.028 in. thick and is fitted with Swagelok™ caps.

In addition to the wide variety of sampling pumps that are manufactured, Spectrex has developed a unique alarm/pump. The New SXC-20 VOC Monitor is a quantitative sampler/detector illustrated in Instrument 17-9b. A miniature pump pulls an air sample across the surface of a heated, multigas, semiconductor detector. The VOC percentage is displayed on a color bar of green, orange, and red LEDs, and sounds a warning beeper at a preselected level. The output triggers a second miniature pump that starts to pull air through a charcoal or adsorber tube. This can be qualitatively and quantitatively analyzed on a gas chromatograph at the end of the sampling period. Finally, a miniature data logger is activated at the beginning of the sampling period. Time scale and quantitative data are easily accessed by any IBM or Apple laptop computer and read automatically. All three features make a precise monitoring system.

17-10. Polyurethane Foam, Active Sampling

Supelco, Inc.

The ORBO-1000 PUF is used for the collection of pesticides and PCBs in air, at sampling rates of 1–5

INSTRUMENT 17-10. Polyurethane Foam Plug (Supelco).

L/min. The polyurethane foam (PUF) plug is 22 mm in diameter by 76 mm long and is made to dimensions and density (0.022 g/cm^3) specified in U.S. EPA methodology. PUF plugs are precleaned and packaged to allow immediate use without further treatment. The PUF plug is housed in a glass holder with tapered end that easily attaches to a personal sampling pump. A filter cartridge containing a 32-mm quartz filter may be attached in front of the PUF to allow collection of aerosols and particulates. The analytical method involves a solvent Soxhlet extraction and concentration followed by gas chromatography. The PUF plug is reusable after appropriate solvent cleanup. Method applications for this sampling device include:

- U.S. EPA Method IP8 - Determination of Organochlorine Pesticides in Indoor Air
- U.S. EPA Method TO10 - Determination of Organochlorine Pesticides in Ambient Air
- ASTM D4861 - Sampling and Analysis of Pesticides and Polychlorinated Biphenyls in Air
- ASTM D4947 - Chlordane and Heptachlor Residues in Indoor Air

17-11. Automated Thermal Desorber Tubes/Desorber

Perkin-Elmer, Ltd.; Perkin-Elmer Corp.; Supelco, Inc.

The Perkin-Elmer Thermal Desorber is available with glass, stainless-steel, or glass-lined stainless tubes (empty or prepacked) for a variety of sampling methods, including TO-14, indoor air, air toxics, ozone precursors, diffusive sampling, and vehicle emissions, as well as solid sample desorption of resins, films, and fragrances in ointments. A wide variety of volatiles can be sampled in the range from C_2 to C_{36} onto user-selectable single- or multibed sorbents. These samples are then loaded onto Perkin-Elmer's 50-sample ATD-400 autosampler for thermal desorption (see Instrument 17-11a). No cryogen is used in the collection or analysis of samples because the ATD-400 utilizes electric (Peltier effect) cooling in conjunction with a sorbent-packed cold trap to concentrate the samples. Also available is a multitube automated sampler for indoor or outdoor environments.

The Supelco Thermal Desorption Unit assumes the role of the injection port of the gas chromatograph and interfaces to a capillary or packed gas chromatograph column via a heated transfer line made of either nickel or fused silica. A secondary flow path is used to prepare on-tube calibration standards using the built-in injection port. It may also be used for transferring analytes from a large-bore, high-capacity sampling tube to a narrow-bore focusing tube before desorption to the gas chromatograph in the primary flow path. This transfer, coupled with the rapid heating capabilities in the primary flow path, provides excellent chromatography of even very volatile gases, without cryogenic cooling. Valve, transfer line, and desorption temperatures are controlled independently (see illustration in Instrument 17-11b).

Passive Samplers and Monitors

The various commercially available passive (dosimeter) monitoring systems and dosimeters are listed alphabetically by contaminant in Table 17-I-1. The table includes manufacturers and brand names. The Pro-Tek™ organic vapor badges are now distributed by Gilian Instrument Co., but their colorimetric badge systems have been discontinued and are not available. 3M diffusive monitors for ethylene oxide, carbon monoxide, formaldehyde, and mercury are listed in Table 17-I-2. The types of badges supplied by SKC are found in Table 17-I-3. Addresses for manufacturers are found at the end of this chapter (Table 17-I-6). Note that the sampling rates for most passive badges are controlled

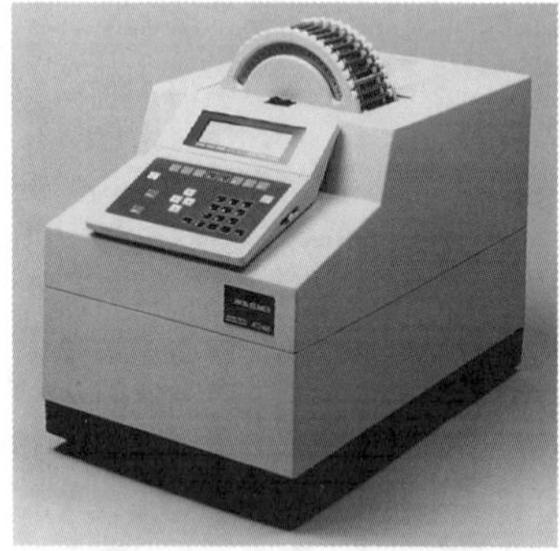

INSTRUMENT 17-11a. Automatic Thermal Desorber (Perkin-Elmer).

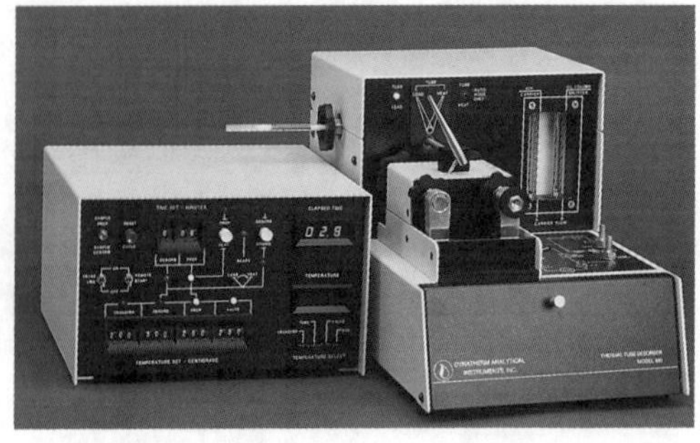

INSTRUMENT 17-11b. Thermal Desorption Unit (Supelco).

by the diffusion and/or permeation rates for each compound and by the specific geometry of the device (example sampling rates for different brands are shown in Table 17-I-4). Thus, each manufacturer must provide the sampling rates for the compounds of interest for their specific badges. Descriptions of specific systems are provided in the paragraphs that follow.

17-12. Pro-Tek™ Badges[87]

Pro-Tek Systems, Inc.

The Pro-Tek G-AA organic vapor air monitoring badge consists of one charcoal strip, two multicavity diffuser elements, and two covers (Instrument 17-12). The charcoal strip contains approximately 300 mg of activated charcoal. The badge offers the choice of two sampling rates of approximately 35 and 70 cm^3/min, depending on whether one or both protective covers is removed. The shortest sampling duration is approximately 0.2 ppm-hrs, and longer duration is limited by saturation of the charcoal strip.

As with charcoal active pumped methods, the analysis is performed using gas chromatography. Desorption coefficients are determined for all contaminants collected on the charcoal. Published values are available, but they should be determined experimentally for each batch being analyzed.

Pro-Tek's Sampling Guide publication lists badge sampling rates for more than 80 compounds. A partial list is found in Table 17-I-4. Sampling rates with an asterisk (*) were determined experimentally. The remaining rates were calculated using published diffusion coefficients or empirical equations modified according to Pro-Tek's experience with its monitor.

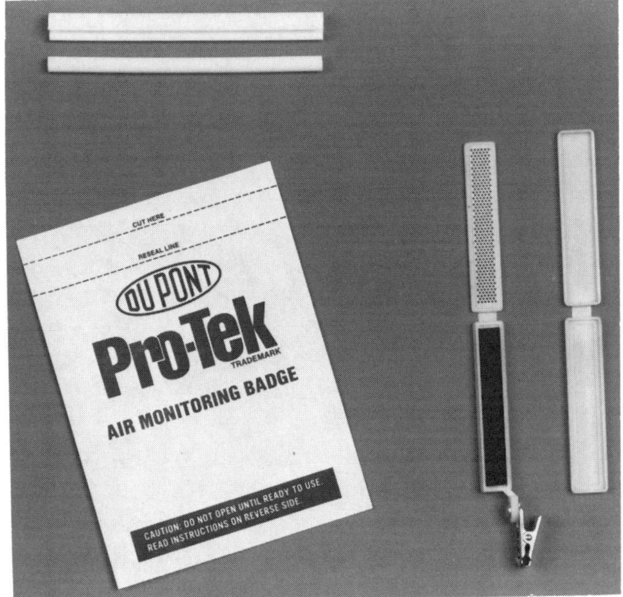

INSTRUMENT 17-12. Organic Vapor Sampling Badge (Pro-Tek).

The Pro-Tek G-BB Organic Vapor Badge is a general purpose device designed to handle most organic vapor requirements. It contains two 300-mg charcoal strips, one in the front section and another in the back-up section. It also has two covers and two precision multicavity diffusers. The shortest sampling duration for G-BB badges is approximately 0.4 ppm-hrs. The longest is determined by saturation of the charcoal.

Monitoring instructions and analysis are the same as for the G-AA badge, but the effective weight collected is calculated from:

$$m = m_1 + 2.2\ m_2$$

The factor 2.2 accounts for the increased diffusion path length to the back-up section.

17-13. TraceAir System OVM Badges

Gilian Instrument Corp.

The single-stage TraceAir organic vapor monitor (OVM) consists of a single strip of activated coconut charcoal sandwiched between two diffuser panels. Two covers are used to seal the unit. The charcoal strip contains 300 mg charcoal. The design of the badge allows the operator to remove either one or both of the covers to activate the badge for sampling. With one cover removed, the unit samples at a rate of approximately 35 cm^3/min (for most organic solvent vapors). Removing both covers doubles the effective sampling rate to the 70 cm^3/min range. This higher range enables the monitor to effectively monitor for short periods of time for short-term exposure limits (STEL) sampling. The limit of detection for this unit is approximately 0.2 ppm-hrs with both covers removed. The Trace Air OVM-2 contains a second charcoal strip that acts as a back-up. This second strip doubles the capacity of the OVM and facilitates sampling in those areas where potential exposures are expected to be higher than the capacity of the single-stage OVM-1. Only one cover can be removed from the OVM-2 because the back cover is used to seal the back-up section in the unit (diagrams of both units are shown in Instruments 17-13a and b). Thus, the limit of detection for the OVM-2 is 0.4 ppm-hrs. The effective mass of sample components collected is based on the same equation as shown above for the Pro-Tek G-BB badges. The TraceAir Technical Reference Guide provides instructions on the use of the badges and the sampling rates for 132 organic compounds (see Table 17-I-4 for example rates).

17-14. Organic Vapor Monitor #3500

3M Company

The 3500 monitor contains a single charcoal sorbent pad separated from a diffusion membrane by spacers (Instruments 17-14a and b). The 3520 has a similar geometry, but incorporates a back-up section that col-

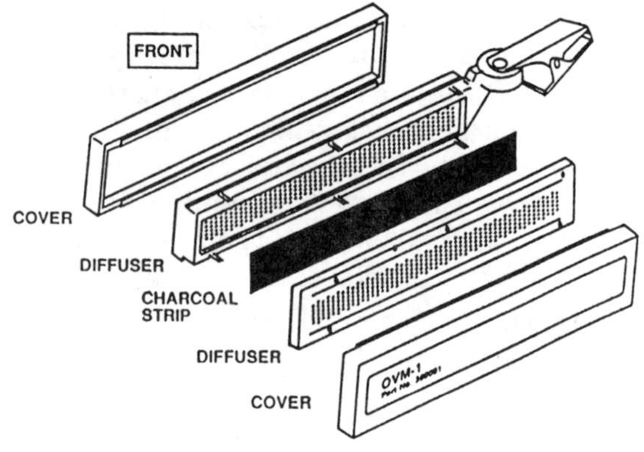

INSTRUMENT 17-13a. TraceAir OVM-1 Badges (Gilian Instruments).

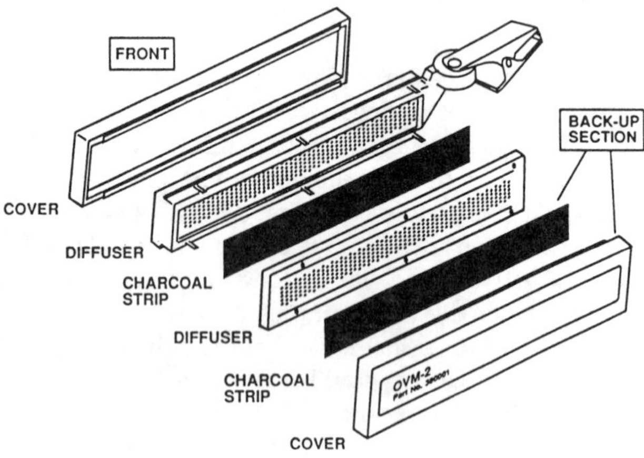

INSTRUMENT 17-13b. TraceAir OVM-2 Badges (Gilian Instruments).

lects gases and vapors when the capacity of the primary sorbent pad has been exceeded. The gas and vapor contaminants enter both types of monitors by molecular diffusion and are adsorbed onto the charcoal pad(s). Sampling rates for gases and vapors are provided by 3M. At the end of a sampling period, the diffusion membrane is removed and a tight-fitting cap is snapped into place. If the 3520 back-up monitor is being used, the primary section is separated from the back-up section, and caps are snapped on both the primary and back-up sections. Design of the capped monitor allows *in-situ* desorption of gases and vapors with carbon disulfide or other suitable solvents. Samples are desorbed for a minimum of 30 min and an aliquot is removed for analysis by gas chromatography. The organic vapor monitors are available with and without laboratory services.

Desorption efficiency values are known to vary with the amount of material on the charcoal and with the type and volume of desorbing solvent used. Therefore, actual desorption efficiencies should always be determined at the time of analysis. The recommended procedure for the 3M Organic Vapor Monitor #3500 is as follows:

> The organic compound in the liquid state is introduced through the elutriation port onto a piece of filter paper placed between the elutriation cap and diffusion plate of the monitor. The port is closed and the organic compound is given sufficient time to vaporize and consequently be absorbed by the charcoal sorbent. The filter is removed and analyzed as a separate sample to determine if complete transfer of the organic compound has occurred. Subsequently, the monitor is desorbed for an appropriate period and the aliquots for the gas chromatographic analysis are taken from the center port of the monitor.

The sampling rate used must be the one supplied by the manufacturer and, if possible, verified by the user (see Table 17-I-4).

17-15. Passive Sampler Series 575

SKC Inc.

This is a miniature sampling device that has a small amount of specially packed sorbent in a circular plastic

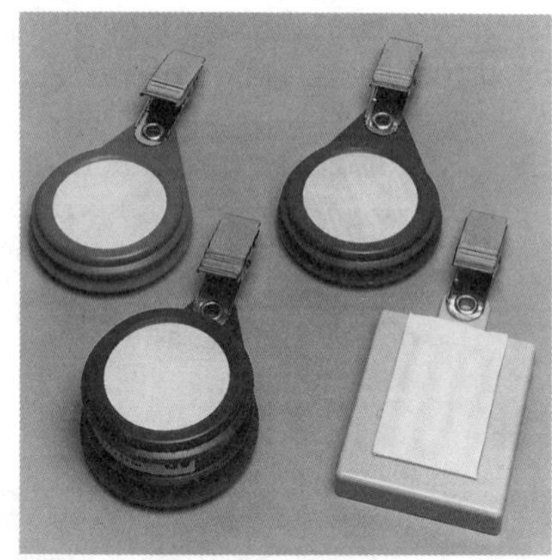

INSTRUMENT 17-14a. Passive Monitoring Badges (3M).

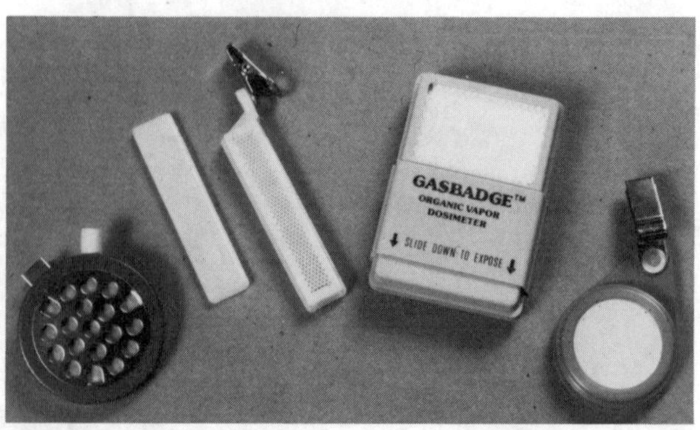

INSTRUMENT 17-14b. Organic Vapor Monitors including #3500 (3M) and Pro-Tek.

disc that is worn as a badge on the collar. It passively takes up airborne chemical vapors by simple diffusion at known sampling rates which have been experimentally determined and validated to NIOSH's strict Level 5 validation protocol.[73] As of this writing, the sampling rates of 35 organic chemicals have been validated. Theoretical sampling rates for other chemicals are also available. The badges are packed with any one of various available sorbents selected to best accommodate the chemicals of interest. The device is pictured in Instrument 17-15.

17-16. Draeger ORSA 5

National Draeger, Inc.

The ORSA is a passive, organic vapor sampler containing 400 mg of activated coconut shell charcoal. The measured contaminants flow automatically into the collecting tube during sampling, as a result of the concentration differential between the ambient air and the interior of the tube, where they are adsorbed on the activated charcoal. For measurements in the TLV range, the sampling time may be as long as 8 hrs. Shorter or longer sampling times are possible for other ranges. The ORSA may be analyzed according to the same laboratory methods used for active sampling charcoal tubes. Pannwitz had published a comparison of the ORSA 5 sampler with other methods, including detector tubes, pumped tubes, and liquid absorption methods. He concluded that there was no essential difference between the results obtained for the active and diffusive methods. See the illustration of the sampler in Instrument 17-16.

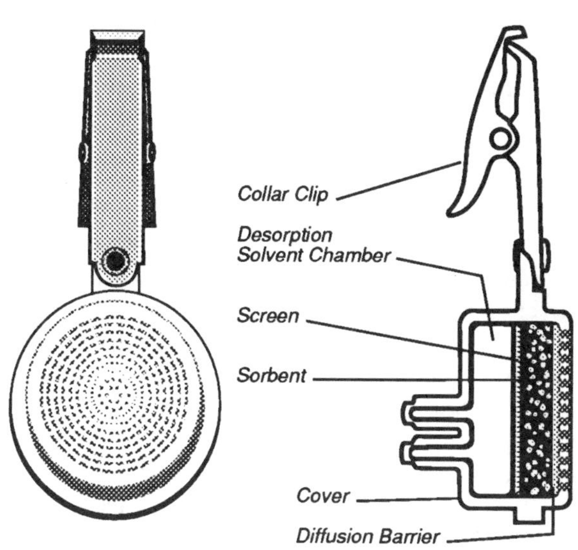

INSTRUMENT 17-15a. Model 575 Organic Vapor Monitor (SKC).

INSTRUMENT 17-15b. Model 575 Organic Vapor Monitor (SKC).

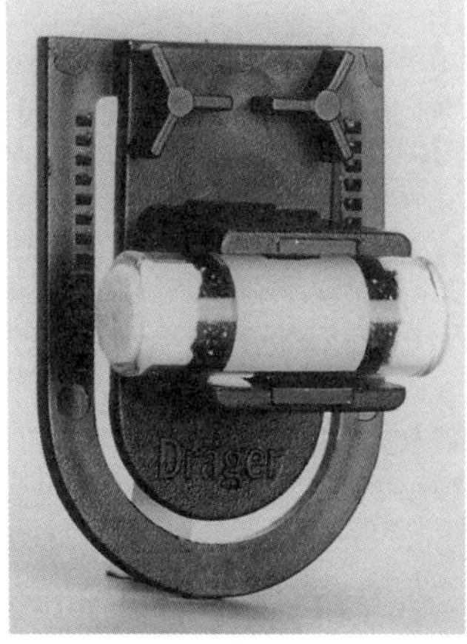

INSTRUMENT 17-16. ORSA 5 Sampler (Draeger).

Samplers for Formaldehyde

17-17. Passive Bubbler 525 for Formaldehyde

SKC Inc.

The patented Passive Bubbler meets OSHA accuracy requirements for STEL and TWA measurements of airborne formaldehyde and permits quick and easy onsite sample analysis. The small, lightweight, 10-ml glass vial can be clipped to a worker's shirt, or used with an area stand. Airborne formaldehyde diffuses into an aqueous solution contained in the sampler through a patented Knudson diffusion disc that precisely controls the rate of sample collection. At the end of the sampling period, a reagent is introduced into the sampler. The formaldehyde concentration is determined using a colorimeter. The complete formaldehyde kit contains 5 vials with clips, supplies for 100 tests, a colorimeter, 5 area stands, a user manual and carrying case. Most kit items are available separately. The sampler is pictured Instrument 17-17.

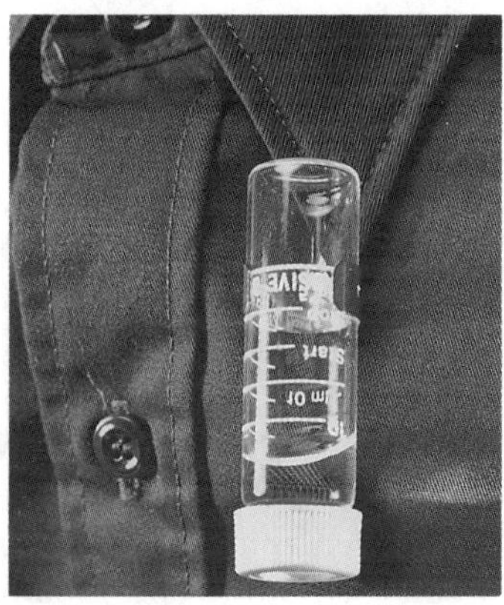

INSTRUMENT 17-17. Passive Bubbler for Formaldehyde (SKC, Inc.).

17-18. Formaldehyde Monitor
3M Company

The formaldehyde monitor contains a bisulfite-impregnated pad separated from a diffusion membrane by spacers. Formaldehyde is sampled by diffusion and collected by chemisorption on the bisulfite pad. At the end of sampling, the diffusion membrane is removed and a tight-fitting cap is snapped into place. The design of the capped monitor allows *in-situ* desorption of the formaldehyde with deionized water and subsequent removal of an aliquot for colorimetric analysis. The formaldehyde monitor is available with and without laboratory services.

17-19. AirScan™ Formaldehyde Monitoring System
AirScan Environmental Technologies, Inc.

The AirScan™ Monitor is a passive dosimeter that employs a crystal growth and nucleation technology to measure concentration of toxic gases. During the exposure period, gas passively diffuses through a sampling port onto a coated film inside the monitor. The film consists of microscopic (1 μm) sites where the analyte of interest reacts and forms crystal seeds. At the end of the sampling period, a supersaturated solution of the reaction product is introduced onto the film and in 5 min, visible crystals grow on the sites where the analyte reaction has occurred. This results in a visible line whose length is proportional to the concentration of the measured compound. The user reads the length of this line in millimeters, and then refers to a lot-specific conversion chart to determine the exposure concentration. See Instrument 17-19.

AirScan monitors exist for STEL (15-min) exposures, TWA (4- to 8-hr) exposures, and indoor air quality (IAQ) (24-hr) exposures, and are accurate to within 25% at the 95% confidence level. The monitors measure formaldehyde, ethylene oxide, and glutaraldehyde, and the crystal growth and nucleation technology is expandable to a large number of other compounds. Lower limits of detection are as follows: formaldehyde—STEL: 0.30 ppm (ceiling value), A2, TWA: 0.03 ppm, IAQ: 0.03 ppm; ethylene oxide—STEL: 1.5 ppm, TWA: 0.10 ppm; glutaraldehyde—STEL: 0.15 ppm.

17-20. Act Monitoring Card System for Formaldehyde
Envirometrics Products Co., Inc.

The ACT™ Electronic Reader is a sophisticated electronic device that is an integral part of the ACT™ Monitoring Card System. Lightweight and portable, the reader contains a lead-acid battery that allows the analysis to be performed at the sampling site. One of the most unique features of the ACT™ reader is the ability to key in the sampling time and the temperature and humidity conditions. All passive monitoring results are affected by these variables. With this system, however, the data that are keyed in allow the reader to factor the conditions directly into the exposure calculations. Accurate results are available seconds after the monitoring period. The system can be applied to formaldehyde, glutaraldehyde, ammonia, hydrogen sulfide, chlorine, sulfur dioxide, carbon monoxide, nitrogen dioxide, ethylene oxide, and methyl ethyl ketone.

Samplers for Oxides of Nitrogen and Ozone

17-21. Palmes Sampler
MDA Scientific, Inc.

The Palmes Sampler can be used to sample for both NO_2 and NO_x, determining NO by difference. In both instances, the sampler is constructed of an acrylic tube with a cross-sectional area of 0.71 cm^2 and length of 7.1 cm. Three stainless-steel grids are coated with triethanolamine evaporated from acetone solution for NO_2 reaction/collection (approximately 0.95 mg per screen) and are placed at the bottom of a 1 × 1 cm, sleeve-type, low-density polyethylene cap. The cap is fixed to one end of the acrylic body. A pen clip and removable cap are added to the other end. The sampler is exposed to NO_2 atmospheres by removing the protective cap. The beginning and ending time of exposure is recorded. The exposure period is terminated by replacing the plastic cap. For collection of NO_x, the tube also has a screen coated with chromic acid (for oxidation of NO to NO_2) and a second triethanolamine-coated screen for collection of the NO_2.

For analysis by NIOSH Method 6700, 2.1 ml of a

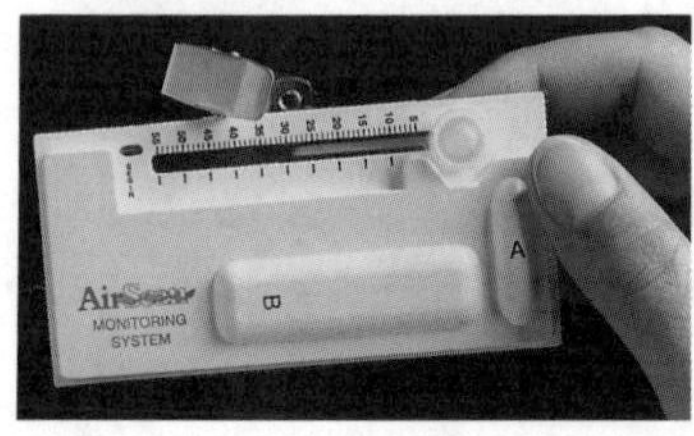

INSTRUMENT 17-19. AirScan Formaldehyde Monitoring System (AirScan).

combined reagent is added directly to the sampler and mixed, and the detector response is read from 10–30 minutes at 540 nm. (Combined reagent: to one part water, add one part sulfanilamide reagent [2a. sulfanilamide in 5 ml concentrated phosphoric acid diluted to 100 ml with water] and one-tenth part N-1-naphthylethylene-diamine dihydrochloride reagent [70 mg dissolved in 50 ml of water]). The Palmes Sampler is presently available as a field monitoring kit that contains the samplers and the spectrophotometric detector.

17-22. Nitrox™

R.S. Landauer, Jr. and Company

Landauer makes a pen-shaped badge for the collection of N_2O. The badge is 14.5 cm long and weighs 46 g. The internal cavity contains two tempered brass cylinders. The first contains a desiccant to remove water, and the second is a molecular sieve collector for N_2O. The second section is returned to the manufacturer for infrared analysis of the collected N_2O (see the illustration of the monitor in Instrument 17-22).

17-23. Harvard Passive Ozone Sampler

Ogawa & Co. USA, Inc.

The passive ozone sampler uses two multitube diffusion barriers with collection on coated glass fiber filters. The principle component of the coating is nitrite ion, which, in the presence of ozone, is oxidized to nitrate ion on the filter medium, $NO_2 + O_3 = NO_3 + O_2$. The filters are extracted with water and analyzed for nitrate ion by ion chromatography. The nominal detection limit is 200 ppb-hrs. Laboratory and field validation tests showed excellent agreement between the passive method and standard ozone monitoring techniques. Sampling is independent of temperature and relative humidity for typical ambient conditions. No significant interferences were found for other atmospheric pollutants. A protective cup is used as a wind screen for outdoor measurements and also acts as a rain cover. The samplers, coated filters, and protective cups are all commercially available (see diagram in Instrument 17-23).

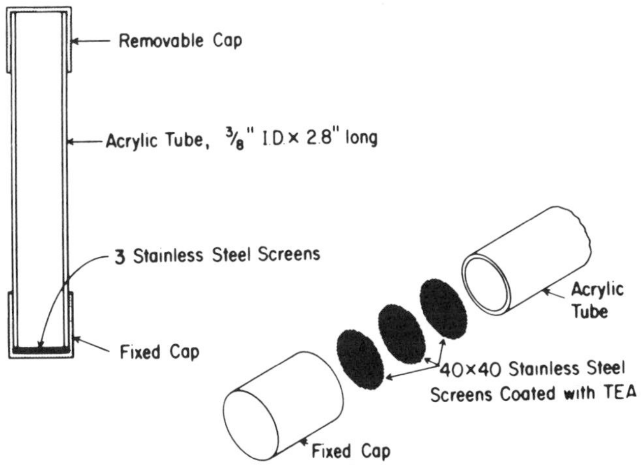

INSTRUMENT 17-21. Passive Palmes Sampler for NO_2.

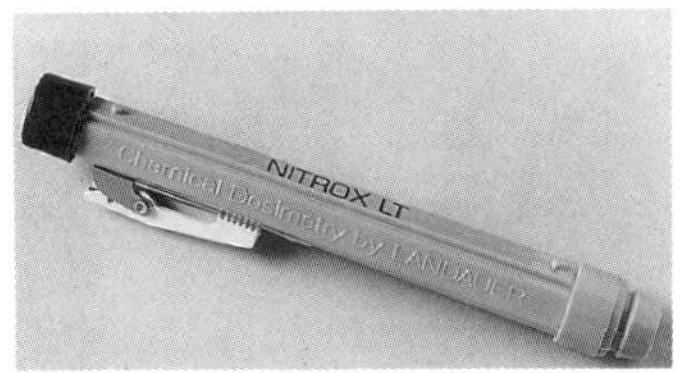

INSTRUMENT 17-22. The Nitrox Monitor for Nitrous Oxide (R.S. Landauer).

The Ogawa Company also markets a passive sampler that collects NO and NO_2 on coated filters which are analyzed by the Saltzmann procedure.

Mercury Samplers

17-24. Monitor #3600 Mercury Badge

3M Company

The 3M Company makes two badges for mercury monitoring. One corrects for chlorine interference, the other is used when chlorine is not present. The badge collects mercury on a gold film, facilitating the formation of a mercury/gold amalgam. The badge is returned to the manufacturer for measurement of the change in electrical conductivity (see illustration in Instrument 17-24).

17-25. GMD Mercury Badge

GMD Systems, Inc.

GMD's Mercury Badge weighs only 14 g and collects mercury via diffusion and adsorption on Hydrar solid sorbent that is contained in a replaceable capsule element. The sorbent capsule is returned to the laboratory for chemical desorption and analysis by flameless atomic absorption.

17-26. Passive Mercury Sampler Badge, 520 Series

SKC Inc.

This is a miniature mercury vapor device that has a small amount of specially packed sorbent in a circular

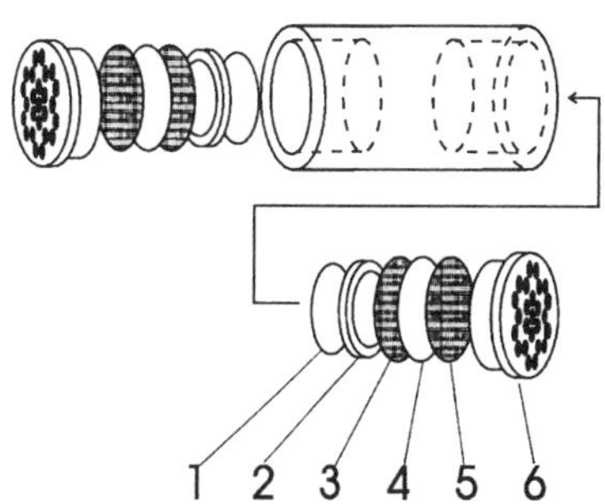

INSTRUMENT 17-23. Harvard Sampler for Ozone (Ogawa & Co.); 1 = Teflon disk, 2 = Teflon ring, 3 = stainless screen, 4 = coated collection filter, 5 = stainless screen, and 6 = diffuser end cap.

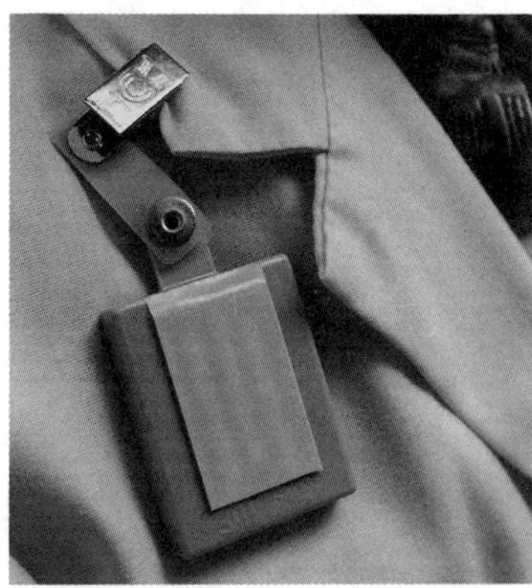

INSTRUMENT 17-24. Passive Sampler for Mercury (3M).

plastic disc that is worn as a badge on the collar. It passively takes up airborne mercury vapors by simple diffusion, after which mercury combines with the sorbent in an irreversible reaction. There is no interference from chlorine or moisture. Analysis is done using standard laboratory equipment. The badge measures worker exposure as a TWA and permits positive analysis for mercury below, between, and above the current OSHA/NIOSH standards of 0.05 mg/m^3. Replaceable sorbent capsules allow for the cleaning and reuse of the badge. This badge follows OSHA Method ID 140 for sampling mercury vapor in workplace atmospheres.

17-27. Ethylene Oxide Monitor
3M Company

The ethylene oxide monitor contains a single, treated sorbent pad separated from a diffusion membrane by spacers. The ethylene oxide vapors are sampled by diffusion and adsorbed on chemically treated activated charcoal, where they are converted to 2-bromoethanol. At the end of sampling, the diffusion cap is removed and a tight-fitting cap is snapped into place. When the sample is ready for chromatographic analysis, a 10% methylene chloride in methanol desorbing solution is added directly to the monitor. The ethylene oxide monitor is available with and without laboratory services and is illustrated in Instrument 17-27.

INSTRUMENT 17-26. Passive Sampler for Mercury (SKC, Inc.).

Other Passive Monitoring Systems

3M diffusive monitors for ethylene oxide, carbon monoxide, formaldehyde, and mercury are listed in Table 17-I-2. The types of badges supplied by SKC are found in Table 17-I-3. Table 17-I-1 lists various monitoring systems alphabetically, along with manufacturers and brand names. Cole-Parmer has a badge for ozone that uses color comparison to determine the exposure after short-term (60-min) and average long-term (8-hr) exposures. Addresses for manufacturers are found in Table 17-I-6.

Additional Reading

Brown, R.H.; Charlton, J.; Saunders, K.J.: The Development of an Improved Diffusive Sampler. Am. Ind. Hyg. Assoc. J. 42:865 (1981).

Calibrated Instruments, Inc.: Technical Bulletin A-5. Ardsley, NY.

Gisclard, J.B.; Robinson, D.B.; Kuezo, Jr., P.J.: A Rapid Empirical Procedure for the Determination of Acrylonitrile and Acrylic Esters in the Atmosphere. Am. Ind. Hyg. Assoc. J. 19:43 (1958).

Guild, L.V.: Assessment of the Reliability of Backup Systems in Diffusive Sorbent Samples. Am. Ind. Hyg. Assoc. J. 52:198 (1991).

Hori, H.; Tanaka, I.: Response Characteristics of the Diffusive Sampler at Fluctuating Vapor Concentrations. Am. Ind. Hyg. Assoc. J. 54:95 (1993).

Lang, H.W.; Freedman, R.W.: The Use of Disposable Hypodermic Syringes for Collection of Mine Atmosphere Samples. Am. Ind. Hyg. Assoc. J. 30:523 (1969).

Merino, M.: Passive Monitors. National Safety News 120:56 (1979).

Mine Safety Appliances Company: MSA Data Sheet 08-00-02. Pittsburgh, PA (1988).

Palmes, E.D.; et al: Personal Sampler for Nitrogen Dioxide. Am. Ind. Hyg. Assoc J. 37:570 (1976).

Pannwitz, K.H.: Comparison of Active and Passive Sampling Devices. Drager Rev. 52:19 (1984).

Pannwitz, K.H.: ORSA 5, a New Sampling Device for Vapours of Organic Solvents. Drager Rev. 48:8 (1981).

Sampling and Analysis of Mine Atmosphere. Miners Circular No. 34 (Revised). U.S. Department of the Interior (1948).

West, P.W.; Reisner, K.D.: Field Tests of a Permeation-type Personal Monitor for Vinyl Chloride. Am. Ind. Hyg. Assoc J. 39:645 (1978).

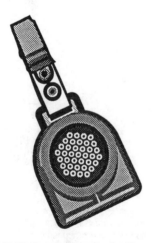

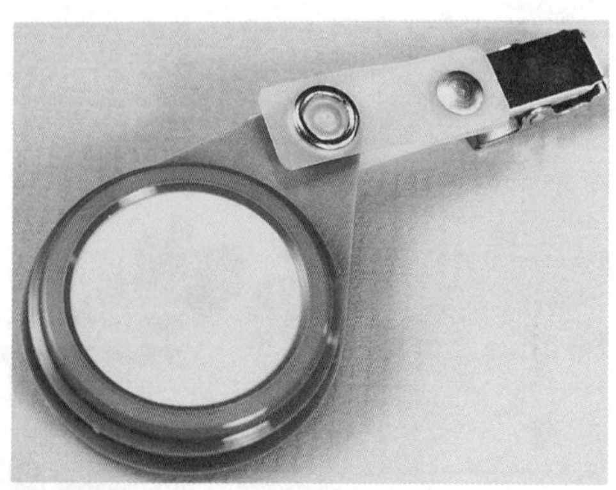

INSTRUMENT 17-27. Passive Monitor for Ethylene Oxide (3M).

TABLE 17-I-1. Manufacturers and Brand Names of Diffusion Monitors

System	Manufacturer	Brand Name
Acetone	SKC	SKC 575-002
Ammonia	SKC	Liquid Sorbent Badge
Carbon monoxide	3M	CO Monitor 3400
Carbon monoxide	Willson Safety Products	Dosimeter Badge
Ethylene oxide	3M	Monitor 3550
Ethylene oxide	AirScan	AirScan Monitor System
Formaldehyde	SKC	Passive Bubbler
Formaldehyde	3M	Monitor 3750
Formaldehyde	AirScan	AirScan Monitor System
Mercury	SKC	Mercury Vapor Badge
Mercury	3M	Monitor 3600, or 3600A
Nitrogen dioxide	Ogawa, USA	Ogawa Passive Sampler
Ozone	Ogawa, USA	Ozone Badge
Ozone	Cole-Parmer	ECO™ Badge
Nitrous oxide	Landauer	Nitrox
Organic vapor monitor	Gilian	TraceAir OVM Badge
Organic vapor monitor	National Draeger, Inc.	ORSA 5
Organic vapor monitor	Perkin-Elmer	ATD tube
Organic vapor monitor	Pro-Tek	GB-AA, GB-BB
Organic vapor monitor	SKC	Passive Sampler 575
Organic vapor monitor	3M	Organic Vapor Monitor 3500

TABLE 17-I-2. 3M Specific Passive Diffusion Monitoring Systems

System	Sampling Range	Interferences	Shelf Life	Brand Name
Organic vapors	Compound dependent	None	18 months	3500 (without analysis) 3510 (with analysis) 3520 (without analysis) 3530 (with analysis)
Ethylene oxide	0.2 to 600 ppm-hrs	None	18 months	3550 (with analysis) 3551 (with analysis)
Formaldehyde	0.8 to 40 ppm-hrs	Phenol, alcohols	18 months	3720 (with analysis) 3721 (without analysis)
Mercury	Up to 0.20 mg Hg/m^3	Strong oxidizers such as halogen vapors. CO, O_3, NO_x, and SO_2 negligible. Organic vapors generally do not interfere.	12 months (for 3600) 6 months (for 3600A)	3600 (with 3M analysis) 3600A (with 3M analysis, for chlorine environments)

TABLE 17-I-3. SKC Monitoring Badges

System	Collection Medium	Analysis	Range
Organic vapor badges	Coconut charcoal Anasorb 747 Anasorb 727	Solvent desorption and GC analysis	Varies with compound
Passive bubbler for formaldehyde	0.05% aqueous MBTH in diffusion cell	Colorimetric	0.03 to 6 mg/m^3 (0.025 to 5 ppm)
Passive mercury sampler	Hopcalite	Acid digestion and cold vapor atomic absorption spectrophotometer	0.061 to 0.020 mg/m^3

MBTH = 3-methyl-2-benzothiazolone hydrazine hydrochloride.

TABLE 17-I-4. Diffusive Monitoring Sampling Rates (cm^3/min)

Compound	Pro-Tek G-AA	3M #3500 Badge Monitor	SKC 575-001	TraceAir Gilian Inst. OVM-1	Perkin-Elmer ATD Tube
Acetone	41.5*	40.1	15.9*	41.5*	
Acrylonitrile	41.9	43.8	21.1	41.9	0.62 (Porapak N)*
Allyl alcohol	40.5	40.4	18.8	40.4	
n-Amyl acetate	24.2	26.0	12.3	24.2	
n-Amyl alcohol	28.4	31.2	14.5	28.4	
Benzene	36.5*	35.5	16.2*	36.5*	0.54 (Chromasorb 106)*
n-Butyl acetate	26.6	31.6	13.27	26.6	0.61 (Tenax TA)*
n-Butyl alcohol	34.1	34.3	16.2	34.1	
Carbon tetrachloride	32.8	30.2	14.1*	32.8	0.48 (Chromasorb 102)*
Chloroform	35.2*	33.5	13.0*	35.2*	0.48 (Chromasorb 102)*
Cyclohexane	28.5*	32.4	15.6*	28.5*	
Dioxane	28.6*	34.5	15.84	28.6*	
Heptane		28.9	13.9*		0.48 (Chromasorb 106)*
Mesityl oxide	22.1*	31.2	13.46	22.1*	
Methyl ethyl ketone	35.8	36.3	17.5*	35.8	
Perchloroethylene	31.6	28.3	12.9*	31.6	0.46 (Chromasorb 106)*
Xylene, o-	28.8	27.3	11.9	28.8	0.52 (Chromasorb 106)*
Xylene, m-	27.2		12.5	27.2	0.48 (Chromosorb 106)*
Xylene, p-	29.0*		12.8	29.0*	0.50 (Chromosorb 106)

* indicates sampling rate determined experimentally.

TABLE 17-I-5. Vendors of Gas and Vapor Collectors

Plastic Bags

AAI Alltech Associates, Inc.
2051 Waukegan Road
Deerfield, IL 60015
(312)948-8600 or (800)255-8324
FAX (708)948-1078

CAL Calibrated Instruments, Inc.
200 Saw Mill River Road
Hawthorne, NY 10532
(914)741-5700 or (800)969-2254
FAX (914)741-5711

EDL Edlon Products, Inc.
117 State Road
P.O. Box 667
Avondale, PA 19311-0667
(215)268-3101

MMM 3M Company
3M Center
Building 275-6W-01
St. Paul, MN 55144-1000
(612)733-1110

PFE Plastic Film Enterprises
1921 Bellaire
Royal Oak, MI 48067
(313)399-0450 or (800)336-3872
FAX (313)399-2534

SKC SKC, Inc.
863 Valley View Road
Eighty Four, PA 15330-9614
(412)941-9701 or (800)752-8472
FAX (412)941-1396

SUP Supelco, Inc.
Supelco Park
Bellefonte, PA 16823-0048
(814)359-3441
FAX (814)359-3044

General Supply Houses

CPI Cole-Parmer Instrument Co.
7425 North Oak Park Avenue
Niles, IL 60714
(708)647-7600
FAX (708)647-9660

FSC Fisher Scientific Company
461 Riverside Avenue
Medford, MA 01752
(617)391-6110

Bubblers and Gas Washers

AGI Ace Glass, Inc.
P.O. Box 688
1430 Northwest Blvd.
Vineland, NJ 08360
(609)692-3333 or (800)223-4524
FAX (800)543-6752

BGI BGI, Incorporated
58 Guinan Street
Waltham, MA 02154
(617)891-9380
FAX (617)891-8151

CGW Corning Glass Works
P.O. Box 5000
Corning, NY 14830
(607)974-4261

MSA Mine Safety Appliances Co.
P.O. Box 427
Pittsburgh, PA 15230
(412)776-8600 or (800)MSA-INST
FAX (412)776-3280

SGI Scientific Glass &
Instrument Company
P.O. Box 6
Houston, TX 77001
(713)682-1481
FAX (713)682-3054

SKC SKC, Inc.
863 Valley View Road
Eighty Four, PA 15330-9614
(412)941-9701 or (800)752-8472
FAX (412)941-1396

SUP Supelco, Inc.
Supelco Park
Bellefonte, PA 16823-0048
(814)359-3441
FAX (814)359-3044

Adsorbents

BCC Barnebey-Cheney Company
P.O. Box 2526
Columbus, OH 43216
(614)258-9501

CSI Columbia Scientific
P.O. Box 203190
Austin, TX 78720
(512)258-5191

PIT Pittsburgh
Division of Calgon Corp.
P.O. Box 1346
Pittsburgh, PA 15230
(412)562-8301

Packaged Sampling Equipment

AJA A.J. Abrams Co., Inc.
P.O. Box 5171
Westport, CT 06881
(203)226-4225

MDA MDA Scientific, Inc.
405 Barclay Blvd.
Lincolnshire, IL 60069
(708)634-2800 or (800)323-2000
FAX (708)634-1371

SAI Sierra Anderson
4801 Fulton Industrial Blvd.
Atlanta, GA 30336
(404)691-1910

ASC Anatole J. Sipin Co.
505 Eighth Avenue
New York, NY 10018
(212)695-5706
FAX (212)695-5916

SKC SKC, Inc.
863 Valley View Road
Eighty Four, PA 15330-9614
(412)941-9701 or (800)752-8472
FAX (412)941-1396

SPE Spectrex Corp.
3580 Haven Avenue
Redwood City, CA 94063
(415)365-6567 or (800)822-3940
FAX (415)365-5845

WSP Willson Safety Products
P.O. Box 622
Reading, PA 19603
(215)376-6161
FAX (215)371-7725

Adsorbents

SUP Supelco, Inc.
Supelco Park
Bellefonte, PA 16823-0048
(814)359-3441
FAX (800)359-3044

WES Westvaco Inc.
Covington, VA 24426
(703)962-1121

TABLE 17-I-6. Sources of Passive Monitors

Code	Source
ASC	Anatole J. Sipin Co., Inc. 505 Eighth Avenue New York, NY 10018 (212)695-5706 FAX (212)695-5916
ASE	AirScan Environmental Technologies, Inc. 197 Meister Ave. Branchburg, NJ 08876 (908)725-1342
DRW	Draegerwerk AG Moislinger Alle 53/55 Postfach 1339D-2400 Lubeck 1, Germany
ENV	Envirometrics Products Company, Inc. 1019 Bankton Drive Charleston, SC 29406 (803)740-1700 or (800)255-8740
GIC	Gilian Instrument Corporation 35 Fairfield Place West Caldwell, NJ 07006 (201)808-3355 FAX (201)808-6680
LAN	R.S. Landauer, Jr. & Co. 2 Science Road Glenwood, IL 60425 (312)755-7000 FAX (708)755-7016
MMM	3M Company Occupational Health & Safety Div. 3M Center, Buildling 220-3E-D4 St. Paul, MN 55144-0001 (612)738-7418 (800)328-1667 FAX (612)736-2555
NDR	National Draeger, Inc. 101 Technology Drive P.O. Box 120 Pittsburgh, PA 15230 (412)787-8383/8389 or (800)922-5518 FAX (412)787-2207 or (800)922-5519
NMS	National Mine Service Co. Safety Systems & Products U.S. Rt. 22 and 30 West Oakdale, PA 15071 (412)429-0800
OGA	Ogawa & Co., USA, Inc. 1230 S.E. 7th Avenue Pompano Beach, FL 33060 (305)781-6223
PEC	Perkin-Elmer Corp. 761 Main Avenue Norwalk, CT 06856 (203)762-1000
PEL	Perkin-Elmer, Ltd. Post Office Lane Beaconsfield, Bucks HP91QA United Kingdom 44-494-676161
PRO	Pro-Tek Systems 95 Brownstone Avenue Portland, CN 06480 (203)342-2306
SKC	SKC, Inc. 863 Valley View Road Eighty Four, PA 15330-9614 (412)941-9704 or (800)752-8472 FAX (412)941-1369
WSP	Willson Safety Products P.O. Box 622 Reading, PA 19603 (215)376-6161 FAX (215)371-7725

Chapter 18

Detector Tubes, Direct-Reading Passive Badges, and Dosimeter Tubes

Bernard E. Saltzman, Ph.D.[A] and Paul E. Caplan[B]

[A]*Department of Environmental Health, University of Cincinnati, Ohio*
[B]*1484 Sigma Circle, Cincinnati, Ohio*

CONTENTS

Development of Detector Tubes

Three types of direct-reading, colorimeteric indicators have been in use for the determination of contaminant concentrations in air: liquid reagents, chemically treated papers, and glass detector tubes containing solid indicating chemicals. An early comprehensive bibliography in this area was prepared by Campbell and Miller.(1)

Convenient laboratory procedures using liquid reagents have been simplified and packaged for field use. Reagents are supplied in sealed ampoules or tubes, frequently in concentrated or even solid forms that are diluted or dissolved for use. Unstable mixtures may be freshly prepared when needed by breaking an ampoule containing one ingredient inside a plastic tube or bottle containing the other. Commercial apparatus of this type is available for tetraethyl lead and tetramethyl lead. Certain liquid reagents, such as the nitrogen dioxide sampling reagents, produce a direct color upon exposure without requiring additional chemicals or manipulations. These permit simplified sampling equipment. Thus, relatively high concentrations of nitrogen dioxide may be determined directly by drawing an air sample into a 50- or 100-ml glass syringe containing a measured quantity of absorbing liquid reagent, capping, and shaking. Liquids containing indicators have been used for determining acid or alkaline gases by measuring the volume of air required to produce a color change. These liquid methods are somewhat inconvenient and bulky to transport and require a degree of skill to use. However, they are capable of good accuracy because measurement of color in liquids is inherently more reproducible and accurate than measurement of color on solids.

Chemically treated papers have been used to detect and determine gases because of their convenience and compactness. An early example of this detection method is the Gutzeit method in which arsine blackens a paper strip impregnated previously with mercuric bromide. Such papers may be freshly prepared and used wet, or stored and used in the dry state. Special chemical chalks or crayons have been used(2) to sensitize ordinary paper for phosgene, hydrogen cyanide, and other war gases. Semiquantitative determinations may be made by hanging the paper in contaminated air.

Inexpensive detector tabs are available commercially which darken upon exposure to carbon monoxide.[3] The accuracy of such procedures is limited by the fact that the volume of the air sample is rather indefinite and the degree of color change in the paper is influenced by air currents and temperature. More quantitative results may be obtained by using a sampling device capable of passing a measured volume of air over or through a definite area of paper at a controlled rate, as is done in a commercial device for hydrogen fluoride. Particulate matter contaminants such as chromic acid and lead may be determined similarly, usually by addition of liquid reagents to the sample on a filter paper. Visual evaluation of the stains on the paper may be made by comparison with color charts or by photoelectric instruments. Recording photoelectric instruments that use sensitized paper tapes operate in this manner and are described in Chapter 19. Accuracy of these methods requires uniform sensitivity of the paper, stability of all chemicals used, and careful calibration. In the case of particulate matter analysis, it may be necessary to calibrate with the specific dust being sampled if the degree of a chemical's solubility is important.

Glass detector tubes containing solid chemicals are another type of convenient and compact direct-reading device. The earliest detector tubes were made for carbon monoxide in 1920. A listing of early references was presented in a previous edition of this text.[4] There has been a great expansion in the development and use of detector tubes,[5–17] and more than 400 different types are now available commercially. Several manuals provide comprehensive descriptions and listings.[18–20] Because of the great popularity and wide use of glass detector tubes, the bulk of this discussion will deal with them, although much of the information will be applicable to the liquid and paper indicators as well.

Applications of Detector Tubes

There are many uses for detector tubes. They are convenient for qualitative[21] and quantitative evaluation of toxic hazards in industrial atmospheres, and for rapid evaluation of spills of hazardous materials.[22] They are also used for air pollution studies, although in most situations, currently available tubes do not have the required sensitivity. Detector tubes may be used for detection of explosive hazards, as well as for process control of gas composition. Confirmation of carbon monoxide poisoning may be made by determining carbon monoxide in exhaled breath or in gas released from a sample of blood (after following an appropriate procedure to release the bound carbon monoxide). Detector tubes may be used for law enforcement purposes, such as determining alcohol in the breath, or to detect gasoline in soil in cases of suspected arson or leakage from underground tanks. Subsoil diffusion of volatile liquid contaminants can be inexpensively tracked.[23] One method of tracking subsoil diffusion involves hammering a Draeger–Stitz probe (a drill rod and probe tip) up to 6 m deep into the soil at each sampling location. The rod is then withdrawn slightly to open the tip, and a detector tube in a capillary probe is lowered inside to the bottom to sample the vapor. It is connected through a capillary tube to a pump above ground. Alternatively, a carbon tube or monitoring instrument probe may be inserted to sample the vapor. Minute quantities of ions in aqueous solutions also may be determined, such as sulfide in wastewater from pulp manufacturing, chromic acid in electrolytic plating wastewater, and nickel ion in wastewater of refineries. Volatile contaminants in sewage or wastewater, such as ammonia, hydrogen cyanide, hydrogen sulfide, benzene, or chlorinated hydrocarbons, may be rapidly estimated with detector tubes. For this detection method, a 100-ml sample is placed in a bubbler. One liter of air is then drawn through a train comprised of a charcoal tube, the bubbler, and a detector tube, which responds to the stripped contaminants.[24]

Detector tubes have been widely advertised as being capable of use by unskilled personnel. Although it is true that the operating procedures are simple, rapid, and convenient, many limitations and potential errors are inherent in this method. The results may be dangerously misleading unless the sampling procedure is supervised and the findings are interpreted by an adequately trained occupational hygienist.

Operating Procedures

The use of detector tubes is extremely simple. After its two sealed ends are broken open, the glass tube is placed in the manufacturer's holder which is fitted with a calibrated squeeze bellows or piston pump. The recommended air volume is then drawn through the tube by the operator. Adequate time must be allowed for each stroke. Even if a squeeze bellows is fully expanded, it may still be under a partial vacuum and may not have drawn its full volume of air. The manufacturer's sampling instructions must be followed closely.

The observer then reads the concentration in the air by examining the exposed tube. Some of the earlier types of tubes were provided with charts of color tints to be matched with the solid chemical in the indicating portion of the tube. This visual judgment depended, of course, on the color vision of the observer and the lighting conditions. In an attempt to reduce the errors due to variations among observers, more recent types of tubes are based on a variable length of stain being produced on the indicator gel. Although in a few tubes a variable volume of sample is collected until a standard length of stain is obtained, in most cases a fixed volume of sample is passed through the tube and the stain length is measured against a calibration scale. The scale may be printed either directly on the tube or on a provided chart.

The range in the interpretation of results by different observers is large because in many cases the end of a stain front is diffuse rather than sharp. Experience in sampling known concentrations is of great value in training an operator to know whether to measure the length up the beginning or end of the stain front, or some other portion of an irregularly shaped stain. In some cases, the stains change with time; thus, the reading should not be unduly delayed.

Care must be taken to see that leak-proof pump valves and connections are maintained. A leakage test to ensure adequate performance may be made by inserting an unopened detector tube into the holder and squeezing the bulb; at the end of 2 min, any appreciable bulb expansion is evidence of a leak. If the apparatus is fitted with a calibrated piston pump, the handle is pulled back and locked. Two min later, it is released cautiously and the piston is allowed to pull back in; it should remain out no more than 5% of its original distance. Leakage indicates the need to replace check valves, tube connections, or the squeeze bellows or to grease the piston.

At periodic intervals, the flow rate of the apparatus should be checked and maintained within specifications for the tube calibrations (generally ± 10%). This may be done simply by timing the period of squeeze bellows expansion. A more accurate method is to place a used detector tube in the holder and draw an air sample through a calibrated rotameter. Alternatively, the air may be drawn from a burette in an inverted vertical position, which is sealed with a soap film, and the motion of the film past the graduations can be timed with a stop watch.[25] The latter method also provides a check on the total volume of the sample which is drawn. In some devices, the major resistance to the air flow is in the chemical packing of the tube; thus, each batch might require checking. An incorrect flow rate may indicate a partially clogged strainer or orifice that should be cleaned or replaced.

With most types of squeeze bellows and hand pumps, the sample air flow rate is variable, being high initially and low toward the end when the bulb or pump is almost filled. This variability has been claimed to be an advantage because the initially high rate gives a long stain and the final low rate sharpens the stain front. If the concentration is rapidly fluctuating during the sampling period, the variable flow rate will cause the reading to be an inaccurate mean value. The stain lengths may depend more on flow rate than on concentration. Colen[26,27] found that flow patterns for six commonly used pumps were different. When five popular brands of carbon monoxide tubes were used with pumps other than their own, grossly erroneous results were obtained, even with identical sample volumes. It should be noted that accuracy requires a close reproduction of the flow rate pattern for the calibrations to be correct.

A number of special techniques may be used in appropriate cases. When sampling in inaccessible places, the indicator tube may be placed directly at the sampling point and the pump operated at some distance away. A rubber tube extension of the same inside diameter as the indicator tube may be inserted between the pump and indicator tube. Such tubes are available commercially as accessories. Lengths as great as 60 ft have been successfully used without appreciable error, provided that more time is allowed between strokes of the pump to compensate for the reservoir effect and to obtain the full volume of sample. This method has the disadvantage that the detector tube cannot be observed during the sampling.

A second arrangement may be used when sampling hot gases such as from a furnace stack or engine exhaust. Cooling the sample is essential in these cases; otherwise, the calibration would be inaccurate and the volume of the gas sample uncertain. A probe of glass or metal, available commercially as an accessory, may be attached to the inlet end of the detector tube with a short piece of flexible tubing.[28] If this tube is cold initially, as little as 10 cm of tubing outside of the furnace is sufficient to cool the gas sample from 250°C to about 30°C. Such a probe has to be employed with caution. In some cases, serious adsorption errors occur either on the tube or in condensed moisture. The dead volume of the probe should be negligible in comparison to the volume of sample taken. Solvent vapors should not be sampled with this method. When sampling air colder than 0°C, clasping the tube in the hand warms it sufficiently to eliminate any error.[28] Critical studies[29,30] of applications to analysis of diesel exhaust showed serious errors for some tubes.

Other special techniques also may be employed. Combustion and decomposition gases from a fire may be rapidly evaluated with a set of five different tubes in a special holder that allows simultaneous sampling using one pump. These systems require special calibration. Some symmetrical tubes can be reversed in the holder and used for a second test. In certain special cases, tubes may be reused if a negative test was previously obtained or after the color has faded. Two tubes also may be connected in series in special cases; e.g., first passing crude gas through a Kitagawa hydrogen sulfide tube and then through a phosgene tube to obtain two simultaneous determinations and remove interferences. These techniques may be used only after testing to demonstrate that they do not impair the validity of the results.

Tubes also have been used in pressures as high as several atmospheres. This situation would exist, for example, in underwater stations. If both the tube and pump are in the chamber, the calibrations and sample volumes both may be altered. It has been reported[28,31] that only the latter occurs for the following Draeger tubes: ammonia 5/a, arsine 0.05/a; carbon dioxide 0.1%/a; carbon monoxide 5/c,10/b; and hydrogen sulfide 1/c,5/b. For these tubes, the corrected concentration is equal to the scale reading (ppm or vol %) divided by the ambient pressure (in atmospheres) at the pump. When tube tips are broken in a pressure chamber, the tube filling should be checked for possible displacement.

Specificity and Sensitivity

The specificity of the tubes is a major consideration for determining applicability and interpreting results. Most tubes are not specific. Chromate reduction is a common reaction used in tubes for detection of organic compounds. In the presence of mixtures, the uncritical acceptance of such readings can be grossly misleading. Comprehensive listings of reactions, as well as a discussion of other major aspects, are available.[18,19,32] Six common reactions and the associated tube types are listed in Table 18-1. The name of the compound listed on the tube often refers to its calibration scale rather than to a unique chemical reaction of its contents.

The lack of specificity of some tubes may be used to advantage for detection of substances other than those indicated by the manufacturer. In this respect, tubes using colorimetric reactions 1, 2, and 6 (Table 18-1) are widely applicable. Thus, the Draeger Polytest screening tube (reaction 2) and ethyl acetate tube (reaction 1) may be used for qualitative indications of reducing and organic materials, respectively.[33] The Draeger trichloroethylene tube (reaction 6a) is also applicable to chloroform, o-dichlorobenzene, dichloroethylene, ethylene chloride, methylene chloride, and perchloroethylene. The methyl bromide tube may be used for chlorobromomethane and methyl chloroform. The chlorine tube may be used for bromine and chlorine dioxide. The toluene tube may be used for xylene. Such use requires specific knowledge of the identity of the reagent and of the proper corrections to the calibration scales.

For some brands of indicator tubes, the units of the calibration scales are in milligrams per cubic meter. Although it has been said that this method of expression eliminates the necessity of making temperature and pressure corrections, such a claim is debatable because the scale calibrations themselves may be highly dependent on these variables. Units of parts per million or percent by volume are most common for industrial hygiene purposes and are used on most of the newer tubes. Conversions may be made from milligrams per cubic meter to parts per million by the formula given in Chapter 8.

Although detector tubes are generally designed for detection of relatively high gas concentrations found in industrial workplaces, some have been applied to much lower outdoor air pollutant concentrations. Kitagawa[34] determined 0.01–2 ppm of nitrogen dioxide using two glass tubes in series, with the temperature controlled at 40°C. The first tube contained diatomaceous earth impregnated with a specific concentration of sulfuric acid to regulate the humidity of the air sample. The second tube, 120 mm long × 2.4 mm inside diameter, contained white silica gel impregnated with ortho tolidine. (It is not clear whether this is identical to the commercial No. 117.) Air was drawn through the tubes for 30 min at 180 ml/min by an electric pump with a stainless steel orifice plate at its inlet. Accuracy was ± 100%; no comments on the specificity were given. Grosskopf[35,36] determined 0.007–0.5 ppm nitrogen dioxide by drawing air through a Draeger 0.5/a nitrous gas tube with a diaphragm pump for 10–40 min at the rate of 0.5 L/min. Readings were not affected by flow rates if the flow rates exceeded 0.5 L/min. No comments were given on the specificity, except that humidity from 30 L of air at 70% relative humidity did not impair the sensitivity. This tube responds to nitric oxide and to oxidants, both of which commonly may be present. Leichnitz[37] reported a tube (Draeger sulfur dioxide 0.1/a) capable of measuring 0.1–3 ppm of sulfur dioxide. This tube requires 100 strokes of a hand bellows pump (each taking 7–14 seconds) or use of the Draeger Quantimeter electric pump in which a motor-driven crank controlled by a microprocessor operates a bellows. This pump is described in the "Instrument Descriptions" section.

Less success was attained when carbon monoxide detector tubes were used for sampling periods of 4 hrs or longer with continuous pumps. It was found that at low concentrations, after an initial period, the stain lengths ceased to increase.[8] However, at higher concentrations, a new calibration could be made[38] (for 3- to 5-hr samples at 8 ml/min through a Kitagawa 100 tube in the range of 30–100 ppm of carbon monoxide). The latter investigator hypothesized that the oxygen in air bleached the black palladium stain and caused the front produced by low concentrations to remain stationary after the first 20–30 min. Effects of water vapor and other contaminants must also be considered in this application. A new calibration is essential under the flow conditions to be used. Studies confirmed that secondary reactions, which bleached the indication and prevented long-term sampling, could be avoided with appropriate reagent systems.[39]

Detector tubes have been developed[40,41] for long

TABLE 18-1. Common Colorimetric Reactions in Gas Detector Tubes

1. Reduction of chromate or dichromate to chromous ion:

Draeger: Acetaldehyde 100/a; acetone 500/a-L; alcohol 100/a; aniline 0.5/a; cyclohexane 100/a; diethyl ether 100/a; ethanol 500/a-L, 1000/a-D; ethyl acetate 200/a, 500/a-D; ethyl glycol acetate 50/a; ethylene oxide 25/a; n-hexane 100/a; hydrocarbons 100/a-L; methanol 50/a; n-pentane 100/a; o-toluidine 1/a.

Gastec: Acetone 151; aniline 181; butane 104; butyl acetate 142; ethanol 112; ethyl acetate 141; ethyl ether 161; ethylene oxide 163; gasoline 101, 101L; hexane 102H, 102L; isopropanol 113; LP gas 100A; methanol 111; methylethylketone 152; methyl isobutyl ketone 153; propane 100B; sulfur dioxide 5H; vinyl chloride 131.

Kitagawa: Acetone 102A; acrylonitrile 128A, 128B; butadiene 168A; butyl acetate 138; cyclohexane 115; dimethyl ether 123; dioxane 154; ether 107; ethyl acetate 111; ethyl alcohol 104A; ethylene oxide 122; furan 161; n-hexane 113; isobutyl acetate 153; isopropanol 150; isopropyl acetate 149; methyl acetate 148; methyl alcohol 119; methyl ethyl ketone 139B; methyl isobutyl ketone 155; propyl acetate 151; propylene oxide 163; sulfur dioxide 103A; tetrahydrofuran 162; vinyl chloride 132.

MSA: Part 95097 for n-amyl alcohol, iso-amyl alcohol, sec-amyl alcohol, tert-amyl alcohol, 2-butoxyethanol (butyl Cellosolve), n-butyl alcohol, isobutyl alcohol, sec-butyl alcohol, tert-butyl alcohol, cyclohexanol, 2-ethoxyethanol (Cellosolve), ethyl alcohol (ethanol), ethylene glycol monomethylether, fufuryl alcohol, 2-methoxyethanol, methyl alcohol (methanol), 2-methylcyclohexanol, methyl isobutyl carbinol (methyl amyl alcohol), n-propyl alcohol, isopropyl alcohol.
Part 460423 for acetone, methyl methacrylate.

2. Reduction of iodine pentoxide plus fuming sulfuric acid to iodine:

Draeger: Benzene 2/a, 5/b, 20/a-L; carbon disulfide 5/a, 10/a-L; carbon monoxide 2/a, 5/c, 8/a, 10/a-L, 10/b, 50/a-L, 0.001%/a, 0.3%/b; ethyl benzene 30/a; hydrocarbon 0.1%/b; methylene chloride 100/a*, 50/a-l*, natural gas*; petroleum hydrocarbons 100/a; polytest; toluene 5/a, 200/a-L.

Gastec: Acetylene 171; benzene 121, 121L; carbon monoxide 1H, 1M; Stoddard solvent 128; toluene 122; vinyl chloride 131; xylene 123.

MSA: Part 93074 for benzene (benzol), chlorobenzene, monobromobenzene, toluene (toluol), xylene (xylol).

3. Reduction of ammonium molybdate plus palladium sulfate to molybdenum blue:

Draeger: Ethylene 0.1/a, 50/a; methyl acrylate 5/a; methyl methacrylate 50/a.

Gastec: Butadiene 174; ethylene 172, 172L.

Kitagawa: Acetylene 101; butadiene 168B; carbon monoxide 106A, 106B, 106C*; ethylene 108B; hydrogen sulfide and sulfur dioxide 120C.

MSA: Part 47134 for carbon monoxide (NBS color change).
Part 85802 for acetylene, ethylene, propylene.

4. Reaction with potassium palladosulfite:

Draeger: Carbon monoxide 50/a-D.

Gastec: Carbon monoxide 1L, 1La, 1LL; hydrogen cyanide 12H.

MSA: Part 91229 for carbon monoxide (length of stain)

5. Color change of pH indicators (e.g., bromphenol blue, phenol red, thymol blue, methyl orange):

Draeger: Acetic acid 5/a, 5/a-L, 10/a-D; acetone 1000/a-D*; acid test; acrylonitrile 1/a*, 5/a*; amine; ammonia 2/a, 5/a, 10/a-L, 20/a-D, 0.5%/a; carbon dioxide 1000/a-L, 500/a-D, 1%/a-D; chlorobenzene 5/a*; cyanide 2/a*; cyclohexylamine 2/a; dimethylformamide 10/b*; formic acid 1/a; halogenated hydrocarbons 100/a**; hydrazine 0.25/a; hydrochloric acid 1/a, 10/a-D, 10/a-L, 50/a; hydrocyanic acid 2/a*, 20/a-D*; hydrogen fluoride 2/a-L; nitric acid 1/a; perchloroethylene 50/a-L; phosphine 0.01/a*; phosphoric acid esters 0.05/a*; sulfur dioxide 0.1/a*, 2/a-L; triethylamine 5/a; vinyl chloride 0.5/a*.

Gastec: Acetaldehyde 92*; acetic acid 81; acrolein 93*; acrylonitrile 191*, 191L*; amines 180; ammonia 3H, 3M, 3L; tert-butyl mercaptan 75; carbon dioxide 2H, 2L; carbon disulfide 13*, 13M; carbonyl sulfide 21; dimethylacetamide 184*; dimethylformamide 183*; formaldehyde 91L*; hydrogen chloride 14L, 14M; hydrogen cyanide 12L*; methacrylonitrile 192; nitric acid 15L; perchloroethylene 133*; pyridine 182; sulfur dioxide 5M, 5L, 5La; trichloroethylene 132H*, 132L*; vinyl chloride 131La*, 131L*.

Kitagawa: Acetaldehyde 133; ammonia 105B; carbon dioxide 126A, 126B; hydrogen cyanide 112B.

MSA: Part 85976 for carbon dioxide. Part 91636 for hydrogen chloride. Part 92030** for 1-chloro-1,1-difluoroethane (Genetron 142B), chlorotrifluoromethane (Freon 13), 1,2-dichloroethane (ethylene dichloride), dichloroethylene (trans-1,2), ethyl chloride, fluorotrichloromethane (Freon 11), methyl chloride, methylene chloride (dichloromethane), propylene dichloride (1,2-dichloropropane),

TABLE 18-1 (con't.). Common Colorimetric Reactions in Gas Detector Tubes

5. MSA (con't.): 1,1,2-trichloro-1,2,2-trifluorethane (Freon 113), vinyl chloride (chloroethylene).
Part 92115 for ammonia, n-butylamine, cyclohexylamine, diisopropylamine, di-n-propylamine, ethylamine, ethylene imine, N-ethylmorpholine, isopropylamine, methylamine, propylene imine, triethylamine, trimethylamine.
Part 92623 for sulfur dioxide. Part 93865 for ozone. Part 95739** for dimethyl sulfoxide.
Part 460021 for acetic acid.
Parts 460103 and 460158 for ammonia.
Part 460425 for hydrazine, monomethyl hydrazine, unsymmetrical dimethyl hydrazine.

6a. Reaction with o-tolidine:

Draeger: Chlorine 0.2/a, 0.3b, 1/a-L, 50/a; chloroform 2/a*; epichlorohydrin 5/b*; fluorine 0.1/a*; nitrogen dioxide 10/a-D; perchloroethylene 10/b, 200/a-D; trichloroethane 50/d*; trichloroethylene 2/a*, 10/a, 10/a-L*, 200/a-D; vinyl chloride 1/a*, 10/a-L*.

Gastec: Chlorine 8H, 8La; chloroform 137*; methyl bromide 136*; methyl chloroform 135*; methylene chloride 138*; nitrogen dioxide 9L; nitrogen oxides 10*, 11*.

Kitagawa: Bromine 114; chlorine 109; chlorine dioxide 116; nitrogen dioxide 117.

6b. Reaction with tetraphenylbenzidine:

MSA: Part 82399 for bromine, chlorine, chlorine dioxide.
Part 83099 for nitrogen dioxide.
Part 85833** for chlorobromomethane; 1,1-dichloroethane; dichloroethylene (cis-1,2 and trans-1,2); ethyl bromide; ethyl chloride; perchloroethylene (tetrachloroethylene); trichloroethylene; 1,2,3-trichloropropane; vinyl chloride (chloroethylene).
Part 85834* for chlorobenzene (mono); 1,2-dibromoethane (ethylene dibromide); dichlorobenzene (ortho); 1,2-dichloroethane

6b. MSA (con't.): (ethylene dichloride); dichloroethyl ether; 1,1-dichloroethylene (vinylidine chloride); methyl bromide; methylene chloride (dichloromethane); propylene dichloride (1,2-dichloropropane); 1,1,2,2-tetrabromoethane; 1,1,2,2-tetrachloroethane; 1,1,3,3-tetrachloropropane; trichloroethane (beta 1,1,2); vinyl chloride (chloroethylene).
Part 87042 for bromine; chlorine.
Part 88536* for carbon tetrachloride; chlorobromomethane; 1-chloro-1,1-difluoroethane (Genetron 142B); chlorodifluoromethane (Freon 22); chloroform (trichloromethane); chloropentafluoroethane (Freon 115); chlorotrifluoromethane (Freon 13); 1,2-dibromoethane (ethylene dibromide); dichlorodifluoromethane (Freon 12); 1,1-dichloroethylene (vinylidine chloride); dichloroethylene (cis-1,2); dichlorotetrafluoroethane (Freon 114); fluorotrichloromethane (Freon 11); Freon 113; Freon 502; methyl bromide; methyl chloroform (1,1,1-trichloroethane); methylene chloride (dichloromethane); perchloroethylene (tetrachloroethylene); trichloroethane (beta 1,1,2); trichloroethylene; 1,1,2-trichloro-1,2,2-trifluoroethane (Freon 113); trifluoromonobromomethane (Freon 13B1).
Part 91624** for acetonitrile; acrylonitrile; 1-chloro-1-nitropropane; cyanogen; 1,1-dichloro-1-nitroethane; dimethylacetamide; dimethylformamide; fumigants (Acritet, Insect-0-Fume, Fume-I-Gate, termi-Gas, Termi-Nate); methacrylonitrile; nitroethane; nitromethane, 1-nitropropane; 2-nitropropane; n-propyl nitrate; pyridine; vinyl chloride.
Part 460225 for chlorine. Part 460424* for nitric oxide.

*Multiple reaction or multiple layer tube for improved specificity or preliminary reaction.
**Pyrolyzer required.

duration sampling (4–8 hrs). These appear to be very similar to the tubes designed for short duration sampling and are effective within the same concentration ranges. They are calibrated for use with a continuous sampling pump, but they operate at lower flow rates. The application of these tubes is to provide time-weighted average concentrations, rather than short-term (few minutes) values. To provide valid averages, the calibrations must be linear both with concentration and time and should display uniformly spaced markings for uniform increments of contaminants. The scales on these tubes usually are in terms of microliters of test gas (ppm × liters), rather than ppm, and the latter is calculated by dividing the scale reading by the liters of air sampled. Over 30 types of long duration tubes are now available commercially. It should be noted that they must be used within the ranges of flow rate and total sampling time established during their calibration by the manufacturer, using the specified continuous sampling pump. A comparison of grab samples and long-term samples for ammonia in swine confinement buildings showed a consistent discrepancy. The long-term values were double the grab sample averages.[42] Low flow MDA Accuhaler pumps were used, with some loss of accuracy.[43] They generally are not suitable for analysis of concentrations in ranges lower than those of ordinary tubes designed for short duration sampling[44] because of the previously mentioned problems of water vapor, oxygen, and other contaminants.

Greater accuracy can be obtained when several detector tubes are used for replicate sampling. A simplified statistical approach based on an assumed normal distribution of values was recommended for 3–10 samples.[45] However, subsequent work indicated that most of the variations were due to the environmental fluctuations rather than to the relatively small analytical errors, and that a lognormal distribution was more appropriate. A step-by-step procedure was presented[46] which categorized the results into noncompliance (less than 5% chance of erroneously citing when actually compliance exists), no decision, and compliance (less than 5% chance of failing to cite when actually noncompliance exists).

Problems in the Manufacture of Detector Tubes

The accuracy, limitations, and applications of detector tubes are highly dependent on the skill with which they were manufactured. Generally, the supporting material is silica gel, alumina, ground glass, pumice, or resin. This material is impregnated with an indicator chemical that should be stable, specific, sensitive, and produce a color which strongly contrasts with the unexposed color and is nonfading for at least an hour. If the reaction with the test gas is relatively slow, a color is produced throughout the length of the tube because the gas is incompletely absorbed and the concentration at the exiting end is an appreciable fraction of that at the entrance. Such a color must be matched against a chart of standard tints. A rapidly reacting indicating chemical is much more desirable and yields a length-of-stain type of tube in which the test gas is completely absorbed in the stained portion.

There is a very wide and unpredictable variation in the properties of different batches of indicating gel. The major portion of the chemical reaction probably occurs on the surface. Therefore, the number of active centers, which are highly sensitive to trace impurities, affects the reaction rate. These problems are well known in the preparation of various catalysts. Close controls must be kept on the purity and quality of the materials, the method of preparation, the cleanliness of the air in the factory or glove box in which the tubes are assembled, the inside diameter of the glass tubes, and even on the size analysis of the impregnated gel, which, in some cases, is important in controlling the flow rate. The manufacturer must also accurately calibrate each batch of indicating gel.

Some tube types are constructed with multiple layers of different impregnated gels with inert separators. Generally, the first layer is a precleansing chemical to remove interfering gases and improve the specificity of the indication. Thus, in the case of some carbon monoxide tubes, chemicals are provided to remove interfering hydrocarbons and nitrogen oxides. In carbon disulfide tubes, hydrogen sulfide is first removed. In hydrogen cyanide tubes, hydrogen chloride or sulfur dioxide are removed first. In other cases, the entrance layer provides a preliminary reaction essential to the indicating reaction. Thus, in some trichloroethylene tubes, the first oxidation layer liberates a halogen which is indicated in the subsequent layer. In some tubes for NO_x gases, a mixture of chromium trioxide and concentrated sulfuric acid is used to oxidize nitric oxide to nitrogen dioxide, which is the form to which the sensitive indicating layer responds. Although such multiple layer tubes are advantageous when properly constructed, they frequently have a shorter shelf life because of diffusion of chemicals between layers and consequent deterioration.

TABLE 18-2. Shelf Life of Draeger Carbon Monoxide Tubes

Temperature °C	Shelf Life
25	>2 years
50	>1/2 year
80	weeks
100	1 week
125	3 days
150	1 day

A shelf life of at least 2 years is highly desirable for practical purposes. A great deal of disappointment with various tube performances is no doubt due to inadequate shelf life. Because some tubes have only been on the market for a short time, the manufacturer may have inadequate experience with the shelf life of the product. Small variations in impurities, such as the moisture content, may have a large effect on the shelf lives of different batches. The storage temperature, of course, greatly affects the shelf life, and it is highly desirable to store these tubes in a refrigerator. The accuracy of tubes stored on the back window shelf of a car may be rapidly destroyed by hot sunlight. In some cases, shelf life has been estimated by accelerated tests at higher temperatures. Such a variation of shelf life (length of time within which the calibration accuracy is maintained at ± 25%) is illustrated by the data listed in Table 18-2 received in a personal communication from Dr. Karl Grosskopf of the Draeger Company. These data plot as an approximately straight line when the logarithm of the shelf life time is plotted against a linear scale of the reciprocal of absolute temperature. Such a plot is usual for the reaction rate of a simple chemical reaction. In other cases, relationships may be more complex.

The shipping properties of tubes must also be controlled carefully. Loosely packed indicating gels may shift, causing an error in the zero point of scales printed directly on the tube, as well as an error in total stain length. When the size analysis includes an appreciable range, the fines may segregate to one side of the bore, causing different flow resistances and rates on each side of the tube. This may cause oval stain fronts that are not perpendicular to the tube bore. If the indicating gel is friable, the size analysis may change during shipping.

Obviously, satisfactory results can be obtained only if the manufacturers take great pains in the design, production, and calibration of tubes.

Theory of Calibration Scales

Up to now, calibration scales have been entirely empirical. The variables that can affect the length of stain are concentration of test gas, volume of air sample, sampling flow rate, temperature, and pressure, as well as a number of factors related to tube construction. There is a striking similarity in the fact that most of the length of stain calibration scales are logarithmic with respect to concentration in spite of the widely differing chemicals employed in different tube types. Although very few data are available for these relationships, a basic mathematical analysis was made by Saltzman.[47] The theoretical formulas discussed below will, of course, have to be modified as more data become available. The relationships were also studied by Grosskopf[36] and Leichnitz.[48]

In the usual case, although the test gas is sorbed completely, equilibrium is not reached between the gas and the absorbing indicator gel because the sampling period is relatively short and the flow rate is relatively high. The length of stain is determined by the kinetic rate at which the gas either reacts with the indicating chemical or is adsorbed on the silica gel. The theoretical analysis shows that the stain length is proportional to the logarithm of the product of gas concentration and sample volume:

$$\frac{L}{H} = \ln (CV) + \ln \left(\frac{K}{H}\right) \quad (1)$$

where: L = the stain length, cm
C = the gas concentration, ppm
V = the air sample volume, cm^3
K = a constant for a given type of detector tube and analyte gas, cm^{-2}
H = a mass transfer proportionality factor having the dimension of centimeters, and known as the height of a mass transfer unit

The factor H varies with the sampling flow rate raised to an exponent of between 0.5 and 1.0, depending on the nature of the process that limits the kinetic rate of sorption. This process may be diffusion of the test gas through a stagnant gas film surrounding the gel particles, the rate of surface chemical reaction, or diffusion in the solid gel particles. If the detector tube follows this mathematical model, a plot of stain length, L, on a linear scale, versus the logarithm of product CV (for a fixed constant flow rate) will be a straight line of slope H. It is important to control the flow rate because it may affect stain lengths more than gas concentrations due to its influence on the factor H.

If larger samples are taken at low concentrations and the value of L/H exceeds 4, the gel approaches equilibrium saturation at the inlet end, and calibration relationships are modified. The solution to the equations for this case has been presented graphically by Saltzman[47] in a generalized chart. However, there is little advantage to be gained in greatly increasing the sample size, because the stain front is greatly broadened and various errors are increased.

For some types of tubes such as hydrogen sulfide and ammonia and for long duration tubes, the reaction rate is fast enough that equilibrium can be attained between the indicating gel and the test gas. Under these conditions, there is a stoichiometric relationship between the volume of discolored indicating gel and the quantity of test gas absorbed. In the simplest case, the stain length is proportional to the product of concentration and volume sampled:

$$L = K\ C\ V \quad (2)$$

If adsorption is important, the exponent of concentration may differ from unity:

$$L = K\ C^{(1-n)}\ V \quad (3)$$

The value of n is the same as that in the Freundlich isotherm equation for equilibrium adsorption, which states that the mass of gas adsorbed per unit mass of gel is proportional to the gas concentration raised to the power n. If the value of n is unity, which is not unusual, Equation 3 indicates that stain length is proportional to sample volume but is independent of concentration. The physical meaning of this is that all concentrations of gas are adsorbed completely by a fixed depth of gel. Such a tube is obviously of no practical value.

Equilibrium conditions may be assumed for a given type of indicator tube if stain lengths are directly proportioned to the volume of air sampled (at a fixed concentration) and are not affected by air sampling flow rate. A log-log plot then may be made of stain length versus concentration for a fixed volume. A straight line with a slope of unity indicates that Equation 2 applies; if another value of slope is obtained, Equation 3 applies.

In some of the narrower indicator tubes, manufacturing variation in tube diameters produces an appreciable percentage variation in tube cross-sectional areas. This results in an error in the calibration as high as 50% because the volume of sample per unit cross-sectional areas is different from that under standard test conditions. An additional complicating factor is the variation produced in flow rate per unit cross-sectional area. If an exactly equal quantity of indicating gel is put into each tube, variations in cross-sectional areas will be indicated by corresponding variations in the filled tube lengths. Correction charts are provided by one manufacturer on which the tube is positioned according to the filled length and a scale is given for reading stain lengths. Although the corrections are rather complex, practically linear corrections are very close approximations that can reduce the errors to 10%. In most tubes, the tube diameters are controlled closely enough that no correction is necessary.

Temperature is another important variable for tube calibrations. The effect is different for different tubes. Because the color tint type of tube depends on the degree of reaction, it is most sensitive to temperature. For example, some old types of carbon monoxide tubes require correction by a factor of 2 for each deviation of 10°C from the standard calibration conditions.

Errors in judging stain lengths produce equal percentage errors in concentration derived from the calibration scale. Errors in measuring sample volume and in flow rate may also result in errors in the final value, although the exact relationships might vary according to the tubes.

Many other complications can be expected in calibration relationships. Thus, for nitrogen dioxide, the proportion of side reactions is changed at different flow rates. Changing sample volumes freely from calibration conditions is not recommended unless the tube is known to be thoroughly free from the effects of interfering gases and humidity in the air.

A crucial factor in the accuracy of the calibration is the apparatus used for preparing known low concentrations of the test gas (this subject is discussed more fully in Chapter 8 of this text). Some manufacturers have used static methods. However, experience has shown that losses of 50% or more by adsorption are not uncommon. Low concentrations of reactive gases and vapors are best prepared in a dynamic system. This has further advantages of capabilities to generate extended volumes and to rapidly change concentrations as required. With either type of apparatus, it is highly desirable to check the concentrations using chemical methods of known accuracy. Some successful systems have been described.[49–55]

A simple and compact dynamic apparatus for accurately diluting tank gas (which may be either pure or a mixture) was developed by Saltzman[50,51] and Avera.[52] The asbestos* plug flowmeter measures and controls gas flows in the range of a few hundredths to a few milliliters per minute. Air-vapor mixtures of volatile organic liquids may be prepared in a flow dilution apparatus using a motor-driven hypodermic syringe. High quality gears, bearings, and screws are needed in the motor drive to provide the uniform slow motion. Some commercial devices have been found unsatisfactory in this regard. Many types of permeation tubes now available have also proven useful.

It is highly desirable for the user, as well as the manufacturer, to have facilities available for checking calibrations. Only in this manner may the user be confident that the tubes and corresponding technique are adequate for the intended purposes. Tubes may also be applied to gases other than those for which they have been calibrated by the manufacturer, in certain special cases, if the user can prepare a new calibration scale.

Stain Length Passive Dosimeters

An important new advance has been the development of direct-reading, passive dosimeters. Passive dosimetry uses diffusion of the test gas and eliminates the need for a sampling pump and its calibration. These attractive devices are compact, convenient, and relatively inexpensive. In early work, detector tubes for toluene, ethanol, and isopropanol were cut open at the entrance of the chemical packing.[56] Later, glass adapters with a membrane (e.g., Millipore®, or silicone rubber) were used[57–59] to provide a draft shield, in some cases a pretreatment chemical layer, and a diffusion resistance. Simpler commercial devices merely provided a score mark which permitted breaking the tube at a controlled point.[60] Some allowed a controlled air space (e.g., 15 mm) upstream from the indicating gel to serve as the initial resistance to diffusion.[61] In some devices, rather than an indicating gel, a strip of chemically impregnated paper is inserted in the glass tube.

The theoretical calibration relationships for these devices rest upon Fick's First Law of Diffusion, which can be expressed as:

$$W = 10^{-6}\, C\, t\, \mathcal{D}\left(\frac{A}{X}\right) \tag{4}$$

where: W = cm^3 of analyte gas collected
t = time, seconds
$\mathcal{D}$ = diffusion coefficient, cm^2/s
A = effective orifice cross-section area, cm^2
X = orifice length, cm

This equation assumes that the concentration is com-

*Because asbestos is no longer generally available, a similar inert packing material may be substituted.

pletely absorbed in the indicating gel and that there is no significant back diffusion pressure. A second common assumption is that the stain length is proportional to the amount absorbed (analogous to Equation 2):

$$L = K\,W \quad (5)$$

The test gas diffuses through a membrane or air space, then through the stained length of indicating gel, and is finally absorbed at the stain front, which is assumed to be relatively narrow. It is convenient to express X in terms of L:

$$X = r + L \quad (6)$$

where: r = effective length, cm, corresponding to the diffusive resistance of the membrane or air space

Combining Equations 4–6 and rearranging yields:

$$r\,L + L^2 = (10^{-6}\,K\,\mathcal{D}\,A)\;C\,t = K'\,C\,t \quad (7)$$

where: K' = a constant equal to the bracketed expression, cm^2/s

This equation has been shown to fit MSA tubes with a 15-mm air space.[61–63] When L was expressed in mm and t in hrs, r was taken as 15 mm, and K' was 0.59 mm^2/hr for carbon monoxide, 11.0 for ammonia, 14.2 for nitrogen dioxide, 22.6 for hydrogen sulfide, 67.3 for sulfur dioxide, and 74.0 for carbon dioxide. For Draeger tubes, which do not use an air space, the equation applied with a zero value for r.[60] For membrane-type devices, the equation was modified by adding another constant:[57–59]

$$C\,t = a + b\,L + c\,L^2 \quad (8)$$

where: a, b, c = empirical constants

These constants may differ for each individual membrane. The inapplicability of a general calibration is a disadvantage of this type of passive monitor.

A more complete mathematical analysis[64] showed that for rapidly changing concentrations the errors would be small. This was experimentally confirmed[65] for both passive dosimeters and for long-term tubes. Most of the published work on passive dosimeters has been by the staffs of manufacturers.[60–63,65] Much larger errors were reported[66,67] by users. Some of the stain boundaries were very diffuse and difficult to read, and some calibrations were inaccurate. Because these tubes are in an early state of development, the values should be checked as much as possible.

Another type of passive dosimeter is the direct-reading colorimetric badge. These dosimeters produce a color tint that is related to the product of time and concentration. Passive badges are more fully treated in Chapter 17. All passive devices require a minimum air velocity at their entrances (0.008 m/s or 15 ft/min) to avoid "starvation" effects (depletion of the air concentration near the entrance).[68,69]

Performance Evaluation and Certification

Evaluations by users of many types of tubes have been reported.[15,70–90] Temperature and humidity were found to be significant factors in some cases.[91,92] Accuracy was found highly variable. In some cases, the tubes were completely satisfactory; in others, completely unsatisfactory. Manufacturers, in their efforts to improve the range and sensitivity of their products, are rapidly changing the contents of their tubes, and these reports are frequently obsolete before they appear in print. Improved quality control, and perhaps greater self-policing of the industry, would greatly increase the value of the tubes, especially for the small consumer who is not in a position to check calibrations.

After reviewing this need, a joint committee of the American Conference of Governmental Industrial Hygienists (ACGIH)–American Industrial Hygiene Association (AIHA) made the following recommendations:[93]

1. Manufacturers should supply a calibration chart (ppm) for each batch of tubes.
2. Length-of-stain tubes are preferable to those exhibiting change in hue or intensity of color.
3. Tests of calibrations should be made at 0.5, 1.0, 2.0, and 5.0 times the ACGIH Threshold Limit Value (TLV).
4. The manufacturer should specify the methods of tests. Values should be checked by two independent methods.
5. Calibration at each test point should be accurate within ±25% (95% confidence limit).
6. Allowable ranges and corrections should be listed for temperature, pressure, and relative humidity.
7. Each batch of tubes should be labeled with a number and an expiration date. Instructions for proper storage should be given.
8. Tolerable concentrations of interferents should be listed.
9. Pumping volumes should be accurate within ±5%, and flow rates should be indicated.
10. Special calibrations should be provided for extended sampling for low concentrations, and flow rates should be specified.

A performance evaluation program was initiated by the National Institute for Occupational Safety and Health (NIOSH). Known concentrations of test substances were generated in flow systems from sources such as cylinder mixtures, vapor pressure equilibration at known temperatures, or permeation tubes. Although few tubes achieved an accuracy of ±25%, many types

TABLE 18-3. Certifications of Detector Tubes by the Safety Equipment Institute as of October 1993*

Substance	Matheson/ Kitagawa	Mine Safety Appliance Co.	National Draeger, Inc.	Sensidyne/ Gastec
Acetone	8014-102SD			151L
Ammonia	8014-105SC	460103	5/a, CH 20501	3La
Benzene	8014-118SC	460754	2/a, 81 01231 5/b, 67 28071	121
Carbon dioxide	8014-126SA	85976	0.1%/a, CH 2351	2L
Carbon disulfide	8014-141SB	492514		13
Carbon monoxide	8014-106SB	91229	5/c, CH 25601 10/b, CH 20601	1La
Chlorine	8014-109SB	460225	0.3/b, 67 28411	8La
Hydrogen chloride	8014-173SB	803948		14L
Hydrogen cyanide	8014-112SB	93262	2/a, CH 25701	12L
Hydrogen sulfide	8014-120SD	460058 487339	2/a, 67 28821 1/c, 67 19001	4LL
Methyl bromide	8014-157SB			136La
Nitrogen dioxide	8014-117SB	83099 487341	0.5/c, CH 30001	9L
Ozone	8014-182U	93865		18L
Phosphine	8014-121U	497101		7La
Sulfur dioxide	8014-124U	92623 487338	0.5/a, 67 28491	5Lb
Toluene	8014-124SA	461371 803947	5/a, CH 23001	122
Trichloroethylene	8014-134S	460328 487342	2/a, 67 28541	132M
Pump model*	8014-400A	Kwik Draw 488543, Kwik Draw Deluxe 487500	Bellows Pump Model 31 6726065	Model 800 Pump 7010657-I

*Tubes are certified only when used with specified pump model of same manufacturer.

showed accuracies in the range of ±25% to ±35%.[77–83]

A formal certification program [94,95] was the next step. In addition to passing performance evaluation tests at the Morgantown, West Virginia, NIOSH laboratory, manufacturers were required to provide information on the contents of the tubes and to conduct a specified quality control program. Because of the dependence of the calibrations on the pumps used with the tubes, certifications were periodically updated and issued[96] for specified combinations of tubes and pumps. By 1981, tubes of four manufacturers for 23 contaminants had been certified. Unfortunately, the program was terminated in 1983 for lack of funding.[97]

The requirements for certification generally followed the recommendations of the joint committee. However, the accuracy requirement was modified to ±35% at 0.5 TLV and ±25% at 1.0, 2.0, and 5.0 times TLV, to be maintained until the expiration date if the tubes were stored according to the manufacturer's instructions. At the TLV concentration, either the stain length had to be 15 mm or greater, or the relative standard deviation of the readings of the same tube by three or more independent tube readers had to be less than 10%. If the stain front was not exactly perpendicular to the tube axis (because of channeling of the air flow), the difference between the longest and shortest stain length measurements to the front had to be less than 20% of the mean length. Color intensity tubes had to have sufficient charts and sampling volume combinations to provide scale values including at least the following multiples of the TLV: 0.5, 0.75, 1.0, 2.0, 2.5, 2.0, 2.5, 3.0, 4.0, and 5.0; the relative standard deviation for readings of a tube by independent readers had to be <10%. Tests were to be conducted generally at

18.3°–29.5°C (65°–85°F) and at relative humidities of 50%, unless the humidity had to be reduced to avoid disturbing the test system. The manufacturer had to file a quality control plan and keep records of inspections of raw materials, finished tubes, and calibration and test equipment. Acceptable statistical quality levels for defects in finished tubes were as follows: critical 0% where tests were nondestructive; otherwise, 1.0%, major 2.5%, minor 4.0%, and accuracy 6.5%. Typical statistical calculations have been described.[98] Certification seals were affixed to approved devices. NIOSH reserved the right to withdraw certification for cause.

Because important legal and economic consequences depend on the accuracy of measurements of contaminant concentrations, enforcement agencies will most likely prefer certified equipment. Standards for detector tubes have been issued by more than 25 organizations,[99] including the Occupational Safety and Health Administration (OSHA),[100] International Union of Pure and Applied Chemistry (IUPAC),[101] Japanese Standards Association,[102] British Standards Institution,[103] American National Standards Institute (ANSI),[104] the International Standards Organization (ISO),[105,106] France, the Soviet Union, The Council of Europe, and a variety of private organizations in the United States and Europe. Requirements are mostly similar to those cited above.

In 1986, the Safety Equipment Institute (SEI) announced a voluntary program for third-party certification of detector tubes.[107] Manufacturers submit tubes for testing as the schedule for each type is announced. Two AIHA-accredited laboratories were selected to evaluate the tubes according to the NIOSH protocol.[94] Another contractor makes onsite, quality assurance audits of manufacturing facilities every 6 months for three audits, and then annually. If the tubes meet all requirements, the manufacturer may apply the SEI certification mark. This program should provide a stimulus for greater acceptance and use and for further improvements in detector tube technology. Tubes will be retested every 3 years. Table 18-3 gives the current listing of certified tubes.[108] Types of tubes for more substances are currently in the testing process.

Conclusions

Use of indicating tubes for analysis of toxic gas and vapor concentrations in air is a very rapid, convenient, and inexpensive technique that can be performed by semiskilled operators. These tubes are in various stages of development, and highly variable results have been obtained. Accuracy depends on a high degree of skill in the manufacture of the tubes. At present, results may be regarded as only range-finding and approximate in nature. The best accuracy that can be expected from indicator tube systems of the best types is on the order of ±25%. Because many of the tubes are far from specific, an accurate knowledge of the possible interfering gases present is very important. The quantitative effect of these interferences depends on the volume sampled in an irregular way. To avoid dangerously misleading results, the operation and interpretation should be under the supervision of a skilled occupational hygienist.

The manufacturers' descriptions for individual instruments are given in the pages which follow this discussion. It was not possible to check the accuracy of every detail of the description and claims made, and the responsibility for this material rests entirely with the individual manufacturers.

References

1. Campbell, E.E.; Miller, H.E.: Chemical Detectors, A Bibliography for the Industrial Hygienist with Abstracts and Annotations. LAMS-2378. Los Alamos Scientific Laboratory, NM (Vol I., 1961; Vol. II, 1964).
2. U.S. Department of the Air Force: Individual Protective and Detection Equipment. In: U.S. Dept. of the Army Technical Manual, TM 3-290, pg. 56–80. Dept. of the Air Force Technical Order, TO 39C-10C-1 (September 1953).
3. McFee, D.R.; Lavine, R.E.; Sullivan, R.J.: Carbon Monoxide, A Prevalent Hazard Indicated by Detector Tabs. Am. Ind. Hyg. Assoc. J. 31:749 (1970).
4. Saltzman, B.E.; Caplan, P.E.: Detector Tubes, Direct Reading Passive Badges and Dosimeter Tubes. In: Air Sampling Instruments for Evaluation of Atmospheric Contaminants, 7th ed., Chapter T, pp. 449–476. S.V. Hering, Ed. Amer. Conf. of Govt. Ind. Hyg., Cincinnati, OH (1989).
5. Ketcham, N.H.: Practical Air-Pollution Monitoring Devices. Am. Ind. Hyg. Assoc. J. 25:127 (1964).
6. Silverman, L.: Panel Discussion of Field Indicators in Industrial Hygiene. Am. Ind. Hyg. Assoc. J. 23:108 (1962).
7. Silverman, L.; Gardner, G.R.: Potassium Pallado Sulfite Method for Carbon Monoxide Detection. Am. Ind. Hyg. Assoc. J. 26:97 (1965).
8. Ingram, W.T.: Personal Air Pollution Monitoring Devices. Am. Ind. Hyg. Assoc. J. 25:298 (1964).
9. Linch, A.L.; Lord, Jr., S.S.; Kubitz, K.A.; Debrunner, M.R.: Phosgene in Air—Development of Improved Detection Procedures. Am. Ind. Hyg. Assoc. J. 26:465 (1965).
10. Linch, A.L.: Oxygen in Air Analyses—Evaluation of a Length of Stain Detector. Am. Ind. Hyg. Assoc. J. 26:645 (1965).
11. Leichnitz, K.: Determination of Arsine in Air in the Work Place (German). Die Berufsgenossenschaft (September 1967).
12. Leichnitz, K.: Cross-Sensitivity of Detector Tube Procedures for the Investigation of Air in the Work Place (German). Zentralblatt für arbeitsmedizin and Arbeitsschutz 18:97 (1968).
13. Linch, A.L.; Stalzer, R.F.; Lefferts, D.T.: Methyl and Ethyl Mercury Compounds—Recovery from Air and Analysis. Am. Ind. Hyg. Assoc. J. 29:79 (1968).
14. Peurifoy, P.V.; Woods, L.A.; Martin, G.A.: A Detector Tube for Determination of Aromatics in Gasoline. Anal. Chem. 40:1002 (1968).
15. Koljkowsky, P.: Indicator-tube Method for the Determination of Benzene in Air. Analyst 94:918 (1969).
16. Grubner, O.; Lynch, J.J.; Cares, J.W.; Burgess, W.A.: Collection of Nitrogen Dioxide by Porous Polymer Beads. Am. Ind. Hyg. Assoc. J. 33:201 (1972).

17. Neff, J.E.; Ketcham, N.H.: A Detector Tube for Analysis of Methyl Isocyanate in Air or Nitrogen Purge Gas. Am. Ind. Hyg. Assoc. J. 35:468 (1974).
18. National Dräger, Inc.: Dräger-Tube Handbook, 101 Technology Dr., Pittsburgh, PA 15275 (1992).
19. Sensidyne/Gastec: Precision Gas Detector System Manual. Sensidyne, Inc., 12345 Starkey Road, Largo, FL 33543 (1985).
20. American Industrial Hygiene Association: Direct Reading Colorimetric Tubes—A Manual of Recommended Practices. AIHA, 2700 Prosperity Ave., Fairfax, VA 22031 (1977).
21. Grote, A.A.; Kim, W.S.; Kupel, R.E.: Establishing a Protocol from Laboratory Studies to be Used in Field Sampling Operations. Am. Ind. Hyg. Assoc. J. 39:880 (1978).
22. Brown, V.R.: Gas and Vapor Detection During Spill Containment. In: Proceedings of the Haztech International Conference, August 11–16, 1986, Denver, CO, pp. 125–136. Colorado Ground Water Assoc. (1986).
23. Loffelholz, R.: Investigation of Contaminated Areas by Means of Dräger Tubes. Dräger Review 63:2 (July 1989).
24. Sieben, O.: Investigation of Oil and Sludge Contaminated Industrial Waste Water by Means of the Dräger Air Extraction Method. Dräger Review 69:11 (May 1992).
25. Kusnetz, H.L.: Air Flow Calibration of Direct Reading Colorimetric Gas Detecting Devices. Am. Ind. Hyg. Assoc. J. 21:340 (1960).
26. Colen, F.H.: A Study of the Interchangeability of Gas Detector Tubes and Pumps. Report TR-71. National Institute for Occupational Safety and Health, Morgantown, WV (June 15, 1973).
27. Colen, F.H.: A Study of the Interchangeability of Gas Detector Tubes and Pumps. Am. Ind. Hyg. Assoc. J. 35:686 (1974).
28. Leichnitz, K.: Use of Detector Tubes Under Extreme Conditions (Humidity, Pressure, Temperature). Am. Ind. Hyg. Assoc. J. 38:707 (1977).
29. Carlson, D.H.; Osborne, M.D.; Johnson, J.H.: The Development and Application to Detector Tubes of a Laboratory Method to Assess Accuracy of Occupational Diesel Pollutant Concentration Measurements. Am. Ind. Hyg. Assoc. J. 43:275 (1982).
30. Douglas, K.E.; Beaulieu, H.J.: Field Validation Study of Nitrogen Dioxide Passive Samplers in a "Diesel" Haulage Underground Mine. Am. Ind. Hyg. Assoc. J. 44:774 (1983).
31. Leichnitz, K.: Effects of Pressure and Temperature on the Indication of Dräger Tubes. Dräger Rev. 31:1 (September 1973).
32. Linch, A.L.: Evaluation of Ambient Air Quality by Personnel Monitoring. CRC Press, Inc., Cleveland, OH (1974).
33. Leichnitz, K.: Qualitative Detection of Substances by Means of Dräger Detector Tube Polytest and Dräger Detector Tube Ethyl Acetate 200 A. Dräger Rev. 46:13 (December 1980).
34. Kitagawa, T.: Detector Tube Method for Rapid Determination of Minute Amounts of Nitrogen Dioxide in the Atmosphere. Yokohama National University, Yokohama, Japan (July 1965).
35. Drägerwerk AG: Information Sheet No. 44: 0.5a Nitrous Gas/Detector Tube, P.O. Box 1339, D-24 Lübeck 1, Federal Republic of Germany (November 1960).
36. Grosskopf, K.: A Tentative Systematic Description of Detector Tube Reactions (German). Chemiker Zeitung-Chemische Apparatus 87:270 (1963).
37. Leichnitz, K.: Determination of Low SO_2 Concentrations by Means of Detector Tubes. Dräger Rev. 30:1 (May 1973).
38. Linch, A.L.; Plaff, H.V.: Carbon Monoxide—Evaluation of Exposure Potential by Personnel Monitor Surveys. Am. ind. Hyg. Assoc. J. 32:745 (1971).
39. Leichnitz, K.: The Detector Tube Method and its Development Tendencies (German). Chemiker-Zeitung 97:638 (1973).
40. Leichnitz, K.: An Analysis by Means of Long-Term Detector Tubes. Dräger Rev. 40:9 (December 1977).
41. Leichnitz, K.: Some Information on the Long-Term Measuring System for Gases and Vapors. Dräger Rev. 43:6 (June 1979).
42. Donham, K.J.; Popendorf, W.I.: Ambient Levels of Selected Gases Inside Swine Confinement Buildings. Am. Ind. Hyg. Assoc. J. 46:658 (1985).
43. Heubener, D.J.: Evaluation of a Carbon Monoxide Dosimeter. Am. Ind. Hyg. Assoc. J. 41:590 (1980).
44. Dharmarajan, V.; Rando, R.J.: Clarification—re: A Recommendation for Modifying the Standard Analytical Method for Determination of Chlorine in Air. Am. Ind. Hyg. Assoc. J. 40:746 (1979).
45. National Institute for Occupational Safety and Health: Criteria for a Recommended Standard—Occupational Exposure to Carbon Monoxide. DHEW (NIOSH) Pub. No. HSM 73-11000. NIOSH, Rockville, MD (1972).
46. Leidel, N.A.; Busch, K.A.: Statistical Methods for Determination of Noncompliance with Occupational Health Standards. DHEW (NIOSH) Pub. No. 75-159. National Institute for Occupational Safety and Health, Cincinnati, OH (April 1975).
47. Saltzman, B.E.: Basic Theory of Gas Indicator Tube Calibrations. Am. Ind. Hyg. Assoc. J. 23:112 (1962).
48. Leichnitz, K.: Attempt at Explanation of Calibration Curves of Detector Tubes (German). Chemiker-Ztg./Chem. Apparatus 91:141 (1967).
49. Scherberger, R.F.; Happ, G.P.; Miller, F.A.; Fassett, D.W.: A Dynamic Apparatus for Preparing Air-Vapor Mixtures of Known Concentrations. Am. Ind. Hyg. Assoc. J. 19:494 (1958).
50. Saltzman, B.E.: Preparation and Analysis of Calibrated Low Concentrations of Sixteen Toxic Gases. Anal. Chem. 33:1100 (1961).
51. Saltzman, B.E.: Preparation of Known Concentrations of Air Contaminants. In: The Industrial Environment—Its Evaluation and Control, Chap. 12, pp. 123–137. National Institute for Occupational Safety and Health, Contract HSM-99-71-45, Cincinnati, OH (1973).
52. Avera, Jr., C.B.: Simple Flow Regulator for Extremely Low Gas Flows. Rev. Sci. Instru. 32:985 (1961).
53. Cotabish, H.N.; McConnaughey, P.W.; Messer, H.C.: Making Known Concentrations for Instrument Calibration. Am. Ind. Hyg. Assoc. J. 22:392 (1961).
54. Hersch, P.A.: Controlled Addition of Experimental Pollutants to Air. J. Air Poll. Control Assoc. 19:164 (1969).
55. Hughes, E.E.; et al: Gas Generation Systems for the Evaluation of Gas Detecting Devices. NBSIR 73-292. National Bureau of Standards, Washington, DC (October 1973).
56. Hill, R.H.; Fraser, D.A.: Passive Dosimetry Using Detector Tubes. Am. Ind. Hyg. Assoc. J. 41:721 (1980).
57. Sefton, M.V.; Kostas, A.V.; Lombardi, C.: Stain Length Passive Dosimeters. Am. Ind. Hyg. Assoc. J. 43:820 (1982).
58. Gonzalez, L.A.; Sefton, M.V.: Stain Length Passive Dosimeter for Monitoring Carbon Monoxide. Am. Ind. Hyg. Assoc. J. 44:514 (1983).
59. Gonzalez, L.A.; Sefton, M.V.: Laboratory Evaluation of Stain Length Passive Dosimeters for Monitoring of Vinyl Chloride and Ethylene Oxide. Am. Ind. Hyg. Assoc. J. 46:591 (1985).
60. Pannwitz, K.H.: Direct-Reading Diffusion Tubes. Dräger Rev. 53:10 (June 1984).
61. McKee, E.S.; McConnaughey, P.W.: A Passive, Direct Reading, Length-of-Stain Dosimeter for Ammonia. Am. Ind. Hyg. Assoc. J. 46:407 (1985).
62. McConnaughey, P.W.; McKee, E.S.; Pretts, I.M.: Passive Colorimetric Dosimeter Tubes for Ammonia, Carbon Monoxide, Carbon Dioxide, Hydrogen Sulfide, Nitrogen Dioxide, and Sulfur Dioxide. Am. Ind. Hyg. Assoc. J. 46:357 (1985).
63. McKee, E.S.; McConnaughey, P.W.: Laboratory Evaluation of a Passive Length-of-Stain Dosimeter for Hydrogen Sulfide. Am. Ind. Hyg. Assoc. J. 47:475 (1986).
64. Bartley, D.L.: Diffusive Samplers Using Longitudinal Sorbent Strips. Am. Ind. Hyg. Assoc. J. 47:571 (1986).
65. Pannwitz, K.H.: The Direct-Reading Diffusion Tubes on the Test Bench. Dräger Rev. 57:2 (June 1986).
66. Cassinelli, M.E.; Hull, R.D.; Cuendet, P.A.: Performance of Sulfur

Dioxide Passive Monitors. Am. Ind. Hyg. Assoc. J. 46:599 (1985).
67. Hossain, M.A.; Saltzman, B.E.: Laboratory Evaluation of Passive Colorimetric Dosimeter Tubes for Carbon Monoxide. Appl. Ind. Hyg. 4:119 (1989).
68. Zurlo, N.; Andreoletti, F.: Effect of Air Turbulence on Diffusive Sampling. In: Diffusive Sampling. An Alternative Approach to Workplace Air Monitoring. Proceedings of an International Symposium, Luxembourg, Sept. 22–26, 1986, pp. 174–176. A. Berlin, R.H. Brown, and K.J. Saunders, Eds. London, Royal Society of Chemistry (1987).
69. Pannwitz, K.H.: Influence of Air Currents on the Sampling of Organic Solvent Vapours with Diffusive Samplers. In: Diffusive Sampling. An Alternative Approach to Workplace Air Monitoring. Proceedings of an International Symposium, Luxembourg, Sept. 22–26, 1986, pp. 157–160. A. Berlin, R.H. Brown, and K.J. Saunders, Eds. London, Royal Society of Chemistry (1987).
70. Dittmar, P.; Stress, G.: The Suitability of Detection of Toxic Substances in the Air; I: Hydrogen Sulfide Detector Tubes (German). Arbeitsschutz 8:173 (1959).
71. Heseltine, H.K.: The Detection and Estimation of Low Concentrations of Methyl Bromide in Air. Pest Technology (England) (July/August 1959).
72. Kusnetz, H.L.; Saltzman, B.E.; LaNier, M.E.: Calibration and Evaluation of Gas Detecting Tubes. Am. Ind. Hyg. Assoc. J. 21:361 (1960).
73. Banks, O.M.; Nelson, K.R.: Evaluation of Commercial Detector Tubes. Presented at the American Industrial Hygiene Conference, Detroit, MI (April 13, 1961).
74. LaNier, M.E.; Kusnetz, H.L.: Practices in the Field of Detector Tubes. Arch. Env. Health 6:418 (1963).
75. Hay, III, E.B.: Exposure to Aromatic Hydrocarbons in a Coke Oven By-Product Plant. Am. Ind. Hyg. Assoc. J. 25:386 (1964).
76. Larsen, L.B.; Hendricks, R.H.: An Evaluation of Certain Direct Reading Devices for the Determination of Ozone. Am. Ind. Hyg. Assoc. J. 30:620 (1969).
77. Morganstern, A.S.; Ash, R.M.; Lynch, J.R.: The Evaluation of Gas Detector Tube Systems; I: Carbon Monoxide. Am. Ind. Hyg. Assoc. J. 31:630 (1970).
78. Ash, R.M.; Lynch, J.R.: The Evaluation of Gas Detector Tube Systems: Benzene. Am. Ind. Hyg. Assoc. J. 32:410 (1971).
79. Ash, R.M.; Lynch, J.R.: The Evaluation of Detector Tube Systems: Sulfur Dioxide. Am. Ind. Hyg. Assoc. J. 32:490 (1971); also see Am. Ind. Hyg. Assoc. J. 33:11 (1972).
80. Ash, R.M.; Lynch, J.R.: The Evaluation of Detector Tube Systems: Carbon Tetrachloride. Am. Ind. Hyg. Assoc. J. 32:552 (1971).
81. Roper, C.P.: An Evaluation of Perchloroethylene Detector Tube. Am. Ind. Hyg. Assoc. J. 32:847 (1971).
82. Johnston, B.A.; Roper, C.P.: The Evaluation of Gas Detector Tube Systems: Chlorine. Am. Ind. Hyg. Assoc. J. 33:533 (1972).
83. Johnston, B.A.: The Evaluation of Gas Detector Tube Systems: Hydrogen Sulfide. Am. Ind. Hyg. Assoc. J. 33:811 (1972).
84. Jentzsch, D.; Fraser, D.A.: A Laboratory Evaluation of Long-term Detector Tubes: Benzene, Toluene, Trichloroethylene. Am. Ind. Hyg. Assoc. J. 42:810 (1981).
85. Septon, J.C.; Wilczek, Jr., T.: Evaluation of Hydrogen Sulfide Detector Tubes. Appl. Ind. Hyg. 1:196 (1986).
86. Leichnitz, K.: Survey of Dräger Long-Term Tubes with Special Consideration of the Long-Term Tubes Sulfur Dioxide 5/a-L. Dräger Review 48:16 (November 1981).
87. Leichnitz, K.: Dräger Long-Term Tubes Meet IUPAC Standard. Dräger Review 52:11 (January 1984).
88. Beck, S.W.; Stock, T.H.: An Evaluation of the Effects of Source and Concentration on Three Methods for the Measurement of Formaldehyde in Indoor Air. Am. Ind. Hyg. Assoc. J. 51:14 (1990).
89. Manninen, A.: Analysis of Airborne Ammonia: Comparison of Field Methods. Ann. of Occ. Hyg. 32:399 (1988).
90. Droz, P.O.; Krebs, Y.; Nicole, C.; Guillemin, M.: A Direct Reading Method for Chlorinated Hydrocarbons in Breath. Am. Ind. Hyg. Assoc. J. 49:319 (1988).
91. Stock, T.H.: The Use of Detector Tube Humidity Limits. Am. Ind. Hyg. Asoc. J. 47:241 (1986).
92. McCammon, Jr., C.S.; Crouse, W.E.; Carrol, Jr., H.B.: The Effect of Extreme Humidity and Temperature on Gas Detector Tube Performance. Am. Ind. Hyg. Assoc. J. 43:18 (1982).
93. Joint Comm. on Direct Reading Gas Detecting Systems, ACGIH–AIHA: Direct Reading Gas Detecting Tube Systems. Am. Ind. Hyg. Assoc. J. 32:488 (1971).
94. National Institute for Occupational Safety and Health: Certification of Gas Detector Tube Units. Federal Register 38:11458 (May 8, 1973); also 43 CFR 84.
95. Roper, C.P.: The NIOSH Detector Tube Certification Program. Am. Ind. Hyg. Assoc. J. 35:438 (1974).
96. National Institute for Occupational Safety and Health: NIOSH Certified Equipment List as of October 1, 1981. DHHS (NIOSH) Pub. No. 82-106. Cincinnati, OH (October 1981; periodically updated and reissued).
97. Centers for Disease Control, National Institute for Occupational Safety and Health: NIOSH Voluntary Testing and Certification Program. Fed. Reg. 48(191):44931 (September 30, 1983).
98. Leichnitz, K.: How Reliable are Detector Tubes? Dräger Rev. 43:21 (June 1979).
99. Leichnitz, K.: Comments of Official Organizations Regarding Suitability of Detector Tubes. Dräger Rev. 49:19 (May 1982).
100. U.S. Department of Labor: Directive 73-4. Use of Detector Tubes. Washington, DC (March 1973).
101. International Union of Pure and Applied Chemistry (IUPAC): Performance Standards for Detector Tube Units Used to Monitor Gases and Vapours in Working Areas. Pure and Applied Chemistry 54:1763 (1982).
102. Japanese Industrial Standard: Detector Tube Type Gas Measuring Instruments. JIS K 0804-1985. Japanese Standards Assoc. 1-24, Akasaka 4, Minato-ku, Tokyo 107, Japan (1986).
103. British Standard: Gas Detector Tubes BS5343. Part 1. Specification for Short Term Gas Detector Tubes. British Standards Institution, 2 Park St., London W1A2BS, England (1986).
104. Industrial Safety Equipment Association: American National Standard for Detector Tube Units-Short Term Type for Toxic Gases and Vapors in Working Environments. ANSI/ISEA 102-1990. American National Standards Institute, 1430 Broadway, New York, NY 10018 (1990).
105. Technical Committee ISO/TC 146, Air Quality: International Standard ISO 8760. Work-Place Air-Determination of Mass Concentration of Carbon Monoxide-Method Using Detector Tubes for Short-Term Sampling with Direct Indication. International Standards Organization, Case Postale 56. CH-1211, Geneva 20, Switzerland (1990).
106. Technical Committee ISO/TC 146, Air Quality: International Standard ISO 8761. Work-Place Air - Determination of Mass Concentration of Nitrogen Dioxide - Method Using Detector Tubes for Short-Term Sampling with Direct Indication. International Standards Organization, Case Postale 56. CH-1211, Geneva 20, Switzerland (1989).
107. Wilcher, Jr., F.E.: SEI Gas Detector Tube Certification. Appl. Ind. Hyg. 3:R-7 (August 1988).
108. Safety Equipment Institute: Certified Products List, October 1993. SEI, 1901 N. Moore Street, Arlington, VA 22209.

Instrument Descriptions

Introduction

Detector tubes, direct-reading passive badges, and dosimeter tubes can be classified by certain general characteristics. For example, many detectors aspirate short-term air samples using a few strokes of a hand piston pump or rubber bulb. The long-term types use a continuous pump at a very low flow rate for periods as long as 8 hrs to give time-weighted average (TWA) concentrations. No pump is required by passive types that rely on diffusion of the analyte from air into the sensing absorbent. Early versions of sensing absorbents exhibited a change in color tint, but more accurate results are obtained with absorbents that produce a length of stain that is related to analyte concentration. The instruments described in this section are classified by these characteristics in Table 18-I-1. Table 18-I-2 is an index of contaminants showing applicable instruments and their characteristics for each analysis. The last table of the chapter, Table 18-I-11, lists the commercial sources for the instruments described. All of the tables in this section are located at the end of the chapter.

18-1. LEAK-TEC Personnel Protection Indicators

American Gas & Chemical Company, Ltd. (AGC)

The Leak-Tec Personnel Protection Indicators (PPI) are plastic badges with pocket clips that chemically react with concentrations of various gases or vapors to give forewarning of excessive exposure to a toxic substance by means of a color change.

The chemicals that can be detected are ammonia, carbon monoxide, chlorine, hydrazine, hydrogen sulfide, nitrogen dioxide, and ozone. A color chart is available for all badges except carbon monoxide and ozone (see Table 18-I-3).

Accumulation

Leak-Tec badges and monitors can accumulate very low concentrations of gas over time. For example, if a chlorine badge is exposed to 0.2 ppm for several days, a color change will eventually result due to the total concentration chlorine exposure. This color change may lead to the false conclusion that 1 ppm of high concentration chlorine was present in the ambient atmosphere during the day of the color change. Because of this accumulation characteristic, the badges and monitors should be changed as often as possible.

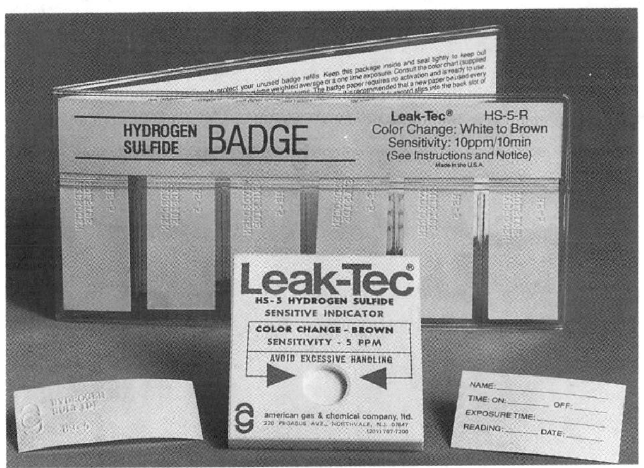

INSTRUMENT 18-1. LEAK-TEC Personnel Protection Indicators.

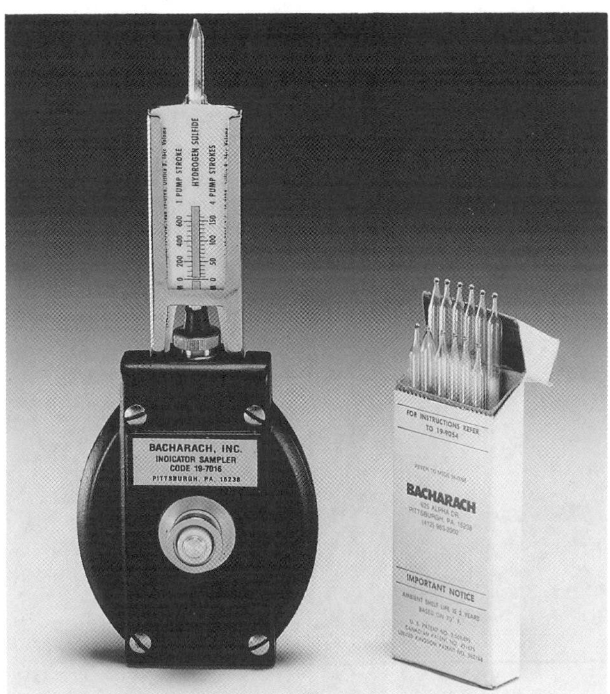

INSTRUMENT 18-2. Bacharach Gas Hazard Indicator.

Color Fading and Reuse of Badge

The chlorine, nitrogen dioxide, ammonia, and ozone indicators can appear to "regenerate" when removed from the contaminated environment. That is, they may return to their original color. The carbon monoxide, hydrazine, and hydrogen sulfide detectors will either fade slightly or not change at all. A badge or monitor that has gone through a distinct color change due to exposure should not be reused even if it has regenerated to the original color. Whenever a badge changes color, a portion of the reagents in the badge has been used. Therefore, the level of sensitivity cannot be guaranteed.

18-2. Bacharach Gas Hazard Indicator

Bacharach, Inc. (BAC)

The Bacharach Gas Hazard Indicator is a portable instrument for the detection of concentrations of hydrogen sulfide, sulfur dioxide, nitrogen dioxide, carbon dioxide, chlorine, and carbon monoxide. Used by safety engineers and industrial hygienists, it finds applications in process industries, refineries, mines, tunnels, sewers, natural gas fields, and confined areas. Hazardous gas content, in ppm, is determined by measuring the length of the stain or bleach. Air is sampled with a

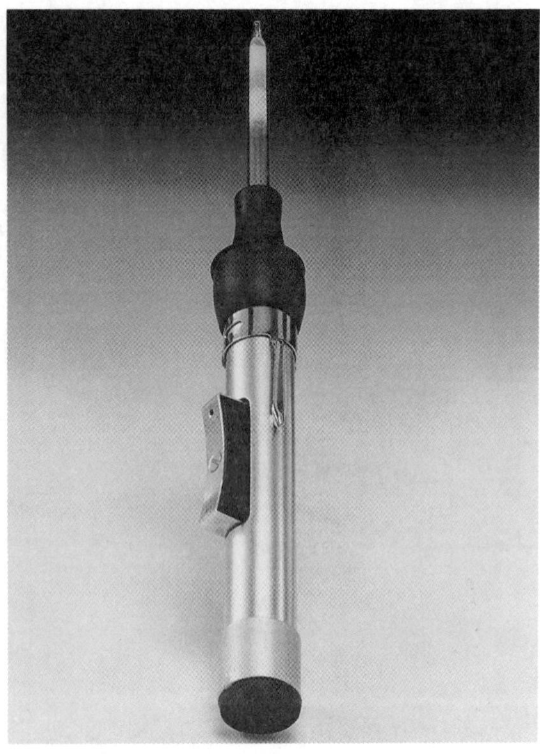

INSTRUMENT 18-3. Monoxor® Carbon Monoxide Detector.

hand-held sampling pump that has interchangeable scales and calibrated tubes. Measurements are read directly from the length of stain, and no color comparison charts or calibration curves are necessary. The ranges of the various tubes are shown in Table 18-I-4.

18-3. Monoxor® Carbon Monoxide Detector

Bacharach, Inc. (BAC)

The Monoxor® Detector (No. 19-7021) is a pocket-sized instrument for detecting dangerous carbon monoxide concentrations; it is not intended for precise measurements of carbon monoxide percentages. Sealed Monoxor indicator tubes contain a short length of yellow carbon-monoxide-sensitive chemical, protected on both ends by a guard gel. This guard gel is unaffected by carbon monoxide and renders the yellow indicating chemical insensitive to smoke, fumes, gases, and vapors other than carbon monoxide. When exposed to carbon monoxide, a brownish-gray stain appears at the end of the yellow chemical. The Monoxor detector has a push-button aspirator pump with a diameter of 3 cm (1 1/16 in.) and a length of 16 1/2 cm (6 1/2 in.). If, after one pump stroke, the stain forms only at the edge of the gel, the concentration is approximately 300 parts carbon monoxide per million parts of air, but the carbon monoxide concentration is much higher as the stain extends over the entire length of the gel. If the stain appears after the second stroke, the carbon monoxide concentration is in the range of 100 to 300 ppm.

18-4. Draeger Haz Mat Kit

National Draeger, Inc. (NDR)

The National Draeger Haz Mat Kit is designed to aid in the initial assessment of potentially hazardous situations. The detector tubes included in the kit have been selected to utilize a systematic sampling matrix. Using the polytest tube as a starting point, the sampling matrix provides a systematic test sequence to obtain information about the chemical group to which an unknown substance may belong. The haz mat kit can also be used for providing quantitative measurement of specific gases and vapors. Evaluation of test results can be performed onsite.

Housed in a durable, lightweight case, the haz mat kit includes the Draeger bellows pump with an automatic stroke counter, a 3-meter extension hose for testing inaccessible areas, and an air current kit for determining wind direction and velocity. Other contents include spare parts and tools for pump maintenance and 17 types of detector tubes. The components fit into a closed-cell foam insert which provides travel protection and organization. The detector tubes in the standard haz mat kit are listed in Table 18-I-5.

18-5. Draeger Diffusion Tubes

National Draeger, Inc. (NDR)

The direct-reading diffusion detector tubes from National Draeger work on the principle of gaseous diffusion to give long-term, TWA measurements without a pump. The contaminant gas diffuses into the tube by means of the concentration gradient between the ambient atmosphere and the interior of the tube. The diffusion tubes have been calibrated in ppm × hrs and volume % × hrs with the calibrated scale printed di-

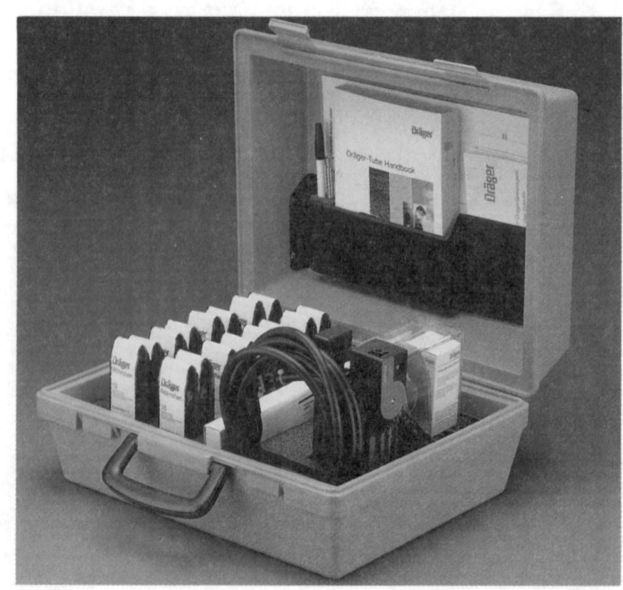

INSTRUMENT 18-4. Draeger Haz Mat Kit.

rectly on the tube. This system consists of a tube holder and a diffusion tube that may be attached to a pocket or lapel. The range of measurement for various Draeger diffusion tubes is given in Table 18-I-6.

18-6. Draeger Long-Duration Detector Tubes and Polymeter

National Draeger, Inc. (NDR)

The Draeger long-term detector tubes and the Draeger Polymeter® measure the mean value of the contaminant concentration over periods of up to 8 hrs. The long-term detector tubes are calibrated in units of microliters and are designed for use over a flow rate range of 10 to 20 ml/min. The TWA concentration in ppm is calculated by dividing the detector tube indication by the sample volume in liters. The Polymeter is a battery-powered peristaltic pump that provides a continuous flow at approximately 15 ml/min. The unit is supplied in a leather carrying bag with a shoulder strap. An extension hose is available as an accessory. Table 18-I-7 indicates the measuring range and usage of Draeger long-term tubes.

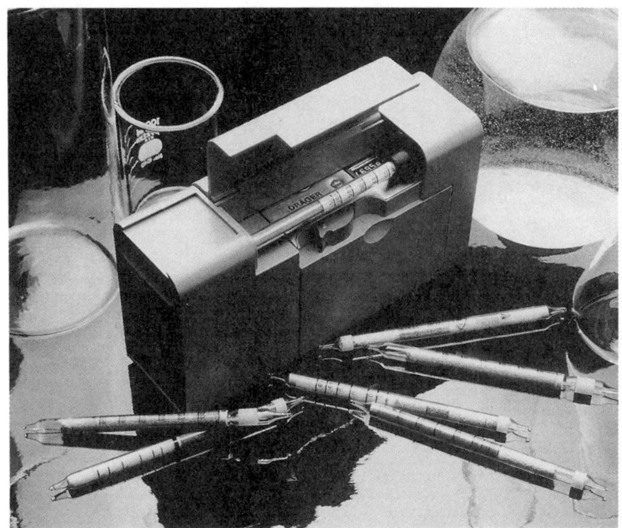

INSTRUMENT 18-6. Draeger Long-duration Detector Tubes and Polymeter.

18-7. Draeger accuro®, accuro 2000, and Quantimeter 1000.

National Draeger, Inc. (NDR)

The National Draeger accuro bellows pump and short-term detector tubes form a portable sampling unit for use in measuring concentrations of various gases and vapors (Instrument 18-7). Draeger detector tubes are available for measuring approximately 350 air contaminants and for technical gas analysis. The pump delivers 100 ml of sample air with each pump stroke. After a prescribed number of pump strokes, the stain length or the discoloration of the tube gives a direct measure of the gas or vapor concentration. Calibration scales are printed directly on most types of tubes. The accuro is a modular system. For large volume measurements, the accuro slides into the electronically programmable accuro 2000. The Quantimeter 1000 is a programmable, battery-operated bellows pump with the same flow characteristics as the hand-operated pump and it is intrinsically safe. The complete Draeger accuro deluxe pump kit with spare parts, tube opener, and screwdriver is contained in a vinyl carrying case and weighs approximately 1.5 kg (3.3 lbs). The detector tubes are essentially specific for particular gases or vapors. This specificity is achieved not only by the use of specific and stable

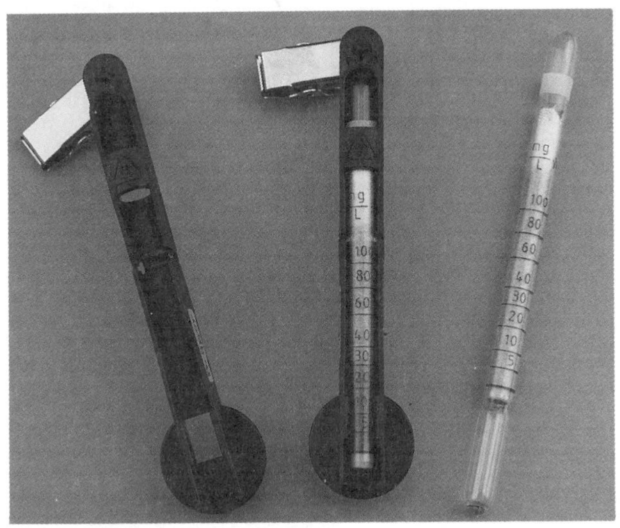

INSTRUMENT 18-5. Draeger diffusion tubes.

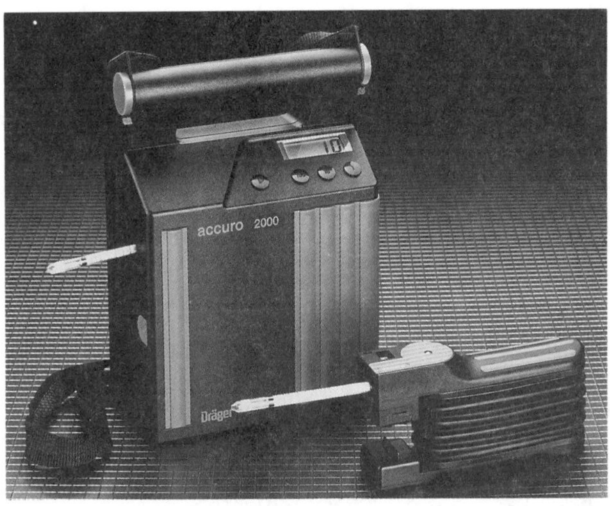

INSTRUMENT 18-7. National Draeger accuro®, accuro 2000, and Quantimeter 1000.

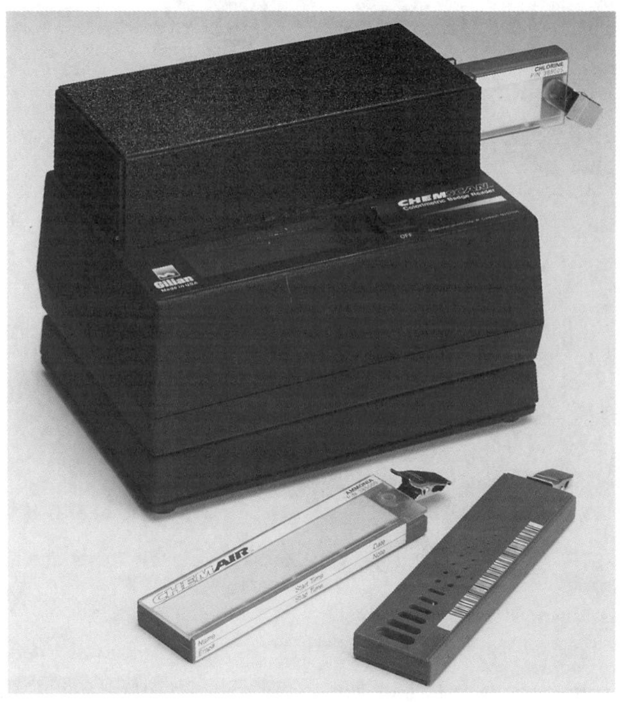

INSTRUMENT 18-8. CHEMAIR™ and CHEMSCAN™ colorimetric badge system.

reagents but also by the use of precleansing layers placed in front of the actual reactive layer to selectively absorb interfering components that may be contained in the gas or vapor sample. The reading deviations for many of the detector tubes are not more than ±25% from the true value.

Table 18-I-2 indicates the use of Draeger short-term detector tubes with the accuro® bellows pump.

18-8. CHEMAIR™ and CHEMSCAN™ Colorimetric Badge System

Gilian Instrument Corp. (GIC)

The new colorimetric passive air sampling badge, the CHEMAIR™ System, provides instantaneous quantitative measurement of gases and vapors. This lightweight (1.5 oz.) badge incorporates a patented, multilayer diffuser design that allows detection of a wide range of concentrations from trace parts per billion (ppb) to high ppm and exceeds NIOSH and OSHA requirements for accuracy and precision.

The patented design of the CHEMAIR badge allows the contaminant to permeate through a hydropic membrane and diffuse onto an indicator film. The contaminant reacts with the reagent-coated film and forms a color stain. Potentially interfering contaminants are trapped on another coated substrate layer and prevented from entering the indicator layer. Color and length are proportional to the exposure dose.

By inserting the exposed CHEMAIR badge into a microprocessor-controlled CHEMSCAN™ optical reader, the color stains on the badge are reduced into their primary components, i.e., red, green, and blue, using a series of LEDs and filters. The CHEMSCAN reader converts the developed color into an exposure dose. The calibration data for the gas being measured are communicated to the optical reader via the bar code on the badge. Once the badge is inserted into the CHEMSCAN reader, total analysis time is just 2 seconds. For area mapping studies, the CHEMAIR badge can be read several times during the exposure period to detect variations in the concentration levels.

CHEMAIR badges will be available for ammonia, carbon monoxide, sulfur dioxide, nitrogen dioxide, hydrogen sulfide, chlorine, carbon disulfide, methanol, ethanol, hydrazine, methyl hydrazine, formaldehyde, ethylene oxide, glutaraldehyde, mercury, methyl ethyl ketone, and acetone.

Contact Gilian to confirm availability.

18-9. CHROMAIR™ Passive Monitoring Badges

Gilian Instrument Corp. (GIC)

Gilian Instrument Corp. introduces CHROMAIR™ passive monitoring badges for indoor air quality and OSHA compliance screening. The easy-to-use badge system allows the user to obtain semiquantitative in-

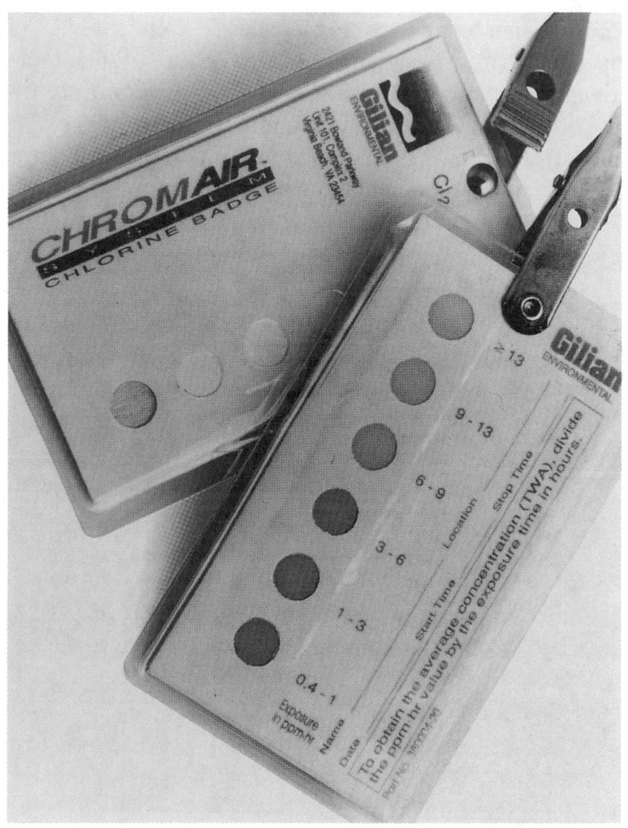

INSTRUMENT 18-9. CHROMAIR™ passive monitoring badges.

formation onsite without laboratory delays. All exposure levels conveniently appear on the badge to show a quick visual indication of the exposure dose.

The passive monitors rely on the principles of diffusion. The contaminant gas or vapor being monitored diffuses through a series of six cells on the front of the badge, each having a proportionally increased resistance to diffusion. After diffusing through the cells, the gas or vapor reacts with an indicator layer containing a specific reagent for the contaminant and the cells change color. When sampling is completed, the exposure dose is clearly indicated on the opposite side of the badge. To obtain the average concentration (ppm) in the sampled atmosphere, divide the exposure dosage (ppm-hrs) by the exposure time in hours.

A convenient exposure dose scale is printed on the back of the badge next to each cell indicating the dose range of that particular cell. The exposure dose scale is read by locating the highest level cell with color. The degree of color saturation of the highest exposed cell determines the interpolated value of the range associated with that cell.

CHROMAIR badges offer accurate exposure measurement without laboratory costs or delays. Chemically similar compounds that are potential interferents are "trapped" from reaching the indicator layer to ensure a valid exposure reading. The unique badge design minimizes the effects of humidity, air velocity, and cross-sensitivities for increased exposure accuracy.

ChromAir badges will be available for ammonia, acetone, chlorine, carbon monoxide, sulfur dioxide, nitrogen dioxide, hydrogen sulfide, carbon disulfide, methanol, ethanol, hydrazine, formaldehyde, and a new glutaraldehyde Ceiling Limit badge for 15-minute exposures.

18-10. Kitagawa Precision® Gas Detector Kit

Matheson Gas Products (MGP)
Roxan, Inc. (ROX)
Enmet Corp. (ENM)

The Model 8014 Precision Gas Detector is used for rapid determination of atmospheric concentrations of toxic gases and vapors. Calibrated detector tubes are available for more than 100 different gases and vapors, as shown in Table 18-I-2. For many gases and vapors, tubes are available for more than one concentration range, bringing the total number of individual tubes currently available to nearly 300. For sampling, a detector tube is inserted in the piston pump inlet. When the pump handle is withdrawn, a 100-cm^3 air sample is drawn through the tube. A single pump stroke is sufficient to produce a color stain, the length of which is proportional to the concentration of the gas or vapor. The detecting reagents are absorbed on particles that are hermetically sealed in the glass detector tubes. The

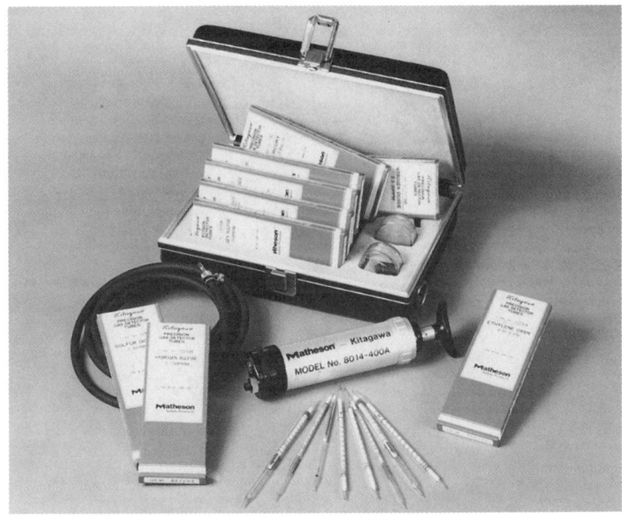

INSTRUMENT 18-10. Kitagawa Precision® Gas Detector Kit.

very fine grain size ensures uniform distribution of air flow through the tubes and provides sharp demarcation lines on all length-of-stain tubes and uniform color changes in color intensity tubes. Typically, the concentration is read directly off the scale etched on each tube. The Gas Detector Kit includes a piston pump, spare parts, and a carrying case with room for seven boxes of tubes. The weight of the pump is 0.6 kg (1.25 lbs); it is 7.3 cm (1.5 in.) in diameter and 20 cm (8 in.) long. The complete unit weighs 1.4 kg (3.5 lbs). Table 18-I-2 lists the detector tubes available. When used within their expiration date, the readings at 20°C (68°F) are designed to be within 5% to 10% of the true concentration. Temperature corrections for operating at other temperatures are normally unnecessary but are provided with those tubes requiring it.

18-11. Kitagawa Qualitative Detector Tubes and Haz Mat Test Kit

Matheson Gas Products (MGP)
Roxan, Inc. (ROX)
Enmet Corp. (ENM)

Matheson's qualitative detector tubes are used for rapid on-the-spot identification of unknown gases and vapors. Unlike conventional "length of stain" tubes that provide quantitative measurements, these tubes are comprised of several indicating sections. Each section contains a unique blend of reagents that will absorb and react with a particular gas or vapor and change color. The unknown gas or vapor is determined by which section(s) changed color, and to what color they changed.

Two types of tubes are available. Model 8014-186B identifies a broad range of organic substances, such as gasoline, alcohols, and hydrocarbons. Model 8014-131 identifies inorganic compounds, such as carbon monox-

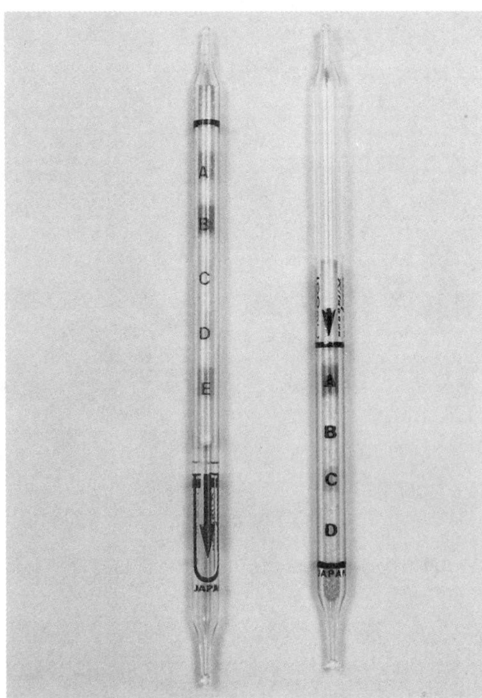

INSTRUMENT 18-11. Kitagawa qualitative detector tubes Models 8014-131 and 8014-186B.

ide, sulfur dioxide, and chlorine. The tubes are also packaged as part of the Model 8070 basic Qualitative Analysis Kit and the Model 8075 deluxe Hazmat Test Kit.

In operation, the qualitative tubes are used similarly to the conventional tubes. That is, a tube is inserted into the inlet of the piston-type Kitagawa sampling pump (Model 8014-400A; also used with conventional detector tubes). The pump handle is withdrawn, accurately drawing a 100-cm^3 air sample through the tube. The sample vue indicator shows when sampling is completed (less than 1 min). Only one pump stroke is required. The presence and identity of the unknown substance, if any, is based upon which sections of the tube change color and to what colors they change. Temperature and humidity corrections are not required.

18-12. Kwik-Draw Detector Tube Pump and Detector Tubes

Mine Safety Appliances Company (MSA)

The Kwik-Draw pump permits detection of gases and vapors with just the squeeze of a hand. The operator places his fingers around the hand grip and pushes the knob in for a precise (100-ml) sample volume. The pump shaft provides the guiding action to drive a spring-loaded bellows pump without cocking.

A mechanical stroke counter shows the exact number of strokes performed and provides a positive stop when the stroke is fully compressed.

The end-of-stroke indicator on the Kwik-Draw deluxe pump "winks" after the precise volume of air is drawn, so operators always know when they have sampled enough air for a successful reading. The Kwik-Draw basic offers a less expensive alternative without the end-of-stroke indicator.

The hand grip is firm and comfortable, even when wearing heavy gloves. A rubber tube holder accepts both 3- and 5-mm tubes, and a carrying pouch holds the pump and several boxes of detector tubes. Approximately 150 detector tubes are available, as shown in Table 18-I-2.

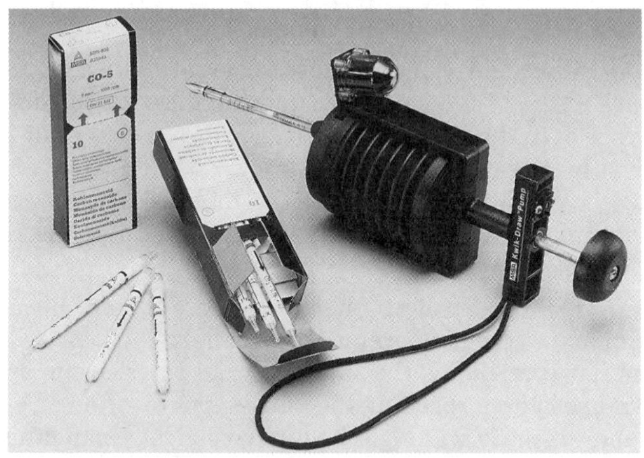

INSTRUMENT 18-12. Kwik-Draw detector tube pump and detector tubes.

18-13. Sensidyne/Gastec Dosimeter Tubes

Sensidyne, Inc. (SEN)

The Sensidyne/Gastec dosimeter tubes contain a reagent that is sensitive to a particular vapor or gas (Table 18-I-8 lists available dosimeter tubes). To operate, snap off the breakaway, prescored end of the tube and insert it in the tube holder. The gas or vapor to be measured immediately enters the tube by diffusion and reacts with the absorbing medium quantitatively to produce a length-of-stain indication. The two-layer construction provides a distinct line of demarcation. The dosimeter tube is read in ppm-hrs. At the end of the sampling period, the ppm-hr calibration mark on the tube at the point where the color stain stops is divided by the number of hours in the sampling period to obtain the TWA ppm concentration. The tube holder is made of a corrosion-resistant, high-impact plastic. It conveniently clips to the worker's collar or shirt, thus preventing the tube holder from dangling far in front of the worker. The dosimeter tube can be read while in the tube holder. A string attachment, secured to the holder and worn around the user's neck, eliminates the possible contamination from a dropped tube. All Sensidyne/Gastec dosimeter tubes are direct-reading.

18-14. Sensidyne/Gastec Pyrotec Pyrolyzer

Sensidyne, Inc. (SEN)

The Pyrotec Pyrolyzer is used in conjunction with Sensidyne/Gastec's Model 800 sampling pump detector tubes for fluorocarbons, nitroparaffins, dimethyl sulfide, and other gases. These gases are listed in Table 18-I-9. These detector tubes are the direct-reading type, with a single calibration scale printed on each tube, so measurements can be made simply and reliably. The method of detection is to first pyrolyze (decompose by heat) the target substance; then measure the level of combustion by-products via a length-of-stain detector tube. The concentration of the by-products of combustion is directly proportional to the concentration of the target substance in the air. The calibration scale printed on the fluorocarbon detector tubes provides a direct reading for refrigerant R-113. Conversions for other common refrigerants are shown in Table 18-I-9. To sample, the operator snaps off both breakaway ends of the tube, inserts the tube into the Pyrotec tube holder, turns the Pyrotec on, and pulls the pump handle out. Construction: high-impact plastic; dimensions: 8.3 × 6.3 cm (3.25 × 2.5 in.); weight 200 g (7 oz.) It screws onto the front of the Model 800 pump. Four standard AA batteries power the instrument for hours of continuous operation. Tube numbers 51, 51L, 51H, 52, and 53 are the only Sensidyne/Gastec tubes that require the Pyrotec Pyrolyzer (see Table 18-I-9).

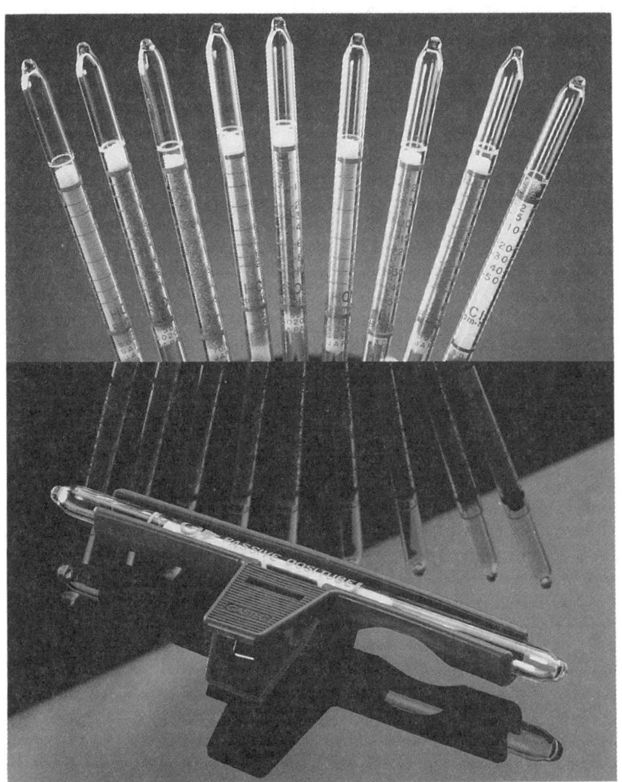

INSTRUMENT 18-13. Sensidyne/Gastec dosimeter tubes.

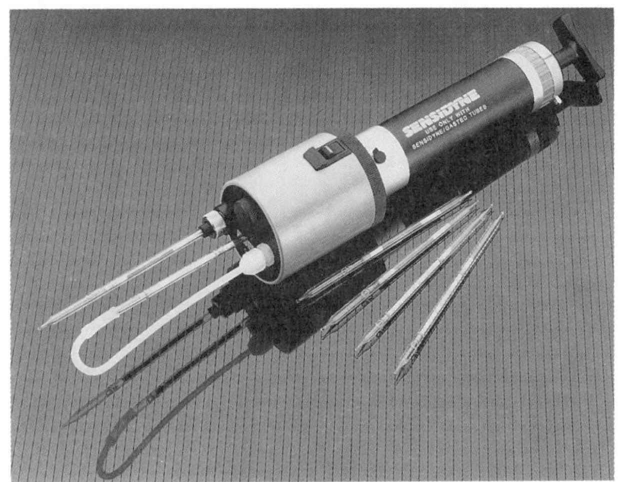

INSTRUMENT 18-14. Sensidyne/Gastec Pyrotec Pyrolyzer.

18-15. Sensidyne/Gastec System

Sensidyne, Inc. (SEN)

The Sensidyne/Gastec system is designed for underground storage tank leak detection of petroleum and other chemicals. It consists of a Model 800 hand-held piston pump, direct-reading detector tubes, and an extension hose. Each detector tube contains a reagent that is sensitive to a particular gas or vapor. These reagents are contained inside a hermetically sealed glass tube with calibration markings printed on the tube. To use, the operator snaps off both breakaway ends of a tube; inserts it into the extension hose; drops the extension hose into the interstitial cavity of a double-walled tank, into a borehole, or into a groundwater monitoring well above the water level; and pulls the pump handle. As the handle is pulled, a measured volume of air is drawn inside the tube where it contacts the reagent to produce a length-of-stain indication. The pump weighs 260 g (9.25 oz.), and tubes may be shipped without special approvals. The system does not require

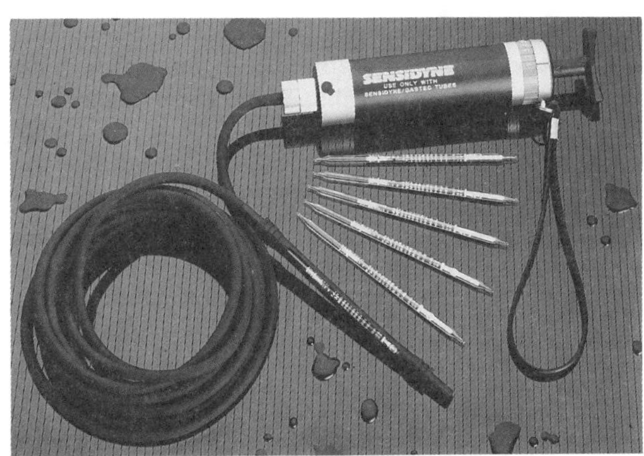

INSTRUMENT 18-15. Sensidyne/Gastec system.

electrical power; it may safely be used in the presence of explosive or flammable gas. It is capable of monitoring over 280 gases and vapors and can discriminate between acids and petroleum products. Gasoline vapors can be detected as low as 3 ppm. Table 18-I-2 lists the detector tubes available.

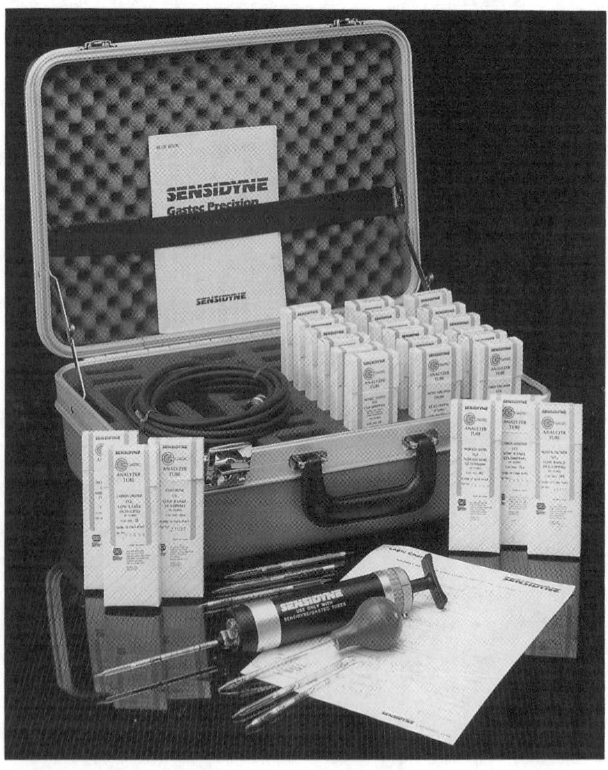

INSTRUMENT 18-16. Sensidyne/Gastec Haz Mat Kit (Deluxe II).

18-16. Sensidyne/Gastec Haz Mat Kits

Sensidyne, Inc. (SEN)

The Sensidyne/Gastec Haz Mat Kits are portable hazardous material detection kits requiring no electrical power or user calibration. The standard kit uses the Model 800 hand-held piston pump and extension cable and incorporates 13 different types of detector tubes for commonly encountered substances, as shown in Table 18-I-10. The kit includes a leather shoulder bag and a laminated sampling logic chart which allows the user to identify unknown compounds using the 13 tubes. The deluxe haz mat kit incorporates all of these elements plus an air flow indicator, smoke tube kit, and 13 boxes of detector tubes in a hardsided carrying case. The Deluxe Haz Mat Kit II uses 23 different types of detector tubes and an expanded logic chart to determine the identity of a wider range of unknown compounds. This system is expandable and is ultimately capable of measuring over 280 gases (see Table 18-I-2 for a list of gas detector tubes available).

18-17. Sensidyne/Gastec Precision Gas Detector System

Sensidyne, Inc. (SEN)

Over 280 gases and vapors can be measured with the High-precision Gas Sampling System using the detector tubes listed in Table 18-I-2. The two major components are 1) direct-reading detector tubes and 2) the high-precision, piston-type volumetric pump. Each detector tube contains a reagent that is specifically sensitive to a particular vapor or gas. These reagents are contained on fine-grain silica gel, activated alumina, or other adsorbing media (depending upon application requirements), inside a constant-inner-diameter, hermetically sealed glass tube. To sample, the operator snaps off both breakaway ends of a tube, inserts the tube into the hand-held pump, and pulls the pump handle out. A measured volume of ambient air is drawn inside the tube. The reagent changes color instantly and reacts quantitatively to provide a length-of-stain indication. The farther the color stain travels along the tube, the higher the concentration of gas. The calibration mark on the tube, at the point where the color stain stops, gives the concentration. Calibration scales for the detector tubes are printed on the basis of individual production lots. Calibration scales are in ppm, mg/L, or %, depending on the substance to be measured and the desired measuring range. Every tube and tube box carries the quality control number, chemical symbol, and the expiration date. The expandable measuring range permits measurement of concentrations above or below the printed scale simply by increasing or decreasing pump strokes.

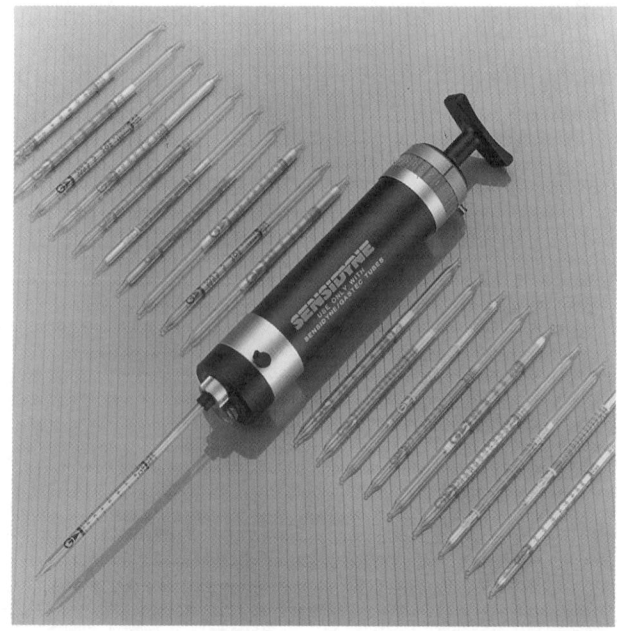

INSTRUMENT 18-17. Sensidyne/Gastec precision gas detector system.

18-18. Sensidyne/Gastec TDI/MDI Analyzer Kit

Sensidyne, Inc. (SEN)

The Sensidyne TDI/MDI Analyzer Kit provides a rapid method for field determination of toluene diisocyanate and methylene bis(4-phenylisocyanate) in air. A sample is drawn through a special absorbing solution using the BDX 55 pump and a midget impinger at 0.1 cfm (2.8 L/min) for 10 min. The solution is transferred to a test tube and a series of reagents are added to produce a blue-red color. The color is compared to a color reference card graduated in ppm by volume. Results within 0.01- to 0.35-ppm limits can be obtained in about 30 min directly in the work environment. It offers accuracy of ± 0.01 ppm when used in accordance with kit instructions. The BDX 55 Super Sampler pump is factory Mutual-approved for Class I, II, and III, Division 1 hazardous locations. It is powered by rechargeable Ni-Cd batteries.

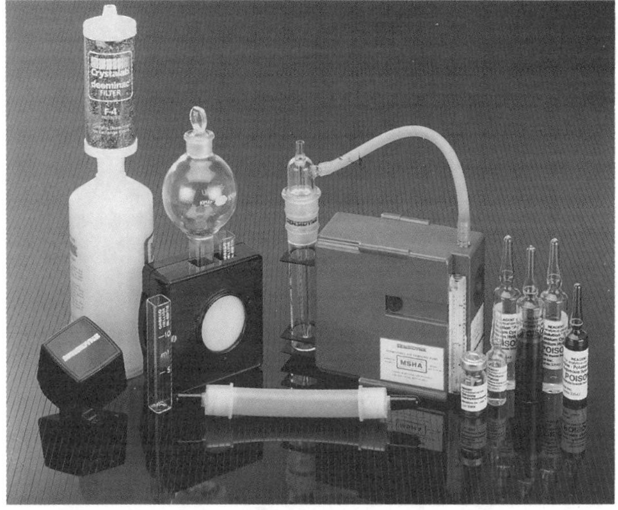

INSTRUMENT 18-19. Sensidyne/Gastec TEL/TMI Analyzer Kit.

18-19. Sensidyne/Gastec TEL/TML Analyzer Kit

Sensidyne, Inc. (SEN)

The Sensidyne TEL/TML Analyzer Kit is used for field sampling of tetraethyl lead or tetramethyl lead in air and for confined space entry testing in gasoline storage tanks. A sample is drawn through a cyanide solution using a BDX 55 pump and midget impinger. The solution is transferred to a comparator tube and reagents are added to form a red color. The color is compared to standard colors in a comparator viewer. The concentration is read directly in μg/ft^3 (conversion to mg/m^3 is: μg/ft^3 × 0.035 = mg/m^3) of lead in air. The performance data on the TEL/TML kit are: measuring range, 1 to 20 μg/ft^3 (=0.035 to 0.7 mg/m^3); accuracy, ± 1 μg; duration of test, about 30 min. The BDX 55 Super Sampler pump may be used in other applications by simply adding appropriate accessories. Factory Mutual-approved for intrinsic safety in Class I, II, and III, Division 1 hazardous locations, the pump may be used continually for up to 8 hrs using rechargeable Ni-Cd batteries.

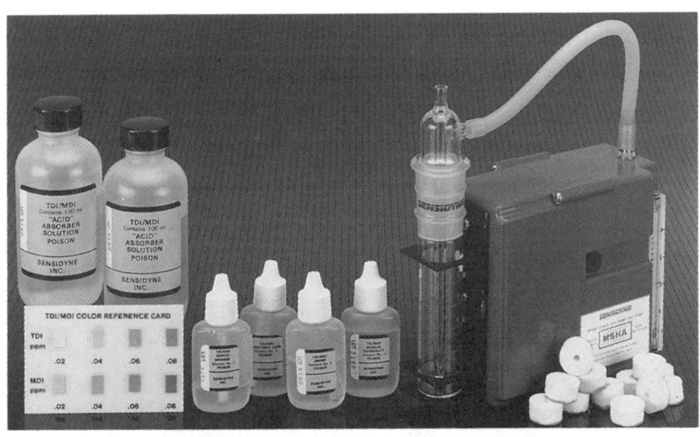

INSTRUMENT 18-18. Sensidyne/Gastec TDI/MDI Analyzer Kit.

18-20. Sensidyne/Gastec Polytec IV Rainbow Tube

Sensidyne, Inc. (SEN)

- Qualitative detection of eight gases simultaneously.
- Fast and simple single pump stroke operation
- Results in 30 seconds.
- Ideal for haz mat, confined space entry, and fire site reentry testing.

The Polytec IV Rainbow detector tube (Catalog No. 27) incorporates a unique multilayer design to qualitatively test for eight common toxic gases simultaneously. These gases are ammonia, hydrogen chloride, hydrogen sulfide, chlorine, sulfur dioxide, nitrogen dioxide, carbon monoxide, and carbon disulfide. An operator simply breaks off the ends of the sealed glass tube and places

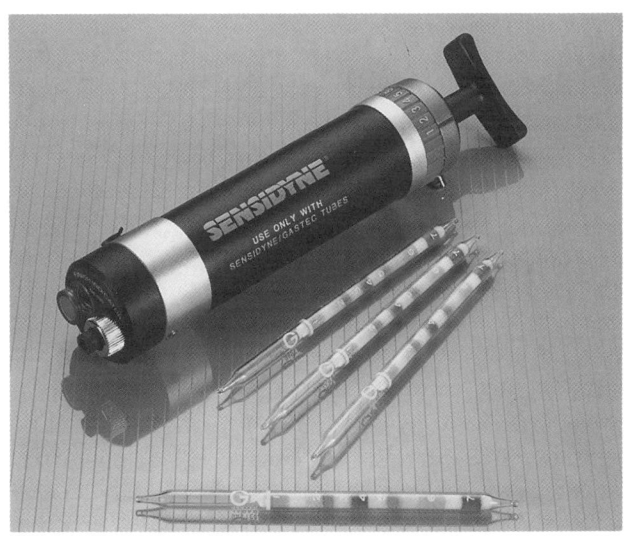

INSTRUMENT 18-20. Sensidyne/Gastec Polytec IV Rainbow tube.

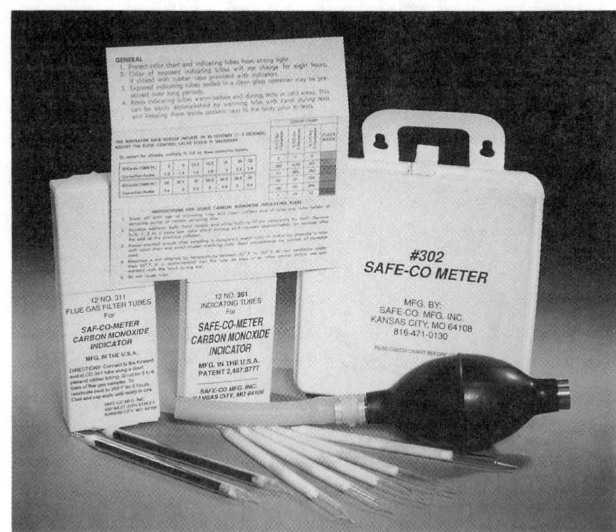

INSTRUMENT 18-21. 302 and 301 Safe-CO meter and tubes.

it into the Model 800 piston pump, observing the directional arrow. After taking one pump stroke, the operator waits 30 seconds and then compares the tube to the chart on the reverse side. The system is expandable with direct-reading quantitative detector tubes for over 280 substances.

18-21. 302 and 301 Safe-CO Meters and Tubes
Safe-CO Manufacturing, Inc. (SAF)

302 Safe-CO Meter with Case Only

The Safe-CO meter consists of an aspirator bulb, four end caps, three rubber bands, tip breaker, and color comparison chart. The meter comes in a lightweight carrying case.

301 Carbon Monoxide Indicator Tubes

Designed as a field instrument to detect and estimate the concentration of carbon monoxide, the detector tubes with meter are used for checking garages, aircraft, mines, passenger vehicles, and all confined areas where carbon monoxide might be suspected. This instrument can also be used in flue gas analysis with the 311 Charcoal Filter Detector Tube Accessory. Carbon monoxide in the air reacts with an indicating gel in the detector tube to produce a color change. The amount of carbon monoxide present is determined by comparing the color in the detector tube after a test with a color chart furnished with the instrument. The 0.5 kg (1 lb) unit is 15 cm (6 in.) high and 8.4 cm (3 5/16 in.) in diameter. The full unit (Instrument 301 detector tubes w/chart, 302 meter w/case) consists of 12 indicating tubes, 4 end caps for tubes, a tip breaker, aspirator bulb, and color comparison chart. These are contained in a lightweight carrying case and meet the quality and accuracy standards set up by the U.S. Bureau of Standards. The five standard colors on the chart represent 0, 0.005, 0.01, 0.02, and 0.04% carbon monoxide (0, 50, 100, 200, and 400 ppm) for one bulb squeeze; for five bulb squeezes, the same colors represent 0, 0.001, 0.002, 0.004, and 0.008% carbon monoxide (0, 10, 20, 40, and 80 ppm). The readings are multiplied by the factors provided in parentheses to correct for high altitudes: altitude 5000 ft. (1.2), 10,000 ft. (1.5), 20,000 ft. (2.2), 30,000 ft. (3.5), and 40,000 ft. (5.4). The standardization is reliable in the temperature range of 65 to 85°F (18–29°C).

311 Activated Carbon Tubes

The activated carbon tubes are recommended for use in flue gas analysis but are not needed for testing for carbon monoxide under normal circumstances. Nitrogen dioxide counteracts the normal development of color in the carbon monoxide colorimetric indicating tube, with a resulting variation in color that makes readings inconsistent.

18-22. SURE-SPOT™ TDI Dosimeter Badge
GMD Systems, Inc. (GMD)

The GMD Systems SURESPOT TDI (toluene diisocyanate) dosimeter badge is a lightweight, direct-reading TDI monitor designed to be worn on the collar of individuals who are potentially at risk from TDI in their working environments. It indicates the presence of TDI by means of a highly specific chemical color reaction in which the amount of color produced is directly proportional to the concentration of TDI and the time of exposure.

The SURE-SPOT TDI badge is designed to be worn during an entire 8-hr workshift. It uses exclusive isomer-independent paper tape detection technology to provide an assessment of the total TDI dose in ppb-hrs. The SURE-SPOT TDI badge is a completely "passive" system that uses the principle of controlled diffusion to provide very accurate results. Its low-end threshold of sensitivity is also sufficient for approximating 15-min-

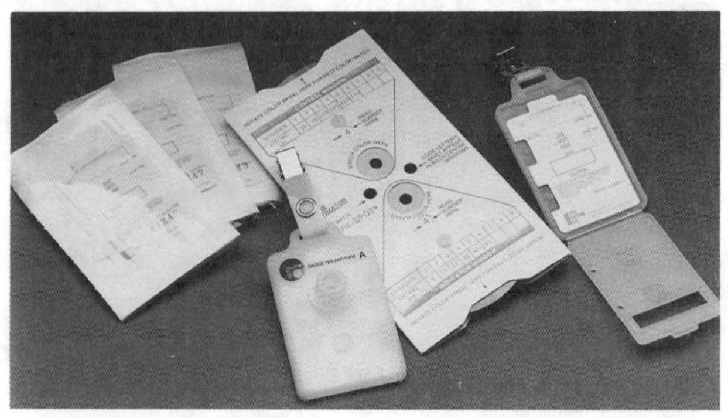

INSTRUMENT 18-22. SURE-SPOT™ TDI dosimeter badge.

ute STEL evaluations.

In operation, a SURE-SPOT TDI Badge Card is activated and mounted in the reusable plastic holder. The unit is then clipped to the collar for sampling in the breathing zone. If TDI is present, a distinct stain develops in either the control or indicator windows or both, depending on the concentration. At the end of the shift, the developed stain is compared against known color standards and the dose in ppb-hrs is calculated.

SURE-SPOT dosimeter badges are also available for exposure to hydrazine/monomethyl hydrazine, hydrides (arsine, phosphine, diborane and silane), and phosgene.

18-23. ACT Monitoring Card System

Envirometrics Products Company, Inc. (EPC)

The ACT Monitoring Card System is a line of colormetric passive monitors designed to give accurate on-site results immediately after the monitoring period. The system includes two components. The first is a qualitative screening card that is read visually by comparing the color developed during exposure to a standard printed on the card. The card allows the user to inexpensively survey a large number of workers and areas to determine where more precise measurements need to be taken. The second component, a Quantitative Card, meets this need when it is used in conjunction with the ACT electronic reader to give precise concentrations in ppm. A unique feature of the system is the ability to correct for the temperature and humidity of the sampling environment. This ensures an overall system accuracy well below the ±25% specified by OSHA.

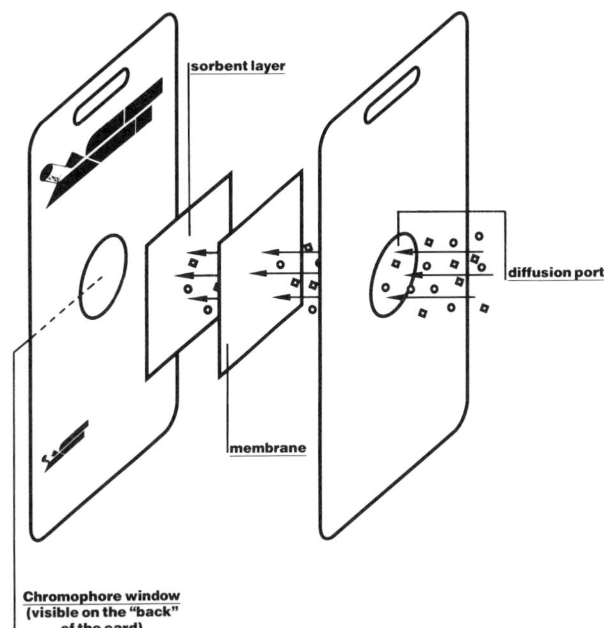

INSTRUMENT 18-23. Schematic of ACT Monitoring Card System.

TABLE 18-I-1. Index of Instruments and Characteristics

		Characteristic					
18-	Instrument	Aspiration	Diffusion	Color Change	Length of Stain	Short-Term	Long-Term
1	LEAK-TEC Personnel Protection Indicators		X	X		X	X
2	Bacharach Gas Hazard Indicator	X			X	X	
3	Bacharach Carbon Monoxide Detector	X		X		X	
4	Draeger Haz Mat Kit	X		X	X	X	
5	Draeger Diffusion Tubes		X		X		X
6	Draeger Long-Duration Detector Tubes & Polymeter	X			X		X
7	Draeger 1000 and 2000 Quantimeters	X		X	X	X	
8	Gilian CHEMAIR and CHEMSCAN Color. Badge System		X	X		X	X
9	Gilian CHROMAIR Passive Monitor Badges			X		X	X
10	Kitagawa Precision Gas Detector Kit	X			X	X	
11	Kitagawa Qualitative Detector Tubes and Haz Mat Test Kit	X		X		X	
12	MSA Kwik-Draw Detector Tube Pump & Tubes	X		X	X	X	
13	Sensidyne/Gastec Dosimeter Tubes		X		X		X
14	Sensidyne/Gastec Pyrotec Pyrolyzer	X			X	X	
15	Sensidyne/Gastec System	X			X	X	
16	Sensidyne/Gastec Haz Mat Kits	X		X	X	X	
17	Sensidyne/Gastec Gas Detection System	X			X	X	
18	Sensidyne/Gastec TDI/MDI Analyzer Kit	X		X		X	X
19	Sensidyne/Gastec TEL/TML Analyzer Kit	X				X	X
20	Sensidyne/Gastec Polytec IV Rainbow Tube	X		X		X	
21	302 Safe-CO Meter and 301 CO Ind. Tubes	X		X		X	
22	GMD SURE-SPOT™ Dosimeter Badges		X	X			X
23	ACT Monitoring Card System		X	X		X	X

TABLE 18-I-2. Index of Contaminants and Applicable Commercial Instruments

Contaminant	Commercial Instruments
Acetaldehyde	7, 10, 12, 15, 17
Acetic acid	5,* 6, 7, 10, 12, 15, 17
Acetic anhydride	7, 15, 17
Acetone	4, 5, 6, 7, 8, 9, 10, 12, 15, 16, 17, 23
Acetone cyanohydrin	15, 17
Acetonitrile	14, 15, 17
Acetylene	7, 10, 12, 15, 17
Acid compounds	7, 15, 17
Acrolein	7, 10, 15, 17
Acrylic acid	15, 17
Acrylonitrile	7, 10, 15, 17
Alcohol	4
Aliphatic hydrocarbons	7, 15, 17
Allyl alcohol	10, 15, 17
Allyl chloride	7, 15, 17
Amines (varied)	15, 16, 17
2-Aminoethanol	7, 15, 17
2-Aminopropane	7, 15, 17
Ammonia	1, 5, 6, 7, 8, 9, 10, 12, 13, 15, 17, 20, 23
n-Amyl acetate	7, 10, 15, 17
n-Amyl alcohol	12
Amyl alcohol (sec. & tert.)	12
n-Amyl chloride (1-chloropentane)	12
Amyl mercaptan	12
Aniline	7, 10, 15, 17
Antimony Hydride (stibine)	7
Aromatics	12
Arsenic trioxide	7
Arsine	7, 10, 12, 15, 17, 22
Arsine compounds (organic)	
Aziridine	7, 15, 17
Basic compounds	7
Benzaldehyde	15, 17
Benzene	4, 6, 7, 10, 12, 15, 16, 17
Benzyl bromide	15, 17
Benzyl chloride	7, 15, 17
Boron trichloride	15, 17
Bromine	7, 10, 12, 15, 17
Bromobenzene (mono)	12
Bromoethane	7, 12, 15, 17
Bromoform	15, 17
Bromotrifluoromethane (R-13B1)	14, 15, 17
Butadiene	5, 7, 10, 12, 13, 15, 17
Butane	7, 10, 12, 15, 17
2-Butanone (MEK)	7, 15, 17
2-Butoxyethanol	12, 15, 17
n-Butyl acetate	7, 10, 15, 17
sec-Butyl acetate	7
tert-Butyl acetate	7
Butyl acrylate	10, 15, 17
Butyl alcohol (n, sec, tert. butanol)	7, 10, 12, 15, 17
n-Butylamine	7, 12, 15, 17
sec-Butylamine	7, 15, 17
Butyl cellosolve	10, 15, 17
Butylene (1 and 2)	7, 12
n-Butyl mercaptan	10, 12, 15, 17
t-Butyl mercaptan	12
Butyro nitrile	15, 17
Carbon dioxide	2, 4, 5, 6, 7, 10, 12, 13, 15, 16, 17, 20
Carbon disulfide	6, 7, 8, 9, 10, 12, 15, 16, 17
Carbon monoxide	1, 2, 3, 4, 5, 6, 7, 8, 9, 10, 12, 13, 15, 16, 17, 20, 21, 23
Carbon tetrachloride	7, 10, 15, 16, 17
Carbonyl chloride (phosgene)	7, 10, 12, 15, 17
Carbonyl sulfide	10, 15, 16, 17
Cellosolve	10, 15, 17
Chlorine	1, 2, 4, 6, 7, 8, 9, 10, 12, 13, 15, 16, 17, 20, 23
Chlorine dioxide	7, 10, 12, 15, 17
Chlorobenzene	7, 10, 12, 15, 17
Chlorobromomethane	12, 15, 17
1-Chlorobutane (n-Butylchloride)	12
Chlorocyclohexane	15, 17
Chlorodifluoroethane (R-142b)	14, 15, 17
Chlorodifluoromethane (R-22)	14, 15, 17
Chloroethane (Ethyl chloride)	12
Chloroform (trichloromethane)	7, 10, 12, 15, 17
Chloroformates	7, 15, 17
Chloronitropropane	
Chloropentafluoroethane (R-115)	
Chloropicrin	7, 10, 15, 17
Chloroprene	7, 10
1- and 2-Chloropropane	12
3-Chloro 1-propene	7,15,17
Chlorotrifluoromethane (R-13)	
Chromic acid	7
Cresol (o, m, and p)	7, 10, 15, 17
Cumene	7, 15, 17
Cyanide ion	7, 15, 17
Cyanogen	12
Cyanogen chloride	7
Cycloheptane	12
Cyclohexane	7, 10, 12, 15, 17
Cyclohexanol	10, 12, 15, 17
Cyclohexanone	10, 15, 17
Cyclohexene	15, 17
Cyclohexylamine	7, 12, 15, 17
Cyclohexylchloride	15, 17
Cyclooctane	12
Cyclopentane	12
Decaborane	
n-Decane	12, 15, 17
Demeton	7

TABLE 18-I-2 (con't.). Index of Contaminants and Applicable Commercial Instruments

Contaminant	Commercial Instruments
Diacetone alcohol	10, 15, 17
1, 2-Diaminoethane	7, 15, 17
Diborane	15, 17, 22
1, 2-Dibromoethane (ethylene dibromide)	7, 10, 12, 15, 17
1, 1-Dibromoethane	7, 15, 17
Dibromomethane (methylene bromide)	12
Dichlorobenzene (o, m, p)	7, 10, 15, 17
Dichlorodifluoromethane (R-12)	14, 15, 17
1, 1-Dichloroethane (ethylidene chloride)	7, 10, 12, 15, 17
1, 2-Dichloroethane (ethylene dichloride)	7, 10, 15, 17
Dichloroethylene (cis and trans)	10, 12, 13, 15, 17
Dichloroethyl ether	10
2, 2-Dichloro-2-fluoroethane (R-141 b)	14, 15, 17
Dichloromethane (methylene dichloride)	6, 7, 10, 12, 15, 17
Dichloronitroethane	
1, 3-Dichloro-1, 1, 2, 2, 3-pentafluoropropane (R-225cb)	14, 15, 17
3, 3-Dichloro-1, 1, 1, 2, 2-pentafluoropropane (R-225 ca)	14, 15, 17
Dichloropropane (1, 2 and 1, 3)	7, 10, 12, 15, 17
Dichlorotetrafluoroethane (R-114)	7, 14, 15, 17
1, 1-Dichloro-2, 2, 2-trifluoroethane (R-123)	14, 15, 17
Dichlorovos (DDVP)	7
Diethanolamine	15, 17
Diethylamine	7, 10, 12, 15, 17
Diethylbenzene	15, 17
Diethylene dioxide	7, 15, 17
Diethylene glycol	15, 17
Diethylenetriamine	15, 17
Diethyl ether	7, 10, 15, 17
Diethyl sulfate	
Diisobutylene	15, 17
Diisobutyl ketone	15, 17
Diisopropylamine	15, 17
Diisopropyl ether	7
Diisopropyl toluene	15, 17
Dimethyl acetamide	7, 10, 15, 17
Dimethylamine	7, 12, 15, 17
Dimethylaminoethanol	15, 17
Dimethylaniline	15, 17
Dimethylbutane	12
Dimethyl disulfide	14, 15, 17
Dimethyl ether	10, 15, 17
Dimethylethylamine	7, 15, 17
Dimethylformamide	7, 10, 15, 17
Dimethylhydrazine (uns) UMDH	7, 12
Dimethyl sulfate	7
Dimethylsulfide	7, 14, 15, 17
Dimethylsulfoxide	
Di-n-propylamine	15, 17
Dioxane	7, 10, 15, 17
1, 3-Dioxolan	15, 17
Divinyl benzene	15, 17
Divinyl methoxysilane	15, 17
Enflurane	14, 15, 17
Epichlorohydrin	7, 10, 15, 17
Ethanolamine (mono)	10
Ethanethiol	7, 15, 17
Ethanolamine	7, 15, 17
2-Ethoxyethanol (Cellosolve)	10, 12, 15, 17
Ethoxyethyl acetate	15, 17
Ethyl acetate	4, 5, 7, 10, 15, 16, 17
Ethyl acrylate	7, 10, 15
Ethyl alcohol	5, 6, 7, 8, 9, 10, 12, 13, 15, 17
Ethylamine	7, 10, 12, 15, 17
Ethyl benzene	7, 10, 12, 15, 17
Ethylbenzyl chloride	15, 17
Ethyl bromide (bromoethane)	7, 15, 17
Ethyl Cellosolve	10, 15, 17
Ethyl Cellosolve Acetate	10, 15, 17
Ethyl chloride (chloroethane)	12, 15, 17
Ethyl chloroformate	7, 15, 17
Ethyl cyanide (propionitrile)	15, 17
Ethylene	7, 10, 12, 13, 15, 17
Ethylene chlorohydrine	15, 17
Ethylenediamine	7, 15, 17
Ethylene dibromide	7, 10, 15, 17
Ethylene dichloride (dichloroethane)	7, 15, 17
Ethylenimine	7, 15, 17
Ethylene glycol	7, 10, 15, 17
Ethylene glycol dinitrate	7
Ethylene glycol monoethyl ether	7
Ethylene oxide	7, 8, 9, 10, 15, 17, 23
Ethyl ether (diethyl ether)	7, 10, 15, 17
Ethyl formate	12
Ethyl glycol acetate	7
Ethyl mercaptan	7, 10, 12, 15, 17
n-Ethylmorpholine	12, 15, 17
Fluorine	7, 15, 17
Fluorochlorocarbons	15, 17
Fluorotrichloromethane (Freon 11)	7, 15, 17
Formaldehyde	7, 8, 9, 10, 12, 13, 15, 17, 23
Formic acid	4, 7, 10, 12, 15, 17
Freons	15, 17
Furan	10
Furfural	10, 15, 17
Furfural alcohol	12
Gluteraldehyde	8, 9, 23
Gasoline (hydrocarbons)	10, 12, 15, 17
Halogenated hydrocarbons	7, 12

TABLE 18-I-2 (con't.). Index of Contaminants and Applicable Commercial Instruments

Contaminant	Commercial Instruments
Halothane (2-bromo-2-chloro-1, 1, 1-trifluoroethane)	14, 15, 17
Heptamethylene diamine	15, 17
n-Heptane	7, 10, 12, 15, 17
n-Hexane	7, 10, 12, 15, 17
Hexamethylene diamine	15, 17
Hexone (MIBK)	7, 15, 17
2-Hexyl alcohol	15, 17
Hexylamine	15, 17
Humidity removal	15, 17
Hydrazine	1, 4, 7, 8, 9, 10, 12, 15, 17, 22
Hydrides (arsine, phosphine, diborane, silane)	22
Hydrocarbons	4, 6, 7, 10, 15, 17
Hydrogen	10, 15, 16, 17
Hydrogen bromide	15, 17
Hydrogen chloride (hydrochloric acid)	5, 6, 7, 10, 12, 15, 16, 17, 20
Hydrogen cyanide (hydrocyanic acid)	4, 5, 6, 7, 10, 12, 13, 15, 16, 17
Hydrogen fluoride	6, 7, 10, 12, 15, 17
Hydrogen peroxide	7
Hydrogen phosphide (phosphine)	12
Hydrogen selenide	10
Hydrogen sulfide	1, 2, 4, 5, 6, 7, 8, 9, 10, 12 13, 15, 16, 17, 20, 23
Hydrogen sulfide/sulfur dioxide (total sulfur)	15, 17
Hydrogen sulfide/sulfur dioxide (simul.)	15, 17
Inorganic espds. (qual.)	11
Iodine	15, 17
Isoamyl acetate	7, 10, 15, 17
Isoamyl alcohol	10, 12, 15, 17
Isobutane	10, 12, 15, 17
Isobutyl acetate	10, 15, 17
Isobutyl acrylate	10
Isobutyl alcohol	8, 10, 12, 15, 17
Isobutylene	12
Isoflurane	14, 15, 17
Isooctane	15, 17
Isopentyl alcohol	10, 15, 17
Isoprene	13
Isophorone	15, 17
Isopropyl acetate	7, 10, 15, 17
Isopropylamine	7, 12, 15, 17
Isopropyl alcohol	7, 10, 15, 17
Isopropyl ether	15, 17
Isopropyl mercaptan	10, 15, 17
Kerosene	15, 17
Lead (inorganic)	
Lead, tetraethyl	19
Lead, tetramethyl	19
LP Gas	15, 17
Maleic anhydride	15, 17
MDI (methylene bisphenyl isocyanate)	18
Mercaptan	7, 10, 15, 17
Mercaptans (total)	15, 17
2-Mercaptoethanol	15, 17
Mercury	7, 8, 10, 12, 15, 17
Mesityl oxide	10
Metaldehyde	15, 17
Methacrylic acid	15, 17
Methacrolonitrile	15, 17
Methane	7
Methanethiol	7, 15, 17
Methoxy-2 propanol	15, 17
Methoxyethyl acetate	7, 15, 17
Methyl acetate	7, 10
Methyl acrylate	7, 10, 15, 17
Methylacrylonitrile	15, 17
Methyl alcohol	7, 8, 9, 10, 15, 16, 17
Methylallyl chloride	15, 17
Methyl amine	7, 10, 12, 15, 17
n-Methyl aniline	15, 17
Methyl bromide	4, 7, 10, 12, 15, 17
2-Methylbutane	12
Methylbutenitrile	15, 17
Methyl Cellosolve	10, 15, 17
Methyl Cellosolve acetate	15, 17
Methyl chloride	14, 15, 17
Methyl chloroform (trichloroethane)	7, 10, 12, 15, 17
Methyl chloroformate	7, 15, 17
Methyl cyclohexane	12, 15, 17
Methyl cyclohexanol	10, 12, 15, 17
Methyl cyclohexanone	10, 15, 17
Methyl cyclopentane	12
Methylene bromide	12
Methylene chloride (R-30)	6, 7, 10, 12, 14, 15, 17
Methylene bis (4-phenylisocyanate) (MDI)	18
Methylene iodide	15, 17
Methyl ether (dimethyl ether)	10, 15, 17
Methyl ethyl ketone (2-Butanone)	7, 8, 9, 10, 15, 17, 23
Methyl formate	12
Methyl hydrazine	8, 9, 15, 17, 22
Methyl iodide	10, 15, 17
Methyl isobutyl ketone	7, 10, 15, 17
Methyl isobutyl carbinol (methyl amyl carbinol)	12
Methyl mercaptan	7, 10, 12, 15, 16, 17
Methyl methacrylate	7, 10, 15, 17
n-Methyl morphaline	15, 17
2-Methyl pentane	12
3-Methyl pentane	12
Methyl proprionate	15, 17

TABLE 18-I-2 (con't.). Index of Contaminants and Applicable Commercial Instruments

Contaminant	Commercial Instruments
Methyl propyl ketone	7
Methyl pyridine	15, 17
Methyl styrene	10
Mineral spirits	15, 17
Monochlorobenzene	10, 15, 17
Monoethylamine	15, 17
Monomethylamine	15, 17
Monomethyl aniline	15, 17
Monomethyl hydrazine	15, 17, 22
Monostyrene	7, 10, 12, 15, 17
Morpholine	15, 17
Naphthalene	10, 15, 17
Natural gas	7
Nickel	7
Nickel carbonyl	7, 10, 15, 17
Nitric acid	7, 10, 15, 17
Nitric oxide	7, 12, 15, 16, 17
Nitroethane	14, 15, 17
Nitrogen dioxide	1, 2, 5, 6, 7, 8, 9, 10, 12, 13, 15, 17, 20, 23
Nitrogen oxides	10, 12, 15, 17
Nitroglycol	7
Nitromethane	14, 15, 17
Nitropropane (1- and 2-)	14, 15, 17
Nitrous fumes	4, 6, 7, 12
Nitrous oxides	12, 14, 15, 17
n-Nonane	12, 15, 17
n-Octane	7, 12, 15, 17
Oil mist	7, 12
Olefins	5, 7, 15, 17
Organic arsenic compounds	7
Organic basic nitrogen	7
Organic compounds	10, 15, 17
Organic compounds, qualitative	10, 11, 15, 17
Oxirane	7
Oxygen	4, 7, 10, 15, 17
Ozone	1, 7, 10, 12, 15, 17
Paraformaldehyde	15, 17
Pentaborane	
Pentachloroethane	12, 15, 17
Pentachloroethanol	
1, 2-Pentadiene	15, 17
Pentamethylenediamine	15, 17
Pentane	7, 10, 12, 15, 17
Pentenenitrile	15, 17
n-Pentyl acetate	10, 15, 17
Peracetic acid	15, 17
Perchloroethylene (tetrachloroethylene)	5, 6, 7, 10, 12, 13, 15, 17
Petroleum ether	15, 17
Petroleum hydrocarbons	15, 17
Phenol	7, 10, 15, 17
Phosgene	7, 10, 12, 15, 17, 22
Phosphine	7, 10, 12, 15, 16, 17, 22
Phosphine in acetylene	10, 15, 17
Phosphoric acid esters	7
4-Picoline	15, 17
Pipenylene	15, 17
Polytec I, II, III	15, 17
Polytec IV Rainbow (qualitative)	16, 20
Polytest	4
Propane (see hydrocarbons)	7, 10, 12, 15, 17
1, 2-Propanediol	15, 17
Proprionaldehyde	15, 17
Proprionic acid	15, 17
Proprionitrile (ethyl cyanide)	15, 17
Proprionic aldehyde	15, 17
n-Propyl acetate	7, 10, 15, 17
n-Propyl alcohol	7, 15, 17
Propyl aldehyde	15, 17
Propylamine	15, 17
Propyl cyanide	15, 17
Propylene	7, 10, 12, 15, 17
Propylene dichloride	7, 15, 17
1, 2-Propylene glycol	15, 17
Propylene glycol monomethyl ether acetate	15, 17
Propylene imine	7, 12, 15, 17
Propylene oxide	10, 15, 17
n-Propyl mercaptan	10, 12, 15, 17
Propyl nitrate	10
Pyridine	7, 15, 17
Qualitest	12
Screening tube	7
Sec-amyl alcohol	12
Sec-butyl alcohol	12
Silane	10, 22
Stibine	7
Stoddard solvent	15, 16, 17
Styrene (monomer)	7, 10, 12, 15, 17
Styrene oxide	15, 17
Sulfur dioxide	2, 5, 6, 7, 8, 9, 10, 12, 13, 15, 16, 17, 20, 23
Sulfuric acid	7
Systox™	7
Tert-amyl alcohol	12
Tert-butyl alcohol	
Tert-butyl mercaptan	12
1, 1, 2, 2-Tetrabromoethane	12, 15, 17
Tetrachlorodifluoroethane (R-112)	15, 17
1, 1, 2, 2-Tetrachloroethane	12, 15, 17
Tetrachloroethylene	5, 6, 7, 10, 12, 13, 15, 17
Tetrachloromethane	7, 15, 17
1, 1, 3, 3-Tetrachloroprene	
Tetraethyl lead	19

TABLE 18-I-2 (con't.). Index of Contaminants and Applicable Commercial Instruments

Contaminant	Commercial Instruments
1, 1, 1, 2-Tetrafluoro-2-chloroethane (R-124)	15, 17
1, 1, 2, 2- Tetrafluoroethane (R-134a)	15, 17
Tetrahydrofuran	7, 10, 15, 17
Tetrahydrothiophene	7, 12
Tetramethyl lead	19
Tetramethylenediamine	15, 17
Thioether	7
Thioglycol	15, 17
Thionyl chloride	15, 17
Toluene	5, 6, 7, 10, 12, 13, 15, 17
Toluene diisocyanate (TDI)	7, 18, 22
Toluidine (ortho)	7, 15, 17
Tribromomethane (bromoform)	12, 15, 17
Trichloroacetic acid	15, 17
1, 2, 3-Trichlorobenzene	15, 17
1, 2, 4-Trichlorobenzene	15, 17
1, 2, 6-Trichlorobenzene	15, 17
1, 1, 1-Trichloroethane (methyl chloroform)	7, 10, 12, 15, 17
1, 1, 2-Trichloroethane	10, 12, 15, 16, 17
Trichloroethylene	4, 5, 6, 7, 10, 12, 13, 15, 16, 17,
Trichlorofluoro-methane (Freon 11)	7, 14, 15, 17
Trichloromethane (chloroform)	7, 12
Trichloropropane	12
Trichlorotrifluoroethane (Freon 113a and 113b)	15, 17
Triethanolamine	15, 17
Triethylamine	7, 10, 12, 15, 17
Trifluoromonobromomethane (R-13B1)	7, 15, 17
1, 1, 1-Trichloro-2, 2, 2-trifluoroethane (R-113b)	7, 15, 17
1,1,2-Trifluoro-1, 2, 2-trichloroethane (R-113)	7, 15, 17
Trimethylamine	10, 15, 17
Trimethylbenzene	10, 15, 17
2, 2, 4-Trimethylpentane	12
Vinyl acetate	10, 15, 17
Vinyl chloride	6, 7, 10, 12, 13, 15, 17
Vinylidine chloride	7, 12, 15, 17
Vinyl pyridine	
Vinyl trimethoxysilane	15, 17
Water vapor	5, 7, 10, 12, 15, 17
Xylene (-o, -m, and -p isomers)	7, 10, 12, 13, 15, 17
Zinc chromate	7

*Underlined instrument number indicates a long-term device (either diffusion tube or badge).

TABLE 18-I-3. LEAK-TEC Personnel Protection Indicators (Instrument 18-1)

Gas	Part #	Sensitivity	Color Change*
Ammonia	A-15	25 ppm/5 min	Yellow to blue
Carbon monoxide	CO-50	50 ppm	Tan to black
Chlorine	C-2	1 ppm/15 min	White to yellow
Hydrazine	H-5	0.1 ppm/15 min	White to yellow
Hydrogen sulfide	HS-5	10 ppm/10 min	White to brown
Nitrogen dioxide	N-1	5 ppm/15 min	White to yellow
Ozone	O-1	0.1 ppm/15 min	White to brown

*A color chart is available for all badges except carbon monoxide and ozone.

TABLE 18-I-4. (Inst. 18-2) Bacharach Gas Hazard Indicator Ranges of Various Tubes

Bacharach Code Complete Kit	Gas Type	Range
19-0247	H_2S	0–650 ppm
19-0248	SO_2	0–2700 ppm
19-0249	CO_2	0–4%
19-0250	NO_2	0–50 ppm
19-0251	Cl_2	0–20 ppm
19-0240	CO	0–0.2%
19-0241	CO	0–0.5%

TABLE 18-I-5. Draeger Haz Mat Kit — Detector Tubes (Inst. 18-4)

	Part Number
Polytest	CH28401
Ethyl acetate 200/a	CH20201
Methyl bromide 5/b	CH27301
Hydrazine 0.25/a	CH31801
Benzene 0.05	CH24801
Hydrocarbons 0.1%/b	CH26101
Acetone 100/b	CH22901
Carbon monoxide 10/b	CH20601
Alcohol 100/a	CH29701
Carbon dioxide 0.1%/a	CH23501
Hydrocyanic acid 2/a	CH25701
Hydrogen sulfide 5/b	CH29801
Nitrous fumes 0.5/a	CH29401
Trichloroethylene 10/a	CH24401
Chlorine 0.2/a	CH24301
Oxygen 5%/B	6728081
Formic acid 1/a	6722701

TABLE 18-I-6. Draeger Diffusion Tubes with Direct Indication (Instrument 18-5)

Draeger Tube	Part No.	Range in Absolute Units	Range of Measurement for Maximum Period of Use (8 hrs)
Acetic acid 10/a-D	81 01071	10–200 ppm × hrs	1.3–25 ppm
Acetone 1000/a-D	81 01431	1,000–30,000 ppm × hrs	125–3,750 ppm
Ammonia 20/a-D	81 01301	20–1,500 ppm × hrs	2.5–188 ppm
Butadiene 10/a-D	81 01161	10–300 ppm × hrs	1.3–40 ppm
Carbon dioxide 500/a-D	81 01381	500–20,000 ppm × hrs	65–2,500 ppm
Carbon dioxide 1%/a-D	81 01051	1–30 vol.% × hrs	0.13–3.8 vol.%
Carbon monoxide 50/a-D	67 33191	50–600 ppm × hrs	6.3–75 ppm
Ethanol 100/a-D	81 01151	1,000–25,000 ppm × hrs	125–3,100 ppm
Ethyl acetate 500/a-D	81 01241	500–10,000 ppm × hrs	63–1,250 ppm
Hydrochloric acid 10/a-D	67 33111	10–200 ppm × hrs	1.3–25 ppm
Hydrochloric acid 20/a-D	67 33221	20–200 ppm × hrs	2.5–25 ppm
Hydrogen sulfide 10/a-D	67 33091	10–300 ppm × hrs	1.3–38 ppm
Nitrogen dioxide 10/a-D	81 01111	10–200 ppm × hrs	1.3–25 ppm
Olefin 100/a-D	81 01171	100–2,000 ppm × hrs	12.5–250 ppm
Perchloroethylene 200/a-D	81 01401	200–1,500 ppm × hrs	25–188 ppm
Sulfur dioxide 5/a-D	81 01091	5–150 ppm × hrs	0.63–18 ppm
Toluene 100/a-D	81 01421	100–3,000 ppm × hrs	13–380 ppm
Trichloroethylene 200/a-D	81 01441	200–1,000 ppm × hrs	25–125 ppm
Water vapor 5/a-D	81 01391	5–100 mg/L × hrs	0.6–12.5 mg/L

TABLE 18-I-7. Draeger Long-Term Tubes (Instrument 18-6)

Draeger Tube	Part No.	Measuring Range	Relative Standard Deviation	Threshold Limit Value (USA 94–95)	Maximum Usage (hrs)
Acetic acid 5/a-L	67 33041	1.25–40 ppm	10–15%	10 ppm	4
Ammonia 10/a-L	67 28231	2.5–100 ppm	10–15%	25 ppm	4
Benzene 20/a-L	67 28221	10–200 ppm	15–20%	10 ppm, A2	2
Carbon dioxide 1000/a-L	67 28611	250–6,000 ppm	10–15%	5,000 ppm	4
Carbon disulfide 10/a-L	67 28621	1.25–100 ppm	10–15%	10 ppm (skin)	8
Carbon monoxide 10/a-L	67 28741	2.5–100 ppm	10–15%	25 ppm	4
Carbon monoxide 50/a-L	67 28121	6.25–500 ppm	5–10%	25 ppm	8
Chlorine 1/a-L	67 28421	0.13–20 ppm	10–15%	0.5 ppm	8
Ethanol 500/a-L	67 28691	62.5–8,000 ppm	15–20%	1,000 ppm	8
Hydrocarbons 100/a-L	67 28571	25–3,000 ppm	10–15%	—	4
Hydrochloric acid 10/a-L	67 28581	1.25–50 ppm	10–15%	C 5 ppm	8
Hydrocyanic acid 10/a-L	67 28441	1.25–120 ppm	10–15%	C 4.7 ppm	8
Hydrogen fluoride 2/a-L	67 28841	0.25–30 ppm	10–15%	C 3 ppm	8
Hydrogen sulfide 5/a-L	67 28141	0.63–60 ppm	5–10%	15 ppm	8
Methylene chloride 50/a-L	67 28881	12.5–800 ppm	15–20%	50 ppm, A2	4
Nitrogen dioxide 10/a-L	67 28281	1.25–100 ppm	10–15%	3 ppm	8
Nitrous fumes 5/a-L ($NO + NO_2$)	67 28911	1.25–50 ppm	10–15%	3 ppm (NO_2)	4
Nitrous fumes 50/a-L ($NO + NO_2$)	67 28191	25–350 ppm	15–20%	3 ppm (NO_2)	2
Perchloroethylene 50/a-L	67 28671	12.5–300 ppm	10–15%	25 ppm, A3	4
Sulfur dioxide 2/a-L	67 28921	0.5–20 ppm	10–15%	2 ppm	4
Sulfur dioxide 5/a-L	67 28151	1.25–50 ppm	10–15%	2 ppm	4
Toluene 200/a-L	67 28271	25–4,000 ppm	10–15%	50 ppm	8
Trichloroethylene 10/a-L	67 28291	2.5–200 ppm	10–15%	50 ppm, A5 100 ppm, A5; STEL	4
Vinyl chloride 10/a-L	67 28131	1–50 ppm	10–15%	5 ppm, A1	10
Sampling Tubes					
Activated charcoal tubes (Type B)	67 33011				
Activated charcoal tubes (Type G)	67 28831				
Silica gel tubes (NIOSH size)	67 28811				
Silica gel tubes (Type B)	67 33021				
Silica gel tubes (Type G)	67 28851				

TABLE 18-I-8. Sensidyne/Gastec Dosimeter Tubes (Instrument 18-13)

Gas or Vapor to be Measured	Tube No.	Range (ppm/hr)	Range (ppm/10 hrs)
Ammonia	3D	25–500	2.5–50
1,3-Butadiene	174D	10–200	1–20
Carbon dioxide	2D	2000–80,000	200–8000
Carbon monoxide	1D	51–1000	5–100
Carbon monoxide	1DL	10–200	1–200
Chlorine	8D	2–50	0.2–5
1,2-Dichloroethylene	174D	30–600	3–60
Ethyl alcohol	112D	1000–25,000	100–2500
Ethylene	174D	12–240	1.2–24
Formaldehyde	91D	1–20	0.1–2
Hydrogen cyanide	12D	10–200	1–20
Hydrogen sulfide	4D	0–200	1–20
Isoprene	174D	20–400	2–40
Nitrogen dioxide	9D	1–30	0.1–3
Perchloroethylene	133D	25–150	2.5–15
Sulfur dioxide	5D	5–100	0.5–10
Toluene	122D	100–2000	10–200
Trichloroethylene	132D	25–300	2.5–30
Vinyl chloride	174D	12–240	1.2–24
Xylene	122D	133–2660	13.3–266

TABLE 18-I-9. Pyrotec Pyrolyzer for Refrigerants and Other Gases (Instrument 18-14)

Refrigerants (Fluorochlorocarbons)

Chemical Name	Use Tube No(s).	Total Measuring Range (ppm)
Trichlorofluoromethane (R-11)	51H, 51, 51L	0.8–2200
Dichlorodifluoromethane (R-12)	51H, 51, 51L	1.8–2600
Bromotrifluoromethane (R-13B1)	51, 51L	4.2–1800
Chlorodifluoromethane (R-22)	51H, 51, 51L	2.5–8000
Tetrachlorodifluoroethane (R-112)	51H, 51, 51L	1–1000
1,1,2-Trichloro-1,2,2-trifluoroethane (R-113)	51H, 51, 51L	1–6000
1,1,1-Trichloro-2,2,2-trifluoroethane (R-113b)	51H, 51, 51L	0.8–1600
Dichlorotetrafluoroethane (R-114)	51H, 51, 51L	1.8–3800
1,1-Dichloro-2,2,2-trifluoroethane (R-123)	51, 51L	1.4–1600
1,1,1,2-Tetrafluoro-2-chloroethane (R-124)	51, 51L	4.2–1800
1,2,2,2-Tetrafluoroethane (R-134a)	81	600–12000
2,2-Dichloro-2-fluoroethane (R-141b)	51, 51L	1–400
Chlorodifluoroethane (R-142b)	51H, 51, 51L	5–41000
3,3-Dichloro-1,1,1,2,2-pentafluoropropane (R-225ca)	51H, 51, 51L	1.1–6000
1,3-Dichloro-1,1,2,2,3-pentafluoropropane (R-225cb)	51H, 51, 51L	1.9–5600

Nitroparaffins

Target Substance	Use Tube No(s).	Total Measuring Range (ppm)
Nitroethane	52	4–240
Nitromethane	52	5–300
1-Nitropropane	52	4.2–252
2-Nitropropane	52	3.7–222

Miscellaneous Substances/Solvents

Target Substance	Use Tube No(s).	Total Measuring Range (ppm)
Acetonitrile	52	3–180
Dimethyl disulfide	53	0.3–3
Dimethyl sulfide	53	0.25–10
Methyl chloride	51, 51L	1.6–480
Methylene chloride	51L	1–46

Anesthetic Gases

Target Substance	Use Tube No(s).	Total Measuring Range (ppm)
Enflurane	51, 51L	25–1200
Halothane	51H, 51, 51L	3–6400
Isoflurane	51, 51L	30–1000
Nitrous oxide	52	50–1000

Ordering Information

Item	Part No.
Model 800 pump kit	7010657-1
Pyrotec Pyrolyzer	7016118
Pyrolyzer detector tubes	51, 51L, 51H, 52, and 53

TABLE 18-I-10. Sensidyne/Gastec Standard Haz Mat Kit and Tubes

Standard Haz Mat Kit, Part Number 7010167-4

The Standard Haz Mat Kit comes complete with the following equipment:

	Part Number
Model 800 pump kit	7010657-1
Shoulder bag carrying case	2417540
5-m extension hose	2417542-2
Gas detection manual (bluebook)	009810
Logic chart	7010167-0
Detector tubes (one box each):	
Carbon monoxide	1La
Hydrogen sulfide	4LL
Benzene	121S
Sulfur dioxide	5Lb
Ammonia	3L
Hydrogen cyanide	12L
Chlorine	8La
Ethyl acetate	141L
Stoddard solvent	128
Hydrocarbons, low class	103
Hydrocarbons, high class	105
Hydrocarbons, petroleum distillates	106
Polytec (qualitative test)	107

TABLE 18-I-11. Commercial Sources of Colorimetric Indicators

Code	Source
AGC	American Gas and Chemical Co. 220 Pegasus Avenue Northvale, NJ 07647 (201)767-7300
BAC	Bacharach, Inc. 625 Alpha Drive Pittsburgh, PA 15238 (412)963-2160
ENM	ENMET Corporation 2308 S. Industrial Way P.O. Box 979 Ann Arbor, MI 48106-0979 (313)761-1270
EPC	Envirometrics Products Company, Inc. 1019 Bankton Drive Charleston, SC 29406 (803)740-1700 or (800)255-8740
GIC	Gilian Instrument Corporation 35 Fairfield Place West Caldwell, NJ 07006 (201)808-3355 FAX (201)808-6680
GMD	GMD Systems, Inc. (a Bacharach affiliate) Old Route 519 Hendersonville, PA 15339 (412)746-3600
MGP	Matheson Gas Products 30 Seaview Drive P.O. Box 1587 Secaucus, NJ 07096 (201)867-4100
MSA	Mine Safety Appliances Company, Instrument Division P.O. Box 427 Pittsburgh, PA 15230 (412)776-8600 or (800)MSA-INST FAX (412)776-3280
NDR	National Draeger, Inc. 101 Technology Drive P.O. Box 120 Pittsburgh, PA 15230 (412)787-8383/8389 or (800)922-5518 FAX (412)787-2207 or (800)922-5519
ROX	Roxan, Inc. 5425 Lockhurst Drive Woodland Hills, CA 91367-5735 (800)228-5775 or (818)703-6108
SAF	SAF-CO Mfg. Inc. P.O. Box 28885 Kansas City, MO 64118 (816)471-0130
SEN	Sensidyne, Inc. Gas and Particulate Detection Systems 16333 Bay Vista Drive Clearwater, FL 34620 (813)530-3602 or (800)451-9444

Chapter 19

Direct-Reading Gas and Vapor Instruments

Mary Lynn Woebkenberg[A] and Charles S. McCammon, Ph.D.[B]

[A]*U.S. Department of Health and Human Services, Public Health Service, Centers for Disease Control and Prevention, National Institute for Occupational Safety and Health, 4676 Columbia Parkway, MS: R-7, Cincinnati, Ohio;* [B]*Department of Health and Human Services, Federal Office Bldg., 1961 Stout Street, Room 1185, Denver, Colorado*

CONTENTS

Introduction

This chapter presents useful information about direct-reading instruments for analyzing airborne gases and vapors. The instrumentation that will be discussed is that which provides an onsite indication, in useful units (e.g. ppm, mg/m^3, etc.), of the presence of the contaminant(s) of interest. Frequently, these instruments are general, nonspecific detectors, but chemispecific detectors are also available.

Direct-reading instruments may be used for area, process, or personal monitoring, and it is convenient to describe three physical classifications for grouping these instruments: *personal* instruments are those instruments small enough to be worn by an individual, *portable* instruments are those easily carried by an individual, *transportable* instruments are those requiring a cart or other support for movement to or from the monitoring site. Ideally, these instruments operate from self-contained battery power, but many require line current.

In this chapter, the reader will find information on operational, physical, and performance characteristics for each of the instruments described. The instruments are grouped into the following classifications: electrochemical instruments, spectrochemical instruments, thermochemical instruments, gas chromatographic instruments, paramagnetic instruments, and an aerosol formation and detection instrument. In each section there is a general definition of the instrumentation to be described, an explanation of the principle of detection, and a brief discussion of conditions of application for the instruments, including capabilities, restrictions, and limitations. At the end of the chapter is a suggested reading list for the reader who requires more in-depth information about a particular technique.

Regardless of the instrument chosen for use and the capabilities of that instrument, there is no substitute for knowledge of the capabilities and limitations of the instrument, as well as conditions in the proposed monitoring situation. Then, the most appropriate instrument can be chosen for a given application, meaningful data can be obtained, and, if necessary, effective solutions for contaminant control can be implemented.

Electrochemical Instruments

Electrochemical techniques involve the measurement of electrical signals associated with chemical systems.(1) These chemical systems are typically incorporated into electrochemical cells. Electrochemical techniques include instruments that operate on the principles of conductivity, potentiometry, coulometry, and ionization.

Conductivity (1.1–1.4)

Instruments that measure conductivity rely on the fact that charged species (ions) conduct electricity. Equally significant is the fact that at low concentrations, such as those concentrations typically found when these species are measured as workplace contaminants, conductivity is proportional to concentration. The fundamental equation for conductivity is given by

$$G = \frac{\Lambda C}{1000\, K}$$

where: G = conductance in Siemens
Λ = equivalent conductance in Siemens per centimeter-equivalent
C = the concentration in equivalents per 1000 cm^3
K = a geometric term describing the electrochemical cell

A conductivity measurement depends on the space between, and area (size) of, a pair of electrodes and also on the volume of solution between them. Because conductance is the reciprocal of resistance, that is,

$$G = \frac{1}{R}$$

where R is resistance in ohms, the latter is sometimes measured since it is a more fundamental property. It should be noted that species monitored by conductivity need not be in an ionic form in the vapor phase but may be gases or vapors that form electrolytes, by chemical reaction, in solution.

Conductivity measurements are temperature dependent, having a temperature coefficient that can be on the order of 2% per °C. Instruments that *control* temperature may use thermostatted cabinets; those that *compensate* for temperature effects do so electronically.

A special case of conductivity instrumentation is one wherein a gold film is used to amalgamate mercury (Hg). In the mercury conductivity detector, the change in resistance of the *solid* film is measured.

Conductivity is, typically, a nonspecific technique in that any species ionizable under the given conditions will affect the measurement. The specific conductance, λ, of each ionizable species is important, for only when the conductivity of interfering electrolytes is either constant and/or negligible can the conductivity of the species of interest be measured.

There also are several solid-state devices that exploit electronic conductivity charges induced in metal oxide semiconductors.(2) Their principle of operation is based on the change in surface conductivity of a semiconductor, such as SnO_2, as a result of gas adsorption. The adsorbed gas may either directly affect the conductivity, or interact with the surface oxygen coverage, which, in turn, affects the conductivity. These instruments are relatively inexpensive, are easy to use, and can be used in oxygen-depleted atmospheres. They are typically used in screening applications and for hazard warning.

Conductivity instruments are primarily used for detection of corrosive gases, e.g., ammonia (NH_3), hydrogen sulfide (H_2S), and sulfur dioxide (SO_2). The conductivity analyzers are numbers 1.1 through 1.4 in the "Instrument Descriptions" section. They are most effectively used in isothermal environments at or near room temperature. Environments with few potential interferences are preferred. Chemical prescrubbers can be helpful.

Potentiometry (2.1–2.45)

Instruments that use a change in electrochemical potential as their principle of detection are most commonly represented by the pH meter. Potentiometry is strictly defined as the measurement of the difference in potential between two electrodes in an electrochemical cell under the condition of zero current. Gases and vapors can react with reagents effecting an oxidation/reduction, the extent of which is proportional to the concentration of the reacting gas. The fundamental equation governing a potentiometric reaction is the Nernst equation:

$$E_{cell} = E^{o}_{cell} - \frac{RT}{nF} \ln \frac{[C]^c[D]^d}{[A]^a[B]^b}$$

where: E_{cell} = cell potential
E^o_{cell} = standard cell potential
$\boldsymbol{R}$ = gas constant
T = temperature
n = number of electrons involved in the electrode reaction
F = Faraday constant

Although the letters in brackets strictly represent the chemical activities of the reacting species, when considering dilute solutions, it is reasonable to approximate the activity using the concentration. This equation is simplified at room temperature (25°C) by converting to the base ten logarithm and substituting for the constants: $\boldsymbol{R}$ = 8.314 Joules mol^{-1} T^{-1}, T = 298 K, F = 96,485 Coulombs/mol. This results in the following equation:

$$E_{cell} = E^o_{cell} - \frac{0.0591}{n}\log\frac{[C]^c[D]^d}{[A]^a[B]^b}$$

The Nernst equation relates potential, E_{cell}, with temperature, the electronic state change of the species being oxidized or reduced, and the concentration of the species. When sampling with a potentiometer, the sampled analyte of interest would most likely be represented in this equation by one of the reactants, A or B.

Whereas potentiometry is basically a nonspecific technique, some degree of specificity may be obtained through the selection of the membrane through which the gaseous analyte must diffuse to enter the electrochemical cell, the selection of the reagent, and the type of electrodes used.

Potentiometers are listed as numbers 2.1 through 2.45 in the "Instrument Descriptions" section. They are used for the measurement of a variety of contaminants including carbon monoxide, chlorine, formaldehyde, hydrogen sulfide, oxides of nitrogen, oxides of sulfur, oxygen, and ozone.

Coulometry (3.1–3.22)

Coulometric analyzers have as their principle of detection the determination of the quantity of electricity required to affect the complete electrolysis of the analyte of interest. The amount of electricity required is proportional to the amount of analyte present. This analyte may be the contaminant requiring monitoring, or it may be a chemical with which the contaminant quantitatively reacts. Regardless, the equation governing coulometry is Faraday's:

$$W = \frac{qM}{nF}$$

where: W = mass of substance that is electrolyzed
q = charge, in Coulombs, required to completely electrolyze the substance
M = formula weight
n = number of electrons per molecule required for electrolysis
F = Faraday's constant: 96,485 Coulombs/mol

The quantity that an instrument must measure is q. This may be done either directly, by determining the integral (controlled-potential coulometry), or indirectly, by measuring the time required for electrolysis under conditions of constant current (constant-current coulometry). Both approaches work because of the following relationship:

$$q = \int i\, dt$$

where: i = current in amperes
t = time

Coulometry is, inherently, a very accurate technique that is fairly sensitive. Coulometric analyzers are numbered 3.1 through 3.22 in the "Instrument Descriptions" section. The vast majority of these instruments are configured as oxygen or oxygen deficiency monitors, although coulometric analyzers are also available for carbon monoxide, chlorine, hydrogen cyanide, hydrogen sulfide, oxides of nitrogen, ozone, and sulfur dioxide.

Ionization (4.1–4.15)

There are three types of ionization detectors: flame ionization (FID), photoionization (PID), and electron capture (ECD). All rely on the ability of their respective energy source (flame, lamp, or radioactivity) to ionize the species of interest.

Flame Ionization

In an FID, a gaseous sample is pyrolyzed in a hydrogen/air flame.[(3)] Pyrolysis produces ions and electrons that are carried through the plasma to an electrode gap, decreasing the gap resistance and allowing current to flow in the external circuit. Figure 19-1 shows a schematic of a typical flame ionization detector. The FID has a wide linear range, on the order of 10^6 to 10^7, and is a very sensitive detector able to detect on the order of nanogram quantities of organic compounds. As a result, this detector is excellent in trace analysis. Flame ionization is a nonspecific detection mechanism ideal for the detection of most organic compounds. The detector does not respond to, or responds very little to, common constituents found in air and water vapor. The user should be aware that electronegative compounds such as chlorine and sulfur (in the vapor phase) will depress the response.

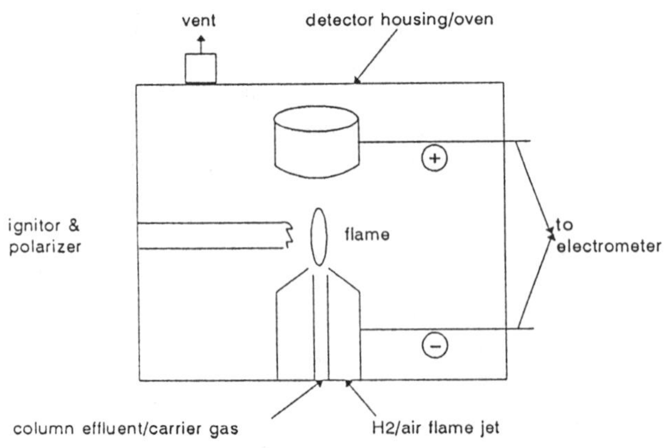

FIGURE 19-1. Schematic of Flame Ionization Detector.

Photoionization

Photoionization is a flameless ionization technique wherein the contaminant gas or vapor is carried into an ionization chamber where an ultraviolet lamp of known constant voltage causes the ionization of any species having an ionization potential less than the energy emitted by the lamp.[4] That is, photoionization occurs when a molecule absorbs a photon of sufficient energy to cause the molecule to lose an electron and become a positively charged ion:

$$RH + h\nu \rightarrow RH^{+} + e^{-}$$

where: RH = molecule to be ionized
h = photon whose energy is greater than the ionization potential of RH
RH^{+} = ionized molecule
e^{-} = electron lost in the process

The PID will have a high voltage positive bias electrode to repel the positively charged molecules accelerating them toward a negatively charged collector electrode. This, in turn, generates a signal at the collector which is proportional to the amount of ionized species. Figure 19-2 shows a schematic of a photoionization detector.

Photoionization is a nondestructive technique and somewhat selective through judicious selection of ultraviolet lamps of varying energies. Under optimum conditions, a PID can detect 5 pg of benzene and has a linear dynamic range on the order of 10^7.

Electron Capture

An ECD uses a radioactive source to generate the ions that are measured by this technique.[3] The radioactive source is usually H^3, Ni^{63}, or Kr^{85}. As the carrier gas, nitrogen, flows past the ion source, the nitrogen is ionized and slow electrons are formed that migrate to the anode, producing a steady current. Some molecules, said to have high electron affinity, have the ability to capture rapidly moving, free electrons from the radioactive source. When the molecules capture the electrons, they become stable, negative ions. This may happen by one of two mechanisms:

$$AB + e^{-} \rightarrow (AB)^{-} + energy \quad AB + e^{-} \rightarrow A^{-} + B \pm energy$$

where: A and B = reactants

Figure 19-3 shows a schematic of an ECD. When samples with high electron affinity components are introduced into the chamber, the current flow, established through the ionization of the nitrogen, is reduced. Because the current reduction is a function of both the amount of sample present and its electron affinity, a calibration must be made separately for each sample component that is to be quantified.

An ECD is very selective, particularly for halogenated compounds, nitrates, conjugated carbonyls, and some organometallic compounds. This detector is very sensitive (as low as 0.1 pg) for the compounds it will detect, but its linear range is very low, about 10^2–10^3.

Both FIDs and PIDs are primarily used for the detec-

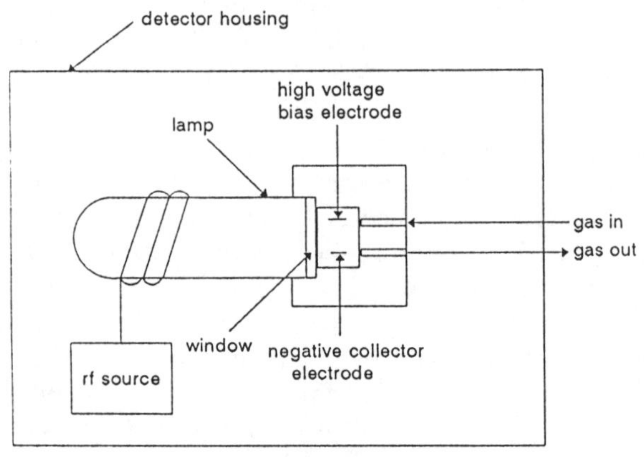

FIGURE 19-2. Schematic of a Photoionization Detector.

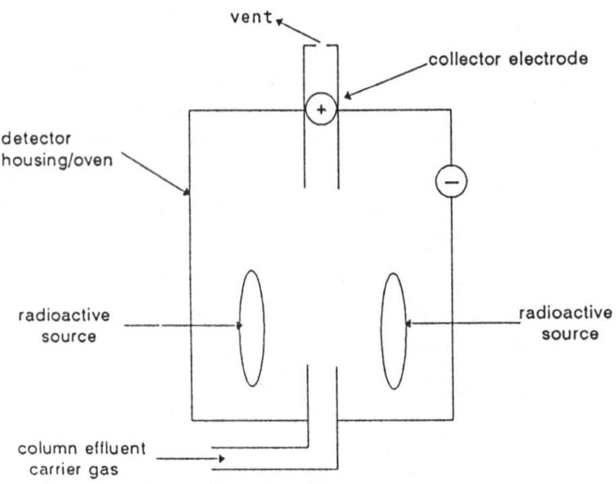

FIGURE 19-3. Schematic of an Electron Capture Detector.

tion of organic compounds, but the PID has some utility for inorganic compounds such as nitric and sulfuric acids, hydrogen sulfide, arsine, and phosphine. The ECD is useful for SF_6 and pesticide detection. Ionization detectors are numbers 4.1 through 4.15 in the "Instrument Descriptions" section. All three detectors are available as stand-alone instruments, as well as detectors for gas chromatographic systems, which will be discussed later in this chapter.

Spectrochemical Instruments

Instruments whose principle of detection is spectrochemical in nature include infrared analyzers, ultraviolet and visible light photometers, chemiluminescent detectors, and photometric analyzers.[5] Photometric analyzers include fluorescent and spectral intensity detectors. In general, spectrochemical analysis involves the use of a spectrum or some aspect of a spectrum to determine chemical species. A spectrum is a display of intensity of radiation that is emitted, absorbed, or scattered by a sample, versus wavelength. This radiation is related to photon energy via wavelength or frequency.

Infrared (5.1–5.16)

Infrared spectrometry (IR) involves the interaction of the infrared portion of the electromagnetic spectrum with matter. Specifically, that portion of the spectrum ranging in wavelength from 770 nm to 1000 μm, or 12,900 cm^{-1} to 10 cm^{-1} in wave number. The infrared portion of the spectrum is subdivided into three regions: the near-infrared (770 nm to 2.5 μm), the mid-infrared (2.5 to 50 μm), and the far-infrared (50 to 1000 μm). The terms "near," "mid," and "far" refer to proximity to the visible portion of the electromagnetic spectrum. Infrared radiation is not energetic enough to cause electronic transitions in molecules, but it does result in vibrational and rotational transitions. Nearly all molecules absorb infrared radiation, making the technique widely applicable. Because the IR spectrum of a given molecule is unique to that molecule, IR can be fairly specific and useful in compound identification. However, the possibility of overlapping peaks makes the use of any single wavelength IR measurement of an uncharacterized mixture risky.

Figure 19-4 shows a schematic of an infrared analyzer. These instruments consist primarily of six major sections: a source of infrared radiation, a wavelength selector, a sample cell, appropriate optics, a detector, and a signal processor/readout. Although Figure 19-4 shows the monochromator after the sample cell, wavelength selection can occur before the sample cell, after the sample cell, or both. Infrared spectrometry may be either a nondispersive or a dispersive technique. A nondispersive IR is a filter photometer employing in-

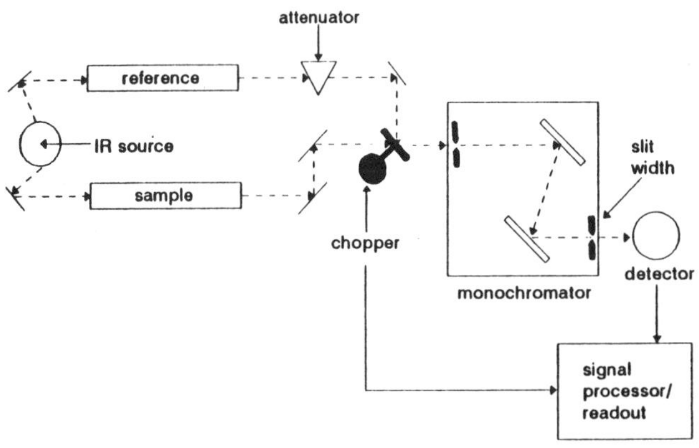

FIGURE 19-4. Schematic of Double Beam Infrared Analyzer.

terference filters designed for the determination of a specific pollutant, whereas a dispersive IR uses prisms or gratings to separate radiation into its component wavelengths to obtain a complete spectrum for qualitative identification.

Because it is an absorption technique, infrared spectrometry is governed by Beer's Law:

$$A = \varepsilon bc$$

where: A = absorbance
ε = molar absorptivity
b = path length
c = concentration

This equation shows the relationships between the amount of energy absorbed and the length of the path through the sample, and between the absorbed energy and the concentration of the species of interest. The dependency of absorbance on path length is significant in discussing parameters of interest because the longer the path length of the instrument, the more sensitive the instrument should be. In introducing Beer's Law, it is significant to note that the absorbance, A, is log P_0/P, where P_0 is the original incident radiation, and P is the energy remaining after some is absorbed by the sample.

An additional instrument parameter of interest is the slit width. The slit width defines the window of energy seen either by the sample or by the detector. Figure 19-4 shows the slit width at the detector end of the instrument. The width of this slit is inversely proportional to selectivity and peak resolution.

The direct-reading infrared instruments are given in the "Instrument Descriptions" section as numbers 5.1 through 5.16. The instruments balance modest precision with selectivity and high throughput. Some instruments are designed as fixed wavelength monitors whereas others are capable of scanning the infrared spectrum. Some of these instruments are designed as general detectors for organics and subgroups such as hydrocarbons; others are more specific monitors for

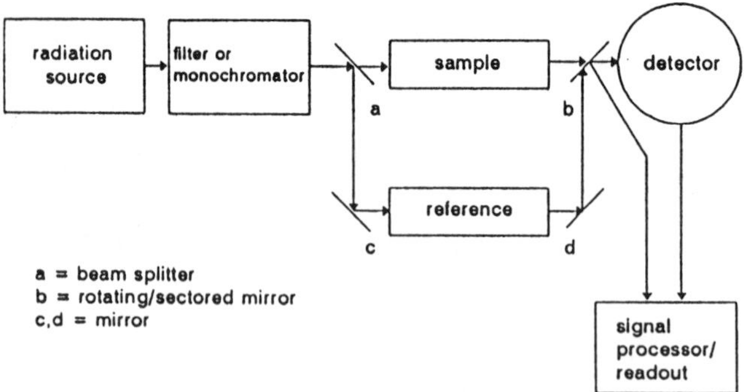

FIGURE 19-5. Schematic of a UV-VIS Spectrophotometer.

compounds such as methane, ethylene, ethane, propane, butane, vehicle emissions, carbon monoxide, carbon dioxide, and several freons. The user needs to be aware that certain ubiquitous compounds, like water, absorb very strongly in the infrared, and care must be exercised to avoid making measurements at or near these absorbances.

Ultraviolet and Visible Light Photometers (6.1–6.10)

Both ultraviolet (UV) and visible (VIS) light photometers operate on the principle of absorption of electromagnetic radiation. The UV is that portion of the electromagnetic spectrum having wavelengths from 10 to 350 nm. The actual spectral range for direct-reading UV instruments is closer to 180–350 nm, which is termed the "near UV," in deference to its proximity to the visible spectrum. The corresponding energy range for the UV is 3.6–7 eV for the near UV and 7–124 eV for the far, or vacuum, UV. The visible spectrum has longer wavelengths than the UV (350–770 nm) and correspondingly lower energies (1.6–3.6 eV). Like their infrared counterparts, the operational principle (energy absorption) of the UV-VIS instruments is governed by Beer's Law, and the techniques have the same relationships between absorption and concentration, and between absorption and path length. Although the relationship between absorbance and concentration is linear, the value typically measured in spectrophotometry is transmittance, T, whose relationship with absorbance is given by:

$$A = 2 - \log \%T$$

Transmittance is the ratio of the amount of energy passing through the sample (not absorbed) to the amount of incident energy. Measuring $\%T$ is preferable because it is a percent scale (as opposed to absorbance which is logarithmic), and the instrument is much easier to zero and span.

Figure 19-5 shows a schematic of a typical UV-VIS photometer. The instruments operating on the principle of energy absorption in the UV-VIS region are given in the "Instrument Descriptions" section as numbers 6.1 through 6.10. Most of these instruments are designed to analyze gaseous samples such as ammonia, mercury vapor (which absorbs very strongly at 253.7 nm), oxides of nitrogen, ozone, and sulfur dioxide.

A special case of visible spectroscopy is colorimetry, wherein the sample is mixed with a reagent selected to react with the contaminant of interest, forming a colored product. The ability of this colored, liquid product to absorb light in the visible region is exploited. This type of instrument, governed by the same chemical principles, can be used as a continuous monitor for a variety of compounds. The UV-VIS instruments are capable of detecting contaminants in the ppm range.

Chemiluminescence (7.1–7.6)

Chemiluminescence is a form of emission spectroscopy wherein spectral information is obtained from nonradiational activation processes.[6] In this case, the emitted energy results from species that are excited by chemical reactions and are returning to the lower energy state by emission of a photon. Chemiluminescence is based on the fact that in some chemical reactions, a significant fraction of the intermediates or products are produced in excited electronic states. The emission of photons from these excited electronic states is measured and, if the reaction conditions are arranged appropriately, is proportional to the concentration of the contaminant of interest. Two common chemiluminescence mechanisms are:

$$\begin{array}{ccc} A + B \rightarrow I + I^{*} & & A + B \rightarrow \boldsymbol{P} + \boldsymbol{P}^{*} \\ \downarrow & + & \downarrow \\ I + h\nu \rightarrow \boldsymbol{P} & & \boldsymbol{P} \rightarrow h\nu \end{array}$$

where: A and B = reactants
I = intermediate
$\boldsymbol{P}$ = product
* = excited state
$h\nu$ = emitted energy

Three conditions must be met in order to have chemiluminescence take place. First, there needs to be enough energy to produce the excited state; second, there must be a favorable reaction pathway to produce the excited state; and, third, photon emission must be a favorable deactivation process.

The direct-reading chemiluminescent detectors are numbered 7.1 through 7.6 in the "Instrument Descriptions" section. They analyze gas phase samples and have been developed primarily for oxides of nitrogen and ozone. Because of the chemical reactions involved, the instruments have a high degree of specificity and have typical limits of detection on the order of 10 ppb.

Photometric Analyzers

This category includes fluorescence analyzers, flame photometric detectors, spectral intensity analyzers, and photometers, primarily reflectance. The first three techniques are all examples of emission spectroscopy wherein the excitation process is radiative in nature; the last category includes automated media advance samplers, branched sequential samplers, and paper tape stain development, all of which utilize photometric analysis.

Fluorescence (8.2, 8.3, 8.5)

Fluorescence is the emission of photons from molecules in excited states when the excited states are the result of the absorption of energy from some source of radiation. For most molecules, electrons are paired in the lowest energy or ground state. If a molecule absorbs energy from a sufficiently powerful radiation source, such as a mercury or xenon arc lamp, the molecule will become "excited," moving an electron to a higher energy state. When the electron returns to the lower, more stable energy condition, it releases the absorbed energy in photons. A significant characteristic of fluorescence is that the emitted radiation is of a longer wavelength (lower energy) than the exciting radiation. Figure 19-6 shows a block diagram of the components of a fluorescence instrument. An excitation wavelength selector is used to limit the energy to that which will cause fluorescence of the sample while excluding energy wavelengths that may interfere with the detection. The emission wavelength selector isolates the fluorescence peak. Detection is at right angles to allow measurement of the longer wavelength light emitted from the sample while avoiding detection of light from the source, which could cause large errors in measurement.

Fluorescence instruments are available for carbon monoxide and sulfur dioxide. They are numbers 8.2, 8.3, and 8.5 in the "Instrument Descriptions" section. Typical limits of detection are in the 5–10 ppb range.

Flame Photometric (8.4, 8.6, 8.14)

Flame photometric detectors can be adjusted to obtain selectivity for nanogram quantities of sulfur or phosphorous compounds. The detector works by measuring the emission of light from a hydrogen flame. Light from the flame impinges upon a mirror and is reflected to an optical filter that allows only light of either 526 μm (for phosphorous) or 394 μm (for sulfur) to pass through to the photomultiplier tube. Calibration with a flame photometric detector is critical because this detector exhibits little or no linearity. From the "Instrument Descriptions" section, numbers 8.4, 8.6, and 8.14 are flame photometric detectors. They have limits of detection in the low ppb range.

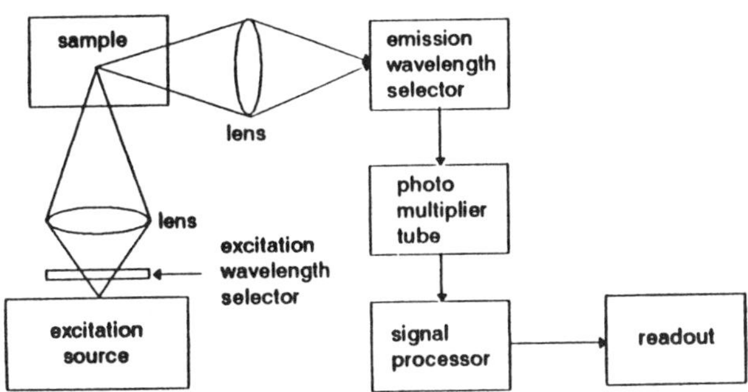

FIGURE 19-6. Schematic of a Fluorescence Spectrometer.

Spectral Intensity (8.8, 8.13)

Spectral intensity analyzers measure the radiant power of emission from an analyte due to nonradiational excitation. Two such instruments are available (numbers 8.8 and 8.13 in the "Instrument Descriptions" section). Both instruments are used for halide detection by measuring the increased spectral intensity of an AC arc (or spark) in the presence of halogenated hydrocarbons. The increased intensity can be related to the concentration of the halogenated compound by using a calibration curve based on the specific compound of interest. These instruments have limits of detection in the tens of ppm range and have limited selectivity, i.e., they can differentiate halogenated compounds from nonhalogenated compounds, but cannot differentiate between halogenated compounds.

Photometers (8.1, 8.7, 8.9–8.12)

The remaining instruments in this category are simply referred to as photometers. The instruments, numbers 8.1, 8.7, and 8.9 through 8.12 in the "Instrument Descriptions" section, have unique sampling characteristics and detection principles relative to the other instruments in this category (spectrochemical techniques), but they operate on spectrochemical principles nonetheless. The majority of these instruments allow for unattended sampling through the use of automated sampling media advance (i.e., tape samplers, rotating drum samplers, rotating disc samplers, and turntable samplers) or branched sequential sampling trains. These samplers typically involve a color change of the sampling medium and the analytic finish is measurement of the light reflected from the sampling medium. These instruments are useful for such toxic species as toluene diisocyanate, ammonia, phosgene, arsine, and hydrogen cyanide. The reflectance instruments can be quite specific through judicious selection of the chemistry for the sampler, and the ability to change the chemistry makes these instruments potentially useful for a wide variety of compounds.

Other instruments in this category include one designed for the determination of CO. This instrument actually measures mercury that is generated via reduction of solid-state mercury oxide. The amount of mercury generated is equal to the quantity of carbon monoxide oxidized in the sample. The mercury is measured using a UV filter photometer. The other three instruments rely on the development of a color stain, wherein the intensity change or the development of the intensity change is measured via a photoelectric cell. These last three instruments are useful primarily for hydrogen sulfide, although one will determine other analytes as a function of the chemically impregnated paper used for color development. All the photometers have limits of detection in the low ppm range and are very specific for the contaminant(s) of interest.

Thermochemical Instruments

Gases and vapors have certain thermal properties that can be exploited in their analysis.[7] Of the instruments available for industrial hygiene applications, one of two thermal properties, conductivity or heat of combustion, is measured.

Thermal Conductivity (9.1–9.3)

Thermal conductivity detectors are relatively simple devices that operate on the principle that a hot body will lose heat at a rate that depends on the composition of the surrounding gas. That is, the ability of the surrounding gas to conduct heat away from the hot body can be used as a measure of the composition of the gas. In actual practice, a thermal conductivity detector consists of an electrically heated element, or sensing device, whose temperature at constant electrical power depends on the thermal conductivity of the surrounding gas. The resistance of the sensing device is used as a measure of its temperature. Thermal conductivity detectors are universal detectors, responding to all compounds. They have large linear dynamic ranges, on the order of 10^5, and limits of detection on the order of 10–8 gram of solute per mL of carrier gas (10–100 ppm for most analytes). Thermal conductivity detectors require good temperature and flow control. They are numbered 9.1 through 9.3 in the "Instrument Descriptions" section.

Heat of Combustion (10.1–10.35)

Heat of combustion detectors, comprising the largest single class of direct-reading instruments for analyzing airborne gases and vapors, measure the heat released during combustion or reaction of the contaminant gas of interest. The released heat is a particular characteristic of combustible gases and may be used for quantitative detection. There are two main mechanisms for the operation of heat of combustion detectors. The first relies on heated filaments. Upon introduction of the contaminant gas into the sample cell, the contaminant comes into contact with a heated source, igniting the contaminant. The resulting heat changes the resistance of the filament. The measured change in filament resistance is related to the gas concentration through the use of calibration standards.

The second mechanism used in heat of combustion instruments employs the use of catalysts via catalytically heated filaments or oxidation catalysts. This second mechanism may use one of two methods of detection: a measured resistance change, or temperature changes measured via thermocouples or thermistors.

Like thermal conductivity detectors, heat of combustion detectors are nonspecific, universal detectors. Some specificity can be introduced by manipulation of the temperature; that is, the combustion temperature may be controlled so that it is insufficient to combust interfering gases. From the second mechanism, some specificity may be introduced by careful selection of the oxidation catalyst.

As the category name implies, heat of combustion detectors are available as generic detectors for combustible gases. Some more specific heat of combustion detectors are available for carbon monoxide, ethylene oxide, hydrogen sulfide, methane, and oxygen deficiency. Most of these monitors read out in terms of percent of the lower explosive limit (LEL) or hundreds of ppm and the limits of detection are a function of the analyte of interest. These instruments are numbered 10.1 through 10.35 in the "Instrument Descriptions" section.

Gas Chromatographs (11.1–11.7)

In terms of detection of airborne gases and vapors, the detectors used in gas chromatographic (GC) analyzers have, for the most part, been discussed earlier in this chapter.[3,4] The most frequently used detectors in GCs designed for industrial hygiene applications are the FID and the PID. The reason gas chromatographs are being discussed separately is fourfold: there are several direct-reading gas chromatographs commercially available; they represent a distinct family of instruments in that they very specifically address the issue of separation (specificity), as well as detection, in industrial hygiene monitoring; they represent one area where a great deal of research and development is ongoing; and they most closely approximate the transfer of laboratory analytical techniques into the field.

Figure 19-7 shows a schematic of a GC. The sample is either injected into the GC using a gas-tight syringe or the instrument may be capable of obtaining its own sample via a built-in sampling pump. If the sample is a liquid, the instrument must be capable of vaporizing the sample (e.g., using a heated injection port).

The actual separation of the sample into its component parts takes place on the GC column.[8] Columns are typically long tubes made of metal, glass, Teflon®, or fused silica. Columns in portable, direct-reading GCs are of two kinds: packed and wall-coated. A packed column contains a granular material used as a solid support which is coated with a chemical chosen for its ability to interact with the components of the sample. This chosen chemical is referred to as the stationary phase. Packed columns are generally from 4 or 5 cm to 1 meter or more in length and have external diameters on the order of 0.3 cm (1/8 in.). A wall-coated column tends to be longer (5 cm to 3 m or more) and narrower (i.d. from 0.1 to 1 mm) than packed columns. In a wall-coated column, there is no granular solid support for the stationary phase. It is, as the name implies, coated directly on the walls of the column. The long, thinner columns (i.d.'s < 0.5 mm) are sometimes referred to as capillary columns.

The sample is carried through the column by an inert (relative to the sample) carrier gas, which, depending on the direct-reading GC, may be helium, hydrogen, nitrogen, argon, carbon dioxide, or air. The separation is governed by the degree of interaction of the sample with the stationary phase and the properties of the carrier gas. All components of a mixture spend the same amount of time in the carrier gas, so their different elution times is a function of the time spent in the stationary phase. The elapsed time from injection until the detector "sees" a component of a mixture is that component's retention time. The retention time is a function of the physical properties of a component in a sample, whereas the size of the peak is a function of the amount. Figure 19-8 shows the component parts of a typical chromatogram.

The degree of separation of two components, as well as their relative retention times, depends, in part, on the temperature at which the system operates. Some portable GCs operate only at ambient temperatures; others are capable of heating the column.

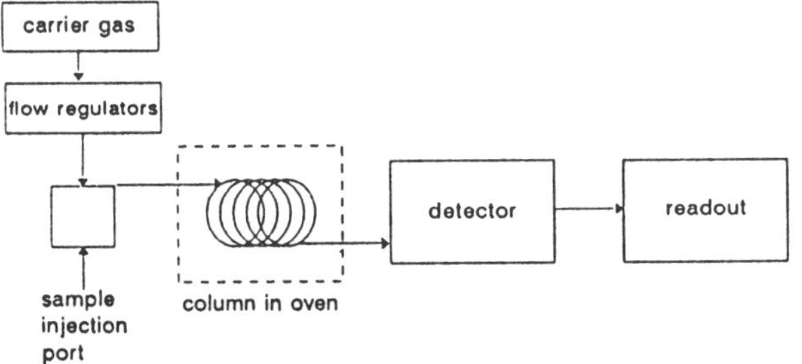

FIGURE 19-7. Schematic of a Gas Chromatograph.

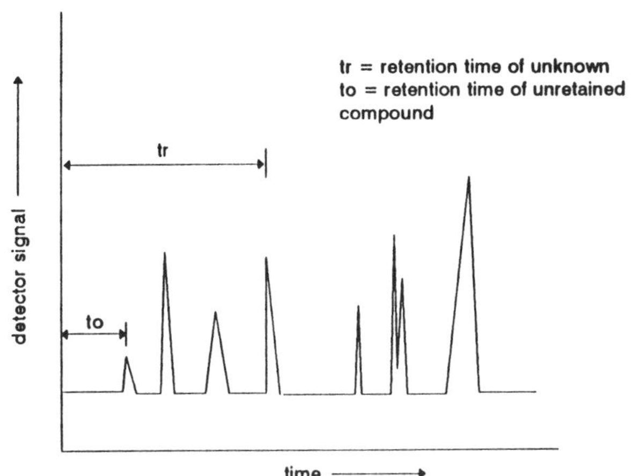

FIGURE 19-8. Schematic of a Typical Gas Chromatogram.

Once the component parts of a mixture elute from the column, they go into the detector. Portable GC detectors include flame ionization, photoionization, electron capture, ultraviolet, flame photometric, and thermal conductivity (which have already been addressed in this chapter), as well as nitrogen-phosphorous and argon ionization.

Because of their separation capabilities, GCs offer excellent selectivity combined with low limits of detection. The limits of detection are primarily a property of the individual detectors and are given in the detector discussions, but portable GCs generally have limits of detection at sub-ppm levels. Some limitations associated with portable GCs include the need for more user knowledge of the technique, size, and cost. The portable GCs are numbers 11.1 through 11.7 in the "Instrument Descriptions" section.

Summary

Many instruments are available for direct-reading analysis of gases and vapors. They operate on a variety of principles of detection and vary in performance characteristics such as linear range, specificity, and limits of detection. Direct-reading instruments represent a powerful tool in developing sampling strategies. That is, direct-reading instruments, when correctly used, can determine, in real or near-real time, those areas of high concentration, those workers at highest risk, and those processes with the highest emissions. Such information is useful in solving a variety of gas and vapor exposure problems. This information can guide the hygienist or safety professional in obtaining other more informative and useful samples requiring laboratory analyses. Used properly, direct-reading instruments can conserve resources, eliminating samples with results of "none detected."

References

1. Strobel, H.A.; Heineman W.R.: Chemical Instrumentation: A Systematic Approach, 3rd ed. John Wiley & Sons, New York (1989).
2. Gentry, S.J.: Appl. Occup. Environ. Hyg., 8(4), 260–266 (1993).
3. David, D.J.: Gas Chromatographic Detectors. Wiley-Interscience, New York (1974).
4. HNU Systems: Gas Chromatograph, Model 301, Instruction Manual. Newton Highlands, MA (1986).
5. Ingle, J.D.; Crouch, S.R.: Spectrochemical Analysis. Prentice-Hall, Inc., New Jersey (1988).
6. Hodgeson, J.A.: A Review of Chemiluminescent Techniques for Air Pollution Monitoring. Toxicol. Environ. Chem. Rev. 11:81 (1974).
7. Skoog, D.A.; West, D.M.; Holler, F.J.: Fundamentals of Analytical Chemistry, 5th ed. Saunders College Publishing, New York (1988).
8. McNair, H.M.; Bonelli, E.J.: Basic Gas Chromatography. Varian Aerograph, Berkeley, CA (1968).

Additional Reading

ACGIH: Volume 1, Dosimetry for Chemical and Physical Agents. William D. Kelley, Ed. American Conference of Governmental Industrial Hygienists, Cincinnati, OH (1981).

Cohen, B.S.: Air Sampling Instrument Performance. Appl. Occup. Environ. Hyg. 8(4) 227–229 (1993).

Cralley, L.J.; Cralley, L.V.: Patty's Industrial Hygiene and Toxicology, Vol.III, Theory and Rationale of Industrial Hygiene Practice. Wiley-Interscience, New York (1981).

Environmental Instrumentation Group, Lawrence Berkeley Laboratory: Instrumentation for Environment Monitoring Air. LBL-1. Technical Information Division, Lawrence Berkeley Laboratory, Berkeley, CA (1973).

Hosey, A.D.: History of the Development of Industrial Hygiene Sampling Instruments and Techniques. American Conference of Governmental Industrial Hygienists, Cincinnati, OH (1981).

Instrumentation for Monitoring Air Quality. R.C. Barras, Symposium Chairman. ASTM Special Publication 555 (74-76066). ASTM, Philadelphia, PA (1974).

Nader, J.S.: Source Monitoring. In: Air Pollution, 3rd ed., Vol. 3. Ch. 15, pp. 589–645. A.C. Stem, Ed. Academic Press, Inc., New York (1976).

Stevens, R.K.; Herget, W.F.: Analytical Methods Applied to Air Pollution Measurements. Ann Arbor Science Publ., Inc., Ann Arbor, MI (1974).

Instrument Descriptions

This section contains tables and short descriptions of the commercially available direct-reading instruments for gases and vapors. The tables are designed to provide an overview of the instrument features, sizes, and capabilities, whereas the descriptions give more detailed information and photographs. Each description is numbered and is cross referenced in the tables that appear at the end of the chapter. The descriptions are grouped by the operating principle upon which the measurement is based. The following instrument tables are included:

Table 19-I-1. Electrical Conductivity Analyzers
Table 19-I-2. Potentiometric Analyzers
Table 19-I-3. Coulometric Analyzers
Table 19-I-4. Ionization Detectors
Table 19-I-5. Infrared Photometers
Table 19-I-6. Ultraviolet and Visible Light Photometers
Table 19-I-7. Chemiluminescent Detectors
Table 19-I-8. Photometric Analyzers
Table 19-I-9. Thermal Conductivity Detectors
Table 19-I-10. Heat of Combustion Detectors
Table 19-I-11. Gas Chromatograph Analyzers

These tables reference instrument manufacturers by code letters; complete names and addresses are given in Table 19-I-12.

Electrical Conductivity Analyzers

19-1-1. Gold Film Mercury Vapor Analyzer
Arizona Instrument Corporation

The Model 411 Gold Film Mercury Vapor Analyzer is a portable instrument designed for mercury surveys in workplace environments. The Model 411 uses a patented Gold Film microsensor as the basis of detection. The sensor absorbs and integrates the mercury present in the sample, registering this as a proportional change in electrical resistance. The sensor's selectivity to mercury eliminates many interferences common to atomic absorption, such as water vapor, SO_2, aromatic hydrocarbons, and particulates. The Model 411 incorporates an internal pump and digital display with microprocessor control. Activating either the 10-second sample or the 1-second survey mode starts the pump that draws a precise volume of air over the Gold Film sensor. Mercury in the sample is adsorbed and integrated by the sensor. The microprocessor computes the concentration of mercury in mg/m^3 and displays the results on the digital meter until the next sample cycle is activated. Response time: sample mode, 10 seconds; survey mode, 1 second. Meter: LCD display. Construction: aluminum alloy. Flow rate: 0.75 L/min.

19-1-2. J-W Toxic Gas Alarms for NH_3, H_2S, and SO_2
Bacharach, Inc.

The Model MHO is used to continuously detect the presence of small concentrations of ammonia, H_2S, and SO_2 in the toxic range. Air is sampled by means of a vibratory pump, and H_2S in the sample is oxidized to SO_2. In the detection cell, the sample contacts a flowing stream of distilled water. Ammonia or SO_2 in the sample dissolves in the water, which increases the conductivity of the water. This conductivity change triggers a thyratron tube to turn on a relay and alarm signal. The complete analyzer is housed in a small, wall-mounted case containing the detection cell, power supply, vibratory pump, flowmeter, alarm circuit, and all other required components. A constant flow of distilled water is fed by gravity from a 1-gal plastic bottle mounted on the wall above the analyzer.

19-1-3. UltraGas-U3S Sulfur Dioxide Analyzer
Calibrated Instruments, Inc.

The UltraGas-U3S is a sampling and analysis device for measuring the concentration of SO_2 in air by the conductivity method. Existing interference components can be eliminated in most cases through suitable absorption traps so that measurement is selective. In the instrument, a constant and continuous stream of air and reagent mix in a reaction chamber. The conductivity of the solution changes in proportion to the concentration of SO_2. The conductivity change is determined in the detector by two electrode sections. The conductivity of the reagent is measured first in one section, and after reaction with SO_2, the conductivity is measured in the second section. The difference in the two alternating currents flowing through the two electrode sections is selected electronically by the recorder. A temperature-dependent resistance compensates for temperature changes.

19-1-4. Gas Analyzer System, Series 9000
Devco Engineering, Inc.

The Devco Engineering Series 9000 is designed specifically for the continuous monitoring of toxic gases or vapors in the atmosphere or of trace concentrations of contaminants in process streams. Typical applications include monitoring for CO_2, Freon®, or ammonia in refrigeration plants; continuous monitoring for SO_2 in air pollution studies; automatic bed cycling by continuously monitoring the effluent in solvent recovery systems; and measuring H_2S in air and hydrocarbon streams in petroleum refineries or sewage treatment plants. Analysis is based on measurement of electrical conductance in water due to ionization of the gas or vapor being monitored.

Prior to analysis, certain gases, such as H_2S or the

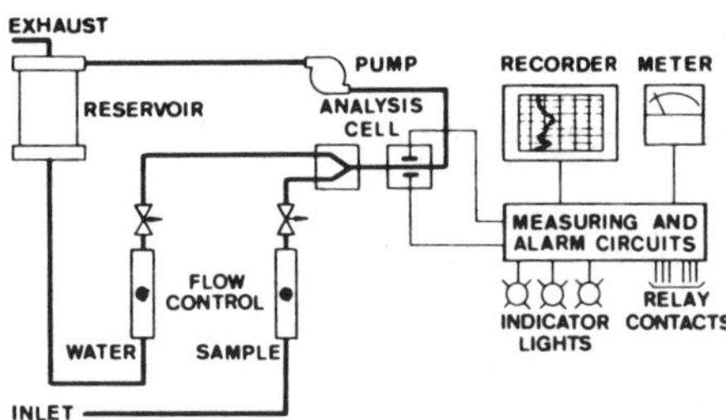

INSTRUMENT 19-1-4. Gas Analyzer System, Series 9000.

halogenated hydrocarbons, are treated by thermal decomposition or oxidation in a pyrolysis train; the emanating combustion products are then passed on to the analysis cell. This system is furnished in wall-mounting varieties, in NEMA type 12 enclosures, in free-standing relay rack-type housings, in portable packages (115 VAC, 60 Hz operated), or in fully explosion-proof construction. No special reagents are required; 2 quarts of water are required approximately every 30 days. Multipoint, sequential sampling systems are available to monitor up to eight points on a single instrument by means of a sample program assembly.

Potentiometric Analyzers

19-2-1. Series 200 and 300 Gas Detectors

AIM USA

The Series 200 and 300 Gas Detectors are designed to detect combustible gases, oxygen, and toxic gases. Applications include:

- Confined space entry survey work
- Industrial safety and hygiene
- Fugitive emissions and leak detection.

Instruments in the 200 and 300 Series are available to detect one, two, or three separate gases. Three data-logging formats are available:

- Alarm incident
- Time-interval sampling
- Location-survey testing.

Sensors are chemical-specific electrochemical for toxic gases and O_2, and nonspecific metal oxide for combustible gases. The metal oxide sensor comes standard with the one sensor version and is optional in the two or three sensor versions.

19-2-2. Series 500 Gas Detectors

AIM USA

The Series 500 Gas Detectors are designed to monitor for combustibles, O_2, H_2S, and CO in confined space entry applications. These instruments use metal oxide or Pellister sensors to detect combustibles and electrochemical sensors to detect O_2, H_2S, and CO.

Features of the 500 Series include audible and visual alarms, shock resistance case, and data logging capabilities for 1300 preset time intervals.

Accessories included with the instruments include:

- Power supply
- Manual
- Quick start card
- Confined space booklet
- Calibration hood
- Carrying case
- QC sheet
- Tool kit.

Operating temperature range: –20 to 50°C. Operating relative humidity range: 5% to 99%, noncondensing.

19-2-3. Sentinel® 44 Personal Multigas Monitor

Bacharach, Inc.

The Sentinel® 44 is designed to measure O_2, combustible gases, CO, and H_2S in confined-space entry applications. The Sentinel® is equipped with audible and visual alarms that are activated when preset instantaneous levels, short-term exposure limits (STELs), or time-weighted averages (TWAs) are exceeded. Other features include:

- Multi-gas LCD display
- Radio frequency interference (RFI) protection
- Data logging capabilities
- Removable battery packs.

Accessories include:

- Hand aspirator or motorized pump
- 10-in. or 36-in. probes
- Calibration kits and gases
- Remote earphone or pocket alarms.

Rechargeable leadacid gel cells can operate the instrument for 8–10 hrs per charge. The Sentinel® can operate in a temperature range of –20 to 50°C and a relative humidity range of 5% to 95%, noncondensing.

19-2-4. Mikrogas® Series Gas Analyzers

Calibrated Instruments, Inc.

Mikrogas® instruments continuously measure concentrations of SO_2, HCl, H_2S, NH_3, Cl_2, $COCl_2$, COS, CS_2, HCN, and other gases in ambient air, industrial process streams, standing tanks, waste treatment facilities, and stack and incineration emissions using the conductimetric measuring principle. Extremely accurate and precise streams of sample gas and a liquid reagent of measured conductivity are volumetrically forwarded to a wet sampling head where they are combined. Thoroughly mixed in a reaction line, the sample gas and chemically changed reagent are then again separated. The reacted conductivity level of the reagent solution is then monitored as it passes a temperature-compensated continuous measuring electrode. An electronic circuit determines the change in conductivity of the reagent solution. This change in conductivity is proportional to the concentration of gas being sampled. Operating temperature: 2 to 40°C.

19-2-5. Ultragas® Series Gas Analyzers

Calibrated Instruments, Inc.

Utilizing the principle of conductivity measurement, Ultragas® instruments provide continuous or batch analysis for laboratory and closed chamber research, and environmental, industrial process, ambient air, and stack applications involving one or more of the following gases: CO, CO_2, CH_4, NH_3, H_2S, SO_2, HCl, $COCl_2$, COS, CS_2, HCN, and other hydrocarbons. High precision pumps continuously forward a liquid reagent and sample gas stream to a temperature-compensated reaction line where both are combined in a constant volumetric ratio and thoroughly mixed. The conductivity of the reagent changes in proportion to the concentration of the gas being sampled and is measured by an electrode. Operating temperature: 2 to 35°C.

19-2-6. Gasman Personal Gas Detector

CEA Instruments, Inc.

The Gasman is a series of single gas, shirt-pocket-sized personal gas monitors for toxic gases, combustible gases, or O_2. All models have a large, front-mounted digital display with built-in back light. Visual and audible alarms are available for toxic gases to provide instantaneous and TWA warnings. The monitors are rugged and water resistant. They are radio frequency (RF) shielded

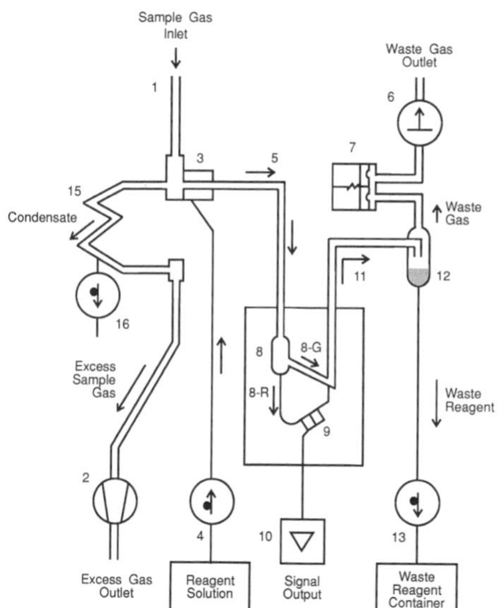

INSTRUMENT 19-2-4. Mikrogas® Series Gas Analyzers.

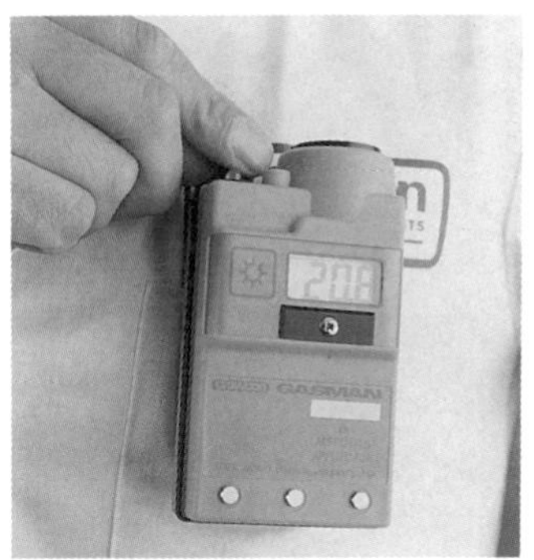

INSTRUMENT 19-2-6. Gasman Personal Gas Detector.

and are powered by four AA or rechargeable batteries. Models are available for O_2, H_2S, CO, SO_2, Cl_2, NO_2, NO, HCl, HCN, NH_3, and combustibles.

19-2-7. Series U Toxic Gas Detectors

CEA Instruments, Inc.

The Series U instruments are dedicated gas detectors in portable, wall-mounted, or multipoint configurations for a variety of contaminants. All instruments in this series use electrochemical-type sensors. The diffusion-type sensors are guaranteed for 2 years, provide rapid response, are solid-state, and are UL approved. Other features include low battery warning lights; built-in battery charger; high poison resistance to sulfur, lead, silicon, and halogenated compounds; and rugged, compact, leather carrying case. Operating temperature: –20 to +65°C.

19-2-8. TG-BA Series Portable Toxic Gas Analyzers

CEA Instruments, Inc.

The TG-BA Series Analyzers use a dedicated gas membrane, galvanic cell sensor. The analyzer is comprised of a sensor unit, a vacuum pump, and an amplifier unit. The gas permeates the membrane, causing a reduction in current at the surface of the working electrode. Response time: typically, one-third of full scale is achieved in less than 30 seconds. Alarm point: one-third of full scale (adjustable) with flashing red lamp (latching) and audible buzzer. Sampling distance: up to 30 ft. Sample flow rate: 0.5 L/min (adjustable). Recorder output: 0–10 mV (option 4 to 20 mA). Alarm contact closures: NO/NC, 250 VAC, 1A capacity. Operating temperature: 0 to 40°C. Dedicated units available for Cl_2, F_2, Br_2, H_2S, and many others.

19-2-9. Triple Plus Confined Space Monitor

CEA Instruments, Inc.

The Triple Plus is a multifunctional portable gas detector that can simultaneously monitor up to four different gases including combustibles, O_2, H_2S, CO, Cl_2, SO_2, NO_2, halons, HCl, HCN, and NH_3. The unit is microprocessor controlled and can be configured to pro-

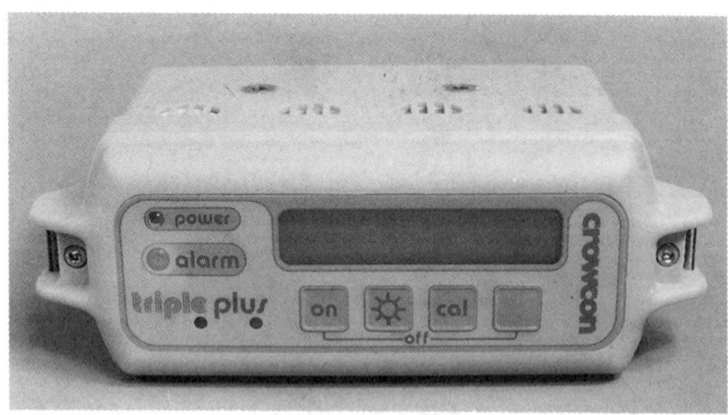

INSTRUMENT 19-2-9. Triple Plus Confined Space Monitor.

vide alarms, TWAs, or peak hold values. Other options include audio or visual alarms, tamper-proof controls, optional air sampling pump, and an internal data logger. The unit weighs 2 lbs and can operate for 12 hrs on a single charge.

19-2-10. XP-302IIE Gas Detection System

COSMOS Gas Detection Systems

The XP-302IIE is an intrinsically safe, microprocessor-controlled portable instrument designed to monitor combustible gases, O_2, H_2S, and CO in ambient working environments and confined spaces. Features include:

- Audible and visual alarms
- 11 diagnostic messages
- Instantaneous and peak concentration
- Chart recorder and printer output capability
- 18-hr battery life.

Response time: within 40 seconds to 90% of final reading. Operating temperature range: 10 to 40°C. Standard accessories include:

- Soft carrying case
- 8-m gas sampling tube with floating probe
- External alarm with 8-m cable
- Dust filters A and B
- Alcohol filter
- Operation manual.

19-2-11. $O_2$25H Oxygen Meter

Dynamation, Inc.

The Dynamation oxygen sensor is a microfuel cell that has a life expectancy of 1 year before replacement is required. Cell replacement requires less than 1 min. The O_2–25H has low maintenance requirements because no chemicals or electrolytes need to be changed or added. The only control is a calibration adjustment that is used to set the meter at 20.9% O_2 before testing. Standard equipment includes a flexible cord and remote cable. This cable can be extended up to 8 ft for remote sampling; a 25-ft extension cord is an available option. Response time: 90% in less than 10 seconds. Temperature range: 0 to 52°C.

19-2-12. MONOGARD and dynaMite Personal Monitors

Dynamation, Inc.

The MONOGARD and dynaMite Series of pocket-sized instruments combine digital LCD and diffusion chemical cell sensing for CO, H_2S, O_2, SO_2, and NO. The units feature an audible, pulsating alarm and a visual flashing light when unsafe atmospheres are encountered. Each unit has a low battery alarm, test switch, and illuminated display switch for reading in dark areas. All alarm points are factory set and customer adjustable. MONOGARDs are enclosed in rugged aluminum cases with leatherette carrying cases. The dynaMite gives more than 250 hrs of continuous operation from its replaceable lithium battery. Operating temperature for the monitors ranges from 0 to 41°C or to 52°C. Response time is 90% of full reading in 30 seconds. Monitors warm up in less than 10 seconds. The expected sensor life is 1.5 years (6-month warranty).

19-2-13. Series 300 Air Pollution Analyzers

Eitel Manufacturing, Inc.

These analyzers are designed to provide drift-free performance and reliability for continuous, unattended monitoring. Systems for single or multigas determinations are available in ranges covering source emissions, occupational exposures, or ambient air concentrations. The gas sample flows across a membrane during its passage through the Faristor sensor. Some gas molecules diffuse through the membrane and dissolve in a thin liquid film where they undergo electrooxidation or reduction. An opposite reaction occurs at the reference, resulting in current flow in the load circuit proportional to the pollutant concentration. The sensor is plugged into the slot in the rear panel of the instrument and gas

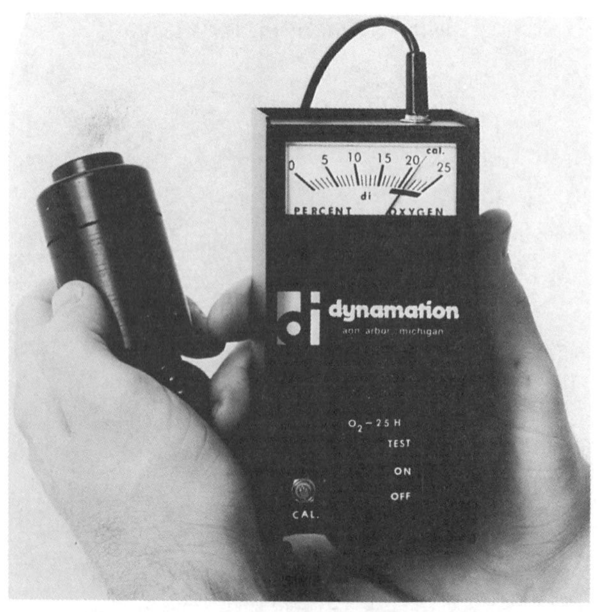

INSTRUMENT 19-2-11. $O_2$25H Oxygen Meter.

connection is made through polypropylene fittings on the outside of the module.

Linearity: ±0.5%. Zero drift: ±0.5%/24 hrs. Span drift: ±1%/week. Response time: 5–15 seconds to 95%. Ambient temperature: 32 to 39°C. Temperature compensation: 4 to 52°C. Sample pressure: not greater than 15 psig. Sample flow: 0.5 to 2 L/min. Recorder output: 100 mV.

19-2-14. CGS Series, Omni 400, and Quad-400 Personal Gas Detectors

ENMET Corp.

These instruments are designed to detect toxic gases, combustible gases, and O_2 deficiency, and they meet all federal Occupational Safety and Health Administration (OSHA) confined space entry standards. Features include:

- Remote sensors
- RFI resistance
- Audible and visual alarms
- LCD displays.

Sensors include microfuel cell for O_2 with average life of 10 months; MOS gas sensor for toxic and combustible gases with average life of 3 years; solid-state, thin-film H_2S sensor; and an electrochemical sensor for CO. Instruments come with case, AC charger, manual, and 20-ft sensor cable. Test gas kits and calibration kits are also available. Operating temperature: –6 to 54°C.

19-2-15. Toximet Series Pocket-Size Toxic Gas Detectors

ENMET Corp.

The Toximet Series are personal, pocket-sized gas detectors that use an electrochemical sensor to monitor for toxic gases, O_2, or H_2. The instrument enclosure incorporates features that provide RFI/electromagnetic interference (EMI) protection, shock resistance, and surface mounting. The instrument normally operates 600 hrs continuously with power supplied by a replaceable 9-V battery. Accessories include a remote oxygen sensor on a 15-ft cable, hand aspirator, motorized sampling pump, and calibration kits for each gas. The Toximet can operate in temperatures from –5 to 45°C. Sensor life is 12 months for O_2 and 2 years for toxic gas cells.

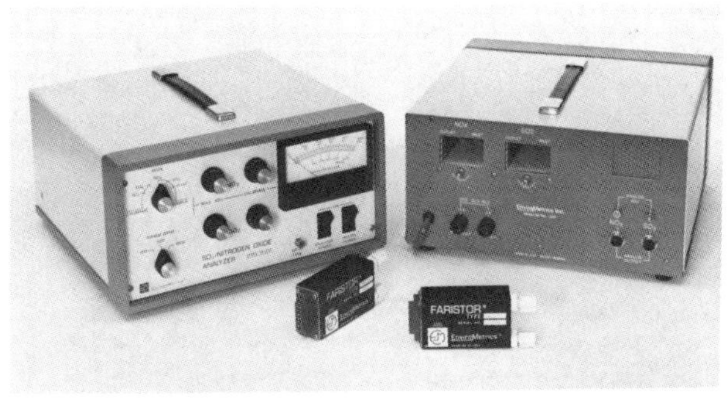

INSTRUMENT 19-2-13. Series 300 Air Pollution Analyzers.

19-2-16. Ethylene Oxide Meter

Environmental Sensors Co.

The Ethylene Oxide Meter is a pocket-sized instrument that can measure ethylene oxide in hospitals, medical product manufacturing, and chemical processing industries. The instrument uses an electrochemical cell, where the working electrode of the cell is maintained at a fixed potential versus a reference electrode. The electrode is a gas diffusion type in which the ethylene oxide diffusing through a porous membrane is electrochemically oxidized. An active catalyst is bonded to a porous Teflon membrane that serves as a physical support and diffusion barrier. The output is governed by Faraday's Law and mass transport of ethylene oxide to the reaction surface. Operating temperature is 20 to 35°C.

19-2-17. Series G3000 Personal Monitors

GfG Gas Electronics, Inc.

The G3000 Series toxic monitors are hand-held, lightweight monitors available for CO (Microco®) and H_2S (Microtox®). Both the Microco and Microtox utilize diffusion input electrochemical cells. The cells are designed to last 1–2 years with little maintenance. A steel mesh diffusion screen and a Teflon membrane protect the unit from dust and splash water. The rechargeable, sintered metal Ni-Cd battery pack powers the unit for over 100 hrs of continuous operation on one charge. Both units use a three-chamber, 8-mm, high digital display. Operating temperature for both units is 0 to 53°C; response time is 15 seconds (T_{90}).

19-2-18. Polytector Personal Multigas Monitor

GfG Gas Electronics, Inc.

The Polytector combines three sensors into one hand-held, personal monitor. The monitor offers the option of diffusion sampling or the use of a continuous diaphragm pump. Several standard versions are available ranging from a three-channel gas detector to an atmospheric monitor and datalogger. The detection principle varies with the application requested; e.g., electrochemical for O_2, H_2S, and CO; catalytic combustion for methane or combustibles; N-type thermocouple sensor for temperature; and a thin film polymer for humidity. A variety of features are available, including automatic datalogging capabilities with 8K of RAM, automatic calibration and zeroing, clock and alarm functions, automatic operating mode, interfaceable with IBM PC, backup power supply, and continuous update of software capabilities. All units are housed in polyamid 12, crack-resistant plastic. Operating temperature for all units is 0 to 53°C. Optical/acoustic alarm system features four-character, 8-mm digital display. Response times vary from 1 (CH_4) to 15 seconds (CO).

19-2-19. Model CO260 Carbon Monoxide Monitor
Industrial Scientific Corporation

The CO260 Carbon Monoxide Monitor carries Mine Safety and Health Administration (MSHA) approval and is suitable for any work environment in which CO is a potential hazard. When equipped with an optional sampling pump and a length of flexible tubing, the CO260 also can take remote air samples of enclosed or confined areas prior to entry. The CO260 utilizes a diffusion-type electrochemical sensor. The digital LCD indicates CO concentrations over the range of 1 to 1999 ppm. Other features include audible and visual alarms for CO and low battery condition, replaceable alkaline batteries that provide 2400 hrs of continuous (non-alarm) operation, backlighting of display for low-light operation, a dust-tight stainless steel case, and many flexible accessories. Operating temperature range is –10 to 40°C.

19-2-20. TMX-410 Multigas Monitor
Industrial Scientific Corp.

The TMX-410 monitors for combustible gases, O_2, and toxic gases and is applicable for use in ambient air monitoring or confined space entry. The TMX-410 can also be upgraded for industrial hygiene applications by installation of a hygiene board that calculates STEL and TWA readings. Electrochemical sensors are used to measure toxic gases and oxygen, whereas combustible gases are measured using a catalytic, diffusion-type sensor. Features of the TMX-410 include audible and visual alarms and a rechargeable battery pack with a life of 10 hrs for continuous operation. Operating temperature: –15 to 40°C. Relative humidity range: 15% to 90%, noncondensing.

19-2-21. Portable Gas Analyzers, Series 1000
Interscan Corporation

The Series 1000 operates on the electrochemical voltammetric sensor principle and is designed for ambient portable survey analysis or fixed, round-the-clock use. The Interscan sensor is a leak-proof, two-electrode sensor, with a gel matrix inside the sensor that emits a free-floating electrolyte. Linearity: ±1% of full scale. Zero drift: ±1% of full scale (in 24 hrs, this is equilibrated and at a constant temperature with sensor properly maintained). Span drift: less than ±2% of full scale (24 hrs, equilibrated and at a constant temperature with sensor properly maintained). Lag time: less than 1 second. Rise time: 20 seconds to 90% of final value or better. Fall time: 20 seconds to 10% of original value or better.

19-2-22. Toxic Gas Dosimeters, Series 5000
Interscan Corporation

The Series 5000 dosimeters are available for monitoring CO, NO_2, H_2S, SO_2, and Cl_2 over a range of up to 10 times the respective TLV. The dosimeters provide alarm features and stored 1-min average concentrations values. The dosimeters utilize a diffusion electrochemical voltammetric sensor. The sensor is a leak-proof, two-electrode sensor, with a gel matrix inside the sensor that emits a free-floating electrolyte. The sample diffuses across a membrane into the sensor where the analog signal is converted to a digital format. One-min averages are computed and stored in random access memory. Nondestructive readout of the data is accomplished by plugging the dosimeter into a Metrosonics Metroreader where a variety of data is printed out. Rise time: 20 seconds to 90% of final value (or better). Fall time: 20 seconds to 10% of original value. Zero drift: ±1.0% of full scale (24 hrs). Span drift: ±1.0% of full scale (24 hrs).

19-2-23. PhD Gas Detector
McNeill International

The PhD and Cannonball® are gas detectors that can monitor up to four gases (O_2, combustible gas, and specific toxic gases) simultaneously. Features include supertwist LCD that automatically lights up in the dark and a built-in memory circuit that allows viewing of data on the screen in the field or downloading to a PC for analyzing, storing, or printing a hard copy. The PhD is classified as intrinsically safe in hazardous locations Class I, Groups A, B, C, and D.

19-2-24. Toxilog Toxic Gas Detectors
McNeill International

The Toxilog gas detectors are small personal monitors for the detection of toxic gases in applications where low cost, ease of use, and durability are prime considerations. The Toxilog is microprocessor controlled, which allows choice of alarms for ceiling values, STELs, or TWAs. It also allows the downloading of data

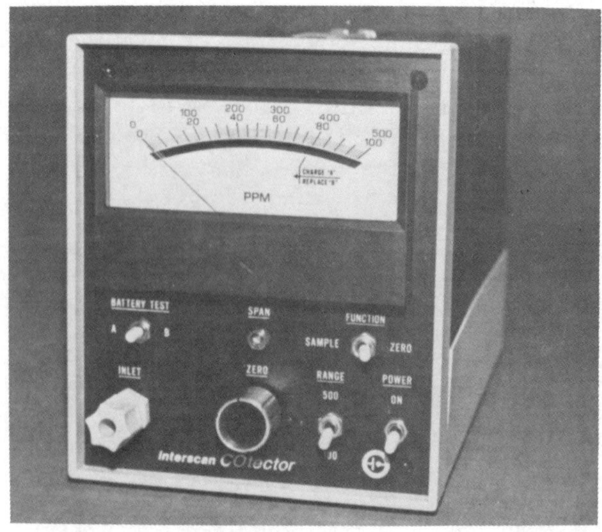

INSTRUMENT 19-2-21. Portable Gas Analyzers, Series 1000.

to a PC. All Toxilog monitors are shipped complete with sensor, calibration adapter, belt clip, a lanyard, and an alligator clip. The Toxilog is intrinsically safe for use in hazardous locations Class I, Groups A, B, C, and D.

19-2-25. Mark II Formaldemeter

MDA Scientific, Inc.

The Mark II Formaldemeter is a direct-reading instrument designed to measure formaldehyde concentrations below OSHA's new STEL. The Formaldemeter detects and measures concentrations from 0.3 to 99.9 ppm and is designed for in-plant screening and surveys. The instrument is compact, portable, and easy to operate with just the push of a button to display formaldehyde levels for compliance purposes. Accuracy at the low ppm levels is ±15%. The Formaldemeter operates from a standard 9-V battery and weighs under 7 oz. The instrument is calibrated using a convenient field kit.

19-2-26. Monitox Personal Alarms

MDA Scientific, Inc.

The Monitox Personal Alarms are pocket-sized monitors that are available for a variety of toxic contaminants. The units are available in digital readout/alarm and alarm only modes. The alarms can be coupled with the Chronotox Data Acquisition System to provide exposure documentation over time. The Monitox utilizes a diffusion gel-type electrochemical sensor. Sophisticated circuitry allows enhanced stability, sensitivity, and reproducibility while minimizing zero drift. Many features are available with the Monitox system, including a variety of alarm configurations, battery level indicator, easy calibration with the gas generator system, and long sensor life. Operating temperature range is 0 to 45°C; low temperature option for operation down to –30°C is available. Gas generator's power source is a 9-V alkaline battery, whose life is 800 functional checks.

INSTRUMENT 19-2-25. Mark II Formaldemeter.

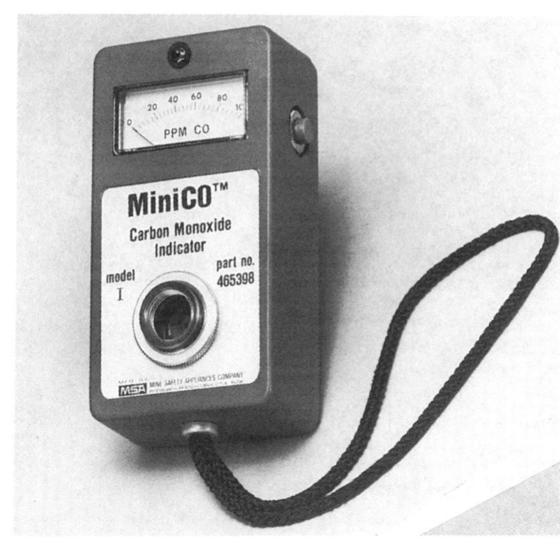

INSTRUMENT 19-2-29. MiniCO™ IV Carbon Monoxide Indicators.

19-2-27. Models 60, 70, 80, and 90 Personal Toxic Gas Monitors

Metrosonics, Inc.

The Models 60, 70, 80, and 90 are compact, hand-held instruments designed to measure ambient air concentrations of CO, SO_2, NO_x, and H_2S, respectively. Three operation modes are available: diffusion mode for area sampling, continuous mode that draws approximately 1000 cm^3/min with a probe connected, and cycling mode where the pump operates for 2 out of every 30 min. Power is supplied by AA rechargeable Ni-Cad batteries that can operate 8 hrs continuous or 24 hrs with the pump off. The electrochemical sensors have a typical life of 1–2 years.

19-2-28. Series PM-7000 Personal Toxic Gas Monitors

Metrosonics, Inc.

The PM-7000 uses electrochemical sensors to detect CO, H_2S, SO_2, Cl_2, NO_2, and NO for personal protection. The sensors utilize capillary diffusion barrier technology, which results in a direct response to volume concentration. The sensors are also cable mounted and can be clipped to clothing for readings taken in the breathing zone. Visual and ear piece audible alarms can be set for two user-selected gas concentrations. The PM-7000 can operate 720 hrs on a 9-V alkaline battery. Operating temperature: –5 to 40°C. Response to 90% of final reading ranges from 30 to 90 seconds, depending on gas.

19-2-29. MiniCO™ IV Carbon Monoxide Indicators

Mine Safety Appliances Company

The MSA MiniCO™ IV Carbon Monoxide Indicators are pocket-sized devices for measuring CO concentra-

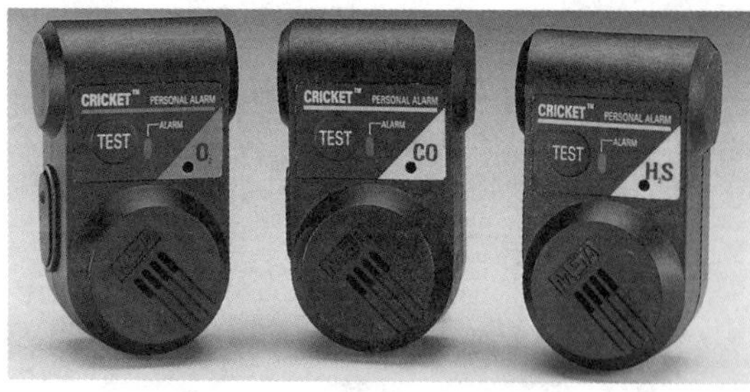

INSTRUMENT 19-2-30. Cricket Personal Alarms.

tions in ambient air. They operate on the principle of an electrochemical polarographic sensor cell. In operation, air samples diffuse through a gas porous membrane and a sintered metal disc to enter a chamber within the cell. The cell electrooxidizes CO to CO_2 in proportion to the partial pressure in the chamber, and the resulting signal is amplified and temperature compensated to drive the meter. An adapter with aspirator bulb, using standard MSA sampling lines, is available for remote sampling. The units are battery powered. The alarm set point is adjustable over the range of 25 to 500 ppm. All models have ±2% precision and accuracy, 90% response time in 30 seconds, a span drift less than 2% full scale/day, and zero drift less than 1% full scale/day. MiniCO indicators can be field-calibrated using the MSA Calibration Check Kit, Model R. Common interferents include SO_2, H_2S, NO_2, ethyl alcohol, and H_2.

19-2-30. Cricket Personal Alarms

Mine Safety Appliances Co.

The Cricket Personal Alarms are very lightweight, weighing less than 3 oz and can be worn clipped to a pocket, belt, lapel, or hard hat for hands-free operation. The instrument is only 1.25 × 3 × 2 in. in size. The Cricket series of personal alarms are miniature, battery-powered instruments designed to provide users with an inexpensive yet dependable way to monitor for O_2 deficiency, CO, or H_2S. The instruments operate continuously and sound an alarm if levels in the environment exceed preset levels (for CO and H_2S) or fall below a preset level (for O_2).

19-2-31. MSTox 8600 Personal Toxic Gas Monitor

MST Measurement Systems, Inc.

The MSTox uses an electrochemical sensor to detect toxic gases for personal protection. Audible and visual alarms can be field adjusted to activate at chosen "warning" and "alert" levels for a specific gas. The 8600 can also be used with an optical earphone or vibrating alarm for use in areas with high noise levels. Three different power supplies are available: a disposable pack that meets applicable intrinsic safety standards, a rechargeable pack that can be recharged 1000 times before needing replacement, and a J-Series pack available in general merchandise stores and intended for use in areas not requiring intrinsic safety. Battery life is approximately 2500 hrs.

19-2-32. ECOLYZER Portable Carbon Monoxide Monitor

National Draeger, Inc.

The Series 2000 ECOLYZER Portable Carbon Monoxide Monitor utilizes electrochemical oxidation at a potential-controlled, Teflon-bonded diffusion electrode for detection. Stability: noncontinuous (spot checking)—typical spot checking operation during a work day, signal decay <1%/24 hrs over the life of the instrument; continuous—signal decays by <1.5%/24 hrs over the first 25 days and <1%/24 hrs subsequently. Response time: 25 seconds. Precision and accuracy: 1.0% full scale. Sampling rate: 700 cm^3/min. Readout mode: meter (110 div. full scale) and recorder.

19-2-33. Personal Carbon Monoxide Monitor

National Draeger, Inc.

The pocket-sized ECOLYZER Personal Carbon Monoxide Monitor for continuous monitoring of CO is designed for the personal protection of workers entering areas where there may be significant accumulations and sudden releases of high concentrations of gas. The monitor features an adjustable stroboscopic visual alarm as well as an audible alarm. The unit employs a diffusion sensor utilizing a three-electrode, electrochemical detection principle. Rise time: <60 seconds to 90% of signal. Accuracy: 5% of reading or ±1.0 ppm. Span drift: 2% of reading per day or 2 ppm. Zero drift: <5 ppm/day. Operating temperature range: 0 to 40°C. Relative humidity range: 5% to 90%.

19-2-34. ENOLYZER Model 7100

National Draeger, Inc.

The ENOLYZER Model 7100 is a portable, direct-reading instrument for simultaneous and separate determination of NO and NO_2. The unit may be operated by rechargeable Ni-Cd batteries or line current. The instrument sensor utilizes an electrochemical reaction at potential-controlled, Teflon-bonded diffusion electrodes. Response time: 90% NO, <5 seconds; 90% NO_2, <30 seconds. Precision and accuracy: ±1% full scale for NO; ±2% full scale for NO_2. Stability: noncontinuous (spot checking)—typical spot checking operation during a work day, NO and NO_2 signal decay <1%/24 hrs.

19-2-35. Dualarm, Trialarm, Quadalarm, and Multi-Pac Portable Multigas Monitors

National Draeger, Inc.

These multigas instruments are designed to monitor for explosive gases, O_2, CO, and H_2S in confined space entry applications or protection of workers in other potentially hazardous areas. Sensors include poison-resistant Pellister for explosives with typical life of 24 months, galvanic fuel cell for O_2 with typical life of 12 months, and 3-electrode electrochemical for CO and H_2S with typical life of 18 months. Response time to 90% concentration: 5–20 seconds for explosives; 5–25 seconds for O_2; and 5–60 seconds for CO and H_2S. Operating temperature: –20 to 40°C. Operating relative humidity: 5% to 95%. Alarms are visual and audible (85dB at 1 ft). Battery life is 8–12 hrs, continuous use.

19-2-36. EXOTOX Triple Gas Monitor

Neotronics

The EXOTOX Monitor offers the capability of monitoring O_2, combustible gases, and CO or H_2S in a single portable monitor. This monitor is specially designed for gas monitoring prior to entry into confined spaces and to give continuous protection to the individual while in the confined space. The EXOTOX utilizes electrochemical sensors for O_2, CO, and H_2S and low power Pellisters for combustible gases. The sample enters the instrument by diffusion or can be aspirated from a confined source to the instrument. Sensor response can be read from an LCD display or via audible or visual alarms. Features include a built-in elapsed time display, computed TWAs and STELs, full RF protection, fast sensor response, minimal drift, small size, and light weight. Operating temperatures: –15 to 50°C. Storage temperature: –20 to 55°C. Humidity: 0% to 100% (noncondensing). Drift 0.6% to 1.5% over 200 days. Digital LCD readout: 20 × 38 mm. Battery life: approximately 10 hrs per charge.

INSTRUMENT 19-2-34. ENOLYZER Model 7100.

19-2-37. NEOTOX Pocket Personal Monitors

Neotronics

The NEOTOX monitors offer individual, lightweight, pocket-sized protection against the hazards of O_2 deficiency and enrichment, CO, and H_2S. The monitor incorporates a visual LCD display and lockable alarms in an intrinsically safe unit that fits in the pocket. The NEOTOX line utilizes the same electrochemical sensors incorporated in the EXOTOX for O_2, CO, and H_2S. Features include a three-digit, top-mounted LCD; water-tight membrane switches; visual and audible alarms; low battery indication; full RF protection; belt clip for easy carrying; water- and dust-proof design; and fast sensor response. Units meet all international intrinsic safety standards. All monitors provide a 6-mm LCD digital display. Total drift for 200 days is between 0.06% and 1.5%. All are powered by 9-V dry batteries which have a life span of 200–300 hrs, depending on the monitor used.

19-2-38. Minigas Multigas Monitor

Neotronics

The Minigas is an intrinsically safe, pocket-sized portable gas monitor that can be used for confined space entry, spot checks, or continuous monitoring in hazardous areas. Models are available to monitor for one, two, or three of the following gases: flammable gas, O_2, CO, or H_2S. The Minigas features a water- and dust-resistant, die-cast metal case with RFI protection, interchangeable alkali dry cell or Ni-Cad battery pack with a low battery warning indicating when the battery is 30 min from exhaustion, and instantaneous audible and visual TWA and STEL alarms. Operating time: 8 hrs on Ni-Cad battery. Operating temperature: 0 to 40°C.

19-2-39. OTOX® 2002/2003 Carbon Monoxide Monitors

Neotronics

The OTOX® 2002/2003 monitors utilize an electrochemical sensor and can be used to detect CO in compressed air/respiratory panels or as an area monitor. The OTOX® features digital displays, two internal quick-set open/closed relays, and either 110- or 12-V power supplies. The battery can operate the instrument for 72 hrs continuously. Operating temperature: –15 to 50°C for the 2002 and 0 to 40°C for the 2003.

19-2-40. Ozone Recorder, Model 03T

Ozone Research and Equipment Corporation

This recorder is designed for atmospheric ozone measurement and ozone measurement in control rooms, laboratories, production plants, warehouses, etc. Ozone measurement is based on the iodometric principle incorporated into an electronic loop feedback servo system that allows continuous measurement of ozone concentrations to as low as 3 ppm. The Model 03T samples at the rate of 4000 cm^3/min, allowing greater unit accuracy and less dependence on slight changes in sample air flow. The instrument will operate for 3-day intervals without change in operation solution, allowing unattended operation over weekends and at night. Response time: normal atmospheric change, 90% of true value in 2 min. Chart speed: 1 in./hr. Chart period: 31 days. Options: alarm circuit and meter for remote signal.

19-2-41. Ozone Measurement Instrument, Model MSA-3
Ozone Research & Equipment Corporation

This portable instrument is used to determine ozone in air or O_2 for applications such as in ozone test chambers, other confined sources, process streams, and in the atmosphere. The principle of measurement is based on the quantitative release of iodine from a buffered solution of potassium iodine in the titration with sodium thiosulfate of the released iodine. The Model MSA-3 employs the electrometric endpoint method, whereby the endpoint of the titration is indicated on a meter. In operation, the instrument is supplied with potassium iodide and sodium thiosulfate solution. With this method, there is no iodine volatilization factor because there is a fixed quantity of thiosulfate, and time (3–5 min) is the only variable. The measurement period ends upon the appearance of iodine, which is sensed electrometrically. Other features include a dry vane vacuum pump and Pyrex-unitized construction of the reaction assembly with integral platinum electrodes and spray jet. Sampling rate: 3000 cm^3/min.

19-2-42. Sulfur Dioxide Analyzer/Recorder
Process Analyzers, Inc.

The Titrilog II is an automatic instrument for the determination of oxidizable sulfur compounds such as H_2S, SO_2, mercaptans, thiophene, and organic sulfides and disulfides. This instrument can be used for measurement in the atmosphere, in gas streams, and in stack gases. The measurement cell consists of an electrolyte containing potassium bromide from which free bromine is being generated electrolytically. In addition to the generating electrodes, there is a set of electrodes sensitive to free bromine. The potential of these electrodes varies with the concentration of free bromine in the solution. To distinguish between some of the different sulfur compounds, liquid absorptive filters are furnished as an accessory. These filters absorb one or more of the compounds of interest, enabling their concentration to be determined by difference. A programming system will route the sample through either of the filters, bypass the filters, and establish a zero level on an automatic repetitive cycle.

19-2-43. S100 Series Portable Gas Indicators
Scott Aviation

The S100 Series are intrinsically safe, portable instruments that can be applied to area monitoring, confined space entry, or personal monitoring. Instruments are available that can monitor for one, two, or three of the following: combustible gas, O_2, H_2S, and CO. Features of the S100 Series include dual low-battery alarms, liquid crystal display that illuminates for low ambient light conditions, and audible alarms for each measured variable. The S100 Series has memory capability to store the highest combustible gas concentration, peak CO or H_2S concentration, or the lowest O_2 measurement. Response time to 63% change: 10 seconds to LEL, 20 seconds for O_2, 45 seconds for H_2S, and 25 seconds for CO. Operating temperature ranges are –10 to 60°C for LEL and 0 to 40°C for the others.

19-2-44. Portable Gas Monitors
Sensidyne, Inc.

Sensidyne markets a wide range of pocket-sized personal monitors (Mini Monitors), portable survey monitors (Series SS2000 and SS4000 for semiconductor gases), and a variety of fixed gas detection systems. The Mini Monitors and Series SS2000 monitors utilize diffusion electrochemical cells specifically designed for each gas to be detected. The lightweight (7 oz), pocket-sized Mini Monitors feature a continuous LED light-illuminated digital display, dual alarm set points, intrinsically safe design, replaceable batteries, RFI/EMI protection, and easy calibration. Additional features on the hand-held Series SS2000 include long-life sensors (3 years expected life), rechargeable batteries, optional continuous operation from AC power, triple alarm system, and ability to withstand temperature extremes. Response time: <20 seconds for Mini Monitors, 10–15 seconds for SS2000, <30 seconds for SS4000. Battery life: over 100 hrs for Mini Monitors, 20 hrs for SS2000, 35 hrs for SS4000. Humidity range: 5% to 95% for Mini Monitors and SS2000; 20% to 90% for SS4000. Temperature range: 0 to 40°C for all monitors.

19-2-45. Portable Flue Gas Analyzer
Teledyne Analytical Instruments

The Model 990 is a completely portable, battery-powered flue gas analyzer designed to rapidly monitor the O_2 and CO content of a combustion process. When these two measurements are combined for the purpose of maximizing fuel-burning efficiencies, boilers and heaters can be fine-tuned for optimum air/fuel ratios.

The CO trace measurement is accomplished by an electrochemical sensor (6-month warranty). The sensor output is directly proportional to the CO concentration. Zero and span drifts are less than 2% in 24 hrs. A 90% of full-scale response is attained in 30 seconds or less. Operating temperature: 0 to 50°C. O_2 analysis is accomplished with Teledyne's Micro-Fuel Cell (1-year warranty), which produces an electrical signal that is directly proportional and specific to the O_2 concentration in the flue gas. A 90% of full-scale response is attained in 13 seconds or less.

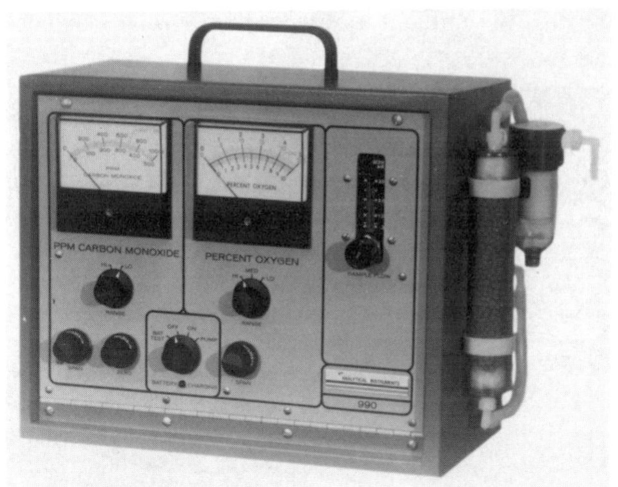
INSTRUMENT 19-2-45. Portable Flue Gas Analyzer.

Coulometric Analyzers

19-3-1. EA-1 Gas Analyzer

Adsistor Technology, Inc.

The EA-1 Gas Analyzer is a portable instrument for detection of flammable and nonflammable gases in the ppm and percent LEL ranges. The EA-1 uses the Cold Sensor™ element, which does not burn vapor to detect gas. The Cold Sensor element operates on the principle of adsorption, the phenomenon that attracts and holds a molecule to the surface of a solid. The measure of this attractive force is known as the van der Waals' constant for the specific molecule. Gaseous diffusion carries the traces of toxic or explosive gas into contact with the adsorptive material in the sensor, changing the sensor's electrical characteristics. The sensor's monitoring system is adjustable to the level of detection desired from small concentrations on the ppm scale (toxic gases) to a percent of the lower explosive limit (combustible gases). The system can transfer data to terminals or computers. Monitoring or alarm systems can be used to trigger corrective control systems.

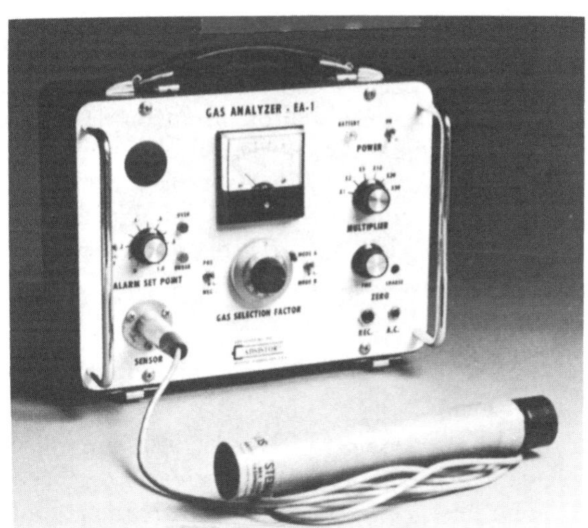
INSTRUMENT 19-3-1. EA-1 Gas Analyzer.

19-3-2. H_2S Sentox

Bacharach, Inc.

This instrument is a diffusion instrument used to detect H_2S gas in the range of 0 to 50 ppm. The H_2S Sentox operates on the oxidation-reduction principle. When exposed to H_2S gas, the metal oxide sensor is reduced and then returns to its normal oxide state when returned to an O_2 atmosphere. This change alters its ability to conduct electricity, which is proportional to the concentration of H_2S.

19-3-3. J-W Oxygen Indicators

Bacharach, Inc.

The K Series of O_2 indicators are available in various models and ranges designed to meet the need for portable, fast-response indicating devices that measure in the low and medium O_2 percentage ranges. The Model GPK is a combined O_2/combustible gas indicating detector. Model HPK is a combination O_2/combustible gas indicator similar to the Model GPK except that it has two combustible gas ranges. Both of the combination detectors are also available in Bureau of Mines-approved versions. In the Model K O_2 indicators, the sample of the atmosphere to be tested is drawn into a self-generating electrolytical cell by means of an aspirator bulb. The current produced is directly proportional to the amount of O_2. Detector cell life for all models is 6 months and the detector cells may be reactivated. The cell plugs into the instrument and may be replaced or reactivated in a matter of minutes. In the combination instruments, the combustible gas detector components are the same as those described under SNIFFER Series Combustible Gas Indicators (19-10-4).

19-3-4. SNIFFER® 103 Portable Oxygen Deficiency Monitor

Bacharach, Inc.

The SNIFFER® 103 O_2 deficiency monitor is a lightweight, compact unit for use in entering into confined areas such as vessels, tanks, manholes, silos, pits, tunnels, shafts, or any other possible O_2-deficient areas. The SNIFFER 103 uses a diffusion electrochemical cell for O_2. The combustible model uses a catalytic (platinum bead) sensor. The sensor response is read on an LCD or it can trigger an audible or visual (LED) alarm. Other features include continuous operation for 10 hrs, low battery indicator, continuous safety (no on/off switch), intrinsically safe, 9-V alkaline battery operation, and a convenient belt/pocket clip.

Continuous operating time: 10 hrs at 25°C. Charging time: 1416 hrs. RFI rejection: no alarms will trigger with 5W radio at 2 ft. Audible alarms include 1-Hz pulse rate for high combustibles, 3-Hz pulse rate for low O_2, and a steady tone for low battery or sensor failure. Visual displays include an alarm symbol for both high combustibles and low O_2, a broken battery symbol indicating low battery, a 100% LEL display, and a 0% O_2 display.

19-3-5. Model 946 Trace Acid/Base Monitoring System
Beckman Instruments, Inc.

The Beckman Model 946 Trace Acid/Base Monitoring System continuously measures trace acid or base concentrations in a variety of process streams. Applications include 1) HCl in vinyl chloride monomer product, 2) HCl in catalytic reformer recycle hydrogen, 3) trace acids in various hydrocarbon streams, and 4) trace ammonia leakage. The system combines the gas or vaporized liquid sample with a metered flow of demineralized water using precise flow control. The gas/liquid mixture flows to a separator where the gas phase is exhausted at the top, and the liquid phase is drained out the bottom into a stainless steel pH flow chamber that measures the pH of the water. The system measures any pH shifts and correlates them to ppm to continuously monitor trace quantities of acids or bases in process streams.

Response: 90% in 3 min. Sample flow rate: liquid from 10 to 25 cm^3/min to vaporizer; gas from 5 to 10 L/min; demineralized water flow rate from 100 to 200 cm^3/min. Quality of water from 1 to 10 megaohm/cm^3 specific resistance (1 to 0.1 microohm/cm specific conductivity). Materials in contact with sample: stainless steel, glass, Teflon, Viton, and PVC. Sample temperature compensation: automatic, from 0 to 100°C. Ambient humidity limits: up to 99% RH. Ambient temperature limits: 0 to 50°C.

19-3-6. Model OM-11EA/OM-11 Oxygen Analyzers
Beckman Instruments, Inc.

The Beckman Models OM-11EA and OM-11 are designed for monitoring vehicle emissions and other applications requiring precise measurement of rapid changes in the concentration of gaseous O_2. They are frequently used in emission measurement consoles and other multiparameter analytical systems. The analyzers use electrochemical technology for polar-graphic O_2 analysis. The Models OM-11EA/OM-11 utilize a factory-charged, factory-sealed, disposable O_2 sensor. The sensor has automatic temperature compensation at both normal and high temperatures. Designed principally for engine exhaust analysis, the Model OM-11EA is suited for console mounting. For applications requiring a remote sensor, the Model OM-11 has a 15-ft interconnection cable that allows the small, compact pick-up head to be remotely located in the most advantageous position.

Speed of response: 100 ms for fast mode (90%). Zero drift: ±0.5% over 24 hrs. Span drift: ±1.0% over 24 hrs. Noise: <0.2% peak-to-peak. Linearity: ±0.2%. Outputs: 10 mV, 100 mV, or 5 VDC. Sample flow rate: 0.14–0.28 m^3/hr (2.36–4.7 L/min). Sensor control temperature: 40°C ± 1°C. Ambient temperature limits: 4.4 to 35°C. Ambient humidity limits: 0% to 95% RH.

19-3-7. Ozone Analyzer, Model 950
Beckman Instruments, Inc.

The Beckman Ozone Analyzer is designed for continuous monitoring of photochemical oxidants. The chemiluminescent method used is based on the principle that ozone reacts with ethylene to produce a light emission. Selectable recorder outputs of 10 mV, 100 mV, 1 V, and 5 V are available by means of a selector switch. During operation, ethylene is directed to the detector at a flow rate of 10–20 cm^3/min. A safety valve is incorporated on the ethylene flow and is designed to shut off the ethylene flow in the event of power failure.

Air samples are introduced at a constant flow rate to the detector by an internal pump and flow control system. A standard for zero calibration is obtained by passing ambient air over a chemical scrubber to remove all traces of ozone. An optical ozone generator, which provides a convenient means of providing span checks, is available. The air flow across the ozone generator provides a known level of ozone to the detector, plus the auxiliary flow permits correlations with the wet chemical KI method. Response time: 90% in 3 seconds. Zero and span drift: less than 1% per day. Operating period: 7 days or more. Noise: 0.5%. Operating temperature: 4 to 38°C.

19-3-8. NO, NO_2, NO_x Monitor, Model 952
Beckman Instruments, Inc.

The Beckman NO, NO_2, NO_x Monitor is used to monitor the ambient atmosphere where the oxides of

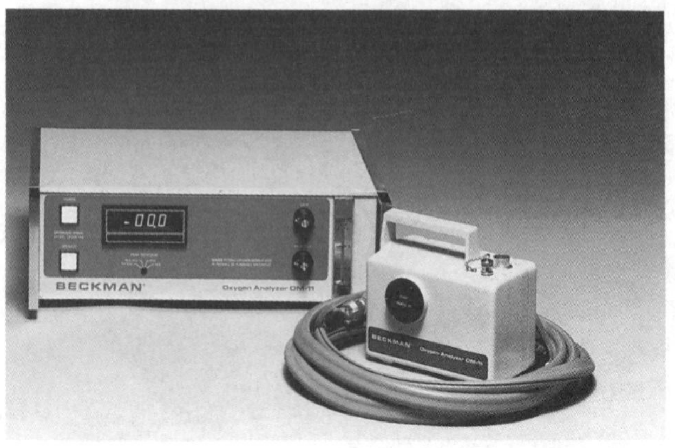

INSTRUMENT 19-3-6. Model OM-11EA/OM-11 Oxygen Analyzers.

nitrogen concentration range between 0.1 and 10 ppm. The chemiluminescent detection principle incorporated in the Model 952 is based on the reaction of NO with O_3 to produce NO_2, about 10% of which is electronically excited to a higher energy state. Return of the NO_2 molecule to its ground state results in emission of ultraviolet light. This light energy is measured by means of a photomultiplier and electronic circuitry and is directly proportional to the concentration of NO present in the sample. NO_x is determined by converting the NO_2 to NO, free of interference from other atmospheric compounds, and subsequent determination of the chemiluminescent reaction. NO_2 is determined by the electronic subtraction of NO from NO_x. Continuous outputs of 10 mV, 100 mV, 1 V, and 5 V are available for recording, telemetry, etc., of each parameter (i.e., NO, NO_x, and NO_2). In the flow control system, ambient air is employed for ozone generation by means of a pump and a UV lamp. Response time: 90% in 3 seconds. Zero and span drift: less than 1% per day. Operating period: 7 days or more. Noise: 0.5%. Operating temperature: 4 to 38°C.

19-3-9. Model OX630 Oxygen Analyzer

Engineering Systems and Designs

The OX630 is a portable unit that utilizes a maintenance-free galvanic electrode to measure atmospheric oxygen levels from 0% to 100%. The electrode has an expected life of 3–5 years at 25°C, 1 atmosphere pressure, and a concentration of 20.9% O_2. The OX630 is sold in a kit containing the meter, an electrode on a 5-ft cable, screwdriver for calibration, and a carrying case. Electrodes up to 100 ft can be manufactured upon request. Operating temperature range: 0 to 40°C. Response time: 95% of final reading in 30 seconds. Power: 9-V battery. Calibration: 20.9% in air.

19-3-10. Personal Oxygen Monitor, Model OX-80

GasTech, Inc.

The GasTech Model OX-80 Personal Oxygen Monitor is a pocket-sized, lightweight instrument designed to continuously monitor O_2 and sound an alarm at a preset level of 19.5%. A pushbutton activates a digital readout. The top-mounted sensor may also be used remotely for tank entry testing. The OX-80 O_2 sensor is a diffusion electrochemical cell in which O_2 produces a chemical reaction directly proportional to the sampled atmosphere. The electrochemical cell is guaranteed for 6 months of operation before reactivation. Standard accessories include a plug-in battery charger, belt clip, and wrist strap; 15-in. and 30-in. O_2 cell extension cables and lapel-mount repeater buzzer are optional.

19-3-11. Microox® Personal Oxygen Deficiency Monitor

GfG Gas Electronics, Inc.

The Microox® is a pocket-sized monitor with an easy-to-read digital display and optical/acoustical alarm to warn of O_2-deficient conditions. It is Model 3012 in the G3000 Series, which are in small, stainless steel cases and operate over 100 hrs continuously between battery charges. The Microox uses a fuel cell sensor and is available with a remote 25-ft sensor, an adjustable alarm, rechargeable batteries, and a stainless steel case that is dust and waterproof. Temperature: 0 to 53.3°C. Response time: T_{90} = 10 seconds. Cross sensitivity: partial pressure chlorine. Lifespan of sensor: 9–14 months. Display: 3-character digital, 8 mm high. Gas transport: diffusion.

19-3-12. Model OX231 Oxygen Monitor

Industrial Scientific Corporation

The OX231 Oxygen Monitor is designed to be intrinsically safe and carries MSHA approval. It is suitable for any work environment in which deficient O_2 levels are a potential hazard. This battery-operated, diffusion-type instrument is recommended for use in confined spaces such as manholes, tunnels, ships' holds, storage tanks, deep vats, closed compartments, and underground installations. The OX231 utilizes a diffusion electrochemical cell that can be replaced in the field without disassembling the case. Percent O_2 is displayed on a liquid crystal readout in increments of 0.1% O_2. Replaceable alkaline batteries provide 2400 hrs of continuous operation. Other features include audible and visual alarms of low O_2 levels and low battery condition, adjustable alarm level, backlighted display for low light situations, on–off switch to prevent accidental shutoff, and dust-tight stainless steel case. Temperature range: –15 to 45°C.

19-3-13. Scen-Trio

Lumidor Safety Products

Scen-Trio is a continuous sensing device for three different categories of gases: explosive, toxic, and O_2. Both visual and audible alarms are activated when preset threshold levels have been exceeded. This portable, battery-powered, multigas detector/alarm has a rechargeable Ni-Cd battery pack and self-powered O_2 fuel cell. It is rated intrinsically safe for Class I, Division I, Groups A, B, C, and D. Scen-Trio operates with reasonable accuracy of alarm settings within the temperature range of –5 to 45°C. Humidity range: 15% to 100% RH when calibrated in 50% RH atmosphere; the device will operate at lower RH (5% to 20% RH) with good accuracy if calibrated in a dry atmosphere.

19-3-14. LP-COM-19GR Oxygen Monitor

Lumidor Safety Products/e.s.p. Inc.

The LP-COM-19GR is a hand-held O_2 deficiency monitor that features a detachable probe for remote monitoring. The monitor is suitable as a personal warning device or as a preentry monitor for confined spaces.

The LP-COM-19GR utilizes a diffusion galvanic cell for measuring percent O_2 over the range of 0% to 50%. The cell should last for 1 year (warranted for 8 months). Other features include visual and audible alarm for low O_2 concentration and low battery, battery test switch, replaceable alkaline batteries, various length probe cords, easy sensor replacement, and a belt clip. Temperature range: –5 to 40°C.

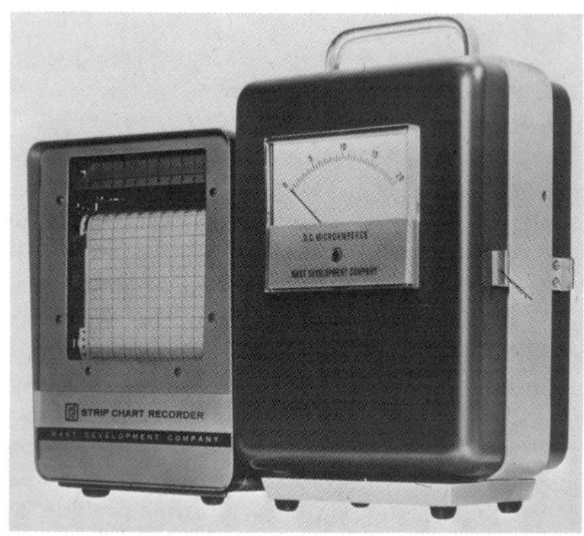

INSTRUMENT 19-3-15. Portable Ozone and Oxidant Recorders.

19-3-15. Portable Ozone and Oxidant Recorders
Mast Development Company

The Model 724-2 Ozone Meter, Model 725-11 Nitrogen Dioxide Meter, and Model 725-21 Microcoulomb Detector are portable, nonspecific electrochemical instruments that are used for the detection of O_3, NO_2, NO, Cl_2, I_2, F_2, and other strong oxidant vapors in low air concentrations. The microcoulomb sensor is used in all three instruments. Selectivity for specific oxidants is related to the concentration, pH, and composition of the electrolyte used. In the Model 724-2 Ozone Meter, the sensing of ozone in the air sample is accomplished by the oxidation-reduction of potassium iodide contained in the sensing solution. High concentrations of SO_2 negatively interfere with ozone determinations, but this interference can be eliminated by using the Model 725-30 SO_2 Filter Kit to trap the SO_2 before it enters the sensor. The microampmeters used on the Model 724-2 Ozone Meter and the Model 725-11 Nitrogen Dioxide Meter are calibrated directly in concentration units. Sampling rate: 140 cm^3/min. Rise and fall time: 1 min. Operating temperature range: 0 to 44°C. Unattended operating time: 3 days (except 30 days for Model 724-2L large reservoir ozone recorder).

19-3-16. Model 3300 Oxygen Monitor
MDA Scientific, Inc.

The Model 3300 is designed for the detection and measurement of percent O_2 in a variety of work environments. Typical applications include preentry monitoring, personal monitoring, and O_2 therapy monitoring. The Model 3300 utilizes a diffusion electrochemical cell that is stable over a wide range of temperatures and humidities. The monitor is internally compensated for temperatures over the range of 0 to 50°C. A variety of features are available, including a choice of ranges (0% to 25% or 0% to 100%), replaceable 9-V batteries, and alarm setting. Sensor charge life: approximately 1 month. Response time: 10 seconds (90% response). Battery life: approximately 300 hrs.

19-3-17. Models 8060/8061 Oxygen Deficiency Monitors
Matheson Gas Products

The 8060 and 8061 are portable oxygen monitors that can be used for monitoring of ambient air or confined space entry. The sensor is a galvanic cell that consists of a noble metal electrode, a base metal electrode, and an electrolyte in aqueous solution. In the preserve of oxygen, current flows from the noble metal electrode to the base metal electrode. Two probes are available: the 8060 has the sensor at the end of an extendable 3-ft coiled cable and the 8061 is equipped with the sensor at the end of a 16-ft cable on a spool. Response time: 2–4 seconds. Operating time: up to 20 hrs powered by 2 AA rechargeable Ni-Cad batteries. Sensor life: 18–24 months. Temperature range: 0 to 45°C.

19-3-18. Oxygen Indicator Models 245, 245R, and 245RA
Mine Safety Appliances Company

MSA Oxygen Indicators are hand-held devices for measuring atmospheric concentrations of O_2 over a range of 0% to 25%. Model 245 is designed primarily for

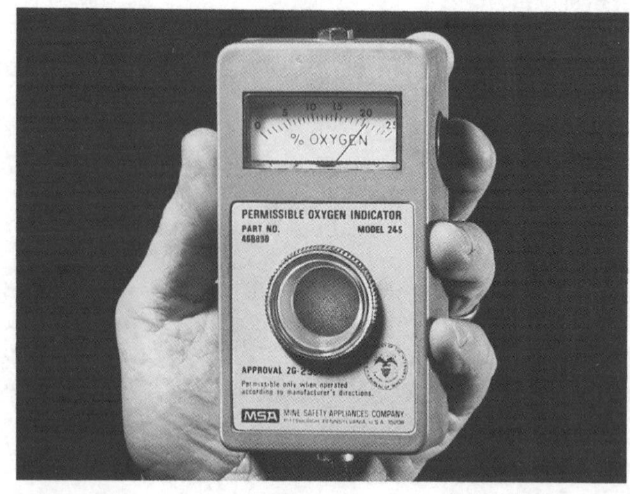

INSTRUMENT 19-3-18. Oxygen Indicator Models 245, 245R, and 245RA.

checking O_2 content in mines, and the sensor is contained in the instrument case. Models 245R and 245RA house the sensor cell in a separate plastic holder at the end of a sampling cable. These models find broader application in industrial areas where remote sampling is frequently required. The oxygen indicator detects O_2 by a galvanic sensor cell containing a gold cathode and lead anode in a basic electrolyte. In operation, O_2 diffuses through the cell face to initiate redox reactions which, in turn, generate a minute current proportional to the O_2 partial pressure. External accessories: Model 245 — adapter for tube sampling, sampling line (5 ft, with couplings, with other lengths available); Models 245R and 245RA — replacement sensor with 10-ft cable, extension cables, 50-ft lengths. Safety provisions: Model 245RA is equipped with an audio alarm that is factory set to activate when the O_2 concentration falls below 19.5%. (Alarm setpoint is adjustable internally.) Once activated, the alarm will sound continuously for up to 24 hrs until manually deactivated or until the O_2 concentration rises above alarm setpoint. Response time: 90% in less than 20 seconds. All models can be calibrated quickly with uncontaminated fresh air, 20.8% O_2.

19-3-19. Passport Personal Alarm
Mine Safety Appliances Company

The Passport is a small, lightweight, water-resistant personal alarm instrument that is capable of monitoring up to five different gases. The instrument is housed in a rugged, easy-to-carry, metal-filled polycarbonate case that is also EMI-resistant and antistatic. The instrument is simple to operate with just the push of a button. It monitors combustibles, oxygen deficiency, and up to three toxic gases (CO, H_2S, SO_2, NO, NO_2, Cl_2, HCN, HCl). An add-on low flow pump module gives the user the option of using diffusion or pumped sampling.

19-3-20. Toxgard® Indicator, Model C
Mine Safety Appliances Company

The MSA Toxgard® Indicator, Model C, is a continuous monitoring instrument for use in the detection of H_2S, HCN, and CO. The instrument operates on the principle of an electrochemical polargraphic cell that oxidizes the gas of interest in proportion to its partial pressure in the sample atmosphere. Safety provisions: tamper-resistant controls, audible and visual alarms. Response time: 50% in 30 seconds, typically 90% in 120 seconds. Span and zero drift: 1%, 1-day maximum.

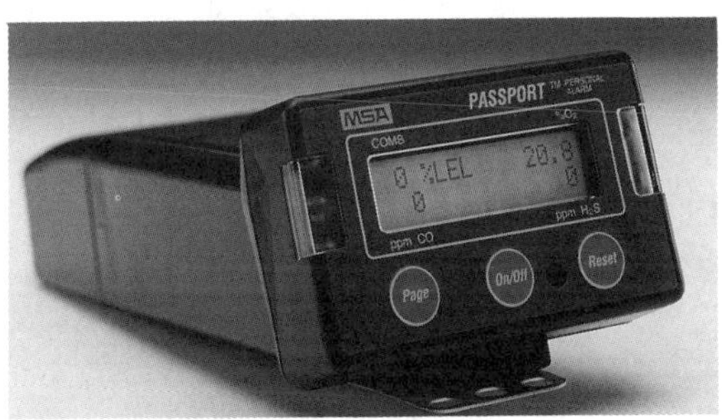

INSTRUMENT 19-3-19. Passport Personal Alarm.

INSTRUMENT 19-3-20. Toxgard® Indicator, Model C.

19-3-21. Multi-Component Monitoring System for Air Pollution
Philips Electronic Instruments

This series of instruments allows continuous, automatic field monitoring of ambient air quality. Five of the measuring modules (SO_2, NO_2, NO, CO, H_2S) use the principle of coulometry, as used for the Model PW 9700. The gas of interest is bubbled through an electrolyte and, as a result, the concentration of one of the components of the electrolyte will change. CO is measured indirectly by the iodine released when CO is passed through heated iodine pentoxide. NO is measured as NO_2 after oxidation. Selective filters ensure that each module is specific for the pollutant it is to measure. Chemiluminescence was chosen for O_3 measurements. This is specific for O_2 and depends on the emission of light by Rhodamine B when exposed to ozone.

The modules are contained in a standard steel-framed, glass-reinforced plastic case for wall or panel mounting. One telemetering module provides up to 19 channels for control and data transmission. Span drift: <2% in 24 hrs after a stabilization period; 5% for O_3. Calibration: span and zero checks can be performed remotely, controlled with built-in standard source and zero filter. Interference error: negligible for all interfering gases in the concentrations occurring in the atmosphere. Climatological influence: the specifications are given for a temperature range of 0 to 30°C. Output signal (before telemetry): 0–20 mA into 0–500 ohm. Maintenance: 3 months continuous operation without the need for service and/or maintenance.

19-3-22. Series 330 Personal Safety Oxygen Monitors

Teledyne Analytical Instruments

The Series 330 uses a disposable electrochemical cell which, in the presence of O_2, produces an output signal linear with and specific to O_2. This instrument has an integral meter readout and is applicable for use in confined space entry and occupational surveys.

Flame Ionization Detectors

19-4-1. Hydrocarbon Gas Analyzer

Columbia Scientific Corporation

The HC5000 performs real time and continuous dry analysis of hydrocarbon gases utilizing a flame ionization detector (FID). Emphasis is focused on stable and reliable performance without a source of clean combustion air required. Thermal control of sample air, hydrogen, and exhaust gas is controlled to within ±1% over 10 to 40°C ambient temperature range. It closely approximates ppm hydrocarbon molecules rather than approximate methane equivalents as provided by FIDs operating in the gas chromatograph (GC) mode. Noise: ±0.05 ppm CH_4. Lag time: <15 seconds. Rise and fall time to 90%: <30 seconds. Zero and span drift: ±0.2 ppm/day; ±0.3 ppm/3 days. Linearity: ±0.1 ppm CH_4. Selectable time constant: 1 second or 10 seconds. Operational specifications: unattended operation (no adjustment of flow or electrical systems), 7 days. Sample flow rate: approximately 200 ml/min; hydrogen flow rate: approximately 140 ml/min.

19-4-2. Organic Vapor Analyzer

Foxboro Company

The Organic Vapor Analyzer (OVA) is designed to measure trace quantities of organic materials in air using a hydrogen flame ionization detection system. It has a single logarithmically scaled readout from 1 to 100,000 ppm or with a lower maximum level, if desired. Designed for use as a portable survey instrument, it can also be readily adapted to fixed remote monitoring or mobile installations. The instrument response is read on a hand-held meter assembly or can be read using the external monitor signal. An audible detection alarm is provided; it can be preset to any desired level and has a frequency modulated tone that varies as a function of the signal level. The standard instrument includes an audible flame-out alarm, battery test indicator, and internal electronic calibration.

Standard accessories include instrument carrying and storage case, high-pressure, fuel-filling hose assembly, and AC battery charger. Response time: <2 seconds. Sample flow rate: nominally 2 L/min. Fuel supply: 75-cm^3 tank of pure hydrogen at maximum pressure of 2300 psig, fillable while in case. Service life: hydrogen supply and battery power — 8 hrs operating time, minimum. The umbilical cord is 5 ft long with connectors for electrical cable and sample hose. In-line disposable and permanent particle filters are standard; activated charcoal filters are optional.

19-4-3. Advanced Vapour Monitor — AVM

Graseby Ionics

The AVM is designed primarily as a survey monitor or a leak detector. A wide variety of toxic vapors can be monitored in ppb levels for short- or long-term periods. This rugged instrument provides real-time monitoring; data can be stored in an ancillary data logger. The hand-held unit can be operated for 5 hrs continuously from internal batteries. Some of vapors that can be detected by this radioactive ionization detector include TDI, TDA, aniline, o-toluidine, dimethyl sulfate, anesthetics, and nerve or blister agents.

19-4-4. Photoionization Analyzer

HNU Systems, Inc.

The Photoionization Analyzer is a portable analyzer used for the measurement of gases in industrial atmospheres. The sensor consists of a sealed UV light source that emits photons which are energetic enough to ionize many trace species (particularly organics) but do not ionize the major components of air such as O_2, N_2, CO, CO_2, or H_2O. The field created on an electrode drives any ions formed by adsorption of the UV light to the collector electrode where the current (proportional to concentration) is measured. This instrument consists of two separate units: a sensor and a readout, connected by a 3-ft, shielded, multiconductor cable with electrical

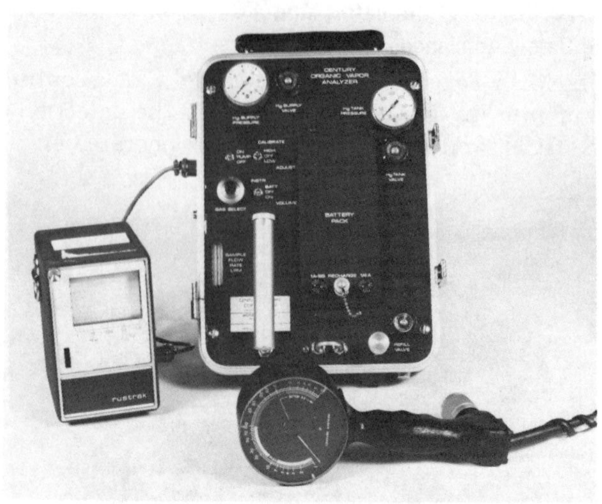

INSTRUMENT 19-4-2. Organic Vapor Analyzer.

connector. The case for the readout module is constructed of drawn aluminum. The sensor's outer body is of aluminum and engineering thermoplastic. Output signal available: 0- to 10-mV recorder jacks. Standard accessories include an AC battery charger and a 3-ft, Teflon-lined telescoping probe for sampling hard-to-reach places. Response time: <5 seconds. Operating time: minimum of 8 hrs on 12-VDC rechargeable batteries.

19-4-5. Atmosphere Monitors

Ion Track Instruments, Inc.

Three units are available from Ion Track Instruments: the Atmosphere Monitor for continuous monitoring of gas streams, the SF_6 Detector/Chromatograph for use as a tracer to detect gas system leaks, and the Leakmeter for use as an industrial leak detector designed for detection of leaks of SF_6 tracer gas or any gases that are responsive to the detector. All three units utilize an electron capture detector; the SF_6 Detector/Chromatograph includes a gas separation column. All three units sample at a rate of 250 cm^3/min and use a meter as the readout mode. The SF_6 Detector/Chromatograph is extremely specific because of the gas chromatograph column. Response time is 1 second for the Leakmeter and the Atmosphere Monitor and 15 seconds for the SF_6 Detector/Chromatograph.

19-4-6. GasCorder Portable Toxic Gas and Vapor Monitor

Mine Safety Appliances Company

The Baseline Series GasCorder Monitor is designed to detect low concentrations of volatile organic compounds (VOCs). It features both a graphic display screen and a built-in disk drive for recording data. It is designed for industrial hygiene applications, fugitive emission monitoring, or use at HazMat or remediation sites for field sampling and analysis of toxic gases, hydrocarbons, organic vapors, and other hazardous materials. It is available as either a flame-ionization detector (FID) or as a photoionization detector (PID). The GasCorder is equipped with user prompts, a flat-panel backlit LCD screen, and both alpha/numeric or trend

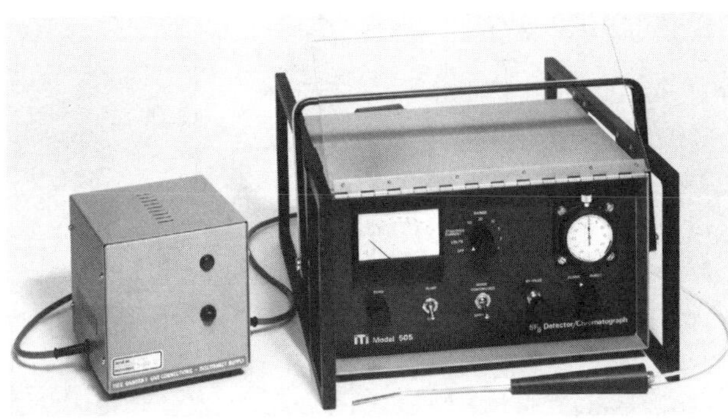

INSTRUMENT 19-4-5. Atmosphere Monitors.

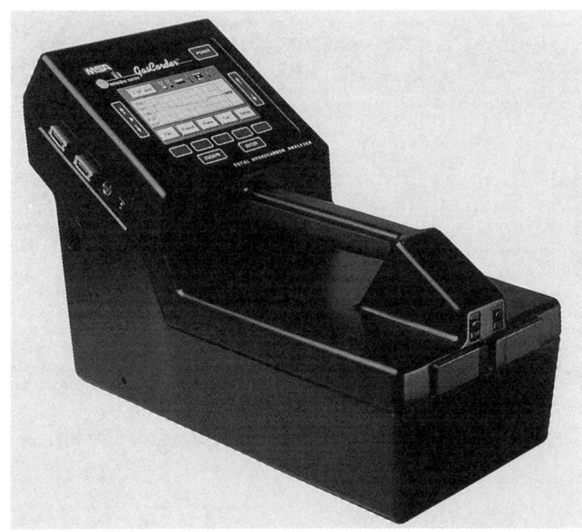

INSTRUMENT 19-4-6. GasCorder Portable Toxic Gas and Vapor Monitor.

data display. The 1.4-megabyte floppy disk records all data generated by the monitor for later review on the display, or for downloading into a PC. Monitoring parameters can be preprogrammed, and long-term unattended operation is possible with optional auto calibration module (and support gases for the FID version).

19-4-7. Photovac TIP

Photovac International, Inc.

The Photovac TIP, which stands for total ionizables present, is designed to measure any airborne contaminant that is detectable by photoionization. In operation, a small pump continuously draws sample air into an ionization chamber that is flooded with UV light. The molecules of most light permanent gases (including the air gases H_2, helium, and N_2) are unaffected because they require an ionization energy higher than that generated by the 10.6-eV lamp in order to become ionized. However, any gases or vapors in the air stream that have ionization energy levels below that generated by the lamp are ionized. Inlet flow rate: 275 ml/min. Display: 3.5-in. LCD (0–1999 counts, illuminated). Charge/discharge time: approximately 16 hrs/4 hrs; charger provided. Low battery indication: at 95% discharge. Signal outputs: 1-V full scale, analog concentration, and modulated pulse for external (optional) earphone. External power: 12 VDC, 0.4 A (TIP has internal regulation). Linearity: 0–100 ppm ± 10%; 100–1000 ppm ± 15%. Response time: 3 seconds (10% to 90% full scale, 10 ppm benzene).

19-4-8. Model 400 Hydrocarbon Analyzer

Rosemount Analytical Inc.

The Model 400 employs the FID method for use in a variety of engine exhaust applications. Its single-unit

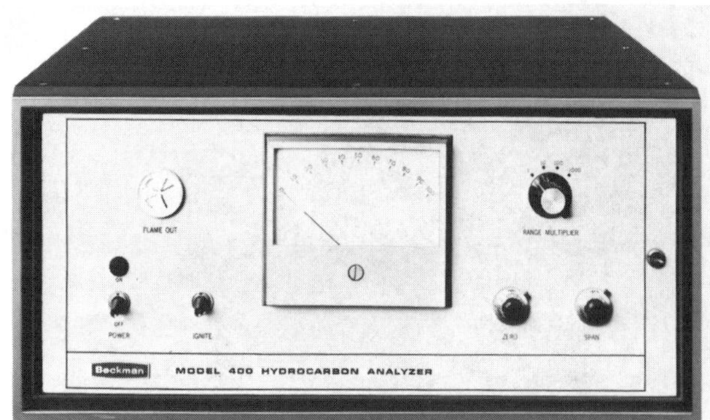

INSTRUMENT 19-4-8. Model 400 Hydrocarbon Analyzer.

case is designed for panel, rack, or bench mounting. Case design permits front, top, and rear access to simplify maintenance. Noise: less than ± 0.5% of full scale. Zero and span drift: ±1% of full scale per 24 hrs. Response time: 90% of full scale in 0.5 seconds at bypass flow rate of 3000 cm^3/min. Output: 10-mV, 100-mV, 1-V, or 5-VDC selectable is standard; 40 to 20 mA, 10 to 50 mA DC, optional. Fuel gas requirement: hydrocarbon-free air. Sample requirements: 500–3000 cm^3/min at 5–10 psig, input, depending on desired response time. Ambient temperature limits: 0 to 43°C. Ambient humidity limits: 95% RH. Safety features: flame-out indicator, integral flame arrestor, and automatic fuel shutoff.

19-4-9. Portable Flame Ionization Meter

Scott Aviation

The Portable Flame Ionization Meter, Model 11-654, is used to detect trace hydrocarbons in air. Applications of the instrument include 1) measurement of hydrocarbons as atmospheric pollutants; 2) monitoring for fuel leaks in storage areas or during fuel transfer and loading operations; 3) measurement of hydrocarbons in liquid oxygen or inert purge gas; 4) monitoring for toxic concentrations of solvents or process chemicals in manufacturing areas, ventilating systems, or storage areas; or 5) monitoring of manholes, sewers, and drains for accumulations of toxic or explosive gases. The basic principle of operation of this detector is ionization of hydrocarbon molecules in a hydrogen flame. Sample flow is obtained by an internal diaphragm-type pump. The fuel flow (40% hydrogen; 60% nitrogen) is controlled in two stages by a pressure regulator followed by a constant differential-type control. All controls necessary for operation of the system are mounted on the front panel. Recorder output terminals are available on the rear panel as are the fuses, sample inlet and exhaust connections, fuel supply controls, and electrical power input. Speed of response: varies directly with sample flow rate; 2–3 seconds, exclusive of external sample transport.

19-4-10. Hydrocarbon Analyzers, 400 Series

Teledyne Analytical Instruments

The TAI Series 400 flame ionization analyzers are continuous monitoring devices designed to measure trace quantities of total hydrocarbon contaminants in a gaseous atmosphere. The analyzer may be used to 1) detect hydrocarbons and atmospheric pollutants, 2) monitor for fuel leakage or toxic solvents, and 3) monitor combustion efficiency by measuring hydrocarbon emissions. In the Series 400, there are three models: Model 402 for positive pressure sampling, Model 403 for portable atmospheric sampling, and Model 404 for portable, high-temperature sampling. Constant temperature is maintained by a solid-state, thermistor temperature controller. Gas flows are regulated by maintaining a constant pressure across a sintered stainless steel restrictor in lieu of capillary tubing. An integral, self-purging manifold for introduction of span, zero, and sample gas is provided, allowing all operations to be performed at the front panel of the instrument.

The low-volume sample path, in conjunction with a variable sample bypass system, provides a fast response to process changes. Only one second is required for 90% response to change from 10 to 1000 ppm. Noise less than ±0.5% full scale. Drift: <1% full scale per day. Output: linear signal meter readout provisions for 0- to 5-mV DC recorder. Ambient temperature: 4 to 38°C. Flow rate: 100–400 ml/min of sample, 40–50 ml of fuel (200 ft^3 cylinder lasts 3 months); fuel mixture of 40% hydrogen and 60% nitrogen. Pressure rating up to 100 psi.

19-4-11. AID Models 580B and 585 Portable Organic Vapor Analyzers

Thermo Electron Instruments

The AID 580 and 585 are portable monitors that use a PID. The PID uses a high-energy UV lamp to ionize a sample that is drawn into the instrument. In general, the PID will respond to most organic compounds. It is

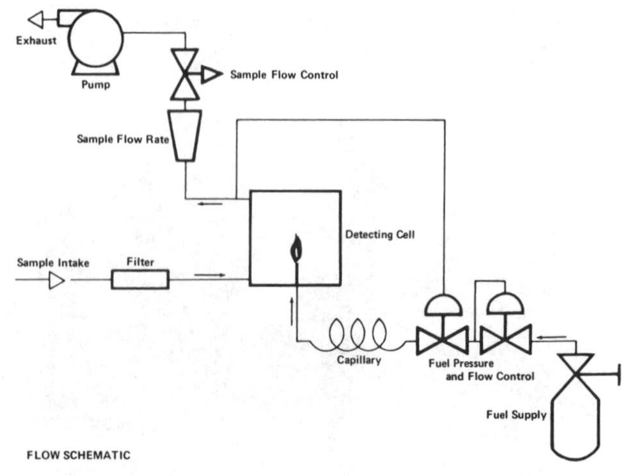

INSTRUMENT 19-4-9. Portable Flame Ionization Meter.

sensitive to methane, ethane, and most of the permanent gases. The sampling rate is 500 ml/min for the AID 580 and 50 ml/min for the AID 585, each regulated by a positive displacement pump. Internal, rechargeable batteries provide 8 hrs of continuous use. No fuel or compressed gases are required. The AID features an integral audio alarm that can be preset to any level. In addition to the normal LCD, an optional strip chart recorder may be operated from the recorder terminals provided on the back panel. The instrument displays information by a linear digital display. As with all PIDs, limited specificity is available by changing the energy of the photoionization lamp. Both instruments are equipped with a 10-eV lamp; an optional 11.8-eV lamp is available. Response time for the AID 580 is 2 seconds at 500 ml/min and 5 seconds for the AID 585 at 50 ml/min. A span and zero calibration control is provided on the front panel of the unit.

19-4-12. Models 710 and 712 Portable Total Hydrocarbon Analyzers

Thermo Electron Instruments

The AID 710 and 712 are designed as portable ambient monitors for use in the detection of fugitive emissions and other types of leaks with FIDs. The AID 710 and 712 are comprised of two units: the side pack and a gun. Samples are drawn in by a positive displacement pump at the rate of 1.5 L/min. The unit requires the availability of an external source of hydrogen to recharge the internal hydrogen supply. The AID 710 and 712 operate off an internal, rechargeable battery pack that supplies a minimum of 8 hrs of power. The unit is provided with a high-level audio alarm and a flame-out indicator to determine when the operations are interrupted. An optional recorder may be connected to the instrument through the terminal jacks on the back of the unit. The response time of the unit is 5 seconds, 90% full scale. A zero and span potentiometer is provided on the front panel of each unit.

19-4-13. Model 910 Organic Vapor Meter

Thermo Electron Instruments

The AID 910 Organic Vapor Meter is designed as a stationary monitor for most organic vapors in air, excluding methane, ethane, propane, and a few others. The AID 910 operation is based on the principle of photoionization. The PID uses a high-energy UV lamp to ionize the sample that is drawn into the instrument. The AID 910 comes confined to two sizes; a bench-mount unit and a NEMA enclosed unit. The sampling rate is variable up to 4 L/min and is user-adjustable. A positive displacement pump provides the source for the air sampling. No external accessories are required to operate the 910; however, a separate module is available to do multiple-point sampling with this unit. No fuel or compressed gases are required. The 910 is equipped with an audible alarm for low-level and high-level indications. Using a standard 10-eV photoionization lamp, the 910 may detect a minimum of 0.1 ppm benzene in air matrix. The instrument displays all data on a linear LCD. As with any PID, the specificity can be varied by the energy of the ionizing lamp. Response time depends on the variable flow rate; 2.5 seconds at maximum flow rate. Span and zero calibration adjustments are found on the front panel of the 910.

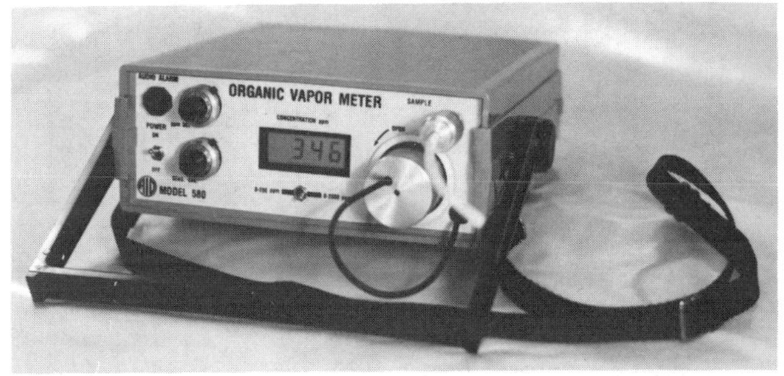

INSTRUMENT 19-4-11. AID Models 580B and 585 Portable Organic Vapor Analyzers.

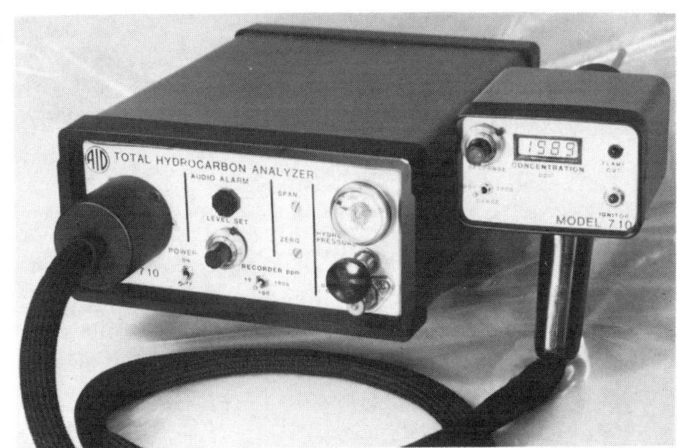

INSTRUMENT 19-4-12. Models 710 and 712 Portable Total Hydrocarbon Analyzers.

19-4-14. Model 680 Portable Hydrocarbon Vapor Meter

Thermo Environmental Instruments, Inc.

The Model 680 is a portable, intrinsically safe fugitive emissions monitoring system. The flame ionization technique utilized by the 680 can sample over a 0–20,000 ppm range, with a sensitivity of 0.1 ppm methane. User programmable software capabilities entail response factor settability, self-calibration adjustment, storage of up to 10 calibrations in memory, and automatic data logging of up to 4000 sample readings by time, date, concentration valve, and location code. Additionally, via bidirectional RS-232 communications, the 680 can interface with commercially available fugitive emission database computer software systems. Operating time: 10 hrs per charge.

INSTRUMENT 19-4-15. 350F Analyzer for CO/CH_4 and Total Hydrocarbons.

19-4-15. 350F Analyzer for CO/CH_4 and Total Hydrocarbons

Tracor, Inc.

The Tracor 350F Analyzer combines a gas chromatographic column with an FID and can be used to measure concentrations of CO, methane, and total hydrocarbons. CO reacts with hydrogen in the presence of reduced nickel catalyst to quantitatively produce methane. The FID is coupled to the reactor for the measurement of the methane reactant. Selectivity is attained by using a precolumn prior to the analytical column that removes all interferents, passing only CO and CH_4. The analytical column then permits separate identification and quantification of both the CO and CH_4. Total hydrocarbons can be analyzed by introducing an ambient air sample directly to the flame during each analytical cycle. An integral flame-out H_2 cutoff is incorporated. The analytical column is housed in a heated mandrel oven. Temperature control is within 0.05°C, assuring reproducibility of analytical time. A panel-mounted pyrometer with a four-position selector switch enables the operator to monitor temperatures of all analytical parameters: valve oven, column oven, reactor, and detector. Fast-response thermocouples permit a full temperature/area profile within seconds.

Infrared Photometers

19-5-1. Open Cell Nondispersive Infrared (NDIR) Gas Detector, Model 5600

Astro International Corporation

The Model 5600 is designed for fixed-station monitoring of combustible gases in chemical plants, ships, well-logging operations, refineries, drying ovens, drilling platforms, sewage digesters, mines, and tunnels. IR energy from the IR source passes alternately through two narrow band interference filters and the sample gas; it is then reflected by a spherical mirror to the solid-state detector. The sample filter wavelength is selected for line spectra absorbed by gases analyzed. Synchronous detection, calculation of dual wavelength ratios, and reference and sample signal processing are then performed to eliminate drift associated with alternate IR detectors. The Model 5600 has compensating circuitry for IR source and detector aging. It employs automatic gain control in the detection process and has a "dirty window" alarm with relay output that activates when insufficient energy reaches the detector. The system verifies "zero" once each second, providing an active detection device. Fail-safe operation and system status are automatic. Output: 0–1 VDC, 0–10 VDC, 4- to 20-mA DC fault alarm (relay); two independent settable alarms. Response time: 8 seconds. Zero and span drift: ±2% (nonaccumulative).

19-5-2. Models 864/865 Nondispersive Infrared Analyzers

Beckman Instruments, Inc.

The Beckman Models 864/865 Nondispersive Infrared Analyzers are designed for precise determination of a given chemical component concentration in vehicle emissions. Applications include vehicle emissions, automotive research and development, and automotive certification testing. The Models 864/865 utilize NDIR radiation absorption, which is produced from two separate energy sources. The infrared beams pass through two cells: a reference cell containing a nonabsorbing background gas and a sample cell containing a continuous flowing sample. Noise: 1% of full scale. Zero and span drift: 1% of full scale/24 hrs. Response time (electronic): variable, 90% in 0.5–26 seconds (15 field-selectable speeds). Sample cell length: 4–38.1 mm. Sample flow rate: nominal 500–1000 cm^3/min. Sample pressure: 15 psig. Maximum ambient temperature range: 1 to 49°C. Output (field selectable): 0–10 mV, 0–100 mV, 0–1 V, 0–5 VDC. Nonlinear output standard; plug-in linear output optional.

19-5-3. Model 866 Ambient CO Monitoring System

Beckman Instruments, Inc.

The Model 866 is designated as a reference method for ambient CO monitoring. Model 867 is also available for monitoring CO in vehicle exhaust. The Model 866 monitoring system combines the Model 865-17 non-

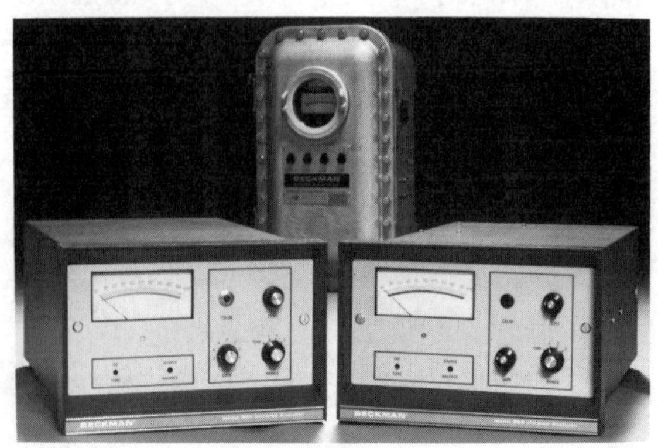

INSTRUMENT 19-5-2. Models 864/865 Nondispersive Infrared Analyzers.

dispersive infrared (NDIR) analyzer, the Automatic Zero/Span Module, a Beckman-developed Automatic Flowing Reference Panel, and a Pump/Sample Handling Module into a self-contained system. Model 866 utilizes NDIR radiation absorption. The infrared beam passes through two cells: a reference cell containing a nonabsorbing background gas, the other cell containing a continuous flowing sample. Noise: <0.2 P/10^6. Total interference equivalent: less than 1.5 P/10^6, per U.S. Environmental Protection Agency (U.S. EPA) specifications. Zero drift: ±0.5 P/10^6 per 12 and 24 hrs. Span drift: ±1%/24 hrs. Electronic response time: 0.5–26 seconds, field selectable, U.S. EPA-designated at 13 seconds. Ambient temperature limits: 0 to 50°C; U.S. EPA designated at 20 to 30°C. Outputs: 10 mV, 100 mV, 1 V, and 5 VDC available from auto zero/span module; 4- to 20-mA DDC optional.

19-5-4. Model 1301 Gas Analyzer

Bruel and Kjaer Instruments, Inc.

The Model 1301 Gas Analyzer is a fully self-contained, transportable Fourier Transform Infrared (FTIR) spectometer that utilizes photoacoustic detection and is designed for field use. The unit can be used as both an analyzer to determine what gases are present and as a monitor for concentration measurements. Any gas or vapor that has an infrared absorbance between 4000/cm and 650/cm can be detected. Detection limits are typically in the range from 0.1 to 10 ppm. The dynamic range is 4 orders of magnitude. The unit has extensive internal data handling and data storage capabilities, along with a built-in disk drive and graphics screen. Serial and parallel interfaces allow for the transfer of data to various peripherals and computers. Zero drift: detection limit over 3 months. Span drift: 5% of reading over 3 months.

INSTRUMENT 19-5-3. Model 866 Ambient CO Monitoring System.

INSTRUMENT 19-5-4. Model 1301 Gas Analyzer.

19-5-5. Toxic Gas Monitor Type 1302

Bruel & Kjaer Instruments, Inc.

The Toxic Gas Monitor Type 1302 is designed for the continuous measurement of various toxic gases. Typical applications are area monitoring for process emissions and perimeter monitoring for accidental releases. The monitor can operate unattended for months at a time. The Multigas Monitor 1302 is a portable unit that has typical applications for occupational exposure, tracer gas analysis, and indoor air quality assessment. The measurement technique used in both instruments is based on infrared photoacoustic spectroscopy. This method is based on the fact that when a gas absorbs modulated light, it emits sound proportional to the concentration of the gas. During operation, air is pumped into the measurement chamber. The chamber is sealed and irradiated with modulated, narrow band, infrared light. If the toxic gas of interest is in the air sample, sound is emitted and measured with a microphone. The signal is processed and the result is transmitted to the controlling computer. Selectivity is controlled by fitting the monitor with the appropriate optical filter for the gas of interest. A wide range of filters is available, covering the useful region of the

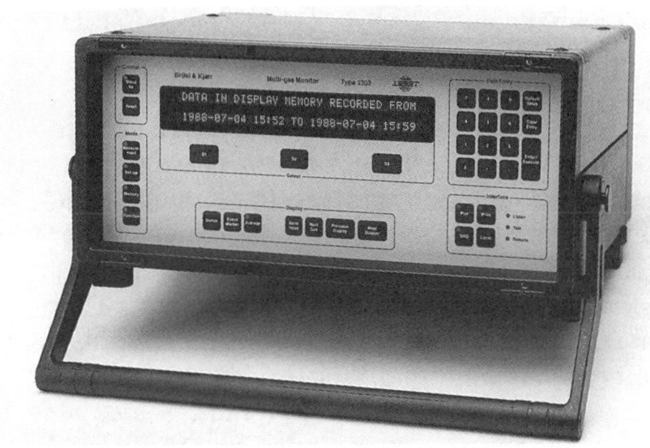

INSTRUMENT 19-5-5. Toxic Gas Monitor Type 1302.

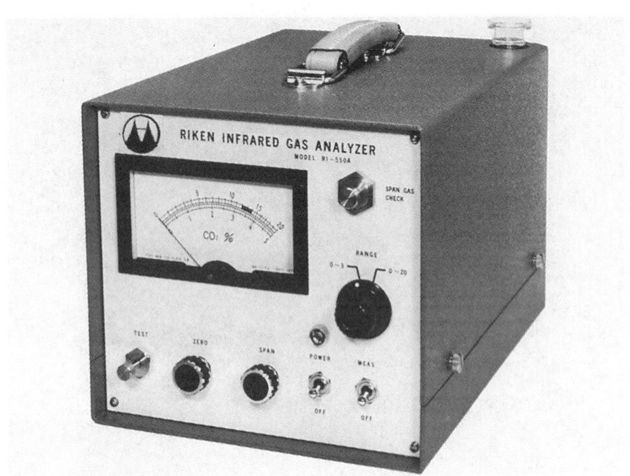

INSTRUMENT 19-5-7. Riken RI-550A Gas Analyzer.

infrared spectrum.

The Toxic Gas Monitor is remotely controlled from a personal computer that can be positioned a considerable distance from the monitor. The monitoring system can incorporate from 1 to 254 monitors connected to one computer. The Model 1302 has 32 KB of memory and 80 character display. It has a measurement time of 30 seconds for one gas and up to 100 seconds for five gases. Span drift: 2.5% of reading in 3 months. Zero drift: detection threshold concentration in 3 months.

19-5-6. Riken RI-411A Portable CO_2 Indicator

CEA Instruments, Inc.

The Riken RI-411 is a lightweight CO_2 infrared gas monitor with digital readout and audible alarm. The unit is applicable to food-related industries, brewers, mushroom growers, greenhouse horticulture, welding, office ventilation systems, cooling systems, hazardous environments, laboratory and research projects, etc. The Riken RI-411 utilizes NDIR absorption to measure CO_2 in air. The unit is Ni-Cd battery operated and microprocessor controlled. The readings of CO_2 concentrations can be continuous or averaged over 1, 3, or 15 min. Averaged readings are held on the display until needed by the user. The RI-411 has a solid-state detector, an illuminated dot-matrix digital display, and a recorder output and can operate on AC using an optional DC power supply. Audible alarms: high CO_2, 5000 ppm (short pulse, optional 25%), averaging period (long tone), and low battery (continuous tone). Response time: 10 seconds to 90% indication. Calibration: zero, calibration using nitrogen or air cylinder (zero gas); span, calibration using cylinder of CO_2 in air. Ambient temperature range: –10 to 40°C. Ambient humidity range: 10% to 90% RH. Recorder output: 0- to 10-mv DC (linear). Auxiliary charger available for charging or continuous operation on 115-VAC adaptor. Operating hrs: about 6 hrs continuous.

19-5-7. Riken RI-550A Gas Analyzer

CEA Instruments, Inc.

The Riken Infrared Gas Analyzer Model RI-550A is a single gas, lightweight, infrared analyzer designed to measure CO, CO_2, methane, ethylene, ethane, propane, or butane levels. This instrument operates on the NDIR absorption principle. The gas stream to be analyzed is drawn into the unit through a sampling probe and sampling line by means of an internal vacuum pump. The sample gas passes through an optical system, and the concentration of the constituent to be measured is read out directly on a meter. Response time: <10 seconds to 90% response. Zero and span drive less than ±2%/8 hrs of full scale. Sample flow rate: 6 L/min, normal, variable. Calibration is by internal span gas canister and/or built-in mechanical reference filter. Ambient temperature range: 0 to 40°C. Ambient humidity range: 0% to 90% RH. Warm-up time: 30 min after power switch ON (usable after 3 min). Recorder output: 0- to 10-mV DC (internal resistance 100 ohms).

19-5-8. Miran Gas Analyzers

Foxboro Company

The Miran Gas Analyzers utilize NDIR absorption. Both the optical path of the gas cell and the wavelength can be varied to give specificity and sensitivity. The instruments are primarily used with a wavelength set for a characteristic absorption band. Ambient air is continuously sampled and either absorbance or percent transmittance measured. The Miran-I Variable Filter Gas Analyzer can be used to scan through the infrared spectrum (2.5–14.5 μm). The Miran 101 is a lighter weight analyzer that reads directly in concentration and is used when a limited number of vapors are to be analyzed. The Miran-II Gas Analyzers are designed for continuous monitoring applications in field installations. Miran-I Variable Filter Gas Analyzer: sampling rate, 28 L/min; readout mode, full scale ranges (0–0.025, 0–0.1, 0–0.25, and 0–1); absorbance units: 0%–100% transmittance. Miran 101 Specific Vapor

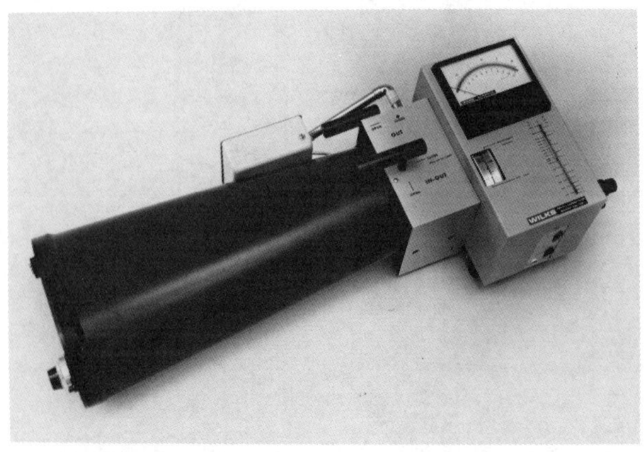

INSTRUMENT 19-5-8. Miran Gas Analyzers.

Analyzer: sampling rate, approximately 15 L/min (cell volume, 2.25 L); readout mode, direct reading in concentrations. Response and averaging time: <1 minute. Stability: drift <0.004 absorbance units at 23.25°C, 3.5 M.

19-5-9. Model RI-413 Portable Freon® Monitor
GasTech, Inc.

The Model RI-413 is a portable instrument capable of measuring Freons® R-11, R-12, R-22, R-113, R-114, and R-502 in ppm concentrations. This instrument is ideal as a leak detector and survey meter around refrigerant or cleaning systems where Freon is typically used. The instrument can be used to obtain continuous output or average readings for 1, 3, or 15 min. The Model RI-413 utilizes NDIR absorption for detection. The Model RI-413 contains a microprocessor for control operations and a durable miniature diaphragm pump to draw in the samples. Other features include a choice of alkaline or Ni-Cd batteries, an adaptor for 115-VAC operation, low battery and high gas level alarms, six detection ranges, self-illuminating digital display, and a 3-ft sampling probe. Response time: 10 seconds to 90%. Operating time: 4 hrs.

19-5-10. IR-702 Infrared Analyzer
Infrared Industries, Inc.

The IR-702 Infrared Analyzer has the capability of detecting two gases simultaneously. Its internal standardization eliminates the need for span gases, and solid-state circuitry allow fast response with low vibration sensitivity. In general, the system compares the optical (infrared) transmittance of two identical optical paths. One optical path passes through the sample of unknown gas, the other optical path passes through the reference path. The difference in optical transmittance between these paths is a measure of the optical absorption. Speed of response: 90% of reading in 1 second. Accuracy: (specification depends on certified calibrations gas) ± 1% of full scale. Noise level: <1% of full scale. Zero and span drift: <1%/24 hrs. Temperature range: 0 to 20°C. Detector type: solid-state (PbSe). Output: 1–100 mV or 0–1 V. Warm-up time: 15 min.

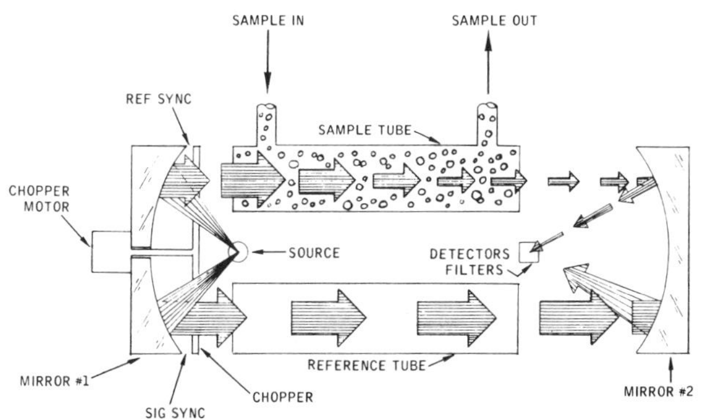

INSTRUMENT 19-5-10. IR-702 Infrared Analyzer.

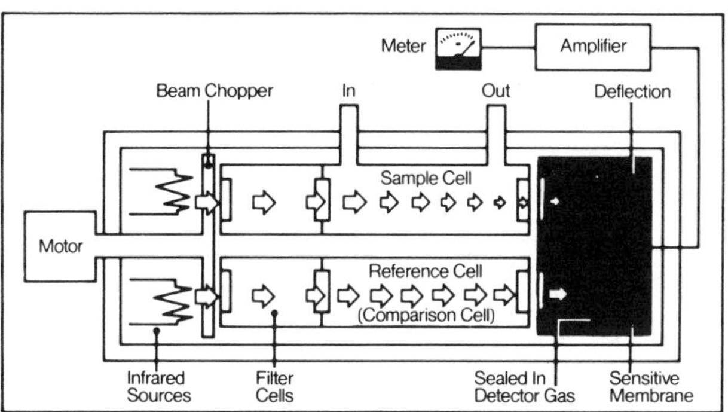

INSTRUMENT 19-5-12. LIRA Model 3000 Nondispersive Infrared Analyzer.

The sampling system is constructed of 316 stainless steel, windows of silicon, and tubing of Teflon. Calibration: internal optical attenuator.

19-5-11. IR-711 Portable Hydrocarbon Analyzer
Infrared Industries, Inc.

The IR-711 Portable Hydrocarbon Analyzer is used for the instantaneous detection and measurement of percent LEL and ppm levels of the alkane family of hydrocarbons in and around fuel tanks and other enclosures. Because of its design, the IR-711 is particularly useful in the monitoring of JP-5 and other kerosene-type fuels. This instrument is an NDIR analyzer for continuously monitoring the concentration of a specific gas in a gas sample stream. Standard recorder outputs (0–100 mV) are provided. The analyzer features a single infrared energy source that eliminates the complex alignment problems associated with dual infrared energy sources. Dual beam optical systems minimize drift effects due to changes in ambient temperature, spectral emission of the source, and power line variations. Reflective coatings are not required on the inside of the sample or reference cells, thereby reducing maintenance, cleaning, and replacement costs. Calibration gas: propane. Accuracy: 5%. Resolution: high range, 2.5% LEL; low range, 25 ppm JP-5. Drift: 1 hr — high range (<2.5% LEL), low range (<25 ppm); 8 hrs — high range (<5% LEL), low range (<50 ppm). Warm-up time: 5 min. Response time for temperature compensation: 2 min.

19-5-12. LIRA Model 3000 Nondispersive Infrared Analyzer
Mine Safety Appliances Company

The LIRA Model 3000 Nondispersive Infrared Analyzer is designed for fixed station use in the detection of any gas or vapor that absorbs infrared energy. Its sample cells and windows are application dependent. Inlet, outlet, and purge fittings are 1/8-in. NPT, and the tubing is made of nylon. Least detectable quantity, sensitivity, and specificity are all application dependent. Response time: 90% in 5 seconds; optional 90% in 3 seconds. Zero and span drift: <1% full scale/day, typically <2% full scale/week. Span check: electrical circuit simulates presence of sample gas when activated by push-button on front panel.

19-5-13. OTOX® Model CO_2 Monitor
Neotronics

The OTOX® can be used as a hand-held and/or wall-mounted CO_2 monitor. The instrument utilizes a nondispersive infrared sensor, which is protected from dust, smoke, and other particulate contaminants by a membrane filter. The OTOX® has a warm-up stabilization time of 5 min and a response time of 20 seconds. The instrument can operate in temperatures from 0 to 50°C and relative humidities between 5% and 95%. A 12-V battery operates the monitor for 1.5–2 hrs.

19-5-14. Series 800 Infrared Analyzers
Rosemount Analytical, Inc.

The Series 800 nondispersive infrared analyzers are designed to monitor CO, CO_2, NO, and hydrocarbons in pollution control, automotive exhaust, or process gas emission applications. Series 800 analyzers produce infrared radiation from one or two separate energy sources. This radiation is modulated by a chopper into pulses. The infrared beam then passes through a flowing sample cell or both sample and reference cells. Based on sample stream characteristics, the reference call may be sealed or flowing. The signal from the infrared detection device(s) is amplified, displayed, and/or transmitted to data acquisition devices. Repeatability: 1% of full scale. Zero/span drift: 1% of full scale/24 hrs.

19-5-15. Model 765-203 Infrared Analyzers
SKC West, Inc.

The Model 765-203 Infrared Analyzer is a wall-mounted/tabletop CO_2 data recorder that can be used to evaluate the efficiency of ventilation systems. The 765-203 has internal memory for storage of time-based data, with the sampling frequency varying from 8 seconds to 30 min. A software package is available to download data to any IBM compatible computer. The software package is menu-driven and allows the user to display, print, and store useful graphs and reports. Power source: 12-V battery with 4.5-hr duration or 12-V, 400-mA AC power adapter. Operating temperature: 10 to 40°C.

Ultraviolet (UV) and Visible Light Photometers

19-6-1. J-W Mercury Vapor SNIFFER®
Bacharach, Inc.

The J-W Model MV-2 Mercury Vapor SNIFFER® is a dual-range, hand-held instrument for the detection and measurement of mercury vapors in working areas. The sample is drawn into the detector and through the UV absorption chamber by a small motor-driven suction fan powered by a battery. To operate the detector, the user turns the control knob to the bias position, adjusts the zero, sets the air knob to sampling position, and reads the vapor concentration on the meter. The vapors of some organic compounds, such as benzene and its compounds, halogenated hydrocarbons, and particulates, absorb UV light at the lamp frequency. Normally, this slight interference does not present a problem. The detector has an efficient built-in filter that permits the meter to be zeroed in a contaminated atmosphere and then switched immediately to read the vapor concentration. The Model MV-2 is a self-contained, battery-powered instrument housed in a lightweight steel case. The indicating meter is calibrated in mg/m^3 of air. All controls and the carrying handle are mounted in the top of the case. The case itself houses the batteries, the 2537 Angstrom UV source lamp, the atomic absorption chamber, the photoelectric cell, and all other operating components. A slip-on connection is provided in the end of the case for an extension probe when used.

19-6-2. AISI Sulfur Dioxide Monitor
Barringer Research, Ltd.

The Barringer AISI Sulfur Dioxide Monitor is used to quantitatively determine the amount of SO_2 emitted by a source such as a stack without physically procuring a sample of the gas. Operation is based on correlation with the absorption spectra of SO_2 in the UV. Hence, normal skylight may be used as the UV source and measurement obtained with the instrument located several hundred feet from the source. In operation, the viewing unit is first sighted on the target plume near the stack mouth. The vertical aperture is then adjusted so that only a small area in the center of the plume fills the field of view. The viewing unit is then moved to one side of the plume to zero out the background SO_2 level, and readings are obtained with the self-contained calibration cells. Finally, the viewing unit is again centered on the plume and the reading is noted. These readings, together with the stack diameter (which is the path length of interest in this case) and the emission temperature of the gas, yield the SO_2 concentration in ppm. The instrument is comprised of three units: the electronic unit, the viewing unit, and the tripod. Sensitivity of Option 1 is 2 ppm-m; Option 2, 40 ppm-m. Field of view: 0.15° horizontal; vertical is adjustable from 0 to 1.5°. Meter and chart recorder are located on the front panel. Option 1 is a high-sensitivity instrument designed for such applications as plume tracing. Option 2 is designed specifically for remote stack monitoring. The units cannot be converted in the field.

19-6-3. Model K-23B Mercury Vapor Meter
Beckman Instruments, Inc.

The Beckman Model K-23B Mercury Vapor Meter is designed to provide an instantaneous reading of mercury vapor in an enclosed environment. Areas where this instrument finds application include: OSHA compliance monitoring, chlorine and caustic plants, mines, chemical laboratories, hospitals, wind tunnels, dry battery manufacturing facilities, thermometer manufacturing facilities, and dental laboratories. The Beckman Model K-23B is a portable, UV filter photometer tuned to a wavelength of 253.7 nm (the wavelength at which mercury vapor absorbs light). To ensure optimum accuracy at all times, a calibration filter assembly is built into the meter. Filters with known absorption factors can be switched into the optical path of the meter to provide standard references for calibration. Output: 0–100 mV plus meter. Noise: 0–0.1 scale, ±1.5% full scale; 0–1.0 scale, ±0.5% full scale.

19-6-4. Model TGM555 Portable Toxic Gas Monitor

CEA Instruments, Inc.

The TGM555 is a portable, ambient air monitor that can be used for continuous colorimetric analysis of numerous compounds. The TGM555 contains a rechargeable DC power source and a constant-volume adjustable air pump. An air sample is continuously drawn into the unit and scrubbed with an absorbing reagent that removes a trace pollutant from the air stream and transfers it into the liquid reagent system. The subsequent color formation is read by a colorimeter and displayed on a built-in meter or on the optional digital readout. A recorder output is also provided.

Operating period: 20 hrs, fully charged internal batteries. Signal output: 0–1.0 V at 0–2.0 mA. Calibration: <1% drift/72 hrs. Sensitivity: 1% of full scale. Nonlinearity: <2%. Zero and span drive: <2%/72 hrs. Air flow drift: <1%/72 hours. Noise: 0.75% of full scale. Lag time: 4 min. Rise time to 90%: 4 min. Fall time 90%: 2.5 min. Temperature range: 4.5 to 49°C. Temperature

INSTRUMENT 19-6-4. Model TGM555 Portable Toxic Gas Monitor.

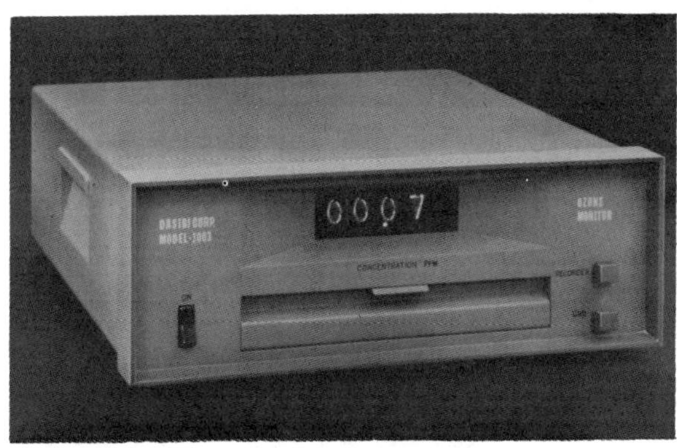

INSTRUMENT 19-6-5. Model 1003 Ozone Monitor.

drift: at laboratory conditions ±3°C, ±1%; from 15 to 30°C, ±2%; from 30 to 50°C, ±4%; from 14 to 50°C, ±8%. Relative humidity range: 5% to 95%. Reagent requirements: SO_2, 3.4 L/week modified West and Gaeke; 3.4 L/week demineralized water; NO_2, 3.4 L/week modified Saltzman (Lyshkow).

19-6-5. Model 1003 Ozone Monitor

Dasibi Environmental Corporation

The Model 1003 Ozone Monitor continuously monitors the concentration of ozone in the air in ppm. An analog output is available for continuous strip-chart recording, and a binary-coded decimal (BCD) output enables direct interfacing with a computer or a printer. Ozone concentration is measured by detecting the absorption level of UV light within a sample volume of air. Accuracy: ±3%. Scale factor: adjustable to any standard. Drift: <0.001 ppm/week noncumulative. Zero span: ±0.4%/°C, corresponding to much less than 0.001 ppm. Interval: 8 or 30 seconds. Flow rate: 7 L/min at 8-second intervals; 1.0 L/min at 30-second intervals. Zero return: 1 interval from 1.0 ppm. Temperature: 0 to 49°C. Meets vibration and shock constraints typically encountered in shipping, aircraft, and mobile vans; maintenance, 1000-hr mean time between maintenance under typical conditions.

19-6-6. Stack Gas Analyzers for SO_2, NO_2, and NO_x

DuPont Company

The DuPont 460 Gas Analyzer Systems are designed for the continuous monitoring of SO_2 and NO_2 in stack emissions at power generating stations and industrial plants. The 461 Analyzer system is designed for source monitoring of nitrogen oxides. It measures NO_2 and analyzes for NO by converting it to NO_2.

The analyses are based on the strong UV absorption of SO_2 and the visible absorption of NO_2. The DuPont 460 Photometric Analyzer, using a split beam configuration, measures the difference in light absorption at two different wavelengths. Either manual- or automat-

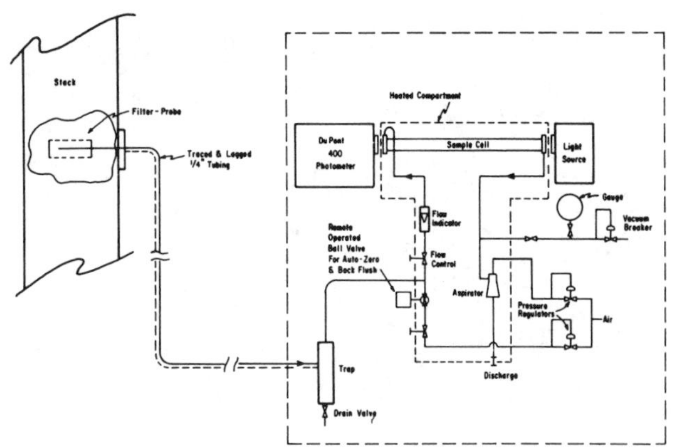

INSTRUMENT 19-6-6. Stack Gas Analyzers for SO_2, NO_2, and NO_x.

ic-operated filter switching mechanisms can be provided to allow one analyzer to be used for both SO_2 and NO_2 measurements. Because NO is essentially transparent in the visible and ultraviolet, quantitative conversion to NO_2 is required for its measurement. Speed of response: 15 seconds or less (5-min cycle for Model 461). Analyzer output: linear, 0- to 10-mV standard; 4–20 mA and 10–50 mA available. Integrally mounted recorder optional. Accuracy: ±2% of full scale. Linearity: better than 2%. An optional calibration filter corresponding to a fixed SO_2 concentration is provided. Compressed air at 30–80 psig.

19-6-7. Autostep Plus

GMD Systems, Inc.

The Autostep Plus is a microprocessor-controlled portable toxic gas detector. The Autostep Plus utilizes a removable, gas-specific ranging or gas-type module to monitor for TDI, MDI, hydrazines, Phosgene "A," Phosgene "B," or acid gas. Multigas modules are available to monitor for TDI, MDI, and HDI or chlorine, hydrides, and acid gas. The detection principle is colorimetric paper tape and reflected light, level measurement controlled by the microprocessor. Other features of the Autostep Plus include 2,000-point data logging capability, built-in audible alarm, and external battery and data connectors. The precision depends on gas and model: 15% of reading or 1 ppb/0.1 ppm, whichever is greater. The Autostep Plus can operate from −10 to 40°C and in 5% to 95% relative humidity, noncondensing.

19-6-8. Model 727-3 UV Ozone Monitor

Mast Development Company

The Model 727-3 UV Ozone Monitor utilizes the technique of UV absorption for fast and specific ozone detection. The monitor is suitable for use in ozone chamber work, environmental chamber work, safety monitoring near ozone generators in industrial or wastewater treatment operations, OSHA-regulated monitoring, quality control for ozone-producing appliances, and plant pathology studies. No expendable reagents of any kind are required. The instrument is portable and designed for both long-term, unattended use and intermittent operation. Off-the-shelf warm-up is less than 20 min. Flow rate: 2 L/min. Ambient temperature range: 0 to 50°C. Relative humidity range: 5% to 95%. Unattended period: up to 30 days. Digital display: 0.00–9.99 ppm. Analog: 1V per 10 ppm. Accuracy: ±4% (based on Beer's law). Lag time: 5 seconds. Rise time: 1 measurement cycle. Fall time: 1 measurement cycle. Zero drift: none. Span drift: 1% of calibration level/24 hrs. Measurement cycle: 20 seconds.

19-6-9. Model 890 SO_2 Analyzer

Rosemount Analytical, Inc.

The Model 890 SO_2 Analyzer uses a nondispersive UV "transflectance" analysis bench to monitor for SO_2. Radiation from a pulsed UV source is collimated and directed onto two multidetector blocks, located before and after the single sample cell. Wavelength isolation is achieved by means of a spectrally selective cold mirror in the detector block. Response time: variable, 90% of full scale in 0.5–20 seconds. Repeatability: ≤1% of full scale. Zero/span drift: ±2% of full scale/week.

19-6-10. Instantaneous Vapor Detector

Sunshine Scientific Instruments

The Instantaneous Vapor Detector is intended primarily for the detection of mercury vapor but can be used for the detection of other vapors in specified ranges of concentration. Applications include the manufacture of electrical apparatus, instruments, bulbs, glassware, fur, and salt; use in the chemical, metal mining, and smelting industries; and use by insurance companies and laboratories. Operation of the detector is based on UV light absorption by mercury vapor. This same principle is also used for the detection of certain other vapors that have selective absorption characteristics for UV radiation. For this reason, the identity of the vapor under test must be known and the vapor must be

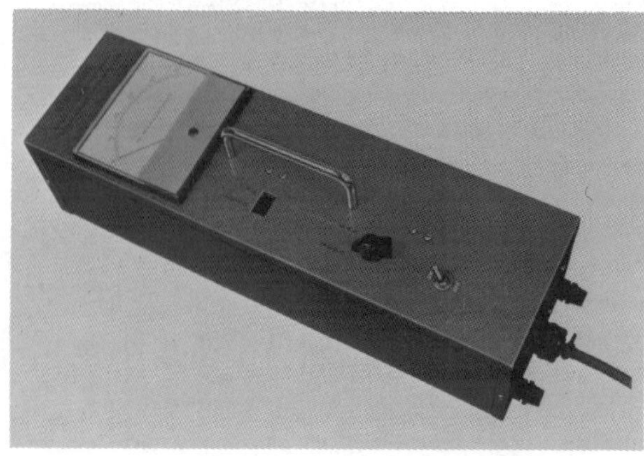

INSTRUMENT 19-6-10. Instantaneous Vapor Detector.

free from other substances which will absorb or obstruct UV light. In addition, the vapor should be relatively uncontaminated by extraneous substances such as fog, dust, or smoke. Features: warm-up time <15 minutes; <1% change in reading for 10% line voltage variation. Low power consumption permits operation from a battery-powered inverter for complete portability. Special options include explosion-resistant Model 38E, recorder output, single- or dual-set point meter (Model 38F), panel or rack mounting, audible/visible alarms, and systems for monitoring multiple locations.

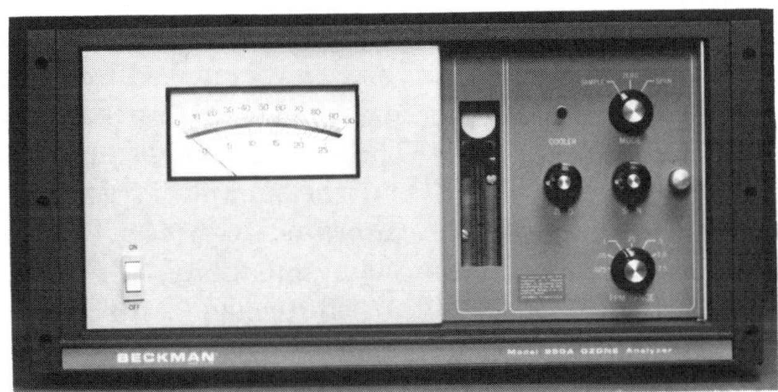

INSTRUMENT 19-7-1. Model 950A Ozone Analyzer.

Chemiluminescence

19-7-1. Model 950A Ozone Analyzer

Beckman Instruments, Inc.

The Model 950A provides ozone analysis over a wide selection of full-scale ranges for ambient air monitoring. The Model 950A utilizes a nonhazardous 90% CO_2/10% C_2H_4 mixture as the reactant gas, instead of pure ethylene typically required for chemiluminescent analysis. The chemiluminescent detection method is based on the principle that ozone mixes with ethylene, resulting in a chemiluminescent reaction that provides a light emission directly proportional to the ozone (O_3) concentration in the ambient air sample. Noise: 0%, 0.002 P/10^6; 80% of span, 0.002 P/10^6. Total interference equivalent: <0.005 P/10^6. Zero drift: <0.005 P/10^6 per 12 hrs; 0.001 P/10^6 per 24 hrs. Span drift: ±2% of full scale/24 hrs. Lag time: <20 seconds. Rise and fall time: <90 seconds. Ambient temperature: 4 to 43°C; U.S. EPA designated at 20 to 30°C. Outputs: 10 mV, 100 mV, 1 V, and 5 VDC.

19-7-2. Model 952A NO/NO_x/NO_2 Analyzer

Beckman Instruments, Inc.

The Model 952A ambient NO_2 monitor is designed for field operation. The Model 952A chemiluminescent detector is based on the principle that NO reacts with ozone to produce NO_2, 10% electronically excited NO_2, and O_2. Following the NO–O_3 reaction, the NO_2 molecules immediately revert to NO_2. This process emits photons that produce a light emission directly proportional to the NO concentration in the ambient air sample. For NO detection, the sample gas and the ozone are introduced directly into the reaction chamber for analysis. To determine NO_x (NO + NO_2) concentration, the sample is first routed through the converter where the NO_2 is converted to NO and then routed to the reaction chamber for analysis. Noise: 0%, 0.002P/10^6; 80% of span, 0.003 P/10^6. Total interference equivalent: 0.01 P/10^6. Zero drift: <0.02 P/10^6 per 12 hrs; <0.005 P/10^6 per 24 hrs. Span drift ±2% of full scale/24 hrs. Lag time: 0.5 min. Rise and fall time: 1.5 min and 1.0 min, respectively. Ambient temperature: 4 to 43°C; U.S. EPA designated at 20 to 30°C. Outputs: individual memory outputs for NO/NO_x/NO_2, switch selectable for 10 mV, 100 mV, 1 V, or 5 VDC; primary output signal, switch selectable for 10 mV, 100 mV, 1 V, or 5 VDC.

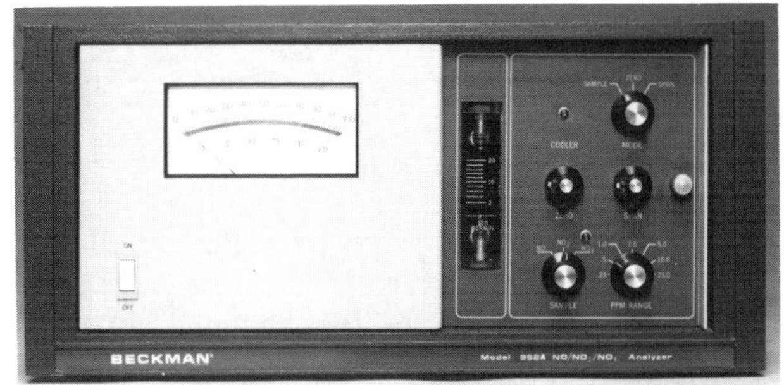

INSTRUMENT 19-7-2. Model 952A NO/NO_x/NO_2 Analyzer.

19-7-3. Model 1100 Ozone Meter

Columbia Scientific Industries Corporation

The Model 1100 Ozone Meter is used for ambient air monitoring and other applications where a specific determination for ozone in the presence of other oxidants is required. The Model 1100 Ozone Meter operates on the Nederbragt principle of the chemiluminescent reaction between ozone and ethylene. Ethylene consumption: 15 cm^3/min. Time constant: selectable 1.0 second or 10 seconds. Known atmospheric interferences: none. Data display: panel meter, mirrored 4.5-in. scale. Electronic: solid-state except for photomultiplier tube. Operating temperature: 10 to 45°C ambient. An optional portable Chemiluminescent Ozone Meter, Model MEC 2000, is also available. It has ranges of 0–0.1, 0–0.2, 0–0.5, and 0–1.0 ppm.

19-7-4. Nitrogen Oxides Analyzer

Columbia Scientific Industries Corporation

The Model NA530R Nitrogen Oxides Analyzer is designed for both research investigations and environmental monitoring for NO, NO_2, and NO_x. It uses the chemiluminescence reaction of ozone with NO in two independent and simultaneous photometric measurement systems to monitor for NO and NO_x. One system contains direct sample air and ozone, and the other contains sample air where all the NO_x has been converted to NO. The signals are subtracted for the NO_2 signal. The chemiluminescence reaction is temperature sensitive, causing a several percent error if allowed to follow ambient temperature. High sensitivity and accuracy are obtained by controlling the temperature of the reaction chamber. Noise (RMS): 0% URL, 0.002 ppm; 80% URL, 0.004 ppm. Interference equivalent: 0.005 ppm each interferent; 0.015 ppm total interferent. Zero drift: ±0.007 ppm/24 hrs; ±0.01 ppm/7 days. Span drift: ± 0.013 ppm/24 hrs; ±0.020 ppm/7 days. Lag time: <5 seconds. Rise and fall time (95%): 0.5–6 min depending on range and TC position. Linearity: ±1%. Unattended operations: 7 days (no adjustment of flow or electrical systems). Sample air flow rate: 1.2 L/min (max). Dry air flow rate: ozone generator, approximately 200 ml/min. Outputs: meter, with selector switch to read NO, NO_2, or NO_x; recorder, each channel has separate outputs of 0–10 V and 0–5 V, adjustable to 0–100 mV. Relative humidity range: 0% to 95%. Ambient temperature range: 10 to 40°C.

19-7-5. Ozone Analyzers

Columbia Scientific Industries Corporation

The Model OA 325-2R and OA 350-2R Ozone Analyzers have been designed to provide real-time, continuous monitoring of ozone in ambient air. Operation of the Ozone Analyzers is based on the gas phase chemiluminescent reaction between ozone and ethylene molecules, which produces light energy in the 300- to 600-nm region. In the presence of excess ethylene, the intensity of light produced is proportional to the concentration of ozone. This reaction has been found to be free of interferences from other gases present in ambient air. The analyzers are identical, except the OA350-2R has an internal UV ozone source to produce a span point and also a zero air source. Noise: 0% URL, 0.003 ppm; 80% URL, 0.002 ppm. Each interferent, ±0.002 ppm or better; total interferents, 0.002 ppm or better. Zero drift: ±0.002 ppm, 12 or 24 hrs. Span drift: (% of reading): 20% URL, ±1.5; 80% URL, ±2.5. Lag time: 0.1 min. Rise and fall time: 0.05 min. Precision: 20% and 80% URL, 0.001 ppm. Temperature range: 20 to 30°C.

19-7-6. Series 900 Analyzers

Rosemount Analytical, Inc.

The Series 900 Analyzers use chemiluminescence detection technology to monitor for oxides of nitrogen. The Model 951A is designed for light-duty engine and source monitoring as well as process applications. The Model 955 is designed for similar applications, but on a wet basis commonly used in heavy-duty engine exhaust monitoring. The Model 951C was specifically designed to meet the requirements of an integrated continuous emissions monitoring system. Zero/span drift: less than ±0.1 ppm or ±1% of full scale/24 hrs at constant temperature or ±0.2 ppm or ±2% of full scale over any 10°C from 4 to 40°C. Repeatability: ±0.1 ppm or 1% of full scale, whichever is greater.

Photometric Analyzers

19-8-1. Model US400 Carbon Monoxide Analyzer

Bacharach, Inc.

The Model US400 is designed for the continuous measurement of low CO concentrations in the field of pollution monitoring and control and when monitoring work areas, garages, ventilation systems, and industrial process streams. Determination of CO is based on the direct measurement of mercury vapor reduced from a heated, solid-state mercury oxide pellet by oxidation of the CO in the sample. The mercury vapor produced is the analog of the CO in the sample stream and permits the readout to be calibrated in terms of CO. The mercury vapor is measured by means of a UV filter photometer. The US400 can be furnished suitable for bench mounting or installed in a standard 19-in. panel, suitable for rack or panel mounting. The sample-drawing pump and remotely operated flow control valves are enclosed in a separate housing. Ambient temperatures: 4 to 43°C. Altitude range: sea level to 1500 m. Warm-up time: 15 min. Sample flow rate: 4.7 L/min. Span drift: ±2% of full scale/day. Lag time: 5 seconds. Response time: <10 seconds for 90% full scale/day. Sensitivity: 0.1 ppm/mV. Recorder outputs: floating or ground reference.

19-8-2. Carbon Monoxide Analyzer DIF 7000

Beckman Instruments, Inc.

The dual-isotope fluorescence (DIF) technique can detect changes in CO concentrations as small as 0.1 ppm and involves producing infrared radiation spectra to match those of two CO isotopes, $^{12}C^{16}O$ and $^{13}C^{16}O$. These spectra "time-share" a single sample chamber, producing a sequence of CO concentration and reference signals that are then sensed by a solid-state photodiode detector. Accuracy is ±1% of reading, ±1% of full

INSTRUMENT 19-8-1. Model US400 Carbon Monoxide Analyzer.

scale (accuracy is relative to calibration source), and linearity is ±1%, 0200 ppm. Specificity: interferent H_2O, rejection — 10,000:1; CO_2, rejection — 20,000:1. The error resulting from all other common interferents is less than 0.5% of range. Opacity tolerance: no degradation of accuracy when measuring in a medium of up to 50% opacity. Noise: 0.5 ppm peak-to-peak on 20-ppm range, increasing to 1.0 ppm on 200-ppm range. Span drift: 1% of reading/month (at constant temp.) Zero drift: 1 ppm/week (at constant temp.) Span and zero temperature coefficient: 0.2% of reading/°C change in ambient temperature. Response time: (90% of final reading) 8 seconds on 200-ppm range; 25 seconds on 20-ppm range. Output: 100 mV (other outputs up to 10 V available on special order). Impedance: <400 ohms. Warm-up time: 30 min to full accuracy. Ambient temperature: 0 to 50°C. Ambient relative humidity: 90%.

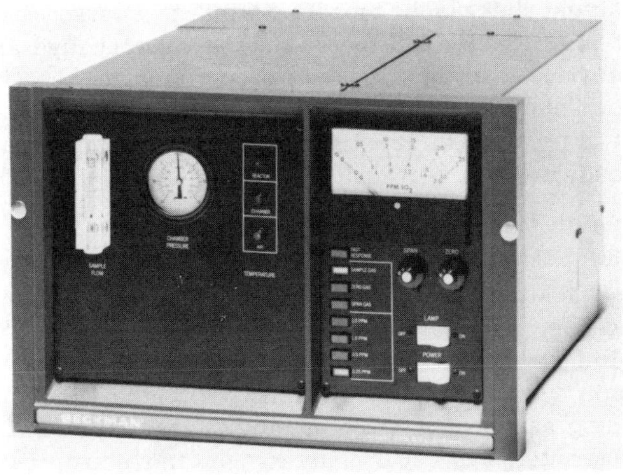

INSTRUMENT 19-8-3. Model 953 Fluorescent Ambient SO_2 Analyzer.

19-8-3. Model 953 Fluorescent Ambient SO_2 Analyzer

Beckman Instruments, Inc.

Utilizing the fluorescent measurement technique, the Model 953 requires no support gases and reagents typically used with flame photometric or coulometric SO_2 analyzers. An internal zero gas scrubber permits ambient air to be used as the zero gas, eliminating the need for zero air cylinders. An added feature is an interferent reactor that eliminates interference due to polycylic aromatic hydrocarbons (PAHs) typically found in samples where dense automotive traffic prevails. Beckman's fluorescent monitoring methodology is based on the principle that SO_2 molecules fluoresce when irradiated by UV light in the 1900–3900 Angstrom wave band. While the phenomenon does occur over this broad spectrum, the optimum excitation wavelength takes place in the narrow 2100–2300 Angstrom band. The Model 953 transmits a broad UV light band via a quartz deuterium lamp, and a narrow UV light band via a light-collimator assembly. The narrow UV light band passes through the sample reaction chamber where a blue sensitive photomultiplier tube then measures the resulting SO_2 fluorescence.

Noise: 0.5 P/10^6 range, 0.001 P/10^6. Lower detectable limit: 0.5 P/10^6 range, 0.004 P/10^6. Zero drift: 0.5 P/10^6 range, less than ± 0.005 P/10^6 per 24 hrs. Span drift: 0.5 P/10^6 range, less than ± 0.006 P/10^6 per 24 hrs. Total interference equivalent: 0.5 P/10^6 range, <0.025 P/10^6. Lag time: 7 seconds. Fall time: 3 min. Ambient temperature: 20 to 30°C. Output: 10 mV, 100 mV, 1 V, or 5 VDC.

19-8-4. Sulfur Analyzer Model SA285

Columbia Scientific Industries Corporation

The Model SA285 Sulfur Analyzer provides continuous, real-time monitoring of sulfur compounds in the ppb range. It utilizes the Meloy-patented Flame Photometric Detector (FPD) to provide dry analysis of sulfur in air samples. The operating principle of the FPD utilizes the photometric detection of the 394-nm centered band emitted by sulfur-containing compounds in a hydrogen-rich air flame. Its specificity arises from a geometric arrangement that optically shields the photomultiplier tube from the primary flame and the employment of a narrow band-pass interference filter. Noise (RMS): ±0.5% of full scale maximum. Zero drift: ±1% full scale/24 hrs. Span drift: ±2% full scale/24 hrs. Lag time: 10 seconds maximum. Rise and fall time: 90%, 25 seconds maximum. Linearity in ppb: ±1% of full scale. Available outputs: a) meter, b) 10-VDC full scale, c) 100-mVDC full scale (adjustable from 10-mV to 5-V full scale). Unattended operation: 14 to 28 days (no adjustment of flow or electrical system). Sample flow rate: approximately 200 ml/min. Hydrogen flow rate: approximately 140 ml/min. Ambient operating temperature range: 10 to 40°C.

19-8-5. Fluorescence SO_2 Analyzer

Columbia Scientific Industries Corporation

The Model SA700 is built for direct ambient air monitoring of SO_2 using a continuous UV source of high intensity and stability. The low noise characteristics provide rapid response and accuracy to better than ±2%, even on the most sensitive ranges. Sample flow rates are less than 500 cm^3/min. Noise (RMS): ±0.5% on 0- to 500-ppb scale. Zero and span drift: meets U.S. EPA specifications. Lag time: 10 seconds maximum. Rise and fall times: to 95%, 2 min maximum. Linearity: ±1% full scale. Operating temperature range: 20 to 30°C to U.S. EPA specifications. Sample flow: <500 cm^3/min. Interferences: meets U.S. EPA specifications. Output: a) 0–10 V; b) 0–100 mV, adjustable to 0–5 V. This instrument is suitable for bench mounting; rack mounting is available.

19-8-6. Phosphorus Gas Detectors/Analyzers
Columbia Scientific Industries Corporation

Columbia Scientific offers monitoring of phosphorus by flame photometric detection as a companion or replacement capability in its sulfur analyzers. The capability is now available in Models PA 460 (integral log-linear amplifier) and PA 465 (a portable, lightweight unit with 12-V battery supply). Rise time for Model PA 460 is 2–3 seconds (nominal), <10 seconds maximum; for the PA 465, it is 10 seconds to 90% of full response. Fall time: <7 seconds for the PA 460 and 3 seconds for the PA 465.

Photometric Analyzers of Surface Deposit

19-8-7. Hydrogen Sulphide Monitor
Fleming Instruments, Ltd.

The Fleming Hydrogen Sulphide Monitor was developed to meet requirements of underground sewer testing or be used in areas where there is a possibility of encountering toxic gases. The basic principle used in the Type 533 Monitor is the continuous elevation, by a sensitive phototransistor, of the intensity of the brown stain produced by the action of H_2S gas on a lead acetate-treated filter paper. Small concentrations of H_2S (as low as 0.1 ppm) result in a staining of the paper, and the degree of stain is continuously evaluated by a stable and sensitive detector circuit. Paper tape: Whatman B.D.H. No. 1 lead acetate filter paper, 1 cm wide × 5 m long (at least 6 working days supply). Paper tape drive mechanism: clockwork motor with drive mechanism that also indicates the remaining operating time. Pump: miniature axial flow. Distilled water is the "wetting" agent. Sampling period to initiate warning signals is approximately 2 min (i.e., when set to 10 ppm sensitivity, the device will trigger after 2 min sampling in a 10-ppm atmosphere).

19-8-8. Halide Detector
GasTech, Inc.

The GasTech Halide Detector utilizes the phenomenon of increased spectral intensity of an AC spark in the presence of halogens in the atmosphere. The brightness of the spark in the UV region is directly proportional to the halogen content of the gas sampled. Its primary field of application is by industrial hygienists in industrial solvent cleaning and fine chemical production facilities. It has also proven useful as a process monitor. Interpretation of this reading is made by relating the meter reading to a calibration curve based on the specific gas being tested. Sampling rate: continuous. Readout mode: panel meter. Recorder output adjustable from 0–10 to 0–50 mV. Detection limits: threshold limit concentrations of most halogen-containing compounds. The instrument also has a range adjust in arithmetic ratios of 1, 3, and 10, permitting expanded readings up to 10,000 ppm. The instrument is generally not subject to interference from nonhalogenated substances, but it is affected by the presence of sulfur and cyanogen compounds. Sensitivity to these compounds is an order of magnitude less than sensitivity to halides. Response time is 3–5 seconds with an accuracy of ±5%. Line voltage changes will have an effect on readings; otherwise stability is in the neighborhood of ±5% per day.

19-8-9. Model 722AEX-A Gas and Vapor Analyzer
Houston Atlas, Inc.

The 722AEX-A is a fixed monitor that measures airborne H_2S either on the close range or on a limitless wide range when equipped with the System 400 orifice/manifold kit accessory. The 722AEX-A operates by the photometric method. The air sample enters the instrument through its louvered hood where it is exposed to a lead acetate-impregnated tape. The H_2S content changes the tape from white to a darker color. A photoelectric cell measures the color change and provides a meter deflection proportional to the H_2S content of the sample. This principle is specific to H_2S. It is accurate to ±2%. Accurate sample readings are ready in 3 min. Zero drift is 5% of full-scale calibration.

19-8-10. Miniguard Personal Alarm Dosimeter
MDA Scientific, Inc.

The Miniguard is designed to function as a personal dosimeter for toxic chemical gases and vapors. The Miniguard uses a dry, chemically impregnated, paper-tape system, specifically sensitive to the substance being sampled. A piece of tape is inserted into the dosimeter, then the dosimeter is put in a shirt pocket, worn on a belt, etc. The tape is exposed either by diffusion or aspiration, depending on the system in-

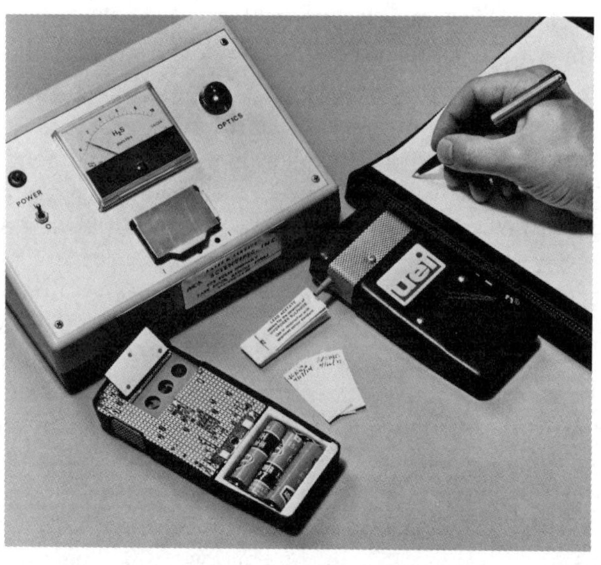

INSTRUMENT 19-8-10. Miniguard Personal Alarm Dosimeter.

volved. The exposed tape section and an unexposed reference section of the tape are continually evaluated by two balanced Cd-S photocells. When a preset stain density equivalent to a dose in ppm/hrs is reached, an audio alarm sounds. At the end of the exposure period, the tape can be removed and inserted into the readout device to provide a direct numerical reading of dose in ppm/hrs. The sampling rate is by diffusion or 0–250 cm^3/min, depending on system and range. Readout is directly in ppm/hrs. Specificity: no significant interference. Response time: variable, depends on alarm setting.

19-8-11. TLD-1 Toxic Gas Detector

MDA Scientific, Inc.

The TLD-1/ChemKey System is a portable, direct-reading instrument capable of measuring over 40 different toxic, corrosive, or pyrophoric gases. This system is designed for use by emergency response teams, industrial hygienists, or anyone who needs to monitor for different hazardous gases. The ChemKey Gas Selection System allows the operator to switch monitoring modes from one gas to another. All that is needed is a simple change of key and interference-free Chemcassette™ sensor. The system detects NH_3, arsine, Cl_2, diisocyanates, diborane, hydrazines, HF, HCl, HCN, H_2S, PH_3, silane, and phosgene.

19-8-12. Series 7100 Continuous Toxic Gas Monitors

MDA Scientific, Inc.

The MDA Series 7100 Monitor can detect ultra-low levels of over 40 hazardous gases in the workplace. Using MDA's Chemcassette™ paper tape detection system, the 7100 can accurately measure gas concentrations without cross-interference to other substances present. The on-board printer reports ppb levels in minute-by-minute, 8-hr average, and alarm-level formats. Other features include digital LCD readout, user-programmability, dual-alarms, alarm relays, serial output, up to 4 weeks unattended operation, and easy calibration.

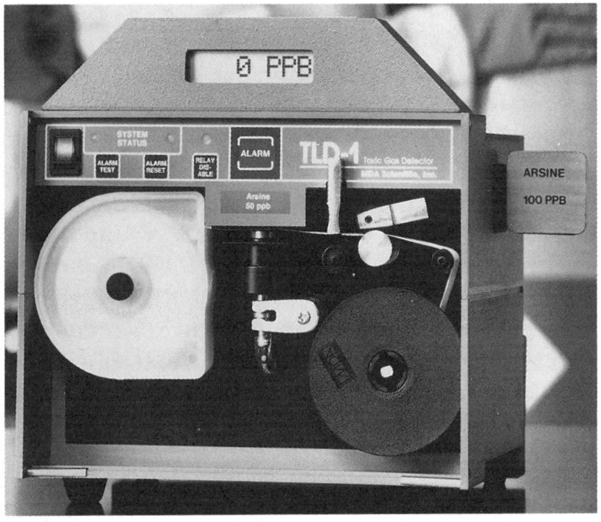

INSTRUMENT 19-8-11. TLD-1 Toxic Gas Detector.

INSTRUMENT 19-8-12. Series 7100 Continuous Toxic Gas Monitors.

19-8-13. Halide Meter

Scott Aviation

The Halide Meter is a portable instrument designed for field determinations of halogenated hydrocarbons in air. The Halide Meter is most often used for determining perchloroethylene, trichloroethylene, carbon tetrachloride, methylene chloride, and similar chlorinated hydrocarbons in air. Air containing halogenated hydrocarbons is passed through a chamber containing an AC electric arc between a copper electrode and a platinum electrode. A bright line spectrum of copper is produced when the air surrounding the arc contains halide vapors. The intensity of this copper spectrum is proportional to the concentration of halide vapors present. The meter readings are converted to ppm using calibration curves. A 20-ft Tygon® sampling hose is also provided with the instrument. Any halogenated material in the air being sampled will cause the instrument to give a reading and, in this sense, the instrument is nonspecific. It cannot, for example, differentiate carbon tetrachloride from trichloroethylene when the vapors are mixed. Nonhalogenated materials, such as hydrocarbons, do not interfere, however, and mixtures of halogenated vapors with other vapors may be evaluated.

19-8-14. Model 271 HA Sulfur Analyzer

Tracor, Inc.

The Model 271 HA was designed primarily as an automated monitor for low-level H_2S and SO_2 (the two common sulfur air pollutants); however, the 270 HA can be used in a variety of other analytical applications simply by changing the column, sample loop size, and/or operating conditions. Operating on gas chromatograph principles and utilizing the Tracor sulfur-specific flame photometric detector, the 270 HA chromatographically separates and independently quantitates vapor-state sulfur compounds in gaseous media. Precise sample volumes, reproducible to within $\pm 0.2\ cm^3$, are injected via fixed F.E.P. Teflon sample

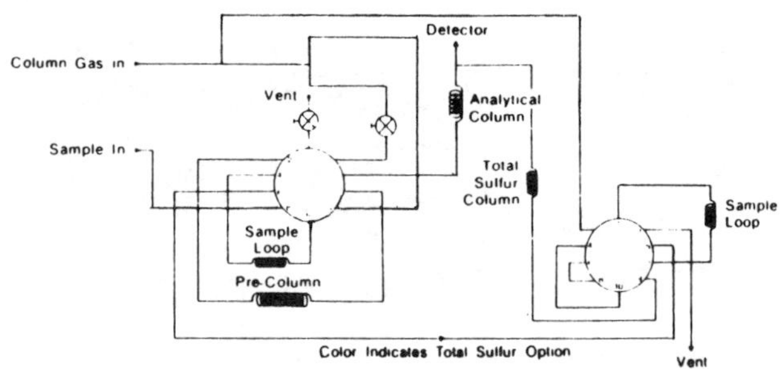

INSTRUMENT 19-8-14. Model 271 HA Sulfur Analyzer.

loops (9 cm^3 standard). The 6-ft analytical column quantitatively separates the low molecular weight sulfur pollutants normally measured in air quality monitoring. Tracor's sulfur selective FPD detects and measures sulfur pollutants as low as 1 ppb (9-cm^3 sample loop) without interference. Sampling rate: cyclic (225 seconds). Readout mode: dual output 0–10 mVFS (chromatographic) and 0–5 VFS (computer or datalogger) for each of two ranges (0–100 ppb and 0–1 ppm). Specificity: sulfur compound specific; possible interferences include high concentrations of CO_2 and/or hydrocarbons (1000 ppm). Response time: sampling is cyclic, maximum response time 225 seconds. Stability: 1%/24 hrs; 2%/week.

Thermal Conductivity Detectors

19-9-.1. Model 7-C Thermal Conductivity Analyzers

Beckman Instruments, Inc.

The Beckman 7-C Series Analyzers utilize the thermal conductivity principle of measurement to analyze the concentration of one component in a mixture of gases. These analyzers may be used in 1) power generating plants to detect hydrogen in generator cooling systems; 2) ammonia plants to measure hydrogen in NO, ammonia, argon, CO, or O_2; 3) petroleum refineries to measure hydrogen in C through C_6 hydrocarbons; or 4) air liquefaction plants to measure argon in O_2 and NO or measure O_2 with argon impurities. The Beckman instruments use heated TC filaments in a Wheatstone bridge to detect gases. Cell response time: 95% of change in 30 seconds at a sample flow rate of 250 cm^3/min. Sample flow rate: nominally 50–350 cm^3/min. Reference gas flow rate: 5–10 cm^3/min; at these flow rates, a cylinder containing 200 ft^3 of gas will last longer than 1 year. Sample pressure is 0–50 psig (69–345 kPa). An indicating meter is available for most ranges. Ambient temperature limits: 4.4 to 38°C. Explosion-proof enclosures are available for use in Class 1, Division 1, Group D, hazardous locations.

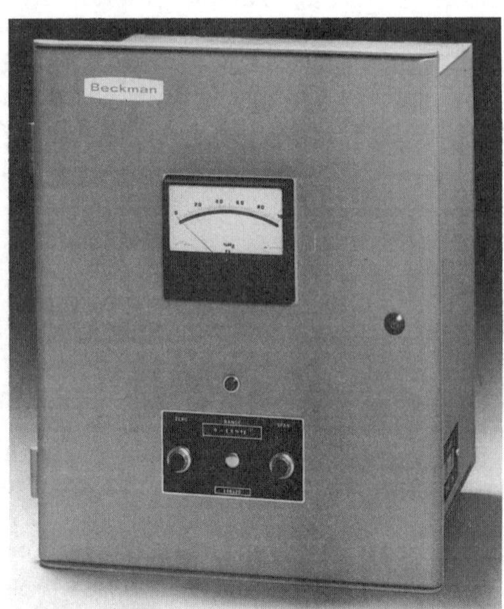

INSTRUMENT 19-9-1. Model 7-C Thermal Conductivity Analyzers.

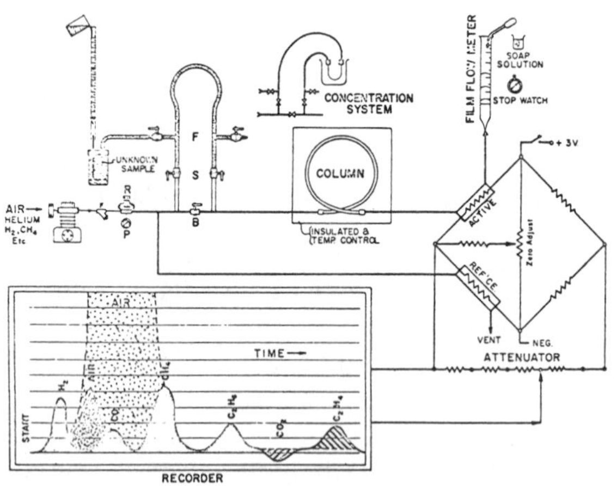

INSTRUMENT 19-9-2. Analograph and Servocorder.

19-9-2. Analograph and Servocorder

Deutsch Engineering & Testing Services

The Analograph uses an air or helium carrier for determinations of selected compounds in air pollution analysis, flue gas analysis, utility gas identification, toxic gases, and breath gas analysis. The Analograph is a chromatograph that uses either catalytic combustion or thermal conductivity detection. A fully transistorized Servocorder is used to handle the detector signal and has full-scale response of 1/8 second, zener reference voltage, multirange switch with an octave span from 1- to 1024-mV full-scale response. Optional dual-column, hot-cold detector in a top-opening metal case permits sharp peaks for fixed gases to C_{15} components.

The Analograph has recorder outlet terminals, fine and coarse zero adjust, and bridge voltmeter. It is supplied with partition column, carrier gas regulator, flowmeter, operating manual, and technical papers complete with built-in thermal conductivity and catalytic combustion detector, three sample tubes, zener diode power supply, and silica gel columns. Optional accessories include AC or DC sampling pumps, plastic sampling jars, special columns, and liquid injection syringes.

The Servocorder is portable in a two-tone black and gray case with carrying handle. Scale: 0–100 Chart: 26059-x with 0–100 range and 10/50 chart ruling, with a #206 synchronous motor rated for 110 V, 60 cycle providing a speed of 3/4 in./min (chart speed selector optional). Maximum source impedance: 100,000 ohms. Zero adjust: full scale.

19-9-3. Leak Hunter Model 8065

Matheson Gas Products

The Matheson Model 8065 Leak Hunter is a portable, hand-held unit designed for leak detection of nonflammable gases. Leak detection is achieved by a microvolume, thermisterized, thermal conductivity detector cell mounted in the front end of the hand unit. Self-diagnostics are included to determine the status of the detection circuitry, current, and low battery conditions (displayed as visual and audible warnings). For noisy environments, earphones are supplied. Gases detected: any gas with a different thermal conductivity to reference ambient air. Response time: <1 second. Recovery time: 1 second. Audio: fixed volume, variable frequency audio generator mounted in gun housing. Diagnostics: low battery indication, detector cell failure alarm. Operating time: maximum 14 hrs from rechargeable batteries. Operating temperature: 0 to 50°C. Storage temperature: –20 to 70°C.

Heat of Combustion Detectors

19-10-1. Series 100 Gas Detectors

AIM USA

The Series 100 Gas Detectors are designed to detect combustible gases, oxygen, and toxic gases in applications that include confined space survey work, industrial safety and hygiene, and fugitive emissions and leak detection. Instruments in the 100 Series are available to detect one, two, or three separate gases. Features include a data entry keypad and alarm incident, time-interval sampling, and location-survey testing data logging formats. Sensors are electrochemical for toxic gases and oxygen, and nonspecific metal oxide for combustible gases.

19-10-2. GasPointer® Combustible Gas Detectors

Bacharach, Inc.

The GasPointer® detectors are intrinsically safe, battery-powered portable instruments designed to measure concentrations of methane and carbon monoxide in ambient air and flue gas. The instrument is particularly designed for locating gas leaks and testing gas appliance installations in residential, commercial, and industrial applications. The GasPointer® operates with three sensors: a capillary diffusion electrochemical CO sensor; a temperature-compensated, catalytic bead, combustible gas sensor for low concentrations of natural gas; and a temperature-compensated, electrochemical oxygen sensor for higher concentrations of natural gas. The GasPointer® can operate in a temperature range of –5 to 50°C and a relative humidity range of 5% to 99%, noncondensing.

19-10-3. Gastron Combustible Gas Detectors

Bacharach, Inc.

The Gastron is a portable instrument used to detect and locate combustible gas leaks. The Model 310 is identical to the Model 282 except that it will detect hydrogen. A continuous sample of air is drawn through a sensing element where controlled catalytic combustion occurs, causing a signal to be generated that feeds both a visual and an audio indicating circuit. When gas is detected, an audio signal is momentarily interrupted and a visual indication is presented on a visual readout meter. The Gastron contains a pump, detector element, filters, control circuit, audio circuit, indicator, switch, and zero adjust. A quick-disconnect cable leads to a battery pack. The probe contains a humidity controlling filter. Response time: <2 seconds. Warm-up time: 2 min. Dust discrimination: filters down to 1 mm. Temperature: operating –34 to 54°C; storage –51 to 66°C. Drift rate: 100% of scale/hr in "Search" range (approximate). Detector cell life: 40 hrs (normal operation) average.

19-10-4. SNIFFER® 500 Series Portable Area Monitors

Bacharach, Inc.

The SNIFFER® 500 Series Portable Area Monitors are instruments designed to alert personnel to the hazards of O_2 deficiency and the presence of dangerous concentrations of combustible gases, CO, and H_2S. The SNIFFER 500 Series combines sensors for two or three different contaminants. The sensors include a heated catalytic bead for combustible gases and electrochemical cells for O_2, H_2S, and CO. Any combination of these contaminants, up to three, is available. Various visual (steady or pulsing LEDs) and audible alarms (using steady, alternating, or pulsed tones) are used for different instruments. In addition to the various alarm options, the 500 Series includes an integral sampling pump, a variety of concentration ranges for combustibles, analog displays, low flow and battery alarms, and use in hazardous areas. Operating temperature: 20 to 50°C. Response time: variable from 5 seconds to 60 seconds (90% response). Operating time: 10 hrs.

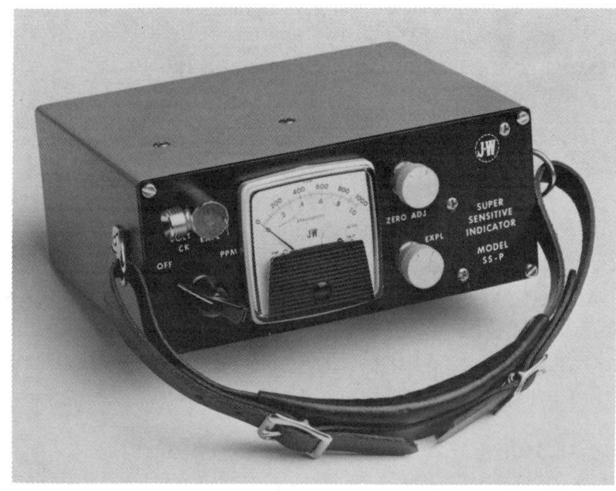

INSTRUMENT 19-10-5. Super Sensitive Indicator.

19-10-5. Super Sensitive Indicator
Bacharach, Inc.

The Super Sensitive Indicator uses a catalytic combustion sensor comprised of two identical platinum elements incorporated as opposite arms of a Wheatstone bridge circuit. One element serves as a reference; the other element, exposed to the sample, reacts catalytically in the presence of low concentrations of combustible gas. Batteries provide up to 8 hrs of continuous operation. Sampling rate: approximately 1.0 L/min. Readout mode: meter. Response time: initial response within 1–2 seconds of exposure. Instrument stability is in keeping with battery-operated instruments of this general design.

19-10-6. TLV SNIFFER®
Bacharach, Inc.

This instrument operates on the principle of catalytic combustion (a process of oxidizing a combustible gas/air mixture on the surface of a heated catalytic bead element). Eight-hour continuous operation is possible with six size D, Ni-Cd batteries or approximately 3 hrs with six size D, carbon-zinc batteries. Sampling rate: 1.65 L/min, nominal. Readout mode: meter, audible alarm, earphone output, and recorder output. Response time: initial response within 12 seconds of exposure. Its stability is in keeping with instruments of similar sensitivity and construction.

19-10-7. Ultra I and Ultra II
Bacharach, Inc.

The Ultra I measures the degree of flammability of any combustible gas or vapor mixture in air. The Ultra II is a dual-scale instrument that indicates both percent LEL and the actual quantity of combustible gas in the sample. Ultra I and Ultra II measure the flammability of gas in the LEL range using the catalytic combustion principle. Each instrument has two scales: 0% to 20% LEL and 0% to 100% LEL. When concentration exceeds 20% LEL, the indicator switches automatically from the lower to the upper scale. The Ultra II also can switch to a thermal conductivity circuit to indicate the actual quantity of combustible gas in the sample. Both units use methane as the calibration gas; have span and zero adjustments through holes in the lower housing; are powered by four size D batteries; and have temperature ranges from –10 to 50°C (limited by battery specifications).

19-10-8. Model 12 Combustible Gas Detector
Chestec, Inc.

The Model 12 is a solid-state detector for all combustible gases. The unit can be worn as a safety monitor for gas meter readers, gas appliance servicemen, petroleum workers, and laboratory workers. The Model 12 utilizes a solid-state semiconductor detector. The detector is silenced by nulling (zeroing) using the sensitivity knob. Any additional combustible gas will start the instrument clicking within seconds. Like a Geiger counter, the click rate increases with combustible gas concentration. The detector can be nulled to silence for gas concentrations up to about 1000 ppm. Any additional gas concentration will cause the instrument to start clicking. The knob pointer and dial scale indicates the approximate concentration in ppm at null. Other features include 12-VDC to 6-VDC charger, belt clip, earphone for noise operations, and rechargeable Ni-Cd batteries. Temperature range: –29 to 66°C. Operating time: 10 hrs.

19-10-9. Model XP-316 High Sensitivity Gas Indicator
COSMOS Gas Detection Systems

The XP-316 employs the principle of solid-thermal conductivity on a semiconductor/platinum filament for the detection of combustible gases and Freons, and for

INSTRUMENT 19-10-6. TLV SNIFFER®.

replacement Freons applications such as safety/compliance monitoring or locating small leaks. The instrument is graduated with a low range (0–1000 ppm) and a high range (0–10,000 ppm). Warm-up time is a maximum of 60 seconds and response time is 3 seconds to start of meter pointer deflection. Battery life: 10 hrs with alkaline cells. Standard accessories include standard AT-3A probe with DF-4 moisture trap and FE-2 filter, standard 1-m hose, carrying case with shoulder strap, four AA dry cell batteries, and FE-2 filter refills.

19-10-10. Model XP-704 Freon Detector
COSMOS Gas Detection Systems

The XP-704 is an intrinsically safe, high sensitivity leak detector for HCFC replacement freons. The minimum detectable leak rate is 3.3×10^{-5} atm-cm^3/sec. and the minimum detectable concentration is 5 ppm. Gas intake is automatic sampling by built-in micropump. The alarm system is an intermittent tone and flashing lamp with frequency proportional to gas concentration. Power is supplied by four AA batteries operate the instrument for 3 hrs continuously. Response time: 3 seconds maximum. Standard accessories include rubber search probe (AT-2), carrying case with shoulder strap, filter/moisture trap, two spare filter refills, and a set of four AA batteries.

19-10-11. Carbon Monoxide Detection System
Devco Engineering, Inc.

The Devco Engineering Carbon Monoxide Detection System is used in air pollution monitoring and to detect the presence of CO in parking garages, vehicle tunnels, steel mills, industrial plants, and warehouses. Devco Series 1000 Carbon Monoxide Detection Systems utilize the "Heat of Reaction" method for the measurement of CO in air. A schematic of the flow system is shown below. The air sample is passed through a heated chamber containing a catalyst bed, which promotes the oxidation of CO. Heat generated by this reaction is proportional to the concentration of CO in the air sample. A solid-state, time-proportioning temperature controller maintains the constant temperature within the analysis cell and cell chamber. All Series 1000 instruments include a "Trouble Alarm" relay circuit. This relay, controlled by instrument failure alarm circuits, illuminates a blue "Trouble" light and provides for external or remote alarm actuation on sample flow failure or low analysis cell temperature. Zero drift: less than ±2% with voltage fluctuations of ±15%. Response to reading: 30 seconds. Error: none due to hydrogen or hydrocarbon gases. Catalyst life: 1–2 years average. Calibration drift: due to relative humidity, error <2% of full-scale reading for relative humidity 50% ± 20%.

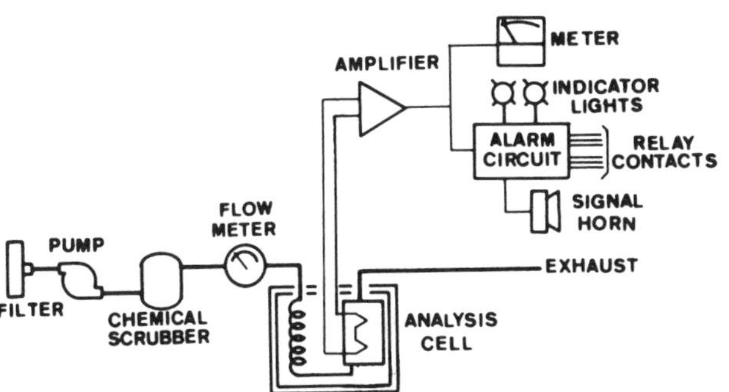

INSTRUMENT 19-10-11. Carbon Monoxide Detection System.

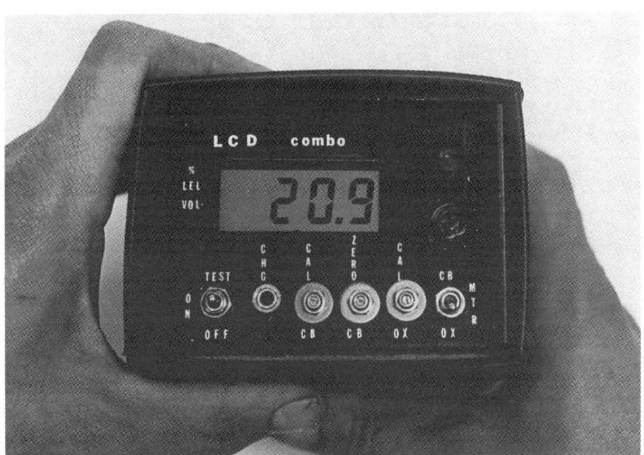

INSTRUMENT 19-10-13. LCD Combo Monitor.

19-10-12. Combustible Gas/Vapor Detection System
Devco Engineering, Inc.

Devco Engineering Series 5000 Combustible Gas and Vapor Detection Systems are designed for continuous monitoring of combustible gases. These systems employ a pair of catalytic hot wire elements forming two legs of a balance Wheatstone bridge. Single point or multiple point units are available for either continuous monitoring of each sample area or for sequential sampling via a single detection system. Two types of remote detector heads are available. The Diffusion Detector Head samples by means of diffusion and convection of the combustion gas in air. The Continuous Flow Detector Head makes use of a suction pump to maintain a continuous flow of the sample through the analysis cell. Speed of response: <1.0 second. Analog signal output for recorders, controllers, or digital display. Solid-state single and dual alarm circuits available. Ambient temperature limits: instrument, 0 to 57°C; detector head, to 93°C standard; to 121°C for high-temperature head.

19-10-13. LCD Combo Monitor
Dynamation, Inc.

The LCD Combo may be used to measure the level of combustible gas and O_2 deficiency. Applications include confined space entry and use as a personal warning device. The unit uses catalytic hot wire sensors for detection of combustible gas and a chemical cell for O_2 detection. The twin combustible sensors are electrically

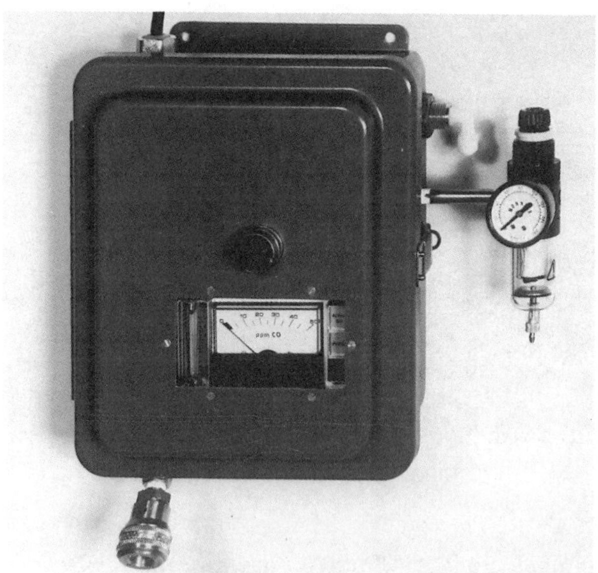

INSTRUMENT 19-10-14. Respiratory Airline CO Monitor/Alarm.

connected in a bridge configuration to compensate for temperature, humidity, and electronic changes. The sensors output is linear from 0% to 100% LEL. The chemical electrolytic cell measures the O_2 level and has up to 18 months of life before replacement. The O_2 cell is temperature compensated with a thermistor that is embedded inside the sensor. The cell can be easily changed and operated from 9 to 49°C. The instrument batteries provide up to 9 hrs of operation. Response time: combustible gas, 90% of maximum reading within 30 seconds. Warm-up time: 3 seconds for combustible gas; 10 seconds for O_2.

19-10-14. Respiratory Airline CO Monitor/Alarm

Dynamation, Inc.

The Model ABL-50 is a CO monitor/alarm specifically designed for respiratory airline breathing applications. It will continuously indicate the level of CO in ppm on its built-in meter and activate external alarms if the concentration exceeds the preset alarm threshold. The Model ABL-50 is connected to a tee fitting in the airline that bleeds off a small, continuous sample of air flowing between the compressor and the user. This sample is filtered for particulate matter, has the oil mist removed, and is regulated to 10 psig before passing over the solid-state, catalytic semiconductor sensor. Enclosure: polyester fiberglass NEMA 4 with cover latch. Controls: calibration and alarm threshold internal. Meter size: 2.5 in. Response: 90% of maximum reading within 2 min with 20 ppm CO concentration; faster at higher concentrations. Alarm adjustment range: 2–50 ppm CO. Recorder output: 0–1 mA. Interferences: other types of organic vapors will be detected if present in high concentrations or at their TLV. Sensor purge period: 1 min nominal. Sensor stabilization period: 10 min nominal.

19-10-15. Combustible Gas/Vapor Detectors

ERDCO Engineering Corporation

The ERDCO Engineering Corporation line of TOX/EX portable combustion gas/vapor indicators are used in safety checks for the presence of combustible gases or vapors. They are used for plant and personnel safety when inspecting, cleaning, or repairing tanks, manholes, ships' holds, and sewage treatment plants. They are widely used in utilities, refineries, laboratories, and combustible storage areas. TOX-EX gas/vapor indicators operate on the basic principle of the catalytic reaction of flammable gases and vapors on an electrically heated platinum filament in a Wheatstone bridge circuit. Accessories available for most models include hose sampling attachment with a 5-ft hose or additional lengths optional, 30-in. semirigid nylon tubing probe, calibrator, and adapter and tank with 25% LEL methane. All models have a response time of less than 3 seconds using 25 ft of sample hose; approximately 5 seconds with 50 ft of hose. All models differentiate methane from petroleum vapor electrically, without adding an absorption filter. In addition, the filament in each model is designed to prevent burnout even when repeatedly exposed to high gas. It is also highly resistant to mechanical shock.

19-10-16. Model EX-10 Personal Combustible Gas Detector

ENMET Corp.

The EX-10 is a pocket-sized combustible gas detector designed for personal protection of workers in hazardous areas or for confined space entry. The catalytic sensor in this instrument has a typical life expectancy of 3–5 years. Alarms are audible and visual, and are adjustable over the full scale. Response time: less than 10 seconds when exposed to 50% LEL methane. Operating temperature range: –10 to 55°C for intermittent exposures. Rechargeable 3.6-V Ni-Cd batteries provide 45 hrs of continuous operation.

19-10-17. Portable Dual Range Combination Combustibles/Oxygen Deficiency Detector and Alarm

GasTech, Inc.

The GX-3A detects combustible gas and O_2 deficiency simultaneously and gives both an audible and a visual alarm whenever either hazardous condition is encountered. It uses a resistive catalytic combustion sensor for combustible gases and an electrochemical cell to measure O_2. The sample is drawn into the instrument by means of an integral pump, and continuous operation of up to 6 hrs is assured by the use of Ni-Cd rechargeable batteries. Solid-state alarm circuits for O_2 and combustibles actuate independent alarm lights and a common audible signal that continues until manually reset. Standard calibration is based on methane. In the ppm range, the detector is calibrated to read directly in ppm of a specific hydrocarbon vapor, normally calibrated on toluene. Calibration curves can be supplied for interpretation of readings of other vapors of interest. Detection limits for O_2 are direct readings from 0% to 25% O_2. Alarms can be set at OSHA limit of 19.5%. The response time is within 3 seconds when using standard sampling hose. Its stability is ±2% full scale/4-hr period.

19-10-18. Exotector® Combustible Gas Meter

GfG Gas Electronics, Inc.

The Exotector® series of combustible gas meters covers three models for confined space entry, gas survey work, and leak detection. The Exotector has two modes of operation: pump operation for sampling from confined spaces and diffusion operation for continuous operation in combustible atmospheres. The different models offer ranges of combustible/methane detection from 0% to 10% LEL for leak detection to 0% to 100% LEL for full-range monitoring. The Exotector uses two sensors: catalytic combustion for 0% to 100% LEL and a hybrid thermal conductivity cell for 0% to 100% by volume detection even in the absence of O_2. Both sensors are mounted in a voltage- and temperature-balanced bridge configuration. Standard features include an analog display, an optical/acoustical alarm, a dual operation mode, 16 hrs of operation on one battery charge, sensor life of 1–3 years, and an intrinsically safe design. The three models (G614/G615, G624/G625, and G634/G635) are housed in antistatic, high-impact Polyamid 12. Response time: T_{90} = 10 seconds; warm-up time <15 seconds.

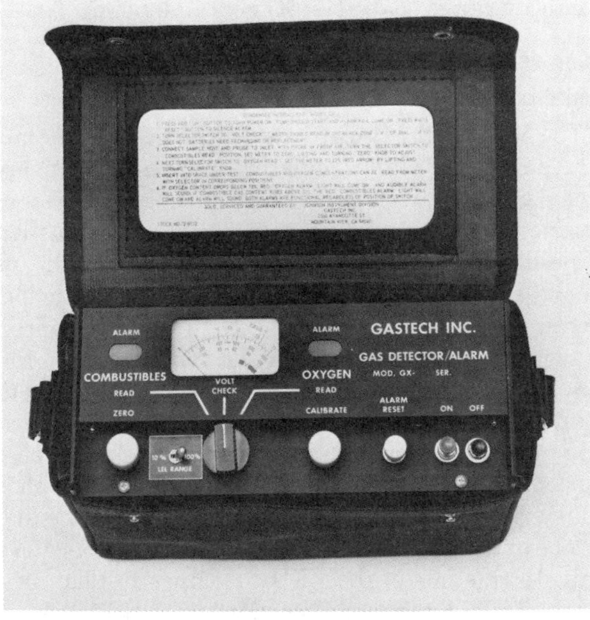

INSTRUMENT 19-10-17. Portable Dual Range Combination Combustibles/ Oxygen Deficiency Detector and Alarm.

INSTRUMENT 19-10-20. Combustible Gas Detectors.

19-10-19. Combustibles Analyzer, Model 647

Hays-Republic Division Corp.

The Hays-Republic Model 647 Heavy-duty Industrial Combustibles Analyzer effectively monitors combustibles levels in flue gases. Other applications include coating ovens and dyers, controlled-atmosphere furnaces, crude-oil handling facilities, distilling operations, engine test cells, electrolytic generators, explosives and fumigant manufacturing, sewage treatment plants, and combustion processes. The Model 647 operates on the principle of catalytic combustion, utilizing a balanced Wheatstone bridge circuit. The sensor consists of two flame arrestors, five layers of fine mesh of woven Monel wire, and a porous metal cup for a double margin of ignition safety. The sensor is further protected by a selective, molecular barrier that reduces catalytic poisoning from tetraethyl lead and silicone compounds. Contaminants: silicone vapors, tetraethyl lead. Integral indications: meter for percent combustibles or LEL; alarms and failure and pilot lights. Output: 0–100 mV. Accuracy: ±5% full scale/day (FSD). Linearity: ±4% FSD. Hysteresis: <1% FSD. Zero drift: 1% FSD/30 days maximum. Speed of response: 90% in 10 seconds. Alarm outputs: isolated NO and NC contacts for warning, alarm, and failure. Alarm reset: integral or remote. Fail-safe features: failures alarm indicating open, short, or low voltage at detector; negative zero drift in excess of 10% FSD; loss of power. Temperature range: 0 to 66°C.

19-10-20. Combustible Gas Detectors

Houston Atlas, Inc.

All of these instruments are capable of detecting the presence of any gas or vapor which, when combined with O_2 in free air, presents a potential explosion hazard. These instruments use the hot wire platinum element for detection. Model 510: portable type in aluminum case with batteries and built-in charger. Its probe is on a 2-m cable. Model 520: a multiunit instrument composed of two to six channels, each similar in operation to the Model 510 above. Either rack- or panel-type mountings. The sensing element is housed in a probe and safety shielded by a Monel metal screen. Up to 100 ft of extension cable may be used with this probe. Response: full scale in 4 seconds.

19-10-21. Model CD212 Methane Gas Monitor

Industrial Scientific Corporation

The CD212 Methane Gas Monitor is designed for use in mines and other work environments to assure optimum protection against hazardous levels of methane gas (CH_4). This monitor is suitable for use by face bosses and equipment operators where continuous monitoring of CH_4 is essential. It also is ideal for maintenance crews performing welding or cutting operations by the last open crosscut. The CD212 and CD210 (High Sensitivity) Methane Monitors utilize diffusion-type catalytic bead sensors in a Wheatstone bridge. The sensor detects methane over the range of 0% to 5% (by volume) and can run continuously for up to 9 hrs on a charge. Other features include an audible alarm for rising methane levels, low battery condition, and malfunction in the sensor; on–off switch that prevents accidental shutoff; digital LCD with illumination; and a rugged stainless steel case. Temperature range: 10 to 50°C.

10-10-22. GASPONDER® Multiple Gas Monitors

Lumidor Safety Products

The GASPONDER® Models (I–IV) offer the capability of monitoring combustibles, percent O_2, CO, and H_2S in any desired combination or all together. These monitors are designed for a wide variety of applications including telecommunications, industrial processes, water and waste treatment plants, sewer and manhole areas, construction, and oil and gas refineries. The GASPONDERs employ a wide variety of sensors, including a poison-resistant catalytic sensor for combustibles, galvanic cell for O_2, and electrochemical cell for CO and H_2S. The monitors use an internal pump at flows of up to 375 cm^3/min for fast instrument response. The monitors also incorporate audible and visual alarms for high or low concentrations, low battery condition, and low flow; charge indicator; automatic battery cutoff circuit; and back-lighted LCD. MSHA approved for mining and methane atmospheres. Temperature range: –5 to 45°C. Operating time: 10 to 12 hrs per charge.

10-10-23. Rechargeable RCM/REM Carbon Monoxide and Ethylene Oxide (EtO) Meters

Macurco, Inc.

The RCM and REM are miniature (shirt pocket-sized) meters specific to CO and EtO, respectively, that are powered by rechargeable Ni-Cd batteries. The units may be plugged into 120 VAC for continuous use or operated on batteries as a portable meter. The RCM and REM use low maintenance, solid-state semiconductor sensors. The readouts are composed of 10 LEDs for display of the concentrations. Other features include special warm-up circuits, low-voltage battery protection, simple operation, and interference-free measurements. Accuracy: continuous use, 10%; intermittent use, 25%. Warranty: 1 year, including batteries.

10-10-24. RGM Flammable Gas Meter

Macurco, Inc.

The RGM is a miniature (shirt-pocket-sized) flammable gas (CH_x) meter that is powered by Ni-Cd rechargeable batteries. The CH_x semiconductor sensor features low maintenance and long life. An electronic meter, composed of 10 LEDs, displays the 0% to 1% or 0% to 5% range of methane gas in air. Other features include special warm-up circuits, low-voltage battery protection, easy calibration, and simple operation. Accuracy: in normal use, 25%; after calibration, 10%. Warranty: 1 year, including batteries.

19-10-25. Gasurveyor 1000 Hydrocarbon Gas Detector

McNeill International

The Gasurveyor is designed to detect combustible gases, O_2, and toxic gases from leaks around pipes, pumps, flanges, and underground tanks in ppm or % LEL. Features include audible and visual alarms, automatic calibration, analogue and digital display, and intrinsically safe BASEEFA and CERCHAR certification. The instrument can operate >12 hrs on alkaline batteries. Operating temperature: –20 to 50°C. Relative humidity range: 20% to 95%, noncondensing.

19-10-26. Model 8057 Hazardous Gas Leak Detector

Matheson Gas Products

The Model 8057 Hazardous Gas Leak Detector monitors laboratory, plant, and process areas; instrumentation; tubing; fittings; storage containers; and production equipment for potentially dangerous leaks of gases and vapors at TLV levels. The Model 8057 uses a solid-state gas sensor with a sintered metallic block. An air sample from the suspected leak-source area is drawn into the unit and over the sensors by the internal, low-power-drain micropump. At intermittent tone sounds, an LED lamp flashes if a gas leak is detected. The tone frequency is proportional to the detected gas concentration; i.e., slow beep for low concentration and a faster beep for higher gas concentrations. The alarm can be silenced by means of a switch on the back of the unit. In this mode, the LED continues to flash in the event of gas detection. Detection time: 10–20 seconds, depending on gas and sensitivity setting. Approximately 6-hr continuous operating time with full charge (charger included). Operating temperature: 0 to 40°C. Warranty: 1 year from date of purchase.

19-10-27. Portable Combustible Gas and Oxygen Alarm, Models 260 and 100
Mine Safety Appliances Company

The Portable Combustible Gas and Oxygen Alarm, Model 260, is a dual-purpose instrument designed to monitor areas for combustible gases and/or O_2 deficiency. Although primarily a portable instrument, Model 260 may be used as a semicontinuous monitor in areas where an audible/visual alarm is required. The Model 100 contains the combustible gas monitor only. The combustible gas portion of the instrument uses a catalytically activated Pelement™ filament in a Wheatstone bridge. The O_2 portion of the instrument operates by means of a diffusion galvanic sensor cell. Sampling rate is 1.6 L/min. Other accessories include standard MSA probe rods, tubes, carrying harness, and sampling lines when used for remote sampling. The combustible gas alarm is factory set to trigger at 50% LEL and the O_2 alarm at 19.5% O_2. Both alarm points are field adjustable. Compounds containing silicon and leaded gasoline vapors may seriously impair instrument response. An inhibitor filter should be used to nullify the effect of leaded gasoline vapors. Response: 90% in <20 seconds. Accuracy: ±5% of full scale for combustibles and ±2% for O_2.

19-10-28. Explosimeter® Combustible Gas Indicator, Model 2A
Mine Safety Appliances Company

The MSA Explosimeter®, Model 2A, measures combustible gases and vapors in concentrations up to 100% of LEL. The instrument operates by the catalytic action of a heated platinum filament in contact with combustible gases. External accessories: sampling line available in length multiples of 5 ft for remote testing; hollow, 3-ft rigid probe tube for sampling from bar holes or manholes; solid, 4-ft probe rod for use in testing tanks that may contain liquids; charcoal filter in external cartridge holder for use as an aid in distinguishing between gases and condensable vapors in sample. Response time: 10–15 seconds. Model 2A is factory-calibrated on pentane in air. Pentane calibration is used because it is representative of petroleum vapors. When testing other combustible gases, readings are generally on the high or safe side.

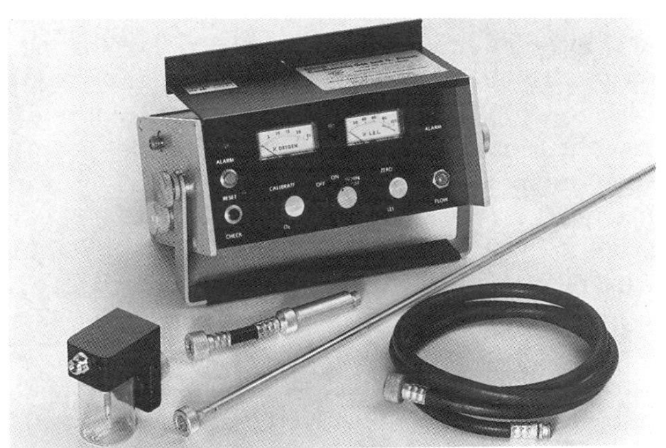

INSTRUMENT 19-10-27. Portable Combustible Gas and Oxygen Alarm, Models 260 and 100.

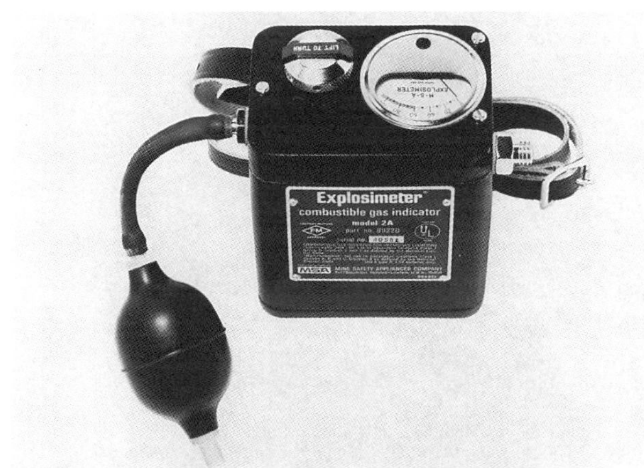

INSTRUMENT 19-10-28. Explosimeter® Combustible Gas Indicator, Model 2A.

19-10-29. Combustible Gas Detection System, Series 5000
Mine Safety Appliances Company

Series 5000 instruments are designed to display gas concentrations from any number of the MSA combustible, toxic, and O_2 gas sensors. These instruments have a high density, yet are reliable and easy to install, start up, and maintain. All Series 5000 instruments provide a three-digit LED readout, three alarm levels, a malfunction indicator, and 4- to 20-mA outputs for each sensor. Sensors may be located up to 5000 ft from the instrument. Different models are available that will accept up to 2, 6, 12, or 24 sensors with NEMA 12 or NEMA 4X enclosures.

19-10-30. Gascope® Combustible Gas Indicator, Models 60 and 62
Mine Safety Appliances Company

MSA Combustible Gas Indicators are portable instruments for use in detecting, measuring, and pinpointing leaks of combustible gases or vapors. Model 60 is calibrated on methane in air by volume in a low range of 0% to 5% and a high range of 0% to 100%. Model 62 is calibrated on pentane in air in a low range of 0% to 100% LEL and a high range of 0% to 100% by volume. MSA Combustible Gas Indicators use two different types of filaments: a catalytic combustion filament for low range operations and a thermal conductivity filament for high range. Sampling rate: 1.5 L/min. The Gascope may be used with MSA 3-ft probe tubes and rods. An external holder for charcoal cartridges at-

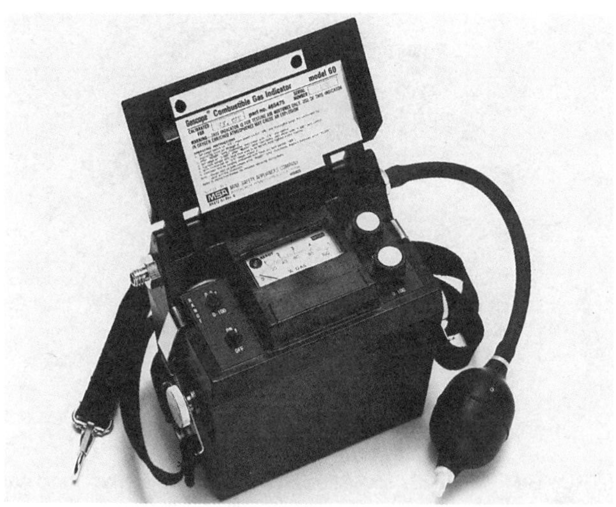

INSTRUMENT 19-10-30. Gascope® Combustible Gas Indicator, Models 60 and 62.

taches to sample line connection of the instrument. Gascope indicators can operate continuously for over 8 hrs on batteries. Silicon compounds may seriously impair response of the instruments. Leaded gasoline vapors can also poison the catalytic combustion filament; an inhibitor filter should be used to nullify this effect. Constant voltage power supply to filaments minimizes zero drift. Calibration: separate adjustment knobs for each measuring circuit of the changings of zero settings.

19-10-31. Methanometer

National Mine Service Company

The G-2000 Methanometer is a pocket-sized, hand-held instrument for measuring the concentration of methane in air. The G-2000 is a diffusion-type methanometer. Gas is admitted to the sensor through two screened ports in the top of the instrument. An LED chain is activated by holding a pushbutton on the side of the case. An additional LED on the front of the instrument gives a constant indication of battery condition while the instrument is in use. The G-2000 is housed in a stainless steel case. MSHA certification: 8C–43. Display: LED chain (0% to 2% CH_4) with underrange and overrange indicators. Detector: catalytic bead on platinum wire. Charging: 50 mA constant current. Approximately 300 readings with fully charged battery.

10-10-32. D-Series Combustible Gas Systems

Scott Aviation

The D-Series are portable instruments that can detect most combustible gases or vapors in air. Two-scale instruments are available. One meter scale range employs catalytic filaments to indicate combustible gas concentration from zero to the LEL. The second scale operates on the thermal conductivity principle and indicates combustible gas or vapor concentration directly from 0% to 100% gas. The D-Series are equipped with aspirator bulb, neck strap, and eight D-cell batteries.

19-10-33. Hydrogen Sulfide Monitor, Model 10HS

Sierra Monitor Corporation

The Sierra Model 10HS monitor continuously measures the concentration of H_2S in the ambient air. Incorporated in the Model 10HS is a solid-state H_2S sensor, microprocessor, concentration display, operating controls, audible alarm, and rechargeable battery or AC power supply. Displays include present concentration, time-weighted average value for exposure on a single shift, or maximum concentration value sensed during a work period. Accessories supplied: earphone for high noise area, instruction manual, and instrument case. Battery gives 8- to 10-hr operation per charge. Device and alarm are intrinsically safe for use in hazardous locations. Operating temperature range: –20 to 40°C. Response time: 80% of full scale in 2 min. Zero drift: <3% of full scale in 8 hrs. Warm-up time: <5 min. Operating controls: on/off switch; display concentration switches for 1) present concentration sensed, 2) time-weighted average value for exposure, 3) maximum concentration value sensed, 4) time unit has been in operation, 5) test for checking operation function and audible alarm, 6) zero screw adjustment to display zero present concentration in fresh air (interior adjustment), and 7) calibration screw adjustment to display 25-ppm present concentration (interior adjustment) when exposed to 25-ppm calibration gas. Alarm levels are factory preset for ceiling concentration level of 20 ppm, time-weighted average value alarm at 10 ppm, evacuation alarm at 50 ppm, and when battery condition is low.

19-10-34. Model 2000 Portable Combustible Gas Detectors

Sierra Monitor Corporation

The Series 2000 detectors are ideal for gas detection in mines, manholes, tanks, natural gas fields, garages and vehicle maintenance facilities, utilities, testing of gas cylinder and new piping connections, etc. The units use solid-state, metal oxide sensors and operate in three different modes: 1) proportional mode — a continuous audible "tick" increases logarithmically as gas concentration rises, 2) low alarm mode — 250 ppm H_2 and 500 ppm CH_4, and 3) high alarm mode — 2500 ppm H_2 and 5000 ppm CH_4. Other features include an alarm for the upper range of gas concentration, an earphone for noisy operation, a 15-ft, 120-VAC power cable, an 18-in. flexible probe, replaceable batteries, and intrinsically safe for use in Class 1, Division 1, Groups B, C, and D. Warm-up time: 30 seconds. Response time: <1 second. Temperature range: –5 to 50°C. Battery life: 8-hrs continuous.

19-10-35. Model 102 Combustible Gas Analyzer

Teledyne Analytical Instruments

The Model 102 uses a catalytic bead sensor. Combustible gases present in the air burn in the presence of O_2, producing a signal proportional to the concentration of the combustible gases. Sample rate: diffusion when placed in air. Readout mode: integral meter with recorder output signal. Detection limits: 100% of LEL of most combustible gases. Specificity: must be calibrated in "equivalent" of a designated combustible gas. Response time: 90% of full scale in <20 seconds. Accuracy: meter ±0.5% of full scale.

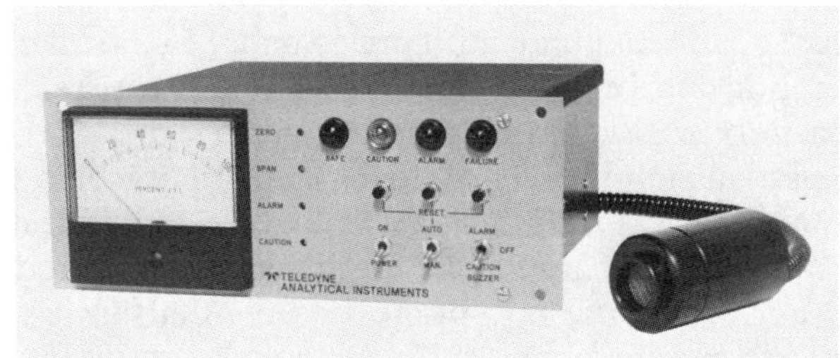

INSTRUMENT 19-10-35. Model 102 Combustible Gas Analyzer.

Gas Chromatographic (GC) Analyzers

19-11-1. Organic Vapor Analyzer

Foxboro Company

Foxboro's Organic Vapor Analyzer is designed to measure trace quantities of organic materials in air using a hydrogen flame ionization detection system. It has a single logarithmically scaled readout from 1 to 100,000 ppm or with a lower maximum level, if desired. Designed for use as a portable survey instrument, it can also be readily adapted to fixed remote monitoring or mobile installations. The instrument response is read on a hand-held meter assembly or can be read utilizing the external monitor signal. An audible detection alarm is provided; it can be preset to any desired level and has a frequency modulated tone that varies as a function of the signal level. The standard instrument includes an audible flame-out alarm, battery test indicator, and internal electronic calibration.

Standard accessories include instrument carrying and storage case, high pressure fuel filling hose assembly, and AC battery charger. Response time: <2 seconds. Sample flow rate: nominally 2 L/min. Fuel supply: 75-cm^3 tank of pure hydrogen at maximum pressure of 2300 psig, fillable while in case. Service life: hydrogen supply and battery power — 8 hrs operating time, minimum. The umbilical cord is 5 ft long with connectors for electrical cable and sample hose. In-line disposable and permanent particle filters are standard; activated charcoal filters are optional.

19-11-2. 300 Series Gas Chromatographs

HNU Systems, Inc.

The 300 Series gas chromatographs offer a range of compact versatility for environmental analysis of organic compounds. Five different detectors are available, including two detectors operational at once. Packed or capillary columns can be used, as well as a a wide range of isothermal or programmed temperatures. The units feature all the extras of a laboratory gas chromatograph, but in a rugged, compact package. Other options include a built-in printer and a choice of injectors.

19-11-3. MSI-301 Organic Vapor Monitor

Microsensor Systems, Inc.

The MS-301 Series Analyzers are designed for high sensitivity, onsite, continuous monitoring of organic vapors. The system contains an isothermal gas chromatograph, a sensitive solid-state sensor, and an onboard microcomputer for control and analysis. Carrier gas is generated by scrubbing ambient air through filters into a pressurized tank. Ambient air samples are collected on concentrator tubes and thermally heated and injected into the column. The system can be remotely controlled via a direct cable or a modem connection. The unit can be operated from 120 VAC or from an optional 12-VDC battery. Other features include ppb sensitivity, multicomponent analysis, self diagnosis, and a simple calibration procedure.

19-11-4. 10S Series Portable Gas Chromatographs

Photovac International, Inc.

The self-contained model 10S air analyzer can be used as a portable or fixed station monitor to provide multicomponent air analyses to the ppb level. The 10S utilizes a photoionization detector that can measure compounds not usually detected by photoionization such as chloromethanes, fluorochloromethanes, and ethane. Automatic sampling is accomplished using a miniature, printed circuit card upon which are mounted very small, three-way solenoid valves, chosen for their extreme reliability and long life. These valves are all under independent computer control and can be interconnected to produce a wide range of different chromatographies. The computer also handles the timing of different valve arrangements, controlling, calibrating, identifying, and quantifying chromatograms; runs the tiny printer/plotter; monitors temperature and battery charge; and provides an auto-zero function at the beginning of each analysis. Chromatography: dual-column, manual injection standard. Multifunction, 6-value (18-ports) option provides variety of gas chromatography arrangements; "quick-scan" and "analytical" columns and "precolumn backflush" are software selectable. A wide range of interchangeable columns is available. Sampling: manual injection or optional automatic injection, computer-controlled internal sampling pump with provision for connection of sampling line. Injection volumes can be software selectable. Carrier gas: normally, air is used but can use other carriers including NO, He, and CO_2. Rechargeable internal reservoir will last about 2 days. Calibration: manual or fully automatic (from portable standard vessel), depending on option chosen. Analysis time: depends on compound sought and any potential interferences. Display mode: internal or external chart recorder shows chromatograph trace and name compounds with concentrations and time-weighted averages (depending on which option is chosen). LCD gives 32 characters, alpha-numeric or bar graph for 10S10. Warm-up time: 5–10 min for most tasks.

19-11-5. SnapShot™ Hand-held Gas Chromatograph

Photovac International, Inc.

The SnapShot™ is designed for specific industrial and environmental monitoring tasks (e.g., benzene, C1–C5 hydrocarbons, and acrylonitrile). Weighing only 8.5 lbs and totally self-contained, the unit is truly hand-held. Single button operation with specific modules means little or no prior training is required. Features include a PID detector, isothermal capillary column, internal software for species identification, LCD readout, internal data logger, automatic injection and backflush, and direct downloading to a PC. A single snap-on lead acid battery allows for 8 hrs of operation and can be easily changed.

19-11-6. Scentograph "Plus II" Portable Gas Chromatograph

Sentex Systems, Inc.

The Scentograph is a portable gas chromatograph designed to provide onsite field analysis with laboratory gas chromatographic quality. Five detector options are available, along with a choice of commercially available columns, either capillary or packed. The units can be heated isothermally or ramped to temperatures up to 180°C. The unit has an internal battery and gas supply for total portability or can be connected to AC power for prolonged use. A detachable lap-top PC with applicable software controls the system and conducts the sample analysis, storing the results on disk for future recall.

19-11-7. Scentoscreen Portable Gas Chromatograph

Sentex Systems, Inc.

The Scentoscreen is a lighter, smaller version of the Scentograph (see Instrument No. 19-11.6) portable gas chromatograph. Not all options available on the Scentograph are available for the Scentoscreen.

TABLE 19-I-1. Electrical Conductivity Analyzers

Instrument No.	Mfg./ Supp.*	Model	Analytes	Range (ppm)	Detection Limit (ppm)	Precision (±)	Dimensions (cm) H	W	L	Weight (kg)	Power	Alarms Aud.	Vis.	Comments
19-1-1	AIC	411	Hg	0.001–1.999	0.001	5%	5.1	2.4	1.6	2.3	7.2 VDC or 110 VAC	—	—	F
19-1-2	BAC	MHO	H_2S, SO_2, NH_3	0–5, 10, 20 0–50, 100	—	—	3.9	4.7	2.4	6.8	115 VAC	X	X	A, B
19-1-3	CAL	U3S	SO_2		0.005	—	6.3	5.5	8.3	27.3	115 VAC	—	—	C, D
19-1-4	DVC	Series 9000	H_2S, Cl_2, CO_2, NH_3, SO_2, halogenated hydrocarbons	0–1	variable	2–5%	NEMA type wall enclosures			—	115 VAC	—	—	A, E

*Manufacturer codes given in Table 19-I-12.

A. H_2S converted to SO_2 in inlet.

B. Absorbs sample in distilled H_2O.

C. Absorbs sample in acidified H_2O_2 solution.

D. Converts SO_2 to H_2SO_4; temperature compensated.

E. Pyrolysis train on inlet for some analytes.

F. Collects a 1- or 10-second sample on a gold film sensor.

TABLE 19-I-2. Potentiometric Analyzers

Instrument No.	Mfg./ Supp.*	Model	Analytes	Range (ppm)	Detection Limit (ppm)	Precision (±)	Dimensions (cm)			Weight (kg)	Power	Alarms		Com-ments
							H	W	L			Aud.	Vis.	
19-2-1	AIM	200 Series 300 Series	O_2, CO, H_2S, SO_2, NO, NO_2, Cl_2, H, HCN, HCl, explosives	—	—	—	39.9 long × 6.4 diameter			1.0	battery	X	X	A, C, N
19-2-2	AIM	500 Series	O_2 H_2S CO combustible gases	0–25% 0–200 0–500 0–100% LEL	—	2.5% FS** 3% FS	19	10.2	6.4	1.4	Pb-acid battery	X	X	A, E, N, O
19-2-3	BAC	Sentinel® 44	O_2 combustibles CO H_2S	0-25% 0–100% LEL 0–999 0–200	—	—	19.7	11.4	5.1	1.1	Pb-acid battery	X	X	C, E
19-2-4	CAL	Mikrogas® Series	SO_2, HCl, H_2S, NH_3, Cl_2, $COCl_2$, COS, CS_2, HCN, etc.	0–1.0 and up	0.04	3% FS		—		—	VAC	X	—	A
19-2-5	CAL	Ultragas® Series	CO, CO_2, CH_4, NH_3, H_2S, SO_2, HCl, $COCl_2$, CKW, COS, CS_2, HCN	0–10 0–5000	0.1	1% FS		—		—	VAC	X	—	A
19-2-6	CEA	Gasman	O_2, H_2S, CO, SO_2, Cl_2, NO_2, NO, HCl, HCN, NH_3, combustibles	variable	variable	—	11.5	6.6	3.9	0.3	4 AA cells	X	X	A, N
19-2-7	CEA	Series U	CO, NH_3, organics, combustibles, Freons	0–250, 500, 100 or %LEL	variable	—	1.7	2.9	1.1	< 0.09	Ni–Cd	X	X	A, D
19-2-8.	CEA	TG-BA Series	Cl_2, H_2S, HCN, HCl, SO_2, $COCl_2$, halogens, NO_x, amines, NH_3, Freons	variable	variable	5%	3.1	3.1	5.1	5.9	110 or Ni–Cd	X	X	A
19-2-9	CEA	Triple Plus	same as Gasman	variable	variable	—	17	8	2	0.9	110 or Pb-acid	X	X	A, C, E, O
19-2-10	COS	XP-302IIE	O_2 combustibles H_2S CO	0–25% 0–100% LEL 0–30 0–100	—	0.7% 5% LEL 1.5 10	23	10.5	17.5	5.0	4-AA	X	X	A, C, M
19-2-11	DYM	O_2-25H	O_2	0–25%	0.5%	1%	1.0	2.0	0.8	0.4	—	X		A
19-2-12	DYM	Monoguard/ dynaMite	CO, H_2S, O_2, SO_2, NO	0–100, 500 100% (O_2)	—	1 ppm	2.0 1.3	1.2 0.9	0.4 0.6	0.3 0.2	9-V lithium 250 hr	X	X	A, B, E

TABLE 19-I-2 (con't.). Potentiometric Analyzers

Instrument No.	Mfg./ Supp.*	Model	Analytes	Range (ppm)	Detection Limit (ppm)	Precision (±)	Dimensions (cm) H	W	L	Weight (kg)	Power	Alarms Aud.	Vis.	Com- ments
19-2-13	EIT	Series 300	SO_2, NO_2, NO_x, H_2S	0–1, 10,000 analyte dependent	0.001 variable	1%	2.6	4.8	5.1	5.5	115–220 VAC	—	—	F
19-2-14	ENM	CGS Series	combustible gases O_2 deficiency	%LEL %vol	—	—	19.2	11.1	6.1	1.6	9.6-V battery	X	X	G
		Omni 4000	CO, H_2S, NH_3, SO_2, Cl_2, HCN, HCl, NO, NO_2, combustible gases, O_2 deficiency	—	—	—		—		—	battery	X	X	C, E
		Quad-400	CO H_2S CH_4 O_2	0–100 5–30 0–60% LEL 0–99.9%	—	—	19.7	14.0	6.6	1.7	7.2-V battery	X	X	A, C, M, O
19-2-15	ENM	Toximet Series	O_2, CO, H_2S, NO, H_2, NO_2, HCl, HCN, SO_2, Cl_2, NH_3	varies by analyte	—	1%	13	6.3	2.8	0.2	9-V alkaline	X	X	A
19-2-16	ENS	Ethylene Oxide Meter	ethylene oxide	0–100	0.1	—	11.4	6.1	2.5	0.1	9-V battery	X	—	A, B
19-2-17	GFG	Series G3000	CO, H_2S	0–200, 50	—	2–3%	1.5	0.9	0.6	0.2	Ni–Cd 100 hr	X	X	A, B
19-2-18	GFG	Polytector	CO O_2 combustibles	0–200, 5000 0–25% 0–5%, 100%	2 0.2% 0.1%	2 ppm 0.2% 1%	3.3	1.4	0.9	0.9	—	—	—	A, B, E
19-2-19	ISC	CO260	CO	0–1999	1		1.9	1.1	0.6	0.4	4 AA cells	X	X	A, B
19-2-20	ISC	TMX 410	combustibles CH_4, O_2, CO, H_2S NO_2, SO_2, Cl_2	0–100% LEL 0–5% vol 0–30% vol 0–999 0–99.9	0.1% 0.1% 0.1% 1, 0.1 0.1		12.1	7.0	5.0	2.0 0.7	Ni–Cd	X	X	A
19-2-21	ITS	Series 1000 & 4000	CO, SO_2, H_2S, Cl_2, NO, NO_2, hydrazines ClO_2, HCN, E_4O, HCHO	0.1–10 × TLV	2% FS	1% FS	2.9 17.8	2.4 10.2	4.5 22.5	3.6 2.0	Ni–Cd	X	X	A, C, E
19-2-22	ITS	Series 5000	CO, NO_2, H_2S, SO_2, Cl_2	0.1–10 times TLV	0.5%	2%	2.4	1.2	0.8	0.7	9V 125 hr	X	X	A, B, E

TABLE 19-I-2 (con't.). Potentiometric Analyzers

Instrument No.	Mfg./ Supp.*	Model	Analytes	Range (ppm)	Detection Limit (ppm)	Precision (±)	Dimensions (cm)			Weight (kg)	Power	Alarms		Com- ments
							H	W	L			Aud.	Vis.	
19-2-23	MCN	PhD Cannonball®	O_2, combustible gases, CO, H_2S, Cl_2, SO_2, NO_2, HCN	—	—	—	5.6	10.9	18.3	0.6	Pb-acid gel	X	X	E, N
19-2-24	MCN	Toxilog	CO, H_2S, SO_2, Cl_2, NO_2, NO, HCN, NH_3, HCl	vary by analyte	—	0.1 ppm	2.2	6.0	10.2	0.2	3-AAA alkaline	X	X	B, N
19-2-25	MDA	Formalde- meter	formaldehyde	0.3–99.9	—	15%	3.0	6.3	12	0.1	9V	X	X	A
19-2-26	MDA	Monitox	CO, Cl_2, N_2H_4, HCN, H_2S, $COCl_2$, SO_2	0–300 analyte dependent	variable	10%	10.5	6.2	2.4	0.15	Px-23 or Px-14 battery	X	X	A
19-2-27	MET	60	CO	0–1999	—	1%	15.0	7.8	4.8	0.9	AA Ni–Cd 120 VAC	X	X	A, B
		70	SO_2	0–1000, 50, 200, 400										
		80	NO_x	0–100, 50, 200, 400										
		90	H_2S	0–400, 5, 10, 25										
19-2-28	MET	PM-7000 Series	CO H_2S, SO_2, NO Cl_2, NO_2	0–1999 0–199.9 0–19.9	—	1%	7.6	10.2	2.3	0.3	9-V battery	X	X	A, E, G
19-2-29	MSA	MiniCO IV	CO	0–100, 250, 500	2	2%	—	—	—	—	—	X	X	A, B
19-2-30	MSA	Cricket	O_2, CO, H_2S, Cl_2	0–25% analyte dependent	2% FS	—	3.2	7.6	5	—	Ni–Cd	X	X	B, M
19-2-31	MST	MSTox 8600	AsH_3, CO, Cl_2, B_2H_6, H_2, HCl, HCN, H_2S, NO_2, O_2, $COCl_2$, PH_3, SiH_4	analyte dependent	—	—	9.3	4.7	2.1	0.1	battery	X	X	A, C
19-2-32	NDR	Ecolyzer Series 2000	CO	0–50, 100, 500, 600, 3000	0.5%	1%	2.8	5.1	2.8	4	Ni–Cd	—	—	A
19-2-33	NDR	210	CO	0–1999	1.0	1 ppm	2.1	1.3	0.5	0.34	9V	X	X	A, B
19-2-34	NDR	7100	NO NO_2	0–10, 50 0–2, 10		1–2%					Ni–Cd	X	X	A

TABLE 19-I-2 (con't.). Potentiometric Analyzers

Instrument No.	Mfg./ Supp.*	Model	Analytes	Range (ppm)	Detection Limit (ppm)	Precision (±)	Dimensions (cm) H	W	L	Weight (kg)	Power	Alarms Aud.	Vis.	Comments
19-2-35	NDR	Dualarm Trialarm Quadalarm Multi-Pac	combustible gases O_2 CO H_2S	0–99% LEL 0–25% vol 0–999 0–199	—	5% LEL 3% 3% 3%	18	8.5	4.5	0.7	Ni–Cd	X	X	A, C, E, N, O
19-2-36	NEO	Exotox	O_2 CO H_2S	0–25% 0–999 0–999	0.5% 1 1	2.5%	6	3.5	2.1	2	Ni–Cd	X	X	A, M
19-2-37	NEO	Neotox	O_2, CO, H_2S	0–35% O_2 0–999	0.1% O_2 1	1–2.5%	1.6	0.9	0.7	2.4	9V 200–300 hr	X	X	A, C
19-2-38	NEO	Minigas	flammable gases O_2 CO H_2S	0–99% LEL 0–25% vol 0–999 0–499	—	2% LEL 0.3% 5 2	4.2	7.2	16.2	0.8	Ni–Cd or 4-AAA	X	X	C
19-2-39	NEO	OTOX® 2002 2003	 CO H_2S, SO_2, Cl_2	 0–100 0–2000	 —	 2.5% 2.5%	 23 20	 13 13	 7 9	 2.0 1.3	 12 VDC 120 VAC	 X	 X	 A
19-2-40	ORE	O3T	O_3	1–100 pph/vol	3 pphm/vol	3%	9.4	5.9	5.1	32	110 VAC	X	—	H
19-2-41	ORE	MSA-3	O_3	5 pphm–0.1% (v)	—	—	6.7	4.7	3.9	21	115 VAC	—	—	H, I
19-2-42	PRA	Titrilog II	oxidizable sulfur compounds (e.g. SO_2, H_2S)		0.01–0.02	—	5.6	5.6	8.3	30	115 VAC	—	—	J, K
19-2-43	SCA	S100 Series	combustibles O_2 H_2S	0–100% LEL 0–25% 0–199	—	0–50%: 3% >50%: 10% 0.8% 0–50: 5 >51: 5% FS	15.9	4.1	7.9	—	Ni–Cd	X	X	C
19-2-44	SEN	Mini Monitor	H_2S, CO, O_2, NO_2, SO_2	0–10, 20, 100, 400, 40%	—	5%	11.8	2.4	7.6	0.2	AA (2) 100 hr	X	X	A, B, C
19-2-45	TEL	990	O_2, CO in flue gas	0–500, 100, 5, 25%	2%	5%	4.8	5.1	2.7	5	Ni–Cd	—	—	A, L, M

*Manufacturer codes given in Table 19-I-12.
**FS = full scale.
A. Electrochemical sensor.
B. Diffusion sampling.
C. Intrinsically safe.
D. Explosion-proof units available.
E. Data logger capabilities.
F. Uses temperature-compensated Faristor sensor.
G. Available in variety of fixed units.
H. Absorbing solution is potassium iodine.
I. Endpoint is a titration with sodium thiosulfate.
J. Cell reagent is KBr, where Br_2 is generated.
K. Liquid prefilters are required for some analytes.
L. Designed for combustion process measurements.
M. Separate sensors for CO and O_2.
N. A variety of sensors available.
O. Designed for confined space entry.

TABLE 19-I-3. Coulometric Analyzers

Instrument No.	Mfg./ Supp.*	Model	Analytes	Range (ppm)	Detection Limit (ppm)	Precision (±)	Dimensions (cm) H	W	L	Weight (kg)	Power	Alarms Aud.	Vis.	Comments
19-3-1	ADS	EA-1	Flammable toxic gases	ppm & % LEL	small concentrations	% of LEL	3.2	4.1	2.2	<4.5	90–120 VAC 190–240 VAC	—	—	A
19-3-2	BAC	Sentox	H_2S	0–50	3	3–10 ppm	4.1	2.7	2.6	3.2	Ni–Cd	X	X	B
19-3-3	BAC	K Series	O_2 combustibles	0–5, 25% O_2 0–1, 4, 100% LEL	0.5% O_2 0.01% LEL	0.1% —	1.2 1.6	1.7 2.2	2.3 3.0	1.3 2.6	battery	X	X	C, D
19-3-4	BAC	Sniffer® 103	O_2 combustibles	0–25% O_2 0–100% LEL	—	—	2.4	1.4	0.9	0.7	9V	X	X	C, D
19-3-5	BEC	946	trace acid base concentration	0–1, 10, 100	0.05	5%	11.8	11.8	4.7	wall mount	107–207 VAC 214–254 VAC	—	—	E
19-3-6	BEC	OM-11EA OM-11	O_2	0-5, 10, 25%	0.05%	1%	—	—	—	wall mount	115/230 VAC	—	—	F
19-3-7	BEC	950	O_3	0–0.025, 0.05, 0.1, 0.25, 0.5, 1.0, 2.5	0.001	1%	—	—	—	wall mount	115/230 VAC	X	—	G
19-3-8	BEC	952	NO, NO_2, NO_x	0.25, 0.5, 1.0, 2.5, 5, 10, 25	0.005	1%	—	—	—	wall mount	115/230 VAC	X	—	H
19-3-9	ESD	OX630	O_2	0–100%	—	1% FS**	15.3	8.9	3.8	—	9V	—		C, J
19-3-10	GAT	OX-80	O_2	0–50%	0.1%	—	2.2	1.2	0.4	0.4	Ni–Cd	X	—	C, J
19-3-11	GFG	G 3000 Microox®	O_2	0–25%	0.1%	0.5%	1.5	0.9	0.6	0.2	Ni–Cd	X	X	C, J
19-3-12	ISC	OX 231	O_2	variable	0.1%	—	1.9	1.1	0.6	0.5	4 AA cells	X	X	B, C, D, J
19-3-13	LSP	Scen-Trio	O_2, toxic gases, combustibles	variable	—	0.5%	3.1	0.8	2.0	1.4	Ni–Cd	X	X	C, J
19-3-14	LSP	LP-COM-19GR	O_2	0–50%	—	0.5%	0.5	1.4	2.4	0.5	Alkaline	X	X	
19-3-15	MDC	724-2 725-11 725-21	O_3 NO_2 Cl_2, F_2	0–100 pphm O_3 0–30 0–1.5	0.003 0.1 0.05					4.8	115 VAC			

TABLE 19-I-3 (con't.). Coulometric Analyzers

Instrument No.	Mfg./ Supp.*	Model	Analytes	Range (ppm)	Detection Limit (ppm)	Precision (±)	Dimensions (cm) H	W	L	Weight (kg)	Power	Alarms Aud.	Vis.	Com-ments
19-3-16	MDA	3300	O_2	0–100% 0–25%	—	2% FS	6 3.0	13 2.4	13 4.5	0.5	9V (2)	X	X	C K
19-3-17	MGP	8060/ 8061	O_2	0–40% vol	—	3%	12	6.6	2.9	0.3	2-AA Ni–Cd	X	—	C
19-3-18	MSA	245 245R 245RA	O_2	0–25%	2% O_2	1% FS	0.8 0.8 0.8	1.0 1.0 1.0	2.0 2.0 2.0	0.3 0.4 0.5	— — 2V alk.	— — X	— — —	C
19-3-19	MSA	Passport	CO, H_2S, SO_2, NO, NO_2, HCN, HCl, Cl_2	variable	variable	—	—	—	—	—	Ni–Cd	X X	X X	C, D, J
19-3-20	MSA	C	H_2S, HCN CO	0–50 0–100	— —	2% FS	3.1	2.4	1.4	3.6	120 VAC	— X	— X	L
19-3-21	PEI	PW 9700	SO_2, NO_2, NO, CO, H_2S, O_3	variable	0.005 NO_2, NO, SO_2, O_3 0.1 CO	2% FS	wall mount			22	110, 125, 200, 220, 240 VAC	—	—	M
19-3-22	TEL	Series 330	O_2	0–25%	—	0.25% O_2	4.0	2.4	1.5	1.7	4 C cells	—	—	C

* Manufacturer codes given in Table 19-I-12.
** FS = full scale.
A. Uses Cold Sensor™.
B. Metal oxide semiconductor sensor.
C. Electrolytic cell for oxygen.
D. Catalytic (platinum) sensor for combustibles.
E. Measures pH shifts and converts to ppm.
F. Designed to measure oxygen in vehicle emissions.
G. Uses chemiluminescent method based on reaction with ozone and ethylene.
H. Measures chemiluminescence of reaction of ozone with NO.
I. Uses electrochemical cell covered with SO_2 permeable membrane.
J. Diffusion sensor.
K. Nonspecific electrochemical sensors for oxidants.
L. Amperometric-type, two-electrode sensor.
M. Measuring modules are electrochemical but are specific for each pollutant of interest.
N. Electrochemical sensors for ambient and stack sampling.

TABLE 19-I-4. Ionization Detectors

Instrument No.	Mfg./ Supp.*	Model	Analytes	Range (ppm)	Detection Limit (ppm)	Precision (±)	Dimensions (cm) H	W	L	Weight (kg)	Power	Alarms Aud.	Vis.	Comments
19-4-1	CSI	HC5000	hydrocarbons	0–10, 50, 100, 500, 1000	0.1 CH_4	0.1 ppm CH_4	4.8	7.5	7.9	18.2	110 VAC	—	—	B
19-4-2	FOX	OVA	organic vapor	1–10^5	1		3.4	4.6	1.7	5.0	12 VDC batt. pack	X	—	A, B, D
19-4-3	GRI	OVA	many toxic vapors	1–80 ppb	1 ppb	—	14.5.	8	39	2.6	Ni–Cd	—	—	E, J, K
19-4-4	HNU	PI-101	organic vapor	0–20, 200, 2000	0.2 (benzene)	1% FS**	4.3	2.1	3.2	4.1	Ni–Cd 12 VDC	X	—	E, F
19-4-5	ITI	505 Leakmeter	SF_6, CCl_4, Freons	—	0.1 (Freons) 0.01 ppb (SF_6)	— 1%	43 45	39 40	23 75	14 10	110 VAC	X	—	H
19-4-6	MSA	Gas Corder	Volatile organic compounds	wide	variable	—	—	—	—	—	battery	—	—	E, F, I
19-4-7	PII	TIP™	organic vapor	0–2000	0.05 (benzene)	vary by element	45 long × 6.3 diameter			1.4	Ni–Cd	X	—	E, F
19-4-8	RAI	Series 400	total hydrocarbons	8 ranges 1–1000	0–4@ 10% scale US CH_4	1% FS	7.4	3.4	6.2	29.5	120 VAC	-	X	A, D
19-4-9	SCA	11-654	hydrocarbons	ppm-vol. % by element	< 2 benzene	1% FS	3.9	4.3	7.1	13.6	110 VAC	—	—	A, B
19-4-10	TEL	TAI 400	total hydrocarbons	10–1000	2 CH_4		6.3	6.7	3.5	—	110 VAC	—	—	A
19-4-11	TEI	580	organic vapors	0–2000	0.1 (benzene)	0.1 ppm (benzene)	7.6	22.8	25.4	3.75	—	X	X	A, B, E
		585		0–10000										
19-4-12	TEI	710 712	total hydrocarbons	0–20000	0.1 1.0	0.1 ppm	25	37	35	6.4	Ni–Cd	— X	— —	A, B, E
19-4-13	TEI	910	organic vapors	0–1000	0.1 (benzene)	—	23	43	46	11.8	110 VAC	X	X	F, G
19-4-14	THE	680	organic vapors	0–100 0–20000	0.5	0.1 ppm 1.0 ppm	31.8	29.2	6.6	5.1	battery 115/220 VAC	—	—	B, E
19-4-15	TRA	350F	total hydrocarbons	0.01–200	0.01	—	—	3.5	7.5	—	115 VAC	—	—	A, D

* Manufacturer codes given in Table 19-I-12.
** FS = full scale.
A. Temperature controlled.
B. Processor controlled.
C. Explosion proof.
D. Gas shutoff.
E. Portable units.
F. PID.
G. Designed for bench mounting.
H. Electon capture detector.
I. FID.
J. Detector uses ^{63}Ni radioactive source.
K. Designed as a leak detector.

TABLE 19-I-5. Infrared Photometers

Instrument No.	Mfg./ Supp.*	Model	Analytes	Range (ppm)	Detection Limit (ppm)	Precision (±)	Dimensions (cm) H	W	L	Weight (kg)	Power	Alarms Aud.	Vis.	Com-ments
19-5-1	ASP	5600	combustible gases	0–100% LEL	—	3%	2.8	2.8	2.6	5.5	110/220 VAC 12-VDC back-up	X	—	A
19-5-2	BEC	864/865	vehicle exhaust	0–100, 500, 1000 CO	—	1% FS**	3.4	5.2	8.8	22.7–27.3	110 VAC	—		B
19-5-3	BEC	866	CO	0–50	—	0.2 ppm	7.2	4.8	10.2	25.9	115 VAC	—		B, C
19-5-4	BKJ	1301	IR absorbing gases	4 orders of magnitude	10.1–10	1% FS	20.5	43	15	18	VAC	—		G
19-5-5	BKJ	1302	IR absorbing gases	5 orders of magnitude	0.01–1	1% FS	17.5	39.5	30	9	VAC or battery	X	X	G, H
19-5-6	CEA	RI-411A	CO_2	0–9950	50	2% FS	3.9	3.0	1.8	—	Ni-Cd 6-D cells 115-VAC adapter	X	—	D
19-5-7	CEA	RI-550A	CO, CO_2, CH_4, ethane, propane, butane, ethylene	—	1% FS	2% FS	3.1	3.4	5.0	9.5	110/220 VAC	—		E
19-5-8	FOX	MIRAN-I	gases that absorb between 2.5–14.5 μm	varies by gas <1 ppm–1%v	varies by gas most <1 ppm	2%	70	28	18	11.4	115/230 VAC	—		E
19-5-9	GAT	RI-413	Freon- R-11, 12, 113, 115, 502	0–9990 (R-11, R-12, R-22, R-502) 0–7900 (R-113) 0–4900 (R-114)	—	5% FS	3.9	3.0	1.8	3.0	Ni-Cd 115-VAC adapter	X	—	B, D
19-5-10	IIT	IR-702	many gases	—	—	1% FS		—		—	90–130 VAC	—		B
19-5-11	IIT	IR-711	hydrocarbons	0–100% LEL (JP-5) 0–1000 ppm	—	2%		—		4.1	—	—		B
19-5-12	MSA	3000	CO, CO_2, SO_2, fluorocarbons, hydrocarbons, etc.	application dependent	application dependent	0.5% FS	8.4	3.7	2.7	20.0	105/220 VAC	—		B

TABLE 19-I-5 (con't.). Infrared Photometers

Instrument No.	Mfg./ Supp.*	Model	Analytes	Range (ppm)	Detection Limit (ppm)	Precision (±)	Dimensions (cm) H	W	L	Weight (kg)	Power	Alarms Aud.	Vis.	Comments
19-5-13	NEO	OTOX® CO_2 Monitor	CO_2	0–1999	—	5% FS	19	9.5	17	0.4	12 VDC 120 VAC	X	X	
19-5-14	RAI	800 Series	CO, CO_2, NO hydrocarbons	—	—	1% FS		—		—	150/230 VAC	—		
19-5-15	SKC	765-203	CO_2	0–40%	—	5% FS	9.5	18.4	7.6	0.6	4-D batteries	—		D

*Manufacturer codes given in Table 19-I-12.
**FS = full scale.
A. Dual wavelength.
B. Dual beam.
C. Model available for vehicle exhaust and bag sampling.
D. Microprocessor controlled.
E. Specified vapor analyzer available.
F. MOD202X suitable for Class I, Groups B, C, D.
G. Utilizes FTIR photoacoustic spectroscopy.
H. Measures up to five gases simultaneously.

TABLE 19-I-6. Ultraviolet and Visible Light Photometers

Instrument No.	Mfg./ Supp.*	Model	Analytes	Range (ppm)	Detection Limit (ppm)	Precision (±)	Dimensions (cm) H	W	L	Weight (kg)	Power	Alarms Aud.	Vis.	Comments
19-6-1	BAC	MV-2	Hg vapor	0.02, 1.0 mg/m^3	0.01 mg/m^3	5% FS**	4.5	1.9	1.7	2.7	12 V Ni-Cd			A, B
19-6-2	BAR	AISI	SO_2	1.0–500, 2000, 40,000	2 or 40 ppm meters	—		—		45.5	battery or 115 VAC	—		B
19-6-3	BEC	K-23B	Hg vapor	0–0.1, 1.0 mg/m^3	0.2% FS	10%	5.1	3.3	1.8	7	115 VAC	—		B
19-6-4	CEA	TGM 555	SO_2, NO_2, NO_x, NH_3, Cl_2, TDI, HCHO, HCN, halides, oxidants	variable 0–0.25, 10	0.025–SO_2	1%	4.7	7.9	2.2	11.4	12 VDC	—		G
19-6-5	DEC	1003	O_3	0.01–9.99	0.01	2%	2.0	5.9	7.3	20.5	115–130 VAC	—		B
19-6-6	DUP	460 461	SO_2, NO_2, NO_x NO_x	0–200, 100% SO_2 or NO_2 0–150, 100% NO_x	4 SO_2/NO_2	1% FS		—		—	115 VAC	—		B, C, E
19-6-7	GMD	Autostep® plus	TDI, MDI, HDI, Cl_2, hydrides, HF, HCl, IPDI, hydrazines, phosgene	varies by analyte	—	15%	21.7	9.8	24.4	2.2	—	X	—	H
19-6-8	MDC	727-3	O_3	0–9.99	0.02	1%	4.3	2.4	9.1	6.8	115 VAC	—		B
19-6-9	RAI	890	SO_2	0–50, 50000	—	≤ 0.1		—		—	115/230 VAC	—		
19-6-10	SSI	38	Hg and organic vapors	0–0.1 mg/m^3	0.01 mg/m^3	5%	1.2	1.6	6.7	3.6	120 VAC	—		A, B, D

*Manufacturer codes given in Table 19-I-12.
**FS = full scale.
A. Organic vapors may interfere.
C. Designed for Class I, Group D.
D. Dual beam.
E. Visible absorption.
F. Utilizes second-derivative spectroscopy in UV and visible spectrum.
G. Liquid reagents required.

TABLE 19-I-7. Chemiluminescent Detectors

Instrument No.	Mfg./ Supp.*	Model	Analytes	Range (ppm)	Detection Limit (ppm)	Precision (±)	Dimensions (cm)			Weight (kg)	Power	Alarms		Com-ments
							H	W	L			Aud.	Vis.	
19-7-1	BEC	950A	O_3	0–0.025 to 25 (7 ranges)	0.01	2% FS**	3.4	7.5	8.4	—	105–125V	—		A, B
19-7-2	BEC	952A	NO, NO_2, NO_x	0–0.25 to 25 (7 ranges)	0.01	0.005 ppm	3.4	7.5	8.4	—	105–125V	X	—	A, C, D
19-7-3	CSI	1100	O_3	0–1, 5, 10	0.01 pphm	1% FS	4.1	6.7	6.9	18.2	105–125 VAC	—		A, B
19-7-4	CSI	530 R	NO, NO_2, NO_x	0–0.1, 0.25, 0.5, 1.0, 5	0.004	0.002 ppm	4.8	6.7	7.9	27.3	105 VAC 130 VAC	X	—	A, C, D
19-7-5	CSI	325-2R 04350-2R	O_3	0–0.1, 0.5, 1.0, 5, 10	0.001	0.001 ppm	4.8	6.7	7.9	18.2	105–125 VAC	—		A, B
19-7-6	RAI	900 Series	NO, NO_2	0–10, 25, 100, 250, 2500, 10,000	—	0.1 ppm		—		—	—	—		

*Manufacturer codes given in Table 19-I-12.
**FS = full scale.
A. Intended for unattended operation.
B. Uses chemiluminescent reactions of O_3 with ethylene as basis for detection.
C. Uses chemiluminescent reaction of NO with ozone as basis for detection.
D. NO_2 converted to NO for analysis.

TABLE 19-I-8. Photometric Analyzers

Instrument No.	Mfg./ Supp.*	Model	Analytes	Range (ppm)	Detection Limit (ppm)	Precision (±)	Dimensions (cm) H	W	L	Weight (kg)	Power	Alarms Aud.	Vis.	Com-ments
19-8-1	BAC	US400	CO	0–5	0.1 ppm/mv	—	panel mounted			15.9	115V ± 10	—		A, C
19-8-2	BEC	DIF 7000	CO	0–20, 50, 100, 200	0.1	1% FS**	2.2	6.7	6.6	14.5	115 VAC ± 10%	—		B, C
19-8-3	BEC	953	SO_2	0.25, 0.5, 1.0, 2.0	0.004	0.003 ppm	4.8	7.5	8.7	40.9	105–125 VAC	—		C, D
19-8-4	CSI	SA 285	sulfur compounds	0–50, 100, 500, 1000 ppb	1% FS	1% FS	4.8	6.7	7.9	22.7	115 ± 10 VAC	X	—	C
19-8-5	CSI	SA 700	SO_2	0–250, 500, 1000, 5000, 10,000 ppb	5 ppb	2% FS	4.8	6.7	7.9	20.0	105–130 VAC 220 VAC	—		C, F
19-8-6	CSI	PA 460	phosphorus gas	0.001–10	0.001	19 (460)	7.5	4.8	7.9	18.2	115 VAC	—		C
		PA 465				20 (465)	3.5	3.9	6.3	9.1	external 115 VAC internal 12 VDC			E
19-8-7	FLM	533	H_2S	—	0.1	—	3.1	2.4	1.2	1.8	9.6-V battery	X	X	H
19-8-8	GAT	Halide	halogenated compounds	1000–10,000	50–100	3%	4.3	2.8	2.8	5.9	120/130 VAC	—		G
19-8-9	HAI	722AEX-A	H_2S	0–100	1	3%	8.3	5.1	5.1	27.3	—	X	—	H
19-8-10	MDA	Miniguard	H_2S, $COCl_2$, TDI, Cl_2, SO_2, NH_3	variable	variable fraction of TLV	—	2.0	0.5	1.0	0.3	3-AA	X	—	H, I
19-8-11	MDA	TLD-1	amines, halides, CO_2, diisocyanates, hydrazines, hydrides, HCN, H_2O_2, H_2S, mineral acids, NO_2, O_3, $COCl_2$, SO_2	ppb-ppm	analyte dep	± 5%@TLV	16.5	21.2	17.7	3.4	110/220 VAC or Pb-acid battery	X	X	H,J
19-8-12	MDA	Series 7100	ibid	ppb-ppm	analyte dep	± 5%@TLV	16.5	43.2	45.7	20.4	115/230 VAC	X	X	H, C
19-8-13	SCA	Halide	halogenated hydrocarbons	0–500	10	10%	6.3	3.8	5.9	15.9	110 VAC	—		G

TABLE 19-I-8 (con't.). Photometric Analyzers

Instrument No.	Mfg./ Supp.*	Model	Analytes	Range (ppm)	Detection Limit (ppm)	Precision (±)	Dimensions (cm) H	W	L	Weight (kg)	Power	Alarms Aud.	Vis.	Comments
19-8-14	TRA	271 HA	sulfur compounds	0–100 ppb < 0–1	4 ppb	< 1%	3.5	7.5	9.4	27.3	115 V	—		C, H

*Manufacturer codes given in Table 19-I-12.
**FS = full scale.
A. Sensors employ analysis of mercury vapor by UV absorption which is generated by oxidation of CO with mercury oxide.
B. Utilizes dual-isotope fluorescence detection.
C. Intended for unattended operation.
D. Utilizes SO_2 fluorescence reaction with UV light for detection.
E. Uses flame photometric detector.
F. Uses SO_2 absorption of UV light.
G. Utilizes increased spectral enhancement of an AC spark by a halogen for detection.
H. Utilizes automatic paper tape sampler.
I. Designed as personal monitoring system.
J. Portable models.

TABLE 19-I-9. Thermal Conductivity Detectors

Instrument No.	Mfg./ Supp.*	Model	Analytes	Range (ppm)	Detection Limit (ppm)	Precision (±)	Dimensions (cm) H	W	L	Weight (kg)	Power	Alarms Aud.	Vis.	Comments
19-9-1	BEC	7-C Series	H_2, Ar, O_2	vary by analyte 0–500 H_2	vary by analyte	2% FS**	7.2	6.0	4.4	—	220 115 VAC	—	—	A, B
19-9-2	DET	Analograph	H_2, He, O_2, CO, CO_2, CH_4, C_2H_6, C_2–C_6 hydrocarbons	vary by analyte	vary by analyte	—	2.8	5.3	5.7	11.4	110 VAC	—	—	C
19-9-3	MGP	Leak Hunter 8065	nonflammable gases	—	He: 1×10^{-5}; CO_2: 3.5×10^{-5}; Freon 12: 1.2×10^{-5}; cc/sec leak rate	—	1.4	3.9	5.5	2.3	4 × 1.5 V dry cell or Ni-Cd	X	X	D

*Manufacturer codes given in Table 19-I-12.
**FS = full scale.
A. Explosion proof available.
B. Corrosion-resistant cells.
C. A separate Servocorder available.
D. Designed for leak detection, not quantification.

TABLE 19-I-10. Heat of Combustion Detectors

Instrument No.	Mfg./ Supp.*	Model	Analytes	Range (ppm)	Detection Limit (ppm)	Precision (±)	Dimensions (cm) H	Dimensions (cm) W	Dimensions (cm) L	Weight (kg)	Power	Alarms Aud.	Alarms Vis.	Comments
19-10-1	AIM	Logic 100 Series	O_2, CO, H_2S, SO_2, NO, NO_2, Cl_2, HCN, HCl, explosive gases	—	—	—	39.9 long 6.4 diameter			1.0	battery	X	X	B, G
19-10-2	BAC	Gas-Pointer® II	combustible gas CO	0–99% LEL 5–99% gas 0–500	—	0.25% 3% 10 ppm	20.6	9.4	5.6	0.9	Ni-Cd	—		A, H, N
19-10-3	BAC	Gastron 282 310	combustible gases	hydro-carbons: 0–500; H_2: 0–25	hydro-carbon: 50; H_2: 10	—	—	—	—	1.9	Ni-Cd	X	X	A
19-10-4	BAC	Sniffer® 500 Series	O_2 deficiency H_2S, CO, combustible gases	O_2: 0–25%; H_2S: 0–100; CO: 0–500; combustibles: 0–10,000	variable	5% FS**	3.0	3.9	2.5	4.3	6 VDC Pb-acid	X	X	A, H
19-10-5	BAC	Super Sniffer®	combustible gases and vapors	0–1000 0–100% LEL	variable	5% FS	1.2	2.4	3.0	3.1	Ni-Cd	—	—	A
19-10-6	BAC	TLV Sniffer®	combustible vapors	0–100, 1000 0–100% LEL	3	5% FS	22.8	9.5	16.8	2.3	Ni-Cd 6 size D	X	—	A
19-10-7	BAC	Ultra I & II	combustible gases and vapors	0–20% LEL 0–100% LEL	—	5% FS	3.3	1.1	2.3	1.4–1.6	4 size D	—	—	A, M
19-10-8	CHI	12	combustible gases	—	1	—	2.3	1.0	0.6	0.5	6 or 12 VDC Ni-Cd	X	—	B, C
19-10-9	COS	XP-316	combustible gases	5 ranges	—	5% FS	19	8.4	4.0	0.7	4-AA	X	X	A, G, N
19-10-10	COS	XP-704	Freon	—	2.1×10^{-5} atm cm^3/sec	—	15.7	6.9	3.3	0.4	4-AA	X	X	I, N
19-10-11	DVC	1000 Series	CO	0–500	—	2% FS	—	—	—	—	115 VAC 220 VAC	—	X	A
19-10-12	DVC	5000 Series	combustible gases and vapors	0–100% LEL	—	3% FS	—	—	—	—	—	—	X	A, D
19-10-13	DYM	LCD combo	combustible gases, O_2 deficiency	0–100% LEL	—		2.8	1.6	1.2	1.4	5 size C	—	—	A, H
19-10-14	DYM	ABL-50	CO	2–50	2	10% FS	5.1	5.5	2.2	7.3	110 VAC 12 VDC	X	X	E, F

TABLE 19-I-10 (con't.). Heat of Combustion Detectors

Instrument No.	Mfg./ Supp.*	Model	Analytes	Range (ppm)	Detection Limit (ppm)	Precision (±)	Dimensions (cm) H	W	L	Weight (kg)	Power	Alarms Aud.	Vis.	Com-ments
19-10-15	EEC	03 HCS 05 HCS 06 HCS 07 HCS	combustible gases and vapors	0–100% LEL 0–10, 100% LEL 0–100% 0–1000 0–100% LEL	— — — —	— — — —	3.1 3.5 2.3 3.5	0.7 1.1 2.5 1.1	1.2 1.4 1.4 1.2	0.8 1.1 1.8 —	2 size D 2 size D 8 size D Ni-Cd or 110 VAC	— X — X	— — — —	A, G A, D, G A A, D
19-10-16	ENM	EX-10	combustible hydrocarbons	0–100% LEL	—	5%	4	6	18	0.5	Ni-Cd or 110/220 VAC	X	X	A
19-10-17	GAT	GX-3A	O_2 deficiency combustible gases	0–25% 0–100% LEL 0–1000	—	5% FS	4.3	2.8	2.2	5.5	6 size D Ni-Cd	X X	X X	A, H
19-10-18	GFG	Exotector®	combustible gases	0–10% LEL 0–100% LEL	variable 0.1–5% LEL	2% LEL	2.0	1.4	0.8	0.6	Ni-Cd	X	X	A, D or F, G, M
19-10-19	HRD	647	combustible gases	0–5% comb. 0–10% comb. 0–100% LEL	0.25% LEL	1% FS	5.0	3.8	3.5	—	115 VAC	—	X	A
19-10-20	HAI	510	combustible gases	0–100%	—	5% FS	2.0	2.8	3.1	5.5	115 VAC	X	—	A, G
19-10-21	ISC	CD212	CH_4	0–5% by volume	0.1% by volume	—	1.9	1.1	0.6	0.5	5 V Ni-Cd	X	—	A, D
19-10-22	LSP	Gasponder® I-IV	combustibles O_2, CO, H_2S	CH_4: 0–100% LEL CO: 0–400 H_2S: 0–100 O_2: 0–30%	variable	CH_4: 5% LEL CO: 2% H_2S: 2% O_2: 0.5%	1.1	2.1	3.0	1.4–1.8	battery	X	X	A, H
19-10-23	MAC	RCM REM	CO EtO	0–100, 500 0–50, 250	10 5	10–25%	0.6	1.1	2.0	0.5	Ni-Cd or 120 VAC	–	X	B
19-10-24	MAC	RGM	combustible gases	0–1, 5%	100	10–25%	0.5	1.1	2.0	0.5	Ni-Cd			
19-10-25	MCN	Gasurveyor 1000	hydrocarbons	0–1000; 0–10%, 100% LEL; 0–100% vol%	10	5%	18	9.5	10.5	1.6	4-D batteries	X	X	G
19-10-26	MGP	8057	Cl_2, AsH_3, H_2, H_2S, PH_3, etc.	—	vary by analyte	—	1.1	2.4	0.5	0.4	4 size AA Ni-Cd	X	X	B, I

TABLE 19-I-10 (con't.). Heat of Combustion Detectors

Instrument No.	Mfg./ Supp.*	Model	Analytes	Range (ppm)	Detection Limit (ppm)	Precision (±)	Dimensions (cm)			Weight (kg)	Power	Alarms		Com- ments
							H	W	L			Aud.	Vis.	
19-10-27	MSA	260 100	combustible gas and O_2	0–100 LEL O_2 0–20% vol.	—	5% FS comb. 2% FS O_2	2.8	3.9	1.5	3.2	2.4 VDC battery pack	X	X	A, H, J
19-10-28	MSA	Explosi-meter® 2A	combustible gas	0–100% LEL	2% LEL	5% FSD	1.3	2.1	2.2	1.8	6 size D cells	—	—	A
19-10-29	MSA	Series 5000	combustible gas	0–100% LEL	—	2%	2.4	5.6	5.3	—	105, 115, 230 VAC	X	X	A, K
19-10-30	MSA	Gascope; Model 60, 62	combustible gases	0–5, 100% CH_4 (vol) 0–100% LEL	—	15% FC	2.6	2.9	1.6	2.3	8 ZnC	—	—	A, L, M
19-10-31	NMS	G-2000	CH_4	0–2% CH_4	—	—	0.8	1.5	0.5	0.3	3.6 VDC Ni-Cd	—	—	A, D
19-10-32	SCA	D Series	combustible gases	% LEL % gas	—	—		—		—	8 size D cells	—	—	
19-10-33	SMC	10HS	H_2S	0–50	—	—	3.0	1.5	0.7	0.7	Ni-Cd	X	—	B, F, G, N
19-10-34	SMC	2000 Series	combustible gases	H_2: 100–5000 CH_4: 200–20,000	H_2: 80 CH_4: 150	—	10.6 × 8 round			0.7	120 VAC	X	—	B, G
19-10-35	TEL	102	combustible gases	0–100% LEL	—	0.5% FSD	1.4	3.7	2.8	3.2	115 VAC	—	—	A, D

*Manufacturer codes given in Table 19-I-12.
**FS = full scale.
A. Heated catalytic combustion sensor.
B. Metal oxide semiconductor sensor.
C. No meter readout; uses rate of clicking relative to concentration.
D. Diffusion sampler.
E. Airline monitor.
F. Continuous line monitor - auto reset.
G. Intrinsically safe for Class I, Groups B, C, D (GG-groups B & D).
H. Electrochemical cell for O_2 deficiency.
I. Designed as leak detector.
J. Model 100, combustible gas only.
K. Explosion-proof model available.
L. Silicon compounds interfere.
M. Thermal conductivity detector for use in absence of oxygen.
N. Models with multiple sensors contained in Table I-19-2.

TABLE 19-I-11. Gas Chromatograph Analyzers

Instrument No.	Mfg./ Supp.*	Model	Analytes	Range (ppm)	Detection Limit (ppm)	Detectors	Dimensions (cm) H	W	L	Weight (kg)	Power	Alarms Aud.	Vis.	Comments
19-11-1	FOX	OVA 128	Organics	0–10,000, 1000	—	FID	13	23	30.5	5.5	Pb-acid	X	—	A, B
19-11-2	HNU	300 Series	Organics	1, 10, 100 (0–1V)	—	FID, PID, ECD, TCD, FPD	26.7 (Model 301)	35	28	11.3	110/230 VAC	—	—	D
19-11-3	MSI	MSI-301	Organics	1 ppb–100 ppm	1 ppb	Solid State	9	37	33	5.5	110 VAC 12 VDC	—	—	C, F
19-11-4	PII	10S Series	Organics	wide	0.1 ppb (benzene)	PID	16	46	34	11.8	battery 110/220 VAC 10–18 VDC	X		C
19-11-5	PII	Snapshot	Organics	wide	0.1 ppb (benzene)	PID	23	12.7	35.6	3.7	Pb-acid	X		C
19-11-6	SST	Scento/ graph Plus II	Organics	0.1–2000 ppm	0.1 ppm	PID, AID, MAID, ECD, TCD	15.2	52	50.8	24	12 VDC 110 VAC	X	—	A, C, E
19-11-7	SST	Scento/ screen	Organics	0.1–2000 ppm	0.1 ppm	PID, AID, MAID, ECD, TCD	16.5	34.2	49.5	10.7	12 VDC	X	—	C, E

*Manufacturer codes given in Table 19-I-12.
A. Intrinsically safe, Class I, Division I, Groups A, B, C, D.
B. Has continuous, direct-reading capabilities.
C. Designed for portable operation.
D. Designed for mobile and environmental laboratories.
E. Can be remotely operated; contains calibration sequence.
F. 12-V battery optional.

TABLE 19-I-12. List of Instrument Manufacturers

Code	Manufacturer
ADS	Adsistor Technology, Inc. Box 51160 Seattle, WA 98115
AIM	AIM USA P.O. Box 720540 Houston, TX 77272-0540
AIC	Arizona Instrument Corp. P.O. Box 1930 Tempe, AZ 85280
ASI	Astro International Corporation 100 Park Avenue League City, TX 77573
BAC	Bacharach, Inc. 625 Alpha Drive Pittsburg, PA 15238 (412)963-2160
BAR	Barringer Research, Ltd. 304 Carlingview Drive Rexdale, Ontario Canada M9W 5G6
BEC	Beckman Instruments, Inc. Process Instruments Division 2500 N. Harbor Boulevard Fullerton, CA 92634
BIO	Biosystems, Inc. 5 Brookside Road Middlefield, CT 06455
BKJ	Bruel & Kjaer Instruments, Inc. 185 Forest Street Marlborough, MA 01752
CEA	CEA Instruments, Inc. 16 Chestnut Street Box 303 Emerson, NJ 07630-0303 (201)967-5660 FAX (201)967-8450
COS	COSMOS Gas Detection Systems P.O. Box 70498 Seattle, WA 98107
CAL	Calibrated Instruments, Inc. 200 Saw Mill River Road Hawthorne, NY 10532 (914)741-5700 or (800)969-2254 FAX (914)741-5711
CAS	Casella London Limited Regent House, Britannia Walk London, N1 7ND, England
CHE	Chestec, Inc. P.O. Box 10362 Santa Ana, CA 92711
CSI	Columbia Scientific P.O. Box 203190 Austin, TX 78720 (512)258-5191
DEC	Dasibi Environmental Corp. 515 W. Colorado Street Glendale, CA 91204
DET	Deutsch Engineering & Testing Services P.O. Box 389 Monsey, NY 10952
DVC	Devco Engineering, Inc. Control Systems Division 36 Pier Lane West Fairfield, NY 07006
DUP	DuPont Company Instrument Products Division Wilmington, DE 19898
DYM	Dynamation Incorporated 3784 Plaza Drive Ann Arbor, MI 48108
ETI	EIT 251 Welsh Pool Road Exton, PA 19341
ENM	ENMET Corp. 2308 S. Industrial Way P.O. Box 979 Ann Arbor, MI 48106-0979 (313)761-1270
EEC	ERDCO Engineering Corp. P.O. Box 1310 Evanston, IL 60204
EDW	Edmont-Wilson Division of Becton Dickinson & Company 1300 Walnut Street Coshocton, OH 43812
EIT	Eitel Manufacturing, Inc. 33208 Paseo Cerveza, Unit G San Juan Capistrano, CA 92675
ESD	Engineering Systems and Design 119A Sandy Drive Newark, DE 19713
ENS	Environmental Sensors Co. 4901 North Dixie Highway Boca Raton, FL 33431
ERI	Ericson Instruments P.O. Box 226 Ossining, NY 10562
FLM	Fleming Instruments, Ltd. Caxton Way, Sevenage Hertfordshire, England
FOX	Foxboro Company Foxboro, MA 02035
GCI	G.C. Industries, Inc. 49050 Milmont Drive Fremont, CA 94538
GFG	GfG Gas Electronics, Inc. 6617 Clayton Rd. Suite 209 Title Bldg. St. Louis, MO 63117
GMD	GMD Systems, Inc. (A Bacharach affiliate) Old Route 519 Hendersonville, PA 15339 (412)746-3600
GAT	GasTech, Inc. 8445 Central Avenue Newark, CA 94560-3431
GMI	General Monitors, Inc. 26776 Simpatica Circle El Toro, CA 92630
GRI	Graseby Ionics Odhams Trading Estate St Albans Road Watford, Herts, UK WD2-5JX
HNU	H-Nu Systems, Inc. 160 Charlemont Street Newton, MA 02161
HRD	Hayes-Republic Division Corp. 3695 Interstate Parkway Riviera Beach, FL 33404
HAI	Houston Atlas, Inc. 9441 Baythorne Drive Houston, TX 77041-7709
ISC	Industrial Scientific 1001 Oakdale Drive Oakdale, PA 15071
ITS	Interscan Corp. P.O. Box 2496 Chatsworth, CA 91313
ITI	Ion Track Instruments, Inc. 340 Fordham Rd. Wilmington, MA 01887
III	Infrared Industries, Inc. 1424 North Central Park Ave. Anaheim, CA 92802

TABLE 19-I-12 (con't.). List of Instrument Manufacturers

Code	Manufacturer
LAT	Lagus Applied Technology, Inc. 11760 Sorrento Valley Road, Suite M San Diego, CA 92121
LER	Lear Siegler Environmental Technology Division 74 Inverness Drive East Englewood, CO 80112
LSP	Lumidor Safety Products 11221 Interchange Circle S Miramar, FL 33025
MDA	MDA Scientific, Inc. 405 Barclay Boulevard Lincolnshire, IL 60069 (708)634-2800 or (800)323-2000 FAX (708)634-1371
MST	MST Measurement Systems, Inc. 327 Messner Drive Wheeling, IL 60090
MAC	Macurco, Inc. 3946 S. Mariposa Street Englewood, CO 80110
MDC	Mast Development Company 2212 East 12th Street Davenport, IA 52803
MGP	Matheson Gas Products 30 Seaview Drive P.O. Box 1587 Secaucus, NJ 07096 (201)867-4100
MCN	McNeill International 37914 Euclid Ave. Willoughby, OH 44094
MET	Metrosonics, Inc. General Products Division P.O. Box 23075 Rochester, NY 14692
MSI	Microsensor Systems, Inc. 62 Corporate Court Bowling Green, KY 42103-4147
MSA	Mine Safety Appliances Company P.O. Box 427 Pittsburgh, PA 15230 (412)776-8600 or (800)MSA-INST FAX (412)776-3280
NDR	National Draeger, Inc. 101 Technology Drive P.O. Box 120 Pittsburgh, PA 15230 (412)787-8383/8389 or (800)MSA-INST FAX (412)787-2207 or (800)922-5519
NMS	National Mine Service Company 600 N. Bell Avenue Carnegie, PA 15106
NEO	Neotronics P.O. Box 370 2144 Hilton Drive, S.W. Gainesville, GA 30503
ORE	Ozone Research and Equipment Corp. 3840 North 40th Avenue Phoenix, AZ 85019
PEI	Phillips Electronics Instruments 85 McKee Drive Mahwah, NJ 07430
PII	Photovac International, Inc. 739B Park Avenue Huntington, NY 11743
PRA	Process Analyzer, Inc. 3 Headly Place Fallsington, PA 19054
RAI	Rosemount Analytical, Inc. 600 South Harbor Blvd. La Habra, CA 90631 (310)690-7600 or (800)441-7245 FAX (310)690-7127
SKC	SKC West, Inc. P.O. Box 4133 Fullerton, CA 92634
SCA	Scott Aviation 225 Erie Street Lancaster, NY 14086
SEN	Sensidyne, Inc. 16333 Bay Vista Dr. Clearwater, FL 34620 (813)530-3602 or (800)451-9444
SST	Sentex Sensing Technology 553 Broad Ave. Ridgefield, NJ 07657
SMC	Sierra Monitor Corp. 1991 Tarob Court Milpitas, CA 95035
SSI	Sunshine Scientific Instruments 1810 Grant Avenue Philadelphia, PA 19115
TEL	Teledyne Analytic Instruments 16830 Chestnut Street City of Industry, CA 91749-1580
TEI	Thermo Electron Instruments 108 South Street Hopkinton, MA 01748
THE	Thermo Electron Instruments, Inc. 8 West Forge Parkway Franklin, MA 02038
TRA	Tracor, Inc. Analytical Instruments Division 6600 Tracor Lane, Building 27 Austin, TX 78725
WPD	Western Precipitation Division 4565 Colorado Boulevard Los Angeles, CA 90039
XON	XonTech, Inc. 6862 Hayvenhurst Avenue Van Nuys, CA 91406

Chapter 20

Denuder Systems and Diffusion Batteries

Yung-Sung Cheng, Ph.D.
Inhalation Toxicology Research Institute, Lovelace Biomedical and Environmental Research Institute, P.O. Box 5890, Albuquerque, New Mexico

CONTENTS

Introduction

The diffusion technique is used to collect ultrafine particles and vapors, and to determine the size distribution of ultrafine particles (<0.2 µm). The technique was first conceived following the observation that losses of atmospheric nuclei in tubes were related to their diffusion coefficients.[1] Mathematical equations for diffusion losses in rectangular or circular tubes were subsequently derived.[2,3] This enabled accurate determination of diffusion coefficients and submicrometer particle sizes from measurement of particle penetration through these tubes.

Diffusion samplers are devices that separate particles or vapors by differential diffusion mobilities. Two types of diffusion samplers are often used in air sampling: a diffusion battery can be used to measure the size distribution of submicrometer particles, and a diffusion denuder is designed to separate and collect gases or vapors from airborne particles. These devices are useful for particles smaller than 0.1 µm, including condensation nuclei, radon progeny, and gas or vapor molecules. The diffusion coefficient of a particle or molecule is inversely proportional to the particle size. The diffusion battery was initially designed to measure the particle size of condensation nuclei in the atmosphere, whereas the diffusion denuder was first designed to determine the diffusion coefficient of gas and vapor molecules. Current applications of diffusion denuders have been extended to atmospheric sampling of SO_2, NH_3, and NO_x, or as a scrubber in an acidic aerosol sampling system to remove certain types of gases to avoid absorption of these gases on particles collected in the filter. Diffusion batteries are frequently used in the laboratory to measure size distributions of ultrafine particles and in indoor environments to determine activity size distributions of radon and thoron progeny.

Diffusion samplers include tubes of different shapes and stacks of fine mesh screens of well-defined characteristics. Principles and operations of diffusion denuders and diffusion batteries have been reviewed.[4,5] A diffusion battery is often used with a condensation nucleus counter in a sampling train to determine the concentration and particle size distribution of an aerosol. However, radioactive aerosols can be sampled by a diffusion battery, and the substrates counted directly for radioactivities. This chapter describes the operating principle, theory, design, applications, and data analyses of diffusion batteries and denuders.

Theories of the Diffusion Technique

The mathematical expressions relating collection or penetration of vapors and particles through cylindrical and rectangular tubes and screens have been derived. These expressions can be used to calculate diffusion coefficients or particle sizes from experimental measurements through diffusion samplers.

These mathematical expressions were derived from the convective diffusion equation describing the concentration profile (c) in various geometries and flow profiles:

$$\frac{\mathcal{D}}{r}\frac{\partial}{\partial r}\left(r\frac{\partial c}{\partial r}\right) = u(r)\frac{\partial c}{\partial z} \quad (1)$$

where: $\mathcal{D}$ = diffusion coefficient
r = radial direction
z = axial direction
$u(r)$ = velocity profile in the axial direction

Several assumptions were made in the derivation of Equation 1: 1) the concentration is in a steady-state condition; 2) the flow field in the device is a function of radial position, r, only; 3) the effect of diffusion in the direction of flow is neglected; 4) no production or reaction of the gas or aerosol occurs in the device; and 5) the sticking coefficient of the gas or particle is 100% on the collection surface (walls or screens). Diffusion devices can be classified as tube (channel)-type or screen-type with different flow profiles. Solutions to Equation 1 for different types of diffusion samplers are summarized in the following section.

Tubes and Channels

Penetration (P) of particles or gases due to the diffusion mechanism has been derived for channels of different geometries, including cylindrical, rectangular, disk, and annular shapes. The general solution of Equation 1 can be expressed as a series of exponential functions:

$$P = \sum_{n=1}^{\infty} A_n \exp(-\beta_n \mu) \quad (2)$$

where: μ = dimensionless argument relating the diffusion coefficient, channel length, and flow rate

The right-hand side of Equation 2 is an infinite series; however, only a finite number of terms are needed to compute or converge to the accurate solution. Convergence of Equation 2 depends on the magnitude of μ. For larger values of μ (low penetration), fewer terms are needed for convergence; at small values of μ (high penetration), many terms are required. For high penetration, alternative equations have been derived.

Solutions of the diffusion equation for tubes or channels depend strongly on the flow field in the tubes, $u(r)$. The flow profile can be laminar or turbulent depending on the flow rate (or Reynolds number), and transient or fully developed depending on the length of the tube and the Reynolds number. A diffusion sampler is always designed to satisfy the fully developed laminar flow condition. Discussions for the effects of flow profile are reported by Ingham.[6] Specific solutions for fully developed laminar flows in tubes or channels of different shapes are described below.

Cylindrical Tubes

Penetration through a circular tube (Figure 20-1) at a flow rate, Q, for particles with a diffusion coefficient of $\mathcal{D}$ has been derived by several investigators as a function of the parameter μ defined as $\pi\mathcal{D}L/Q$.[3,6–10] The numerical solution obtained by Bowen *et al.*[11] for μ between 1×10^{-7} and 1 is most accurate. Results obtained by Davis and Parkins,[8] Tan and Hsu,[9] Sideman *et al.*,[7] and Lekhtmakher[10] agree substantially with those of Bowen *et al.*[11] By comparison of various expressions, the following analytical solutions have the accuracy of four significant figures as compared to Bowen's result in the entire range of μ:[12]

$$P = 0.81905 \exp(-3.6568\,\mu) + 0.09753 \exp(-22.305\,\mu) + 0.0325 \exp(-56.961\,\mu) + 0.01544 \exp(-107.62\,\mu) \text{ for } \mu > 0.02 \text{ and} \quad (3)$$

$$P = 1.0 - 2.5638\,\mu^{2/3} + 1.2\,\mu + 0.1767\,\mu^{4/3} \text{ for } \mu \le 0.02 \quad (4)$$

The formula for small values of μ is taken from Gormley and Kennedy,[3] Newman,[13] and Ingham.[6]

Rectangular Channels and Parallel Circular Plates

Particle penetration through a parallel narrow rectangular tube (Figure 20-1) of width W and separation H, where $H \ll W$, has been derived as a function of μ defined as $8\mathcal{D}LW/3QH$ (Gormley cited by Nolan and

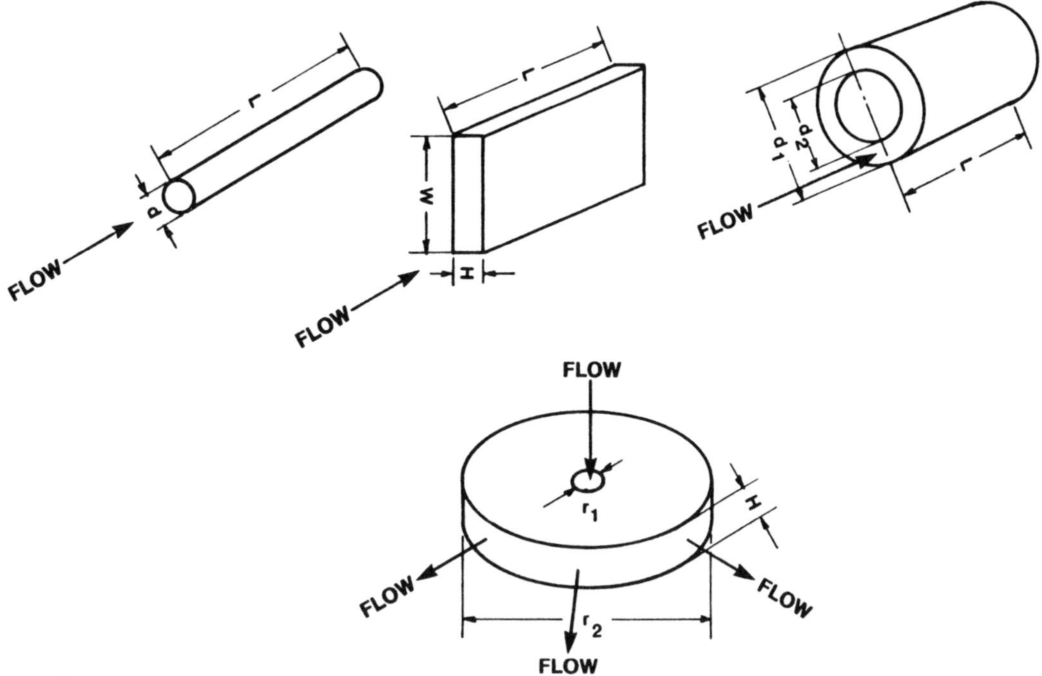

FIGURE 20-1. Schematics of different shapes of tubes.

Nolan.(2,7,11,14–16) The same equation can be used to calculate penetration for inward flow between parallel circular plates (Figure 20-2), where the diffusion parameter μ is defined as $8\pi\mathcal{D}(r_2^2 - r_1^2)/3QH$, where r_2 and r_1 are outer and inner radii of the disks.(15) The most accurate solution was given by Tan and Thomas(16) and Bowen *et al.*;(11) other investigators agreed substantially with their results. The most accurate analytical formulas (as to the accuracy of four significant figures) for the entire range of μ are:(12)

$$P = 0.9104 \exp(-2.8278\,\mu) + 0.0531 \exp(-32.147\,\mu) + 0.01528 \exp(-93.475\,\mu) + 0.00681 \exp(-186.805\,\mu) \text{ for } \mu > 0.05, \text{ and} \quad (5)$$

$$P = 1 - 1.526\,\mu^{2/3} + 0.15\,\mu + 0.0342\,\mu^{4/3} \text{ for } \mu \le 0.05 \quad (6)$$

The formula for small values of μ is given by Ingham.(17) Kennedy (quoted by Nolan and Kennedy(18)) derived a similar formula with different coefficients, but the results vary by only 1%.

Annular Tubes

A theoretical equation has not been derived for diffusional losses through an annular tube (Figure 20-2). The following empirical equation for the annular tube was derived from a sorption study with SO_2:(19)

$$P = (0.82 \pm 0.10) \exp[\,(-22.53 \pm 1.22)\,\mu\,] \quad (7)$$

where: $\mu = \pi\mathcal{D}L(d_1 + d_2)/4Q(d_2 - d_1)$
d_1 = inner diameter
d_2 = outer diameter

Equation 7 is valid only for annular tubes where μ is large, and penetration through the device is less than 10%.

Wire Screens

Aerosol penetration through a stack of fine mesh screens with circular fibers of uniform diameter and arrangement has been derived.(20–22) A stack of fine mesh screens simulates a fan model filter(23,24) in terms of flow resistance and aerosol deposition characteristics.(25) The theoretical penetration was derived based on the aerosol filtration in the fan model filter:

$$P = \exp\left[-Bn\left(2.7Pe^{-2/3} + \frac{1}{k}R^2 + \frac{1.24}{k^{1/2}}Pe^{-1/2}R^{2/3}\right)\right] \quad (8)$$

where: $B = 4\alpha h/\pi(1-\alpha)d_f$
n = number of screens
d_f = fiber diameter
h = thickness of a single screen
α = solid volume fraction of the screen
k = hydrodynamic factor of the screen
$= -0.5 \ln(2\alpha/\pi) + (2\alpha/\pi) - 0.75 - 0.25(2\alpha/\pi)^2$
$R = d_p/d_f$, the interception parameter
$Pe = Ud_f/\mathcal{D}$ is the Peclet number
U = superficial velocity

Equation 8 includes the diffusional and interceptional losses of aerosol on screens and is valid for particles up to 1 μm in size.(25) For particles larger than 1 μm, inertial impaction becomes an important mecha-

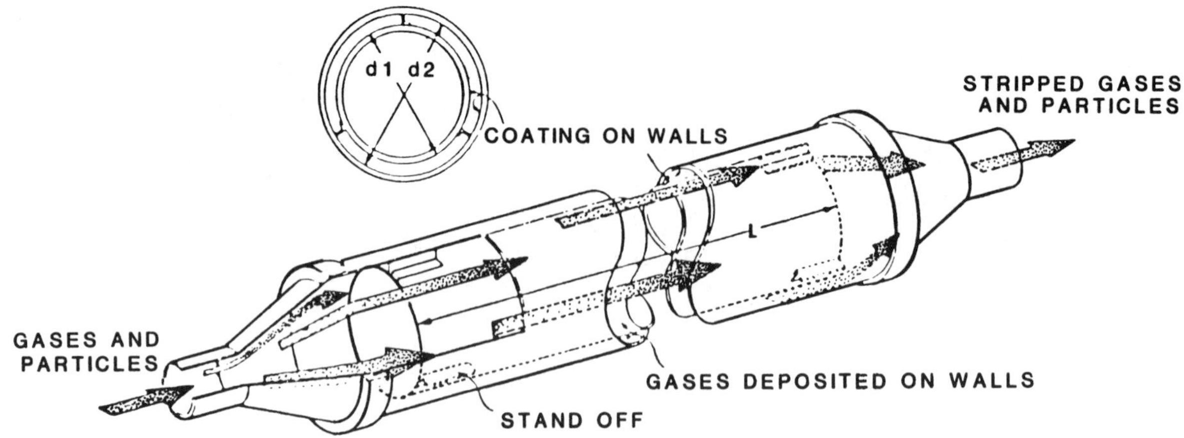

FIGURE 20-2. Schematic of an annular denuder.

nism, and Equation 8 may not be adequate. For smaller particles (d_p < 0.01 μm), diffusional deposition is the dominant mechanism, and Equation 8 is simplified to:

$$P = \exp(-2.7 Bn Pe^{-2/3}) \quad (9)$$

Diffusion Denuders

Gas or vapor molecules diffuse rapidly to the wall of a diffusion sampler and adsorb onto the wall coated with material suitable for collecting the gas. Diffusion tubes have been used to measure diffusion coefficients of several gases in the air.[26–28] Since 1980, diffusion denuders followed by a filter pack have been developed to sample atmospheric nitric acid vapors and nitrate particulate aerosols. Using this sampling technique, called the denuder difference method, gaseous species, such as HNO_3 and NH_3, can be separated from particulate nitrates and thus minimize sampling artifacts due to the presence of these gases.[29–34] Diffusion denuders are also used to monitor vapors, such as formaldehyde, chlorinated organic compounds, and tetra alkyl lead, in the ambient air or work environments.[35–37] Some personal samplers have also been developed for industrial hygiene use.[38,39]

Description of Diffusion Denuders

Two types of diffusion denuders have been designed: the cylindrical tube and annular tube.

Cylindrical Denuders

In cylindrical denuders, a single cylindrical glass or Teflon® tube is often used for collecting gases or vapors. The diameter and length of the tube and the sampling flow rate are designed to have greater than 99% collection efficiency. For example, a glass tube of 3-mm i.d. and 35 cm long would have over 99% efficiency for ammonia ($\mathcal{D}$ = 2.47 × 10^{-5} m^2/s) at 3 L/min.[40] For higher sampling flow rates, parallel tube assemblies have been designed,[29,32] consisting of 16 glass tubes 5-mm i.d. and 30 cm long. The sampling flow rate was 50 L/min, and the collection efficiency for ammonia was over 99%.[29]

Penetration through the tube-type denuders can be estimated by taking the first term of Equation 3 only:

$$P = 0.819 \exp(-3.66\ \mu) \quad (10)$$

This simplified equation is accurate at higher values of μ (> 0.4) and at lower penetrations (P < 0.190). The error of the estimated penetration from Equation 3 increases with the decreasing value of μ(–0.25% error for μ = 0.2 and P = 0.395, and –1.8% for μ = 0.1 and P = 0.579). Equation 10 is applicable for the fully developed laminar flow region in the tube. The flow Reynolds number in the tube should be less than 2300 for laminar flow:

$$Re = \frac{4\rho Q}{\eta \pi D} < 2300 \quad (11)$$

where: Q = volumetric flow rate
D = diameter of the tube
ρ = gas density
η = gas viscosity

In the entrance of the tube, the flow is in a transition region from plug flow to developed flow. The length of entrance, L_e, is defined by the following equation and should be minimized:

$$L_e = 0.035\ d\ Re \quad (12)$$

Annular Denuders

Higher sampling flow rates are desirable, especially for sampling trains consisting of denuders and filters or dichotomous samplers.[31] An annular tube denuder was recently designed for this purpose.[19] It consists of two coaxial cylinders with the inner one sealed at both ends, so that air is forced to pass through the annular space (Figure 20-3). The collection efficiency of the annular tube can be estimated from Equation 7 for lower Reynolds numbers ($Re < 2300$) defined as:

$$Re = \frac{4\rho Q}{\eta\pi\,(d_1 + d_2)} \quad (13)$$

Comparing the performance of the cylindrical and annular denuders in removing a gas from an air stream, a typical annular denuder ($d_2 = 3.3$ cm and $d_1 = 3.0$ cm) is possible by equating Equations 7 and 10. It can be shown that:

$$\frac{Q}{L}\Big|_{annular} = 31.5\,\frac{Q}{L}\Big|_{cylinder} \quad (14)$$

This relationship shows that for a given tube length, the annular denuder can operate at 30 times the flow rate of the cylindrical denuder and still have the same removal efficiency. Also, the Reynolds number would still indicate laminar flow conditions for the annular tube system. A multi-channel annular diffusion denuder has been tested and used in ambient air sampling.[35]

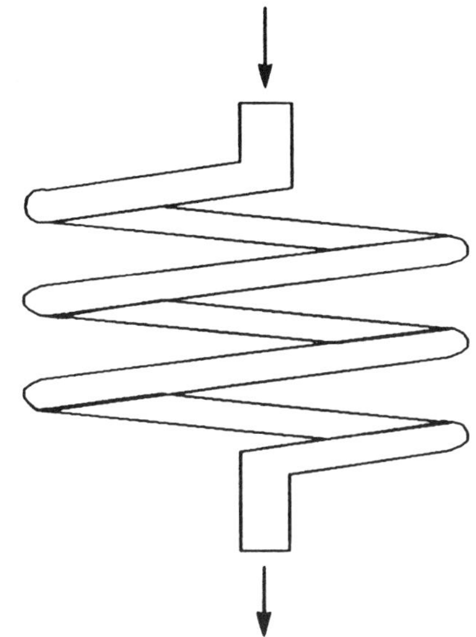

FIGURE 20-3. Schematic of a compact coil denuder.

Compact Coil Denuders

A compact coil denuder consisting of a 1.0-cm-i.d. and 95-cm-long (L) glass tube bent into a three-turn helical coil with a 10-cm diameter (Figure 20-3) has been designed by Pui *et al.*[41] The heat and mass transfer rates to the tube wall in a curved tube are much higher than those in a straight tube operated at the same conditions.[42,43] This denuder is operated at 10 L/min (Q) with a Reynolds number of 1400. The penetration through the denuder can be expressed as:[41]

$$P = 0.82\,\exp(-\frac{\pi L \mathcal{D}}{Q}\,Sh) \quad (15)$$

$$Sh = \frac{0.864}{\delta}\,De^{1/2}(1 + 2.35\,De^{-1/2}) \quad (16)$$

where: Sh = Sherwood number
De = Dean number, the flow Reynolds number divided by the square root of the radius of curvature
δ = thickness ratio of the concentration boundary to the momentum boundary layer

This unit has a 99.3% collection efficiency for SO_2 with less than 6% loss for particles between 0.015 and 2.5 μm in diameter. It is compact and easy to operate.

Transition-Flow Denuders

Both cylindrical and annular denuders are operated in laminar flow conditions, and they are designed to remove all gases of interest from the air stream. Particle evaporation may increase the concentration of some gases in passing through such denuders, especially in the case of the decomposition of NH_4NO_3 into HNO_3 and NH_3 gases. To avoid biases due to evaporation of particles, one approach to sampling such gases is to collect only a known fraction of gases in the denuder and then calculate the gas concentration.

A transition-flow denuder was designed by Durham *et al.*[44] to permit higher sampling flow. The cylindrical denuder has an i.d. of 0.95 cm with a 6-cm distance of the first active surface to allow for development of a stable flow profile. The denuder section is lined with a 3.2-cm-long nylon sheet. By assuming complete mixing in the active section, the penetration can be expressed as:

$$P = \exp(-\frac{2\pi\alpha L}{Q}) \quad (17)$$

where: L = length of the active surface
Q = flow rate
$\alpha = r\mathcal{D}/\delta$ = a function of the diffusion coefficient
r = radius of the tube
δ = boundary thickness, which is a function of the Reynolds number

The penetration must be determined empirically. Operating the denuder at 16.1 L/min ($Re = 2500$), Durham *et al.*[44] obtained a retention of 0.911 for HNO_3.

Scrubber-Type Diffusion Denuders

Most diffusion denuders have a solid coating on the wall to collect gaseous species, and the coating substrates are washed after sampling for analysis. For continuous analysis of gas species, diffusion scrubbers

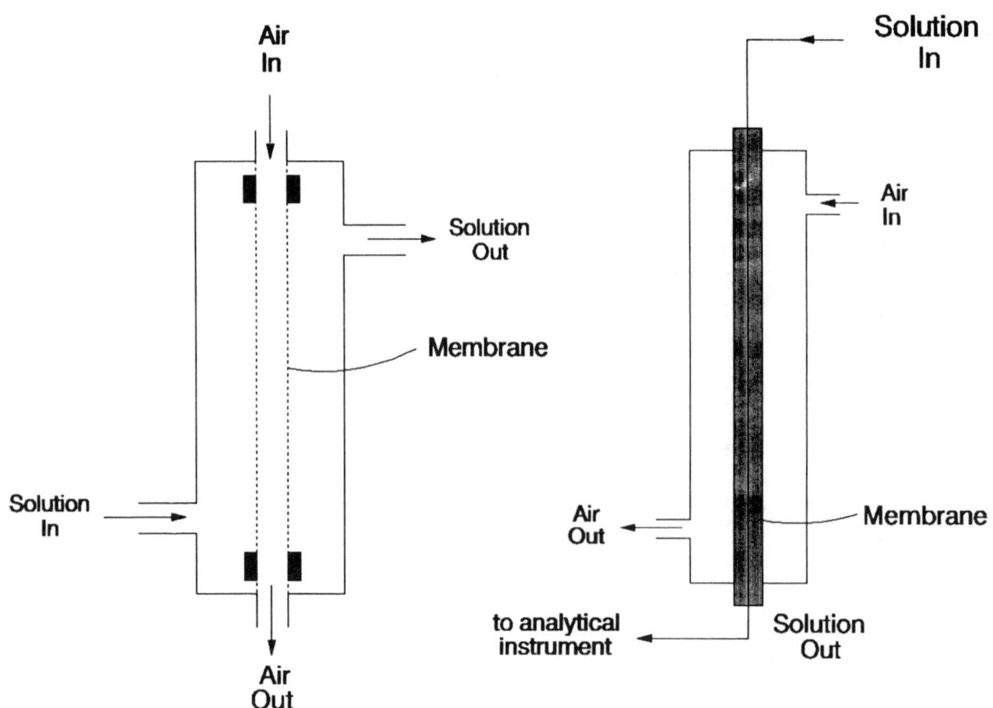

FIGURE 20-4. Schematics of diffusion scrubbers.

are used; the absorbent or solvent in the liquid form is continuously flowing along the tube wall, and the analyte can be analyzed in real-time.[45,46] A tubular scrubber is made by inserting a membrane tube into the glass tube to form a jacket between the glass wall and the membrane (Figure 20-4). Porous membranes, such as PTFE and polypropylene, allow gases (but not particles) to permeate and dissolve in the solution that flows continuously through the jacket. The collection characteristics of this diffusion scrubber should be similar to the tube diffusion denuder. Another type of diffusion denuder consists of a tube with a membrane tube at the center, in which air flows through the annular space while the solvent passes through the membrane tube.

Coating Substrates

Absorbent material can be coated onto the tube wall of a denuder to collect the gas of interest from the air stream. Table 20-1 lists substrates for removal of some gases as reported in the literature. Some materials absorb more than one gas. For example, sodium carbonate can absorb acidic gases found in the ambient air, including HCl, HNO_2, HNO_3, and SO_2. The method of application of material to the tube wall depends largely on the nature of the material. Most materials are first dissolved then applied to the tube wall. Solvents are allowed to evaporate, leaving the absorbent on the glass tube wall. In some cases, the glass denuder wall has been etched by sand blasting the surface to increase the capacity of walls to support the denuding chemical substrate.[19] Absorbent paper impregnated with liquid or solution substrate, such as oleic acid, has been used to line the inside of the denuder wall.[26] A nylon sheet has also been used as a liner.[44] Anodized aluminum surfaces have recently been found to be a good absorb-

TABLE 20-1. Materials for Absorbing Gases in the Diffusion Denuder

Coating Material	Gas Absorbed	Reference
Oxalic acid	NH_3, aniline	38, 40
Oleic acid	SO_3	26
H_3PO_3	NH_3	29
K_2CO_3	SO_2, H_2S	47
Na_2CO_3	SO_2, HCl, HNO_3, HNO_2	32
$CuSO_4$	NH_3	26
PbO_2	SO_2, H_2S	47
WO_3	NH_3, HNO_3	48
MgO	HNO_3	29
NaF	HNO_3	49
NaOH and guaiacol	NO_2	50
Bisulfite-triethanolamine	Formaldehyde	36
Nylon sheet	SO_2, HNO_3	44
Tenax powder	Chlorinated organics	35
Silica gel	Aniline	39
ICl	Tetra alkyl lead	37

ing surface for nitric acid. Annular denuders made of anodized aluminum do not need coating.[51] Tenax or silica gel powder is more difficult to apply; however, these materials adhere to the glass wall coated with silicon grease.[35,39]

Sampling Trains

When sampling ambient or working atmospheres, it is sometimes necessary to collect gases and particulate materials separately. In this case, a sampling train consisting of diffusion denuders and a filter pack has been used. A more complex system (as shown in Figure 20-5), including a cyclone precutter, two Na_2CO_3-coated annular denuders, and a filter pack with a Teflon and a nylon filter, has been used to collect acidic gases (HNO_3, HNO_2, SO_2 and HCl) separately from nitrate and sulfate particles.[34] The first denuder removes gases quantitatively, whereas the second accounts for the interference from particulate material deposited on the wall under the assumption that particle deposition on each denuder is the same.[37] The denuders are placed vertically to avoid particle deposition on the walls by sedimentation. A diffusion scrubber can be connected to an ion chromatograph or other analytical instruments for real-time analysis of gases.[46,52] Further discussion can be found in Chapter 4.

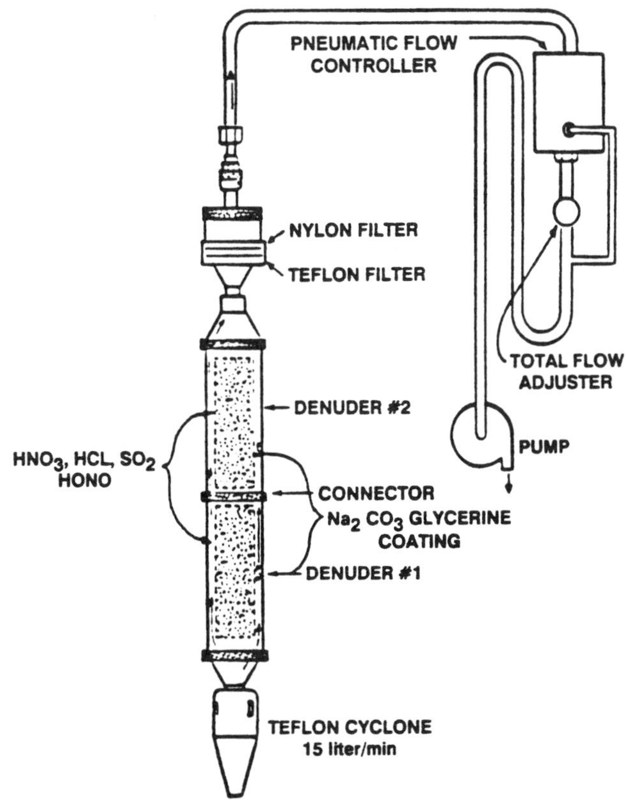

FIGURE 20-5. An ambient acidic aerosol sampler consisting of a precutter, two annular denuders, and a filter pack.[34]

Diffusion Batteries

Diffusion batteries were originally developed to measure the diffusion coefficient of particles less than 0.1 μm in diameter. They have since been used for determination of particle size distributions by converting the diffusion coefficient to the particle size. Diffusion batteries are one type of only a few instruments that are applicable in measuring ultrafine particles between 0.1 μm and about 1 nm, corresponding to the size of molecular clusters. In this section, various designs of the instrument, detection of particles, and methods of data analysis will be discussed.

Description of Diffusion Batteries

Several types of diffusion batteries have been designed. Those based on rectangular channels and parallel circular plates are single-stage diffusion batteries. Cylindrical-tube and screen-type diffusion batteries usually have several stages.

Rectangular Channel

Rectangular channel diffusion batteries usually consist of many rectangular plates forming parallel channels of equal width. These plates are separated by spacers and glued to a container with an airtight seal. For example, a diffusion battery consisting of 20 parallel channels (0.01 cm wide, 12.7 cm high, and 47.3 cm long) made from graphite plates has been designed for a 1 L/min sampling flow rate.[26] Other instruments have been made from aluminum or glass plates with similar construction.[2,53–56] Each channel should be parallel and have the same width. Deviation of channel width results in a nonuniform flow rate through each channel, which in turn causes the deviation of penetration from the theoretical prediction of Equations 5 and 6. A diffusion battery of 10 single channels, each separately housed in a box, has been designed by Pollak and Metnieks.[57]

A single-stage diffusion battery can be used to measure the diffusion coefficient of monodisperse aerosols at one flow rate. When it is used to measure polydisperse aerosols, such as those found in ambient air, several measurements taken at different flow rates are necessary to determine the distribution of diffusion coefficients.

Parallel Disks

A diffusion sampler has been designed by Kotrappa *et al.*[58] It is based on the diffusional losses of particles from a fluid flowing radially inward between two coaxial, parallel, or circular plates as originally proposed by Mercer and Mercer.[15] Stainless steel plates (3.77-cm diameter) with a central hole of 0.2-cm diameter in the upper plate are the collecting substrate. Separation between the plates is 0.225 cm. An absolute filter is used to collect material penetrating the device. This sampler has been used to determine the diffusion coefficient of radon decay products which have diffusion coefficients of the order of 0.05 cm^2/sec. The amount of radioactivity collected at the plates and the absolute filter was determined, and the diffusion coefficient was calculated from Equation 5, simplified to contain only the first term:

$$P = 0.9104 \exp\left(-2.8278 \frac{8\pi \mathcal{D} (r_2^2 - r_1^2)}{3QH} \right) \quad (18)$$

Cylindrical Tubes

Tube-type diffusion batteries made of cylindrical tubes usually consist of a cluster of thin-walled tubes with diameters less than 0.1-cm i.d. Large equivalent length (actual length × number of tubes) is required for measurement of particle size, because particles have much smaller diffusion coefficients than do gas molecules. Several cluster tube diffusion batteries have been designed.[59–61] Figure 20-6 shows the schematic of a tube-type diffusion battery as reported by Scheibel and Porstendörfer.[61] Three diffusion batteries with 100, 484, and 1000 single tubes were used with lengths of 5.0, 9.3, and 39.03 cm, respectively. Tube-type diffusion batteries use materials that are commercially available and are also easier to construct than the parallel-plate diffusion battery. A lightweight material such as aluminum is often used; however, this type of diffusion battery is still heavy, bulky, and expensive. Most cluster tube diffusion batteries consist of one to three stages,[60,61] although an eight-stage diffusion battery has been constructed.[59]

Compact diffusion batteries with many stages have been designed by using collimated hole or honeycomb structures (CHSs). The CHSs are discs containing a large number of near-circular holes. Figure 20-7 shows a 1 3/4-in.-diameter CHS disc made from stainless steel containing 14,500 holes of 0.009-in. diameter (Brunswick Co., Chicago, IL). With a thickness of 1/8 to 1 in., the equivalent length ranged from 46 to 369 m. A portable 11-stage diffusion battery has been designed with CHS elements.[62] The total length is 60 cm, and the equivalent length is 5094 m. Figure 20-8 shows the schematic of a five-stage diffusion battery made from CHS elements. A multiple-stage diffusion battery is required to measure the size distribution of a polydisperse aerosol. The development of a multiple-stage CHS diffusion battery opens up the possibility of routine measurements of submicrometer aerosols. However, the commercial sources for the CHS are not currently available and, therefore, only a few diffusion batteries are still being used in some laboratories. Other CHS discs made from glass capillary tubes of 25 or 50 mm in diameter and a thickness of 0.5 to 2.0 mm are commercially available (Galileo Electro Optical Corp., Struburg, MA). A six-stage CHS diffusion battery made from glass has been designed.[63]

Wire Screens

Diffusion batteries using stacks of filters as the cell material have been used by Sinclair and Hinchliffe[64] and Twomey and Zalabsky.[65] This filter material is lightweight and inexpensive to build. However, com-

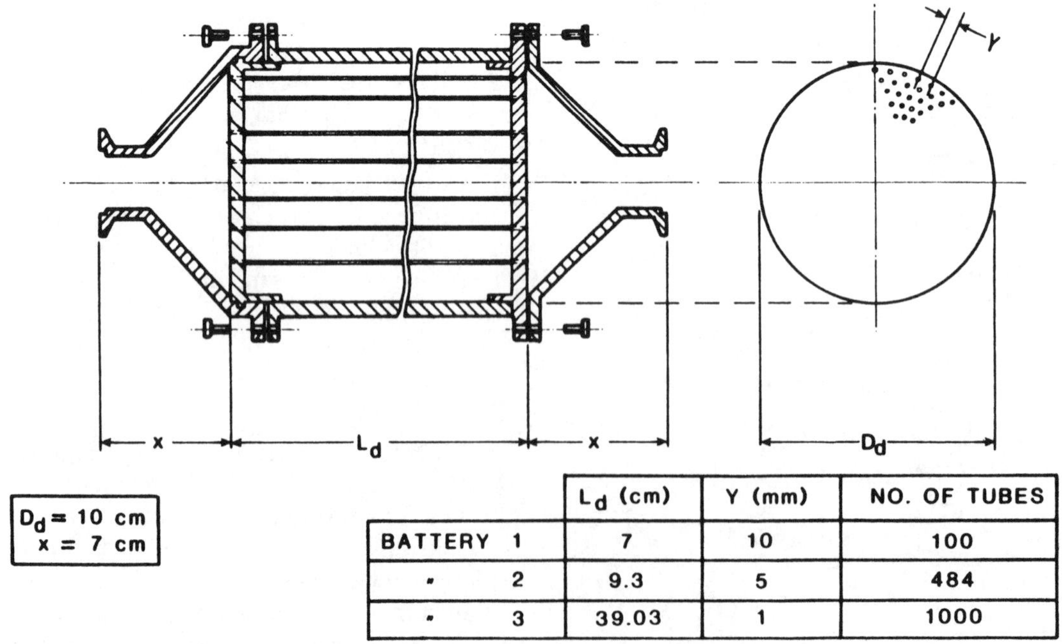

	L_d (cm)	Y (mm)	NO. OF TUBES
BATTERY 1	7	10	100
" 2	9.3	5	484
" 3	39.03	1	1000

FIGURE 20-6. Schematic of a cluster-tube diffusion battery.[61]

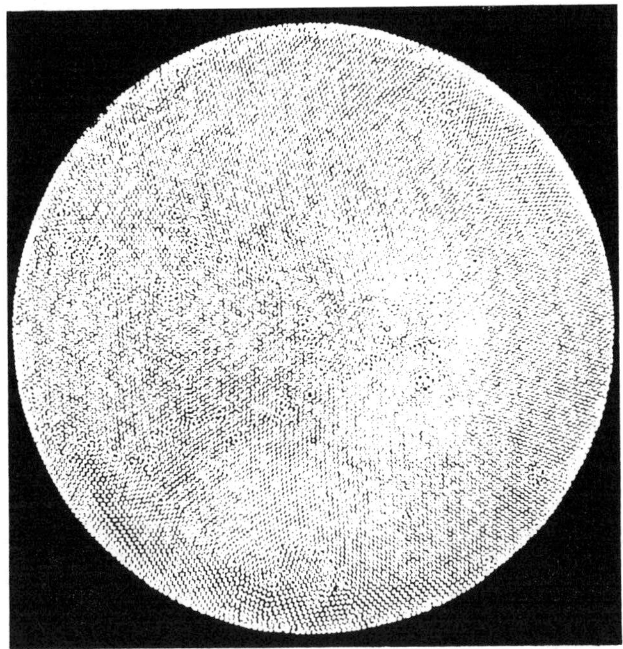

FIGURE 20-7. A stainless steel, collimated hole structure disc.

mercial fiber or membrane filters are not ideal materials because of the nonuniformity in the fiber diameter and porosity. Aerosol penetration through the filter may not be consistent and could not be predicted accurately by filtration theory. Sinclair and Hoopes[66] designed a 10-stage unit using stainless steel 635-mesh screens of uniform diameter, opening, and thickness (Figure 20-9). The designed flow rate ranged from 4 to 6 L/min. Stacks of these well-defined screens simulate a fan model both in geometry and in flow resistance.[25] Penetration through screens can be predicted by the fan model filtration theory (Equation 8).[20,21] Subsequently, this unit has become commercially available

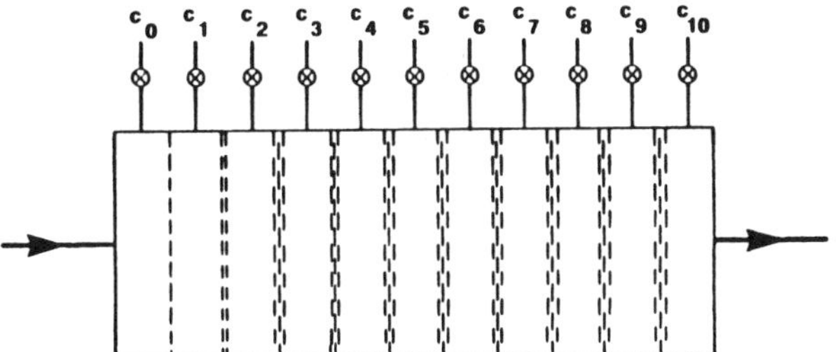

FIGURE 20-9. Schematic of a 10-stage screen-type diffusion battery.

(Model 3040, TSI Inc., St. Paul, MN). Other types of screens have also been tested and found useful.[22,25] Table 20-2 lists characteristics of the different screens as shown in Figure 20-10. Screen-type diffusion batteries are compact in size and simple to construct. Screens can be cleaned and replaced easily when they are contaminated or worn out.

Most multistage diffusion batteries described here are arranged in a series so that the aerosol concentration decreases continuously through the cells. Aerosol penetration is usually detected by a condensation nucleus counter (CNC). Based on parallel flow and mass collection principles, a parallel flow diffusion battery (PFDB) has been designed by Cheng *et al.*[67] This unit measures the penetration by mass or radioactivity without a particle detecting unit. It is also more useful to detect unstable aerosols with fluctuating size and concentration. A schematic diagram of the PFDB is shown in Figure 20-11. The PFDB consists of a conical cap and a collection section containing seven cells. Each diffusion cell contains a different number of stainless steel 200-mesh screens followed by a 25-mm Zefluor filter (Gelman, Ann Arbor, MI). The seven cells typically contain 0 through 35 screens. Critical orifices provide a 2 L/min flow rate through each cell resulting

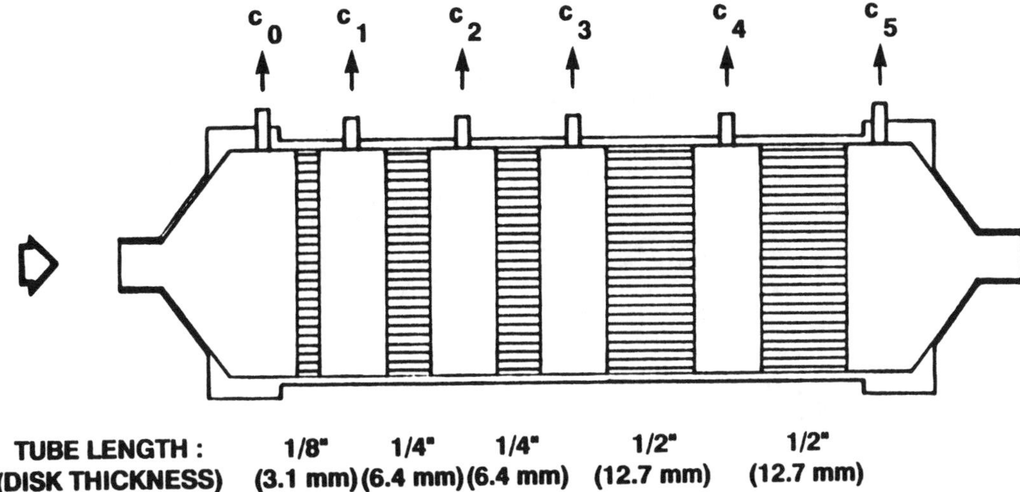

FIGURE 20-8. Schematic of a five-stage diffusion battery consisting of a stainless steel, collimated hole structure.

TABLE 20-2. Characteristic Dimensions and Constants for Various Types of Screens in Screen-Type Diffusion Batteries

Screen Mesh	145	200	400	400	635
Weave	Square	Square	Square	Twill	Twill
Screen diameter (μm)	55.9	40.6	25.4	25.4	20
Screen thickness (μm)	122	96.3	57.1	63.5	50
Solid volume fraction	0.345	0.244	0.230	0.292	0.313

in a total flow rate of 14 L/min. Gravimetric determination of collected filter samples from each cell provides the direct mass penetration as a function of screen number for the determination of aerosol size distribution, thereby eliminating the sometimes inaccurate conversion of number to mass.

Screen diffusion batteries have been used routinely to determine the activity size distribution of radon progeny. A single screen and a filter have been used to estimate the unattached fraction. The screen and flow rate were chosen such that 4- to 10-nm particles can penetrate the screen with 50% efficiency. The radioactivity collected on the screen and the filter are counted, and the amount of activity collected on the screen is assumed to be the unattached radon progeny. The activity size distribution of the radon progeny can be measured with either a graded screen diffusion battery[68] or a PFDB.[69,70] A graded diffusion battery consists of several stages, each with a different type of screen. The screens with a lower mesh number are used to collect particles in the nm size range, whereas screens of a larger mesh number are used to collect larger particles. Figure 20-12 shows a schematic of a graded diffusion battery including five stages of screens

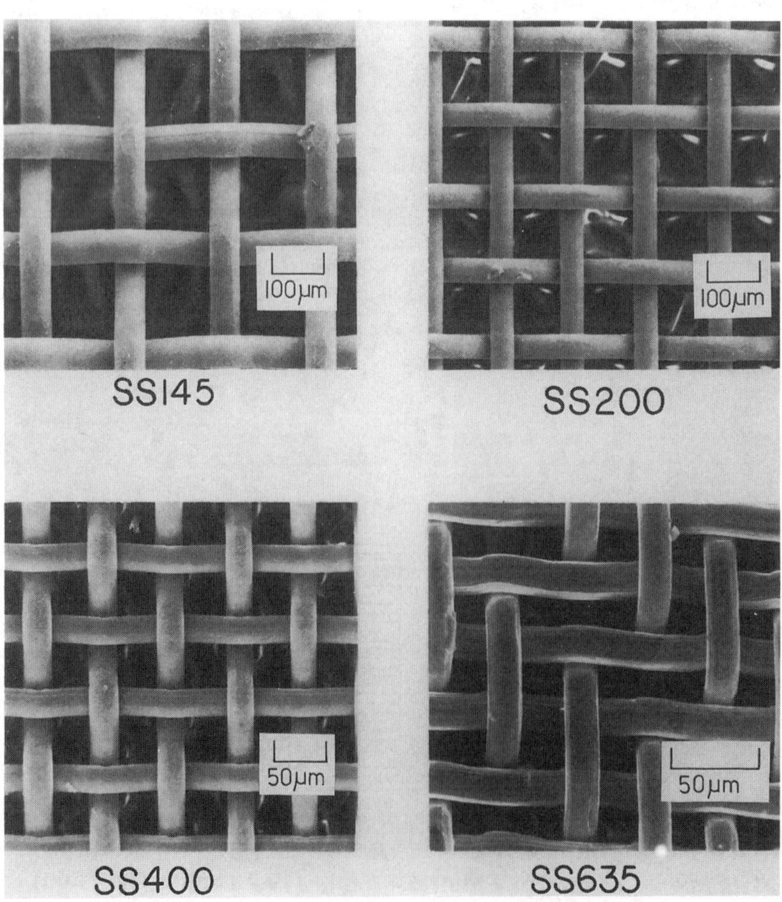

FIGURE 20-10. Photomicrograph of stainless mesh screens.

and a back-up filter.[71] After a brief sampling time (5–10 min), the screens and filters are counted directly for radioactivity. Because of the geometry of the screens, the efficiency of the alpha counting is not 100%, and corrections should be made to allow for a lower counting efficiency on screens.[72] PFDBs with much higher flow rates (over 30 L/min) are used to collect indoor radon progeny, which often have very low concentrations. Usually, only the back-up filters for each stage of the PFDB are counted for radioactivity. Thus, this method eliminates possible errors due to the attenuation of alpha rays by the screen.

Use and Data Analysis

Aerosol penetration through a diffusion battery provides data for the determination of particle size distribution. Aerosol penetration through a diffusion cell is obtained by measuring the number, mass, or activity concentrations at the inlet and outlet of each cell. A CNC is used to measure the number concentration. Figure 20-13 shows a schematic diagram of a system including a diffusion battery, an automatic switching valve, and a CNC. With the automatic sampling system, it takes 3 min to complete an 11-channel measurement.

For radioactive aerosols, penetration based on activity can be obtained by collecting samples at the diffusion cell and a back-up filter at the end of the diffusion battery. The single-stage parallel disk diffusion sampler[58] and screen diffusion batteries have been used for this purpose. Screens can be counted directly for radioactivity.[69] Penetration based on the mass can be obtained by using a PFDB.

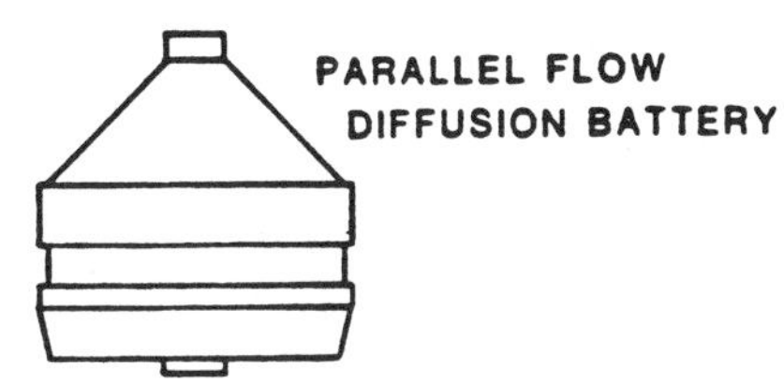

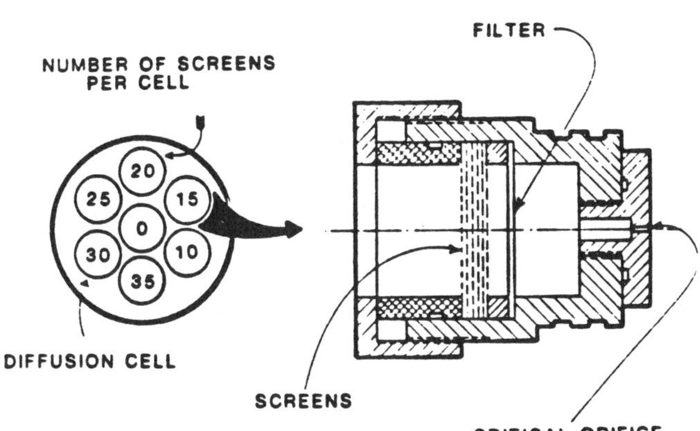

FIGURE 20-11. Schematic of a parallel flow diffusion battery.

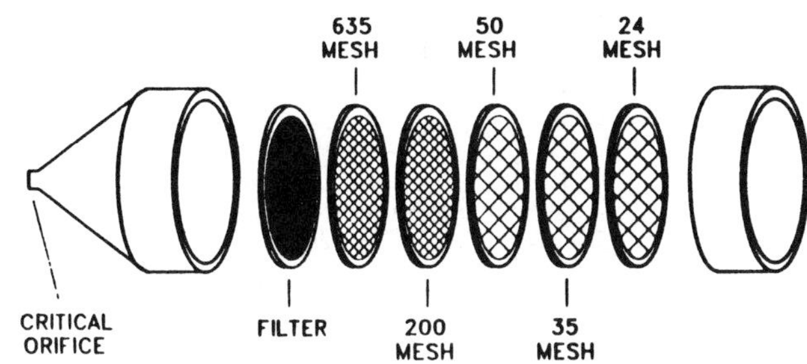

FIGURE 20-12. Schematic of a graded diffusion battery.

Data Analysis

Monodisperse Aerosols

Particle size distributions are calculated from penetration data obtained from the measurements by the diffusion battery. For a monodisperse aerosol, the diffusion coefficient, $\mathcal{D}$, can be calculated directly from the corresponding Equations 3–9. The particle size, d_p, is then calculated from the following relationship:

$$\mathcal{D} = \frac{kTC(d_p)}{3\pi\eta d_p} \tag{19}$$

$$C(d_p) = 1 + \frac{2\lambda}{d_p}\left[\,1.142 + 0.558\exp\left(-0.999\frac{d_p}{2\lambda}\right)\right] \tag{20}$$

where: k = Boltzmann constant (1.38×10^{-16} erg K^{-1})
T = absolute temperature (K)
C = "Cunningham" slip correction factor
λ = mean free path of air (0.0673 μm at 23°C and 760 mm Hg)

With monodisperse particles, measurements from a single-stage diffusion battery are sufficient, and measurements from multiple-stage devices should improve the accuracy.

Polydisperse Aerosols

Most aerosols in ambient environments and work places have polydisperse size distributions, and the method described in the previous section does not apply. Three penetration data points are the minimum required, but more will improve the accuracy of the size determination. Both graphical and numerical inversion methods have been developed for the size determination from penetration data.

Fuchs *et al.*[73] have generated a family of penetration curves for rectangular channel diffusion batteries assuming the aerosol size distribution is lognormally

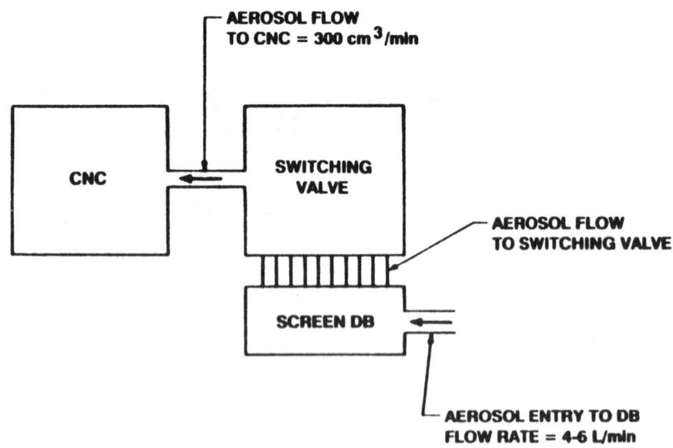

FIGURE 20-13. Schematic of a diffusion battery, automatic switch valve, and condensation nuclei counter.

distributed. Mercer and Greene[74] have provided curves representing the penetration of aerosols in both cylindrical and rectangular channels as functions of the diffusion parameter, m, and the geometric standard deviation from 1 to 5. Once the data are properly aligned with one of the curves, this method gives a rough estimate of the mean and geometric standard deviation of the diffusion coefficient. Similar curves have been derived for screen-type diffusion batteries.[75] This method does not apply to aerosols that do not follow lognormal size distributions.

Sinclair[59] used a graphical "stripping" method to estimate the particle size distribution from penetration data through a multistage, cylindrical-type diffusion battery. A family of penetration curves has been calculated for monodisperse particles over a range of equivalent lengths. The experimental penetration data are plotted on a different paper of the same scale. The experimental curve is matched against the theoretical curves, and the one having the best fit at the right end of experimental curves (i.e., where penetration is least) is subtracted, leaving a new experimental curve. The process is repeated until the original experimental curve is entirely eliminated. Particle size and fractions of each size in the original aerosol are indicated by the matched theoretical curves and their intercepts with the ordinate of the graph. A similar method has been applied to the screen-type diffusion battery.[76] This method does not assume a certain size distribution and thus is more useful. However, results for both graphical methods depend on judgement in matching curves.

More consistent results can be obtained by using numerical inversion methods. In a diffusion battery, aerosol penetration through stage i, P_i, can be expressed mathematically as the integration of the aerosol penetration equation for monodisperse aerosol $P_i(x)$:

$$P_i = \int_0^\infty P_i(x)\, f(x)\, dx \tag{21}$$

where: $f(x)$ = size distribution
$P_i(x)$ = aerosol penetration of size x in stage i

Each observed penetration for stage $i = 1$ through n can be expressed in the form of Equation 21. Several numerical inversion methods have been developed to obtain the aerosol size distribution, $f(x)$. Raabe[77] has developed a nonlinear least square regression to solve Equation 21 under the assumption of a lognormal distribution for $f(x)$. A similar method is used by Soderholm[12] for diffusion battery data analysis. A nonlinear iterative method proposed by Twomey[78] was applied to diffusion batteries by Knutson and Sinclair.[79] Modification of Twomey's method is used for data analysis of screen-type diffusion batteries.[80,81] An expectation-maximization algorithm has been developed for the screen-type diffusion battery and appears to work as well as or better than the least square regression and Twomey's method.[82] Further recommendations for calculating particle size distribution from data obtained with a diffusion battery can be found in Chapter 6.

Conclusion

Diffusion denuders are instruments used to separate and collect gas or vapor from particles, and diffusion batteries are used to determine the particle size distribution of ultrafine particles. These instruments are based on similar sampling principles and mathematical formulas. These techniques are important tools in studying ultrafine particles, gases and vapors, and molecular clusters such as radon progeny.

References

1. Nolan, J.J.; Guerrini, V.H.: The Diffusion Coefficient of Condensation Nuclei and Velocity of Fall in Air of Atmospheric Nuclei. Proc. R. Iri. Acad. 43:5–24 (1935).
2. Nolan, J.J.; Nolan, P.J.: Diffusion and Fall of Atmospheric Condensation Nuclei. Proc. R. Iri. Acad. A45:47–63 (1938).
3. Gormley, P.G.; Kennedy, M.: Diffusion from a Stream Flowing Through a Cylindrical Tube. Proc. R. Iri. Acad. A52:163–169 (1949).
4. Cheng, Y.S.: Diffusion Batteries and Denuders. In: Air Sampling Instruments for Evaluation of Atmospheric Contaminants, 7th ed., pp. 406–419. S.V. Hering, Ed. American Conference of Governmental Industrial Hygienists, Cincinnati, OH (1989).
5. Cheng, Y.S.: Diffusion and Condensation Techniques. In: Air Measurement, Principles, Techniques, and Applications, pp. 427–451. K. Willeke and P.A. Baron, Eds. Van Nostrand Reinhold, New York (1993).
6. Ingham, D.B.: Diffusion of Aerosols from a Stream Flowing Through a Cylindrical Tube. J. Aerosol Sci. 6:125–132 (1975).
7. Sideman, S.; Luss, D.; Peck, R.E.: Heat Transfer in Laminar Flow in Circular and Flat Conduits with (Constant) Surface Resistance. Appl. Sci. Res. A14:157–171 (1965).
8. Davis, H.R.; Parkins, G.V.: Mass Transfer from Small Capillaries with Wall Resistance in the Laminar Flow Regime. Appl. Sci. Res.

22:20–30 (1970).
9. Tan, C.W.; Hsu, C.J.: Diffusion of Aerosols in Laminar Flow in a Cylindrical Tube. J. Aerosol Sci. 2:117–124 (1971).
10. Lekhtmakher, S.O.: Effect of Peclet Number on the Precipitation of Particles from a Laminar Flow. J. Eng. Physics 20:400–402 (1971).
11. Bowen, B.D.; Levine, S.; Esptein, N.: Fine Particle Deposition in Laminar Flow Through Parallel-plate and Cylindrical Channels. J. Colloid Interface Sci. 54:375–390 (1976).
12. Soderholm, S.C.: Analysis of Diffusion Battery Data. J. Aerosol Sci. 10:163–175 (1979).
13. Newman, J.: Extension of the Leveque Solution. J. Heat Transfer 91:177–178 (1969).
14. DeMarcus, W.; Thomas, J.W.: Theory of a Diffusion Battery. Oak Ridge National Laboratory Report ORNL-1413. ORNL, Oak Ridge, TN (1952).
15. Mercer, T.T.; Mercer, R.L.: Diffusional Deposition from a Fluid Flowing Radially Between Concentric, Parallel, Circular Plates. J. Aerosol Sci. 1:279–285 (1970).
16. Tan, C.W.; Thomas, J.W.: Aerosol Penetration Through a Parallel-plate Diffusion Battery. J. Aerosol Sci. 3:39–43 (1972).
17. Ingham, D.B.: Simultaneous Diffusion and Sedimentation of Aerosol Particles in Rectangular Tubes. J. Aerosol Sci. 7:373–380 (1976).
18. Nolan, P.J.; Kennedy, P.J.: Anomalous Loss of Condensation Nuclei in Rubber Tubing. J. Atmos. Terrestrial Phys. 3:181–185 (1953).
19. Possanzini, M.; Febo, A.; Aliberti, A.: New Design of a High-performance Denuder for the Sampling of Atmospheric Pollutants. Atmos. Environ. 17:2605–2610 (1983).
20. Cheng, Y.S.; Yeh, H.C.: Theory of a Screen-type Diffusion Battery. J. Aerosol Sci. 11:313–320 (1980).
21. Cheng, Y.S.; Keating, J.A.; Kanapilly, G.M.: Theory and Calibration of a Screen-type Diffusion Battery. J. Aerosol Sci. 11:549–556 (1980).
22. Yeh, H.C.; Cheng, Y.S.; Orman, M.M.: Evaluation of Various Types of Wire Screens as Diffusion Battery Cells. J. Colloid Interface Sci. 86:12–16 (1982).
23. Kirsch, A.A.; Fuchs, N.A.: Studies of Fibrous Aerosol Filters-III. Diffusional Deposition of Aerosols in Fibrous Filters. Ann. Occup. Hyg. 11:299–304 (1968).
24. Kirsch, A.A.; Stechkina, I.B.: The Theory of Aerosol Filtration with Fibrous Filter. In: Fundamentals of Aerosol Science, pp. 165–256. D.T. Shaw, Ed. Wiley, New York (1978).
25. Cheng, Y.S.; Yeh, H.C.; Brinsko, K.J.: Use of Wire Screens as a Fan Model Filter. Aerosol Sci. Technol. 4:165–174 (1985).
26. Thomas, J.W.: The Diffusion Battery Method for Aerosol Particle Size Determination. J. Colloid Sci. 10:246–255 (1955).
27. Fish, B.R.; Durham, J.L.: Diffusion Coefficient of SO_2 in Air. Environ. Lett. 2:13–21 (1971).
28. Durham, J.L.; Spiller, L.L.; Ellestad, T.G.: Nitric Acid-nitrate Aerosol Measurements by a Diffusion Denuder, a Performance Evaluation. Atmos. Environ. 21:589–598 (1987).
29. Stevens, R.K.; Dzubay, T.G.; Russwurm, G.; Rickel, D.: Sampling and Analysis of Atmospheric Sulfates and Related Apecies. Atmos. Environ. 12:55–68 (1978).
30. Appel, B.R.; Tokiwa, Y.; Haik, M.: Sampling of Nitrates in Ambient Air. Atmos. Environ. 15:283–289 (1981).
31. Shaw, R.W.; Stevens, R.K.; Bowermaster, J.; et al.: Measurements of Atmospheric Nitrate and Nitric Acid; The Denuder Difference Experiment. Atmos. Environ. 16:845–853 (1982).
32. Forrest, J.; Spandau, D.J.; Tanner, R.L.; Newman, L.: Determination of Atmospheric Nitrate and Nitric Acid Employing a Diffusion Denuder with a Filter Pack. Atmos. Environ. 16:1473–485 (1982).
33. Ferm, M.: A Na_2CO_3-coated Denuder and Filter for Determination of Gaseous HNO_3 and Particulate NO in the Atmosphere. Atmos. Environ. 20:1193–1201 (1986).
34. Stevens, R.K.: Modern Methods to Measure Air Pollutants. In: Aerosols: Research, Risk Assessment, and Control Strategies, pp. 69–95. S.D. Lee, Ed. Lewis, MI (1986).
35. Johnson, N.D.; Barton, S.C.; Thomas, G.H.S.; et al.: Development of Gas/Particle Fractionating Sampler of Chlorinated Organics. 78th Annual Meeting of Air Pollution Control Assocation, Detroit, MI (1985).
36. Cecchini, F.; Febo, A.; Possanzini, M.: High Efficiency Annular Denuder for Formaldehyde Monitoring. Anal. Lett. 18:681–693 (1985).
37. Febo, A.; DiPalo, V.; Possanzini, M.: The Determination of Tetraalkyl Lead Air by a Denuder Diffusion Technique. Sci. Total Environ. 48:187–194 (1986).
38. DeSantis, F.; Perrino, C.: Personal Sampling of Aniline in Working Site by Using High Efficiency Annular Denuders. Ann. Chimica 76:355–364 (1986).
39. Gunderson, E.C.; Anderson, C.C.: Collection Device for Separating Airborne Vapor and Particulates. Am. Ind. Hyg. Assoc. J. 48:634–638 (1987).
40. Ferm, M.: Method for Determination of Atmospheric Ammonia. Atmos. Environ. 13:1385–93 (1979).
41. Pui, D.Y.H.; Lewis, C.W.; Tsai, C.J.; Liu, B.Y.H.: A Compact Coiled Denuder for Atmospheric Sampling. Environ. Sci. Technol. 24:307–312 (1990).
42. Mori, Y.; Nakayama, W.: Study on Forced Convective Heat Transfer in Curved Pipes. Int. J. Heat Mass Transfer 10:37–59 (1967a).
43. Mori, Y.; Nakayama, W.: Study on Forced Convective Heat Transfer In Curved Pipes. Int. J. Heat Mass Transfer 10:681–695 (1976b).
44. Durham, J.L.; Ellestad, T.G.; Stockburger, L.; et al.: A Transition-flow Reactor Tube for Measuring Trace Gas Concentrations. J. Air Pollut. Control Assoc. 36:1228–1232 (1986).
45. Dasgupta, P.K.: A Diffusion Scrubber for the Collection of Atmospheric Gases. Atmos. Environ. 18:1593–1599 (1984).
46. Dasgupta, P.K.; Dong, S.; Hwang, H.; et al.: Continuous Liquid-phase Fluorometry Coupled to a Diffusion Scrubber for the Real-time Determination of Atmospheric Formaldehyde Hydrogen Peroxide and Sulfur Dioxide. Atmos. Environ. 22:946–963 (1988).
47. Durham, J.L.; Wilson, W.E.; Bailey, E.B.: Application of an SO_2 Denuder for Continuous Measurement of Sulfur in Submicrometric Aerosols. Atmos. Environ. 12:883–886 (1978).
48. Braman, R.S.; Shelley, T.; McClenny, W.A.: Tungstic Acid for Preconcentration and Determination of Gaseous and Particulate Ammonia and Nitric Acid in Ambient Air. Anal. Chem. 54: 358–364 (1982).
49. Slanina, J.; Lamoen-Doornebal, L.V.; Lingerak, W.A.; Meilof, W.: Application of a Thermo-denuder Analyzer to the Determination of H_2SO_4, HNO_3, and NH_3 in Air. Int. J. Environ. Anal. Chem. 9:59–70 (1981).
50. Buttini, P.; Di Palo, V.; Possanzini, M.: Coupling of Denuder and Ion Chromatographic Techniques for NO_2 Trace Level Determination in Air. Sci. of Total Environ. 61:59–72 (1987).
51. John, W.; Wall, S.M.; Ondo, J.L.: A New Method for Nitric Acid and Nitrate Aerosol Measurement Using the Dichotomous Sampler. Atmos. Environ. 22:1627–1635 (1988).
52. Lindgren, P.F.; Dasgupta, P.K.: Measurement of Atmospheric Sulfur Dioxide by Diffusion Scrubber Coupled Ion Chromatography. Anal. Chem. 61:19–24 (1988).
53. Nolan, P.J.; Doherty, D.J.: Size and Charge Distribution of Atmospheric Condensation Nuclei. Proc. R. Iri. Acad. 53A:163–179 (1950).
54. Pollak, L.W.; O'Conner, T.C.; Metnieks, A.L.: On the Determination of the Diffusion Coefficient of Condensation Nuclei Using the Static and Dynamic Methods. Geofis. Pura Appl. 34:177–194 (1956).
55. Megaw, W.J.; Wiffen, R.D.: Measurement of the Diffusion Coefficient of Homogeneous and Other Nuclei. J. Rech. Atm. 1:113–125 (1963).
56. Rich, T.A.: Apparatus and Method for Measuring the Size of Aerosols. J. Rech. Atmos. 2:79–85 (1966).
57. Pollak, L.M.; Metnieks, A.I.: New Calibration of Photo-electric Nucleus Counters. Geofis. Pura Appl. 43:285–301 (1959).
58. Kotrappa, K.; Bhanti, D.P.; Dhandayutham, R.: Diffusion Sampler

Useful for Measuring Diffusion Coefficients and Unattached Fractions of Radon and Thoron Decay Products. Health Phys. 29:155–162 (1975).
59. Sinclair, D.: Measurement and Production of Submicron Aerosols. In: Proceedings of the 7th Conference on Condensation and Ice Nuclei, pp. 132–137. Prague, Vienna (1969).
60. Breslin, A.J.; Guggenheim, S.F.; George, A.C.: Compact High Efficiency Diffusion Batteries. Staub-Rein. Luft 31(8):1–5 (1971).
61. Scheibel, H.G.; Porstendörfer, J.: Penetration Measurements for Tube and Screen-type Diffusion Batteries in the Ultrafine Particle Size Range. J. Aerosol Sci. 15:673–682 (1984).
62. Sinclair, D.: A Portable Diffusion Battery. Am. Ind. Hyg. Assoc. J. 33:729–735 (1972).
63. Brown, K.E.; Beyer, J.; Gentry, J.W.: Calibration and Design of Diffusion Batteries for Ultrafine Aerosols. J. Aerosol Sci. 15:133–145 (1984).
64. Sinclair, D.; Hinchliffe, L.: Production and Measurement of Submicron Aerosols. In: Assessment of Airborne Particles, pp. 182–199. T.T. Mercer et al., Eds. Thomas, Springfield, IL (1972).
65. Twomey, S.A.; Zalabsky, R.A.: Multifilter Technique for Examination of the Size Distribution of the Natural Aerosol in the Submicrometer Size Range. Environ. Sci. Technol. 15:177–184 (1981).
66. Sinclair, D.; Hoopes, G.S.: A Novel Form of Diffusion Battery. Am. Ind. Hyg. Assoc. J. 36:39–42 (1975).
67. Cheng, Y.S.; Yeh, H.C.; Mauderly, J.L.; Mokler, B.V.: Characterization of Diesel Exhaust in a Chronic Inhalation Study. Am. Ind. Hyg. Assoc. J. 45:547–555 (1984).
68. Holub, R.F.; Knutson, E.O.; Solomon, S.: Tests of the Graded Wire Screen Technique for Measuring the Amount and Size Distribution of Unattached Radon Progeny. Radiat. Protect. Dosim. 24:265–268 (1988).
69. Reineking, A.; Porstendörfer, J.: High-volume Screen Diffusion Batteries and -spectroscopy for Measurement of the Radon Daughter Activity Size Distributions in the Environment. J. Aerosol Sci. 17:873–880 (1986).
70. Ramamurthi, M.; Hopke, P.K.: An Automated, Semicontinuous System for Measuring Indoor Radon Progeny Activity-weighted Size Distributions, dp: 0.5-500 nm. Aerosol Sci. Technol. 14:82–92 (1991).
71. Cheng, Y.S.; Su, Y.F.; Newton, G.J.; Yeh, H.C.: Use of a Graded Diffusion Battery in Measuring the Radon Activity Size Distribution. J. Aerosol Sci. 23:361–372 (1992).
72. Solomon, S.; Ren, T.: Counting Efficiencies for Alpha Particles Emitted from Wire Screens. Aerosol Sci. Technol. 17:69–83 (1992).
73. Fuchs, N.A.; Stechkina, I.B.; Starosselskii, V.I.: On the Determination of Particle Size Distribution in Polydisperse Aerosols by the Diffusion Method. Br. J. Appl. Phy. 13:280–281 (1962).
74. Mercer, T.T.; Greene, T.D.: Interpretation of Diffusion Battery Data. J. Aerosol Sci. 5:251–255 (1974).
75. Lee, K.W.; Connick, P.A.; Gieseke, J.A.: Extension of the Screen-type Diffusion Battery. J. Aerosol Sci. 12:385–386 (1981).
76. Sinclair, D.; Countess, R.J.; Liu, B.Y.H.; Pui, D.Y.H.: Automatic Analysis of Submicron Aerosols. In: Aerosol Measurement, pp. 544–563. W.E. Clark and M.D. Durham, Eds. University Press of Florida, Gainesville, FL (1979).
77. Raabe, O.G.: A General Method for Fitting Size Distributions to Multi-component Aerosol Data Using Weighted Least-squares. Environ. Sci. Technol. 12:1162–1167 (1978).
78. Twomey, S.: Comparison of Constrained Linear Inversion and an Alternative Nonlinear Algorithm Applied to the Indirect Estimation of Particle Size Distribution. J. Computation Physics 18:188–200 (1975).
79. Knutson, E.O.; Sinclair, D.: Experience in Sampling Urban Aerosols with the Sinclair Diffusion Battery and Nucleus Counter. In: Proc. Advances in Particle Sampling and Measurement, EPA 600/7-79-065, pp. 98–120. W.B. Smith, Ed. Cincinnati, OH (1979).
80. Kapadia, A.: Data Reduction Techniques for Aerosol Size Distribution Measurement Instruments. Ph.D. Dissertation, University of Minnesota (1980).
81. Cheng, Y.S.; Yeh, H.C.: Analysis of Screen Diffusion Battery Data. Am. Ind. Hyg. Assoc. J. 45:556–561 (1984).
82. Maher, E.F.; Laird, N.M.: EM Algorithm Reconstruction of Particle Size Distributions from Diffusion Battery Data. J. Aerosol Sci. 16:557–570 (1985).

Instrument Descriptions

Commercial sources for vendors listed in this section are provided in Table 20-I-1.

20-1. Screen Diffusion Battery, Model 3040

TSI Incorporated

The TSI diffusion battery has 10 stages with stainless steel 635-mesh screens. The screen holder is made of either stainless steel or aluminum. The flow rate through the diffusion battery is between 4 to 6 L/min. The useful particle size range is from 0.003 to 0.5 µm. The aerosol concentration in each stage is usually measured by a continuous flow CNC (Model 3022 or 3025), and an automatic switch valve (Model 3042) is used to measure the concentration in successive stages automatically. Dimensions: 25 × 6.3 × 9 cm.

20-2. Parallel Flow Diffusion Battery

In-Tox Products

The parallel flow diffusion battery uses the principle of screen diffusion battery and parallel flow. The unit is made of aluminum. It consists of a conical cap and a collection section containing seven cells. Each diffusion cell contains a different number of stainless steel 200-mesh screens followed by a 25-mm Zefluor filter (Gelman, Ann Arbor, MI). The seven cells typically contain 0–35 screens. Critical orifices provide a 2 L/min flow rate through each cell, resulting in a total flow rate of 14 L/min. Gravimetric determination of collected filter samples from each cell provides the direct mass penetration as a function of screen number for the determination of aerosol size distribution. Dimensions: 23 × 23 × 23 cm.

20-3. Annular Denuders

URG Corporation

The company has several types of annular denuders designed to be used alone for collecting gases or to be

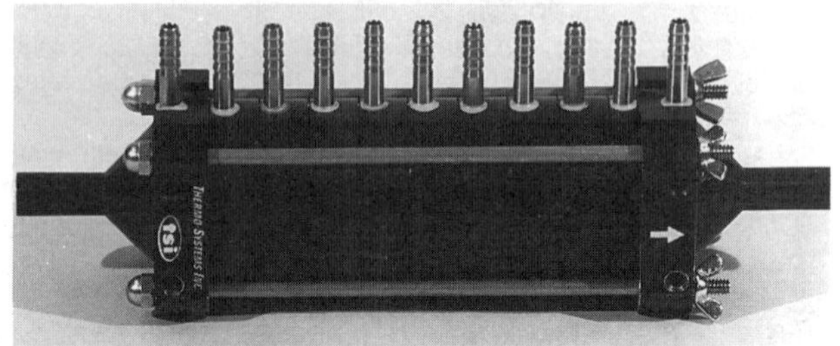

INSTRUMENT 20-1. Screen diffusion battery, TSI Model 3040.

INSTRUMENT 20-2. Parallel flow diffusing battery.

used in a series with a filter, impactor, or cyclone for collecting ambient and indoor aerosols as well as acidic gases. Model URG-2000-30B is a glass denuder with a length of 242 mm and a diameter of 30 mm. It has 1 mm annular space. Inside glass surfaces are etched to provide greater surface area for coating.

Model URG-2000-30 × 100-3CSS has two inner glass tubes (1-mm separation) positioned around a solid glass rod. The outer stainless steel tube is Teflon-coated. The diameter is 30 mm, and the lengths are 100, 150, or 242 mm.

The glass surfaces can be coated with Na_2CO_3 to collect HCl, SO_2, HNO_2, and HNO_3, or citric acid to collect NH_3.

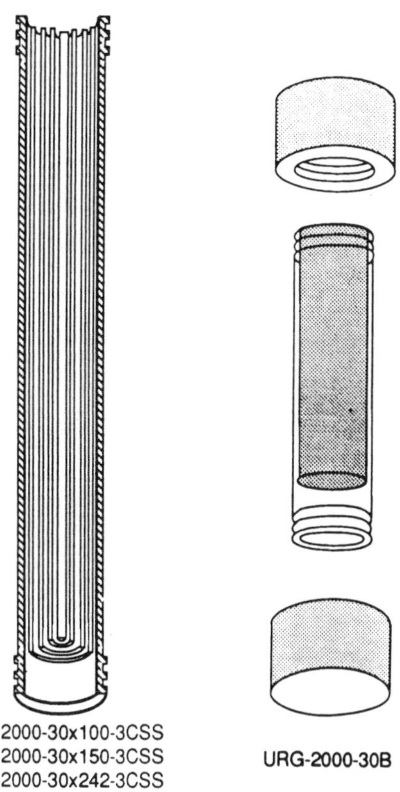

INSTRUMENT 20-3. Annular denuders from URG showing a single channel and three channel glass denuders.

TABLE 20-I-1. Commercial Sources

Symbol	Source
TSI	TSI Incorporated 500 Cardigan Rd. P.O. Box 64394 St. Paul, MN 55164 (612)483-0900
ITP	In-Tox Products 115 Quincy, NE Albuquerque, NM 87108 (505)265-1180 FAX (505)265-1181
URG	URG Corporation 116 Merritt Mill Rd. P.O. Box 368 Carrboro, NC 27510 (919)942-2753

Chapter 21

Sampling from Ducts and Stacks

Charles E. Billings, Ph.D.[A]; Dale A. Lundgren, Ph.D., P.E.[B]

[A]*Acting Director, Environmental Medical Service, Massachusetts Institute of Technology, 77 Massachusetts Avenue, Room 20C-204, Cambridge, Massachusetts;* [B]*Environmental Engineering Sciences, University of Florida, 410 Black Hall, Gainesville, Florida*

CONTENTS

Introduction

Sampling of a flowing gas stream has a number of important applications in industrial hygiene and environmental health. The purposes of this chapter are 1) to develop the general principles and procedures for those with little previous experience (basic considerations) and 2) to review current techniques used primarily for air pollution control.

The objectives of gas stream sampling are 1) to obtain a representative sample (or specimen) from a flowing gas stream and 2) to determine flow characteristics, fluid composition, or properties of constituents. Table 21-1 presents a list of parameters that may be required to characterize the gas flow, fluid composition, or fluid properties; these parameters may be obtained by gas stream sampling and appropriate analysis.

The objective of the sampling activity must be clearly

TABLE 21-1. Parameters Obtained by Gas Stream Sampling*

Parameter	Example
Gas composition	Molecular composition
Thermodynamic properties	Temperature
Transport properties	Viscosity
Gas motion characteristics	Velocity
Other phases	Solid particulate matter

*To define magnitude and transport of mass, energy (heat, momentum), chemical species, and phases (also applies with modifications to any fluid stream).

identified and correctly stated because it will constrain selection and application of sampling methods. Typical purposes include:

1. The measurement of air pollution source emission rates for specific constituents (e.g., gases or particulate matter).
2. Evaluation of total collection efficiency and pressure drop of a gas cleaning device.
3. Measurement of source emission rate by species and spectra (e.g., particle size distribution, or an individual substance such as lead).
4. Evaluation of the particle size-efficiency of a control device or system.
5. Research and development on processes, apparatus, or methods.

Sampling of gas cleaning devices or sampling of air pollution emissions is used frequently to satisfy legal, contractual, or regulatory compliance requirements. Specific details of acceptable gas stream sampling procedures must be agreed to by owners, vendors, and agencies. Much of this type of sampling may be conducted by consultant contractors retained for an individual project. A written purpose, details of acceptable practice, and a clear work statement will help ensure satisfactory results and assist in obtaining qualified contractors at realistic cost. Approval of written plans and stack sampling methods may be required by state and/or federal agencies.

Purposes of gas stream sampling include 1) process evaluation studies, 2) air pollution control activities, 3) industrial air and gas cleaning device performance evaluations, and 4) industrial hygiene applications. In each of the possible applications, data may be obtained on one or more of the parameters given in Table 21-1. Broadly speaking, gas streams of interest can be identified as process gas streams, fuel gas streams, or waste gas streams (e.g., flue gases, ventilation system exhausts, etc.).

One common application of gas stream sampling is to determine stack discharge (emission) rates or concentrations from an industrial air pollution source. Data to be obtained in this case include gas composition, temperature, pressure, gas velocity, volumetric flow rate, nature and concentration of contaminants, and process information related to emissions. The purpose is to provide valid information to management with respect to legally allowable contaminant discharge concentration or rate; data are also provided for evaluating the performance of the control device.

This procedure is typically called air pollutant source emission sampling (or source sampling, stack sampling, stack testing, emission testing, or source evaluation). During the past 20 years, and especially since the formation of the U.S. Environmental Protection Agency (U.S. EPA) in 1971, highly specific methods of manual gas stream sampling have been developed and promulgated in regulations for individual industrial source emission categories. These methods will be discussed in more detail below.

Principles

Essential Aspects

Selection of the general method to be followed (i.e., the apparatus and procedures) includes consideration of the system, flow, and contaminants that interact to affect selection of a particular sampling method and where it is best applied to the flowing gas system to obtain valid (i.e., statistically, physically, and chemically representative) samples of components. Individual aspects to be considered in the planning and implementation of a sampling activity are listed in Table 21-2. Information on the general process and specific operation under consideration must be obtained. Such information includes process flow sheets; nature, composition, and quantities of materials in the operation and their phases; flow rates; possible plans and specifications; principal dimensions; whether the process is continuous or steady-state (e.g., enclosed or automated) or cyclic, intermittent, or otherwise noncontinuous (e.g., batch, open, or manual); and details on the control system design (plans and specifications

TABLE 21-2. Essential Aspects of Gas Stream Sampling

Purpose of samples
Nature of process
Nature of the flow
Nature of components in fluid
Sampling and analysis

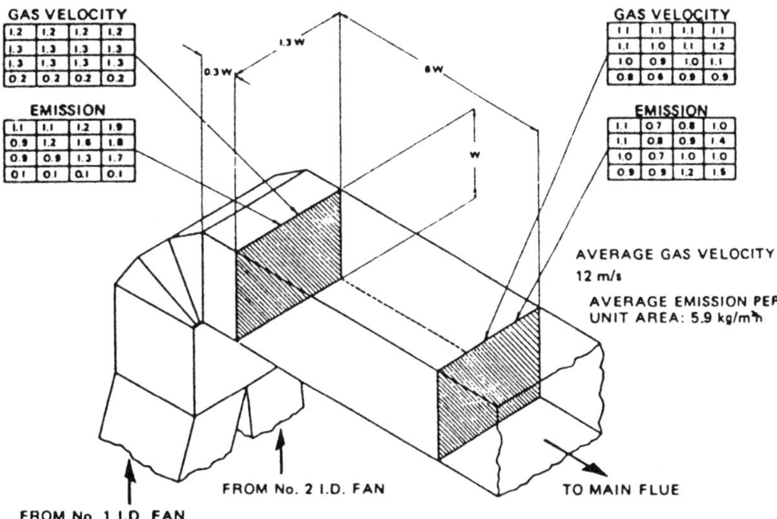

FIGURE 21-1. Measured velocity and concentration profiles after a bend.[1] Average gas velocity, 39 ft/sec (13.6 m/s); average emission per unit area = 1.2 lb/ft^2-hr (14.1 mg/m^2-sec); equivalent round diameter, D_e = 2LW/(L+W) = 6.8 ft (173 mm); distance between planes 1 and 2 = 36/6.8 = 5.4 D.

on hoods, ductwork, fans, collectors, and stack design). This background information is used to plan the sampling activity.

For many air pollutant sources, U.S. EPA now requires continuous sampling and analysis of emissions, and this may be done by *in-situ* procedures. The usual method for industrial hygiene and air pollution control sampling (and for process sampling) involves manual extraction of a sample of the fluid (gas) and separation of the components of interest for subsequent analysis either directly at the site or in an analytical laboratory. The following discussion refers specifically to extractive sampling for components and contaminants of the fluid (gas) stream.

Nature of Flow and Selection of Sampling Location

To select an appropriate location for introduction of extractive sampling apparatus, consideration must be given to the effects on velocity and concentration profiles caused by the gas flow system (i.e., ductwork, elbows, tees or junctions, fans, collectors, expansions, contractions, valves, gates, dampers, and flowmeters) and by the velocity profile of the flow stream. Each flow system component produces specific effects on the gas flow pattern transverse to the flow at each location in the stream, and the velocity and concentration profiles are modified by each of the components in the ductwork, at points immediately downstream.

Illustrations of these effects have been presented from field studies in breechings of coal-fired boilers.[1] Figure 21-1 shows an example of velocity profiles and particle concentration after a junction and elbow. Velocities and particle concentrations (actually flux or mass/area-time) are shown here as the ratio of the value determined at a point (an equal area traverse point, as will be discussed below) to the numerical average value, across the whole flue, such that the concentration or velocity at each point is expressed as its ratio to the overall average. Hawksley *et al.*, in discussing effects illustrated in Figure 21-1, state:[1]

> Figure [21-1] gives data at sampling positions after (a) 90° bend. Solids are centrifuged to the outside of the bend but the uniformity is gradually restored by turbulent mixing, as shown, although in this instance the pattern is complicated by an unequal supply of solids from the two i.d. fans. The degree of uniformity obtained at two to six diameters from a bend is shown. About three to five diameters is sufficient to establish a tolerable uniformity, although this may not be the case when the quantity of grit is high. When there is little grit, one to three diameters is adequate. Even at the bend or within one diameter or so of it (Figure 21-1) the local mass flows do not vary greatly. The direction of variation lies in the plane of the bend and the effect of previous bends is not usually apparent . . . Gentler bends tend to give less centrifuging of solids . . .
>
> If the velocity is high and the bend sharp, the gas flow may separate from the inner wall of the bend and not become reattached until one or two flue diameters downstream from the bend. The fluid in the dead space will tend to circulate in a large eddy, the direction of rotation being forwards near the main stream and

> backwards near the wall. The circulation velocity is not high but may be sufficient for the reversed flow to be detected by means of a Pitot tube. The solids flow is contained in the main stream and the emission can be measured in the presence of a reversed flow if it is possible to define the effective cross-sectional area of the main stream. Separation may occur if a flue diverges too rapidly; it arises also, with the shedding of free eddies or vortices, after obstacles such as the blades of dampers. A converging flue tends to produce a more uniform distribution of gas and solids flow.
>
> There is usually a steep gradient of solids flow immediately after a fan . . . and the solids may be displaced also to the side of the flue opposite to the inlet of the fan. But depending on the design features of the fan, the distribution may not be markedly non-uniform . . .

Obtaining a representative sample of particulate matter from a flowing gas stream requires a more complex procedure and more attention to details of apparatus than sampling for gases and vapors. As indicated in Figure 21-1, the concentration of particulate matter in the gas stream may be expected to vary across any transverse section and longitudinally along the stream as well. One may expect a reasonably uniform particulate concentration profile if the stream has a fully developed velocity profile with good turbulent (transverse) mixing. This is usually stated (expected) to occur some 5–10 diameters downstream of any flow disturbance such as an elbow, damper, etc., and at least 2 diameters upstream from any such disturbance. The particulate concentration profile uniformity at any given transverse section also depends on the particle size spectrum. Larger, heavier particles ($\rho_p d_p^2 >> 1$; where ρ_p = particle apparent density in g/cm^3 and d_p = particle diameter in µm) tend to settle in a flowing stream even with moderate turbulence (transverse fluid dynamic mixing of eddies), so the particle concentration profile would be expected to indicate a higher mass concentration (or a larger number concentration of larger diameter particles) in the bottom half of the flow channel as compared to the top half. In square and rectangular ducts, there are also eddies (vortices) in the corners which tend to affect particle concentrations as well. The persistence of cyclonic, vortex, spiralling flow in the outlet ducts of centrifugal collectors and fans also may cause distortions in the particle size concentration distribution spectrum for larger, heavier particles. Vortex flow may persist in a cylindrical conduit (e.g., pipe, flue, or stack) for 50–100 diameters before the energy is dissipated and the flow pattern returns to the turbulent profile. In these cases, flow straighteners are normally required to restore uniform axial flow at the cost of some added system pressure drop.

One widely used experimental procedure for laboratory and pilot plant studies to produce uniform (flat) velocity and concentration profiles at 5 duct diameters downstream is the annular orifice or Stairmand disc ($D_{disc} = 0.707D_{duct}$). This device works best at duct velocities of the order of 2000–4000 fpm (10–20 m/s), at the cost of an unrecoverable pressure drop of about one velocity head. It can be mounted on a single axial shaft and rotated out of the stream when not in use. With suitable static taps (one duct radius upstream and downstream of the obstruction), it can be used as a conventional total flowmeter. Because of the pressure loss penalty, it has not found wide use in process, fuel, or waste gas streams of high volume flow rate.

Selection of a suitable location for sampling thus involves judgment based on experience with flow phenomena. As a general rule, sampling should be done at least 5–8 diameters downstream from a disturbance and at least 2 diameters upstream from one. A selection guideline from the U.S. EPA standard method is discussed below when these criteria cannot be met.

Selection of Number and Arrangement of Traverse Points

To obtain a representative sample of a fluid property, substance, or characteristic that varies across the duct (flue, etc.), a series of samples are taken at a multiple number of points in an equal area traverse in a plane transverse to flow. The total cross-sectional area of the duct is divided into a number of equal areas, and samples are taken at locations which best represent the center of the smaller areas (centroid). In the case of square or rectangular ducts, the equal areas will be squares or rectangles, and samples are taken from the center of each of them. For round ducts, the smaller areas are concentric circles, and samples are commonly taken on two perpendicular diameters, although segments may be used. The procedure required by U.S. EPA for dividing a duct into smaller areas is illustrated in Figure 21-2.[2] Selection of the appropriate number of points depends upon the size of the duct and an estimate of degree of disturbance of the flow and expected concentration profiles (i.e., distance to upstream and downstream disturbances).

U.S. EPA uses a selection guide that adjusts the minimum number of sampling points in a traverse according to distance of the sampling plane with respect to upstream or downstream disturbance, increasing the number above 12 when the traverse or sampling plane is closer than 8 diameters downstream from the disturbance or 2 diameters upstream, as shown in Figure 21-3.[2] The U.S. EPA selection rule requires a smaller number of sampling points for velocity and nonparticulate sampling traverses as contrasted to the number required for particulate sampling traverses. Smaller numbers of traverse points are also required in small ducts (< 24 in. in diameter [< 610 mm]) as shown by the lower curves in Figure 21-3a and 21-3b. Use of the U.S. EPA selection rules may lead to a conservatively high number of sampling points for many situations if the flow is reasonably uniform and constituents are well mixed.[3] The equivalent round diameter (D_e) of square and rectangular ducts used to determine the required number of sampling points is given in Figure 21-1 (*viz.*, $D_e = 2LW/[L + W]$; where: L = the height and W = the width of the duct). *Industrial Ventilation — A Manual of Recommended Practice*[4] provides tables (9-2, 9-3, and 9-4) that give actual dimensions for 6, 10, and 20 velocity traverse points for duct diameters from 3 to 80 in. (80 to 2000 mm), as summarized in Table 21-3.

After choosing the sampling plane or site and determining the number of sampling points, openings are made in the duct wall to permit the apparatus to be inserted. For lighter gauge ventilation ductwork under slight negative pressure, a hole-saw is used to cut a suitable round hole (typically 1.5 to 3 in. diameter [38 to 76 mm]). For heavier ductwork, (>16 gauge; flues, breeching, stacks, etc.), a 3- or 4-in.-diameter (76- or 101-mm-diameter) coupling (or short nipple) is welded onto the wall, and a round hole is flame-cut out of the wall. Access to the sampling ports, platforms, ladders, rails, toeboards, jib booms, and other fixtures and utilities at the sampling location are arranged as required (e.g., temporary scaffolding and extension cords versus fabricated platforms and ladders welded in place). (See the Occupational Safety and Health Administration [OSHA] regulations [29 CFR 1910 and 1926] for proper designs.)

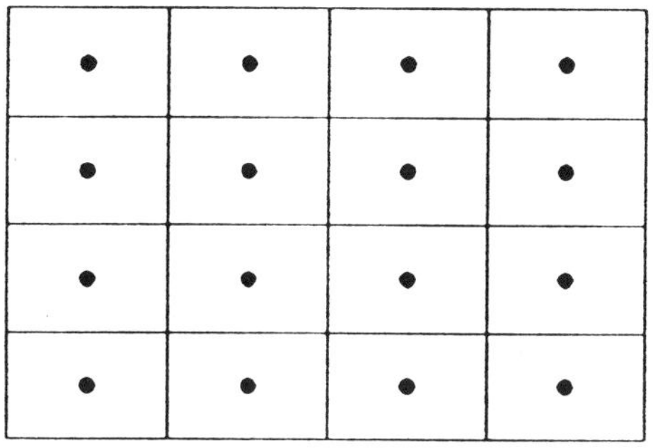

Example showing rectangular stack cross section divided into 16 equal areas, with a traverse point at centroid of each area.

Number of Traverse Points	Matrix Layout
9	3 × 3
12	4 × 3
16	4 × 4
20	5 × 4
25	5 × 5
30	6 × 5
36	6 × 6
42	7 × 6
49	7 × 7

FIGURE 21-2a. U.S. EPA cross-section layout for rectangular stacks.

Measurement of Velocity Profile and Gas Flow Rate

Composition, temperature, and pressure of the gas are determined by methods appropriate to the particular industry and gas stream. Standard guides for these determinations are provided in U.S. EPA methods for specific industrial stack emission sources,[2] discussed below.

Temperature and static pressure are measured in the duct at the sampling point with a thermometer and static pressure tap, respectively.[4] If the operation (or process) involves combustion, flue gas analysis would be performed for oxygen, carbon dioxide, and, if suspected, carbon monoxide, by standard Orsat Analysis or Fyrite® analyzers.[3,5] For process gases, gas analysis, temperature, and pressure would be determined by individual industry or company practices. Methods for specific industrial air pollution source emissions to the atmosphere are also presented below.[2] Water vapor will be present in combustion gases to the extent of 5% to 10%, depending on the amount of excess air, hydrogen, and water in fuel (e.g., gas versus coal or oil). Water scrubber outlets will contain water vapor up to saturation at the temperature of the outlet gas and may equal from 15% (outlet temperature of 130°F [55°C]) to 70% (outlet temperature of 195°F [90°C]). Kilns, dryers, and refuse incinerators may have outlet gas moisture contents from 10% to 30% depending on fuel, material, moisture content, excess air, etc. Initially, estimation of moisture content may be based on experience and judgment; then, moisture content can be measured during sampling by condensation in a cooled impinger followed by silica gel (the water volume is measured and the silica gel is weighed). Conventional psychrometric wet bulb and dry bulb thermometers can be used under certain conditions, i.e., relatively clean air at moderate temperatures.[6] Knowing the molecular composition and the moisture content of the gas, density can be calculated at the stack temperature and pressure using the fractional composition and gas laws. Details of this procedure can be found in the literature.[2,3,6–8]

Velocity pressure (h_v) at each traverse point is measured using a Pitot-static tube of standard design for relatively particulate-free gases or using reverse-impact-type tubes for dusty gas (Figures 21-4a through 4c).[2,4] Each leg of the Pitot-static tube is connected by rubber tubing to a U-tube manometer (vertical or inclined). Effects of flow characteristics (e.g., turbulence, yaw, or vorticity), wall proximity, viscosity, and related problems affect Pitot tube calibrations.[2,9] The stand-

Traverse Point	Distance, % of Diameter
1	4.4
2	14.6
3	29.6
4	70.4
5	85.4
6	95.6

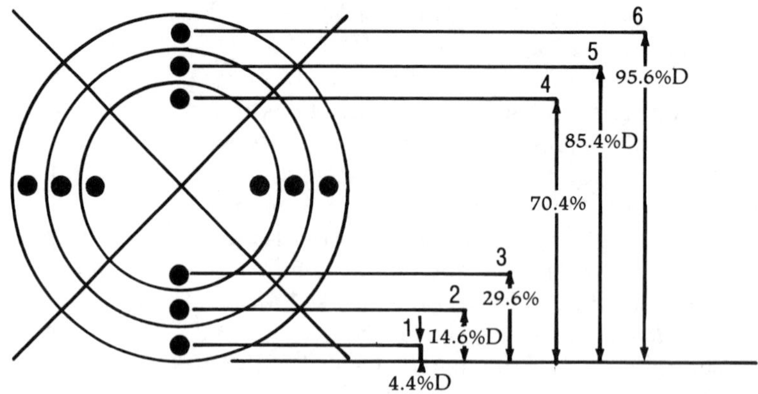

Example showing circular stack cross section divided into 12 equal areas, with location of traverse points indicated (6 points on a diameter).

Traverse Point No. on a Diameter	Number of Traverse Points on a Diameter											
	2	4	6	8	10	12	14	16	18	20	22	24
1	14.6	6.7	4.4	3.2	2.6	2.1	1.8	1.6	1.4	1.3	1.1	1.1
2	85.4	25.0	14.6	10.5	8.2	6.7	5.7	4.9	4.4	3.9	3.5	3.2
3	—	75.0	29.6	19.4	14.6	11.8	9.9	8.5	7.5	6.7	6.0	5.5
4	—	93.3	70.4	32.3	22.6	17.7	14.6	12.5	10.9	9.7	8.7	7.9
5	—	—	85.4	67.7	34.2	25.0	20.1	16.9	14.6	12.9	11.6	10.5
6	—	—	95.6	80.6	65.8	35.6	26.9	22.0	18.8	16.5	14.6	13.2
7	—	—	—	89.5	77.4	64.4	36.6	28.3	23.6	20.4	18.0	16.1
8	—	—	—	96.8	85.4	75.0	63.4	37.5	29.6	25.0	21.8	19.4
9	—	—	—	—	91.8	82.3	73.1	62.5	38.2	30.6	26.2	23.0
10	—	—	—	—	97.4	88.2	79.9	71.7	61.8	38.8	31.5	27.2
11	—	—	—	—	—	93.3	85.4	78.0	70.4	61.2	39.3	32.3
12	—	—	—	—	—	97.9	90.1	83.1	76.4	69.4	60.7	39.8
13	—	—	—	—	—	—	94.3	87.5	81.2	75.0	68.5	60.2
14	—	—	—	—	—	—	98.2	91.5	85.4	79.6	73.8	67.7
15	—	—	—	—	—	—	—	95.1	89.1	83.5	78.2	72.8
16	—	—	—	—	—	—	—	98.4	92.5	87.1	82.0	77.0
17	—	—	—	—	—	—	—	—	95.6	90.3	85.4	80.6
18	—	—	—	—	—	—	—	—	98.6	93.3	88.4	83.9
19	—	—	—	—	—	—	—	—	—	96.1	91.3	86.8
20	—	—	—	—	—	—	—	—	—	98.7	94.0	89.5
21	—	—	—	—	—	—	—	—	—	—	96.5	92.1
22	—	—	—	—	—	—	—	—	—	—	98.9	94.5
23	—	—	—	—	—	—	—	—	—	—	—	96.8
24	—	—	—	—	—	—	—	—	—	—	—	98.9

FIGURE 21-2b. U.S. EPA location of traverse points in circular stacks (percent of stack diameter from inside wall to traverse point).

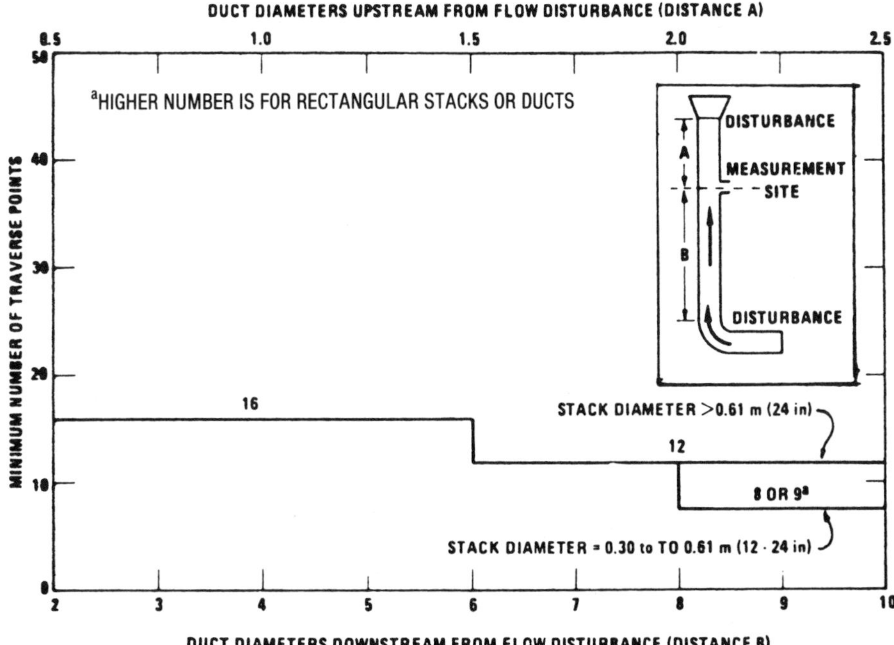

FIGURE 21-3a. Minimum number of traverse points for velocity (nonparticulate) traverses.[(2)]

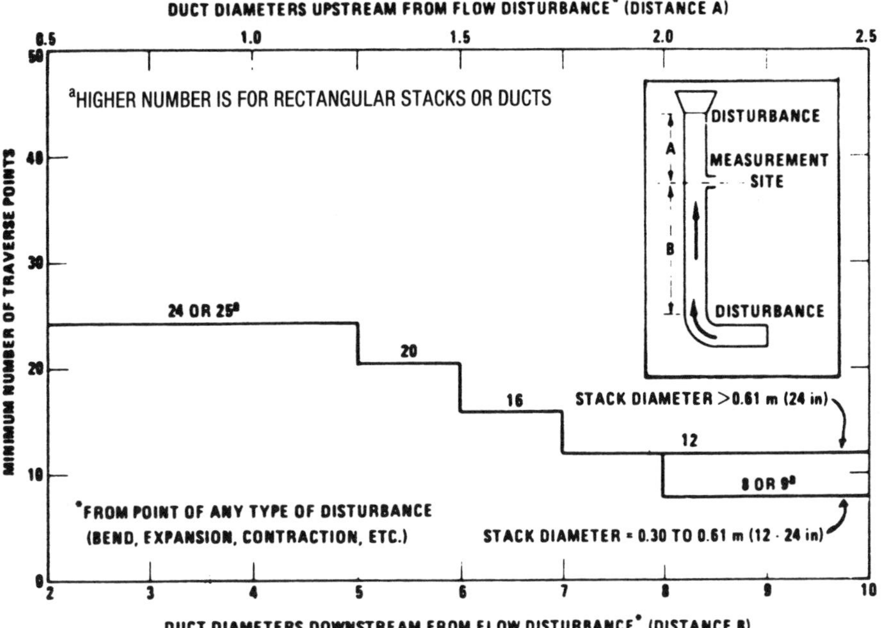

FIGURE 21-3b. Minimum number of traverse points for particulate traverses.[(2)]

TABLE 21-3. Selection of Number of Velocity Traverse Points[(4)]

Diameter			Cross-sectional Area		Number of Test Points
in.	ft	mm	ft^2	m^2	
3–6	0.25–0.5	76–152	0.05–0.2	0.005–0.0186	6
4–48	0.3–4	102–1219	0.09–12.6	0.008–1.17	10
40–80	3.3–6.7	1016–2032	8.7–34.9	0.81–32.4	20

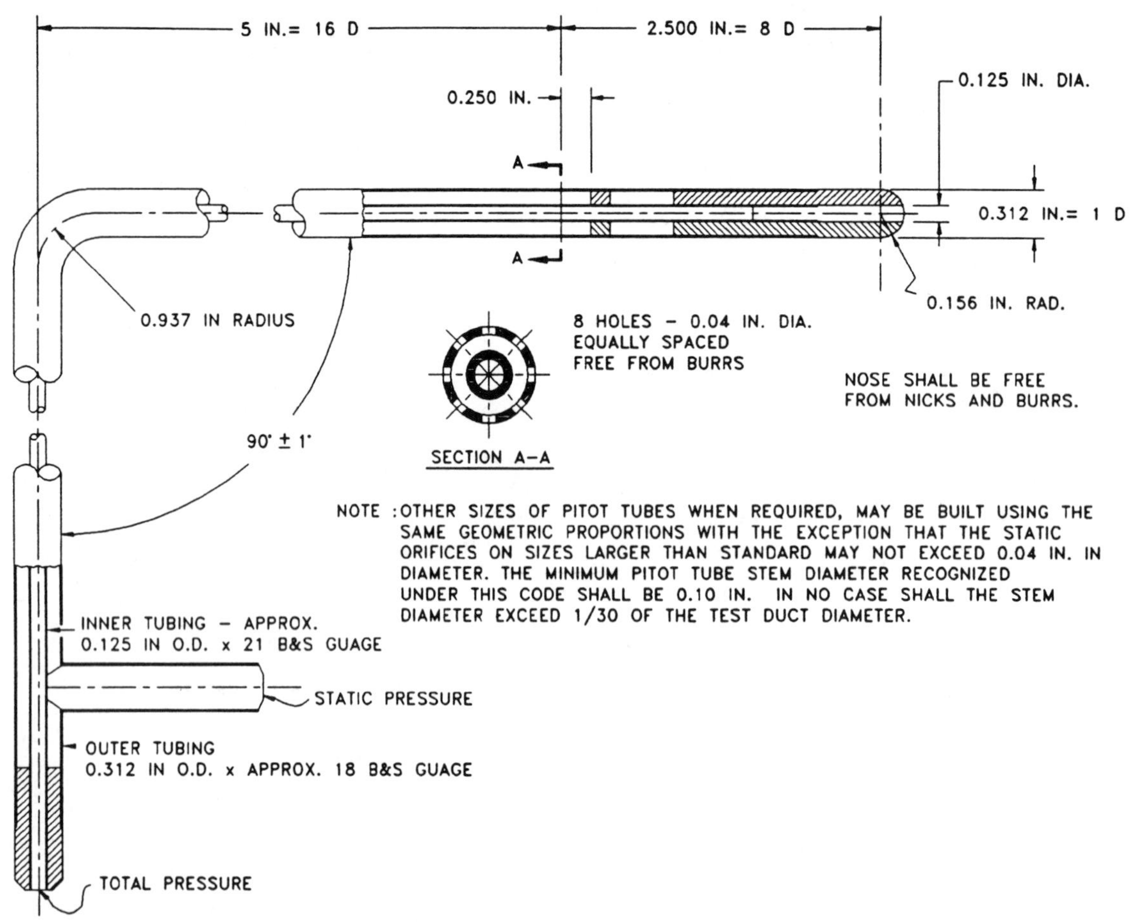

FIGURE 21-4a. Standard Pitot tube for duct gas velocity determination.[4]

ard Pitot-static tube design has a calibration coefficient near 1 for most typical air flows, but it is not exactly constant.[9] In general, the reverse-impact tube has a calibration coefficient of $Kp > 1$, from the induced negative pressure due to the wake downstream of the reverse-static opening (i.e., it will produce a slightly higher h_v, about 20%). This device should be calibrated in about the same conditions in which it will be used and used in the same orientation as it was calibrated.[2] Calculations for velocity are indicated elsewhere.

For practical purposes in the field, with normal fluctuations in flow, the standard Pitot tube or the reverse-impact-type tube can be used with an inclined manometer down to about 0.1 in. (2 mm) of water (i.e., 1.0 in. [25 mm] of displacement on a 10:1 inclined manometer) and can measure velocities down to about 1000 fpm (≈ 5 m/s) with a small error.[9] To measure lower velocities, a variety of more sensitive devices are available.[10] Further details on measurement of air velocity and instruments are presented in Chapter 9 of *Industrial Ventilation — A Manual of Recommended Practice*.[4] Velocities at all traverse points are summed and averaged to determine the average velocity at the cross section.[2,6,7] The total volumetric flow rate is the product of the average velocity and the cross-sectional area at the plane of measured velocity.

Special instruments or procedures are required for measurement of flow characteristics and properties in the general regime of gas dynamics, which includes high Reynolds number flow ($Re > 10^6$), non-negligible Mach number ($M > 0.1$), or where sufficient energy is present in the flow to cause important interactions with probes. These situations include high velocities (>25,000 fpm [>127 m/s]), compressible flow, shock flows, and high temperatures and pressures.[11] Other flow phenomena requiring special procedures include measurement of turbulence structure and intensity.[12] A recommended method to detect the presence of a rotary component of flow (vortical, spiralling flow) is described in U.S. EPA Method 1. Cyclic or random pulsations in flow also require special consideration.

Sampling and Analysis

General Considerations

The most general form of an extractive gas sampling system is shown in Figure 21-5a. A sampling probe is connected to a sample collection device followed by a

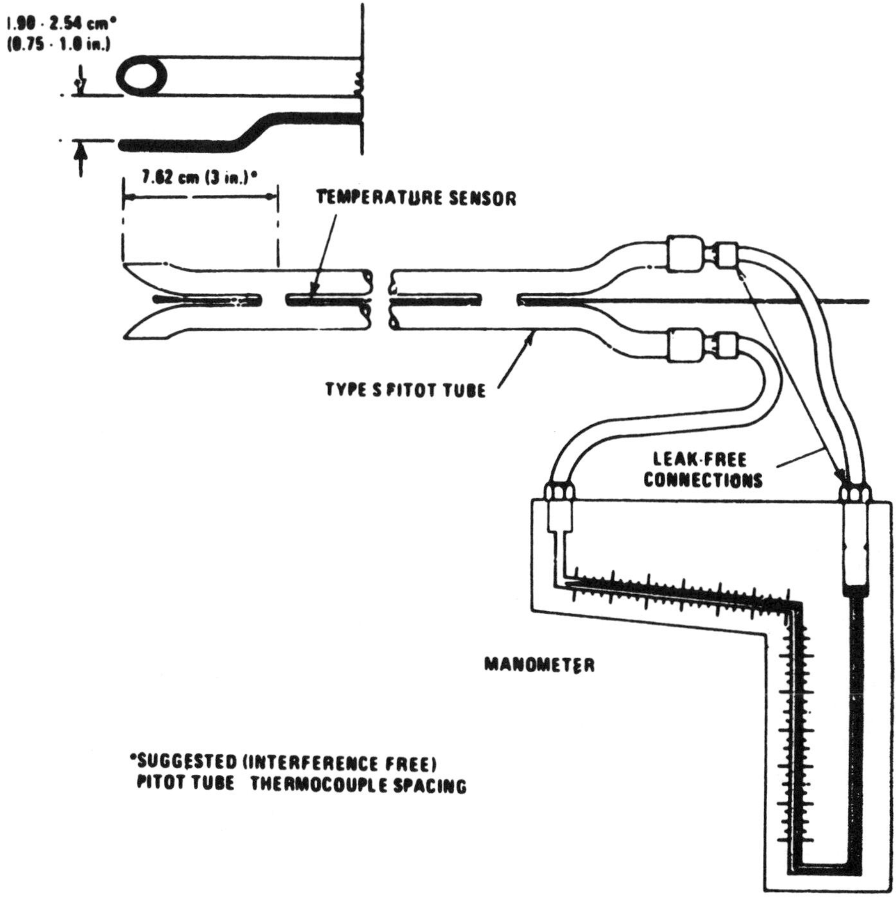

FIGURE 21-4b. Type S Pitot tube for duct gas velocity determination.[2]

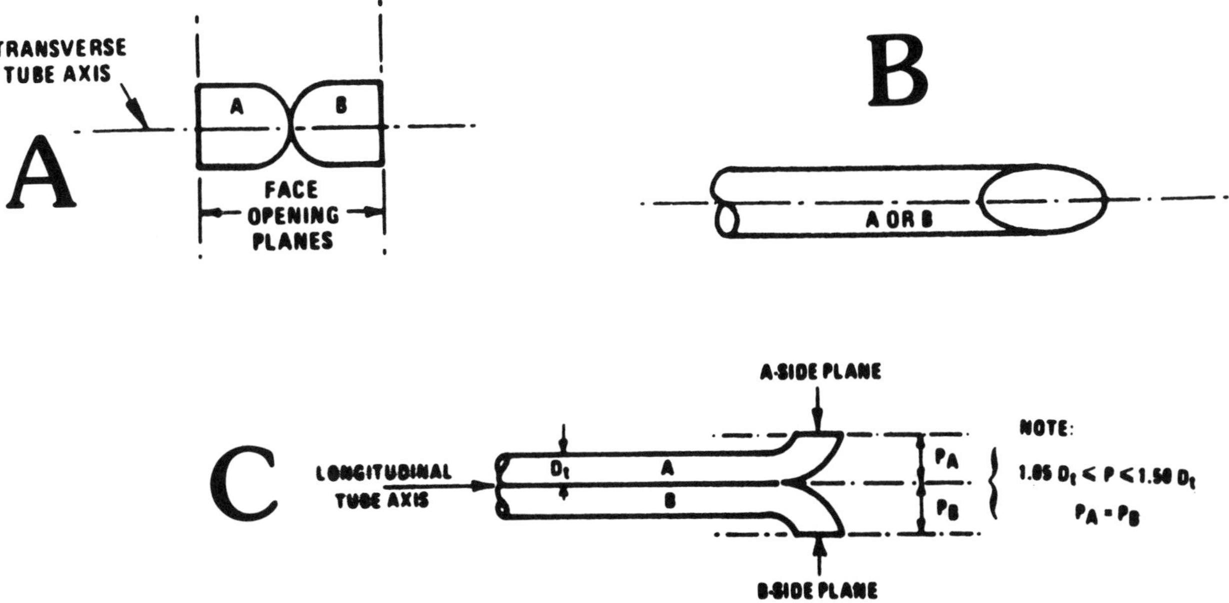

FIGURE 21-4c. Type S Pitot tube. A: end view; B: side view; C: top view.

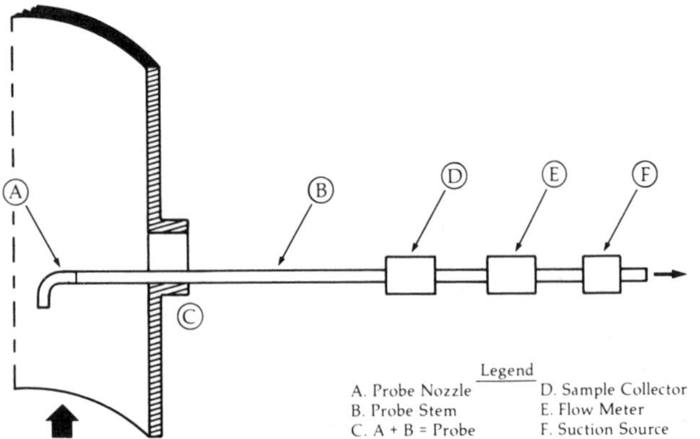

FIGURE 21-5a. Gas stream sampling train schematic: out-stack collector.

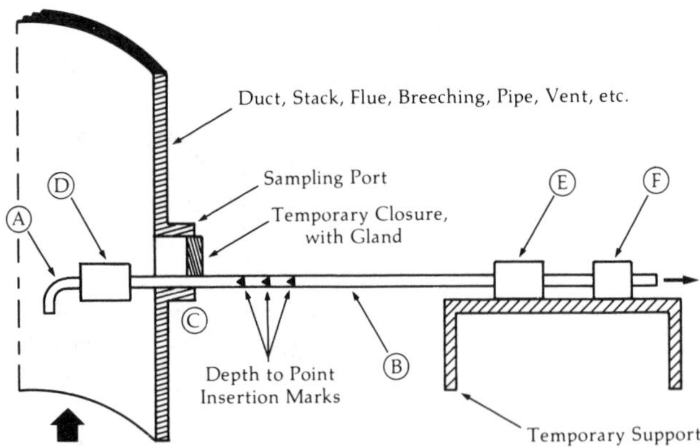

FIGURE 21-5b. Gas stream sampling train schematic: in-stack collector.

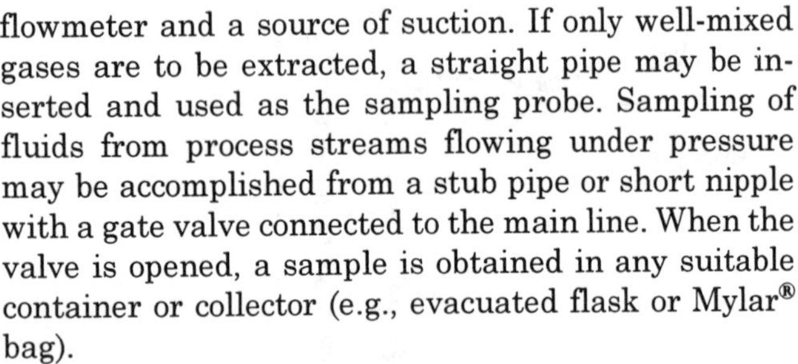
flowmeter and a source of suction. If only well-mixed gases are to be extracted, a straight pipe may be inserted and used as the sampling probe. Sampling of fluids from process streams flowing under pressure may be accomplished from a stub pipe or short nipple with a gate valve connected to the main line. When the valve is opened, a sample is obtained in any suitable container or collector (e.g., evacuated flask or Mylar® bag).

When sampling particulate material from the stream, a curved tip is added to point into the oncoming stream to sample properly as shown at (A) in Figure 21-5a. Particulate matter will deposit on the interior surfaces of the probe nozzle (A) and probe stem (B). This material must be cleaned out and included in the total amount caught in the collector (D) to obtain a reliable estimate of gas stream concentration. In the case of dry granular materials, particulate matter may be brushed or washed out of the nozzle and stem easily. In other situations where condensation or reaction occurs, such as with oil smokes, asphalt fumes, or other tarry or sticky materials, cleaning the probe becomes more of a chore, and may require washing with suitable solvents.

To overcome particulate deposition problems and to eliminate condensation effects on the collected sample in hot moist gases, the collector may be mounted on the end of the probe stem and inserted into the stream, as shown in Figure 21-5b. A nozzle is added to face into the stream to sample for particulate matter properly. The order of the major components is nozzle, collector, probe, flowmeter, and suction source. Other auxiliary apparatus shown in Figure 21-5b include a closure with gland to seal the sampling port (necessary if the stream pressure is positive to the outside, to reduce exposures of sampling personnel or protect the process stream) and a temporary support to hold the sampling train steady while a sample is obtained at each traverse point in the stack, duct, flue, breeching, pipe, etc. Other auxiliary apparatus not shown may include provision

TABLE 21-4. Advantages and Disadvantages of In-stack versus Out-stack Collector Location

Advantages

In-stack:

1. Immediate collection in or close to gas stream.
2. No deposition in probe.
3. No condensation in collector.
4. Smaller equipment generally required.

Out-stack:

1. Large sample volume may be taken (long time).
2. Large holding capacity in collector.
3. Smaller and simpler probe design (small stack hole).
4. Easier to change collector or remove sample.
5. Sample can be cooled before collection.
6. Less likelihood of sample loss.
7. More flexibility in choice of collector.
8. Optimum collector velocity can be used.
9. Sample volume may be metered before collector, if desired.

Disadvantages

In-stack:

1. Choice of collector limited.
2. Sampling volume limited.
3. Holding capacity smaller.
4. Larger stack hole.
5. Stack suction may cause some sample loss.
6. Optimum collector velocity may be exceeded.
7. Sample may be more difficult to remove.

Out-stack:

1. Deposition of material occurs in probe.
2. Condensation may occur in probe or collector.
3. Probe cleanout required between samples.
4. Larger equipment may be required, such as heated sampling filter box, heated probe, etc.

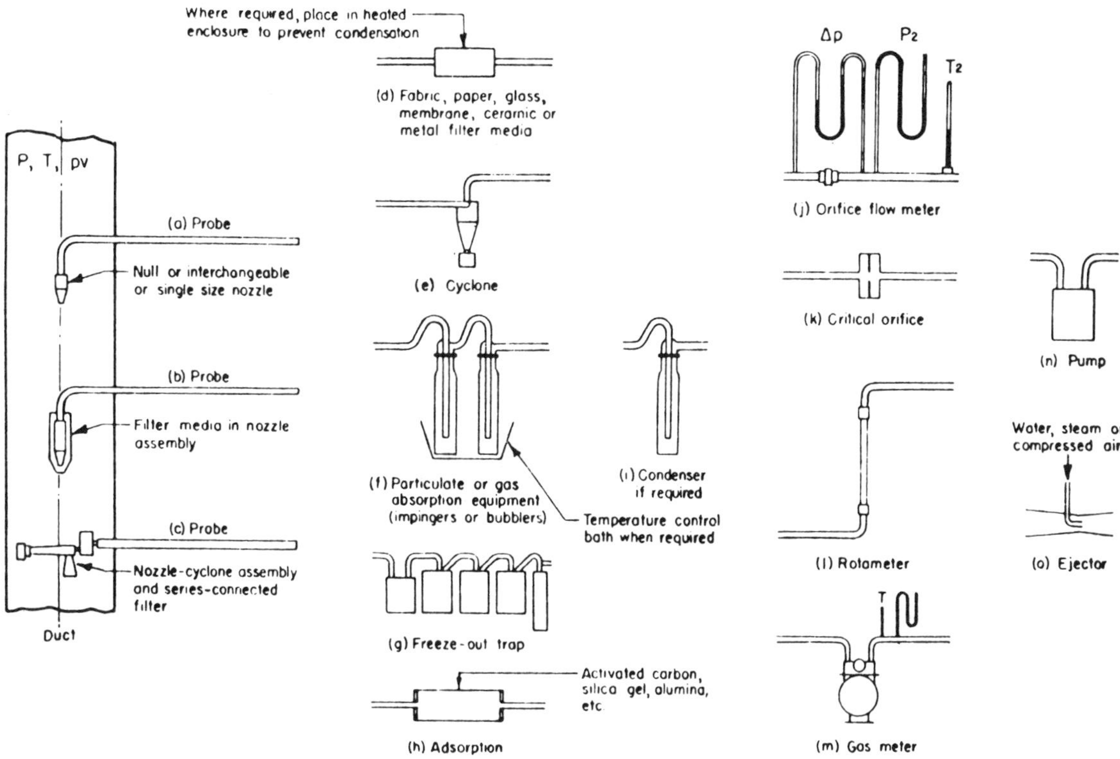

FIGURE 21-6. Sampling system components. (Courtesy of Academic Press, New York.)

for a jacketed probe to be heated (or cooled) to maintain the sample temperature to the collector, moisture or other condensible collectors, other flowmeters, stack Pitot-static tube, stack thermocouple, thermometers in sample stream at collector and at flowmeter, pressure gauges and manometers, and flow volume totalizer. These apparatus are illustrated below (e.g., see "U.S. EPA Appendix Methods 1–5 and 17," Figure 21-11). Advantages and disadvantages associated with collector location are given in Table 21-4. Typical stack sampling collector, flowmeter, and pump alternatives are illustrated schematically in Figure 21-6. The "Instrument Descriptions" section at the end of this chapter describes these major components and indicates suppliers.

Isokinetic Sampling for Particulate Matter

Because aerosol particles have an inertial behavior different than the gas in which they are suspended, a representative sample must be extracted from a flowing gas stream at the stream velocity. That is, the nozzle tip opening area (A_n, ft^2 or mm^2) and sample volumetric flow rate (Q_m, cfm or L/min at stack T and P conditions) must be adjusted to obtain a velocity $V_n = Q_m/A_n$ equal to the gas stream velocity, V_s, at the point of sampling. The sampling constraint $V_n = V_s$ is called "isokinetic" or "equal-velocity" sampling. Because V_s varies across the transverse section at the sampling location (and has been determined by the Pitot traverse above), the sampling volume flow rate, Q_m, is varied as the sampling probe nozzle tip is sequentially located at each of the sampling points in the traverse. A sampling probe nozzle diameter (D_n, in. or mm) is selected to yield the appropriate velocities with a knowledge of the sampling pump volume flow rate capability. Typically, 1.0 ft^3/min (28.3 L/min) sampling volume flow rate is used because this rate is within the capability of most portable vane-type vacuum pumps with a 1/4- or 1/3-HP electric motor.

Typical calculations for determination of the isokinetic sampling nozzle tip size are derived from the requirement $V_n = V_s$. Assume that the total mass concentration is to be determined, that the total flow is steady, the temperature and pressure are near ambient, and the process that generates the particulate matter is continuous. When the velocity at one traverse point in the duct has been measured to be 3000 fpm (15.24 m/s), and it is desired to sample at 1.0 cfm (28.3 L/min), the appropriate nozzle tip size and sampling volume flow rate is determined as follows:

$$V_n A_n = (1.0 \text{ cfm})(144 \text{ in.}^2/\text{ft}^2), \text{ or} \quad (1)$$

$$= 28.3 \text{ L/min}\left(16.67 \frac{\text{m/s}}{\text{L/m}^3}\right) \text{(metric units)}$$

$$V_n = V_s = 3000 \text{ ft/min, or} \quad (2)$$

15.24 m/s (metric units), then

$$A_n = 1 \times \frac{144}{3000} = 0.048 \text{ in.}^2\text{, or} \tag{3}$$

$$= 28.3 \times \frac{16.67}{15.24} = 31.7 \text{ mm}^2 \text{ (metric units)}$$

The diameter of the nozzle tip is therefore:

$$D_n^2 = 4\frac{A_n}{\pi} = 0.061 \text{ in.}^2\text{, or} \tag{4}$$

$$= 4\frac{A_n}{\pi} = 40.3 \text{ mm}^2 \text{ (metric units)}$$

$$D_n = 0.25 \text{ in., or} \tag{5}$$

$$= 6.35 \text{ mm (metric units)}$$

There are various practical precautions in the gas stream sampling literature regarding minimum size of probe tip, particularly for larger particles at higher concentrations (e.g., stoker-fired coal fly ash grits), but as a general rule, 0.25 in. (6 mm) or larger is a reasonable size for most field situations.

If the temperature (or pressure) in the gas stream is substantially different from ambient temperature outside the stack where the sample flowmeter and pump are located, temperature and pressure corrections to gas volume must be made in accordance with the perfect gas law (Boyle's Law, Charles' Law) or any suitable state equation for the fluid of interest. Temperature (and pressure) changes cause a change in volume (usually a reduction as temperature drops) as the sample is drawn out of the stack and passed through the collector. The temperature (and pressure) at the flowmeter must be measured, and the volume corrected back to stream conditions, to achieve isokinetic conditions. In addition, the orifice flowmeter has a characteristic performance equation:

$$Q_m = K\left(\frac{\Delta h}{\rho}\right)^{1/2} \tag{6}$$

where: Q_m = sample volume flow rate (cfm)
K = dimensional constant containing area, coefficients, etc.
Δh = orifice pressure drop (inches of water)
ρ = gas density

Gas density varies with absolute temperature (T_i) and pressure (P_i) as follows:

$$\frac{\rho_i}{\rho_o} = \left(\frac{P_i}{P_o}\right)\left(\frac{T_o}{T_i}\right) \tag{7}$$

so that if the gas passing through the flowmeter is not at the same temperature and pressure when calibrated, then these corrections must be performed as well. All of the above calculations are usually combined in a standard meter rate equation in typical sampling methods or as a nomograph which solves the equation. Effects on gas volume of removal of condensibles (e.g., moisture) in the collection train prior to the flowmeter must be included in the meter rate equation as well.[2,6,7]

Sampling at the probe nozzle tip with a velocity that is substantially different from the stream velocity is termed "nonisokinetic" sampling. This procedure may cause a size-selective segregation of particulate matter entering the probe tip. Broadly, for larger, heavier particles (i.e., for $\rho_p d_p^2 >> 1$, μm²-g/cm³), oversampling (nozzle velocity > stack velocity, $V_n > V_s$) gives underestimation of the mass concentration because of the inability of larger particles to turn with the gas flow into the nozzle tip. The actual effect on measured concentration due to nonisokinetic sampling is shown elsewhere. Undersampling ($V_n < V_s$) results in overestimation of concentration, with parallel arguments to those given above, which leads to inclusion of greater numbers of larger, heavier particles in the sample. Isokinetic and null-balance sampling probes are discussed below in "Special Apparatus and Applications."

Effects of Flow on Representative Sampling

The situation for isokinetic sampling assumes that the probe walls are of ideally thin material, of negligible thickness, far from all other flow disturbances. The actual situation in practice is rather more complicated, as shown in Figures 21-7a through 7c. First, the probe nozzle is typically made of thick-walled tubing tapered to a fine, sharp edge at the actual inlet opening (Figures 21-7a and 7b). Second, within an inch or two from the opening, other apparatus distort the flow field upstream of the nozzle (Figures 21-7c and 7d). Third, the flow over the outside of the nozzle is accelerating and a laminar boundary layer is forming, possibly with some flow separation at the junction of the nozzle taper and the main tubing which affects the external flow field upstream of the nozzle. Finally, flow in any real gas stream is turbulent approaching the probe nozzle opening with an unknown (i.e., unmeasured) amount of

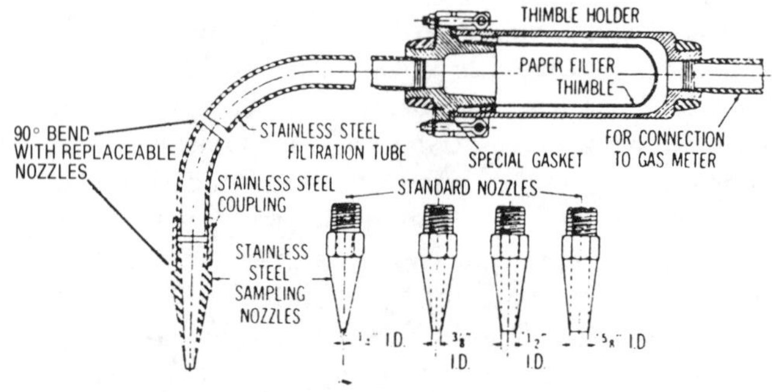

FIGURE 21-7a. Paper filter thimble holder with replaceable nozzles. The filtration tube has 90° bend.

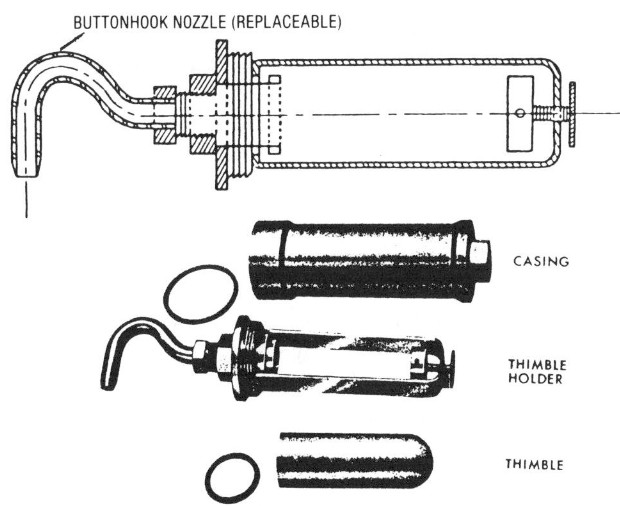

FIGURE 21-7b. Alundum® filter thimble holder with replaceable buttonhook nozzle. (Alundum is a registered trademark of Norton Company, Worcester, MA.)

transverse motion of the fluid and the particles, not necessarily in phase (because the particle motions will lag the fluid motion due to greater particle inertia). These latter effects are illustrated schematically in Figure 21-8. Rouillard and Hicks[13] have made measurements of the velocity field in the upstream vicinity of common sampling probes and tips and report the following conclusions:

> In isokinetic sampling from a gas stream it is usually assumed that the flow pattern upstream of the sampling probe is not affected by the presence of the probe. That some probes do seriously affect the gas streamlines is shown by velocity traverses taken with a hot wire anemometer under controlled flow conditions in a wind tunnel. The degree to which the streamlines are affected depends on the wall thickness and taper of the nozzle, the stem diameter, as well as on the size and proximity of sampling accessories in the vicinity of the nozzle. For a probe to cause negligible disturbance under isokinetic conditions it should have a sharp-edged nozzle with little or no outside bevel, and the stem of the probe should be at least 11 stem diameters downstream from the nozzle inlet.

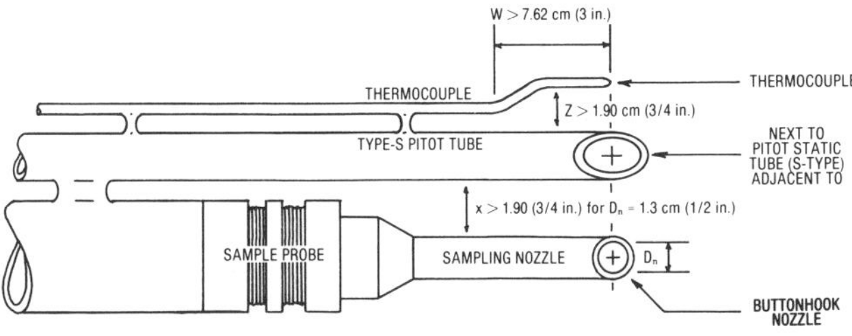

FIGURE 21-7c. Proper thermocouple placement to prevent interference on U.S. EPA probe.[2]

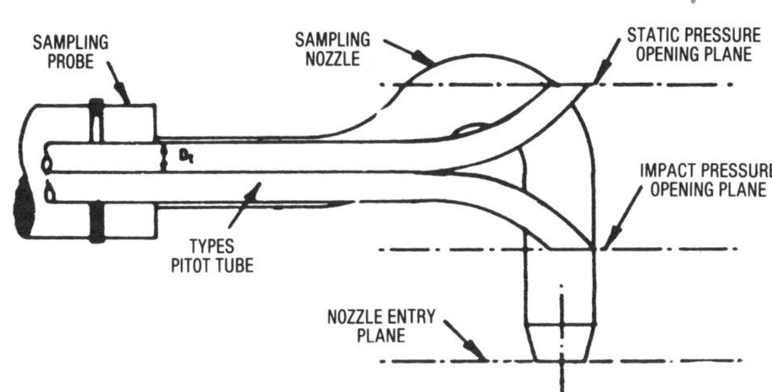

FIGURE 21-7d. Side view of probe.[2] To prevent Pitot tube from interfering with gas flow streamlines approaching the nozzle, the impact pressure opening plane of the Pitot tube shall be even with or above the nozzle entry plane.

Definite flow effects are transmitted upstream of sampling probes. Obstruction to the flow by nozzle walls and sampling accessories in the vicinity of the nozzle mouth can result in a stagnation-like region in the flow field. The magnitude of the associated inertial sampling error increases with increasing length of the upstream interference zone.

Inertial errors can be reduced by locating the nozzle at least 11 stem diameters upstream of the stem of the probe and selecting a constant outside diameter nozzle/stem geometry. The bevelling of the nozzle should be on the inside.

The upstream flow disturbance obtained with

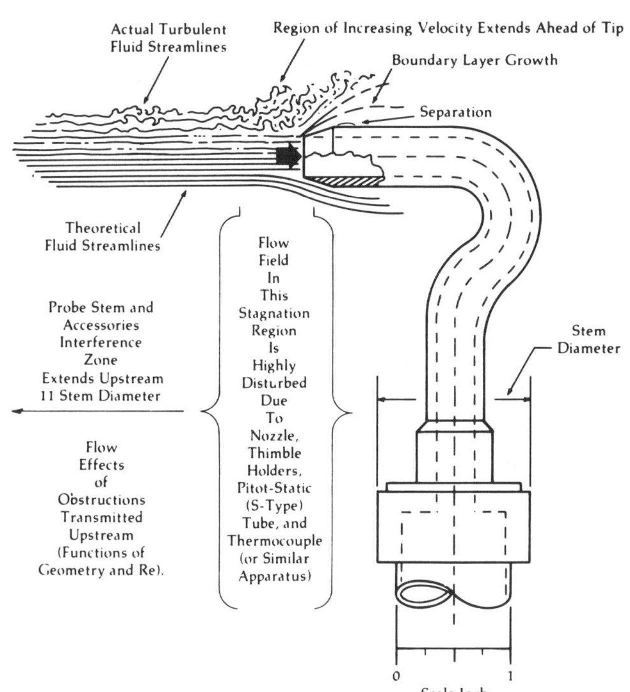

FIGURE 21-8. Actual approach zone flow phenomena in gas stream sampling.

such a streamlined probe is restricted to velocity profile development which, provided the sampling is isokinetic, does not cause inertial sampling errors.

Applications

Introduction

This section contains details on specific methods of manual gas stream sampling (MGSS) that may be applied to individual industrial processes and operations. A general guideline for planning a survey is given, followed by a presentation of MGSS methods promulgated and proposed as regulations by U.S. EPA and a summary review of methods developed, recommended, or required by other groups. Certain special applications of gas stream sampling for issues of current interest are reviewed. Accuracy of methods, qualifications of technical personnel, and other selected issues are considered, followed by a brief review of literature of the past decade.

There are three kinds of methods that may be considered in any gas sampling situation: 1) an individual method developed as above, using apparatus selected for the project, 2) standard methods (apparatus and procedures) to be discussed below, and 3) modified standard methods.

Some useful information can be obtained from a simple center-line sample of a dusty gas taken with an out-stack filter holder (closed face) or an impinger, attached to a piece of bent soft copper refrigeration tubing for a probe and connected through a critical orifice to a vacuum pump. Such typical systems include dust collecting and waste-conveying systems such as for wood wastes, rubber grinder dust, abrasives, etc. These types of inexpensive data can be used in many situations to assess process wastestream loadings, to estimate collector efficiency, to define a need for collectors on emission streams, etc. Use of standard methods (described below) requires more elaborate equipment and procedural time but, of course, yields more valid information in a legal sense. When planning a gas stream sampling project, judgment must be used to select an appropriate method consistent with project objectives.

There are also two levels of difficulty of sampling to be considered:

1. Routine sampling, in which the setup has been done before, where there are data available on previous tests, and the project can be redone by one or two senior technicians in a relatively straightforward way.
2. Nonroutine sampling, in which the setup has not been done before, or new types of data are required. Examples of nonroutine sampling include data on particle-size and/or composition parameters,(14) data on a new process or one substantially changed, data on a high temperature-high pressure gas line, or data on newer sampling methods with limited field evaluation experience.(15–17)

In either case, there is need for information on the nature, characteristics, and quantities of materials to be expected in the gas stream. Each of these is process-dependent, and a general rule is to obtain information on the process initially. Expected emission concentrations can be calculated from air pollutant emission factors, with data on process parameters (i.e., size of process), flue gas flow rates, fuel rate, operation rate, etc.(18)

After determining the general process parameters and expected concentrations of substances of interest contained in the gas stream, apparatus and procedures can be selected or developed to obtain required data. The following sections consider these topics.

Guideline for Planning and Implementing a Gas Stream Sampling Project

Table 21-5 has been prepared to identify necessary steps in the process of preparing for and conducting, assisting with, or observing a stack sampling project. It is a reasonably complete outline of necessary steps in the process, based on extensive experience. Each item can be developed in greater detail to prepare a checklist for conduct of each part of the project.

U.S. EPA Reference Methods for Stationary Source Air Pollutant Emission Sampling

Gas stream sampling and the underlying principles are used by U.S. EPA to measure emissions from air pollution sources 1) for determination of quantity and composition of emission species; 2) for development of emission inventories; 3) for development of emission factors; 4) for source emission surveillance, reporting, and assessment; 5) for monitoring status of compliance with emission standards and enforcement activities; 6) for permit and application support for a variety of regulatory purposes; 7) for validation of source continuous emission monitoring systems (CEMS); 8) for assessment of best control technology in use; 9) for validating performance of control devices; 10) for development of better, novel, or new control technology; 11) for development of better or new measurement methods, devices, etc.; and 12) for developing or validating air dispersion models, etc.

One major provision of the Clean Air Act Amendments of 1970 was the establishment of uniform national standards or new source performance standards (NSPS).(2) These are specific allowable emissions for individual new (or substantially modified) stationary

TABLE 21-5. Guidelines for Planning and Implementing a Gas Stream Sampling Project*

1. Identify purpose of tests: pollutant emission compliance, control equipment tests, process evaluation, other.
2. Identify data to be obtained: process, operation rates, etc.; gas composition and properties; flow character.
3. Obtain plant and process information: operational plans and specifications, general and specific site details, materials, flows, etc.
4. Select and specify test methods: individual design, standard method, modified method; obtain written agreement on method(s).
5. Site visit: discuss plans, prepare preliminary schedule of activities, assess and evaluate status of equipment.*
6. Select site(s): location(s) for tests and need for supporting facilities, such as arrangements for space, laboratories, etc.*
7. If to be contractor implemented (or for budget estimating purposes): prepare work statement, identify bidders, select evaluation criteria, send request for proposal, get back proposals, apply evaluation criteria, evaluate, select contractor, meet, negotiate, award contract or purchase order.
8. Select equipment.*
9. Assign crew.*
10. Plan for access arrangements: ladders, scaffolds, platforms, jib booms and tackle, shelters, utilities, space, etc.
11. Schedule activities (final) (budget final).
12. Assemble equipment.
13. Prepare necessary supplies, reagents, weighed filters, etc.
14. Calibrate flowmeters, leak checks, etc.
15. Pack for shipment.
16. Ship or take.
17. Travel to site.
18. Meet with plant personnel, test observers, inspect, advise, etc.*
19. Unpack equipment, set up, leak checks, calibration checks.
20. Run preliminary test, check for cyclonic flow, unusual moisture, etc.
21. Analyze preliminary data, prepare preliminary result.
22. Discuss preliminary result with the plant personnel and observers, modify test procedures.*
23. Conduct test(s): three repetitions for U.S. EPA methods typically may require 3 separate days in sequence.*
24. Analyze preliminary samples and data; calculate % isokinetic (%I) for particulate tests; identify problems and need to modify, change, or abort test plans.*
25. Evaluate and discuss preliminary results with plant personnel/observers.*
26. Remove equipment, clean up site, secure ports, etc.
27. Repack equipment, prepare samples for transport to analytical laboratory.
28. Ship or take back.
29. Travel back.
30. Unpack equipment, clean up, repair, recalibrate or recheck leaks.
31. Discuss analysis of samples for desired data with analyst.
32. Analyze samples.
33. Prepare results and calculations.
34. Prepare report:
    Report contents (minimum required for legally valid reporting): title page, letter of transmittal, table of contents, list of figures, list of tables, summary or abstract page, 1) introduction, 2) background, 3) apparatus and procedure, 4) test results, 5) discussion of results, 6) conclusions, 7) recommendations, 8) appendices including copies of all field data, process flow chart, sample and analytical results (raw data), fuel analysis, data pages and tables filled out in the field, field observations, chain-of-custody affirmations, calibrations, preliminary filing data, test crew names and other identifiers (e.g., SSN), etc., and all other appropriate field test and backup data, e.g., copies of standard test methods or other pertinent regulations, stack opacity observations, typical calculations performed, etc.
35. Present report results, decide on course of action.

*State and federal air pollution control agency personnel may require pretest review and approval and onsite supervision of tests for regulatory compliance.

source categories and facilities. Each NSPS, when issued as a regulation, applies to new construction. These are also generally used by state air pollution control agencies as a guide to good practice for existing sources. Principal contents of the regulation include emission standards for each substance and methods for determination of compliance. Emission standards are typically expressed either in mass of material per unit of material processed, or per unit of energy input or product output rate, or in terms of outlet concentration directly. Table 21-6 lists an example of the promulgated NSPS for one source and the facilities affected (e.g., unit

TABLE 21-6. Sample of the Standards of Performance Table — 40 CFR Part 60[2]

Source Category	Affected Facility	Pollutant	Emission Level	Monitoring Requirement[A]
Subpart D: Fossil-fuel-fired steam generators for which construction commenced after August 17, 1971 (>250 million Btu/hr)	Fossil-fuel-fired boilers[B]	Particulate	0.10 lbs/million Btu	No requirement
		Opacity	20% (27% for 6 min/hr)	Continuous
		SO_2	1.20 lbs/million Btu	Continuous
		NO_x	0.70 lbs/million Btu	Continuous

[A]Continuous monitors are used to determine excess emissions only, unless noted as "continuous compliance."
[B]Includes boilers firing solid or liquid fuel and wood residue mixtures.

operation or process equipment).[19,20] The remainder can be obtained directly from a U.S. EPA publication. Table 21-6 also lists the allowed emission level from the facility and whether a CEMS is required on the stack discharge for compliance. Each NSPS also lists the reference test methods required to demonstrate compliance and for recordkeeping and reporting purposes (surveillance procedures).

Standards of Performance for New Stationary Sources are compiled and updated annually.[2] A semi-annual update service is available from U.S. EPA. Most practicing professionals accumulate the *Federal Register* announcements on a daily review basis and also use current awareness reporting systems.[21,22]

As indicated above, U.S. EPA has developed and published (and occasionally revised) standard reference methods for MGSS for about 70 source/facility categories. Table 21-7 lists the appendix test method number and its title for methods used in the NSPS and 16 methods used in National Emissions Standards for Hazardous Air Pollutants (NESHAPS). With a few exceptions (e.g., Methods 9, 22, 24, and 28), these are all manual methods involving specific apparatus and procedural instructions. Applications of each method to individual NSPS are indicated in the Code of Federal Regulations.[2] For example, Subpart D (steam generators) requires use of Methods 1 through 5 for determination of particulate emissions, Methods 6 and 7 for SO_2 and NO_x, and Method 9 for opacity (visual). From the U.S. EPA publication[2] and updates, method details can be obtained for other applications.

U.S. EPA is also developing or investigating MGSS methods for toxic substances that may present a unique community health hazard, such as methylene chloride,[23–25] nickel, cadmium, dioxins, furans, and ethylene oxide.[26]

U.S. Environmental Protection Agency Appendix Methods 1–5 and 17

U.S. EPA Appendix Methods 1–5 or 17 are used in more than half of the NSPS. These methods are described briefly here. The full text describing apparatus and procedures may be obtained from Reference 2.

Method 1 describes the selection of a sampling site and determination of the appropriate number of sampling traverse points, as described previously in conjunction with Figure 21-3. The method of application of Figure 21-3 is described as follows: When the 8- and 2-diameter criteria can be met, the minimum number of traverse points shall be 1) 12, for circular or rectangular stacks with diameter (or equivalent diameters) >0.61 m (24 in.); 2) 8, for circular stacks with diameters between 0.30 and 0.61 m (12–24 in.); and 3) 9, for rectangular stacks with equivalent diameters between 0.30 and 0.61 m (12–24 in.).

When the 8- and 2-diameter criteria cannot be met, the minimum number of traverse points is determined from Figure 21-3a or 21-3b. The distances from the chosen measurement site to the nearest upstream and downstream disturbances are determined, and each distance is divided by the stack diameter or equivalent diameter to determine from Figure 21-3a the minimum number of traverse points that correspond to 1) the number of duct diameters upstream and 2) the number of diameters downstream. The higher of the two minimum numbers of traverse points, or a greater value, is selected, so that for circular stacks the number is a multiple of four (from Figure 21-2b), and for rectangular stacks, the number is one of those shown in Figure 21-2a.

Method 2 describes the conduct of a velocity traverse. Upon determining the traverse points, the traverse is conducted by the principles discussed above. Actual details of procedures are given in Method 2.[2] Training and apprenticeship experience are most valuable for valid implementation of any of these procedures.

Method 3 contains details for determination of flue gas composition in conjunction with moisture content determination by Method 4. Figure 21-9 indicates apparatus for withdrawing a grab sample to a Fyrite (or Orsat) analyzer. A more representative sample can be obtained by pumping an integrated sample into a plastic bag held in a box, as shown in Figure 21-9. A sample rate of 0.5–1.0 L/min and a bag volume of the order of 50 L are recommended (30 L final sample volume). The

TABLE 21-7. U.S. EPA Manual Gas Stream Sampling (MGSS) Reference Methods for New Source Performance Standards (NSPS) and National Emissions Standards for Hazardous Air Pollutants (NESHAPS) (7/92)*

Appendix A Test Method No.	Title
1	Sample and velocity traverses for stationary sources
1A	Sample and velocity traverses for stationary sources with small stacks or ducts
2	Determination of stack gas velocity and volumetric flow rate (Type S Pitot tube)
2A	Direct measurement of gas volume through pipes and small ducts
2B	Determination of exhaust gas volume flow rate from gasoline vapor incinerators
2C	Determination of stack gas velocity and volumetric flow rate in small stacks or ducts (standard Pitot tube)
2D	Measurement of gas volumetric flow rates in small pipes and ducts
3	Gas analysis for carbon dioxide, oxygen, excess air, and dry molecular weight
3A	Determination of oxygen and carbon dioxide concentrations in emissions from stationary sources (instrumental analyzer procedure)
4	Determination of moisture content in stack gases
5	Determination of particulate emissions from stationary sources
5A	Determination of particulate emissions from the asphalt processing and asphalt roofing industry
5B	Determination of nonsulfuric acid particulate matter from stationary sources
5C	[Reserved]
5D	Determination of particulate emissions from positive-pressure fabric filters
5E	Determination of particulate emissions from the wool fiberglass insulation manufacturing industry
5F	Determination of nonsulfate particulate matter from stationary sources
5G	Determination of particulate emissions from wood heaters from a dilution tunnel sampling location
5H	Determination of particulate emissions from wood heaters from a stack location
6	Determination of sulfur dioxide emissions from stationary sources
6A	Determination of sulfur dioxide, moisture, and carbon dioxide emissions from fossil fuel combustion sources
6B	Determination of sulfur dioxide and carbon dioxide daily average emissions from fossil fuel combustion sources
6C	Determination of sulfur dioxide emissions from stationary sources (instrumental analyzer procedure)
7	Determination of nitrogen oxide emissions from stationary sources
7A	Determination of nitrogen oxide emissions from stationary sources—ion chromatographic method
7B	Determination of nitrogen oxide emissions from stationary sources (ultraviolet spectrophotometry)
7C	Determination of nitrogen oxide emissions from stationary sources—alkaline-permanganate/colorimetric method
7D	Determination of nitrogen oxide emisisons from stationary sources—alkaline-permanganate/ion chromatographic method
7E	Determination of nitrogen oxides emissions from stationary sources (instrumental analyzer procedure)
8	Determination of sulfuric acid mist and sulfur dioxide emissions from stationary sources
9	Visual determination of the opacity of emissions from stationary sources
Alternate method 1	Determination of the opacity of emissions from stationary sources remotely by lidar
10	Determination of carbon monoxide emissions from stationary sources
10A	Determination of carbon monoxide emissions in certifying continuous emission monitoring systems at petroleum refineries
10B	Determination of carbon monoxide emissions from stationary sources
11	Determination of hydrogen sulfide content of fuel gas streams in petroleum refineries
12	Determination of inorganic lead emissions from stationary sources
13A	Determination of total fluoride emissions from stationary sources—SPADNS zirconium lake method
13B	Determination of total fluoride emissions from stationary sources—specific ion electrode method
14	Determination of fluoride emissions from potroom roof monitors for primary aluminum plants
15	Determination of hydrogen sulfide, carbonyl sulfide, and carbon disulfide emissions from stationary sources
15A	Determination of total reduced sulfur emissions from sulfur recovery plants in petroleum refineries
16	Semicontinuous determination of sulfur emissions from stationary sources
16A	Determination of total reduced sulfur emissions from stationary sources (impinger technique)
16B	Determination of total reduced sulfur emissions from stationary sources
17	Determination of particulate emissions from stationary sources (in-stack filtration method)
18	Measurement of gaseous organic compound emissions by gas chromatography
19	Determination of sulfur dioxide removal efficiency and particulate, sulfur dioxide, and nitrogen oxides emission rates

TABLE 21-7 (con't.). U.S. EPA Manual Gas Stream Sampling (MGSS) Reference Methods for New Source Performance Standards (NSPS) and National Emissions Standards for Hazardous Air Pollutants (NESHAPS) (7/92)*

Appendix A Test Method No.	Title
20	Determination of nitrogen oxides, sulfur dioxide, and diluent emissions from stationary gas turbines
21	Determination of volatile organic compound leaks
22	Visual determination of fugitive emissions from material sources and smoke emissions from flares
23	Determination of polychlorinated dibenzo-p-dioxins and polychlorinated dibenzofurans from stationary sources
24	Determination of volatile matter content, water content, density, volume solids, and weight solids of surface coatings
24A	Determination of volatile matter content and density of printing inks and related coatings
25	Determination of total gaseous nonmethane organic emissions as carbon
25A	Determination of total gaseous organic concentration using a flame ionization analyzer
25B	Determination of total gaseous organic concentration using a nondispersive infrared analyzer
26	Determination of hydrogen chloride emissions from stationary sources
27	Determination of vapor tightness of gasoline delivery tank using pressure-vacuum test
28	Certification and auditing of wood heaters
28A	Measurement of air to fuel ratio and minimum achievable burn rates for wood-fired appliances
101	Determination of particulate and gaseous mercury emissions from chlor-alkali plants—air streams
101A	Determination of particulate and gaseous mercury emissions from sewage sludge incinerators
102	Determination of particulate and gaseous mercury emissions from stationary sources (hydrogen streams)
103	Beryllium screening method
104	Determination of beryllium emissions from stationary sources
105	Determination of mercury in wastewater treatment plant sewage sludges
106	Determination of vinyl chloride from stationary sources
107	Determination of vinyl chloride of inprocess wastewater samples, and vinyl chloride content of polyvinyl chloride resin, slurry, wet cake, and latex samples
107A	Determination of vinyl choride content of solvents, resin-solvent solution, polyvinyl chloride resin, resin slurry, wet resin, and latex samples
108	Determination of particulate and gaseous arsenic emissions
108A	Determination of arsenic content in ore samples from nonferrous smelters
108B	Determination of arsenic content in ore samples from nonferrous smelters
108C	Determination of arsenic content in ore samples from nonferrous smelters
111	Determination of ^{210}Po emissions from stationary sources
114	Test methods for measuring radionuclide emissions from stationary sources
115	Monitoring for ^{222}Rn Emissions
201	Determination of PM_{10} emissions (exhaust gas recycle procedure)
202	Determination of condensible particulate emissions from stationary sources

*Source: Reference 2.

integrated sample can be made more representative of the total gas stream by traversing across the flow field during sampling (see Reference 2 for details). Analysis for carbon dioxide and oxygen (dry molecular weight determination) can be made with a Fyrite analyzer. For more accurate data, an Orsat analysis is required. Procedures for leak testing, calibration, use, and calculations are also given in Reference 2.

Method 4 describes apparatus and procedures for determination of moisture in stack gases from combustion sources, pyrometallurgical processes, or in the discharge from wet scrubbers. As shown in Figure 21-10, a heated probe conducts a gas stream sample through a heated filter to an ice-water-cooled condenser. Moisture condenses and its volume is measured. The condenser consists of four Greenburg–Smith impingers or a coil of tubing, immersed in an ice bucket. In the first arrangement, it is recommended that the fourth impinger be filled with silica gel. In the second case, silica gel or other dessicant should be included after the tubing coil to dry the gas completely and to protect downstream components from acid attack. For example, condensibles and (sulfur) acids in the gas passing through a dry gas meter rapidly rust, corrode, and freeze up the motion, rendering the meter inoperable.

Method 5 is used to sample for particulate matter, using an out-of-stack filter contained in a heated box. Standard components, considered in series, are 1) a glass-lined heated probe with a button-hook nozzle (outside taper), 2) an attached thermocouple, 3) an attached reverse-impact (Type S) Pitot-static tube (these three items comprise the pitobe), 4) a heated, fibrous filter holder and chamber, 5) four Greenburg–Smith impingers in a series, 6) a leak-free vacuum pump, 7) a dry gas meter, and 8) an outlet orifice. Pressure gauges, temperature probes, flowmeter manometer and Pitot tube manometer, flow control and shutoff valving, and electrical switching, fuses, etc., are arranged at the point of use in the system or are transmitted to gauges in a central meter box. Construction details for standard models are contained in a U.S. EPA technical publication.[27] Methods for maintenance, calibration, and operation of the equipment are described in a companion U.S. EPA publication.[28] The apparatus and procedures were developed during the early 1960s by the U.S. Bureau of Mines and the National Air Pollution Administration (now the U.S. EPA).[29,30]

Procedures for calibration, leak checks, preparation of consumable supplies, use in the field, sample recovery, recording of data and observations, and calculations required are contained in Reference 2. Each of the several manufacturers listed in Table 21-I-1 (located in the "Instrument Descriptions" section at the end of this chapter) provides an operating instruction manual for their specific design. To use the system, the sampling probe is mounted on the sample box and the sample box is connected to the meter box by means of the umbilical cord. The sampling probe or its support is marked with

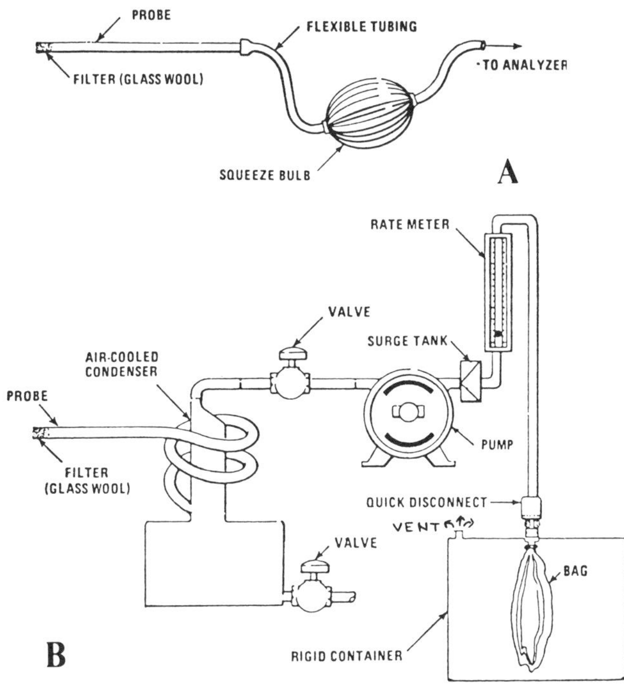

FIGURE 21-9. U.S. EPA Reference Method 3 gas sampling train.[2] A. Grab sampling train. B. Integrated gas sampling train.

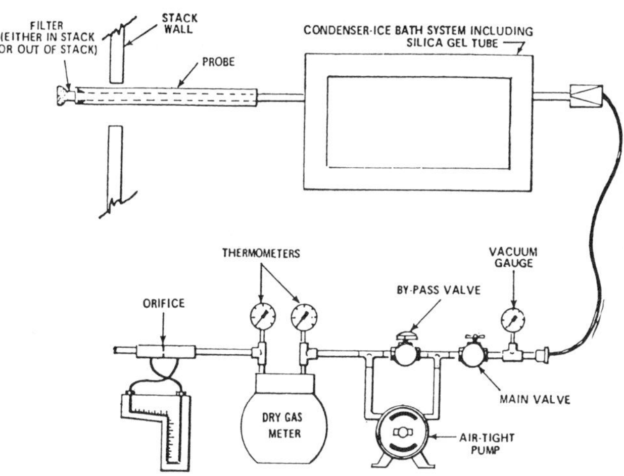

FIGURE 21-10. U.S. EPA Reference Method 4 moisture sampling train.[2]

glass cloth tape at traverse cross-sectional depth of insertion points. After leak-checking, the assembly is then mounted on a suitable framework for sliding in and out of the stack. Typically, operation is maintained at isokinetic flow conditions at about 1.0 cfm (28.3 L/min) at each traverse point by adjusting sampling volume with a fixed probe nozzle tip size. Three major methods of adjusting the flow rate are commonly used: 1) a nomograph that solves the isokinetic equation graphically, as described by Rom,[28] and is furnished by the manufacturer of the train; 2) a meter rate equation that contains all the factors and is reduced for simple calculation in the field on a hand-held scientific calculator; 3) a small, programmable, hand-held computer may be used; or 4) a slide rule calculator.

Sampling with the Method 5 train is somewhat more complex than with others used in the past (e.g., WP-50).[7] It is especially necessary to obtain some training and experience before using Method 5 to determine parameters that may be used later for economic estimating or legal purposes.

To reduce some of the operational complexity from the Method 5 train used for sampling from gas streams where the particulate concentration is independent of the temperature, U.S. EPA has developed Method 17, as shown in Figure 21-11.[2] The heated filter holder in the sample box has been removed as a requirement, and a flat (or thimble) filter holder is attached to the stack end of the probe for direct insertion into the gas stream. This in-stack filter method collects particulate matter at stack temperature and removes the need to clean out the probe liner and filter front half with acetone or other solvents at the end of each test. A simple, unheated steel (instead of glass) probe is attached to the moisture condenser by a flexible hose (Teflon®-lined). Moving this simple filter-probe assembly to each point in the traverse is easier and cleanup is quicker at the end.

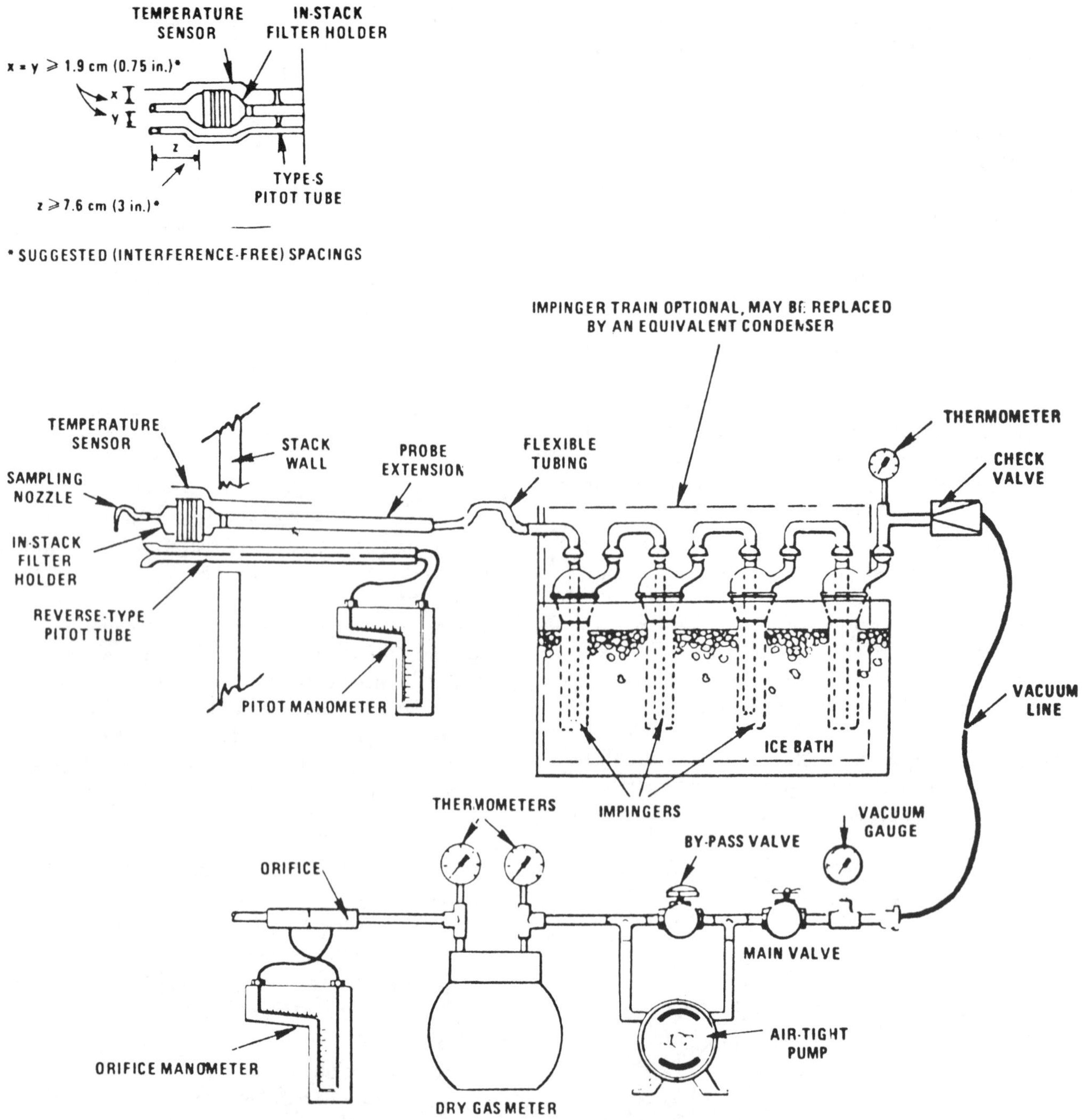

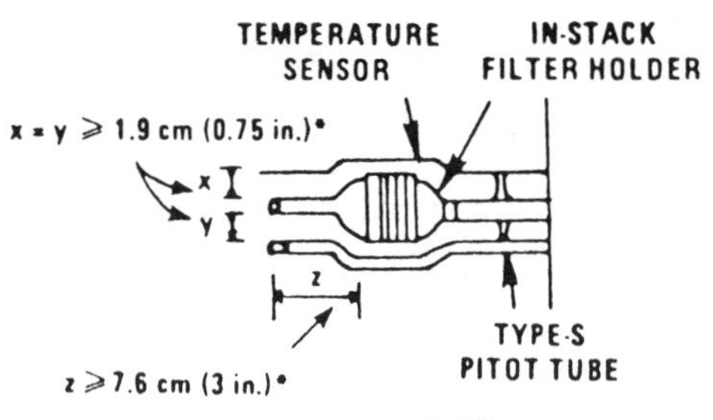

FIGURE 21-11. U.S. EPA Reference Method 17 particulate sampling train, equipped with in-stack filter.[2]

Both Method 5 and Method 17 usually require two persons to operate in the field. Prior training and supervised experience are necessary in order to be aware of and compensate for potential problems with leaks, breakage, precision, etc.

Safety Precautions

Safety and health considerations for gas stream sampling teams include potential hazards associated with climbing and working at heights, electrical shock, confined space entry and work, and exposure to chemicals from pressurized openings in ducts. Common health concerns include 1) confined space entry procedures, permits, etc., for work inside dust collectors, boilers, flues, breeching, etc.; 2) avoiding exposure to chemical hazards from gases or contaminants in a flowing pressurized stream when opened for probe insertion and traversing; and 3) discontinuing the use of asbestos products for thermal protection or for gaskets on probe glands, etc.

Electrical or fire hazards can occur occasionally when a ground fault develops. The glass-lined Pitot tube is electrically heated and the outer sheath can reach 110 volts, unless it is grounded. None of the standard, commercially available Method 5 equipment is intrinsically safe for Class I Group D explosive atmospheres. Exposed resistance heaters exist in older designs. One of the major difficulties with the Method 5 train is obtaining a satisfactory leak check (<0.02 cfm [<0.57 L/min] at 0.5 atm; Method 5 section 4.1.4[2]). There are about 100 joints, junctions, connections, etc. (permanent and temporary), and any one or several may leak on any given test setup. In addition, the glass-lined probe has been known to break during setup. There are no specific universal guidelines for leak location; each instance is unique when it occurs. Experience and judgment are essential.

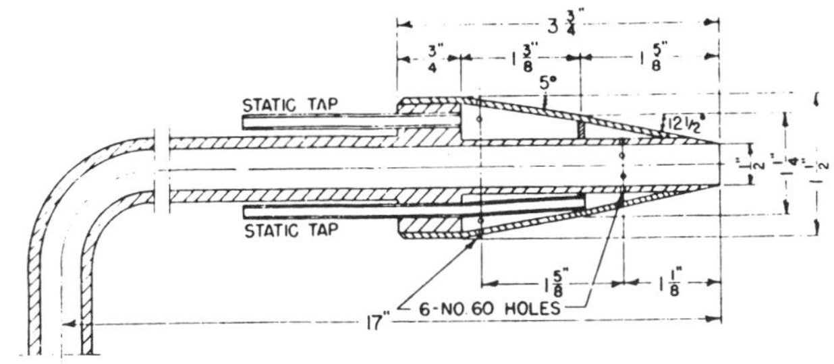

FIGURE 21-12a. Typical null-type isokinetic sampling nozzle, probe A. (Courtesy of Western Precipitation Corp.)

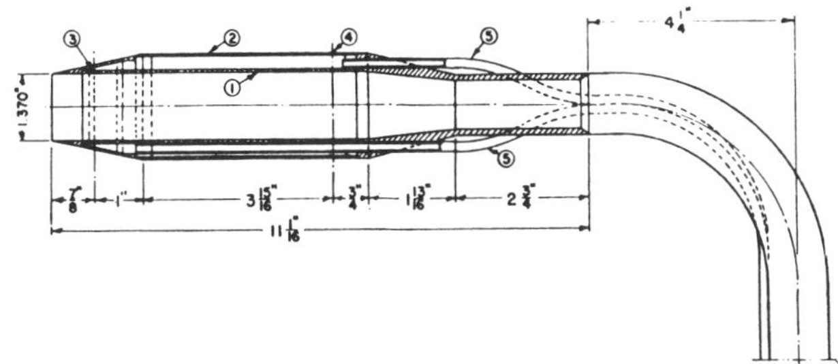

FIGURE 21-12b. Typical null-type isokinetic sampling nozzle, probe B: 1.5-in. (38.1-mm) o.d. tube, No. 16 gauge, 1.370-in. (34.8-mm) i.d. (1); 2.125-in. (54-mm) o.d. tube, No. 18 gauge, 2.037-in. (51.7-mm) i.d. (2); inside static 8.125-in.- (206.4-mm-) diameter holes equally spaced (3); 12.125-in.- (308-mm-) diameter holes equally spaced (4); static tubes, 3/16-in. (4.8-mm) o.d., 0.117-in. (3-mm) i.d. (5). (Courtesy Bethlehem Steel Company.)

Other MGSS Guidelines, Codes, and Standards

Many other organizations and agencies have developed stack sampling methods for various operations or emissions.[31–47] Methods are also discussed in the American Public Health Association (APHA) Intersociety manual.[38,39] There are also companion developments of stack sampling methods in other industrialized countries such as the design of the British Coal Utilization Research Association.[1]

Special Apparatus and Applications

This section deals briefly with four major topical areas alluded to in previous sections: 1) isokinetic sampling probes, 2) high-volume stack samplers, 3) high temperature–high pressure (HiT–HiP) sampling systems, and 4) selected systems.

Isokinetic Sampling Nozzles

Null-type isokinetic sampling nozzles are usually three-chamber designs that operate by measuring static pressure on the outside of the probe nozzle body and static pressure inside the inlet opening of the nozzle, as illustrated in Figures 21-12a and 12b.[48] The null-static pressure balance is achieved when zero static pressure differential (null) is developed between the inside and outside static pressure taps. This is assumed to indicate that isokinetic velocity is being obtained.

Dennis *et al.*[48] found that calibration of these probes was required because errors in isokinetic velocity of –28% to +8% occurred at null static pressure balance over a velocity range from 1000 to 7000 fpm (5.08–35.56 m/s). The general conclusions from this extensive investigation are that 1) null balance static pressure probes must be calibrated in a duct of the same general size and configuration as the field installation and at the velocity, temperature, etc. at which they will be used; 2) isokinetic velocity actually will be achieved at some positive (or negative) value of the static pressure difference; and 3) the calibration will change with duct velocity and size/configuration. Null-type sampling probes cannot theoretically achieve isokinetic velocities except possibly in a very limited range because the location of static tap holes, probe and nozzle size and shape, inlet configuration, etc., all interact with boundary layer growth and consequent static pressure distribution over the outside of the probe nozzle and along the inside of the nozzle inlet tube (in the entrance length region). Other designs of isokinetic null-balance probe nozzles are illustrated in Figures 21-13a through 13c.[49–53]

High-Volume Stack Samplers

Normal in- and out-stack sampling apparatus are designed to operate usually with a small, easily portable vane-type vacuum pump having a flow capability of about 1.0 cfm (28.3 L/min). There are a number of applications in which a higher volume flow rate is desirable and a suitable collector and vacuum source combination must be obtained, e.g., for sampling of the outlet concentration of a fabric filter operating at 99.99% plus efficiency or for fuel and waste gas streams containing particulate concentrations below 1.0 mg/m^3 (<0.5 grains/1000 ft^3).

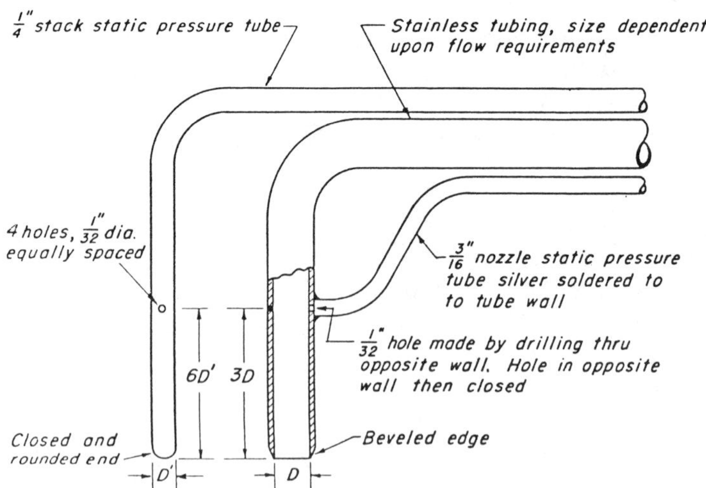

FIGURE 21-13a. Industrial Hygiene Foundation simplified "null" nozzle design.[49]

A 50- to 75-cfm (1400–2100 L/min) model, developed as the Boubel-CS3 hi-volume sampler, is shown in Figure 21-14.[54] A cast aluminum, gasketed filter holder contains a flat 8-in. × 10-in. (203 × 245-mm) rectangle of all-glass, high-efficiency fiber filter paper (MSA-1106B or HV-70). Flow is conducted through (1) sampling nozzle tip (1 7/8-in. [47.6-mm] i.d. for low velocity, < 2000 fpm [10 m/s]; 1 3/8-in. [34.9-mm] i.d. for midrange velocities, 2000–4000 fpm [10–20 m/s]; and 15/16-in. [23.8-mm] i.d., high velocity, >4000 fpm [> 20 m/s]), then through (3) aluminum extension tubing (3 or 4 ft [760–1020 mm]), through the filter and housing (5), through an orifice meter whose upstream and downstream static pressure taps are connected to a 0- to 4-in. water gauge (w.g.) (0–100 mm w.g.) Magnehelic® gauge, through a butterfly control valve, and through flexible tubing to a conventional Cadillac® Blower. Flow is adjusted with valve (10). The technical instructions contain nomographs to adjust flow rate using the Pitot-static tube (2) readings shown on the second 0- to 2-in. w.g. (0–50 mm w.g.) Magnehelic gauge and the temperature at the measuring orifice (8).

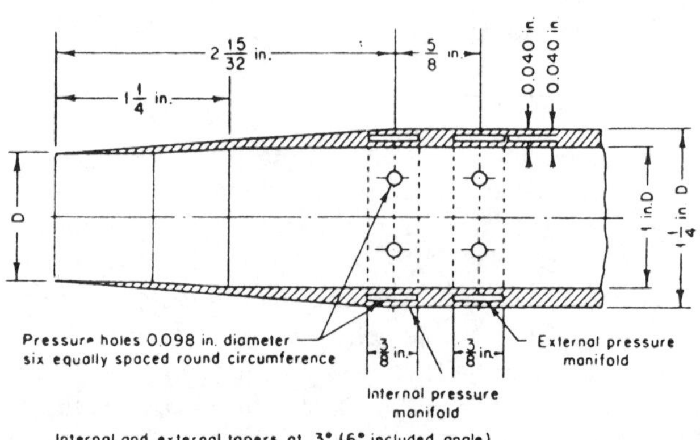

FIGURE 21-13b. Sampling probe (pressure leads from manifold not shown).[50]

A high-volume stack sampler (HVSS) was developed by the Aerotherm Division of Acurex Corporation for U.S. EPA. It is a U.S. EPA Method 5 train operating at 4 cfm (113 L/min) with a stainless steel probe liner and General Electric's Lexan® polycarbonate impingers. It operates at 6 cfm (170 L/min) with a heated cyclone in place and 7.5 cfm (212 L/min) when the cyclone is removed. The pump is a 10 cfm, oil-less vane type, custom modified and rated at 10 cfm (283 L/min) at 0 mm Hg vacuum. Stated weight is 38 lbs (17 kg) for the sample box and 50 lbs (33 kg) for the control unit.

High Temperature–High Pressure Gas Stream Sampling

Sampling from a confined flowing gas stream at high temperature or high pressure may require special consideration for insertion of apparatus to reduce ambient leakage outward for personnel safety or process reasons and to preserve sampled material. These are common problems in the pyrometallurgical, natural and producer fuel-gas, chemical process, petroleum, and related industries. Typical devices developed for leak-limiting insertion of MGSS systems are shown in

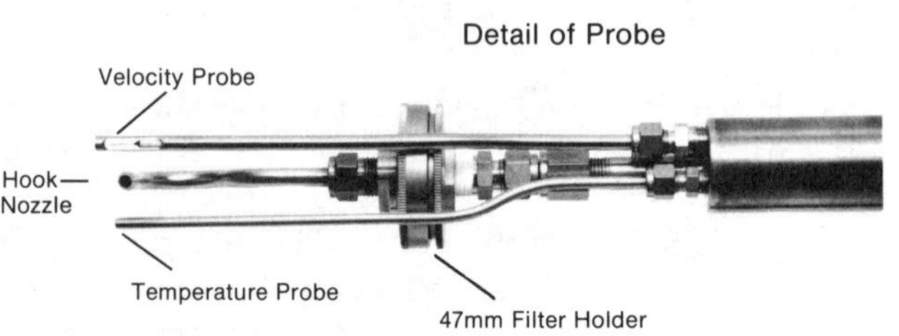

FIGURE 21-13c. Automatic isokinetic Method 5 sampling attachment.[51]

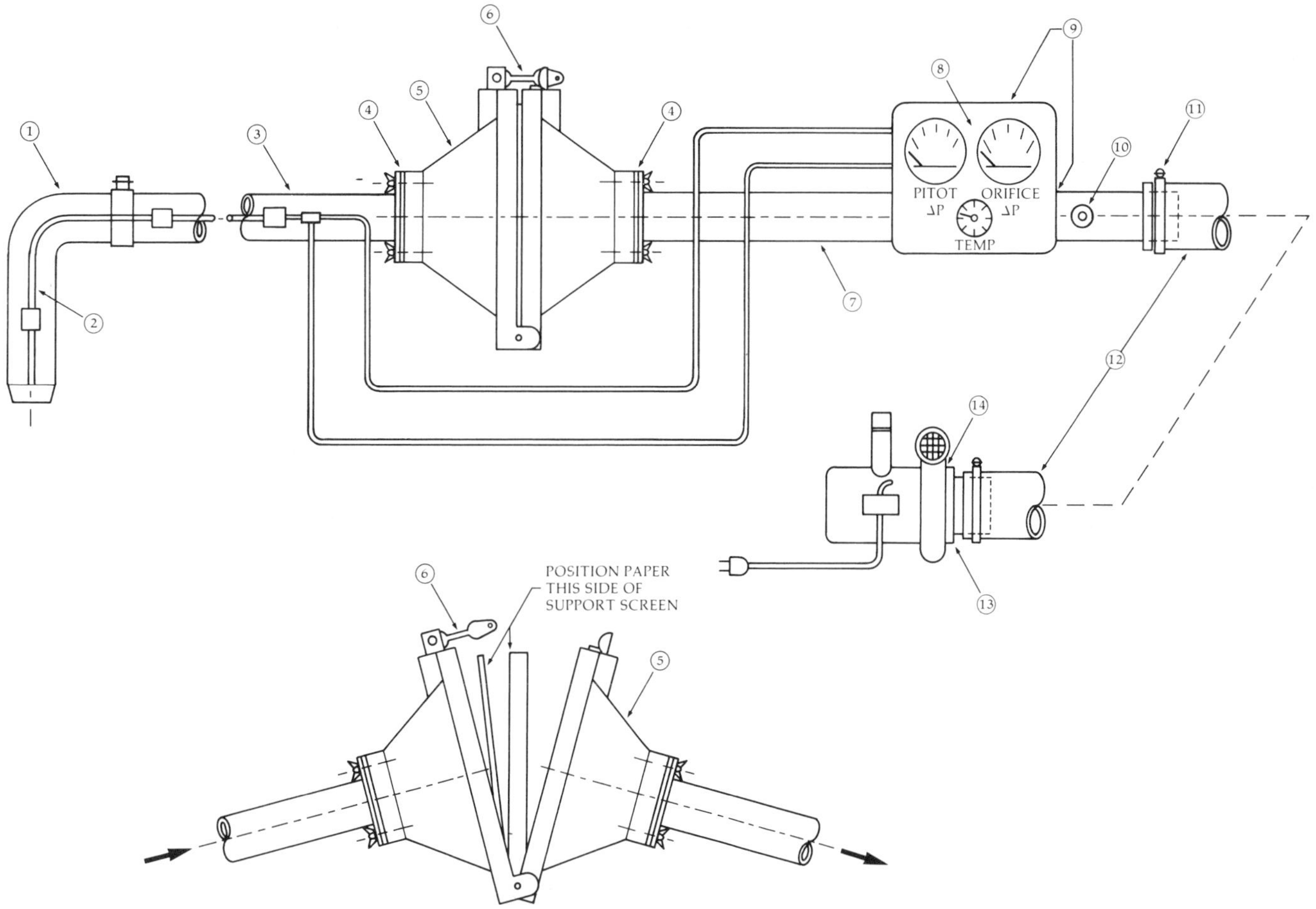

FIGURE 21-14. Boubel-CS3 hi-volume sampler:[54] inlet nozzle (1); Pitot-static tube (2); inlet section, 30 in. (762 mm) and 48 in. (1219 mm) (3); Neoprene gaskets (4); filter housing assembly (5); housing fastener (6); control section (7); test panel (8); flow control orifice (9); control valve (10); hose clamps (11); flex hose (12); blower hose adaptor (13); suction blower (Cadillac) (14).

Figure 21-15.[55,56] The out-stack design for a few millimeters of mercury pressure indicates a typical method of insertion of the probe through a gate valve and sliding gland arrangement. It has a large capacity fabric filter bag, plus provision for determining local velocity (Figure 21-15a).[55] The Accurex sampling system, shown in Figure 21-15b, is designed to determine the efficiency of particulate removal before fluidized-bed coal combustion gas enters a gas turbine. A remotely located computer automatically positions the water-cooled sampling probe at a given traverse point and maintains isokinetic sampling rate. As shown in Figure 21-15b, the sampling probe enters the pressurized duct through block and bleed valves. The gas

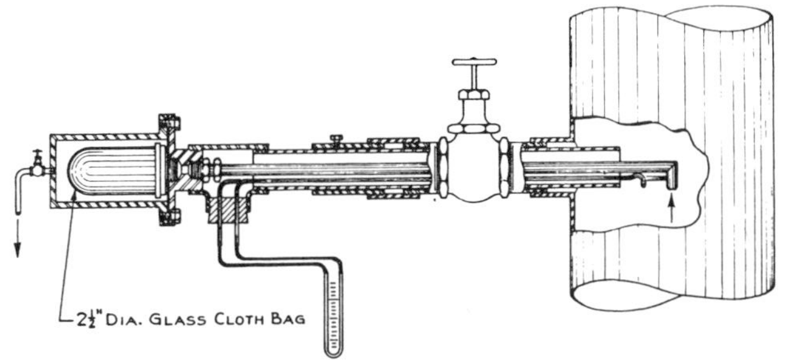

FIGURE 21-15a. Sampling high pressure blast furnace gas (25 mm Hg, 540°C).[55]

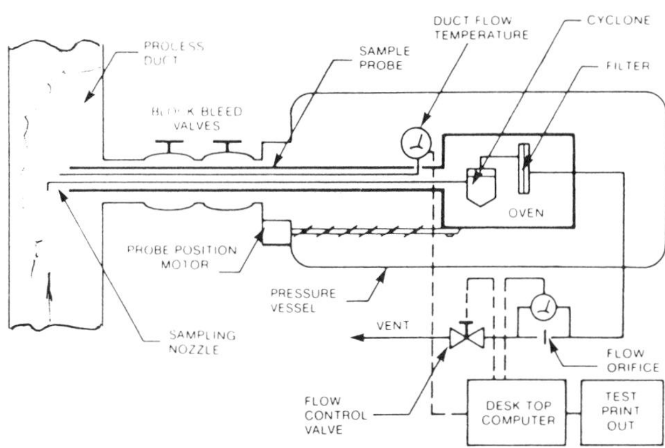

FIGURE 21-15b. Sampling high temperature and pressure fluidbed combustion gas (12 atm, 1100°C).[56]

stream velocity and temperature are measured by instruments at the end of the probe. A computer controls sampling by opening a gas flow control valve and maintains the isokinetic sampling rate by adjusting it. Large particles are removed in a cyclone, and fine particles are caught by a filter. Gas passes out through an orifice used to calculate sampling flow rate. The entire sampling system is suspended from a hanger to allow for thermal expansion. The computer controls probe movement to each sample point.(56)

Special Systems

The source assessment sampling system (SASS), developed by Accurex for U.S. EPA, represents a special, commercially available system designed for research purposes. It extracts a 4-cfm (113-L/min) sample and separates particulate matter by size fractions (cyclones). It filters the undersize fraction (filter holder), removes organics (porous sorbent), and then removes condensibles (in impingers). "SASS is an integrated sampling system, capable of measuring particulate loading and size distribution, determining trace element concentration, and trapping organic substances. Stainless . . . or water-cooled, quartz-lined probes can be supplied for high temperature sampling."(57) It contains three cyclones plus a filter to separate particulate matter by aerodynamic diameter. Organics are collected on an adsorber and trace elements are collected in impingers.(15)

Determination of Particle Size and Chemical Composition

Introduction

This section discusses special requirements in gas stream sampling methods used to determine size and composition of particulate materials transported by the stream. Objectives for determination of size and composition include evaluation of properties or effects that vary with size or composition, or evaluation of process yield or equipment performance in terms of size or composition.

Particulate Air Pollutant Source Emissions

The traditional approach to the control of particulate air pollutants from stationary sources has been accomplished by measurement of the emission concentration of the total amount of particulate matter conveyed by the gas stream. Continuing developments in the understanding of the complexity of particulate air pollution have, over the past 15 years or so, led to the design, commercial production, and use of a variety of size-discriminating instruments and apparatus with application to particulate air pollution source emissions. Devices used for source emission sampling are broadly divided into 1) inertial classifiers (mechanical collectors) and 2) others such as light scatter, electrical mobility, or diffusion battery analyzers. In general, the devices in the first group include cascade impactors and cyclones. Their use for source evaluation is a technically sophisticated procedure. Both of these device categories have particle removal characteristic curves that are functions of particle properties (size, shape, density, etc.); operating flow characteristics (flow rate or velocity, temperature, gas composition, and content of moisture or other condensibles, etc.); and the amount of material presented to and contained (deposited) within.

Comparisons of results of particle size analysis obtained with four different cascade impactors were found to vary among the various available designs and upon circumstances of use.(58) Recommendations for use of in-stack impactors are summarized in Table 21-8.(58) Decision-making guidelines are presented in Table 21-9.(59) Also see the operating instruction manual for each device to obtain information on stage collection performance calibrations, recommended collection substrates, adhesives versus operating temperature, interstage losses, tolerable deposit per stage versus analytical sensitivity required and its relation to expected particulate concentration in the gas stream, interferences between substrate or adhesive and collected particulate matter or its analysis, etc.(60)

Use of impactors for higher temperature sampling in process gas streams introduces additional limits on adhesives, namely volatilization (weight loss) and reaction with process or flue gases (weight gain). The adhesive selected should also be considered with respect to possible analytical interferences, i.e., organic adhesives might provide too high a background for subsequent analysis for organic components. In some circumstances, manufacturers may furnish properly cut-out pieces of fibrous substrate (e.g., all glass fiber filter material) to collect impacted particles and reduce bounce-off or to reduce tare weight of substrate.

Comparative interstage wall losses have been reported, as shown in Figure 21-16.(60,61) Wall losses are a function of impactor design, substrate treatment, particle size, type of aerosol material (solid versus liquid), and jet velocity and flow rate. In practice, operating flow rate, collector plate adhesive, and the amount of material collected on a stage will interact to affect wall loss and deposit bounce-off. The amount of material collected on a single stage is recommended not to exceed 5–15 mg (see Table 21-8). Operating time thus depends on the concentration of particulate material in the gas stream as well as expected particle size. Impactors have significant limitations for *in-situ* separation of solid particulate matter into size fractions based on aerodynamic equivalent diameter. Upper stages may be overloaded, causing material to bounce off and to be deposited on a lower stage, thus distorting apparent

TABLE 21-8. Summary of Recommendations for In-stack Impactor Use[58]

Selection of Collection Surfaces

1. Grease (spray silicone or Apiezon H)
   a. Use at a temperature less than 200°C.
   b. Apply a thickness equal or greater than the size particles to be impacted.
   c. Precondition the surface for 1 hour at a temperature about 25°C above the expected sampling temperature.

2. Glass fiber
   a. Use at temperatures less than approximately 500°C.
   b. Precondition to avoid SO_2 uptake.
   c. Precondition for 1 hour at 25°C above the temperature of sampling.
   d. Note that the measured aerosol mass median diameter could be 30% greater than actual.
   e. If possible, avoid sampling "hard" aerosols because of increased particle bounce.

3. Uncoated metal
   a. Use at temperatures up to 500°C.
   b. Precondition for 1 hour at or above the temperature of sampling.
   c. Avoid sampling oil or "hard" aerosols because of bounce and unstable collection characteristics.

General Selection of Flow Rate

1. Maintain jet velocities less than 75 m/sec when sampling either oil or hygroscopic-type aerosols.
2. Maintain jet velocities less than 50 m/sec when sampling "hard" aerosols.
3. Choose a flow rate that will provide sizing information over the range of the expected mass median diameter, within the above limits.

Stage Loadings

1. Hygroscopic-type aerosols: 5–7 mg maximum per stage.
2. Oil aerosols: 15 mg maximum per stage.
3. Stage loading checks:
   a. Observe back side of nozzle for increased deposition.
   b. Observe primary deposits for uniformity.
4. General minimum stage loading:
   a. Collect 10 times the stage weighing sensitivity.

Treatment of Interstage Losses

Exclude losses from calculations of particle size distribution due to errors involved in trying to recover these losses. Include losses as collected mass if calculating total aerosol mass concentration.

Treatment of Sizing Data

Consider that the error associated with a mass measurement is inversely proportional to the mass collected; therefore, when constructing the distribution, give greater weight to the data points representing the majority of the collected mass.

size. They overload rapidly at high concentrations (e.g., on the inlet to a collector). To overcome some of these overload limits, U.S. EPA and manufacturers have developed precutter or scalping cyclone inlets for use as a preseparator ahead of the impactor.

A series cyclone design has been developed and calibrated by SoRI, as shown in Figure 21-17.[62–64] These instruments may be used to evaluate source emission of thoracic or inhalable particles. A formal sampling method for PM_{10} emissions has also been developed as U.S. EPA Methods 201 and 201A.

Particle Size-Efficiency of Collection Systems

There has been an increasing interest in the particle size-specific collection performance of control devices during the past several years. A number of field studies have been undertaken on inlet and outlet particle size distributions for a variety of sources and collection systems.[65–67] A review of the coal fly ash emission program undertaken by the Electric Power Research Institute (EPRI) for electrostatic precipitators has been reported.[68] Principal test apparatus used in these studies include in-stack cascade impactors for up-

TABLE 21-9. Impactor Decision-making[59]

Item	Basis of Decision	Criteria
Impactor	Loading and size estimate	a. If concentration of particles smaller than 5 μm is less than 0.46 g/am³ (0.2 grain/acf), use high flow rate impactor (0.5 acfm [14.a L/min]). b. If concentration of particles smaller than 5 μm is greater than 0.46 g/am³ (0.2 grain/acf), use low flow rate impactor (< 0.05 acfm [1.41 L/min]).
Sampling rate	Loading and gas velocity	a. Fixed, near isokinetic. b. Limit so that last jet velocity does not exceed: –60 m/sec greased –35 m/sec without grease.
Nozzle	Gas velocity	a. Near isokinetic, ± 10%. b. Sharp edged; minimum 1.4-mm i.d.
Precutter	Size and loading	If precutter loading is comparable to first stage loading, use precutter.
Sampling time	Loading and flow rate	a. Refer to Reference 59, Section 5.5 b. No stage loading greater than 10 mg.
Collection substrates	Temperature and gas composition	a. Use metallic foil or fiber substrates whenever possible. b. Use adhesive coatings whenever possible.
Number of sample points	Velocity distribution and duct configuration	a. At least two points per station. b. At least two samples per point.
Orientation of impactor	Dust size, port configuration, and size	Vertical impactor axis whenever possible.
Heating	Temperature and presence of condensible vapor	a. If flue is above 177°C, sample at process temperature. b. If flue is below 177°C, sample at 11°C above process temperature at impactor exit external heaters.
Probe	Port not accessible using normal techniques	a. Only if absolutely necessary. b. Precutter on end in duct. c. Minimum length and bends possible.

stream or downstream concentrations. Some data on submicrometer fractions have been obtained in various studies using an electric mobility analyzer, light-scattering photometers, condensation nuclei counters, and diffusion batteries; in at least one instance, electron microscopic analysis was used as well. The low-pressure cascade impactor described by Hering *et al.*[69] has been adapted for gas stream sampling by Pilat[70] of the University of Washington.

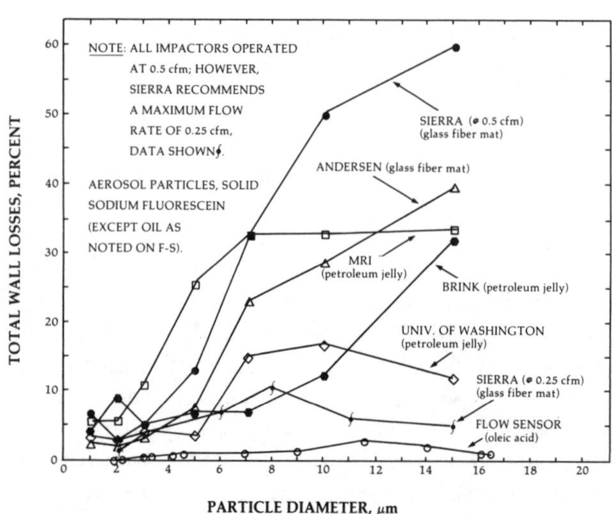

FIGURE 21-16. Comparison of impactor wall losses.[60,61]

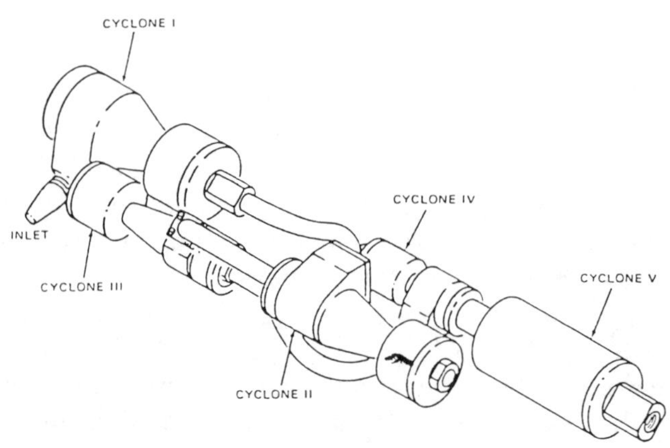

FIGURE 21-17. U.S. EPA/SoRI five-stage cyclone.

Method Validation, Accuracy, Precision, and Sampling Statistics

Validation Between Methods

The foregoing discussions have indicated the diversity of methods that have been used within the United States to determine characteristics or components in flowing gases. Legal and economic consequences of the results of these measures have also been mentioned. Prior to 1972, intermethod comparisons were not generally undertaken. The original use of U.S. EPA Method 5 (commencing in the late 1960s) to determine particulate emissions required the inclusion of the dried impinger residue as part of the total emission concentration, in addition to material collected in the probe and cyclone and on the filter. These two quantities of particulate material are referred to as front-half (i.e., material brushed or washed from nozzle, probe liner, and cyclone plus filter particulate matter) and back-half (dried residue from three impingers). For many years, combustion engineers and related specialists have used techniques such as the filter thimble method in Bulletin WP-50[7] equivalent to the apparatus suggested in the American Society of Mechanical Engineers (ASME) Power Test Code used for performance tests on steam generators, incinerators, fly ash collectors, etc. When U.S. EPA began to include the back-half catch as a surrogate for materials that form particulate matter later in the plume downwind, concentrations from the sources were determined to be greater than had been customarily obtained with the front-half of Method 5 or with an in-stack filter thimble alone.[71] Increased particulate matter in out-stack configurations has been attributed to sulfur dioxide conversion to sulfates. There have been a number of reports on intermethod results from pulverized coal-fired boilers, oil-fired boilers, electric furnace fume, incinerators, etc., under the sponsorship of U.S. EPA, the American Society for Testing and Materials' (ASTM) Project Threshold, ASME, and individual industrial organizations.[72] Typical issues and early data are contained in U.S. EPA reports and other references.[46,73–75] Subsequent studies have determined that careful field practices and maintenance of U.S. EPA Method 5 probe and filter heated to stack temperature yield largely equivalent mass loadings for both methods (ASME/WP-50 and U.S. EPA Method 5) at least for steam generator fly ash, if condensation is avoided.

Interlaboratory Validation of Methods

ASTM in Project Threshold and U.S. EPA have performed collaborative tests on a single source using ASTM D-3685 or U.S. EPA Method 5 for particulate matter. Typically, four stack sampling teams, using more or less identical equipment and procedures, sample simultaneously from four sampling ports on the same stack.[76] U.S. EPA has issued a performance standard that requires existing and new hazardous waste incinerators to operate at a particle destruction and removal efficiency of 99.99% (99% hydrochloric acid removal). Therefore, in this case, gas stream sampling is used to determine performance of the incinerator as well as performance of associated gas cleaning equipment.[77] Collaborative test results are discussed in several references.[37,77–85] One report presents results of collaborative tests of several U.S. EPA methods within and among laboratories.[86] The typical coefficient of variation reported by U.S. EPA for particulates by Method 5 is about 10% (standard deviation/mean value); for Method 17, it is about 6%.

Requirements for precision and accuracy have led U.S. EPA to require quality assurance programs and interlaboratory surveys.[87–90] A critical review of analytical methods for air sampling has been prepared by Katz[91] and critiqued by associates.[92] Current state-of-the-art has been summarized by Farthing.[93] Consensus data on precision and accuracy can be found in an article by DeWees.[94]

Education, Training, Certification, and Accreditation for Gas Stream Sampling

In order to obtain a reasonably representative and valid sample of a flowing gas stream, one needs to have some education, training, and experience. Source evaluation sampling has become fairly complex, costly, and more widespread in the past 15 years. Typical instruction may be obtained on U.S. EPA Methods 1–10 from U.S. EPA course number 450 — Source Sampling (Air Pollution Training Institute, Research Triangle Park, NC 27711). Courses are also provided by manufacturers of the sampling equipment and at the annual meetings of the Air Pollution Control Association and the American Institute of Chemical Engineers.

There is also a national association of source sampling principals (Source Evaluation Society [SES], P.O. Box 12124, Research Triangle Park, NC 27709), with about 300 members. The SES has a biennial (about every 1.5 years) meeting under the auspices of the Engineering Foundations at a Conference on Stack Sampling and Stationary Source Evaluation. It also meets *ad hoc* as part of the annual meeting of the Air and Waste Management Association (formerly the Air Pollution Control Association).

The SES is preparing to establish programs for the accreditation of organizations involved with source emissions testing and analysis, and for the certification of individuals who conduct or direct emissions testing or analysis. Current recommendations for laboratory accreditation are summarized below.

- *Education, Training, Experience*—one individual onsite (e.g., team leader) to be certified by test in the method that will be used.
- *Proficiency Demonstration*—review of test reports and analysis of audit samples.
- *Equipment Specifications*—possess up to 80% of major listed equipment specified in a method including calibration, field, and laboratory.
- *Recordkeeping/Reporting*—retain records for 10 years, including quality assurance (QA), calibration and test data, and sample retention for reanalysis.
- *Quality Assurance*—formal plan including calibration, sample identification and custody, QA responsibility chart, implementation procedures, and onsite audits.[21]

Dedication

This chapter is respectfully dedicated to the memory of Bernard D. Bloomfield (1922–1971). He was the original author of this chapter which appeared in the fourth and fifth editions of the *Air Sampling Instruments* manual. He lectured widely and wrote chapters for several texts on this topic from his broad experience with the Michigan Department of Public Health.

References

1. Hawksley, P.G.W.; Badzioch, S.; Blackett, J.H.: Measurement of Solids in Flue Gases, 2nd ed., pp. 114–116. The Institute of Fuel, London (1977).
2. U.S. Environmental Protection Agency: Standards of Performance for New Stationary Sources, pp. 195–1142. 40 CFR 60 (Rev. July 1, 1992). U.S. Government Printing Office, Washington, DC (and U.S. Government Bookstores in 22 U.S. cities) (1992).
3. American Society of Mechanical Engineers: Flue and Exhaust Gas Analyses, Part 10, Instruments and Apparatus, Supplement to ASME Performance Test Codes, PTC 19.10-1981, p. 9. ASME, United Engineering Ctr., 345 E. 47th St., New York, NY 10017 (1980).
4. American Conference of Governmental Industrial Hygienists: Industrial Ventilation — A Manual of Recommended Practice, 21st ed., Chap 9. ACGIH, Cincinnati, OH (1992).
5. Air Test Kit Bacharach 5220. Bacharach Instruments Co., Div. of AMBAC Industries, Inc., 625 Alpha Dr., Pittsburgh, PA 15238.
6. American Society of Mechanical Engineers: Performance Test Code PTC 38-1980. In: Determining the Concentration of Particulate Matter in a Gas Stream, p. 79. ASME, United Engineering Ctr., 345 E. 47th St., New York, NY 10017 (1980).
7. Andersen Samplers, Inc.: Methods for Determination of Velocity, Volume, Dust and Mist Content of Gases, Bulletin WP-50, 7th ed. H.A. Haaland, Ed. Andersen Samplers, Inc., 4215 Wendell Dr., Atlanta, GA 30336 (1968).
8. American Society of Mechanical Engineers: Performance Test Code PTC 38-1980, p. 81. ASME, United Engineering Ctr., 345 E. 47th St., New York, NY 10017 (1980).
9. Ower, E.; Pankhurst, R.C.: The Measurement of Air Flow, 5th ed., Chap. III. Pergamon Press, Inc., Elmsford, NY (1977).
10. Ower, E.; Pankhurst, R.C.: The Measurement of Air Flow, 5th ed., Chap. X. Pergamon Press, Inc., Elmsford, NY (1977).
11. Ower, E.; Pankhurst, R.C.: The Measurement of Air Flow, 5th ed., Chap. IV. Pergamon Press, Inc., Elmsford, NY (1977).
12. Bradshaw, P.: An Introduction to Turbulence and Its Measurement. Pergamon Press, Inc., Elmsford, NY (1975).
13. Rouillard, E.E. A.; Hicks, R.E.: Flow Patterns Upstream of Isokinetic Dust Sampling Probes. J. Air Pollut. Control Assoc. 20(6):599 (1978).
14. Moseman, R.F.; Bath, D.B.; McReynolds, J.R.; et al.: Field Evaluation of Methodology for Measurement of Cadmium in Stationary Source Stack Gases. EPA/600/S4-86/048. NTIS No. PB 87-145 355/AS. National Technical Information Service, 5285 Port Royal Road, Springfield, VA 22161 (April 1987).
15. Schlickenrieder, L.M.; Adams, J.W.; Thrun, K.E.: Modified Methods and Source Assessment Sampling System Operator's Manual. EPA/600/S8-85/003. NTIS No. PB 85-169 878/AS. National Technical Information Service, 5285 Port Royal Road, Springfield, VA 22161 (April 1985).
16. Farthing, W.E.; Williamson, A.D.; Dawer, S.S.; et al.: Investigation of Source Emission PM_{10} Particulate Matter: Field Studies of Candidate Methods. EPA/600/S4-86/042. NTIS No. PB 87-132 841/AS. National Technical Information Service, 5285 Port Royal Road, Springfield, VA 22161 (March 1987).
17. Margeson, J.H.; Knoll, J.E.; Midgett, M.R.; et al: An Evaluation of the Semi-Vost Method for Determining Emissions for Hazardous Waste Incinerations. J. Air Pollut. Control Assoc. 37(9):1067 (1987).
18. U.S. Environmental Protection Agency: Compilation of Emission Factors, AP-42, 3rd ed., and all supplements to current year (1993). National Technical Information Service, 5285 Port Royal Road, Springfield, VA 22161, and U.S. Government Printing Office, Washington, DC (and U.S. Government Bookstores in 22 U.S. cities).
19. Pahl, D.: EPA's Program for Establishing Standards of Performance for New Stationary Sources of Air Pollution. J. Air Pollut. Control. Assoc. 33(5):486 (1983).
20. U.S. Environmental Protection Agency: Background Information for NSPS: Primary Copper, Zinc, and Lead Smelters, Vol. 1, Proposed Standards. Report No. EPA-450/2-74-002a. U.S. EPA, Research Triangle Park, NC (1974).
21. Source Evaluation Society Newsletter. P.O. Box 12124, Research Triangle Park, NC 27709.
22. EPA Stationary Source Sampling Methods. The McIlvaine Company, 2970 Maria Avenue, Northbrook, IL 60062.
23. Lipton, S.; Lynch, J.R.: Health Hazard Control in the Chemical Process Industries. John Wiley and Sons, Inc., New York (1987).
24. U.S. Environmental Protection Agency: Methylene Chloride: Initiation of Regulatory Investigation. Fed. Reg. 50:42037 (October 17, 1985).
25. Butter, F.E.; Coppedge, E.A.; Suggs, J.C.; et al: Development of a Method for Determination of Methylene Chloride Emissions from Stationary Sources. J. Air Pollut. Control Assoc. 38(3):272 (1988).
26. Jayanty, R.K.M.; Hochberger, J.: Summary of the 1987 EPA/APCA Symposium on Measurement of Toxic and Related Air Pollutants. J. Air Pollut. Control Assoc. 37(8):898 (1987).
27. Martin, R.M.: Construction Details of Isokinetic Source-Sampling Equipment. EPA Report No. APTD-0581. U.S. EPA, Research Triangle Park, NC (1971).
28. Rom, J.J.: Maintenance, Calibration, and Operation of Isokinetic Source-Sampling Equipment. EPA Report No. APTD-0576. U.S. EPA, Research Triangle Park, NC (1972).
29. Gerstle, R.W.; Cuffe, S.T.; Orning, A.A.; Schwartz, C.H.: Air Pollution Emissions from Coal-Fired Power Plants, Report No. 2. J. Air Pollut. Control Assoc. 15(2):353 (1964).
30. Gerstle, R.W.; Cuffe, S.T.; Orning, A.A.; Schwartz, C.H.: Air Pollution Emissions from Coal-Fired Power Plants, Report No. 2. J. Air Pollut. Control Assoc. 15(2):59 (1965).
31. Guidelines for Stack Sampling in the State of Maryland. Technical Memorandum AMA-TM-81-05 IIA-F. State of Maryland, Dept. of Health and Mental Hyg., Air Management Admin., Baltimore, MD 21201 (1981).
32. 310 Code of Massachusetts Regulations 7.00, *et seq.*, cities appli-

cable EPA, NSPS regulations.

33. Devorkin, H.; Chass, R.L.; Fudurich, A.P.: Source Testing Manual. Air Pollution Control District — Los Angeles County, Los Angeles, CA; now South Coast Air Quality Management District, El Monte, CA 91731 (1972).
34. Karels, G.G.: Improved Sampling Method Reduces Isokinetic Sampling Errors. Presented at the 12th Methods Conference in Air Pollution and Industrial Hygiene Studies, University Southern California, Los Angeles, CA (April 6–8, 1971).
35. American Society of Mechanical Engineers: Power Test Code 28-1965. In: Determining the Properties of Fine Particulate Matter. ASME, United Engineering Ctr., 345 E. 47th St., New York, NY 10017 (1965).
36. American Society of Mechanical Engineers: Test Code for Dust Separating Apparatus 1941. Personal communication from PTC-21 Dust Separating Apparatus Committee (November 1988).
37. American Society for Testing and Materials: Standard Test Method for Particulate Independently or for Particulates and Collected Residue Simultaneously in Stack Gases. ANSI/ASTM D-3685-78. ASTM, Philadelphia, PA 19103 (1979).
38. American Public Health Association: Methods of Air Sampling and Analysis, 2nd ed. APHA, Washington, DC (1977).
39. Intersociety Committee: Methods of Air Sampling and Analysis, 3rd ed. Lewis Publishers, Inc., Chelsea, MI (1989).
40. Research Cottrell, Inc.: Test Method for the Determination of 1. Gas Velocity; 2. Moisture; 3. Dry Dust; 4. Acids; 5. Tar Content of Gases; 6.Calculation of Efficiency of Dust Collection Apparatus. Research Cottrell, Inc., Bound Brook, NJ (1957).
41. Industrial Gas Cleaning Institute: Test Procedures for Determining Performance of Particulate Emissions Control Equipment. Pub. No. 101. IGCI, Alexandria, VA (1973).
42. American Petroleum Institute: Manual of Disposal of Refinery Wastes, Vol. V, Sampling and Analysis of Waste Gases and Particulate Matter. Am. Pet. Inst., Div. of Refining, New York (1954).
43. Incinerator Institute of America: Incinerator Testing Bulletin T6-71. Incinerator Inst. of Am., Arlington, VA (1971).
44. U.S. Public Health Service: Specifications for Incinerator Testing at Federal Facilities. BDP&EC, NCAPC (unnumbered document). U.S. PHS, Research Triangle Park, NC (1967).
45. Funkhauser, T.; Peters, E.T.; Levent, P.L.; et al.: Manual Methods for Sampling and Analysis of Particulate Emissions from Municipal Incinerators. U.S. EPA Report No. EPA 650/2-73-023. U.S. EPA, Office of Research and Development, Washington, DC (1973).
46. Achinger, W.C.; Gair, J.J.: Testing Manual for Solid Waste Incinerators. Unnumbered report. U.S. EPA, Office of Solid Waste Mgmt. Programs, Cincinnati, OH (1974).
47. U.S. Environmental Protection Agency: Guidelines for Stack Testing at Municipal Waste Combustion Facilities. EPA/600/58-88/085. National Technical Information Service, 5285 Port Royal Road, Springfield, VA 22161 (1988).
48. Dennis, R.; Samples, W.R.; Anderson, D.M.; Silverman, L.: Isokinetic Sampling Probes. Ind. Eng. Chem. 49(2):294 (1957).
49. Haines, G.R.; Hemeon, W.C.L.: Measurement of Dust Emission in Stack Gases. Information Circular No. 5. to the American Iron and Steel Institute. Industrial Hygiene Foundation of America, Inc., Pittsburgh, PA (1953); test results appear in Air Repair. J. Air Pollut. Control Assoc. 4:159 (1954).
50. Toynbee, P.A.; Parks, W.J.S.: Isokinetic Sampling Probes. Int. J. Air Water Pollut. 6:13 (1962).
51. Kurz Instruments, Inc., 24H Garden Road, Monterey, CA 93940.
52. Steen, B.: A New Simple Isokinetic Sampler for the Determination of Particle Flux. Atmos. Environ. 11(7):623 (1977).
53. Steen, B.; Keady, P.N.; Sem, J.G.: A Sampler for Direct Measurement of Particle Flux. TSI Q. VII(1):3 (1981); from TSI Inc., P.O. Box 64394, St Paul, MN 55164.
54. Boubel, R.W.: A High Volume Stack Sampler. J. Air Pollut. Control Assoc. 21(12):783 (1971).
55. Arbogst, A.H.: The Quantitative Determination of Dust in Gas. Iron and Steel Engineer, pp. 1–8 (October 1948).
56. Accurex Corp.: Aerotherm Accurex High Temperature-High Pressure Sampling System Product Literature. Accurex Corp., Mountain View, CA (1981).
57. U.S. Environmental Protection Agency: Modified Method 5 Train and Source Assessment Sampling Systems Operations Manual. EPA Report 600/8-85; NTIS No. PB85-1G9578. National Technical Information Service, 5285 Port Royal Road, Springfield, VA 22161 (1985).
58. Lundgren, D.A.; Balfour, W.D.: Size Classification of Industrial Aerosols Using In-stack Cascade Impactors. J. Aerosol Sci. 13:181 (1982).
59. Harris, D.B.: Procedures for Cascade Impactor Calibration and Operation in Process Streams. U.S. EPA Report No. EPA-600/2-77-004. U.S. EPA, IERL/ORD, Research Triangle Park, NC (1977).
60. Cushing, K.M.; McCain, J.D.; Smith, W.B.: Experimental Determination of Sizing Parameters and Wall Losses of Five Commercially Available Cascade Impactors. Paper No. 76-37.4, presented at the APCA Annual Meeting, Portland, OR. APCA, Pittsburgh, PA (1976); also see Environ. Sci. Technol. 13(6):726 (1979).
61. McFarland, A.R.: Evaluation of Wall Losses in Flow Sensor Source Test Impactor. Unpublished report to Flow Sensor, McLean, VA (June 1981).
62. Smith, W.B.; Cushing, K.M.; WIlson, R.R.: Cyclone Samplers for Measuring the Concentration of Inhalable Particles in Process Streams. J. Aerosol Sci. 13(3):259 (1982).
63. Parsons, C.T.; Felix, L.G.: Operating Manual for Five-Stage Series Cyclone. Report No. SORI-EAS-80-845. Southern Research Institute, Birmingham, AL (1980).
64. Smith, W.B.; Wilson, Jr., R.R.; Harris, D.B.: A Five-Stage Cyclone System for in-situ Sampling. Environ. Sci. Technol. 13(11):1387 (1979).
65. Bradway, R.M.; Cass, R.W.: Fractional Efficiency of a Utility Boiler Baghouse: Nucla Generating Plant. Report No. EPA-600/2-75-013a to U.S. EPA. GCA Corp., Bedford, MA (August 1975).
66. Cass, R.W.; Bradway, R.M.: Fractional Efficiency of a Utility Boiler Baghouse: Sunbury Steam-Electric Station. Report No. EPA-600/2-76-077a to U.S. EPA. GCA Corp., Bedford, MA (March 1976).
67. Cass, R.W.; Langley, J.E.: Fractional Efficiency of an Electric Arc Furnace Baghouse. Report No. EPA-600/7-77-023 to U.S. EPA. GCA Corp., Bedford, MA (March 1977).
68. McElroy, M.W.; Carr, R.C.; Ensor, D.S.; Markowski, G.R.: Size Distribution of Fine Particles from Coal Combustion. Science 215(4528):13 (1982).
69. Hering, S.V.; Friedlander, S.K.; Collins, J.J.; Richards, L.W.: Design and Evaluation of a New Low-pressure Impactor. Environ. Sci. Technol. 13(2):184 (1979).
70. Lundgren, D.A.; Lippmann, M.; Harris, F.S.; et al., Eds.: Aerosol Measurement. University Presses of Florida, Gainesville, FL (1979).
71. Hemeon, W.C.L.; Black, A.W.: Stack Dust Sampling: In-stack Filter or EPA Train. J. Air Pollut. Control Assoc. 22(7):516 (1972).
72. Selle, S.J.; Gronhovd, G.H.: Some Comparisons of Simultaneous Gas Particulate Determinations Using the ASME and EPA Methods. ASME Reprint 72-WA/APC-4. ASME, United Engineering Ctr., 345 E. 47th St., New York, NY 10017.
73. Govan, F.A.; Terracciano, L.A.: Source Testing of Utility Boilers for Particulate and Gaseous Emissions. Paper No. 72-72, presented at APCA Annual Meeting, Miami Beach, FL. Air Pollution Control Association, Pittsburgh, PA (1972).
74. American Public Health Assoc.: Methods of Air Sampling and Analysis, 2nd ed., pp. 939–940. APHA, Washington, DC (1977).
75. Crandall, W.A.: Determining Particulates in Stack Gases. Mech. Eng. 14 (December 1972).
76. Cowherd, C.: Personal communication from Midwest Research Institute, Kansas City, MO (August 1982).
77. Environmental Health Letter, July 1, 1982 (refers to January 23, 1981 RCRA standards).
78. Hamil, H.F.; Thomas, R.E.: Collaborative Study of Particulate Emis-

sion Measurements by EPA Methods 2, 3, and 5 Using Paried Particulate Sampling Trains (Municipal Incinerators). Report No. EPA-600/4-76-014. U.S. EPA, Research Triangle Park, NC (1976).
79. Midgett, M.R.: The EPA Program for the Standardization of Stationary Source Emission Test Methodology — A Review. Report No. EPA-600/4-76-044. U.S. EPA, Research Triangle Park, NC (1976).
80. Howes, J.E.; Pesut, R.N.; Foster, J.P.: Interlaboratory Cooperative Study of the Precision of Sampling Stacks for Particulate and Collected Residue. ASTM DS 55-56. Am. Soc. for Testing and Materials, Pittsburgh, PA (1975).
81. Hamil, H.F.; Thomas, R.E.: Collaborative Study of Method for the Determination of Particulate Matter Emissions from Stationary Sources (Fossil Fuel-fired Steam Generators). Report No. EPA-650/4-74-021. U.S. EPA, Research Triangle Park, NC (1974).
82. Hamil, H.F.; Camann, D.E.: Collaborative Study of Method for the Determination of Particulate Matter Emissions from Stationary Sources (Portland Cement Plants). Report No. EPA-650/4-74-029. U.S. EPA, Research Triangle Park, NC (1974).
83. Hamil, H.E.; Thomas, R.E.: Collaborative Study of Method for the Determination of Particulate Matter Emission from Stationary Sources (Municipal Incinerators). Report No. EPA-650/4-74-022. U.S. EPA, Research Triangle Park, NC (1974).
84. Mitchell, W.J.; Midgett, M.R.: Means to Evaluate Performance of Stationary Source Test Methods. Environ. Sci. Technol. 10(1):85 (1976).
85. Midgett, M.R.: How EPA Validates NSPS Methodology. Environ. Sci. Technol. 11(77):655 (1977).
86. Source Evaluation Society Newsletter, Vol. VIII, No. 1. SES, Research Triangle Park, NC (February 1983).
87. U.S. Environmental Protection Agency: Quality Assurance Handbook for Air Pollution Measurement Systems, Vol. III, Stationary Source Specific Methods, Sec. 3.5.8 and 3.6.8. Pub. No. EPA-600/4-77-027b. U.S. EPA, Research Triangle Park, NC (August 1977).
88. Fuerst, R.G.; Denny, R.L.; Midgett, M.R.: A Summary of the Interlaboratory Source Performance Surveys for EPA Reference Methods 6 and 7 — 1977. Pub. No. EPA-600/4-79-045. U.S. EPA, Research Triangle Park, NC (August 1979).
89. Fuerst, R.G.; Midgett, M.R.: A Summary of the Interlaboratory Source Surveys for EPA Reference Methods 5, 6, and 7 — 1978. Pub. No. EPA-600/4-80-029. U.S. EPA, Research Triangle Park, NC (May 1980).
90. Shigehara, R.T.; Curtis, F.: Methods 6 and 7 Quality Assurance/Control Background Information. U.S. EPA, Emission Measurement Branch, ESED, OAQPS, Research Triangle Park, NC (November 1981).
91. Katz, M.: Advances in the Analysis of Air Contaminants, A Critical Review. J. Air Pollut. Control Assoc. 30(5):528 (1980).
92. Saltzman, B.E.: Comments and Discussion Papers. J. Air Pollut. Control Assoc. 30(9):983 (1980).
93. Farthing, W.E.: Particle Sampling and Measurement. Environ. Sci. Technol. 16(4):237A (1982).
94. DeWees, W.: Letter to the Editor. Source Evaluation Society Newsletter, Vol. VIII, No. 1. SES, Research Triangle Park, NC (February 1983).

Instrument Descriptions

U.S. EPA Method 5 type stack gas sampling equipment is available from the manufactures listed in Table 21-I-1. Fundamentally, all equipment is similar and will meet the U.S. EPA requirements for isokinetically withdrawing a gas sample from a stack and collecting out the particulate matter on a glass fiber filter maintained at a prescribed temperature. Most of the units described below consist of the following components:

Sampling probe: Available in various standard effective lengths (e.g. 3, 5, and 10 ft [0.9, 1.5, and 3 m]) with standard probe liners of stainless steel or borosilicate glass (some manufacturers also have inconel and quartz liners). Probes are equipped with a Type S Pitot tube and thermocouple. Normally, the probe liner is covered by a resistance wire heater and probe thermocouple.

Sampling unit: A two-piece, modular unit consisting of a heated filter box (capable of maintaining a set temperature around the filter holder) and a condenser unit. The condenser is normally an ice-bath compartment capable of holding about six glass impinger assemblies (minimum of four required), with a quick-connect fitting for the umbilical cord.

Umbilical cord: A flexible length of tubing that connects the sampling unit outlet to the meter box (or sample control box) inlet. Incorporated with the sampling line tubing are electrical lines and thermocouple cable that transmit temperature readings to the control unit. Standard 25, 50, 75, and 100 ft (7.5, 15, and 30 m) lengths are available from most manufacturers. Some umbilical cords can be connected to form longer lengths.

Control unit (or meter box): Contains the system's vacuum pump, gas volume meter, gas flow rate meter, two manometers (or other pressure gauges), temperature gauges, operating values, and electrical connections. The control unit is used to adjust and monitor the sample flow rate to achieve isokinetic sampling conditions.

21-1. Universal Stack Sampler

Graseby Andersen

This is a typical U.S. EPA Method-5-type stack sampling system. The control unit (meter box) contains a 4 cfm rotary-vane pump, dry gas meter, double-column manometer, LED readout digital temperature meter, operating values, and all electrical connections (with circuit breakers). Control unit weight is 73 lbs (33 kg). The sampling unit (heated filter housing and condenser) is a modular, two-piece case of stainless steel construction. Umbilical cords of 25–300 ft (7.5–90 m) lengths can be connected for longer lengths. Sampling probes have detachable Pitot tube tips and stack and probe liner thermocouples.

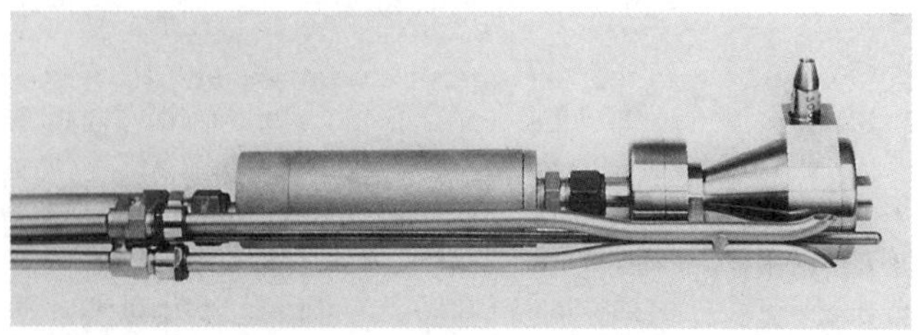

INSTRUMENT 21-1. Universal Stack Sampler.

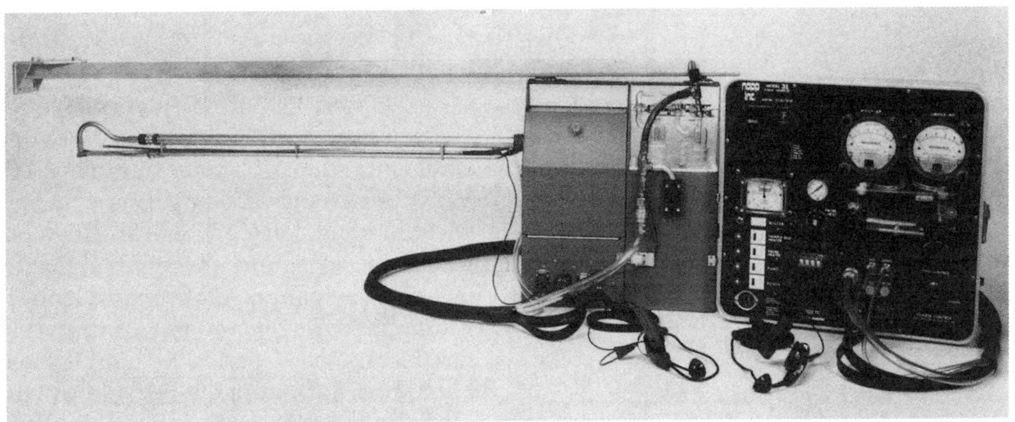

INSTRUMENT 21-7. Manual stack sampling equipment.

21-2. Emission Parameter Analyzer
Graseby Andersen

This is another U.S. EPA Method-5-type stack sampling system. This equipment was formerly manufactured by the Western Precipitation Division of Joy Manufacturing.

21-3. U.S. EPA Method 5 Source Sampling Equipment
CAE Express

CAE Express manufactures complete Method 5 sampling trains, as well as equipment items or systems to be used with several of the other U.S. EPA methods. CAE Instrumental Rental also rents Method 5 and other equipment. Many of the components are interchangeable between manufacturers.

21-4. Isokinetic Source Sampler
Apex Instruments

Apex Instruments manufactures a complete line of source sampling instruments, including meter box consoles, sample cases, probe assemblies, and many glassware items. This equipment is of standard design and operation and meets the normal U.S. EPA criteria for source sampling.

21-5. AP 5500-E-S Stack Sampling System
Scientific Glass and Instruments, Inc.

SGI has a complete line of Method 5 (particle), Method 6 (SO_2), Method 7 (NO_x), Method 8 (H_2SO_4), and other sampling equipment. This equipment is similar to the Method 5 equipment previously described.

21-6. Model 2010 Method 5 Stack Sampling System
Graseby Nutech

This Method 5 stack sampling equipment is constructed to meet U.S. EPA specifications for isokinetic sampling. The Model 2010 system includes a control console, sample case, stainless steel probe, umbilical cord, and glassware. Nutech also manufactures the volatile organic sampling train (VOST); the semivolatile organic sampling train, which is now U.S. EPA Method 23 (previously called Modified Method 5); and many other stack sampling equipment items.

21-7. Stack Sampling Systems
NAPP Inc.

Since 1969, NAPP Inc., has been manufacturing a line of stack sampling equipment. They now produce a very complete line of equipment for most of the U.S. EPA sampling method requirements. In addition to the general Method 5 equipment, Napp provides a volatile organic sampling system, in-stack thimble filter holder assemblies, and PM_{10} stack sampling equipment, and recently has listed a computerized Model 31 stack sampler.

21-8. Automated Method 5 (Auto-5)
Graseby Andersen

A new automated Method 5 sampler is available from Graseby Andersen. This system is programmed to solve U.S. EPA Method 5 sampling equations, calculate sampling traverses, record temperatures and pressures, and automatically adjust the isokinetic sample rate. All measurements are displayed on a single LED screen and automatically recorded for a final printout. The manufacturer has stated that this system conforms to 40 CFR 60 requirements.

21-9. PM_{10} Source Sampling System
Graseby Andersen

The PM_{10} source sampler is designed to collect the PM_{10} size particulate emissions from an industrial source. Procedures for measurement of size-specific particulate emissions are more complex, but similar to, particulate sampling by U.S. EPA Method 5. Size-specific source emission measurements are obtained using an inertial size-separation device such as a cyclone or cascade impactor. A proper size sampling nozzle is used to allow isokinetic sampling at a calculated flowrate to obtain the 10-μm cut size for the cyclone.

Incorporation of emission gas recycling (EGR) allows a variable fraction of conditioned filtered exhaust gas from the sampler to be added back to the sample nozzle and the inertial classifier. This action maintains a constant flowrate through the inertial classifier while the gas flowrate into the sample nozzle is adjusted to remain isokinetic while traversing the stack.

21-10. Stacksamplr LCO™

Graseby Andersen

The Stacksamplr™ is a portable, stack gas sampler used for isokinetically collecting solids, mists, and gaseous pollutants from most chemical and combustion processes. The probe is a combination probe and Pitot tube assembly. Several interchangeable inlet nozzles are provided. Probes are available in various effective lengths. The sampling case contains a filter holder for particle removal and impingers for water and gas removal. The control case contains flowmeter, draft gauge, temperature controls, valves, timer, switches, and all the necessary components for control of the isokinetic sampling. A separate pump is used. An umbilical cord connects the sampling case and the control case.

21-11. Automatic High-Volume Stack Sampler

Cascade Stack Sampling Systems

The automatic high-volume stack sampler is designed for high-volume stack sampling. The integrated sampling system consists of a probe with Pitot tube, large filter holder, and air mover with orifice flowmeter. Isokinetic setting is controlled by a microprocessor. Flow rates are from 10 to 60 cfm (300–1700 L/min). The system is also available in a manual configuration. Probe assembly is constructed of aluminum with three nozzles available for velocities of 800–1200 fpm (4–6 m/s). The filter housing is designed for an 8- × 10-in. (20- × 25-cm) glass fiber filter. The balance of the sampler consists of a control system; a flexible sampling hose; a two-speed, heavy-duty suction-blower; and a microprocessor.

21-12. Dust and Fume Determination Assembly, Models D-1000 and D-1027

Graseby Andersen

This equipment was designed to measure aerosol concentrations in a gas as it passes through a flue. The measurement involves withdrawing a controlled flow rate of gas from the flue and separating the particulate matter from the gas. The type of particle, the temperature, and the moisture content of the carrier gas will determine the method to be used in making the separation. The paper thimbles (Model D-1000) may be used up to 120°C (250°F) and suction pressures of up to 4 in. (10 cm) Hg. Alundum thimbles (Model D-1027) are used where it is important to have high wet strength, chemical resistance, or high temperature resistance.

The complete dust and fume sampling equipment employing the Alundum thimble method (Model D-1027) consists of an aspirating eductor, thermometer, vacuum gauge, dry gas meter, condenser, heavy-duty rubber hose, Alundum thimble holder, and various nozzles. The paper thimble equipment differs from the Alundum arrangement only in that different sampling nozzles are used and the thimble holder is made of aluminum for placement outside the flue. Filter thimble holders are described in greater detail elsewhere.

21-13. Stack Sampling Nozzles and Thimble Holders

BGI Incorporated

These are components of sampling trains for in-stack particulate sampling. BGI thimble holders have been designed for use with U.S. EPA-type probes for Methods 16 and 17. They can also be used for Method 5 and other sampling applications. They are constructed of polished 316 stainless steel. Various sizes are available for use with cellulose and fiberglass thimbles (19 × 90 mm, 30 × 100 mm, and 43 × 123 mm). The 30- × 100-mm unit can also be used with Alundum thimbles. The BGI button-hook nozzle is designed to fit U.S. EPA-type sampling trains that accept nozzles terminating in 5/8-in. (1.59-cm) o.d. tubing. Nozzles are available in nominal inside diameters from 1/8 to 1 in. (0.32–2.5 cm).

21-14. Isokinetic Sampling Systems

Kurz Instruments, Inc.

The Kurz systems employ thermal mass flow sensors to sense both stack and sample gas velocities to control sampling rate automatically to achieve isokinetic sampling. The Series 1275 systems are singlepoint systems in which the stack and sample sensors can be operated in a differential mode to provide automatic sample flow control and isokinetic sampling at a single point. The Series 4200 systems are multipoint systems in which the average stack velocity is measured by sensors at several points, and the average sample velocity is measured by a single sensor in the combined sample from all the sample points. Although this ensures overall average isokinetic conditions, sampling at individual points may be anisokinetic.

Series 1275 components include probe assembly consisting of isokinetic sampling head, probe support, and filter box (or other collecting device at user's option); system enclosure housing flow sensor electronics, electronic sample valve controller, and sample valve; and pump. Series 4200 components include multipoint stack velocity sensor probe; single or dual sampling nozzles and manifold; and system electronics, including flow control valve, pump, and sample collection device at user option.

TABLE 21-I-1. List of Manufacturers

Code	Manufacturer
GRA	Graseby Andersen 500 Technology Court Smyrna, GA 30082-5211 (404)319-9999 or (800)241-6898 FAX (404)319-0336
	Apex Instruments P.O. Box 172 Apex, NC 27502 (919)387-8369 FAX (800)882-3214
BGI	BGI Incorporated 58 Guinan Street Waltham, MA 02154 (617)891-9380 FAX (617)891-8151
	CAE Express 500 W. Wood Street Palaline, IL 60067 (800)223-3977 FAX (708)991-6577
CSS	Cascade Stack Sampling Systems P.O. Box 5186 Bend, OR 97708 (503)388-4729
	Graseby Nutech 4022 Stirrup Creek Drive Suite 325 Durham, NC 27703 (800)637-6312 FAX (919)544-3770
KRZ	Kurz Instruments, Incorporated 2411 Garden Road Monterey, CA 93940
	Napp, Inc. 2104 Kramer Lane Austin, TX 78758 (512)836-5110 FAX (512)837-4532
SGI	Scientific Glass & Instruments, Inc. P.O. Box 6 Houston, TX 77001 (713)682-1481 FAX (713)682-3054

Chapter 22

Sampling Airborne Radioactivity

Beverly S. Cohen, Ph.D.
Nelson Institute of Environmental Medicine, New York University School of Medicine, Tuxedo, New York

CONTENTS

Introduction

Radioactivity is the spontaneous transformation of the nucleus of an atom by the emission of corpuscular or electromagnetic radiation. Radioactive contaminants have historically been considered apart from chemical contaminants because it is their radiological properties that determine their biological and environmental impact. Additionally, they have been regulated by special government agencies concerned with radiological protection. Prior to the 1940s, there was essentially no concern about airborne radioactivity. The role of the short-lived decay products of radon in the etiology of lung cancer in underground miners was not yet appreciated. Small amounts of naturally occurring radionuclides were released to air from burning of fossil fuels, but there was almost no potential for other contaminant airborne radionuclides. Protection from significant exposure to ionizing radiation was required for only a limited number of scientists and physicians. This was provided by adherence to guidelines recommended by groups such as the International Commission on Radiological Protection (ICRP) and the National Council on Radiation Protection and Measurements (NCRP).

Radioactive contaminants are also distinguished by the specialized and very sensitive methods available for the detection of radioactivity. Measurements of concentrations of a few thousand atoms per liter are not uncommon. Average indoor air concentrations of radon (^{222}Rn), for example, are less than 2×10^4 atoms per liter, or about 7×10^{-13} ppm. Concentrations of the short-lived decay products of radon normally total fewer than 30 atoms per liter. The sensitivity with which radioactivity can be detected results from the ionization produced in matter by the radiation. This ionization also produces responses in biological tissue at very low levels of irradiation, so that in a sense, the measurement capabilities are commensurate with the significance of the quantities measured. Yet, complex questions result from the ability to measure very small quantities of radiation, e.g., "What is the significance of a radiation dose to tissue that is a small fraction of the dose from natural background radiation?" and "How low is 'as low as reasonably achievable' (ALARA),[1] when implementing radiation protection guidelines?"

Special constraints on sampling methods that derive from the specific radiological properties of a contaminant must be integrated with good basic air sampling practices. Guidance may be obtained from other parts of this text for activities ranging from design of appropriate sampling strategies through design and calibration of the entire sampling train; including consideration of inlet bias, isokinetic sampling, efficiency of the collection substrate, sample loss and stability, and air flow calibration. Special consideration must be given to the radiometric properties of the particular nuclide to evaluate the need for sample processing. Chemical separations are frequently unnecessary because of the ease with which radioactive materials can be detected. Source preparation and the radiation detection system must be suited to the type of radiation emitted, and rapid decay of the sample is sometimes a significant problem.

This chapter will discuss some special aspects of sampling that result from the radioactivity of the airborne material.

Units

Background

Three separate physical entities must be considered: 1) the source of the radiation, 2) the radiation, and 3) the absorber. It is important to recognize the separateness of these items. Sources of ionizing radiation include the sun and other extraterrestrial objects, radioactive isotopes, and particle accelerators (including common X-ray machines). The only airborne sources are radioactive isotopes. The radiation travels outward from the source carrying away energy; it can continue indefinitely with essentially undiminished energy if traversing a vacuum. The absorber is the material in which the radiation will deposit energy by ionization and excitation of the atoms. In some cases, source and absorber are inextricably meshed, but they are nonetheless inherently separate entities with different physical properties which are not transferable from one to the other.

Convenient measurement units such as the curie, roentgen, and rad (see below) were developed over the years by scientists working with ionizing radiation. As knowledge and measurement processes improved, these historical units were occasionally reevaluated and standardized. As a result of international agreement, a new set of units consistent with the System Internationale (SI) was adopted in 1975.[2] These new units have been generally accepted since 1985.[3] A few important units are given below. These units apply to 1) sources, 2) the radiation, and 3) the absorber. Both historical and SI units are listed. A complete list of units with conversion factors is presented in Table 22-1.

Definitions

Sources

The quantity of a radioactive source is defined by its "activity" or the rate of spontaneous nuclear transformation (see Equation 1). The unit of activity is the becquerel (Bq):

$$1 \text{ Bq} = 1/s$$

Thus, 1 Bq represents one transformation, or disintegration, per second.

The historical unit of activity is the curie (Ci):

$$1 \text{ Ci} = 3.7 \times 10^{10} \ s^{-1} \text{ (exactly)}$$

Radiation

Exposure is a measure of the quantity of X or gamma radiation. It is defined by the electric charge the radiation produces as it traverses an air mass. Exposure does not have a special unit in the SI system but combines the basic units of charge in coulombs (C) and mass in kilograms (kg). The units of exposure are C/kg.

The conventional unit of exposure is the roentgen (R):

$$1 \text{ R} = 2.58 \times 10^{-4} \text{ C/kg (exactly)}$$

Thus, 2.58×10^{-4} C is the charge of the ions of one sign produced in one kg of air by one roentgen of X or gamma radiation.

Energy: Corpuscular radiation is generally defined by stating the particle identity and its kinetic energy. The SI unit of energy is the joule, but conventional units in multiples of the electron volt (eV) are used almost

TABLE 22-1. Conversion Between SI and Conventional Units*

Quantity	Symbol for Quantity	Expression in SI Units	Expression in Symbols for SI Units	Special Name for SI Unit	Symbols Using Special Name	Conventional Unit	Symbol for Conventional Unit	Value of Conventional Unit in SI Units
Activity	A	1 per second	s^{-1}	becquerel	Bq	curie	Ci	3.7×10^{10} Bq
Absorbed dose	D	joule per kilogram	J/kg	gray	Gy	rad	rad	0.01 Gy
Absorbed dose rate	$\dot{D}$	joule per kilogram second	$J\ kg^{-1}\ s^{-1}$		Gy/s	rad	rad/s	0.01 Gy/s
Average energy per ion pair	W	joule	J			electron volt	eV	1.602×10^{-19} J
Equivalent dose	H	joule per kilogram	J/kg	sievert	Sv	rem	rem	0.01 Sv
Equivalent dose rate	$\dot{H}$	joule per kilogram second	$J\ kg^{-1}\ s^{-1}$		Sv/s	rem per second	rem/s	0.01 Sv/s
Electric current	I	ampere	A			ampere	A	1.0 A
Electric potential difference	U, V	watts per ampere	W/A	volt	V	volt	V	1.0 W/A
Exposure	X	coulomb per kilogram	C/kg			roentgen	R	2.58×10^{-4} C/kg
Exposure rate	$\dot{X}$	coulomb per kilogram second	$C\ kg^{-1}\ s^{-1}$			roentgen per second	R/s	2.58×10^{-4} C/kg s
Fluence	Φ	1 per meter squared	m^{-2}			1 per centimeter squared	$1/cm^2$	$1.0 \times 10^4/m^2$
Fluence rate	$\dot{\Phi}$	1 per meter squared second	$m^{-2}\ s^{-1}$			1 per centimeter squared second	$1/cm^2s$	$1.0 \times 10^4/m^2s$
Kerma	K	joule per kilogram	J/kg	gray	Gy	rad	rad	0.01 Gy
Kerma rate	$\dot{K}$	joule per kilogram second	$J\ kg^{-1}\ s^{-1}$		Gy/s	rad per second	rad/s	0.01 Gy/s
Lineal energy	y	joule per meter	J/m			kiloelectronvolt per micrometer	keV/μm	1.602×10^{-10} J/m
Linear energy transfer	L	joule per meter	J/m			kiloelectronvolt per micrometer	keV/μm	1.602×10^{-10} J/m
Mass attenuation coefficient	μ/ρ	meter squared per kilogram	m^2/kg			centimeter squared per gram	cm^2/g	$0.1\ m^2/kg$
Mass energy transfer coefficient	μ_{tr}/ρ	meter squared per kilogram	m^2/kg			centimeter squared per gram	cm^2/g	$0.1\ m^2/kg$
Mass energy absorption coefficient	μ_{en}/ρ	meter squared per kilogram	m^2/kg			centimeter squared per gram	cm^2/g	$0.1\ m^2/kg$
Mass stopping power	S/ρ	joule meter squared per kilogram	$J\ m^2/kg$			million electron volts centimeter squared per gram	$meV\ cm^2/g$	$1.602 \times 10^{-14}\ J\ m^2/kg$
Power	P	joule per second	J/s	watt	W	watt	W	1.0 W
Pressure	P	newton per meter squared	N/m^2	pascal	Pa	torr	torr	(101325/760)Pa
Radiation chemical yield	G	mole per joule	mol/J			molecules per 100 electron volts	molecules/100 eV	1.04×10^{-7} mol/J
Specific energy	z	joule per kilogram	J/kg	gray	Gy	rad	rad	0.01 Gy

*Adapted from NCRP Report No. 82.[(3)]

TABLE 22-2. Radiation Weighting Factor, w_R[A,B]

Type and energy range		w_R
X and γ rays, electrons, positrons and muons		1
Neutrons, energy	<10 keV	5
	10 keV to 100 keV	10
	>100 keV to 2 MeV	20
	>2 MeV to 20 MeV	10
	>20 MeV	5
Protons, other than recoil protons and energy >2 MeV		2
Alpha particles, fission fragments, nonrelativistic heavy nuclei		20

[A]Adapted from NCRP No. 116.[4]
[B]For detailed explanations and constraints on usage, see ICRP No. 60[5] or NCRP No. 116.[4]

exclusively. Common multiples are keV (10^3 eV) and MeV (10^6 eV). One eV is the kinetic energy acquired by an electron accelerated through a potential difference of 1 volt.

$$1 \text{ eV} = 1.602 \times 10^{-19} \text{ J}$$
$$= 1.602 \times 10^{-12} \text{ ergs}$$

Dose

Absorbed Dose: Dose is the energy transferred to the absorber by the ionizing radiation. The SI unit of absorbed dose (D) has been given a special name, the gray (Gy):

$$1 \text{ Gy} = 1 \text{ J/kg}$$

The historical unit of absorbed dose is the rad, which is equal to 100 ergs per gram of absorber.

$$1 \text{ rad} = 10^2 \text{ Gy}$$

Equivalent Dose: A special unit used in radiation protection is the equivalent dose ($H_{T,R}$). It is the product of the average absorbed dose in a specified organ or tissue ($D_{T,R}$) and a radiation weighting factor (W_R) that accounts for biological effectiveness of the ionizing radiation producing the dose. Thus, equivalent dose is:

$$H_{T,R} = W_R D_{T,R}$$

where: $D_{T,R}$ = the absorbed dose in a specified tissue
W_R = the radiation weighting factor

The subscript T refers to the specific tissue; subscript R refers to the specific radiation. Values of W_R are given in Table 22-2. When several types or energies of radiation are present, the average equivalent doses must be summed. The unit of equivalent dose is the sievert (Sv):

$$1 \text{ Sv} = 1 \text{ J/kg}$$

The historical unit is the rem:

$$1 \text{ rem} = 10^{-2} \text{ J/kg}$$

Fundamentals of Radioactivity

Radioactive Decay

The transformation, or decay, of a nucleus is a random process so that if there are a large number (N) of identical radioactive atoms, the rate at which they decay (dN/dt) in a given time period will be a constant fraction of N.

$$\frac{dN}{dt} = -\lambda N \quad (1)$$

where: dN = the number of unstable nuclei which transform in a time interval dt
λ = the proportionality constant, or the fraction which decay per unit time.

λ is known as the decay constant and is characteristic of a given nuclide or atomic species. dN/dt is the "activity" of a source. Decay is a stochastic or random process; thus, Equation 1 only applies to sufficiently large samples of a nuclide.

Integration of Equation 1 from time $t = 0$ to t yields the number of nuclei which survive to time t:

$$N = N_o e^{-\lambda t} \quad (2)$$

where: N_o = the number of nuclei at $t = 0$
N = the number present at time t.

The time (T) at which half the nuclei will have transformed or decayed ($t = T$ when $N/N_o = 1/2$) is then:

$$T = \frac{0.693}{\lambda} \quad (3)$$

where: T = the half life of the species; a characteristic time that is always the same for a particular nuclide.

Radiation Properties

The physical properties of the emitted radiation determine both the biological significance of the radiation and various requirements for sampling and detection. The most common corpuscular radiations are alpha or beta particles. Electromagnetic radiation is emitted in the form of high energy photons called gamma rays.

Alpha Particles

Alpha particles are helium nuclei. They are emitted mainly from nuclei with high atomic mass leaving behind an atom with atomic number reduced by 2 and mass reduced by 4 mass units. Their energies range from about 2 to 11 MeV. Alpha particles emitted from a given nuclear species are monochromatic; that is, they all have the same kinetic energy. Alpha particles are massive enough so that they are not easily deflected as they traverse matter and, typically, their paths are straight lines. The double charge and relatively high mass causes dense ionization along the track. A 5.0-MeV alpha particle, for example, will cause several thousand ion pairs per micrometer (μm) of water or tissue, transferring about 100 keV of energy per μm to the molecules of the absorber. The rate at which energy is transferred per unit path length of an absorber is called the linear energy transfer (LET). Alphas are classified as high LET particles. They can only traverse a few centimeters of air or a few micrometers of tissue before losing all of their initial kinetic energy. This very limited range prevents alpha particles from penetrating the skin. Unless an alpha particle source (i.e., a radioactive alpha-emitting particle) is inhaled or ingested, significant irradiation of internal tissue cannot occur. Any absorber in the path of an alpha particle will significantly reduce its energy. Self-absorption by the source itself can be substantial. The efficiency with which alpha particles may be detected when particulate material is collected on a filter is highest if samples are very thin. The detection efficiency for alpha particles on a dust-laden filter will be reduced significantly by self-absorption.

Beta Particles

Beta particles are positive or negative electrons. When an atom decays by beta emission, the atomic number changes by ± 1, but the atomic mass does not change if an electron (e^-) is emitted because an orbital electron will replace the lost mass to balance the extra positive charge gained by the nucleus. If a positron (e^+) is emitted, the atomic mass is reduced by twice the mass of an electron. When a nucleus decays by beta emission, a neutrino or antineutrino is also emitted and the energy loss is shared between the particles. Thus, betas from a given species are emitted with a range of energies up to a maximum that is specific to the nuclear transition. The average share of the energy carried off by the beta particle (from a collection of the same atoms) is about one-third of the total energy of the nuclear transition. Typical energies range from 10 keV to 4.0 MeV. Beta particles are easily deflected by interactions with orbital electrons because they have the same mass, so they travel erratic paths causing ionization and excitation of atoms as they pass until all of their initial kinetic energy has been transferred to the absorber. The trail of ion pairs left behind will be much less dense than that of an alpha particle. Beta particles will typically lose energy to the absorber at a few keV per micrometer and are thus low LET radiation. Positrons will ultimately interact with an electron causing both to annihilate with the emission of two 0.511-MeV gamma rays. Beta particles, depending on energy, may travel from a few centimeters to 10 or 15 m in air, or from a few micrometers to about 2.0 cm in tissue.

Gamma Rays

Gamma rays are photons and exhibit both wave and particle properties. The energy (E) is proportional to the frequency (f) of the radiation; $E = hf$, where h is Planck's constant. Photons from a particular nuclear transition are monochromatic, but some nuclear decays result in emission of several different photons. Typical energies range from a few keV to a few MeV. The manner in which high energy photons, or gamma rays, interact with matter to ionize atoms in the absorber varies with energy and the specifics of the absorbing material. The energy of a beam of gamma radiation will be attenuated exponentially because interactions between the gamma rays and the atoms of the absorber are stochastic. Gamma rays do not exhibit a finite range but the mean free path, i.e., the average distance a photon will travel before having a collision, gives a measure of the penetration. The mean free path is also known as the relaxation length. The mean free path in air for a 1.0-MeV gamma ray is about 120 m; in water or tissue, it is about 14 cm.

Other Emissions

A variety of particles other than alpha particles, beta particles, and gamma rays are emitted less commonly in nuclear transformations. These include protons, neutrons, conversion electrons, Auger electrons, and X-rays. Further information may be found in NCRP Report No. 58[(6)] and Knoll.[(7)] A comprehensive listing of detailed decay schemes is presented in Lederer and Shirley.[(8)]

Table 22-3 presents a list of major radiations of some isotopes used in medicine and industry, identified in materials or air around accelerators, or found in reactor coolant and corrosion products.

Radiation Detectors

Radiation detectors in common use are gas-filled chambers, scintillation detectors, semiconductor detectors, thermoluminescent dosimeters, and etched-track detectors. Ionization chambers, proportional counters, and Geiger–Mueller counters are gas-filled chambers. The incident radiation interacts with the gas to form ion pairs. An electric field is established across the gas volume by collecting electrodes. The electrons are collected at the anode and the positive ions at the cathode. Semiconductor detectors similarly collect the ion pairs

TABLE 22-3. Half Life and Major Radiations of Selected Isotopes[A]

Nuclide	Half life[B]	Major Radiations	Approximate Energies (MeV) and Intensities[B]
$^{3}_{1}H$	12.33y	β⁻	0.0186 max
$^{7}_{4}Be$	53.3d	γ	0.478 (10.3%)
$^{14}_{6}C$	5730y	β⁻	0.156 max
$^{13}_{7}N$	9.96m	β⁺ γ	1.19 max 0.511 (200%, annihilation radiation)
$^{15}_{8}O$	122.s	β⁺ γ	1.723 max 0.511 (200%, annihilation radiation)
$^{22}_{11}Na$	2.602y	β⁺ γ	0.545 max (90.57%) 1.275 (100%)
$^{24}_{11}Na$	15.02h	β⁻ γ	1.389 max 1.369 (100%), 2.754 (100%)
$^{32}_{15}P$	14.28d	β⁻	1.711 max
$^{35}_{16}S$	87.4d	β⁻	0.167 max
$^{41}_{18}Ar$	1.837h	β⁻ γ	2.49 max, 1.198 max 1.293 (99%)
$^{42}_{19}K$	12.36h	β⁻ γ	3.519 max 1.524 (18.8%), 0.312 (0.3%)
$^{47}_{20}Ca$	4.536d	β⁻ γ	1.988 max (16%), 0.684 max (83.9%) 1.297 (77%), 0.807 (7%), 0.49 (7%)
$^{51}_{24}Cr$	27.70d	 γ	V X-rays 0.320 (10.2%)
$^{54}_{25}Mn$	312d	 γ	Cr X-rays 0.835 (100%)
$^{55}_{26}Fe$	2.7y		Mn X-rays
$^{59}_{26}Fe$	44.6d	β⁻ γ	0.273 max (48.5%), 0.475 max (51.2%), 1.573 max (0.3%) 0.143 (1.02%), 0.192 (3.08%), 1.099 (56.5%), 1.292 (43.2%)
$^{57}_{27}Co$	271d	γ	0.122 (86%), 0.136 (11%), 0.014 (9%), Fe X-rays
$^{60}_{27}Co$	5.271y	β⁻ γ	0.318 max (99.88%) 1.173 (99.90%), 1.332 (99.98%)
$^{85}_{36}Kr$	10.7y	β⁻ γ	0.672 max 0.514 (0.43%)
$^{89}_{38}Sr$	50.5d	β⁻	1.488 max (99.99%)
$^{90}_{38}Sr$	28.8y	β⁻	0.546 max
$^{90}_{39}Y$	64.1h	β⁻	2.288 max (99.98%)
$^{99m}_{43}Tc$	6.02h	 γ	Tc X-rays 0.141 (89%)
$^{125}_{53}I$	60.2d	γ	0.035 (6.7%) Te X-rays
$^{131}_{53}I$	8.04d	β⁻ γ	0.336 max (13%), 0.606 max (86%), 0.81 max (0.6%) Xe X-rays 0.284 (6.04%), 0.0802 (2.61%), 0.364 (81%), 0.637 (7.21%), 0.723 (1.79%)
$^{138}_{54}Xe$	14.1m	β⁻ γ	2.720 max, 2.460 max 0.605 (32%), 0.434 (20%), 1.768 (17%), 2.015 (12%), 0.396 (6%)

TABLE 22-3 (con't.). Half Life and Major Radiations of Selected Isotopes[A]

Nuclide	Half life[B]	Major Radiations	Approximate Energies (MeV) and Intensities[B]
$^{137}_{55}Cs$	30.17y	β^- γ	0.5116 max (94.6%), 1.176 max (6%) 0.662 (85%)
$^{192}_{77}Ir$	74.2d	β^- γ	0.672 max (47%), 0.536 max (41%), 0.256 max (6%) 0.316 (83%), 0.468 (48%), 0.308 (30%), 0.296 (28.7%), 0.588 (4.6%), 0.604 (8.3%) Os X-rays, Pt X-rays
$^{198}_{79}Au$	2.696d	β^- γ	0.961 max, 0.290 max 0.4118 (96%), 0.676 (1%), 1.088 (2.5%)
$^{210}_{82}Pb$	22.26y	β^- γ	0.063 max (18%), 0.016 max (82%) 0.0465 (4%) Bi L X-rays
$^{222}_{86}Rn$	3.8235d	α	5.489 (100%)
$^{224}_{88}Ra$	3.66d	α γ	5.686 (95%), 5.449 (5%) 0.241 (4%) Rn X-rays
$^{226}_{88}Ra$	1600y	α γ	4.784 (94%), 4.602 (6%) 0.186 (3%) Rn X-rays
$^{241}_{95}Am$	433y	α γ	5.486 (86%), 5.443 (13%), 5.387 (1.3%) 0.060 (36%) Np L X-rays

[A]After Schleien and Terpilak.[(9)]
[B]Common time units: y (years); d (days); m (minutes); s (seconds). Data from *Table of Isotopes*.[(8)]

produced in a small volume of a semiconducting solid. Scintillation counting is based on the detection of visible light that is emitted by certain materials when they are irradiated. Recent technical developments have increased the use of etched-track detectors and thermoluminescent dosimeters. Other less used methods include photographic film, calorimetric measurements, and chemical reaction vessels. These latter methods are not normally used for air sampling and will not be discussed further. Additional information may be obtained from NCRP,[(6)] Knoll,[(7)] and Eichholz and Poston.[(10)]

Gas-Filled Detectors

Ionization Chambers

In an ionization chamber, the ions produced in the gas by radiation are collected as a result of the applied electric field, the electrons moving to the anode and the positive ions to the cathode. With sufficient voltage across the electrodes, all ions will be collected before recombination can occur. The current produced is measured by a microammeter or a sensitive current integrating device. Either the total amount of charge or the rate at which charge is collected is a measure of the intensity of the radiation. Small portable ionization chambers are available for use as survey meters. If they are to be used for alpha or beta particle detection, there must be a very thin "window" that the particles can penetrate to reach the detection volume. For photons, penetration is not a problem, but few ion pairs will be produced in a small gas volume, resulting in very low detection efficiency. The number of ion pairs formed in the gas depends on the gas density; thus, increased sensitivity may be obtained by increasing the gas pressure. Pressure ionization chambers containing argon, which operate at about 20 atmospheres, can be used to measure environmental gamma ray fields.

Ionization chambers may be used for detecting individual pulses rather than current flow. If an ionizing particle produces a number of ion pairs in the chamber, a current pulse will result, and the rate at which pulses are registered is a measure of the radiation intensity. The number of events in a measured time period may also be used, with calibration and geometric corrections, to determine source activity. If all of the energy of the original ionizing particle is absorbed in the gas volume, the size of the pulse will be proportional to the initial energy of the particle. Suitable electronics must be used to shape the pulse and provide time resolution. Ionization chambers are particularly useful for radiation with high linear energy transfer, such as alpha particles, which produce many ion pairs within the detection volume.

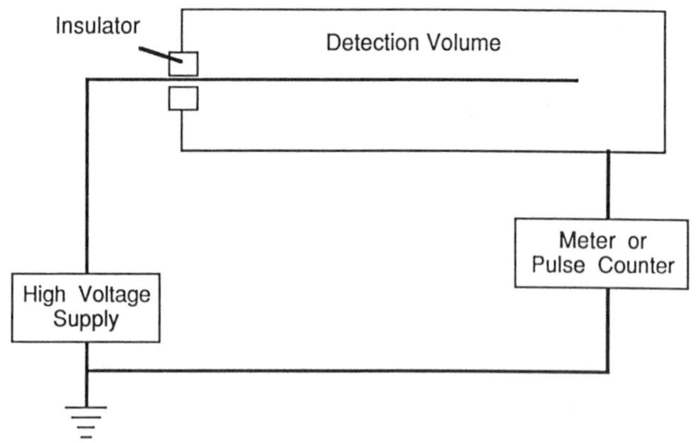

FIGURE 22-1. Block diagram of a gas-filled radiation detector system. A pulse height analyzer may be added when the detector is used as a proportional counter.

Proportional Counters

As the voltage across a chamber increases, the initial electron from each ion pair gains sufficient kinetic energy as it moves toward the anode to ionize some of the gas molecules. The resultant secondary ion pairs will amplify the pulse. The higher the applied voltage, the more energetic the initial electrons will become, and the more secondary ion pairs will be produced. The pulse size thus increases with voltage. A chamber operating in this region of amplification is a proportional counter.

Proportional counters generally utilize a cylindrical configuration, with a central high-voltage electrode as the anode and an outer conducting surface as the cathode (Figure 22-1). This configuration produces a high gradient field around the central electrode. If the voltage is carefully maintained, the pulse size will be proportional to the original quantity of ionization. The pulses of current may then be sorted and recorded electronically according to size by a multichannel analyzer, or specific sizes may be selected for counting using discriminators to remove smaller and larger pulses. The size of the pulse represents the amount of energy absorbed in the gas volume, and with proper calibration, the energy resolution can be used to identify specific nuclides. The presence of a particular nuclear emission will be indicated by a peak occurring at a given energy which can be separated from the general spectrum of background radiation. In practice, gas-filled detectors are rarely used for energy analysis. They have been replaced by crystalline and solid-state detectors, which are described below.

Gas-filled counters may be operated in the proportional region at atmospheric pressure with one end open so that the source can be placed directly into the counting volume. This is valuable for very low energy radiations which cannot penetrate the window of a counting chamber.

Geiger–Mueller Counters

As the voltage across a gas volume increases further, a region will be reached where a single ionization within the chamber will result in secondary ionization of all of the gas molecules in the volume. This is the Geiger–Mueller (G–M) operating region. The response of the chamber will be nearly constant over a considerable voltage range (the plateau) until the voltage becomes so high that the applied electric field will pull electrons from the gas molecules and the chamber will enter a self-discharge region. Along the G–M plateau, any ionization will result in a pulse of the same magnitude, and the chamber is used to simply count the number of ionizing events which take place within. If a chamber is operated in the G–M region, quenching gasses or electronic quenching must be used to stop the electrical discharge after each pulse. The external circuitry provides pulse shaping for time resolution, but the counter will not be able to respond to a second ionizing event during the discharge, and measured count rates need to be corrected for dead time. In regions of very high gamma-ray flux, such instruments may be unable to respond. They should be designed to then give maximum readout; otherwise, a false zero may be indicated.

G–M tubes are useful for detecting gamma radiation that may cause only a single ionizing event in a gas volume; however, the detection efficiency is low. They can be built with thick walls and are relatively sturdy. Many radiation survey instruments are comprised of a small portable power supply and meter to which a G–M tube "probe" is attached by a flexible cable. G–M tubes with thin end-windows can be used to scan surfaces for beta or alpha particle contamination or to count small sources.

Scintillation Detectors

Many substances emit visible light when exposed to ionizing radiation. These include phosphors such as zinc sulfide crystals, sodium iodide and cesium iodide crystals, and various organic materials. Liquid scintillators to detect low energy beta particles are frequently used in biological studies but are rarely used with air samples. NCRP[(6)] provides references to information sources on the subject.

Detector crystals are made with specific impurities to improve their scintillation properties. NaI and CsI crystals activated with thallium are commonly used for photon detection. They are much more efficient absorbers of photons than gas-filled chambers. If the photon is completely absorbed in the scintillator, the quantity of light emitted will be proportional to the energy of the incident photon. Because the amount of energy absorbed increases with the volume of the absorber, large

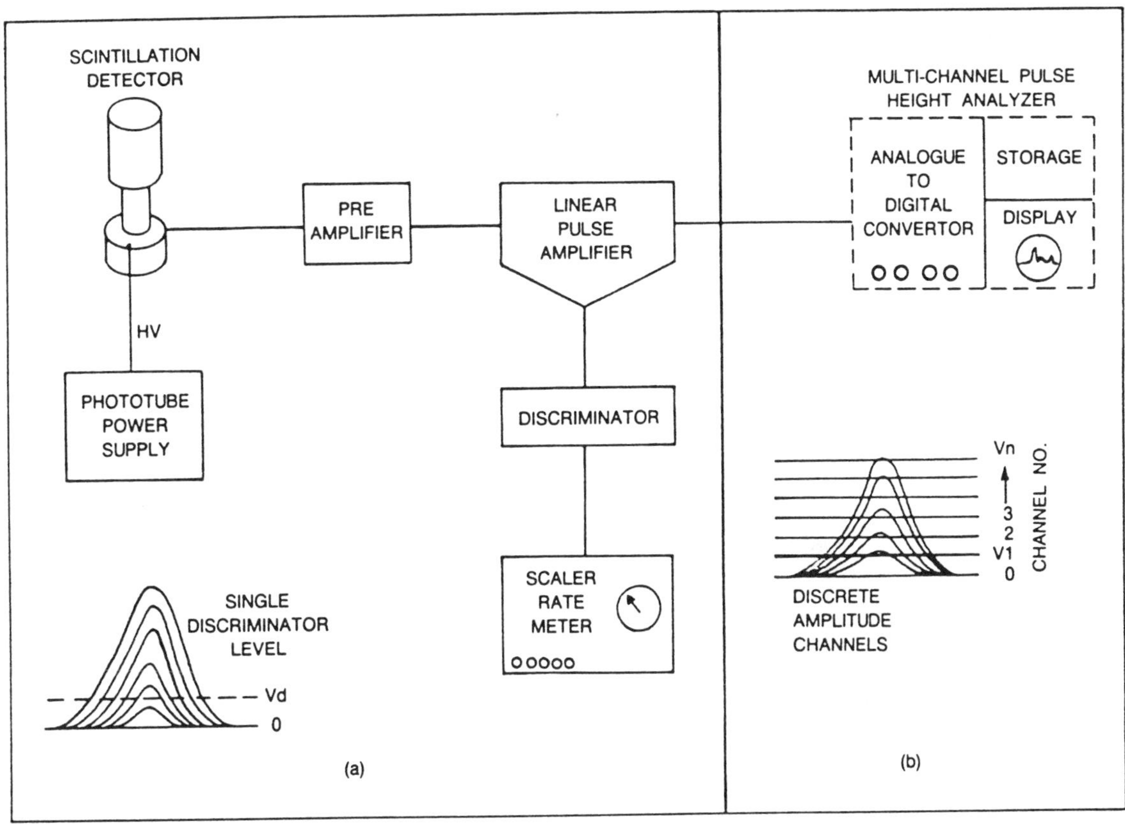

FIGURE 22-2. Block diagram of typical scintillation-counter systems: (a) for integral count-rate measurements for photon energies above those corresponding to a discriminator voltage V_d; (b) for "pulse-height-spectrometer" measurements at different photon energies corresponding to discriminator voltage intervals $V_1, V_2 \ldots V_n$.[6] Reprinted with permission, National Council on Radiation Protection and Measurements.

crystals are desirable. To be useful, the scintillator must be transparent to the emitted light; therefore, single crystals are needed for large detectors.

The emitted light is converted to an electrical pulse by a photomultiplier tube. The signals from the photomultiplier tube are amplified and electronically counted (Figure 22-2). Pulses greater than or less than a certain size may be counted or the pulses may be accumulated by size in a multichannel analyzer, as described above for a proportional counter. Relatively good energy resolution for gamma rays may be obtained with a crystal scintillation detector.

An example of the use of scintillation crystals to quantify airborne radioactivity is the measurement of radon gas adsorbed on charcoal. Charcoal-containing canisters are deployed for periods of 4–7 days. Radon gas will diffuse into the container and be adsorbed onto the charcoal. The radon gas will decay through a series of short-lived nuclides, several of which emit photons (Table 22-4). The photons specific to radon decay can be selectively counted by a scintillation detection system.

ZnS activated with silver is the most commonly used phosphor for alpha particle detection. It is available coated on Mylar® sheets or discs which may be placed directly onto an alpha particle source for high detection efficiency. An extremely low background arrangement for alpha-particle counting uses phosphor-coated Mylar discs.[11] It is particularly effective for very low activity samples such as filters used to collect environmental levels of the short-lived decay products of ^{222}Rn. Each filter is placed on a small plastic mount, covered with the phosphor disc, and then wrapped with Mylar. Alternatively, phosphor-coated material may be incorporated into a fixed detection system and the sample filter placed in a source holder near the phosphor. ZnS phosphor is also used to coat the interior surface of grab samplers known as "Lucas flasks" for detection of alpha radioactivity in air (Figure 22-3).[12]

Semiconductor Detectors

Detectors fabricated from solid semiconducting materials, primarily silicon or germanium, are essentially solid-state ionization chambers. Ionization takes place within the detector volume, producing pairs of charge carriers consisting of an electron and a hole. The charge is collected by a voltage placed across the detection volume. The electrons can be collected from the solid, at least for very thin solids (maximum thickness about

TABLE 22-4. Uranium Series from ^{222}Rn to ^{210}Pb

Nuclide	Historical Name	Half life*	Major Radiation Energies (MeV) and Intensities[7,9]		
			α	β	γ
$^{222}_{86}$Rn ↓	Emanation radon (Rn)	3.823 d	5.49 (99.92%)	—	—
$^{218}_{84}$Po	Radium A	3.05 m	6.00 (99.98%)	—	—
99.98% → $^{214}_{82}$Pb; 0.02% → $^{216}_{85}$At					
$^{214}_{82}$Pb	Radium B	26.8 m	—	0.178 (2.4%) 0.665 (46.1%) 0.722 (40.8%) 1.02 (9.5%)	0.295 (18.4%) 0.352 (35.4%) 0.768 (1.04%)
$^{216}_{85}$At	Astatine	~ 2 s	6.65 (6.4%) 6.99 (90%) 6.76 (3.6%)	—	—
$^{214}_{83}$Bi	Radium C	19.9 m	—	1.06 (5.56%) 1.15 (4.25%) 1.41 (8.15%) 1.50 (16.9%) 1.54 (17.5%) 1.89 (7.56%) 3.27 (19.8%)	0.609 (44.8%) 0.768 (4.76%) 1.12 (14.8%) 1.24 (5.83%) 1.76 (15.3%) 2.20 (4.98%)
99.98% → $^{214}_{84}$Po; 0.02% → $^{210}_{81}$Tl					
$^{214}_{84}$Po	Radium C'	164 μs	7.69 (100%)	—	—
$^{210}_{81}$Tl	Radium C''	1.30 m	—	1.86 (24%) 2.02 (10%) 2.41 (10%) 4.20 (30%) 4.38 (20%)	0.298 (79.1%) 0.800 (99.0%) 1.07 (12%) 1.21 (17%) 1.36 (21%)
$^{210}_{82}$Pb ↓	Radium D	22.3 y	—	0.0165 (87%) 0.063 (18%)	0.046 (4.18%)

*Common time units: y (years); d (days); m (minutes); s (seconds).

1.5–2.0 cm), because they have been raised to conduction bands by the excitation; the holes in the valence band move toward the opposite electrode. As with gas ionization chambers, the collected charge is proportional to the amount of energy deposited in the sensitive volume. Various methods are used to create as large a sensitive region in the solid as possible. This requires that holes and electrons be balanced properly when a collecting voltage is applied. One of the methods involves drifting lithium ions through the detector. It is then necessary to keep the detector at cryogenic temperatures to maintain the lithium gradient. Other methods result in detectors that can be maintained at room temperature, e.g., silicon surface barrier detectors. These detectors have very thin detection regions that are useful for alpha or beta particle spectrometry but not for gamma ray photons. High-purity germanium (HPGe) detectors, which are not lithium drifted, must be operated at cryogenic temperatures because the electrons can be raised to the conduction band by transfer of thermal energy at room temperatures, thus adding unwanted background noise to the system. Semiconductor detectors, because they are solids, have much higher detection efficiency for gamma rays than do gas-filled detectors. Ge, with a higher density and atomic number than Si, is preferred for gamma detection. The energy resolution is superior to that of a NaI crystal (Figure 22-4).

Etched Track Detectors

Solid-state nuclear track detectors have been developed relatively recently. They consist of a large group of inorganic and organic dielectrics that register tracks

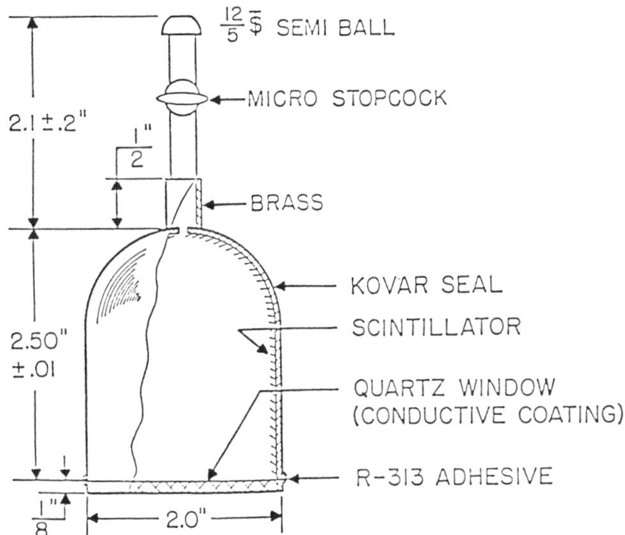

FIGURE 22-3. Alpha particles produced in the gas volume during decay of radon and short-lived progeny interact at the walls to produce scintillations. The light is transmitted through the circular quartz window at the base to a photomultiplier tube. The signal may then be amplified and counted.[12] Reprinted with permission, Atomic Industry Forum.

when traversed by heavy charged particles. The first observation of charged particle tracks in a crystal was reported in 1958.[13] The track is more vulnerable than the bulk material to dissolution by etching agents, which makes possible enlargement of the tracks to a size that can be observed optically. There is a threshold in the amount of linear energy transfer by an ionizing particle to the detector that must be exceeded for tracks to register. Only a few materials have been identified which will respond to alpha particles. These materials include cellulose nitrate and polycarbonates. The detectors do not respond to light, beta particles, or gamma ray photons and thus provide a very low background system for the measurement of extremely low levels of alpha radioactivity. In addition, no power source or electronic equipment is required. Detectors are exposed, collected, and returned to the laboratory for chemical etching and the counting of tracks. Extreme care must be taken in the handling and calibration of these detectors in order to obtain reproducible and reliable results. Allyl diglycol carbonate and cellulose nitrate detectors are currently in use for long-term integrated sampling of environmental radon.

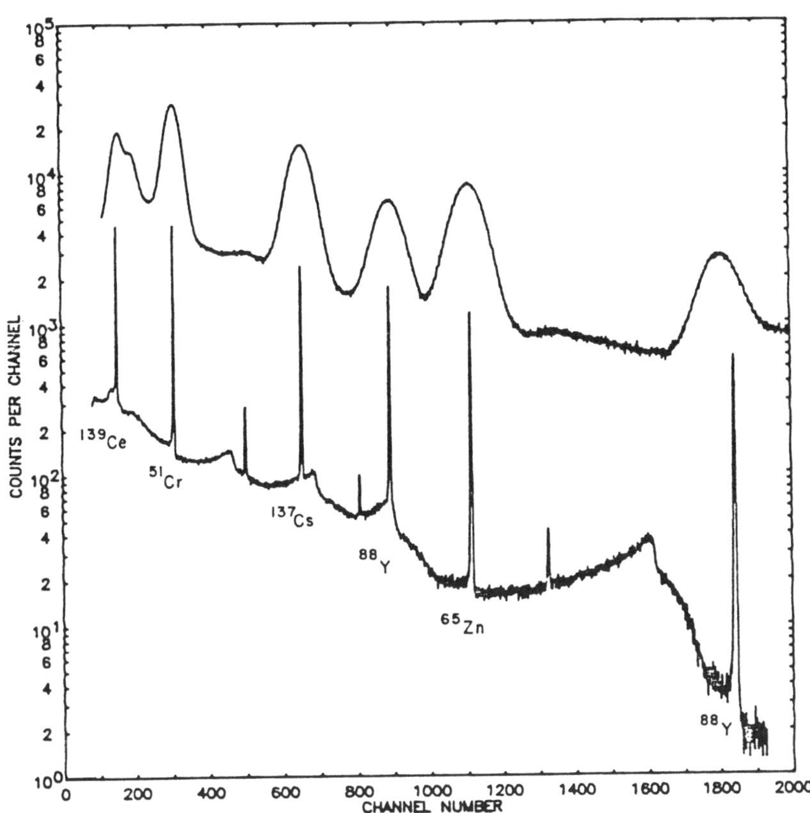

FIGURE 22-4. Gamma-ray spectra of a 5-ml mixed-radionuclide-solution source taken with the source within a 5-in. NaI(Tl) well crystal (upper curve) and at the face of a 60-cm^3 Ge(Li) detector (lower curve). The counting time in each case was 2000 s (from measurements made at the National Bureau of Standards).[6] Reprinted with permission, National Council on Radiation Protection and Measurements.

Thermoluminescent Dosimeters

Thermoluminescent dosimeters (TLDs) are crystalline materials in which electrons displaced by an interaction with ionizing radiation become trapped at an elevated energy level and emit visible light when released from that energy level. The number of trapped electrons is related to the radiation exposure. The trapped electrons are released by heating the TLDs, and the amount of light emitted during the heating process (the glow curve) is related to the exposure via calibration. The TLDs must be annealed prior to an exposure measurement. The crystals used most commonly are CaF_2 and LiF, with volumes of a few cubic millimeters. As with etched-track detectors, no power or electronic equipment is needed at a measurement site. A laboratory-based readout unit is required. TLDs respond to alpha, beta, and gamma radiation. These detectors are useful for long-term environmental monitoring and have been incorporated into integrating radon detection systems.(14,15)

Detector Calibration

The proper calibration of most radiation detection systems requires knowledge of the properties of both source and detector. Careful investigation of calibration methods must be made for specific cases. An extensive discussion on the preparation of calibration sources can be found in NCRP Report Nos. 58 and 97.(6,16) Standard sources can be obtained from the National Institute of Standards and Technology (NIST), formerly the National Bureau of Standards (NBS), and some government laboratories. The use of such sources, while an essential ingredient in quality control, does not itself ensure measurement accuracy. Use of a standard source with a given geometry will determine the counting efficiency for a specific setup, but any change in source characteristics (e.g., source substrate, thickness) can introduce significant differences. One or two specialized laboratories maintain chambers with well-characterized atmospheres of radon that are available for calibration of radon detectors.

The energy of the radiation to be measured may have important effects on the detector response. It is therefore prudent to calibrate for the specific radiation to be measured. Etched-track detectors, for example, will respond to ionizing particles only when the linear energy transfer is within a specific range. Calibration, as a function of gamma-ray energy, is important for survey instruments with gas-filled detectors (for guidance see NCRP Report No. 112).(17) Response may decrease rapidly for low energy gamma rays because of absorption in the chamber walls. Energy calibrations are essential in the case of spectrometric analysis (e.g., with a scintillation crystal or a semiconductor detector) or when electronic discrimination is used.

Background Reduction

Because background radiation is ubiquitous, it is always desirable and frequently essential to reduce the background count rate for counting samples with very low activity. Lead shielding is commonly used around photon detectors to reduce terrestrial and cosmic gamma ray background. Very heavy lead shielding is required for sensitive crystalline photon detectors. Little shielding is needed for thin, alpha-detection phosphors or surface-barrier detectors. Methods other than shielding include counting only simultaneous beta-gamma emissions, energy spectrometry, or very sophisticated double crystal (CsI/NaI combination) scintillation counting.

Statistical Considerations

Counting Statistics

Counting data belong to a population where events are discrete and a relatively small number of events occur in the time that is available. This type of population is best described by the Poisson distribution. For this distribution, the variance is equal to the number of counts, and the best estimate of the standard deviation is the square root of the number of counts. If a total of N sample counts is acquired in time t, the standard deviation (SD) of N is $\sqrt{N}$. The probability that the true mean count lies within the interval $N \pm \sqrt{N}$ is 0.675, within $N \pm 2\sqrt{N}$ it is 0.95, and within $N \pm 3\sqrt{N}$ it is 0.997. The uncertainty (often called the "error") in the count may be represented by the standard deviation. The count rate, $R = N/t$; the standard deviation of the count rate, $SD_R = \sqrt{N}/t$; and the coefficient of variation of the count rate, $CV_R = SD_R/R = 1/\sqrt{N}$.

When establishing sampling and counting protocols, sampling times should be balanced against counting time for the desired level of precision. If a source with a count rate of 100 counts per minute (cpm) is counted for 1, 10, 100, or 1000 min, the CVs of the count rate will be 0.10, 0.03, 0.01, and 0.003. An increase in counting time from 1 to 10 min reduces the uncertainty from 10% to 3%. This is desirable if other sampling errors are in the range of a few percent. An increase in counting time from 10 min to 1.67 hrs to reduce the uncertainty to 1%, or to 16.7 hrs to reduce it to 0.3%, may not be warranted. Similar considerations apply to increasing sampling duration in order to increase the count rate of the sample. Clearly, for radionuclides with half lives that are the same order of magnitude as the sampling duration, the loss of sample by decay must be considered.

Background counts are always detected because of the presence of natural terrestrial and cosmic radiation. Then:

$$R_n = R - R_b \quad (4)$$

where: R_n = the net sample count rate
R = the total sample count rate
R_b = the background count rate.

The errors in the background (SD_b) and sample count rates (SD_R) are independent and are therefore propagated by summing the variances. The SD of the net count rate, SD_n, is then estimated as the square root of the total variance (Chapter 10).

$$SD_n = \left[(SD_R)^2 + (SD_b)^2\right]^{1/2} = \left[\frac{N}{t_s^2} + \frac{N_b}{t_b^2}\right]^{1/2} \quad (5)$$

where: N_b = the number of background counts
N = the total number of counts
t_s = the sample count time
t_b = the background count time.

Lower Limits of Detection

When the amount of radioactivity contained in a sample will result in a count rate that is very close to background, it is not always clear whether activity is present and, if so, how well the quantity of activity can be measured. There are a number of ways in which detection limits are defined for counting data.

Three lower limits of activity have been distinguished.(18,19) The first is a limit at which it is decided whether activity is present, the second is the amount of activity that may be detected with a given level of reliability, and the third is the quantity of activity that may be measured with given precision. Detailed discussions and derivations of these limits are found in Currie,(18) Altshuler and Pasternack,(20) and Pasternack and Harley.(21) Which of these limits should be chosen depends on the specifics of the measurement, but the limit reported should be defined clearly.

A convenient measure is given by Pasternack and Harley.(21) They define the "lower limit of detection" (LLD) of a radioactivity counter as "the smallest amount of sample activity that will yield a net-count sufficiently large so as to imply its presence."

The LLD is approximated as:

$$\text{LLD} = \gamma\,(k_\alpha + k_\beta)\left(\frac{N}{t_s^2} + \frac{N_b}{t_b^2}\right)^{1/2} \quad (6)$$

where:

k_α and k_β represent the value corresponding to the preselected risk for concluding falsely that activity is present (α) and the predetermined degree of confidence for detecting its presence ($1-\beta$). For $\alpha = \beta = 0.05$, $k_\alpha = k_\beta = 1.645$
γ = a calibration constant to convert counts into activity
N = the measured sample plus background count in time t
N_b = the measured background count in time t_b

For $\alpha = \beta = 0.05$, this can be written as:

$$\text{LLD} = 3.29\,\gamma\,SD_n \quad (7)$$

where: SD_n = the standard deviation of the net count rate as defined in Equation 5

LLDs may be reduced by repeated measurements to obtain better estimates for the variance of the background count rate (Equation 5).

Sampling Methods

Sampling methods must be designed specifically for particular nuclides to incorporate an appropriate radiation detection system. Detectors must be fitted to both the type and energy of the radiation. Half lives, if short, may limit the procedure, but a simple measurement of half life may permit identification and quantification, even in the presence of interferences. Specific air sampling methods for certain nuclides have been published. Some are contained in NCRP publications.(19,22,23) The third edition of *Methods of Air Sampling and Analysis*,(24) a publication of the American Public Health Association, gives methods for measuring atmospheric ^{131}I, ^{222}Rn, elemental tritium, and tritium present as water vapor. For further discussion of radioactive aerosols in general, and specific information on radon and its short-lived decay products, References 25 and 26 are recommended. A recent review of tritium sampling and measurement can be found in Reference 27.

Recognition of the magnitude of the radiation dose to the population from naturally occurring levels of the short-lived decay products of radon(28–30) has resulted in the development and improvement of a substantial number of measurement techniques. The decay series from ^{222}Rn through ^{210}Pb is shown in Table 22-4. The terms short-lived "decay products" or "daughters" or "progeny" refer to the series from ^{218}Po through ^{214}Po. As seen from the varying decay rates and emissions, either alpha, beta, or gamma ray detectors may be used and energy resolution or series decay times employed to separate the various decay products. It is difficult to quantify each decay product, or "daughter," in most environments because of the extraordinarily low levels of activity. However, the concentration of each of the short-lived progeny must be known for a complete determination of the radiation dose to the respiratory tract tissue. If significant concentrations of ^{220}Rn (commonly known as thoron) and its decay products are present, these too must be quantified.

Either radon (gas) or progeny (particles) concentrations may be measured. Concentrations of radon as low as 3.7 Bq/m^3 (0.1 pCi/L) can be measured in grab samples, and much lower concentrations can be measured with integrating samplers. When the progeny are measured, the concentration is frequently reported in "working level" (WL). The WL is a measure of the potential alpha energy concentration in air (PAEC). PAEC is defined as the number of decay product atoms multiplied by the alpha particle energy that will be released as each atom decays to ^{210}Pb. The SI unit of PAEC is J/m^3. The WL is any combination of short-lived decay products in one liter of air that will result in the emission of 1.3×10^5 MeV potential alpha energy and is equal to 2.08×10^{-5} J/m^3. This is equivalent to 3700 Bq/m^3 (100 pCi/L) of ^{222}Rn in equilibrium with its short-lived progeny. If each decay product formed in the series remained airborne and in the space, the concentrations would be in equilibrium, but removal by ventilation and deposition to walls and other surfaces disturbs the equilibrium. The WL is a historical unit that avoids the problem of equilibrium.

Very low background alpha particle detection systems permit detection of radon progeny concentrations as low as 0.0005 WL for a 5-min filter sample. The air is filtered for exactly 5 min onto a 0.8-µm pore size membrane filter. A ZnS (Ag)-coated phosphor is placed over the filter, and the light flashes are counted by a photomultiplier tube with appropriate electronics. Counts are taken for three specific time intervals. The activity of each of the short-lived nuclides and the WL level can then be calculated by taking into account the decay time of each nuclide, the efficiency of counting, and the air volume sampled.[31] Table 22-5, reproduced from George,[32] summarizes many of the instruments and methods for measuring radon and its short-lived decay products in air. An extensive report detailing radon measurement methods may be obtained from NCRP.[16] The U.S. Environmental Protection Agency (U.S. EPA) has published a set of recommended protocols for measurement of radon in homes.[33] The purposes of these protocols are to ensure quality control and to obtain measurements under stable and standardized conditions. The latter will facilitate comparisons but may not represent average concentrations in the home. The working level month (WLM) is a historical unit of exposure and is an exposure rate of 1 WL for a working month of 170 hrs (1 WLM = 0.0035 Jh/m^3). Remedial action is recommended by NCRP if an annual exposure exceeds 2 WLM (7×10^{-3} Jh/m^3) (Table 22-6). This translates roughly to an air concentration of 300 Bq/m^3 (8 pCi/L) of ^{222}Rn, but will vary because the radiation dose from radon daughter inhalation depends on occupancy factors and other variables. U.S. EPA recommends that indoor air concentrations of radon be reduced to below 148 Bq/m^3 (4 pCi/L).

Sampling Strategy

Radioactive gases or particles in air may be sampled by grab sampling, continuous monitoring, or integrated sampling methods. Grab samples will give the concentration of a contaminant at a particular location at the instant the sample was collected. The equipment is usually quite simple, and this sampling method is useful for screening on a small scale. Periodic grab sampling may be used to assess average concentrations. For average ambient concentrations, grab sampling should span several seasons. Samples may be counted immediately, as is necessary for short-lived isotopes (e.g., the overall half life of the short-lived radon progeny is about 30 min), but it is frequently possible to return the sample to the laboratory for counting, thereby avoiding the difficulties associated with transporting electronic counting equipment.

Continuous air monitoring is required for an in-depth assessment of airborne radioactivity because of spatial and temporal variations. With continuous sampling it is possible to observe variability and concentration peaks. Sources can be identified and effects of ventilation or weather patterns on ambient concentrations may be observed. Continuous monitoring is normally required for protective surveillance at nuclear reactors and processing facilities. Several regulatory guides issued by the U.S. Nuclear Regulatory Commission (NRC) contain guidance on air sampling (Regulatory Guides 8.21, 8.23, 8.24, 8.25, and 8.30); the most detailed is "Air Sampling in the Workplace," Regulatory Guide 8.25.[34]

Integrated sampling over extended time periods will result in a single average concentration value. Detection methods are often simpler and less expensive than either continuous or grab sampling methods. For the case of radon and its short-lived decay products, both passive and active samplers are available for integrated monitoring of environmental indoor air concentrations.

Gas Phase Sampling

Radioactive gases or vapors may be sampled directly into a detector volume. The Lucas flask (Figure 22-3) for ^{222}Rn is an example. The bottom of the container is made of optically clear glass. The remaining interior surfaces are lined with ZnS (Ag) scintillator. Air is drawn into the evacuated flask by opening the valve on top. The dimensions of the flask ensure that most alpha particles emitted in the flask will reach the walls and produce scintillations. The scintillations are detected and quantified by placing the bottom of the flask into contact with a photomultiplier tube coupled to a counting device. Integrated air samples may be metered into an impermeable, nonreactive sampling bag or tank, and later transferred to an appropriately designed detection volume. Gases may be collected on charcoal actively or by

TABLE 22-5A. Instruments and Methods for Measuring Radon in Air*

Instrument and Method	Application	Principle of Operation	Sensitivity
Scintillation cell	Grab sampling	Scintillation alpha counting.	< 0.1–1.0 pCi/L
Ionization chamber	Grab (laboratory only)	Sample transferred into ion chamber. Pulse of current counting.	< 0.05 pCi/L
Active continuous scintillation cell monitor	Continuous	Flow through scintillation cell. Alpha counted.	<0.1–1.0 pCi/L
Passive diffusion electrostatic monitor	Continuous	Radon diffusion into sensitive volume. ^{218}Po collected on scintillation detector electrostatically.	0.5 pCi/L for 10-min counting intervals
Passive diffusion radon-only monitor	Continuous	Radon diffusion into sensitive volume. Radon progeny removed by electret. Count alpha particles from radon only with alpha scintillation counter.	0.1 pCi/L for 60-min counting intervals
Passive track etch monitor	Integrating	Alpha sensitive film registers tracks. Visible when etched in NaOH.	0.2–0.4 pCi L^{-1} $month^{-1}$ depending on size
Passive activated carbon monitor	Integrating	Radon adsorption on activated carbon. Gamma counting with gamma analyzer for ^{114}Pb and ^{214}Bi gamma rays.	0.2 pCi/L for 100-hr exposure
Passive electrostatic-thermoluminescence monitor	Integrating	Radon diffusion into sensitive volume. ^{218}Po collects on thermoluminescence detector electrostatically.	0.03–0.3 pCi/L depending on size for 170-hr exposure

*References for specific methods are listed in George.[32]

TABLE 22-5B. Instruments and Methods for Measuring Radon Progeny in Air*

Instrument and Method	Application	Principle of Operation	Sensitivity
Kusnetz-Rolle	Grab sampling for WL	Collect sample on filter for 5–10 min. Alpha count.	0.0005 WL
Tsivoglou and modifications	Grab sampling for individual radon progeny and WL	Collect sample on filter for 5–10 min. Alpha count.	0.1 pCi/L each of ^{218}Po, ^{214}Pb, ^{214}Bi, and 0.005 WL
Tsivoglou and modifications	Continuous — Instant radon progeny and WL monitoring	Collect sample on filter for 2–3 min. Alpha and beta counting.	0.1–1.0 pCi/L 0.001–0.01 WL depending on flow rate
Tsivoglou and modifications	Continuous	Collect on filter for 5–10 min. Alpha count. One measurement every 30 min.	0.1–1.0 pCi/L 0.001–0.01 WL depending on flow rate
Thermoluminescence radon progeny integrating sampling unit (RPISU)	Integrating	Collect sample on filter for 1–4 weeks. Detect with thermoluminescence material (CaF_2: Dy).	0.0001 WL
Thermoluminescence modified WL monitor	Integrating	Collect sample on filter for 1–2 weeks. Detect with thermoluminescence material (LiF).	0.0005 WL
Surface barrier WL monitor	Integrating	Collect sample on filter continuously. Detect alpha radio-activity with silicon surface barrier detector.	0.00005–0.005 WL depending on flow rate
Radon/thoron monitor	Integrating	Collect sample on filter continuously. Detect radon and thoron daughter alpha radioactivity with alpha-sensitive film.	0.001 WL in 240 hrs

*References for specific methods are listed in George.[32]

TABLE 22-6. Summary of Recommendations on Limits for Exposure to Ionizing Radiation[A,B,C,D]

A. Occupational exposures[D]	
1. Effective dose limits	
a) Annual	50 mSv
b) Cumulative	10 mSv × age
2. Equivalent dose annual limits for tissues and organs	
a. Lens of eye	150 mSv
b. Skin, hands, and feet	
B. Guidance for emergency occupational exposure[D]	(see Section 14 of Reference 4)
C. Public exposures (annual)	
1. Effective dose limit, continuous or frequent exposure[D]	1 mSv
2. Effective dose limit, infrequent exposure[D]	5 mSv
3. Equivalent dose limits for tissues and organs[D]	
a) Lens of eye	15 mSv
b) Skin, hands and feet	50 mSv
4. Remedial action for natural sources:	
a) Effective dose (excluding radon)	> 5 mSv
b) Exposure to radon decay products	> 7×10^{-3} Jh/m^3
D. Education and training exposures (annual)[D]	
1. Effective dose limit	1 mSv
2. Equivalent dose limit for tissues and organs	
a) Lens of eye	15 mSv
b) Skin, hands, and feet	50 mSv
E. Embryo-fetus exposures[D] (monthly)	
1. Equivalent dose limit	0.5 mSv
F. Negligible individual dose (annual)[D]	0.01 mSv

[A]Adapted from NCRP Report No. 116.[4]
[B]Excluding medical exposures.
[C]See Tables 22-2 and 22-7 for recommendations on w_R and w_T, respectively.
[D]Sum of external and internal exposures but excluding doses from natural sources.

passive diffusion[35] and either de-emanated into a counting volume or gamma-counted directly if the emitted radiation is sufficiently energetic to penetrate the container. The entire charcoal container may be placed on a NaI crystal or a lithium-drifted germanium detector. In the latter case, geometric considerations have a significant effect on counting efficiency, and the counting efficiency for the distributed source must be determined. Effects of interferences, such as water vapor, on collection efficiency must be evaluated. Canisters containing 100 g of activated charcoal are commonly used to detect environmental radon. Exposure is for 7 days, followed by counting with a NaI crystal detector system.[36,37]

A passive monitor for tritiated water vapor (HTO) consists of a standard scintillation vial containing water, or other sorbent, that has a precisely defined orifice in the lid. The vapor diffuses into the sampler and is collected by the sorbent. Vial and contents are then prepared for liquid scintillation counting.[27]

Internal ionization chambers are also used for radioactive gases. A known volume of sample is admitted into an evacuated ionization chamber and the current is measured. The current may be compared with that of an identical chamber containing pure, aged air.

Particle Sampling

The concentration of radioactive particles in air is most frequently determined by collecting all the particles in a known volume of air onto a filter and counting the activity on the filter. The counting efficiency of the system must be calibrated for the specific source, filter, and detector geometry. Continuous air monitors frequently operate in a semicontinuous manner by filtering airborne particles onto a portion of continuous tape for a specified time period. The sample is then counted by a detector just above or beneath the tape after which the tape moves to provide a clean substrate for the next sample. For alpha particles or very low energy beta particles, substantial absorption may occur in the filter or even in the air gap between source and detector. Calibration specific for radiation energy is required for each geometry unless it has been determined previously that the response is not energy dependent.

The size distribution of the airborne radioactive particles may introduce sample bias. Overall sampling efficiency for aerosols depends strongly on aspiration efficiency, entry efficiency, and transport efficiency of the collecting probe[38,39] (Chapter 11) . These are all particle-size-dependent processes. Sampling of large particles ($d > 10$ µm) is particularly susceptible to bias as a result of these factors. Large radioactive airborne particles may result directly from accidental releases, or indirectly from deposition of fallout onto soil particles that are subsequently resuspended. The number concentration may be very low so that detection depends on sampling large volumes of air. A review of these problems, which includes analysis of equipment designed for large particle sampling in this context, is presented in Reference 40. If some specific fraction of the ambient aerosol is desired (e.g., only the inspirable, thoracic, or respirable mass fraction),[41] such separation may be incorporated into the sampling train (Chapter 5). Other appropriate sampling instruments, such as the cascade impactor,[42] may also be used. Counting of the individual stages will determine an activity-particle size distribution (Chapter 14).

Radiation Safety Sampling Programs

An operational radiation safety program requires continuous air monitoring systems coupled to alarm systems.[43,44] Surveillance for airborne contaminants is most commonly done by continuous air monitors (CAMs). Particles are collected on a filter and counted with a conventional detector, which is usually a thin window G–M counter, scintillation detector, or a solid-state detector. Energy discrimination may be incorporated in the detection system when monitoring for a known emitter. CAM performance for continuous alpha air monitoring is an area of ongoing investigation.[45] Fiber-supported membrane filters such as Fluoropore FSLW (Millipore Corp.) are recommended for monitoring alpha emitters[46,47] (see Chapter 13). Selecting a specific pulse height to be counted will significantly reduce interferences from background such as radon daughters. Where plutonium and other alpha emitters are of concern, alpha spectrometry will provide specificity in the detection-alarm system. The American National Standards Institute (ANSI) has issued a number of guides for the performance of instrumentation used to monitor airborne radioactivity (e.g., ANSI N13.1[48] and ANSI N42.17B.[49] When using monitor-alarm systems, a check source should be used routinely to ensure that the system is operating properly.

Radiation Protection Criteria

Evaluation of airborne radioactive contaminant concentrations for radiation protection differs from that of chemical contaminants because protection criteria for ionizing radiation are based on the radiation dose ultimately delivered to an individual. Evaluation of airborne contamination must be based on the complex relationships between exposure to a given concentration and dose. For protection purposes, the dose, or energy delivered to tissue, is modified to include the concept of biological *equivalence* for different types of radiation, as well as *effectiveness*, which normalizes for organ sensitivity.

Responsibility for recommending limits for exposure to ionizing radiation for both the occupational and nonoccupational (general public) exposures in the United States has been delegated by Congress to the NCRP. Regulations are promulgated by various agencies including the U.S. EPA, the NRC, the Occupational Safety and Health Administration (OSHA), and others. A guide to the many radiation standards and guidances can be found in the *Health Physics and Radiological Health Handbook*,[50] but it is necessary to check for current published standards. The dose limits recommended by NCRP[4] are given in Table 22-6. These guidelines conform with, but extend, the recommendations of the ICRP,[5] which are in use in most other countries.

"The goal of radiation protection is to prevent the occurrence of serious radiation induced-conditions (acute and chronic deterministic effects) in exposed persons and to reduce stochastic effects in exposed persons to a degree that is acceptable in relation to the benefits to the individual and to society from the activities that generate such exposure."[4] Radiation protection guidance for occupational exposure in the United States is thus based on risk and benefit considerations. There are three basic principles: 1) any activity involving radiation exposure should be justified as useful enough to society to warrant the exposure, 2) exposures that result from carrying out such activities should be kept as low as reasonably achievable, and 3) the maximum annual dose to an individual worker should be limited to specified numerical values. The numerical value specified is an upper limit of acceptability rather than a design criterion. Exposure of any individual to

TABLE 22-7. Tissue Weighting Factor (w_T) for Different Tissues and Organs[A,B]

0.01	0.05	0.12	0.20
Bone surface	Bladder	Bone marrow	Gonads
Skin	Breast	Colon	
	Liver	Lung	
	Esophagus	Stomach	
	Thyroid		
	Remainder[C,D]		

[A]Adapted from ICRP Report No. 60[(5)] and NCRP Report No. 116.[(4)]

[B]The values have been developed for a reference population of equal numbers of both sexes and a wide range of ages. In the definition of effective dose, they apply to workers, to the whole population, and to either sex. These w_T values are based on rounded values of the organ's contribution to the total detriment.

[C]For purposes of calculation, the remainder comprises the following additional tissues and organs: adrenals, brain, small intestine, large intestine, kidney, muscle, pancreas, spleen, thymus, and uterus. The list includes organs that are likely to be selectively irradiated. Some organs in the list are known to be susceptible to cancer induction. If other tissues and organs subsequently become identified as having a significant risk of induced cancer, they will then be included either with a specific w_T or in this additional list constituting the remainder. The remainder may also include other tissues or organs selectively irradiated.

[D]In those exceptional cases in which one of the remainder tissues or organs receives an equivalent dose in excess of the highest dose in any of the 12 organs for which a weighting factor is specified, a weighting factor of 0.025 should be applied to that tissue or organ, and a weighting factor of 0.025 should be applied to the average dose in the other remainder tissues or organs (see ICRP Report No. 60[(5)]).

the maximum dose for any substantial portion of a lifetime is discouraged. Limits for exposure of the general public are based on these same principles.

The limiting numerical values for assessed dose are based on risk of fatal cancer. They are specified as "effective dose" (E) to an individual. E is defined as:

$$E = \sum_{T} w_T H_T \tag{8}$$

where: w_T = a tissue weighting factor (Table 22-7)
H_T = the equivalent dose received by tissue T.

The limits are established based on radiation risk for individual organs. The factors (w_T) provide for weighting if more than one organ is exposed in order to limit the total risk for an individual.

Dose limits apply to the sum of external and internal exposures. External exposures are assessed via effective dose. For internal exposures, "committed effective dose" must be calculated. This type of dose takes into account the continuing irradiation of organs and tissues that occurs after intake of a radionuclide.[(5)] Because of this continuing radiation, ICRP established the "Annual Limit on Intake" (ALI) (ICRP 61). The ALI limits the committed effective dose from an intake in a single year to 20 mSv. NCRP recommends that ALI be used as reference levels and adopts the ICRP values as "Annual Reference Levels of Intake" (ARLI). Air concentrations must be controlled so that individuals will not be exposed to more than the ARLI.

The maximum air concentration to which a worker may be exposed, in compliance with these limits, is called the "Derived Reference Air Concentration" (DRAC). The DRAC for each radioactive nuclide is derived from the ARLI. A series of calculations relates the air concentration to organ and tissue concentrations via inhalation and metabolic processes, along with dosimetric calculations based on the emitted radiation. The calculation requires knowledge of the physical properties of the inhaled nuclide, lung deposition efficiency, solubility of the particle in the lung, transfer coefficients between body compartments, retention times, organ and tissue geometric factors, and so forth. The publications *Reference Man*[(51)] and *Annual Limits for Intake of Radionuclides by Workers*[(52)] provide numerical values and models for these calculations. Both NCRP and ICRP are currently revising the lung models used for the dosimetry of inhaled nuclides. Portions of the proposed new models have been published.[(53,54)]

In addition to annual dose limits, NCRP recommends for occupational exposure that the cumulative effective dose not exceed the age of the individual in years × 10 mSv. Exposure to individuals under 18 is discouraged, but occasional exposure for educational and training purposes is acceptable within strict guidelines.[(4)]

National radiation protection standards for the public are also shown in Table 22-6. The limits for public exposures do not include background or medical exposure. Remedial action is recommended for natural exposures beyond the limits specified in Table 22-6. The numerical values are considered an upper limit, and all exposures should be kept as low as practicable. There is, however, a level of risk considered to be so low as to be negligible and to require no attention or action. This "Negligible Individual Dose" (NID) is set at an effective dose of 0.01 mSv (1 mrem) per year.

Summary

Airborne radioactive contaminants must be sampled by methods appropriate to the type and energy of the radiation emitted. Sampling and detection equipment must be selected and calibrated for specific nuclides. Very sensitive detection methods are currently available and extremely low levels of contamination may be quantitated with properly selected equipment. Natural background radiation will limit the level of radioactivity that can be measured because of the statistical nature of the decay process so that efforts to reduce the detection of background radiation are often needed. Sampling of airborne radioactivity in the workplace and in the environment must ensure that recommended dose limits for both workers and the public are not exceeded and that all exposures remain as low as reasonably achievable.

References

1. Code of Federal Regulations: Radiation Protection Guidance to Federal Agencies for Occupational Exposure. Fed. Reg. 52:2822 (1987).
2. International Commission on Radiological Protection: Radiation Quantities and Units. ICRU Report 33. ICRP, 7910 Woodmont Avenue, Washington, DC 20014 (1980). *Note*: A revised version of this report is in preparation.
3. National Council on Radiation Protection and Measurements: SI Units in Radiation Protection and Measurements. NCRP Report No. 82. NCRP. Bethesda, MD (1985).
4. National Council on Radiation Protection and Measurements: Limitation of Exposure to Ionizing Radiation. NCRP Report No. 116. NCRP, Bethesda, MD (1993).
5. International Commission on Radiological Protection: Radiation Protection: 1990 Recommendations of the International Commission on Radiological Protection. ICRP Publication 60. Annals of the ICRP, 21(1–3). Pergamon Press, Elmsford, NY (1991).
6. National Council on Radiation Protection and Measurements: A Handbook of Radioactivity Measurement Procedures, 2nd ed. NCRP Report No. 58. NCRP, Bethesda, MD (1985).
7. Knoll, G.F.: Radiation Detection and Measurement. John Wiley and Sons, Inc., New York (1979).
8. Lederer, C.M.; Shirley, V.S.; Eds.: Table of Isotopes, 7th ed. John Wiley and Sons, Inc., New York (1978).
9. Schleien, B.; Terpilak, M.S.: The Health Physics and Radiological Health Handbook, Supplement 1. Nucleon Lectern Associates, Inc. (1986).
10. Eichholz, G.G.; Poston, J.W.: Principles of Nuclear Radiation Detection. Ann Arbor Science Publishers, Ann Arbor, MI (1979).
11. Hallden, N.A.; Harley, J.H.: An Improved Alpha-counting Technique. Anal. Chem. 32:1861 (1960).
12. Lucas, Sr., H.F.: Alpha Scintillation Radon Counting in Workshop on Methods for Measurement of Radiation In and Around Uranium Mills. Atomic Indust. Forum, Vol. 3, No. 9 (1977).
13. Young, D.A.: Etching of Radiation Damage in Lithium Fluoride. Nature 182:375 (1958).
14. Schiager, K.J.: Integrating Radon Progeny Air Sampler. Am. Ind. Hyg. Assoc. J. 35:165 (1974).
15. Maiello, M.L.; Harley, N.H.: EGARD: An Environmental X-ray and ^{222}Rn Detector. Health Phys. 53:301 (1987).
16. National Council on Radiation Protection and Measurements: Measurement of Radon and Radon Daughters in Air. NCRP Report No. 97. NCRP, Bethesda, MD (1988).
17. National Council on Radiation Protection and Measurements: Calibration of Survey Instruments Used in Radiation Protection for the Assessment of Ionizing Radiation Fields and Radioactive Surface Contamination. NCRP Report No. 112. NCRP, Bethesda, MD (1991).
18. Currie, L.A.: Limits for Qualitative Detection and Quantitative Determination. Anal. Chem. 40:586 (1968).
19. National Council on Radiation Protection and Measurements: Tritium Measurement Techniques. NCRP Report No. 47. NCRP, Bethesda, MD (1976).
20. Altshuler, B.; Pasternack, B.: Statistical Measures of the Lower Limit of Detection of a Radioactivity Counter. Health Phys. 9:293 (1963).
21. Pasternack, B.S.; Harley, N.H.: Detection Limits for Radionuclides in the Analysis of Multi-component Gamma Ray Spectrometer Data. Nucl. Instrum. Methods 91:533 (1971).
22. National Council on Radiation Protection and Measurements: Environmental Radiation Measurements. NCRP Report No. 50. NCRP, Bethesda, MD (1976).
23. National Council on Radiation Protection and Measurements: Carbon-14 in the Environment. NCRP Report No. 81. NCRP, Bethesda, MD (1985).
24. Lodge, Jr., J.P., Ed.: Methods of Air Sampling and Analysis, 3rd ed. Intersociety Committee. Lewis Publishers, Inc., Chelsea, MI (1989).
25. Hoover, M.D.; Newton, G.J.: Radioactive Aerosols. In: Aerosol Measurement: Principles, Techniques, and Applications, pp. 768–798. K. Willeke and P.A. Baron, Eds. Van Nostrand Reinhold, New York (1993).
26. Cohen, B.S.: Radon and Its Short-Lived Decay Product Aerosols. In: Aerosol Measurement: Principles, Techniques, and Applications, pp. 799–815. K. Willeke and P.A. Baron, Eds. Van Nostrand Reinhold, New York (1993).
27. Wood, M.J.; McElroy, R.G.C.; Surette, R.A.; Brown, R.M.: Tritium Sampling and Measurement. Health Phys. 65:610–627 (1993).
28. National Council on Radiation Protection and Measurements: Exposures from the Uranium Series with Emphasis on Radon and Its Daughters. NCRP Report No. 77. NCRP, Bethesda, MD (1984).
29. National Council on Radiation Protection and Measurements: Evaluation of Occupational and Environmental Exposures to Radon and Radon Daughters in the United States. NCRP Report No. 78. NCRP, Bethesda, MD (1984).
30. National Council on Radiation Protection and Measurements: Ionizing Radiation Exposure to the Population of the United States. NCRP Report No. 93. NCRP, Bethesda, MD (1987).
31. Thomas, J.W.: Measurement of Radon Daughters in Air. Health Phys. 23:783 (1972).
32. George, A.C.: Instruments and Methods for Measuring Indoor Radon and Radon Progeny Concentrations. In: Radon, Proceedings of an APCA International Specialty Conference. Air Pollution Control Association, Pittsburgh, PA (1986).
33. U.S. Environmental Protection Agency: Interim Indoor Radon and Radon Decay Product Measurement Protocols. EPA 520/1-86-04. U.S. Environmental Protection Agency, Office of Radiation Programs, Washington, DC (1986).
34. U.S. Nuclear Regulatory Commission. Air Sampling in the Workplace, Regulatory Guide 8.25. Superintendent of Documents, U.S.

Government Printing Office, P.O. Box 37082, Washington, DC (1992).

35. Underhill, D.W.: Basic Theory for the Diffusive Sampling of Radon. Health Physics 65:17–24 (1993).
36. Cohen, B.L.; Nason, R.: A Diffusion Barrier Charcoal Absorption Collector for Measuring Rn Concentrations in Indoor Air. Health Phys. 50:457 (1986).
37. George, A.C.; Weber, T.: An Improved Passive Activated C Collector for Measuring Environmental ^{222}Rn in Indoor Air. Health Phys. 58:583–589 (1990).
38. Vincent, J.H.: Aerosol Sampling: Science and Practice. John Wiley and Sons, New York (1989).
39. Willeke, K.; Baron, P.; Eds.: Aerosol Measurement: Principles, Techniques, and Applications. Van Nostrand Reinhold, New York (1993).
40. Garland, J.A.; Nicholson, D.W.: A Review of Methods for Sampling Large Airborne Particles and Associated Radioactivity. J. Aerosol Sci. 22:479–499 (1991).
41. American Conference of Governmental Industrial Hygienists: Particle Size-Selective Sampling in the Workplace. ACGIH, Cincinnati, OH (1985).
42. Lodge, J.P.; Chan, T.L.; Eds.: The Cascade Impactor. American Industrial Hygiene Association, Akron, OH (1986).
43. National Council on Radiation Protection and Measurements: Operational Radiation Safety Program. NCRP Report No. 59. NCRP, Bethesda, MD (1978).
44. National Council on Radiation Protection and Measurements: Radiation Alarms and Access Control Systems. NCRP Report No. 88. NCRP, Bethesda, MD (1986).
45. Hoover, M.D.; Newton, J.G.: Statistical Limitations in the Sensitivity of Continuous Air Monitors for Alpha-emitting Radionuclides. In: Inhalation Toxicology Research Institute Annual Report 1991–1992, pp. 1–4. Lovelace Biomedical Environmental Research Institute, Albuquerque, NM (1992).
46. Moore, M.E.; McFarland, A.R.; Rodgers, J.C.: Factors that Affect Alpha Particle Detection in Continuous Air Monitor Applications. Health Physics 65:69-81 (1993).
47. Hoover, M.D.; Newton, J.G.: Update on Selection and Use of Filter Media in Continuous Air Monitors for Alpha-emitting Radionuclides. In: Inhalation Toxicology Research Institute Annual Report 1991–1992, pp. 5–7. Lovelace Biomedical Environmental Research Institute, Albuquerque, NM (1992).

INSTRUMENT 22-1. Electret-passive environmental radon monitoring (E-PERM®) system.

48. ANSI: American National Standard Guide to Sampling Airborne Radioactive Materials in Nuclear Facilities. ANSI N13.1-1969. American National Standards Institute, New York (1969).
49. ANSI: American National Standard on Performance Specifications for Health Physics Instrumentation — Occupational Airborne Radioactivity Monitoring Instrumentation. ANSI N42.17B-1989. American National Standards Institute, New York (1989).
50. Shleien, B.: The Health Physics and Radiological Health Handbook, Revised Edition. Scinta, Inc., Silver Springs, MD (1992).
51. International Commission on Radiological Protection: Reference Manual: Anatomical, Physiological, and Metabolic Characteristics. ICRP Publication 23. Pergamon Press, Oxford (1975).
52. International Commission on Radiological Protection: Annual Limits on Intake of Radionuclides by Workers Based on the 1990 Recommendations. ICRP Publication 61. Annals of the ICRP 21(4). Pergamon Press, Elmsford, NY (1991).
53. Phalen, R.F.; Cuddihy, R.G.; Fisher, G.L.; et al.: Main Features of the Proposed NCRP Respiratory Tract Model. Radiat. Protect. Dosimetry 38:179–184 (1991).
54. James, A.C.; Stahlhofen, W.; Rudolf, G.; et al.: The Respiratory Tract Deposition Model Proposed by the ICRP Task Group. Radiat. Protect. Dosimetry 38:159–165 (1991).

Instrument Section

A complete list of instrument manufacturers is provided in Table 22-I-1, which is located at the end of this section.

22-1. Electret-Passive Environmental Radon Monitoring (E-PERM®) System

Rad Elec Inc.

The E-PERM system employs electret ion chamber technology to provide an accurate, passive measurement of airborne radon over a period from 2 days to 1 year. The system consists of an electret (permanently charged Teflon® piece) loaded into an electrically conducting plastic chamber. Radon diffuses into the chamber and causes ionization. The electret collects the ions, thereby depleting the charge on the electret. A portable electret surface voltage reader is used to measure the change in surface voltage of the electret, which is related to the radon concentration and the exposure duration. With suitable adaptation, the system is usable for measuring airborne radon progeny, thoron, tritium, and other radioactive noble gases.

22-2. Radon Monitoring System

Genitron Instruments GMBH Frankfurt and AlphaGUARD Inc., Northbrook, IL

AlphaGUARD PQ2000 is a portable instrument with long-term battery or line operation for use indoors or in the field. Air temperature, relative humidity, and atmospheric pressure are recorded in 10-min intervals together with radon gas levels between ambient and 50,000 pCi/L. Operation is based on ionization chamber pulse counting. Response time is 30 min for a change from ambient to 30 pCi/L, which it negotiates in three steps of 10 min. The detection efficiency is 1.7 cpm per pCi/L. AlphaGUARD is accessed through the software package AlphaVIEW, which requires a 286 or better main processor with a 512-kB capacity and VGA compatible monitor. The interactive system is able to present and interpret stored data of up to 21 days. Thermal or laser printer options are available. The instrument weighs 10 lbs. Dimensions are 17 × 34 × 12 cm.

22-3. Radon Gas Monitor

Eberline Instrument Corp.

The Model RGM-3 is a microcomputer-based portable system for continuously measuring radon gas. The detector assembly consists of a metal chamber coated on the inside with zinc sulfide doped with silver powder for alpha sensitivity. Prefiltered air is drawn through the chamber by a vacuum pump. The RGM-3 supports two modes of operation. In the continuous mode, the pump runs while the onboard counting computer maintains a 1-hr file of count versus time. In the grab sampling mode, a sample is pulled into the chamber, monitored, and then flushed. Background compensation is automatically calculated based on a calibration flush with zero activity air and an estimate of previous plate out of the short-lived progeny. Sensitivity is 5 cpm/pCi/L, pump flow rate is 10 L/min, and battery life is 2–4 hrs for continuous sampling. The monitor is 41 × 25 × 30 cm and weighs 13.6 kg.

22-4. Rapid Radon Monitor

Technical Associates

The Model FR-5R-FS (not pictured) provides rapid testing; first appraisal results in just 6 min. Radon is collected onto charcoal in a cannister at a high flow rate. Sensitivity is 0.3 pCi/L at the 90% confidence level. Easy-to-operate digital scaler/analyzer. High-volume pump pulls over 200 L/min. Optional shielding permits in-house testing for standard 2 1/2-in. and 2 7/8-in. canisters.

22-5. Radon Measurement System

Pylon Electronics Inc.

Pylon's fully integrated AB-5 radon measurement system provides a full range of detection, monitoring, and measurement capabilities. The AB-5 combines a lightweight, portable radon monitor with a wide range of attachable probes, detectors, and other accessories for active and passive continuous radon gas measurement, working level and nuclide concentration measurement and analysis, surface contamination detection and wipe testing, and soil and water analysis. AB-5 dimensions are 21.6 × 9.6 × 24.1 cm; it weighs 3.2 kg (with internal battery).

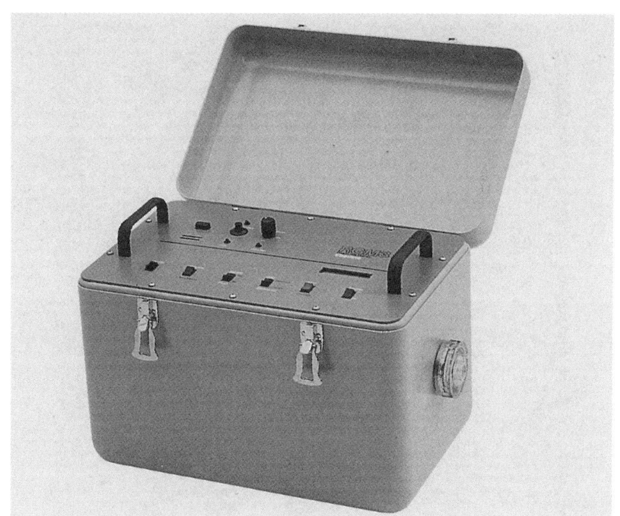

INSTRUMENT 22-3. Radon gas monitor.

22-6. Radon Gas Monitor

Sun Nuclear Corporation

The Model 1023 professional radon gas monitor is a microcomputer-based continuous radon monitor. Radon gas is allowed to diffuse into a chamber. Decay products are blocked from entry by a filter. In the chamber, the decay products plate out on a diffused-junction photodiode detector by means of an electrostatic field.

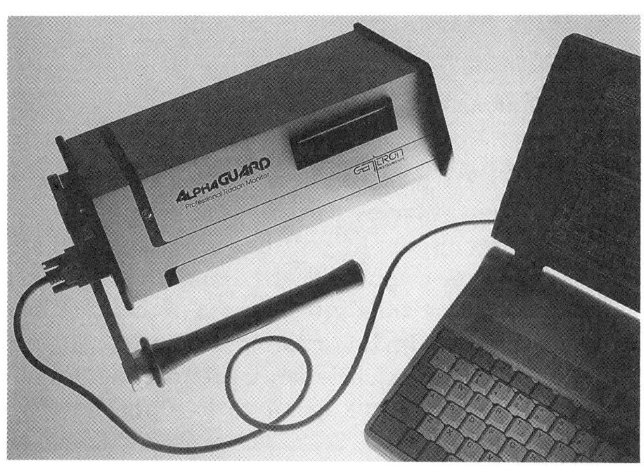

INSTRUMENT 22-2. Radon monitoring system.

INSTRUMENT 22-6. Radon gas monitor.

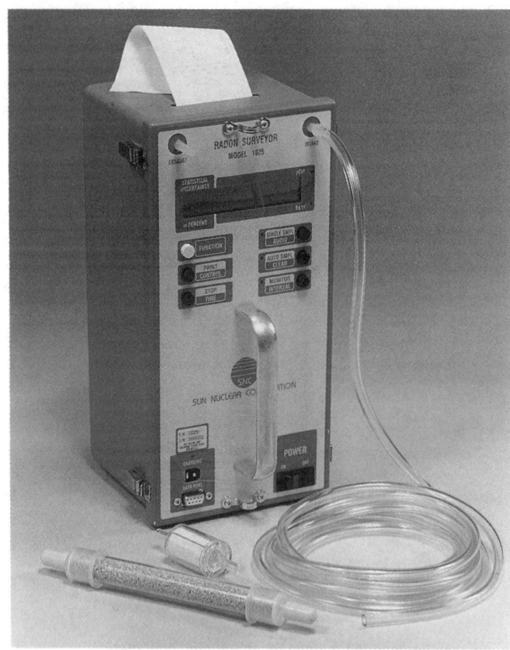

INSTRUMENT 22-7. Radon gas grab-sampler/monitor.

The system is completely solid-state with software calibration. Overall sensitivity is 2.5 cph pCi^{-1} L^{-1}. On demand, the Model 1023 displays the longer-term (since last reset) and short-term (12 hr) average radon gas concentration on a 3-digit LED display in pCi/L. The Model 1023 provides a hard-copy printout of the long-term memory data. It is line operated through the use of an AC to DC power adapter. It contains nonrecharging batteries which provide up to 7 hrs of uninterrupted power. The monitor contains mercury switches that place an indication, on the printout, of any movement of the instrument. The system is cylindrical in shape, approximately 5 in. in diameter and 7 in. high; it weighs 2 lbs. The simpler, but similar, Model 1024 Residential Radon Gas Monitor does not provide printer output.

22-7. Radon Gas Grab-Sampler/Monitor
Sun Nuclear Corporation

The Model 1025 radon gas surveyor is a completely self-contained, portable radon gas measurement and data collection system. The instrument is microcomputer-based and employs a diffused-junction photodiode as its alpha detector. It has three measurement modes. The single grab sample mode allows the user to initiate a grab sample measurement on demand. The automatic grab sample mode provides programmed grab sample capability. During both grab sample modes, the instrument discriminates against counts generated by ^{214}Po, avoiding the need to "flush" the system between individual grab samples. Sensitivity is 20 cph pCi^{-1} L^{-1} in both grab sample modes. The continuous monitor mode operates the pump continuously, logging measurements to memory in intervals defined by the user. No count discrimination technique is employed while in the continuous monitor mode; this results in an overall sensitivity of 40 cph pCi^{-1} L^{-1}. The Model 1025 radon gas surveyor contains an integral thermal printer, internal air pump, and rechargeable battery. The instrument has a liquid crystal display and includes a standard RS-232 serial computer interface. It operates on either line or battery power. A field calibration kit requires the availability of a known radon concentration.

22-8. Continuous Radon Measurement System
Pylon Electronics Inc.

Pylon's AB-4 Continuous Radon Measurement System for the measurement of radon gas concentrations in air is based on zinc sulfide scintillators and photo multiplier tubes. The AB-4 is qualified by U.S. EPA as a primary and/or a secondary device, as well as a mail-in device in U.S. EPA's Radon Measurement Proficiency program. Automatic field calibration (operating point), phone modem and alarm capabilities, optional internal printer, check source, and environmental sensors for pressure, temperature, and humidity have been incorporated. AB-4 dimensions are approximately 29 × 26 × 17 cm; it weighs 5.0 kg (with internal batteries).

22-9. Working Level Measurement System
Pylon Electronics Inc.

The Pylon Model WLx detects, measures, and discriminates radon and thoron progeny using a silicon solid-state particle detector for spectroscopic analysis. The portable WLx can be used as a continuous working level meter or as a grab sample monitor with variable counting routines. The WLx is preprogrammed with standard protocols, but operators may override these and create their own using the instrument keypad. Lower level of detection is 1 mWL, nominal. Included on this instrument are graphic display and graphic printer output; audible alarm with remote alarm facility; built-in, servo-controlled air pump; and user replaceable ni-cad or alkaline batteries.

22-10. Continuous Working Level Monitor
alphaNUCLEAR Company

The CIRAS II for measuring radon or thoron at residential sites provides periodic and cumulative average WL measurements. Recording memory is built in, as is PC computer compatibility through a serial port. Air is sampled at a constant flow rate of 125 cm^3 by a servo-controlled pump. Radon progeny are deposited on the filter collector, which is adjacent to a solid-state, diffused-junction detector sensitive to alpha particles only. Time resolution is 1 hr. There is a built-in rechargeable battery for 24-hr support. The monitor is 8 × 2.5 × 3 in.

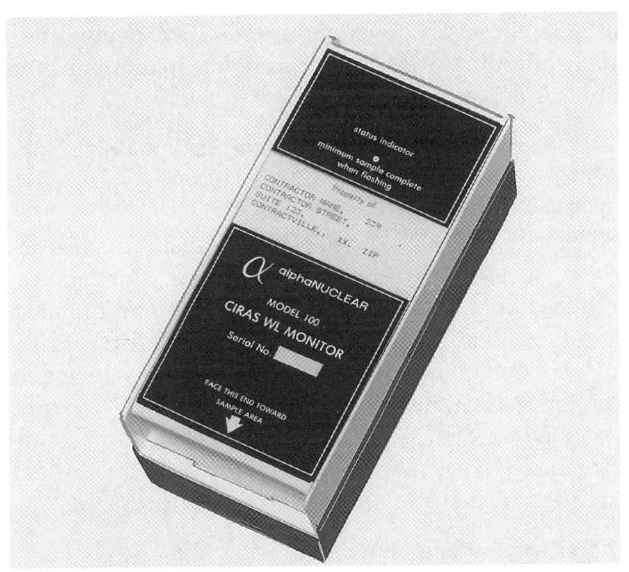

INSTRUMENT 22-10. Continuous working level monitor.

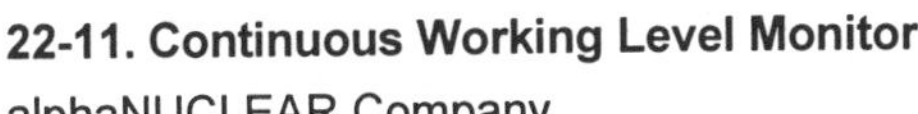

22-11. Continuous Working Level Monitor

alphaNUCLEAR Company

The PRISM II is a rugged, waterproof, tamperproof monitor for use in demanding or extreme environments (e.g., underground mines). Operation is similar to the CIRAS II. Sensitivity is 25 cph/mWL. Data logging memory is for 27 days of continuous operation with 10-min resolution. A built-in rechargeable battery allows 4 days of autonomous operation on a single charge. The unit is 2 × 5 × 6 in.

A version of the PRISM II (Model 570/PRISM) that is available incorporates red, yellow, and green indicator lights to give prompt local and remote indication of ambient WL conditions. The user can program threshold values. It includes a serial port and modem communications for remote annunciation through PLCs, SCADA, and central computer monitoring systems for automatic single or multisite monitoring.

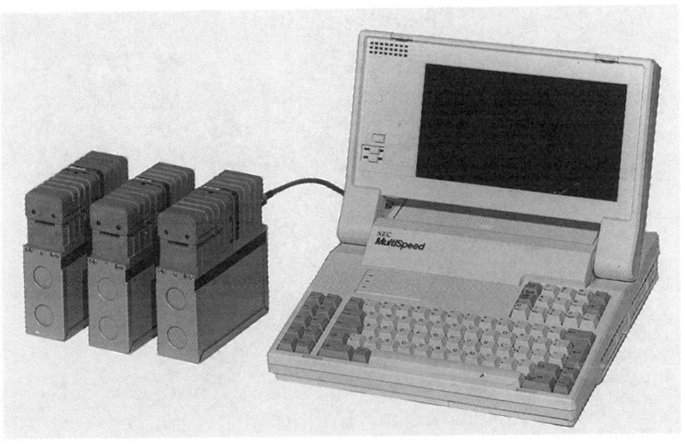

INSTRUMENT 22-11. Continuous working level monitor.

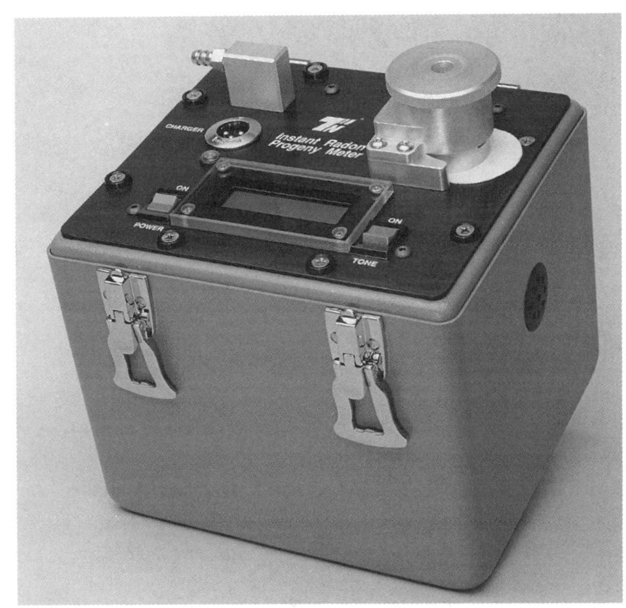

INSTRUMENT 22-12. Instant radon progeny meter.

22-12. Instant Radon Progeny Meter

Thomson & Nielson Electronics Ltd.

The Model TN-IR-21 employs an integral regulated 8 L/min pump to collect radon progeny on a glass microfiber filter that is positioned over a semiconductor alpha detector. The pump, filter, detector, display, rechargeable battery, and controlling electronics are all contained in a single 21 × 20 × 18 cm package weighing 6 kg. The instrument provides an estimate of radon progeny concentration in only 5 min and calculates more accurate (± 10% @ 20 mWL) results in 22.5 min.

22-13. Tritium in Air Monitor to Public Release Levels

Technical Associates

The Model STG-5ATL is a sensitive, rugged, down-to-public-release-level monitor (10^{-7} μCi/cm^3). It measures tritium as HTO in the presence of radioactive noble gases and varying external radiation background. The air being monitored is filtered, deionized, and divided into two streams. In one of the streams, HTO is removed. The two streams are then passed through two balanced detectors operated in subtractive mode. The net reading is presented directly with outputs for alarm (included) and printer and computer interface. Alarm and hard copy are standard features. Provision is made for interface with external computer or control system.

22-14. Alpha Air Monitor

Eberline Instrument Corp.

Model Alpha-6 is a continuous alpha monitor employing a solid-state detector with a 256-channel analyzer to separate energies in order to identify specific isotopes and minimize interference from radon-thoron alpha emitters. The air flow is adjustable from 10–100 L/min.

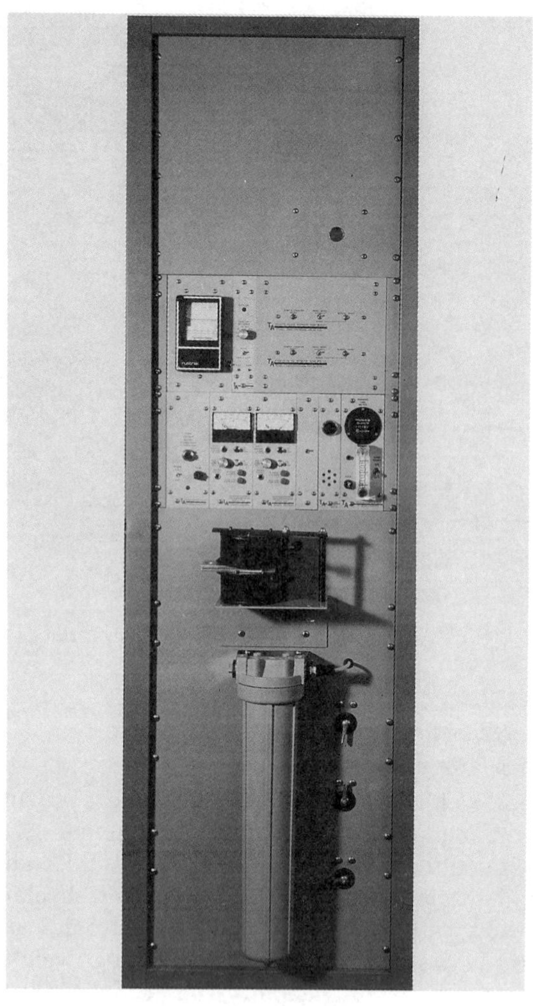

INSTRUMENT 22-13. Tritium in air monitor to public release levels.

The instrument provides immediate readout and connection to computer storage. An adjustable alarm is provided. The detector head comes in a variety of configurations to support inline and ambient monitoring of the air. The instrument measures approximately 35 × 32 × 38 cm and weighs about 6.6–7 kg, depending on the head. A CAM (ACS-1) system based on the Alpha-6 monitor is also available.

INSTRUMENT 22-14. Alpha air monitor.

22-15. Particulate, Iodine, and Noble Gas Air Monitoring System

Eberline Instrument Corp.

The Model PING-1A is shielded with 3 in. of lead in a 4π geometry to reduce background. Particulate is collected onto a 47-mm-diameter filter and monitored by a 2-in.-diameter × 0.010-in.-thick plastic beta scintillation detector and a solid-state alpha particle detector for radon background subtraction. Iodine is adsorbed on TEDA-impregnated charcoal and counted with a 2- × 2-in. NaI(Tl) detector and pulse height analyzer. The system is mounted on a cart.

22-16. Beta Particle Air Monitor

Eberline Instrument Corp.

The AMS-4 collects and monitors beta radiation on particles. The AMS-4 provides direct concentration readout that is continuously compared to alarm setpoints. The user can specify the DAC to concentration unit conversion factor. The detector head assembly may be placed up to 1000 feet from the instrument. The head supports two 2-in.-diameter, gas-proportional sensor detectors; one for monitoring the beta activity of the particulate filter and a second for real-time gamma background subtraction. An optional pump module supplies a nominal 60 L/min flow rate. A hot wire anemometer monitors actual flow rate. All count data are stored in the instrument's memory for later retrieval to a computer or printer. The radial sampling head and optional pump weigh 31 lbs.

INSTRUMENT 22-15. Particulate, iodine, and noble gas air monitoring system.

22-17. Beta Air Monitor

Ludlum Measurements, Inc.

The Ludlum Model 333-2 beta air monitor and the Model 333-IP rotary, carbon-vane air pump form a complete monitoring system. The 333-2 is configured for continuous sampling of airborne beta-emitters. Dual alarm setpoints provide independent setting of the ALERT level (strobe) and the ALARM level (bell). Set points may be checked via the front panel push-buttons. Failure detection is provided for loss of count in the primary detector. Two recorder outputs are provided. A low/no air flow indicator flashes when air flow drops below a preset rate. The critical air chamber components are constructed of stainless steel. Two pancake G–M tubes with window density of 1.5–2.0 mg/cm^2 mica are contained in a lead shield. The primary detector faces the filter paper and the secondary detector is positioned behind the primary detector for gamma subtraction. The Model 333-2 has a range of 10–100,000 cpm. Counting efficiency for ^{99}Tc is 36% (2 pi). This instrument is 27.75 × 15.875 × 13 in. and it weighs approximately 160 lbs (less pump and regulator).

INSTRUMENT 22-17. Beta air monitor.

22-18. Portable Continous Airborne Monitor, BAB

Novelec, North America, Inc.

The BAB is a family of real-time portable airborne alpha- and beta-emitting particulate monitors. Particles are collected on filter paper at a continuously monitored air flow rate. Using solid-state detectors and digital electronics, it reports ambient airborne concentrations directly in μCi/cm^3 over a wide range of concentrations. Detection sensitivity depends on background and counting time. This instrument operates in typical nuclear power plant background gamma radiation and radon levels. Gamma background compensation is accomplished with a guard detector; radon background via several spectrometry channels. Its portability allows it to be used at the work site to provide continuous coverage of the job. It provides preset alarm thresholds and built-in self testing. Data capture options allow for real-time control point monitoring of remote job sites by radio or RS-232 link to a PC and/or historical data capture on a RAM card for reading and storing in a PC.

22-19. Mobile Cart Type, Air Sampling System MRV-14 C

Hi-Q Environmental Products Company

This "golf cart/goose neck"-type unit is used for particulate and radioiodine sampling at adjustable operational breathing levels from 4 to 7 ft. These units use

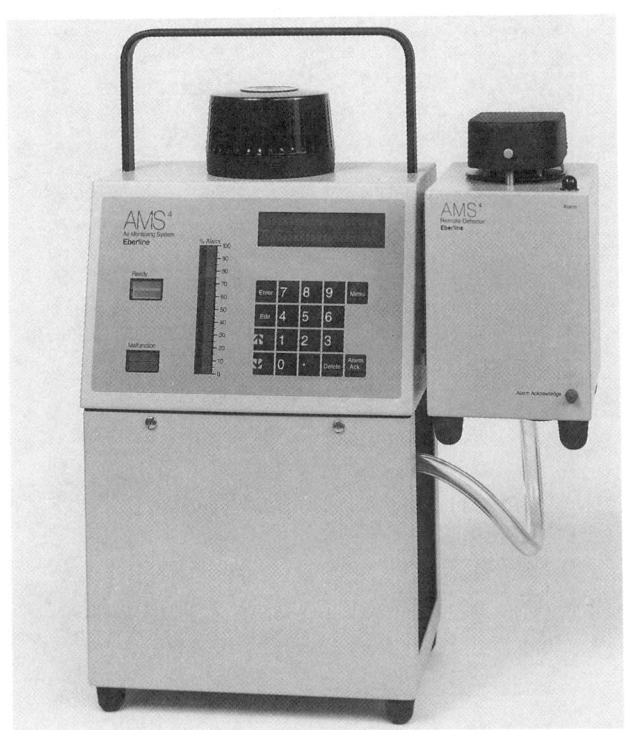

INSTRUMENT 22-16. Beta particle air monitor.

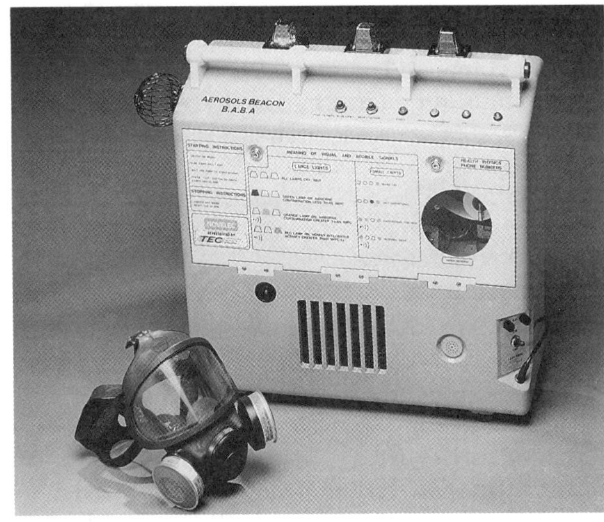

INSTRUMENT 22-18. Portable continous airborne monitor, BAB.

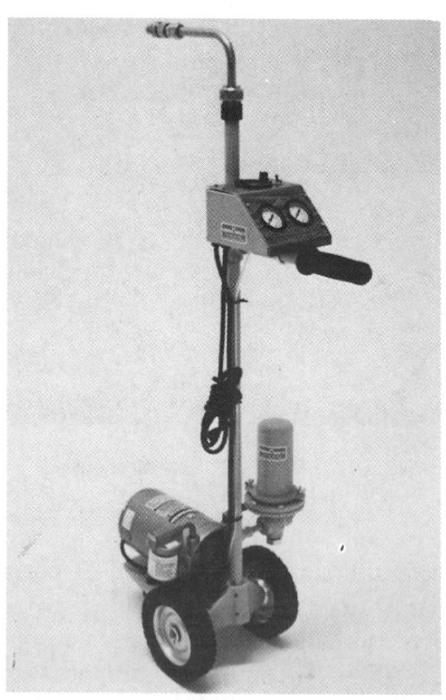

INSTRUMENT 22-19. Mobile cart type, air sampling system MRV-14 C.

oil-less, quiet, rotary carbon-vane pumps. The unit also comes with two vacuum gauges to measure the pressure differential between the pump and the filter head, which are mounted along with an electronic elapse timer. Iodine is collected with either TEDA-impregnated carbon cartridges available in three mesh sizes or silver-impregnated zeolite cartridges for subsequent radioactivity counting. The latter cartridges 1) permit analysis of radioiodine without interference from any radioactive noble gases in the air stream and 2) remove any radioiodine from the air stream to permit accurate analysis of radioactive noble gases. The Hi-Q AGX Series silver-impregnated zeolite cartridges contain a highly efficient inorganic adsorbent for the collection and removal of elemental and organic forms of radioactive iodine. Laboratory tests indicate that radioactive xenon, krypton, and other noble gases are not retained to any significant degree by the silver zeolite (approximately 1/15,000th or less than that retained by carbon). Various cartridge and filter holders are available to satisfy individual sampling requirements.

22-20. Iodine Air Monitor

Technical Associates

The Model FM-5-ABNI air monitor samples airborne radioiodine contamination and has alarm record capability. It also provides integrated exposure information and provides hard copy. The contaminant is collected in a standard charcoal filter cartridge. The filter is under constant surveillance via a scintillation detector. Limit of sensitivity (as ^{131}I) is 10^{-9} $\mu Ci\ ml^{-1}\ min^{-1}$ exposure.

INSTRUMENT 22-20. Iodine air monitor.

22-21. Air Monitor-Gas, Gross Beta-Gamma Particulate, and Iodine (or Gross Alpha)

Technical Associates

The Model BAM-3H three-channel air monitor simultaneously measures gross beta-gamma particulates,

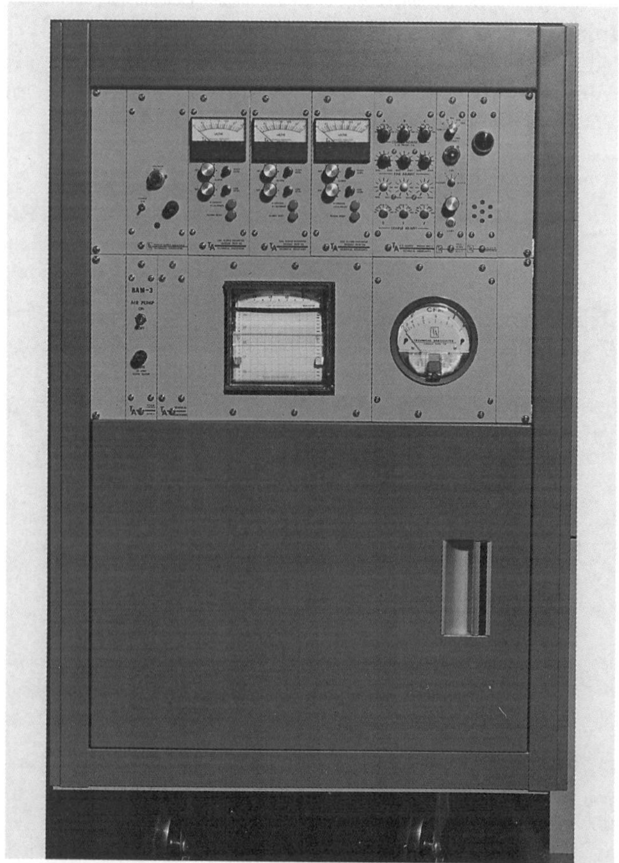

INSTRUMENT 22-21. Air monitor-gas, gross beta-gamma particulate, and iodine (or gross alpha).

gaseous radioactivity, and iodine (gross alpha in BAM-3HC). It is a continuous duty, high capacity, rugged skid or caster-mounted system. Electronics are plug-in modules allowing change or addition of function and rapid repair by substitution of modules in the field. Shields are 3-in., void-free, and lead encased in welded steel; they have stainless steel liners for easy decontamination. Filters are changed via a quick disconnect, o-ring, sealed filter holder. Air flow is factory set at 3 ft^3/min, but can be set at flows up to 10 ft^3/min without equipment change.

22-22. Moving Filter Alpha Plus Beta-Gamma System

Technical Associates

Model SAAM-1 filter tape A/BG air monitor system is a line-operated, continuous-duty, long period air monitor that automatically integrates over a preset period and prints results. It incorporates an alarm as well as hard copy. Standard configuration reads gross alpha and gross beta-gamma. It has plug-in capacity for one or more channels of specific radiation energies (e.g., ^{239}Pu, ^{238}U). This system draws air through a section of filter tape and measures the activity on the tape after a predetermined time; usually 20 min. It has a dwell time of 20 min, and sensitivity on the order of 1% of the most restrictive alpha or beta-gamma contamination standard.

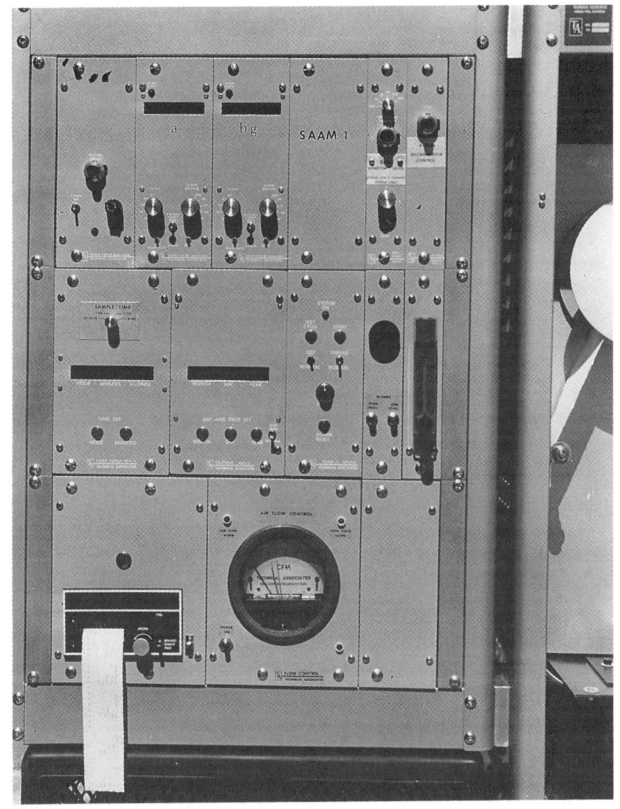

INSTRUMENT 22-22. Moving filter alpha plus beta-gamma system.

TABLE 22-I-1. List of Instrument Manufacturers

AlphaGUARD Inc. 3334 Commercial Avenue Northbrook, IL 60082 (708)206-0708 FAX (708)206-0114	Hi-Q Environmental Products Co. 7386 Trade Street San Diego, CA 92121 (619)549-2820 FAX (619)549-9657	Rad Elec Inc. 5714-C Industry Lane Frederick, MD 21701 (301)694-0011 FAX (301)694-0013
alphaNUCLEAR Company 1125 Derry Road East Mississauga, Ontario, Canada L5T 1P3 (416)564-1383 FAX (416)564-1297	Ludlum Measurements, Inc. P.O. Box 810 501 Oak Street Sweetwater, TX 79556 (915)235-5494 FAX (915)235-4672	Sun Nuclear Corporation 425-A Pineda Court Melbourne, FL 32940-7508 (407)254-7785 FAX (407)259-7979
Eberline Instrument Corp. P.O. Box 2108 504 Airport Road Santa Fe, NM 87504 (505)471-3232 FAX (505)473-9221	Novelec, North America, Inc. 113 W. Outer Drive P.O. Box 6621 Oak Ridge, TN 37831 (615)482-9287 FAX (615)483-0305	Technical Associates 7051 Eton Avenue Canoga Park, CA 91303 (818)883-7043 FAX (818)883-6103
Genitron Instruments GMBH Heerstrabe 149 D-6000 Frankfurt/Main-90 Germany	Pylon Electronics Inc. 147 Colonnade Road Ottawa, Ontario, Canada K2E 7L9 (613)226-7920 FAX (613)226-8195	Thomson & Nielson Ltd. 1050 Baxter Road Ottawa, Ontario, Canada K2C 3P1 (613)596-4563 FAX (613)596-5243

Chapter 23

Sampling Airborne Microorganisms and Aeroallergens

Janet M. Macher, Sc.D, M.P.H.,[A] Mark A. Chatigny, B.S.,[B] and Harriet A. Burge, Ph.D.[C]

[A]*California Department of Health Services, Environmental Health Laboratory, Berkeley, California;* [B]*University of California (Ret.), San Lorenzo, California;* [C]*Department of Environmental Health, Harvard School of Public Health, Boston, Massachusetts*

CONTENTS

Introduction

Environmental scientists rely on air monitoring to measure chemical and mineral contaminants outdoors and in workplaces. Airborne microorganisms and other biological materials also cause disease and can be studied by collecting air samples. Airborne microorganisms are potential problems outdoors (e.g., human, animal, and plant pathogens from natural sources and agricultural activities) and indoors (e.g., in operating rooms and food and drug processing facilities). Health-care professionals increasingly recognize bioaerosols as a cause of preventable airborne infections and hypersensitivity diseases, as well as related absences and lowered productivity in classrooms and workplaces.[(1)]

This chapter provides a discussion of the diversity of airborne biological particles and some suggestions on how to select the most suitable equipment for a variety of sampling situations. Also discussed are sampling for "viable" or "culturable microorganisms" (i.e., those that grow on artificial media in the laboratory, such as bacteria and fungi) and collection of "aeroallergens" (i.e., biological particles analyzed microscopically or chemically, such as pollen grains, fungus spores, amorphous allergens, and other biological debris). Some inhaled microorganisms cause infectious disease (e.g., measles, Legionnaires' disease, tuberculosis, and histoplasmosis). Many microorganisms and other biological particles cause hypersensitivity reactions (e.g., allergic asthma and rhinitis). Some biological particles also contain toxins and irritants (e.g., endotoxins from gram-negative bacteria and mycotoxins from fungi).

Although researchers from a variety of fields monitor airborne microorganisms and other bioaerosols, this chapter focuses primarily on the study of problems related to human health and well-being. Currently, there are no occupational exposure limits for bioaerosols and no universally accepted sampling methods, as explained below in an excerpt from the 1994–1995 *Threshold Limit Values and Biological Exposure Indices* Booklet from the American Conference of Governmental Industrial Hygienists (ACGIH):[2]

Threshold Limit Value for Biologically Derived Airborne Contaminants

Biologically derived airborne contaminants include bioaerosols (airborne particulates composed of or derived from living organisms) and volatile organic compounds released from living organisms. Bioaerosols include microorganisms (culturable, nonculturable, and dead microorganisms) and fragments, toxins, and particulate waste products from all varieties of living things. Biologically derived airborne contaminant mixtures are ubiquitous in nature and may be modified by human activity. All persons are repeatedly exposed, day after day, to a wide variety of such contaminants. At present, gravimetric Threshold Limit Values (TLVs) exist for some wood dusts, which are primarily of biological origin, and for cotton dust, which is at least in part biological. There are no TLVs for concentrations of total culturable or countable organisms and particles (e.g., "bacteria" or "fungi"); specific culturable or countable organisms and particles (e.g., *Aspergillus fumigatus*); infectious agents (e.g., *Legionella pneumophila*); or assayable biological-source contaminants (e.g., endotoxin or volatile organic compounds).

A. A general TLV for a concentration of culturable (e.g., total bacteria and/or fungi) or countable bioaerosols (e.g., total pollen, fungal spores, and bacteria) is not scientifically supportable because:

1. Culturable organisms or countable spores do not comprise a single entity, i.e., bioaerosols are complex mixtures of different kinds of particles.
2. Human responses to bioaerosols range from innocuous effects to serious disease and depend on the specific agent and susceptibility factors within the person.
3. Measured concentrations of culturable and countable bioaerosols are dependent on the method of sample collection and analysis. It is not possible to collect and evaluate all of these bioaerosol components using a single sampling method.

Terminology, Methods, and Limitations

"Microorganism," as used in this chapter, includes viruses, bacteria (also rickettsia and chlamydia), fungi (yeasts and molds), and spores. The term "spore" refers to clusters or single particles from fungal fruiting bodies, or resistant dormant structures some bacteria produce. Microorganisms, in particular bacteria and viruses, often occur in aggregates or attached to other material when airborne, e.g., skin flakes, soil particles, or the dried residue of water droplets.[3] Methods for collecting bioaerosols are similar to those for collecting other airborne particles (Table 23-1); however, the analytical techniques used to detect and quantify bioaerosols may impose limitations on collection methods (see discussion of "Assay Methods," below).

Available devices for collecting bioaerosols, at present, tend to be somewhat less sophisticated, although no less diverse, than those for other particles. There are no direct-reading sampling instruments to detect airborne microorganisms or biologically derived contaminants, or to identify them immediately after collection, except for particles that can be recognized by microscopic examination. Although automated identification systems for cultured bacteria are becoming more available and reliable, samples still require fairly time-consuming processing before these can be applied. Even rapid detection methods based on gene amplification or immunoassay require several hours of laboratory processing. Unique to sampling viable organisms is a requirement for aseptic equipment and specimen handling. Microorganisms are present almost everywhere, e.g., in air and water, and on inanimate objects and the human body. Bioaerosol sampling results may be incorrect and misleading if the personnel collecting the samples do not appreciate the need to practice appropriate sterile techniques.

The amount of material in an infectious, allergenic, or toxic dose of a bioaerosol can be very small compared with the amount of airborne dust or number of fibers needed to produce other diseases. Infectious agents multiply after entering the body, and very little allergen, toxin, or irritant may trigger a response in a sensitive individual. Microbiologists frequently use the ability of microorganisms to multiply to achieve very sensitive detection and very specific identification. Some allergen assays, on the other hand, require relatively large amounts of material and concentration, multiplication, or amplification steps.

There is no one group of "indicator organisms" to measure biological air quality, unlike the use of coliform bacteria to assess drinking water quality. Neither can an investigator always decide clearly when a bioaerosol's presence reflects normal occurrence and when it represents undesirable contamination. Overviews on the subject of bioaerosol sampling discuss the types and concentrations of material typically found in a variety of environments,[4–8] but authorities seldom venture to recommend allowable or desirable bioaerosol concentrations.[2]

Literature Overview

It is neither possible to include in this chapter a review of the extensive literature on sampling bioaerosols, nor is it necessary for an investigator to be familiar with the great variety of instruments and procedures that have been developed. Several books cover the field of aerobiology more broadly,[9–11] and a number of reviews discuss specific types of samplers and their uses and limitations.[12–18] The references cited in this chapter provide detailed discussions of the topics briefly presented here. Readers are encouraged to review the references listed in previous editions of this chapter for a historical perspective of the field, because many earlier references were omitted from this edition to allow space for more recent and accessible materials.

Bioaerosols in Indoor Environments

A World Health Organization document provides a good overview of the current state of knowledge on airborne viable particles, allergens, and other biologically derived material.[1] The indoor environment usually contains a different variety of bioaerosols than outdoor air; e.g., there are greater numbers of airborne bacteria from humans indoors than outdoors, but more airborne fungi from environmental sources outdoors than indoors.

Medical researchers and microbiologists developed much of the technology for collecting pathogenic airborne microorganisms to study infectious disease transmission. Plant pathologists developed many of the methods used to collect airborne agents of crop infections, toxin-producing fungi, and nonculturable bioaerosols.

Bioaerosol sampling methods have been used indoors to evaluate measures to reduce wound infections during surgery,[5,19,20] to survey the types and concentrations of microorganisms in residences,[6–8,21–25] and to evaluate respiratory exposures to endotoxin.[26,27] Bioaerosol sampling has also been used to measure allergens in residential and occupational settings[28–33] and to examine microbiological air quality in food processing plants and animal containment buildings.[34–38] Water-cooled, heat-transfer equipment has been implicated in outbreaks of Legionnaires' disease with transmission often occurring indoors.[39,40] Air sampling has helped investigators confirm possible modes of legionellosis transmission, although the source of infection is usually determined by sampling water sources, not air.[41–44]

Respiratory complaints and other possibly building-related symptoms in offices and elsewhere indoors appear to be increasingly common.[11,45–47] Exposures to microorganisms or their by-products,[21] as opposed to chemicals (e.g., formaldehyde and volatile organic compounds) or nonbiological particles (e.g., glass fibers), account for an unknown fraction of building-related complaints. Guidelines for sampling indoor bioaerosols emphasize the importance of good medical assessment of building occupants and a thorough visual inspection of a facility before undertaking air sampling.[4,11]

Bioaerosols in Outdoor Environments

Outdoors, as compared to indoors, bioaerosols 1) are generated by a wider variety of sources, 2) are suspended in moving rather than often virtually still air, 3) must be collected during a variety of weather conditions, and 4) have undergone greater stress from changes in relative humidity, ultraviolet radiation, and exposure to air pollutants, which may inactivate sensitive microorganisms or change the chemical or physical structure of allergens and toxins.

A variety of microorganisms and biologically derived material has been recovered from ambient outdoor air[9–11,28,48,49] and from air near local sources including wastewater treatment plants[50] and waste handling facilities.[27,51,52] Bioaerosol sampling has been used to demonstrate the possibility of viral or bacterial release from ocean surf[53] and to investigate long-distance transport of animal pathogens.[9,10,54]

Aerosol Chamber Experiments

Researchers have learned a great deal from studies with test aerosols generated in experimental chambers in addition to studies on naturally occurring indoor and outdoor bioaerosols. Researchers have studied the survival of airborne viruses and bacteria to understand respiratory disease transmission,[55,56] explore the ef-

TABLE 23-1. Commercially Available Samplers for Collecting Bioaerosols

Sampler[A]	Operation	Sampling Rate (L/min)	Suggested Sampling Time (min)	Manufacturer/ Supplier[B]	Price[C]	Applications and Remarks
23-1. ROTATING SLIT or SLIT-TO-AGAR IMPACTORS: a–c. (vp/sc)[D]	Impaction onto agar in a 10- or 15-cm culture plate on a rotating surface	28–50, 700	0.5–60, depending on model/ situation	BC, BGI, CLL, NBS	III	Provide information on aerosol concentration over time. Some models available with variable rotational speeds.
23-2. MULTIPLE-HOLE IMPACTORS:						
a. Single-stage impactors						
i. 100-hole impactor (sc)	Impaction onto agar in a 9-cm plate	10 or 20	1–30	BMC	II	Compact.
ii. 219- or 487-hole impactors (sc)	Impaction onto agar in a 6.5- or 9-cm contact plate	90 or 180	0.5–5	SBI	III	Widely used. 219- and 487-hole heads available with 0.5- or 1-mm holes.
iii. 400-hole impactor (N-6) (vp,co)	Impaction onto agar in a 10-cm culture plate	28	1–30	GRA	III	Widely used.
b. Two-stage, 200-hole impactor (vp,co)	See 2a(iii), above	28	1–30	GRA	III	Divides samples into less and more respirable fractions.
c. Six-stage, 400-hole impactor (vp,co)	See 2a(iii), above	28	1–30	GRA	III	Widely used. Provides information on particle size distribution.
d. Eight-stage, personal impactor (vp)	Impaction onto 3.4-cm substrates or media in special trays	2	≤480 with filters, 5–30 with media	GRA, SKC	III	Provides information on particle size distribution. For viable recovery, sampler useful only in highly contaminated environments.
23-3. CENTRIFUGAL SAMPLERS:						
a. Agar strip impactors						
i. Standard impactor (sc)	Impaction onto agar in plastic strips	40 (nominal)	0.5–8	BDC	III	Widely used. Collection strips available only from supplier.
ii. Plus impactor (sc)	See 3a(i), above	50 (nominal)	0.2–20	BDC	III	Collection strips available only from supplier.
b. Cyclone sampler (sc)	Reverse flow cyclone	≤ 20	≤ 99	BMC	III	Useful for collecting large amounts of bioaerosols.
23-4. LIQUID IMPINGERS:						
a. Single-stage, all glass impingers, AGI-4 and AGI-30 (vp,co)	Impingement into liquid, jet 4 mm or 30 mm above impaction surface	12.5	1–30	AGI, MIL	I	Cells on or in larger particles broken apart. Suitable for collecting viruses as well as other bioaerosols. More vigorous impaction with AGI-4 than AGI-30.
b. i–ii Three-stage impingers (vp,co)	Impingement into liquid	10, 20, or 50	1–30	BMC, HG	I to II	See 4a, above. Provides information on particle size distribution.

TABLE 23-1 (con't.). Commercially Available Samplers for Collecting Bioaerosols

Sampler[A]	Operation	Sampling Rate (L/min)	Suggested Sampling Time (min)	Manufacturer/ Supplier[B]	Price[C]	Applications and Remarks
23-5. FILTERS						
a. Cassette filters (vp)	Filtration	1–5	5–60	CC, GS, MIL, SKC	I to II	Portable, inexpensive, allow personal monitoring. Some loss of viability due to cell desiccation. Collection efficiency depends on pore size. Assay efficiency depends on nature of filter material.
b. High-volume filters (vp)	Filtration	150–2000	up to 24 hrs	BGI, GMW, SKC	II to III	Useful for collecting large amounts of aeroallergens and toxins. Noisy indoors. Collection efficiency depends on pore size.
23-6. SETTLING SURFACES:						
a. Open culture plate, settle plate	Gravity settling onto agar in culture plate	undefined	≤240	—	I	Widely available and simple, but collection biased toward large particles. Used to estimate surface deposition.
b. Adhesive-coated surface	Gravity settling onto coated surface, e.g., glass microscope slide	undefined	minutes to days	—	I	See 6a, above. Used to collect aeroallergens for microscopic identification.
23-7. POLLEN, SPORE, AND PARTICLE IMPACTORS:						
a. i–ii. 1- to 7-day tape/slide impactors (sc)	Impaction onto a rotating drum with tape strip or glass slide	10	1–7 days	BMC, L	II to III	Used outdoors to collect pollen and large spores for microscopic identification.
b. i–iii Moving slide impactors (sc)	Impaction and settling onto moving glass slide	10, 15	Continuous or intermittent, minutes to days	ABP, BMC, L	III	Used indoors to collect pollen and large spores for microscopic identification. Used outdoors protected from rain and snow.
c. Stationary slide impactor (sc)	See 7b, above, glass slide stationary	10	30 s to 30 min	BMC	II	Compact. See 7b, above. Used primarily indoors.
d. Rotating rod impactors (sc)	Impaction onto rotating rods	48 (nominal)	Continuous or intermittent, minutes to days	STI	II to III	Used outdoors to collect pollen and large spores for microscopic identification.

[A] See "Instrument Descriptions" section.
[B] See Table 23-I-1, Manufacturers and Suppliers of Samplers to Collect Bioaerosols.
[C] Price range (sampler only, see Footnote D, below): I = < $100 (U.S.), II = $100 to $1000 (U.S.), III = > $1000 (U.S.).
[D] co = A critical orifice may be incorporated into the sampler. Requires a vacuum pump with sufficient capacity.
sc = Self-contained with built-in air mover.
vp = Requires a vacuum pump and flow control device that may be available from the sampler manufacturer.

fects of environmental factors on bioaerosol survival,[9,56] and evaluate air sampler performance.[57–60]

Bioaerosol Sampler Selection

As in any sampling program, having clearly defined objectives is essential when collecting bioaerosols. An investigator must consider possible sampling locations, sample number, sample collection time, effects of seasonal and temporal variations in bioaerosol concentration, and assay system limitations. The investigator must also specify the desired level of identification and quantification of the recovered material. The last two factors are especially important because the biological, chemical, and physical condition of bioaerosols is often critical for accurate identification and quantification, and the need to collect material with minimal damage can outweigh other considerations (see "Assay Methods").

Table 23-1 describes several widely used and readily available samplers, and Table 23-2 lists samplers suitable for indoor and outdoor air monitoring, separating them by the form in which cells and particles carrying cells are collected, i.e., left intact or washed apart (see the following section). Almost all of the devices listed in Table 23-2 are suitable for sampling intermediate concentrations of culturable particles indoors without sizing them. Samplers can be compared by scanning the columns in Table 23-2, noting the types of bioaerosols and analyses for which instruments are suited. The "Instrument Descriptions" section of this chapter provides illustrations and detailed information on the samplers listed in Tables 23-1 and 23-2. Investigators also must choose suitable collection and culture media and incubation temperatures to measure culturable microorganisms, as outlined in Table 23-3 (see also "Assay Methods — Culture").

Collecting Intact Particles

When studying bioaerosols, the only information that may be needed is the concentration of particles containing cells, spores, etc., without concern for whether the particles contain one or more individual units. Collection of bioaerosols directly on agar-based culture media, on which the microorganisms form discrete colonies, is the simplest method to determine the concentration of airborne particles carrying culturable microorganisms (Instruments 23-1a–c, 23-2a–d, 23-3a–b, and 23-6a; also see "Assay Methods"). In addition, some bioaerosols can be collected on slides and filters for microscopic examination, counting intact particles and estimating the number of individual cells or spores in each aggregate.[3,66,67]

Knowing the concentration of intact bioaerosols may be sufficient in an operating room where viable microorganisms are often limited to a few species on dust particles, skin flakes, etc., which can deposit on open wounds and sterile instruments.[5] Sampling relatively large volumes of air for culturable particles and identifying known or opportunistic pathogens can provide a useful assessment of the potential for wound infection. However, investigators must determine the total number of culturable microorganisms in air when measuring the concentration of airborne pathogens to estimate respiratory infectious dose, i.e., the concentration of intact respirable particles multiplied by the number of cells per particle.

Aerosols sampled to measure the concentration of individual cells typically are collected in or transferred to a liquid (Instruments 23-2d, 23-3b, 23-4a–b, and 23-5a), and the resulting cell suspensions transferred to culture media or delivered to other assay systems.[63,64] Investigators will often also wish to have parallel samples to measure intact particles, as described above.

The number of cells or spores in bioaerosol aggregates varies widely, depending on microorganism type and source.[68] Fišar *et al.*[66] found an average of 1.4 bacteria or yeast per particle in urban air, and Lundholm[69] found 13 bacteria per particle in a cotton mill, 24 in a sewage plant, and 147 on human skin fragments. Karlsson and Malmberg[67] observed an average of three spores per particle in agricultural air and reported that more than half of the spores occurred alone or in respirable aggregates. Lacey[3] reviewed and summarized a number of studies that examined the effects of aggregation on bioaerosol aerodynamic behavior and infectivity.

The Physical Sampling Environment

This section considers some practical aspects of air monitoring, not the least of which is whether samples are collected indoors or outdoors, as discussed earlier and outlined in Table 23-2. Devices that operate at fairly high flow rates but are quiet and unobtrusive are recommended for sampling in residences, offices, and healthcare settings. Samplers that require auxiliary electrical power are not a problem indoors [Instruments 23-1a–c, 23-2a(iii), and 23-2b–c], but battery-operated samplers may be more convenient [Instruments 23-2a(i)–(ii) and 23-3a–b]. Sampling in a cleanroom often requires that measurements be taken at many sampling points, but the contaminants of concern are usually hardy environmental microorganisms present at low concentrations, in which case a simple filtration device may be suitable[70,71] (Instrument 23-5a, and Chapter 13). Sampling for spores and pollen outdoors requires self-contained, low-power, robust samplers able to withstand adverse weather conditions [Instruments 23-7a(i)–(ii)].

Typical Sampling Train

A typical sampling train for bioaerosol collection includes the following components, in order: air inlet, particle collector, flowmeter, flow rate controller, and air mover (Figures 12-1 and 13-1). Air inlets should minimize particle entry and wall losses before the particle collector. The particle collection section of a sampler should have known efficiency and be reliable. Chapters 4, 5, 13, 14, and 15 describe the principles by which particles are separated from a suspending air stream. A particle collector may be a single element, e.g., a filter, or single-stage impinger or impactor (Figure 23-1), or there may be more than one unit in series, e.g., a multiple-stage impinger or cascade impactor (Figure 23-2). Pressure drop across the particle collection section of a sampling train should be as low as possible to minimize the size of air mover needed.

An in-line rotameter is commonly used to measure air flow rate in bioaerosol samplers (Figure 23-3 and Chapter 7). In-line flowmeters and pressure gauges should be calibrated with all sampling elements connected, including filters, culture plates, and collection fluids (see also Chapter 14). Power supply for a vacuum pump may be electrical line current or replaceable or rechargeable batteries (see also Chapter 12). An instrument may have only an indicator light to show that it is functioning if flow rate is constant or automatically controlled. Otherwise, air flow rate may be controlled manually or a critical orifice may be used to maintain constant flow. Critical-flow orifices operate on the principle that for a given set of upstream conditions, the velocity of air from a restricted opening increases with decreasing downstream-to-upstream pressure ratio until air reaches sonic velocity. The pressure and air velocity in the throat of an orifice will not fall below the conditions at the critical point even if one further reduces downstream pressure. The capillary nozzle in an all-glass impinger (Instrument 23-4a) functions as a critical orifice, and some multiple-hole impactors also have built-in flow-control devices.

Sampler Maintenance and Calibration

Users should check samplers for proper functioning each time they are operated, e.g., measure air flow rate, verify vacuum pressure if using a critical orifice, and clear blockage from sampling slits or holes. Users should confirm air flow rate periodically with an independent flow measuring device (Chapter 7), and never assume that built-in flow meters or critical orifices operate accurately until verified.

Obstruction of the sampling inlets in multiple-hole impactors occurs more readily with small openings than with large, e.g., the 0.25-mm-diameter holes in stage six of Instrument 23-2c. Unobstructed openings are critical for impactors where, for a given flow rate, the size of an orifice controls jet velocity. Jet velocity, in part, determines an impactor's cutpoint or d_{50}, i.e., the particle aerodynamic diameter (d_a) for which 50 percent of the particles are collected. Aerodynamic diameter is the diameter of a smooth, spherical, unit-density particle with the same gravitational settling velocity as the particle in question (see also Chapter 5). The curve produced from plotting percent particles collected against particle d_a^2 for a specific impactor approximates a cumulative lognormal relationship characterized by cutpoint diameter and geometric standard deviation (σ_g) (Chapter 14). Impactor collection efficiency reaches 99 percent at a particle diameter equal to $d_{50} \bullet 3(\sigma_g)$.

The distance between an impaction nozzle or jet and a collection surface (e.g., agar, glass slide, or adhesive tape) is also critical to particle collection efficiency[15] (see also Chapter 14 and the section on "Sampling 'Efficiency'" in this chapter). Slit-to-agar impactors frequently have adjustable stage heights to ensure proper slit-to-agar distance (Figure 23-3), but for other impactors, the distance varies with the type of plate used and the amount of agar added. Most impactors are designed for a jet-to-plate distance approximately equal to nozzle width, e.g., 0.25 to 1 mm. Agar volume should comply closely to a manufacturer's specification for size-separating samplers to ensure collection of particles close to an impactor's d_{50} cutpoint. Agar depth is less critical for general bioaerosol sampling as long as 1) the agar surface is fairly level and smooth, 2) all plates have approximately the same amount of agar (e.g., ± 3 ml of the desired volume for a 10-cm plate), 3) the jet-to-plate distance in "overfilled" plates is not less than half the nozzle width, and 4) agar in "underfilled" plates is not so thin it dries out during sample incubation.

It is essential that sample specimens be protected from contamination during collection and while being transported to and from a laboratory. Viable microorganisms may be carried over from one sampling session to another if a device is not sanitized between uses (e.g., by dipping in or wiping with 70% ethanol and air drying). This consideration is of particular concern when sampling outdoors and in highly contaminated environments where hardy bacterial and fungal spores may be abundant.

Air Velocity and Sampling Rates

One of the most critical physical differences between indoor and outdoor environments often is the velocity of the air from which samples are taken. Air velocities outdoors can range from 0 to 15 m/s, with rapid and radical changes of direction, whereas low ambient air speeds can usually be expected indoors, typically <0.5

TABLE 23-2. Outline for Selecting a Bioaerosol Sampler

Sampling Location	Form of Recovered Particles	Separation of Particles by Size	Aerosol Concen-tration[A]	Rotating Slit Impactors [23-1a–c][B]	Multiple-hole Impactors: Single-Stage Impactors 100-Hole [23-2a(i)]	219-Hole [23-2a(ii)]	487-Hole [23-2a(ii)]	400-Hole [23-2a(iii)]	2-Stage, 200-Hole [23-2b]	6-Stage, 200-Hole [23-2c]	8-Stage, Personal [23-2d]	Centrifugal Samplers: Agar Strip Impactors [23-3a(i–ii)]	Cyclone Sampler [23-3b]
Indoors or Outdoors	Intact particles	No size separation	Low	C[C]	C	C	C	C	C	C	M	C	—
			Interm.	C	C	C	C	C	C	C	M	C	—
			High	C	C	—	C	C	C	C	M	C	—
		Size separation	Low	—	—	—	—	—	C	C	M	—	—
			Interm.	—	—	—	—	—	C	C	M	—	—
			High	—	—	—	—	—	C	C	M	—	—
	Dispersed particles[D]	No size separation	Low	C	C	C	C	C	C	C	I,B,M	—	I,B,M,H
			Interm.	C	C	C	C	C	C	C	I,B,M	—	I,B,M,H
			High	C	C	—	C	C	C	C	I,B,M,H	—	I,B,M,H
		Size separation	Low	—	—	—	—	—	C	C	I,B,M	—	—
			Interm.	—	—	—	—	—	C	C	I,B,M	—	—
			High	—	—	—	—	—	C	C	I,B,M,H	—	—

[A]Low concentration: <100 CFU/m^3, e.g., cleanrooms and operating rooms; collect >0.5 m^3 (>500 L) of air.
Intermediate concentration: 100–1000 CFU/m^3, e.g., general indoor and outdoor concentrations; collect 0.25–1 m^3 (250–1000 L) of air.
High concentration: >1000 CFU/m^3, e.g., animal and plant handling areas, outdoor construction and excavation sites; collect <0.25 m^3 (<250 L) of air.
[B]Numbers refer to listing of samplers in Table 23-1.
[C]B = Bioassay for toxins, e.g., endotoxin and mycotoxin.
C = Culture of sensitive and hardy microorganisms, e.g., vegetative cells and spores.
H = Culture of hardy microorganisms only, e.g., spore-forming bacteria and fungi.
I = Immunoassay for allergens.
M = Microscopic examination.
[D]When particles washed from the collection surface or when glycerol-gelatin or other soluble medium used (see text).

TABLE 23-2 (con't.). Outline for Selecting a Bioaerosol Sampler

				Liquid Impingers			Filters		Settling Surfaces		Pollen, Spore, and Particle Impactors			
				Single-Stage [23-4a(i–ii)]										
Sampling Location	Form of Recovered Particles	Separation of Particles by Size	Aerosol Concen-tration	AGI-30	AGI-4	Three-Stage [23-4b(i–ii)]	Casette Filters [23-5a]	Hi-Vol Filters [23-5b]	Settle Plates [23-6a]	Coated Surface [23-6b]	1- to 7-Day [23-7a(i–ii)]	Moving Slide [23-7b(i–iii)]	Station-ary Slide [23-7c]	Rotating Rods [23-7d]
Indoors	Intact particles	No size separation	Low	—	—	—	I,H	—	M	M	M,I	M,I	—	M
			Interm.	—	—	—	I,M	—	M,C	M	M,I	M,I	M	M
			High	—	—	—	I,M	—	M,C	M	M,I	M,I	M	M
		Size separation	Low	—	—	—	I,H[E]	—	—	—	—	—	—	—
			Interm.	—	—	—	I,M[E]	—	—	—	—	—	—	—
			High	—	—	—	I,M[E]	—	—	—	—	—	—	—
	Dispersed particles	No size separation	Low	—	—	I,B,M,C	I,B,H	—	M	M	M,I	M,I	—	I,B,M,H
			Interm.	I,B,M,C	I,B,M,H	I,B,M,C	I,B,M,H	—	M,C	M,H	M,I	M,I	M	I,B,M,H
			High	I,B,M,C	I,B,M,H	I,B,M,C	I,B,M,H	—	M,C	M,H	M,I	M,I	M	I,B,M,H
		Size separation	Low	—	—	I,B,M,C	I,B,H[E]	—	—	—	—	—	—	—
			Interm.	—	—	I,B,M,C	I,B,M,H[E]	—	—	—	—	—	—	—
			High	—	—	I,B,M,C	I,B,M,H[E]	—	—	—	—	—	—	—
Outdoors	Intact particles	No size separation	Low	—	—	—	I,H	I	—	—	M,I	M,I	—	M
			Interm.	—	—	—	I,M	I	—	—	M,I	M,I	M	M
			High	—	—	—	I,M	I	—	—	M,I	—	M	M
		Size separation	Low	—	—	—	I,H[E]	I[E]	—	—	—	—	—	—
			Interm.	—	—	—	I,M[E]	I[E]	—	—	—	—	—	—
			High	—	—	—	I,M[E]	I[E]	—	—	—	—	—	—
	Dispersed particles[D]	No size separation	Low	—	—	I,B,M,C	I,B,H	I,B	—	—	M,I	M,I	—	I,B,M,H
			Interm.	I,B,M,C	I,B,M,H	I,B,M,C	I,B,M,H	I,B	—	—	M,I	M,I	M	I,B,M,H
			High	I,B,M,C	I,B,M,H	I,B,M,C	I,B,M,H	—	—	—	M,I	—	M	I,B,M,H
		Size separation	Low	—	—	I,B,M,C	I,B,H[E]	I,B[E]	—	—	—	—	—	—
			Interm.	—	—	I,B,M,C	I,B,M,H[E]	I,B[E]	—	—	—	—	—	—
			High	—	—	I,B,M,C	I,B,M,H[E]	—	—	—	—	—	—	—

[A–D]See previous page.
[E]When used with a cyclone or other size-selective particle separator.

TABLE 23-3. Collection and Culture Media for Culturable Microorganisms

Microorganism	Liquid Collection Media[A,B]	Agar-based Culture Media[B]	Incubation Temperature	Incubation Time
Bacteria				
Human flora, potential pathogens	Sterile distilled water Physiological saline Phosphate buffered saline Nutrient broth Brain/heart infusion broth Peptone water	Soybean-casein digest agar (SCDA) Heart infusion agar Nutrient agar Blood agar	35 to 37°C	18–48 hrs
Environmental saprophytes	(see above)	R2A SCDA	25 to 30°C	>24 hrs
Thermophilic bacteria	(see above)	SCDA	50 to 55°C	>18 hrs
Total coliform	(see above), Endo broth	EMB agar Endo agar	35 to 37°C	18–48 hrs
Fungi				
Environmental saprophytes	Sterile distilled water Physiological saline Phosphate buffered saline Peptone water (wetting agents and antifoams needed)	Malt extract agar Sabouraud dextrose agar Rose Bengal agar (with Streptomycin) Inhibitory mold agar	Room temperature, approx. 20 to 25°C	>24 hrs, often several days to weeks
Potential pathogens	(see above)	(see above)	35 to 37°C	(see above)
Xerophilic fungi	(see above)	Malt extract agar with added NaCl, sucrose, or dichloran-glycerol	20 to 25°C	(see above)
Viruses	Sterile distilled water Physiological saline Phosphate buffered saline Minimum essential medium Nutrient broth Brain/heart infusion broth	Appropriate cell or tissue culture	Generally 35 to 37°C	>18 hrs, dependent on cell line

[A]Antifoams (e.g., Dow Corning Antifoam A [Dow Corning Corp., Midland, MI] or GE 60 [G.E., Co., Waterford, NY]) can be added, as well as wetting agents (e.g., Tween - 0.1%) to disperse clusters, gelatin to prevent clumping of collected particles, and other compounds (e.g., betaine to reduce osmotic stress[(61)] and catalase to enhance resusitation).[(62)]
[B]Selected antibiotics can be added to reduce the growth of contaminants.[(63–65)]

m/s. Exposed culture plates (Instrument 23-6a) or glass slides (Instrument 23-6b) have been used to estimate bioaerosol concentration. These methods over-sample large particles because of their higher settling rates and because they are less affected by turbulence than smaller particles, but such samples can be informative when measuring surface contamination by bioaerosol deposition,[(57,60)] e.g., in laboratories, operating rooms, and food preparation areas.

Sampling particles >7 μm from an air stream >2 m/s requires isokinetic collection, as discussed in Chapters 5 and 21 (e.g., when sampling inside a ventilation duct or outdoors). Isokinetic sampling takes place when air velocity into a sampler inlet matches ambient air velocity. Considerable variation is tolerable in inlet configuration when collecting small particles not affected greatly by anisokinetic sampling conditions.[(72)] Inlet velocity can be adjusted to achieve isokinetic sampling by varying air flow rate or probe cross-sectional area. Investigators generally cannot or do not wish to change a sampler's flow rate; therefore, they may prefer to vary the effective size of a sampling inlet, keeping it as short as possible to minimizes losses.

Particle Size

The previous section discussed the effects of air velocity on particle collection. Chapter 5 provides more precise definitions of particle size, along with methods for measuring this parameter.

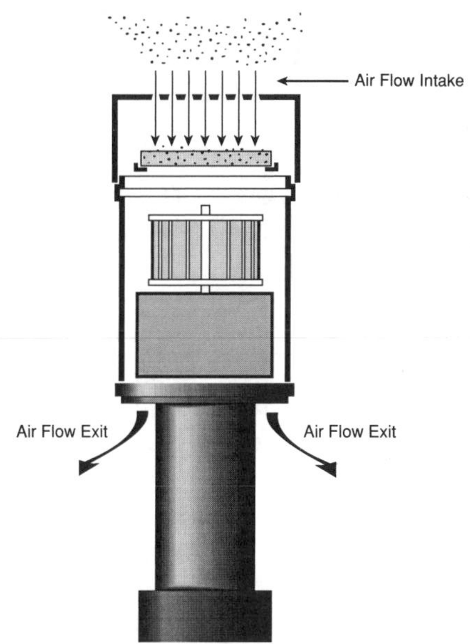

FIGURE 23-1. Single-stage impactor [Instrument 23-2a(ii)]

Bioaerosol Particle Sizes

Individual viral particles range from 0.01 to 0.25 μm, bacterial cells from 0.1 to 10 μm, fungus spores and fragments from 1 to 100 μm, and pollen grains from 10 to 100 μm. Measurements of cell dimensions made under a microscope, as quoted above and in microbiology texts,[63,64,73] will not always predict bioaerosol aerodynamic behavior accurately.[3] Large bioaerosols (e.g., pollen grains and some fungus spores) of less than unit density, and nonspherical particles (e.g., rod-shaped bacteria, fungus spores, and mycelial fragments) behave aerodynamically like smaller, unit-density spherical particles[74] (see Chapter 14).

Microorganism-laden particles released by humans have been found to range from 4- to 20-μm d_a, leading investigators to conclude that microorganisms become aerosolized in association with other materials (e.g., respiratory secretions or skin flakes) or on particles from intermediate resting places (e.g., soil or dust) because many bacteria and viruses are smaller than the particles on which they occur.[75] Nonviable allergens and toxins, on the other hand, can be airborne on particles <1 μm (e.g., ragweed allergen and bacterial endotoxin)[29,32,76,77] or in the 10- to 30-μm size range (e.g., mite fecal particles, fungus spores, and pollen grains).[31,48,49,78,79]

The aerodynamic size range from 1 to 10 μm is most important for airborne respiratory pathogens because these particles remain airborne longer than larger particles and penetrate to varying depths in the respiratory tract. Infectious agents on particles ≤5 μm are retained in the nonciliated airways and alveoli long enough to multiply. Particles ≥10 μm may impact in the nasal passages during nose breathing but penetrate to the trachea and bronchi during mouth breathing.

The concentration of airborne microorganisms usually cannot be predicted from the concentration of total suspended particles despite an association of microbiological cells with particles in a limited particle size range.[35,80] The number of microorganisms in ambient aerosols is usually small relative to the total particle load, except where other airborne particles were removed intentionally and the microbiological aerosol dominated.[57]

Size-Separating Bioaerosol Samplers

Several accepted methods for measuring the size distribution of airborne dusts and mineral particles are also suitable for sizing bioaerosols. The best method of bioaerosol size separation is that which is simplest, provides the required size information, and is compat-

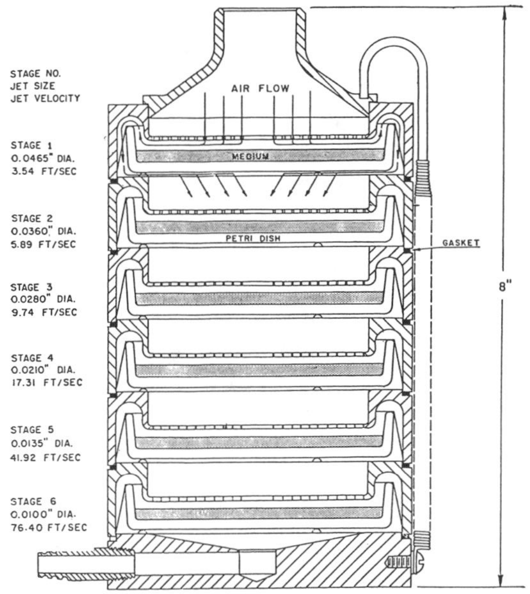

FIGURE 23-2. Cascade impactor (Instrument 23-2c)

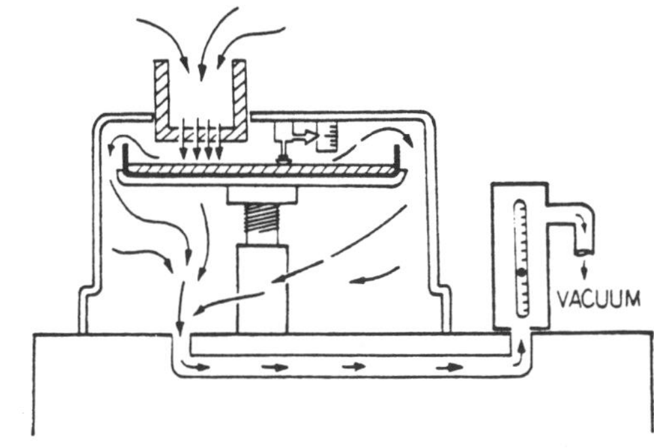

FIGURE 23-3. Rotating slit-to-agar impactor showing flowmeter and adjustable stage height (Instruments 23-1a–c)

ible with the assay system to be used.

The curved neck of an all-glass impinger (AGI) traps particles >8 µm, and these particles can be recovered by rinsing the inlet tube (Instrument 23-4a). Better size separation is available with three-stage impingers [Instruments 23-4b(i)–(ii)] designed to reproduce collection in the nasopharyngeal, tracheobronchial, and alveolar regions of the lungs;[81–83] see Chapter 5 for definitions of these regions.

A widely used multiple-stage impactor (Instrument 23-2c, and Figure 23-2) collects particles in six size fractions.[84] Many investigators use the final stage alone [the N-6 method, Instrument 23-2a(iii)] when they do not need particle size information.[85] The fifth stage of this sampler (the holes of which are not as small and therefore not as susceptible to blockage) may work equally well, especially when viable particles <1 µm are not expected in a sampled aerosol. A similar two-stage impactor (Instrument 23-2b) separates particles larger and smaller than 7 µm.[84]

A more recently developed personal inertial spectrometer collects bioaerosols at 4 L/min onto filters (Chapter 5; available from BGI, see Table 23-I-1).[86] Sample air enters around a core of filtered air and particles deposit at radial positions dependent on d_a. Exposed filters can be divided into sections with known particle size cutpoints and the sections analyzed separately by culture or direct microscopic examination.

Sampling "Efficiency"

There are several types of sampling efficiency that must be considered when studying bioaerosols: 1) the efficiency with which particles are collected, 2) the efficiency with which collected particles are transferred to an assay system, and 3) the efficiency with which bioaerosol viability and other critical characteristics are preserved during sample collection and transfer. For example, a 0.4-µm-pore membrane filter has very high collection efficiency; transfer and detection efficiencies also can be very good if particles are allowed to grow in place on a filter or the filter surface is examined directly with a microscope. However, there may be transfer losses if collected particles must be washed from the filter, and culture recovery for many microorganisms may be lower with filters than with impactors or impingers due to cell damage during the collection and transfer processes. It is a combination of such considerations, not just particle collection efficiency, that determines which devices are most suitable for a given bioaerosol sampling situation.

Bioaerosol Concentrations

Indoor and outdoor concentrations of airborne viable particles, most of them nonpathogenic, can range from tens to thousands per cubic meter of air. A person inhales approximately 20 m^3 of air in the course of a day, and with the air, whatever microorganisms it contains. Nonpathogenic microorganisms are seldom a concern for healthy people at the concentrations typically found in indoor or outdoor air. However, people with compromised immune systems may be susceptible to opportunistic pathogens (e.g., fungi in the genus *Aspergillus* and environmental species of *Mycobacterium*), and at sufficiently high doses, some microorganisms can overwhelm even a healthy body's defenses (e.g., *Legionella* bacteria that cause Pontiac fever).

Sampling when the concentration of culturable bioaerosols is high (>1000 colony-forming units [CFU]/m^3; see "Assay Methods — Culture") may present problems of rapid sample overload on impactor plates, but the accurate measurement of low concentrations of microorganisms (<10 CFU/m^3) also may be difficult (Table 23-2). An investigator must anticipate bioaerosol concentration at a study site, e.g., from preliminary sampling results or reported surveys in similar settings, to select a sampler that will accommodate a reasonable sampling time.[15] Investigators may choose to collect several air volumes when studying previously untested environments, so at least one sample yields a countable number of colonies or particles (e.g., collect at one flow rate for 1, 5, and 30 min).

Collecting as many samples as possible is advised because bioaerosol concentration varies throughout space and over time. Reporting median or geometric mean air concentrations makes more sense than reporting averages because bioaerosol measurements tend to be distributed lognormally rather than normally (Chapter 2). The information from uncountable under- or overloaded samples need not be lost entirely when using median values because these measurements may cluster at the extreme ends of a sampled concentration range. Reported σ_gs for residential bioaerosol concentrations[8] have ranged from 2 to 9 and coefficients of variation from 6% to 50% for sufficiently large sample sizes[22,24,51,52,59,87] (see also Chapter 2).

A range of 25 to 250 CFU per standard 100-mm culture plate is considered optimal to count and identify bacterial or fungal colonies accurately.[63,64] However, this range is only suitable for colonies of small to medium size and uniform shape. Microbiologists may prefer to work with <100 CFU per culture plate to reduce colony interference and overlap if an environment contains a variety of microorganisms. An investigator could aim for an upper limit of 2 bacterial CFU/cm^2 and 1 fungal CFU/cm^2 for smaller plates [Instrument 23-2a(ii)]. Similar guidelines apply for achieving optimal numbers of particles for microscopic examination.[15] Investigators should realize that these restrictions and those discussed immediately below determine a sampling method's detection limits, i.e., the minimum and maximum bioaerosol concentrations a method can measure.

Measuring Bioaerosol Concentration with Impactors

Collecting too much material, mentioned above, may be a problem when sampling culturable bioaerosols [Instruments 23-1a–c, 23-2a–d, 23-3a(i)–(ii), and 23-6a] or collecting particles on stationary glass slides (Instrument 23-7c). Tables have been published for 200- and 400-hole impactors [Instruments 23-2a(iii) and 23-2b–c] to adjust colony counts for the probability that more than one particle impacted at the same site.[88–91] Tables for 219- and 487-hole impactors [Instrument 23-2a(ii)] are available from the supplier, and adjustments for other samplers can be computed fairly easily.[88,90,91] These adjustments become increasingly significant as the number of filled holes increases.

Investigators often shorten collection times to avoid overloading stationary impaction slides and plates when sampling in heavily contaminated environments. Collection times of ≤10 s have been reported when using relatively high sampling rates, e.g., a six-stage impactor at 28 L/min. This method of avoiding oversampling is not advisable because the time required to clear the internal air through a sampler represents a significant fraction of the total sampling period, resulting in significant errors on the lower impactor stages. Also, size separation of particles in a cascade impactor may be incorrect if collection time is very short because the air will not have reached a steady flow rate. At the other extreme, however, sampling times cannot be so long that collection surfaces are overloaded, and prolonged sampling (e.g., >20 min), when impacting directly onto agar-based media, may kill sensitive microorganisms or dry or deform the collection surface at an impaction site, thereby changing a sampler's collection characteristics.

Particle bounce may complicate the collection of bioaerosols with inertial impactors (Chapter 14). Bounce depends on the hardness of the particles and the impaction surface, and increases with increasing material hardness, particle size, and air velocity. A biological particle striking moist agar generally will stick, but a "bouncy" particle hitting a previously deposited particle may rebound and be carried away in the air stream. Particle bounce may be significant when using an uncoated glass slide as an impaction surface. Coating the slide would improve retention, but not guarantee it, if the energy stored in particle deformation during impaction overcomes adhesive retention forces.

A potential source of confusion with multiple-jet impactors is the occurrence of satellite colonies or particles around impaction sites. Stray colonies or particles may result from clusters of cells that separated during collection or from particles that bounced. Particles may migrate from an impaction site if water or excess adhesive spreads during sampling. Satellites also might represent previously unimpacted particles that moved, because of air turbulence, sufficiently close to a collection surface to deposit some distance from a primary impaction site. A build-up of deposited particles, deformation of a collection surface at an impaction site (e.g., a dimple formed in drying agar), or interference between adjacent jets may disturb smooth air flow.

Measuring Bioaerosol Concentration with Impingers

Collection into liquid (Instruments 23-4a–b) offers the advantage that high concentration samples can be diluted with sterile liquid, and low concentration samples can be concentrated by centrifugation or filtration. Therefore, impingers are useful when it is difficult to anticipate bioaerosol concentration or when concentration varies a great deal between samples. Impingers should not be used for >30 min when collecting culturable bioaerosols or in very dry environments because increasing concentration of additives in a collection liquid (due to water evaporation) and prolonged vigorous scrubbing may damage collected microorganisms. Final collection fluid volume must be measured and taken into account when calculating sample concentration. Impingers must be used with particular care when collecting hydrophobic particles (e.g., fungus spores), in which case a downstream filter should be added to collect particles not captured in the impinger fluid.[17]

Apparently minor sampler modification can significantly alter the recovery of culturable microorganisms. For example, the all-glass impinger (Instrument 23-4a) comes in two versions, the AGI-30 and the AGI-4, with corresponding jet-to-plate distances of 30 mm and 4 mm. Although an AGI-30 collects fewer small particles because of the increased jet-to-plate distance, more of the collected cells remain viable because they suffer less damage. Researchers evaluating the effect of altering impinger jet position for a personal sampler found that increasing sampling rate to compensate for a d_{50} shift when they raised the impinger jet resulted in greater splashing and particle loss.[92]

Measuring Bioaerosol Concentration with Filters and Gelatin-based Media

Filters: Bioaerosols in highly contaminated environments have been collected with smooth-surface polycarbonate filters (Chapters 13 and 14). Material collected on filters can be washed into suspension for transfer to an assay system,[68,93] or filters can be examined directly with a microscope.[67,94] The type of filter used to collect some bioaerosols may affect assay results. For example, endotoxin affinity for filter material may vary and may also depend on the wash medium used.[76,77]

Filters moistened with glycerin have been used as collection surfaces in a personal cascade impactor[93,95] (Instrument 23-2d, and Figure 14-14). The low flow rate of a pump for a personal impactor or filter cassette (e.g., 2 L/min) may permit extended operation without overload and provide a better long-term estimate of average air concentration. Personal sampling devices are recommended for monitoring individual worker exposure and in highly contaminated environments.[86,92,93,95,96]

Gelatin-based Media: Some researchers have used a glycerol-gelatin mixture (500 ml glycerol, 500 ml distilled water, and 7 g gelatin) in place of agar-based media for collecting viable particles with impactors.[93] The gelatin medium is dissolved after sampling to obtain a liquid specimen, which can be diluted and plated, or filtered. Gelatin was used as the solidifying agent because it melts at 40°C, a temperature that does not damage many cells, as compared with agar which does not melt until it reaches 100°C. The glycerol-gelatin mixture contains less water than standard culture media (approximately 50% versus 95%); therefore, the impaction surface changes less during sampling, thereby permitting longer collection times.[93] European investigators report good results with soluble foamed-gelatin filters not used as often in the United States.[24]

Assay Methods

Investigators must consider the biological, chemical, and physical characteristics of bioaerosols as well as physical particle behavior when selecting a sampler and an assay system. An experienced aerobiologist or microbiologist can select the material of interest from the other bacteria, fungi, viruses, and other nonbiological debris also found in air by careful choice of assay procedures.

Investigators should consult reference texts for details on preparing, storing, and handling sampling equipment and media, and on including appropriate quality assurance samples, e.g., positive and negative laboratory controls and field blanks.[63,64,73] Investigators may wish to conduct laboratory tests or field trials to evaluate proposed collection methods and assay procedures. Evaluation tests might include spiking samples to assess recovery efficiency and evaluate the effects of the assay procedure on the material of interest. In addition, laboratory isolates or actual samples should be analyzed with and without wetting agents, evaporation retardants, antifoams, antibiotics, or other additives to ensure they do not interfere with cell growth or other detection characteristics.

Culture

The primary use of culture procedures for bioaerosol samples is to recover microorganisms identifiable by visible characteristics such as colony appearance; cell size, shape, and staining reaction; and spore morphology. Laboratory procedures for handling bacteria and fungi are similar and facilities for such work are widely available. This generally is not the case for culturing and identifying cell-dependent microorganisms, i.e., viruses, chlamydia, and rickettsia. However, investigators seldom are requested to monitor airborne infectious agents or respiratory pathogens (e.g., measles, Q-fever, tuberculosis, or Legionnaires' disease agents) except for research purposes or to detect certain opportunistic pathogens (e.g., *Aspergillus* spp.). The air concentration of infectious agents may be many times lower than the concentrations of other microorganisms, even in epidemic outbreak situations. Therefore, it generally is more productive to study disease transmission by focusing on the activities of infected people or animals, or on the presence and concentration of pathogens in reservoirs rather than in air.[54,97]

Culturable bioaerosols may be collected directly on agar-based medium in culture plates (frequently called "plates" or "Petri dishes") or in liquid in impingers (Chapter 14). Cells suspended in impinger fluid can be inoculated directly onto agar or filtered. Cyclone samplers and high-volume and polycarbonate filters can be used to collect large amounts of bioaerosols, which can be examined directly or washed into suspension for assay (Chapters 13 and 14).

Reporting Culturable Bioaerosol Concentrations

Viable bacteria and fungi multiply on the surface of semisolid culture media into visible areas of growth or "colonies." Bacterial and fungal colonies also can grow on the surfaces of cellulose ester membrane filters (Chapter 13) placed face-up on agar or a support pad moistened with culture medium. Each collected particle that contains ≥1 viable bacterial cell or reproducible fungal particle is counted as a CFU. Chlamydia, rickettsia, and viruses, on the other hand, do not multiply alone but infect host cells in tissue or cell cultures. Patches of burst host cells, appearing as cleared areas in cell lawns, are called "plaques." Other agents change the size or appearance of infected host cells, producing a "cytopathic effect." Each particle containing ≥1 active virus is counted as a "plaque-forming unit" (PFU) or a "cytopathic-effect unit" (CPU).[98,99] Often it is sufficient to count the number of culturable particles as CFU, PFU, or CPU directly, and to express aerosol concentration per cubic meter of air, but investigators occasionally wish to know the total number of airborne microorganisms when some particles carry more than one cell or virus, as discussed earlier in this chapter.

Culture Conditions

Table 23-3 lists typically used liquid and agar-based media, along with incubation times and temperatures for collecting and growing bacteria, fungi, and viruses.[65] Many of the listed media are nonselective, and therefore suitable for a wide range of microorganisms. Media specifically designed to collect stressed organisms (e.g., 2% malt extract agar for fungi and R2A for bacteria) may be more appropriate than richer media, which may even harm damaged cells (e.g., enriched malt extract agar and soybean-casein digest agar, also known as tryptic or trypticase soy agar).[50] Additives to the usual formulations for culture media and impinger liquids may improve recovery of airborne microorganisms.[61,62,100]

It sometimes may be necessary to include growth inhibitors in culture media because environmental samples generally contain a variety of organisms, some of which are not of interest, and others may grow at different rates. The higher pH (approximately pH 7) of most bacterial media limits fungal growth, but fungicides are helpful for bacterial samples from fungi-rich environments (e.g., agricultural settings) and when plates will be held more than a week to detect slow-growing bacteria. Similar considerations apply when attempting to recover fungi from bacteria-rich environments, e.g., occupied indoor settings. Fortunately, most bacteria grow poorly on the lower pH (approximately pH 5) media commonly used to culture fungi. Various media have been recommended to support the growth of the greatest number of fungi while restricting their spreading.[24,65,87,100,101,102] However, these media may suppress the growth of some important fungi completely[101] and should be used with controls; either in parallel with a less restrictive medium or with a collection method that allows microscopic sample examination. Conidia of *Penicillium* spp. and sporangiospores of *Rhizopus* and *Mucor* spp. have been partitioned in a two-phase, aqueous polymer system to separate slow- and rapid-growing fungi.[103]

The temperature at which samples are incubated also affects recovery of culturable microorganisms. Most environmental bacteria and fungi grow well between 20°C and 30°C, and may not be recovered if samples are incubated at higher temperatures. Human pathogens and normal flora do better near body temperature (35°C to 37°C), and only thermotolerant and thermophilic microorganisms survive above 50°C. Some researchers have suggested that it is also important to culture indoor air samples specifically for xerophilic fungi, which prefer drier growth conditions and may not be recovered if standard high-water-content media are the only types used.[7,21,22,24,87,102]

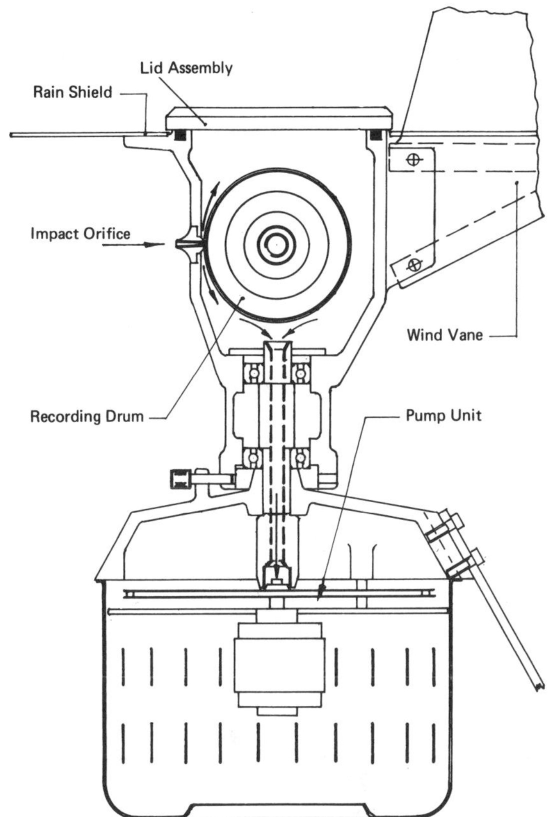

FIGURE 23-4. Rotating adhesive tape impactor [Instrument 23-7a(i)]

Direct Examination

Investigators repeatedly have found that culturing air samples to determine microbiological content identifies only a fraction of the total numbers and types of bioaerosols present.[67,68,94,104,105] Fungi, bacteria, spores, pollen grains, and dust mites can be viewed and counted with a light microscope, and these examples plus viruses can be examined in more detail with a scanning electron microscope (SEM).[63,64,67,68,73,94,105–107] Microscopic analysis is especially useful when total counts of organisms are required and viability is not a concern. Samples for microscopic analysis can be collected by impaction onto adhesive-coated tape (Figure 23-4), by impaction directly onto adhesive-coated glass slides, or by filtration.

Heikkila *et al.*[94] cultured air samples to recover viable fungi and identified isolates by standard laboratory methods. The investigators then used spores from these reference cultures to identify spores collected on filter air samples from the same environments. Application of methods other than culture is especially important when investigating bioaerosols responsible for hypersensitivity diseases for which microorganisms need not be viable to produce an effect, and when collecting microorganisms that grow poorly on standard culture media (e.g., mushroom spores). Culturing bioaerosols in these cases allows accurate identification of isolates, whereas direct microscopic counting of particles allows determination of total air concentration.

Bacterial stains (e.g., Gram and acridine orange stains) show cell shape, but beyond categorization into general groups (e.g., gram-positive cocci, gram-negative rods, or just cocci, rods, etc.), bacteria cannot be identified by these simple tests alone. Labelled antibody stains detect specific bacteria and fungi, but the cells must be fairly abundant for these methods to be practical for air samples. Even SEM examination generally provides too little information to identify bacteria, but many pollen grains and fungus spores can be identified to genus level with a light microscope or SEM.[48,67,94,106,108–115]

Immunoassays

The fact that antigens (including allergens) elicit specific antibody responses in exposed organisms is used to facilitate analysis of antigenic microorganisms and amorphous particles.[116] Immunoassays for airborne antigens include radioimmunoassay staining techniques (RAST), enzyme linked immunosorbent assays (ELISA), and radioimmunoassays (RIA).[117,118] All of these tests use antigens or antigen-specific antibodies adsorbed or covalently bound to solid surfaces, and either radioactive- or enzyme-labelled antibodies to detect bound antigen or antibody.

Immunochemical assays are especially appropriate when monitoring allergens because the effector agent, rather than an indicator, is measured (i.e., the allergen itself, not a spore that may or may not contain the allergen). Immunoassays are specific to particular antigens and there is no method to measure "total" antigens in a sample or evaluate all the types of antigen that might be present. Immunoassays may be more or less specific depending on the targeted antigen. For example, an assay for Alt aI, the major allergen from fungi in the genus *Alternaria*, will detect that allergen only and ignore all other alternaria allergens as well as those from other organisms.

Immunoassays may be conducted on filter-collected air samples, impinger liquids, or material washed from impactor plates.[78] More commonly, however, at least for indoor samples, allergens are measured by immunoassay of "house" dust elutions, not air samples.

Other Bioassays

Biological toxins and mutagens elicit specific responses in test cells and these responses can be used to assay air samples for specific biological materials. For example, the Limulus amoebocyte assay detects bacterial endotoxin, and other tests measure mutagenicity and cytotoxicity.[7,77,119,120] These assays can be performed on eluted bulk dust, filter or impactor samples, or on impinger fluids.

The development of gene "probes" (which detect specific genetic sequences) and polymerase chain reaction methods (which amplify selected genetic sequences)[70] show promise for detecting and quantifying bioaerosols. As with immunoassays, the microorganisms of interest must be known in advance and an appropriate system to detect the microorganisms must be available. These methods offer rapid, sensitive, and specific detection, and may be especially useful for microorganisms that are difficult or dangerous to culture, or present at low concentrations relative to other materials.

Assessment of Infectivity

Infectivity, the ability of a pathogen to multiply within a host, is discussed here in its broadest terms and related directly to microorganism viability. In most cases, determining microbiological dose required to produce infection by inhalation requires a living host system. Placing susceptible sentinel animals in a test environment has demonstrated the presence of pathogenic microorganisms when other sampling methods failed.[54] Susceptible hosts can be inoculated with concentrated liquid samples collected with suitable air sampling devices if it is not possible or desirable to expose animals directly in a study environment.[54,98] Alternatively, isolates from sampled environments can be grown in pure culture and used to inoculate or otherwise expose test animals.

Received bioaerosol dose can be calculated from measured bioaerosol concentration, the time people or test animals were exposed, and their breathing rates. However, as with any aerosol, not all inhaled bioaerosols are retained. Particle retention in various regions of the respiratory tract depends on airway size, breathing rate, and particle aerodynamic behavior (see also Chapter 5 and the section on "Particle Size," above). Potentially infectious particles deposited at sites not susceptible to the microorganisms on those particles may not result in disease.

Comparing Samplers

Verhoeff[24] evaluated bioaerosol samplers and culture media using the following criteria:

1. Yield in terms of the measured air concentration: considering techniques that produced higher concentration estimates better
2. Yield in terms of the number of species isolated: considering techniques that recovered greater numbers of different species better
3. Reproducibility of sequential and parallel sam-

ples with the same types of instruments: considering more reproducible techniques better

4. Correlations among samplers: considering techniques that correlated well with others better.

Two samplers (a multiple-stage [Andersen] impactor and the AGI-30; Instruments 23-2c and 23-4a) were suggested some years ago as "standard" samplers to which others should be compared.[121] Comparison among samplers for culturable microorganisms is only valid when all samplers are tested with the same microorganisms, in the same environments, using defined culture media and conditions. Reasonable comparisons can be made among impactors such as the slit-to-agar, multiple-hole, and centrifugal impactors (Instruments 23-1a–c, 23-2a–d, and 23-3a–b). Samplers that collect culturable particles can be compared with samplers that separate particles into their component cells if a test aerosol contains predominantly single cell particles[57,58,83] or a soluble collection medium is used in the impactors.[93]

Other considerations also play a role when choosing among samplers. Although impingers are less expensive to purchase than impactors, impactors are easier to reuse in the field; after sampling, the exposed plate is removed, the instrument is disinfected, and a fresh plate is inserted. Impinger samples also require more processing in the laboratory, which entails additional technician time and increases opportunities for error.[83] An advantage of an impinger sample over an impactor, on the other hand, is that investigators often can carry out several assays on one sample, e.g., use the liquid to measure both culturable bacteria and fungi, and perhaps also assay antigen, specific DNA, or endotoxin concentration. Investigators also may have greater assurance of obtaining countable samples with impingers because the collected material can be diluted or concentrated to cover a wider range of possible air concentrations.

Investigators recently have discussed establishing performance criteria for bioaerosol samplers[122] and certifying laboratories for bioaerosol assays and related environmental testing.[123] No formal sampler performance criteria have yet been proposed, in part due to the inappropriateness of establishing a single comprehensive set of criteria to cover all bioaerosols and bioaerosol samplers.[2] The variety of microorganisms and biological materials called bioaerosols and their range of physical, chemical, and biological properties is great. The use of summary criteria for bioaerosol collection or assay is complicated further by the variety of uses to which such samplers are put, and the many different health effects and other consequences bioaerosols may cause. Nevertheless, it should be possible to recommend accuracy and precision levels for bioaerosol sampling and analysis, and to suggest desirable collection and recovery efficiencies for the sizes and types of bioaerosols of greatest interest, perhaps similar to criteria for size-selective air samplers. Many microbiology and industrial hygiene laboratories already subscribe to accreditation and proficiency testing programs for other analytical work. The addition of a program to certify laboratories for processing bioaerosol samples may overlap readily with the requirements of these other programs.

Conclusions

This chapter was written with the recognition that few occupational health or air pollution scientists specialize in the study of biological agents and that more of them are chemists or engineers than microbiologists. However, public and professional awareness of health hazards associated with bioaerosols is increasing, and there is a concomitant need for industrial hygienists and health and safety practitioners to consider the impact of airborne biological material when judging overall air quality.

Much of the information in this chapter for selecting a bioaerosol sampler and sample assay procedure is summarized in Tables 23-1 to 23-3 and in the "Instrument Descriptions" section. The available numbers and types of bioaerosol samplers have grown in recent decades and investigators have shown a preference for impactors, especially self-contained units. Regardless of what samplers investigators use, they should have evidence (from trial studies or published literature) that the sampler adequately recovers the specific bioaerosols of interest.

References

1. World Health Organization: Indoor Air Quality: Biological Contaminants. Report on a WHO meeting, Rautavaara, August 29–September 2, 1988. WHO Regional Publications, European Series No. 31, Copenhagen (1990).
2. American Conference of Governmental Industrial Hygienists: 1994–1995 Threshold Limit Values for Chemical Substances and Physical Agents and Biological Exposure Indices, pp. 9–11. ACGIH, Cincinnati, OH (1993).
3. Lacey, J.: Aggregation of Spores and Its Effect on Aerodynamic Behaviour. Grana. 30:437–445 (1991).
4. Burge, H.A.; Feeley, J.C., Sr.; Kreiss, K.; et al.: Guidelines for the Assessment of Bioaerosols in the Indoor Environment. American Conference of Governmental Industrial Hygienists, Cincinnati, OH (1989).
5. Hambraeus, A.: Aerobiology in the Operating Room — A Review. J. Hosp. Inf. 11(Suppl. A):68–76 (1988).
6. Miller, J.D.: Fungi as Contaminants in Indoor Air. Atmos. Environ. 26A(12):2163–2172 (1992).
7. Miller, J.D.; Laflamme, A.M.; Sobol, Y.; et al.: Fungi and Fungal Products in Some Canadian Houses. Inter. Bioterior. 24:103–120 (1988).
8. Reponen, T.; Nevalainen, A.; Jantunen, M.; et al.: Normal Range Criteria for Indoor Air Bacteria and Fungal Spores in a Subarctic Climate. Indoor Air. 2:26–31 (1992).
9. Cox, C.S.: The Aerobiological Pathway of Microorganisms. John

Wiley & Sons, New York (1987).

10. Edmonds, R.L.; Ed.: Aerobiology. The Ecological Systems Approach. Dowden, Hutchinson & Ross, Stroudsburg, PA (1979).
11. Morey, P.R.; Feeley, J.C.; Otten, J.A.; Eds.: Biological Contaminants in Indoor Environments. American Society for Testing and Materials, Philadelphia (1990).
12. Burge, H.A.; Solomon, W.R.: Sampling and Analysis of Biological Aerosols. Atmos. Environ. 21(2):451–456 (1987).
13. Fannin, K.F.: An Approach to the Study of Environmental Microbial Aerosols. Wat. Sci. Tech. 13:1103–1114 (1981).
14. May, K.R.: Assessment of Viable Airborne Particles. In: Assessment of Airborne Particles, pp. 480–494. T.T. Mercer, P.E. Morrow, and W. Stber, Eds. Charles C. Thomas, Springfield, IL (1980).
15. Nevalainen, A.; Pastuszka, J.; Liebhaber, F.; Willeke, K.: Performance of Bioaerosol Samplers: Collection Characteristics and Sampler Design Considerations. Atmos. Environ. 26A(4):531–540 (1992).
16. Raynor, G.S.: Sampling Techniques. In: Aerobiology, The Ecological Systems Approach. Dowden, Hutchison and Ross, Inc., Stroudsberg, PA; distributed by Academic Press, New York (1980).
17. Stetzenbach, L.D.: Airborne Microorganisms. In: Encyclopedia of Microbiology, Volume 1, pp. 53–65. Academic Press, NY (1992).
18. Stetzenbach, L.D.; Hern, S.C.; Seidler, R.J.: Field Sampling Design and Experimental Methods for the Detection of Airborne Microorganisms. In: Microbial Ecology, Chapter 27, pp. 543–555. McGraw–Hill, New York (1992).
19. Favero, M.S.; Bond, W.W.: Sterilization, Disinfection, and Antisepsis in the Hospital. In: Manual of Clinical Microbiology, 5th ed., pp. 183–200. A. Balows, Ed. American Society for Microbiology, Washington, DC (1991).
20. Humphreys, H.: Microbes in the Air — When to Count! (The Role of Air Sampling in Hospitals.) J. Med. Microbiol. 37:81–82 (1992).
21. Flannigan, B.; McCabe, E.M.; McGarry, F.: Allergenic and Toxigenic Micro-organisms in Houses. J. Appl. Bacteriol. Symp. Suppl. 70:61–73S (1991).
22. Hunter, C.A.; Grant, C.; Flannigan, B.; Bravery, A.F.: Mould in Buildings: The Air Spora of Domestic Dwellings. Inter. Biodeter. 24:81–101 (1988).
23. Su, H.J.; Rotnitzky, A.; Burge, H.A.; Spengler, J.D.: Examination of Fungi in Domestic Interiors by Factor Analysis: Correlations and Associations with Home Factors. Appl. Environ. Microbiol. 58(1):181–186 (1992).
24. Verhoeff, A.P.; van Wijnen, J.H.; Boleij, J.S.; et al.: Enumeration and Identification of Airborne Viable Mould Propagules in Houses. A Field Comparison of Selected Techniques. Allergy 45(4):275–84 (1990).
25. Verhoeff, A.P.: Presence of Viable Mould Propagules in the Indoor Air of Houses. Toxicol. Indus. Health, 6(5):133–145 (1990).
26. Olenchock, S.A.: Quantitation of Airborne Endotoxin Levels in Various Occupational Environments. Scand. J. Work Environ. Health. 14(Suppl 1):72–73 (1988).
27. Rahkonen, P.; Ettala, M.; Laukkanen, M.; Salkinoja-Salonen, M.: Airborne Microbes and Endotoxins in the Work Environment of Two Sanitary Landfills in Finland. Aerosol Sci. Technol. 13(4):505–513 (1990).
28. Agarwal, M.K.; Swanson, M.C.; Reed, C.E.; Yunginger, J.W.: Immunochemical Quantitation of Airborne Short Ragweed, Alternaria, Antigen E, and Alt-1 Allergens: A Two Year Prospective Study. J. Allergy Clin. Immunol. 72:40–45 (1983).
29. Habenicht, H.A.; Burge, H.A.; Muilenberg, M.L.; Solomon, W.R.: Allergen Carriage by Atmospheric Aerosol II. Ragweed Pollen Determinants in Submicronic Atmospheric Fractions. J. Allergy Clin. Immunol. 74(1):64–67 (1984).
30. Knysak D.: Animal Aeroallergens. Immunol. Allergy Clin. North Amer. 9(2):357–364 (1989).
31. Platts-Mills, T.A.E.; Heymann, P.W.; Longbottom, J.L.; Wilkins, S.R.: Airborne Allergens Associated with Asthma: Particle Sizes Carrying Dust Mite and Rat Allergens Measured with a Cascade Impactor. J. Allergy Clin. Immunol. 77:850–857 (1986).
32. Solomon, W.R.; Burge, H.A.; Muilenberg, M.L.: Allergen Carriage by Atmospheric Aerosol. I. Ragweed Pollen Determinants in Smaller Micronic Fractions. J. Allergy Clin. Immunol. 72(5):443–447 (1983).
33. Swanson, M.C.; Campbell, A.R.; Klauck, M.J.; Reed, C.E.: Correlations Between Levels of Mite and Cat Allergens in Settled and Airborne Dust. J. Allergy Clin. Immunol. 83(4):776–83 (1989).
34. Al-Dagal, M.; Fung, D.Y.C.: Aeromicrobiology - A Review. Food Sci. Nutrition. 29(5):333–340 (1990).
35. Butera, M.; Smith, J.H.; Morrison, W.D.; et al.: Concentration of Respirable Dust and Bioaerosols and Identification of Certain Microbial Types in a Hog-growing Facility. Can. J. Anim. Sci. 71:271–277 (1991).
36. Kang, Y-J.; Frank, J.F.: Evaluation of Air Samplers for Recovery of Biological Aerosols in Dairy Processing Plants. J. Food Prot. 52(9):655–659 (1989).
37. Kang, Y-J.; Frank, J.F.: Comparison of Airborne Microflora Collected by the Andersen Sieve Sampler and RCS Sampler in a Dairy Processing Plant. J. Food Prot. 52(12):877–880 (1989).
38. Radmore, K.; Holzapfel, W.H.; Luck, H.: Proposed Guidelines for Maximum Acceptable Air-borne Microorganisms Levels in Dairy Processing and Packaging Plants. Inter. J Food Microbiol. 6:91–95 (1988).
39. Thornsberry, C.; Balows, A.; Feeley, J.C.; et al.: Legionella. In: Proceedings of the Second International Symposium. W. Jakubowski, Ed. American Society for Microbiology, Washington, DC (1984).
40. World Health Organization: Epidemiology, Prevention and Control of Legionellosis: Memorandum from a WHO Meeting. WHO Bull. OMS. 68:155–164 (1990).
41. Bollin, G.E.; Plouffe, J.F.; Para, M.F.; Hackman, B.: Aerosols Containing *Legionella pneumophila* Generated by Shower Heads and Hot-water Faucets. Appl. Environ. Microbiol. 50:1128–1131 (1985).
42. Breiman, R.F.; Cozen, W.; Fields, B.S.; et al.: Role of Air Sampling in Investigation of an Outbreak of Legionnaires' Disease Associated with Exposure to Aerosols from an Evaporative Condenser. J. Infect. Dis. 161:1257–1261 (1990).
43. Breiman, R.F.; Fields, B.S.; Sanden, G.N.; Barbaree, J.M.: Air Sampling for Legionella - Reply. JAMA 264(20):2626 (1990).
44. Zingeser, J.A.; Birkhead, G.S.; Mamolen, M.; Vogt, R.L.: Air Sampling for Legionella. JAMA 264(20):2625–2626 (1990).
45. Burge, H.A.: The Fungi. In: Biological Contaminants in Indoor Environments, pp. 136–162. P.R. Morey, J.C. Feeley, and J.A. Otten, Eds. American Society for Testing and Materials, Philadelphia (1990).
46. Harrison, J.; Pickering, C.A.C.; Faragher, E.B.; et al.: An Investigation of the Relationship Between Microbial and Particulate Indoor Air Pollution and the Sick Building Syndrome. Resp. Med. 86:225–235 (1992).
47. Problem Buildings: Building-associated Illness and the Sick Building Syndrome. In: Occup. Med.: State of the Art Reviews, Volume 4(4). J.E. Cone and M.J. Hodgson, Eds. Hanley & Belfus, Philadelphia (1989).
48. Lewis, W.H.; Vinay, P.; Zenger, V.E.: Airborne and Allergenic Pollen of North America. The Johns Hopkins University Press, Baltimore (1983).
49. Solomon, W.R.: Aerobiology of Pollinosis. J. Allergy Clin. Immunol. 74:449–461 (1984).
50. Laitinen, S.; Nevalainen, A.; Kotimaa, M.; et al.: Relationship Between Bacterial Counts and Endotoxin Concentrations in the Air of Wastewater Treatment Plants. Appl. Environ. Microbiol. 58(11):3774–3776 (1992).
51. Lembke, L.L.; Kniseley, R.N.; Van Nostrand, R.C.; Hale, M.D.: Precision of the All-glass Impinger and the Andersen Microbial Impactor for Air Sampling in Solid-waste Handling Facilities. Appl. Environ. Microbiol. 42:222–225 (1981).

52. Lembke, L.L.; Kniseley, R.N.: Airborne Microorganisms in a Municipal Solid Waste Recovery System. Can. J. Microbiol. 31:198–205 (1985).
53. Baylor, E.R.; Baylor, M.B.; Blanchard, et al.: Virus Transfer from Surf to Wind. Science 198:575–580 (1977).
54. Regnery, R.L.; McDade, J.E.: *Coxiella burnetii* (Q Fever), A Potential Microbial Contaminant of the Environment. In: Biological Contaminants in Indoor Environments, pp. 115-135. P.R. Morey, J.C. Feeley, and J.A. Otten, Eds. American Society for Testing and Materials, Philadelphia (1990).
55. Adams, D.J.; Spendlove, J.C.; Spendlove, R.S.; Barnett, B.B.: Aerosol Stability of Infectious and Potentially Infectious Reovirus Particles. Appl. Environ. Microbiol. 44:903–908 (1982).
56. Ijaz, M.K.; Sattar, S.A.; Johnson-Lussenburg, C.M.; Springthorpe, V.S.: Effect of Relative Humidity, Atmospheric Temperature, and Suspending Medium on the Airborne Survival of Human Rotavirus. Can. J. Microbiol. 31:681–685 (1985).
57. Buttner, M.P.; Stetzenbach, L.D.: Monitoring Airborne Fungal Spores in an Experimental Indoor Environment to Evaluate Sampling Methods and the Effects of Human Activity on Air Sampling. Appl. Environ. Microbiol. 59(1):219–226 (1993).
58. Jensen, P.A.; Todd. W.F.; Davis, G.N.; Scarpino, P.V.: Evaluation of Eight Bioaerosol Samplers Challenged with Aerosols of Free Bacteria. Am. Ind. Hyg. Assoc. J. 53(10):660–667 (1992).
59. Kang, Y-J.; Frank, J.F.: Evaluation of Air Samplers for Recovery of Artificially Generated Aerosols of Pure Cultures in a Controlled Environment. J. Food Prot. 52(8):560–563 (1989).
60. Lundqvist, G.R.; Aalykke, C.; Bonde, G.J.: Evaluation of Children as Sources of Bioaerosols in a Climate Chamber Study. Environ. Int. 16:213–218 (1990).
61. Marthi, B.; Lighthart, B.: Effects of Betaine on Enumeration of Airborne Bacteria. Appl. Environ. Microbiol. 56(5):1286–1289 (1990).
62. Marthi, B.; Shaffer, B.T.; Lighthart, B.; Ganio, L.: Resuscitation Effects of Catalase on Airborne Bacteria. Appl. Environ. Microbiol. 57(9):2775–2776 (1991).
63. American Public Health Association: Compendium of Methods for the Microbiological Examination of Foods, 2nd ed., pp. 47-123. APHA, Washington, DC (1984).
64. American Public Health Association: Standard Methods for the Examination of Water and Wastewater, 17th ed., pp. 9.4–9.8; 9.52–9.66. American Water Works Association and Water Pollution Control Federation, Washington, DC (1989).
65. Nash, P.; Krenz, M.M.: Culture Media. In: Manual of Clinical Microbiology, 5th ed., pp. 1226–1288. A. Balows, Ed. American Society for Microbiology, Washington, DC (1991).
66. Fišar, Z.; J., Hysek; Binek, B.: Quantification of Airborne Microorganisms and Investigation of Their Interactions with Non-living Particles. Biometerol. 34:189–193 (1990).
67. Karlsson, K.; Malmberg, P.: Characterization of Exposure to Molds and Actinomycetes in Agricultural Dusts by Scanning Electron Microscopy, Fluorescence Microscopy and the Culture Method. Scand. J. Work Environ. Health. 15:353–359 (1989).
68. Eduard, W.; Lacey, J.; Karlsson, K.; et al.: Evaluation of Methods for Enumerating Microorganisms in Filter Samples from Highly Contaminated Occupational Environments. Am. Ind. Hyg. Assoc. J. 51(8):427–436 (1990).
69. Lundholm, I.M: Comparison of Methods for Quantitative Determinations of Airborne Bacteria and Evaluation of Total Viable Counts. Appl. Environ. Microbiol. 44:179–183 (1982).
70. Favero, M.S.; Puleo, J.R.: Techniques Used for Sampling Airborne Microorganisms Associated with Industrial Clean Rooms and Spacecraft Assembly Areas. In: Airborne Contagion, pp. 241–254. R.B. Kundsin, Ed. Volume 353, Annals of New York Academy of Sciences. New York Academy of Sciences, New York (1980).
71. Fields, N.D.; Oxborrow, G.S.; Puleo, J.R.; Herring, C.M.: Evaluation of Membrane Filter Field Monitors for Microbiological Air Sampling. Appl. Microbiol. 27:517–520 (1974).
72. Willeke, K.; Grinshpun, S.A.; Chang, C.-W.; et al.: Inlet sampling efficiency of bioaerosol samplers. J. Aerosol Sci. 23:S651–S654 (1992).
73. American Society for Microbiology: Manual of Clinical Microbiology, 5th ed. A. Balows, Ed. ASM, Washington, DC (1991).
74. Madelin, T.M.; Johnson, H.E.: Fungal and Actinomycete Spore Aerosols Measured at Different Humidities with an Aerodynamic Particle Sizer. J. Appl. Bacteriol. 72:400–409 (1992).
75. Noble, W.C.; Lidwell, O.M.; Kingston, D.: The Size Distribution of Airborne Particles Carrying Microorganisms. J. Hyg. 61:385–391 (1963).
76. Gordon, T.; Galdanes, K.; Brousseau, L.: Comparison of Sampling Media for Endotoxin-contaminated Aerosols. Appl. Occup. Environ. Hyg. 7(7):472–477 (1992).
77. Milton, D.K.; Gere, R.J.; Feldman, H.A.; Greaves, I.A.: Endotoxin Measurement: Aerosol Sampling and Application of a New Limulus Method. Am. Ind. Hyg. Assoc. J. 51:331–337 (1990).
78. Yoshizawa, S.; Sugawara, F.; Yasueda, H.; et al.: Kinetics of the Falling of Airborne Mite Allergens (Der I and Der II). Arerugi 40(4):435–438 (1991).
79. Solomon, W.R.; Burge, H.P.; Boise, J.R.; Becker, M.: Comparative Particle Recoveries by the Retracting Rotorod, Rotoslide, and Burkard Spore Trap Sampling in Compact Array. Int. J. Biometeor. 24(2):107–116 (1980).
80. Seal, D.V.; Clark, R.P.: Electronic Particle Counting for Evaluating the Quality of Air in Operating Theatres: A Potential Basis for Standards? J. Appl. Bacteriol. 68:225–230 (1990).
81. Bradley, D.; Burdett, G.J.; Griffiths, W.D.; Lyons, C.P.: Design and Performance of Size Selective Microbiological Samplers. J. Aerosol Sci. 23:S659–S662 (1992).
82. May, K.R.: Multistage Liquid Impinger. Bacteriol. Rev. 30:559–570 (1966).
83. Zimmerman, N.J.; Reist, P.C.; Turner, A.G.: Comparison of Two Biological Aerosol Sampling Methods. Appl. Environ. Microbio. 53(1):99–104 (1987).
84. Gillespie, V.L.; Clark, C.S.; Bjornson, H.S.; et al.: A Comparison of Two-stage and Six-stage Andersen Impactors for Viable Aerosols. Am. Ind. Hyg. Assoc. J. 42:858–864 (1981).
85. Jones, W.; Morring, K.; Morey, P.; Sorenson, W.: Evaluation of the Andersen Viable Impactor for Single Stage Sampling. Am. Ind. Hyg. Assoc. J. 46:294–298 (1985).
86. Prodi, V.; Belosi, F.; Mularoni, A.; Lucialli, P.: PERSPEC: A Personal Sampler with Size Characterization Capabilities. Am. Ind. Hyg. Assoc. J. 49(2):75–80 (1988).
87. Smid, T.; Schokkin, E.; Boleij, J.S.M.; Heederik, D.: Enumeration of Viable Fungi in Occupational Environments: A Comparison of Samplers and Media. Am. Ind. Hyg. Assoc. J. 50(5):235–239 (1989).
88. Andersen, A.A.: New Sampler for the Collection, Sizing and Enumeration of Viable Airborne Particles. J. Bacteriol. 76:471–484 (1958).
89. Leopold, S.S.: "Positive Hole" Statistical Adjustment for a Two-stage, 200-Hole-per-stage Andersen Air Sampler. Am. Ind. Hyg. Assoc. J. 49:A88–A90 (1988).
90. Macher, J.M.: Positive-hole Correction of Multiple-jet Impactors for Collecting Viable Microorganisms. Am. Ind. Hyg. Assoc. J. 50(11):561–568 (1989).
91. Somerville, M.C.; Rivers, J.C.: An Alternative Approach for the Correction of Bioaerosol Data Collected with Multiple Jet Impactors. Am. Ind. Hyg. Assoc. J. 55(2):127–131 (1994).
92. Fängmark, I., Wikström, L.E.; Henningson, E.W.: Collection Efficiency of a Personal Sampler for Microbiological Aerosols. Am. Ind. Hyg. Assoc. J. 52(12):516–520 (1991).
93. Blomquist, G.; Palmgren, U.; Ström, G.: Improved Techniques for Sampling Airborne Fungal Particles in Highly Contaminated Environments. Scand. J. Work Environ. Health 10:253–258 (1984).
94. Heikkilä, P.; Kotimaa, M.; Tuomi, et al.: Identification and Counting of Fungal Spores by Scanning Electron Microscope. Ann. Occup.

Hyg. 32(2):241–248 (1988).
95. Rubow, K.L.; Marple, V.A.; Olin, J.; McCawley, M.A.: A Personal Cascade Impactor: Design, Evaluation and Calibration. Am. Ind. Hyg. Assoc. J. 48(6):532–538 (1987).
96. Macher, J.M.; First, M.W.: Personal Air Samplers for Measuring Occupational Exposures to Biological Hazards. Am. Ind. Hyg. Assoc. J. 45:76–83 (1984).
97. Burge, H.A.: Risks Associated with Indoor Infectious Aerosols. Toxicol. Indus. Health, 6(2):263–274 (1990).
98. Gerba, C.P.; Goyal, S.M.: Methods in Environmental Virology. Marcel Dekker, Inc., New York (1982).
99. Sattar, S.A.; Mohammad, K.I.: Spread of Viral Infections by Aerosols. CRC Crit. Rev. Environ. Control. 17(2):89–131 (1987).
100. Madelin, T.M.: The Effect of a Surfactant in Media for the Enumeration, Growth and Identification of Airborne Fungi. J. Appl. Bacteriol. 63:47–52 (1987).
101. Burge, H.A.; Solomon, W.R.; Boise, J.R.: Comparative Merits of Eight Popular Media in Aerometric Studies of Fungi. J. Allergy Clin. Immunol. 60:199–203 (1977).
102. Morring, K.L.; Sorenson, W.G.; Attfield, M.D.: Sampling Airborne Fungi: A Statistical Comparison of Media. Am. Ind. Hyg. Assoc. J. 44:662–664 (1983).
103. Blomquist, G.K.; Ström, G.B.; Söderström, B.: Separation of Fungal Propagules by Partition in Aqueous Polymer Two-phase Systems. Appl. Environ. Microbiol. 47:1316–1318 (1984).
104. Hysek, J.; Fišar, Z.; Zizka, et al.: Airborne Microorganism Monitoring: A Comparison of Several Methods, Including a New Direct Counting Technique. Zentralbl. Mikrobiol. 146:435–443 (1991).
105. Palmgren, U.; Ström, G.; Blomquist, G.; Malmberg, P.: Collection of Airborne Micro-organisms on Nuclepore Filter, Estimation and Analysis — CAMNEA Method. J. Appl. Bacteriol. 61:401–406 (1986).
106. Muilenberg, M.L.: Aeroallergen Assessment by Microscopy and Culture. Immunol. Allergy Clin. North Amer. 9(2):245 (1989).
107. Reed, C.E.; Swanson, M.C.; Lopez, M.; et al: Measurement of IgG Antibody and Airborne Antigen to Control an Industrial Outbreak of Hypersensitivity Pneumonitis. J. Occup. Med. 25:207–210 (1983).
108. Barnett, H.L.; Hunter, B.B.: Illustrated Genera of Imperfect Fungi. Burgess Pub. Co., Minneapolis, MN (1972).
109. Burge, H.; Boise, J.R.; Rutherford, J.A.; Solomon, W.R.: Comparative Recoveries of Airborne Fungus Spores by Viable and Nonviable Modes of Volumetric Collection. Mycopathologia 61(1):27–33 (1977).
110. Burge, H.; Chapman, J.; Jelks, M.: Quality Control of Multisource Aeroallergen Data. Grana 25:247–250 (1986).
111. Carmichael, J.W.; Kendrick, W.B.; Conners, I.L.; Sigler, L.: Genera of *Hyphomycetes.* University of Alberta Press, Edmonton, Alberta, Canada (1980).
112. Ellis, M.B.: Dematiaceous *Hyphomycetes.* Comonwealth Mycological Institute, Kew, Surrey, England (1971).
113. Ellis, M.B.; Ellis, J.P.: Microfungi on Land Plants. MacMillan Pub. Co., New York (1985).
114. Smith, E.G.: Sampling and Identifying Allergenic Pollens and Molds. Blewstone Press, San Antonio, TX (1986).
115. Solomon, W.R.: Sampling Airborne Allergens. Ann. Allergy 52(3):140–149 (1984).
116. Platts-Mills, T.A.E.; Chapman, M.D.; Heymann, P.W.; Luczynska, C.M.: Measurements of Airborne Allergen Using Immunoassays. Immunol. Allergy Clin. North Amer. 9(2):269–283 (1989).
117. Brown, M; Aalberse, R.; Platts-Mills, T.; Chapman, M.: Monoclonal Immunoassay for Quantitative Analysis of Fel d I(Cat-1) in House Dust Extracts. J. Allergy Clin. Immunol. 79(1):221 (abstr.) (1987).
118. Gleich, G.J.; Larson, J.B.; Jones, R.T.; Baer, H.: Measurement of Potency of Allergy Extracts by their Inhibitory Capacities in the Radioallergosorbent Test. J. Allergy Clin. Immunol. 53:158 (1974).
119. Milton, D.K.; Feldman, H.A.; Neuberg, D.S.; et al.: Environmental Endotoxin Measurement: The Kinetic Limulus Assay with Resistant-Parallel-Line Estimation. Environ. Res. 57:212–230 (1992).
120. Olenchock, S.A.: Endotoxins. In: Biological Contaminants in Indoor Environments, pp. 190–200. P.R. Morey, J.C. Feeley, and J.A. Otten, Eds. American Society for Testing and Materials, Philadelphia (1990).
121. Brachman, P.S.; Ehrlich, R.; Eichenwald, H.F.; et al.: Standard Sampler for Assay of Airborne Microorganisms. Science 144:1295 (1964).
122. Macher, J.M.; Willeke, K.: Performance Criteria for Bioaerosol Samplers. J. Aerosol Sci. 23:S647–S650 (1992).
123. Cole, E.C.; Colvert, R.J.: Draft Concept. Laboratory Accreditation and Proficiency Testing for Microbiological Analysis. Presented at the American Industrial Hygiene Conference, New Orleans, LA (May 1993).
124. Lach, V.: Performance of the Surface Air System Air Samplers. J. Hosp. Infection. 6:102–107 (1985).
125. Clark, S.; Lach, V.; Lidwell, O.M.: The Performance of the Biotest RCS Centrifugal Air Sampler. J. Hosp. Inf. 2:181–186 (1981).
126. Macher, J.M.; First, M.W.: Reuter Centrifugal Air Sampler: Measurement of Effective Airflow Rate and Collection Efficiency. Appl. Environ. Microbiol. 45:1960–1962 (1983).

Instrument Descriptions

23-1. Rotating Slit or Slit-to-Agar Impactors

23-1a. Mattson-Garvin Air Sampler (BC)

Air is drawn at 28 L/min through a fixed 0.15- × 41-mm slit and impacted directly onto semisolid medium on a rotating turntable. Two models are available: M/G 220 to monitor room air and M/G P-320 to monitor compressed gases. Model 220 has a built-in vacuum pump; Model P-320 has a constant pressure reducing valve (maximum 645 cm Hg, minimum 25 cm Hg). Both models have airflow gauges and adjustment valves. Samplers available with drive motors for rotational speeds of 5, 15, 30, or 60 min per revolution. Adjustable electric timer shuts off sampler at cycle end. Gauge to adjust slit-to-agar distance to 2–3 mm. High efficiency particulate air (HEPA) filter on air exhaust (Model 220).

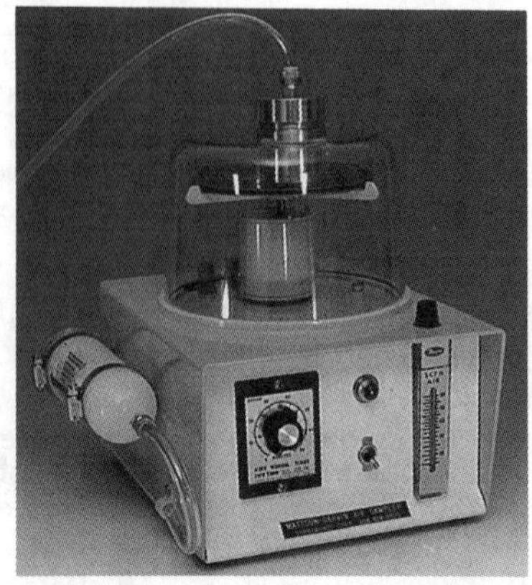

INSTRUMENT 23-1a. Mattson-Garvin Model 220 rotating slit or slit-to-agar impactor; shown with HEPA filter and probe assembly.

d_{50} cutpoint: 0.5 μm[58]

Collection substrate: 40–50 ml semisolid medium in 15- × 1.5-cm disposable culture plates.

Power: 120 V 60 Hz or 240 V 50 Hz.

Materials: Dome - Lexan plastic; base - metal; nozzle - metal.

Dimensions: 30 cm high × 25 cm wide × 30 cm front to back.

Weight: Model 220 - 7 kg; Model P-320 - 5 kg.

INSTRUMENT 23-1b. Casella Airborne Bacteria Sampler MK-II, a rotating slit or slit-to-agar impactor.

23-1b. Airborne Bacteria Sampler MK-II (BGI; CLL)

Air is drawn through fixed narrow slits and impacted directly onto semisolid medium on a rotating turntable. Two models are available: small model has one 0.3- × 28-mm slit and samples at 30 L/min onto 10-cm plates; large model has four 1- × 44.5-mm slits and samples at 700 L/min onto 15-cm plates. Both models have airflow gauges and adjustment valves. Rotational speed variable at 0.6, 2.4, or 6 min per revolution with automatic shutoff at cycle end. Turntable height adjusts for slit-to-agar distance of 2 mm. Template available for reading individual segments of impaction plates. Carrying handle attached.

d_{50} cutpoint: Small model - 0.67 μm (calculated);[15] large model - approximately 1 μm (calculated).

Collection substrate: 15–25 ml or 40–50 ml semisolid medium in 10- or 15-cm disposable culture plates.

Power: 120 V, 6 amp, 60 Hz.

Auxiliary air mover: Small sampler - approximately 0.1-hp vacuum pump able to move 30 L/min air flow at 2.2-cm-Hg pressure drop; large sampler - approximately 0.5-hp vacuum pump capable of moving 700 L/min air flow at 3.0-cm-Hg pressure drop.

Materials: Aluminum; plated and painted steel.

Dimensions: 32 × 25 × 37 cm.

Weight: Small model - 9.5 kg; large model - 11 kg.

INSTRUMENT 23-1c. New Brunswick rotating slit-to-agar biological air sampler.

23-1c. Slit-to-Agar Biological Air Sampler (NBS)

Air is drawn at 50 L/min through a fixed 25-mm-long × 0.1- to 0.2-mm-wide slit and impacted directly onto semisolid medium on a rotating turntable. Three models are available: STA-101 manually operated air sampler, STA-203 variable speed air sampler, and STA-303 console air sampler. Models 101 and 203 require air movers; Model 303 has a built-in, 1/3-hp, oil-less vacuum pump. All models have a metering orifice calibrated at 50 L/min. Models 203 and 303 can be operated at rotational speeds of 24, 40, or 60 min per revolution with automatic shutoff at cycle end. Turntable height adjustable. Template available for reading individual segments of impaction plates.

d_{50} cutpoint: Not reported.

Collection substrate: 40–50 ml semisolid medium in 15- × 1.5-cm disposable culture plates.

Power: 120 V 60 Hz; 220/230 V 50 Hz; or 220 V 50 Hz single fuse.

Auxiliary air movers (Models 101 and 203): Vacuum pump able to move 50 L/min at 55-cm-Hg pressure drop.

Materials: Bonnet - plastic composite; base - metal and plastic; nozzle - stainless steel.

Dimensions: Model 101 - 20 cm high × 22 cm wide × 29 cm front to back; Model 203 - 32 × 30 × 23 cm; Model 303 - 104 × 51 × 46 cm.

Weight: Model 101 - 3 kg; Model 203 - 4 kg; Model 303 - 55 kg.

23-2. Multiple-Hole Impactors

23-2a. Single-Stage Impactors

23-2a(i). 100-Hole Impactor

Portable Air Sampler for Agar Plates (BMC Sampler 2B)

Air is drawn at 10 or 20 L/min through 100 1-mm holes and impacted directly onto semisolid medium. Sampler can be run continuously or using a built-in 1-

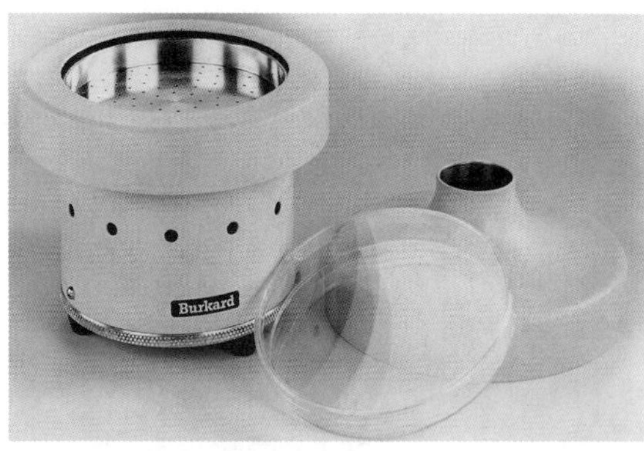

INSTRUMENT 23-2a(i). Burkard portable air sampler for agar plates, a single-stage 100-hole impactor.

to 9-min timer.

d_{50} cutpoint: 4.1 μm at 10 L/min; 2.9 μm at 20 L/min (calculated).

Collection substrate: 27 ml semisolid medium in 9-cm disposable culture plates.

Power: Rechargeable 6 V battery or AC adaptor. Indicator light and audible signal.

Materials: Aluminum inlet (autoclavable); plastic housing.

Dimensions: 15 cm high × 12 cm in diameter.

Weight: 0.7 kg.

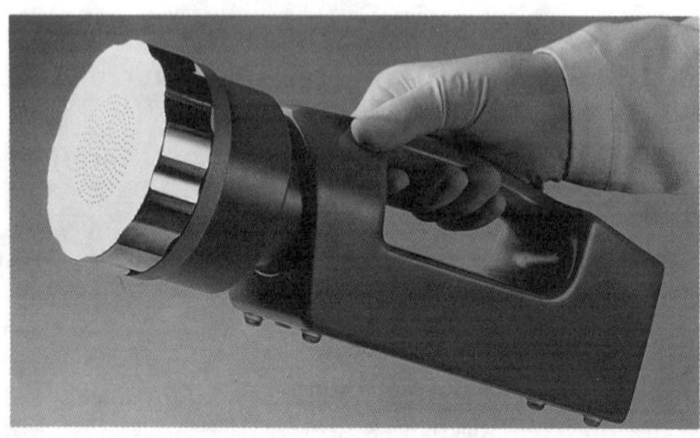

INSTRUMENT 23-2a(ii). Spiral Biotech surface-air sampler (SAS); Super 90, a single-stage 219- or 487-hole impactor.

23-2a(ii). 219- or 487-Hole Impactors

Surface-Air Sampler (SAS) (SBI)

Air is drawn through 219 or 487 holes (0.5 or 1 mm in diameter) and impacted directly onto semisolid medium. Three models are available: Super 90 and compact models sample at 90 L/min; high flow model samples at 180 L/min. Sampling heads with 219 or 487 holes attach to any model for use with 6.5- or 9.2-cm disposable contact plates. Hot-wire probe for air flow validation. Carrying cases included.

d_{50} cutpoint:

- 219 1-mm holes: 90 L/min - 2.0 μm (calculated); 180 L/min - 1.45 μm (calculated),[15] 1.9 μm (experimental).[124]
- 219 0.5-mm holes: 90 L/min - 0.7 μm; 180 L/min - 0.5 μm (calculated).
- 487 1-mm holes: 90 L/min - 3.1 μm; 180 L/min - 2.2 μm (calculated).
- 487 0.5-mm holes: 90 L/min - 1.1 μm; 180 L/min - 0.7 μm (calculated).

Collection substrate: 12–14 ml or 13–15 ml semisolid medium in 6.5- or 9.2-cm disposable culture (contact) plates.

Power: Rechargeable 6 V or 12 V battery; high flow model - AC adapter; Super 90 model - LCD display and timer; compact and high flow models - indicator lights and timers.

Materials: Sampler heads - autoclavable aluminum or stainless steel. Super 90 model - polyurethane resin housing; compact and high flow models - aluminum housings.

Dimensions: Super 90 - 12 cm high × 11 cm wide × 32 cm long; compact - 22 × 10 × 31 cm; high flow - 10 × 10 × 32 cm, (battery pack - 18 × 11 × 16 cm).

Weight: Super 90 - 2.1 kg; compact - 2.4 kg; high flow - 2.0 kg (battery pack - 5.0 kg).

23-2a(iii). 400-Hole Impactor (N-6)

Model 10-880, Single-Stage Bioaerosol Sampler (GRA)

Air is drawn at 28 L/min through 400 0.25-mm holes and impacted directly onto semisolid medium.

d_{50} cutpoint: 0.57 μm (calculated),[15] 0.65 μm (experimental).[88]

Collection substrate: When using last stage of six-stage impactor (Sampler 2c) - 45–50 ml semisolid medium in 10- × 1.5-cm disposable culture plates or 27 ml in manufacturer's glass plates; when using Model 10-880 or N-6 version - 20–25 ml semisolid medium in 10- × 1.5-cm disposable culture plates.

INSTRUMENT 23-2a(iii). Graseby Andersen Model 10-880 single-stage bioaerosol sampler, a 400-hole impactor.

Auxiliary air mover: Rotary-vane or diaphragm vacuum pump able to move 28 L/min at 2-cm-Hg pressure drop.

Materials: Aluminum (autoclavable).

Dimensions: 7.5 cm high × 9 cm in diameter.

Weight: 0.6 kg.

23-2b. Two-Stage, 200-Hole Impactor

Microbial Air Sampler (GRA)

Air is drawn at 28 L/min through two stages, with 200 1.5- or 0.4-mm holes, and impacted directly onto semisolid medium. Critical orifice incorporated into base.

d_{50} cutpoint: Stages 0 and 1 - 8.0 and 0.95 μm (calculated).[58]

Collection substrate: 20–25 ml semisolid medium in 10- × 1.5-cm disposable culture plates.

Auxiliary air mover: Vacuum pump able to maintain a pressure difference of 25 cm Hg required to operate critical orifice.

Materials: Aluminum (autoclavable).

Dimensions: 7 cm high × 12 cm in diameter.

Weight: 1.2 kg.

23-2c. Six-Stage, 400-Hole Impactor

Particle-Fractioning Viable Sampler (GRA)

Air is drawn at 28 L/min through six stages, each with 400 holes, and impacted directly onto semisolid medium. Hole diameters from Stage 1 to 6 - 1.18, 0.91, 0.71, 0.53, 0.34, and 0.25 mm. Sampler available with carrying case.

d_{50} cutpoint: Stages 1 to 6 - 7.0, 4.7, 3.3, 2.1, 1.1, and 0.65 μm (experimental).[88]

Collection substrate: 45–50 ml semisolid medium in 10- × 1.5-cm disposable culture plates or 27 ml in manufacturer's glass plates; 20–25 ml semisolid medium in 10- × 1.5-cm disposable culture plates.

INSTRUMENT 23-2b. Graseby Andersen microbial air sampler, a two-stage 200-hole impactor.

INSTRUMENT 23-2c. Graseby Andersen particle-fractioning viable sampler, a six-stage 400-hole impactor.

Auxiliary air mover: Rotary-vane or diaphragm vacuum pump able to move 28 L/min at 2-cm-Hg pressure drop.

Materials: Aluminum (autoclavable).

Dimensions: 20 cm high × 11 cm in diameter.

Weight: 7 kg.

23-2d. Eight-Stage, Personal Impactor (GRA, SKC)

Air is drawn at 0.5–5 L/min through one to eight stages, each with six tapered radial slots or pairs of holes, and impacted onto removable substrates. The slot or hole diameters from Stage 1 to 8 are 2.6 × 9.5, 1.4 × 9.5, 0.81 × 9.5, 0.43 × 9.5, 0.25 × 9.5, 0.17 × 4.8, 0.46, and 0.32 mm. Inlet shroud available.

d_{50} cutpoint (2 L/min): Stages 1 to 8 - 21.3, 14.8, 9.8, 6.0, 3.5, 1.55, 0.93 and 0.52 μm, plus a back-up filter (experimental).[95]

Collection substrate: 34-mm removable Mylar or aluminum substrates, or special trays with soluble medium.

Auxiliary air mover: Personal vacuum pump able to move 0.5–5 L/min at 1.5-cm-Hg pressure drop.

Materials: Aluminum with nickel-plated impactor stages.

Dimensions: Depending on number of stages used, 7–9 cm high × 6 cm in diameter.

Weight: Depending on number of stages used, 0.17–0.20 kg.

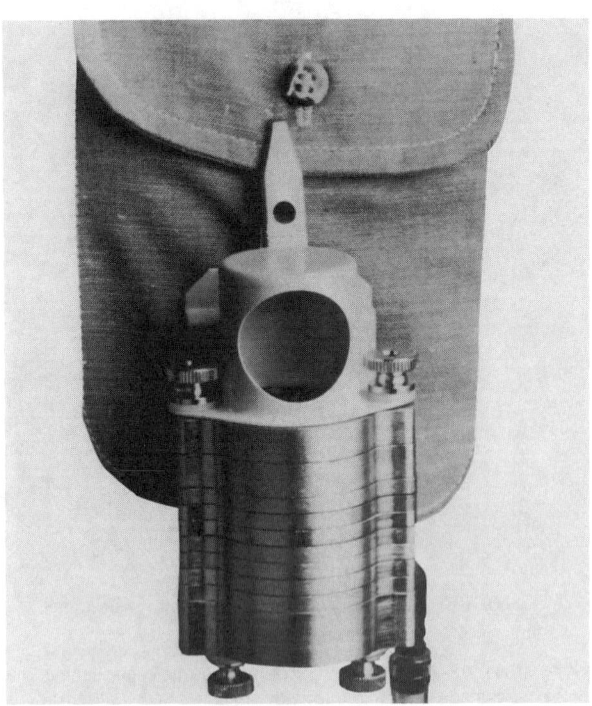

INSTRUMENT 23-2d. Graseby Andersen eight-stage, personal impactor.

23-3. Centrifugal Samplers

23-3a. Agar Strip Impactors, Reuter Centrifugal Samplers (RCS)

23-3a(i). RCS Standard Air Sampler (BDC)

Air is drawn by a rotating impeller, at a nominal rate of 40 L/min, and impacted onto semisolid medium. Air enters and exits through the same opening. Explosion-proof model available. Sampler available with carrying case.

d_{50} cutpoint: Approximately 5 µm,[125] approximately 3–4 µm,[126] > 2 µm[58] (all estimated).

Collection substrate: Semisolid medium in disposable culture strips. Strips contain 34 sections, 1 $cm^2 \times 0.5$ cm deep.

Power: Operates on four "D" cell batteries or AC adapter. Indicator light and timer. Remote control cable available.

Materials: Impeller blades and drum autoclavable.

Dimensions: 6-cm head diameter, 34 cm long.

Weight: 1.1 kg.

23-3a(ii). RCS Plus Air Sampler (BDC)

Air is drawn by a spinning rotor assembly, at a nominal rate of 50 L/min, and impacted onto semisolid medium. Air enters and exits through separate ports. Anemometer available for calibration. Sampler available with carrying case. Programmable by sample volume.

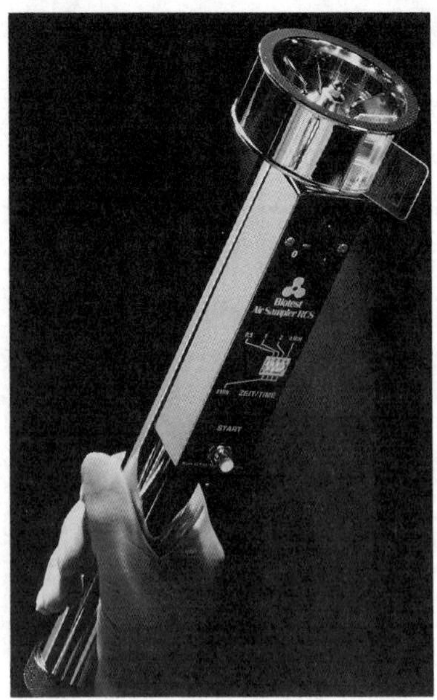

INSTRUMENT 23-3a(i). Biotest RCS Standard air sampler; a centrifugal, agar strip impactor.

d_{50} cutpoint: 80% efficient for 2-µm particles and ≥ 98% efficient above 4 µm (manufacturer).

Collection substrate: Semisolid medium in disposable culture strips. Strips contain 34 sections, 1 $cm^2 \times 0.5$ cm deep.

Power: Rechargeable 7.2-V battery. Indicator display. Infrared remote control available.

Materials: Polycarbonate housing, anodized aluminum rotor (autoclavable), steel protection cap (autoclavable).

Dimensions: 13 cm high × 11 cm wide × 30 cm long.

Weight: 1.5 kg.

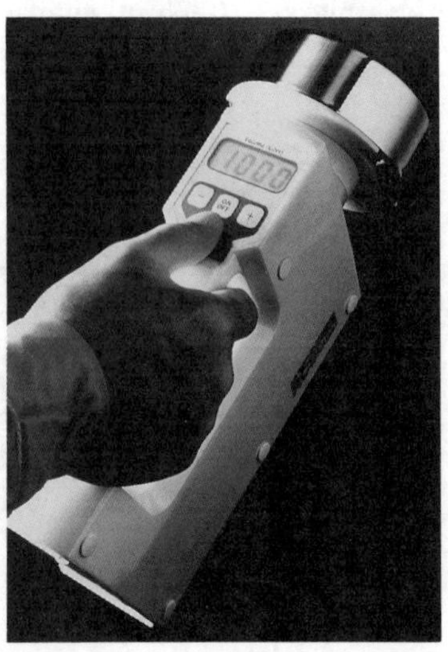

INSTRUMENT 23-3a(ii). Biotest RCS Plus air sampler; a centrifugal, agar strip impactor.

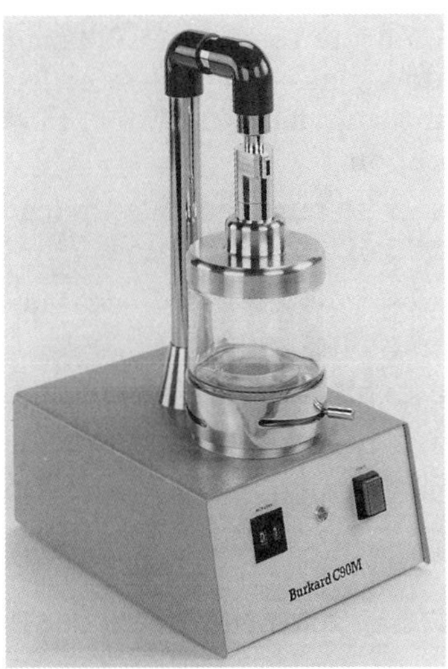

INSTRUMENT 23-3b. Burkard cyclone sampler for airborne particles, a centrifugal sampler.

23-3b. Cyclone Sampler

Cyclone Sampler for Airborne Particles (BMC Sampler 8)

Air is drawn at 10 L/min through a 0.9- × 0.3-cm vertical orifice into a reverse-flow cyclone. Flowmeter available for calibration.

d_{50} cutpoint: 1.2 μm (experimental, data available from manufacturer).

Collection substrate: Particles collected dry in catchpot or in liquid medium.

Power: Rechargeable battery pack or AC adaptor. Indicator light and timer.

Materials: Glass catchpot (autoclavable, dry heat sterilizable). Two sizes available.

Dimensions: 33 cm high × 17 cm wide × 22 cm front to back.

Weight: 4.6 kg.

23-4. Liquid Impingers

23-4a. Single-Stage, All-Glass Impingers (AGI)

AGI-30 and AGI-4 (AGI; MIL)

Air is drawn at 12.5 L/min through a capillary (critical orifice) jet and impacted against a wetted surface. Samplers come in two sections with ground-glass connections.

d_{50} cutpoint: 0.31 μm (calculated).[15]

Collection substrate: 10–20 ml liquid in a 125-ml capacity bottle.

Auxiliary air mover: Vacuum pump able to maintain a pressure difference of 20 cm Hg required to operate critical orifice.

Materials: Glass (autoclavable, dry heat sterilizable).

Dimensions: 28 cm high × 4 cm wide × 10 cm front to back (including vacuum attachment).

Weight: 0.15 kg.

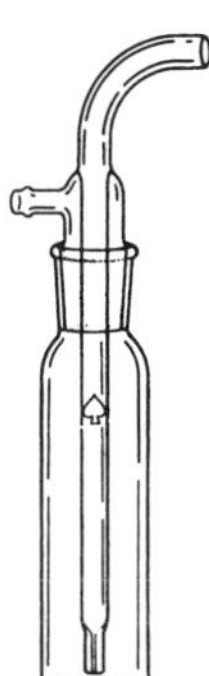

INSTRUMENT 23-4a. Ace Glass single-stage, all-glass impinger (AGI-4).

23-4b. Three-Stage Impingers

23-4b(i). Multiple-Stage Liquid Impinger (BMC Sampler 4D)

Air is drawn at 20 L/min through three stages and impacted against wetted surfaces. Entrance has a stagnation-point shield to improve aspiration efficiency in moving air. A critical orifice is incorporated into the sampler.

d_{50} cutpoint: Stages 1 to 3 - $\geq$ 10, 4 to 10, and < 4 μm.[82]

Collection substrate: 6 ml liquid in each stage.

Auxiliary air mover: Vacuum pump able to maintain a pressure difference of 18 cm Hg required to operate critical orifice.

Materials: Anodized aluminum alloy or stainless steel (heat sterilizable).

Dimensions: 14.5 cm high × 10 cm wide × 11.5 cm front to back.

Weight: 0.7 kg.

23-4b(ii). Three-Stage Impinger (HG)

Air is drawn at 10, 20, or 50 L/min through three stages and impacted against wetted surfaces. Jet di-

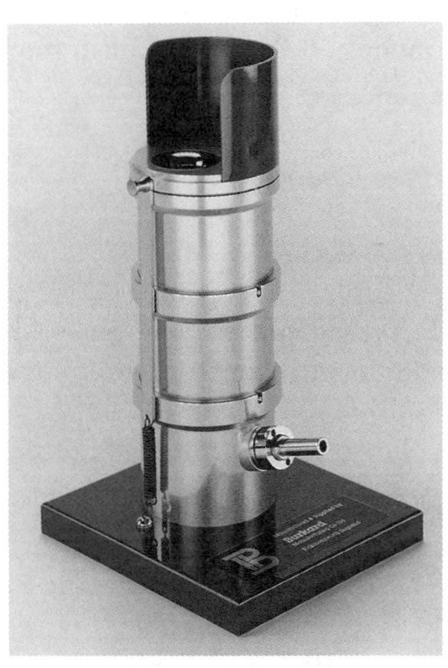

INSTRUMENT 23-4b(i). Burkard multiple-stage liquid impinger.

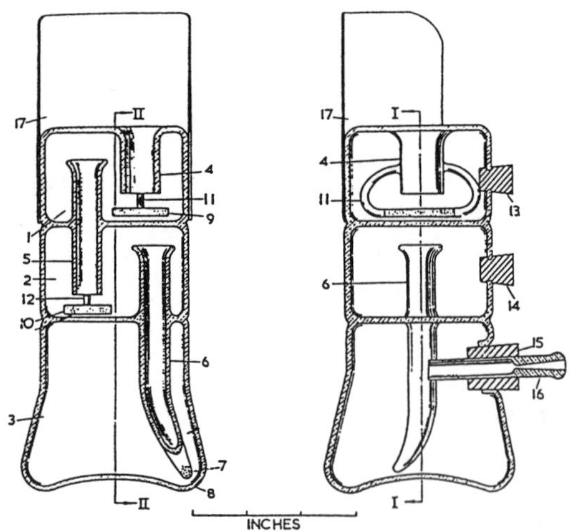

INSTRUMENT 23-4b(ii). Hampshire Glassware three-stage impinger.

ameters for stages 1 to 3, 10-L/min model - 0.8, 0.5, and 0.14 cm; 20-L/min model - 1.5, 0.75, and 0.2 cm; 50-L/min model - 1.5, 1.0, and 0.33 cm. A critical orifice may be incorporated into the sampler.

d_{50} cutpoint: Stages 1 to 3, 10-L/min model - ≥ 7, ≥ 3, and ≥1 m; 20-L/min model - 10 μm, 4 μm, and lower respiratory tract equivalent; 55-L/min model - same as 10-L/min model.[82]

Collection substrate: 10-L/min model - 2 ml liquid each stage; 20-L/min model - 4 ml liquid each stage; 50-L/min model - 7 to 10 ml liquid in stages 1 and 2, 10 ml liquid in stage 3.

Auxiliary air mover: Vacuum pump able to maintain a pressure difference of 10–13 cm Hg required to operate critical orifice.

Materials: Hand-blown glass (autoclavable, dry heat sterilizable).

Dimensions: Outer diameters, 10-L/min model - 4.5 cm; 20-L/min model - 6.0 cm; 50-L/min model - 7.5 cm.

Weight: Not reported.

23-5. Filters (see Chapter 13)

23-6. Settling Surfaces

(Prepared culture plates and glass slides commercially available from laboratory suppliers.)

23-7. Pollen, Spore, and Particle Impactors

23-7a. 1- to 7-Day Tape/Slide Impactors

23-7a(i). 1- to 7-Day Recording Volumetric Spore Trap (BMC Sampler 9)

Air is drawn at 10 L/min through a 2- × 14-mm slot (other orifices also available) and impacted onto a tape supported on a drum rotating at 0.2 cm/hr (7-day collection) or onto a glass slide (24-hr collection). A wind vane maintains sampler orientation. Flowmeter available for calibration.

d_{50} cutpoint: 2- × 14-mm slot - 5.2 μm (calculated); 1- × 14-mm slot - 2.52 μm (calculated).[15]

Collection substrate: Adhesive-coated transparent plastic tape or glass slide.

Power: Operates off battery or electrical connection.

Materials: Parts treated to prevent corrosion.

Dimensions: 94 cm high, 53-cm vane radius.

Weight: 16 kg.

23-7a(ii). 1- to 7-Day Volumetric Pollen and Particle Sampler

(L Sampler VPPS 2000)

Air is drawn at 10 L/min (adjustable from 0.5 to 11.0 L/min) through a 2- × 14-mm slot and impacted onto a tape supported on a drum rotating at 0.2 cm/hr (7-day collection) or onto a glass slide (24-hr collection). A wind vane maintains sampler orientation. Flowmeter available for calibration.

d_{50} cutpoint: 10 μm; 70% efficient for 30-μm particles (manufacturer).

Collection substrate: Adhesive-coated transparent plastic tape or glass slide.

Power: 220 V, 50 Hz, or 115 V, 60 Hz.

Materials: Stainless steel, brass and aluminium alloy.

Dimensions: Without legs - 77 cm high, 47-cm vane radius; legs - 35 or 85 cm long.

Weight: 16 kg.

INSTRUMENT 23-7a(i). Burkard 1- to 7-day recording volumetric spore trap.

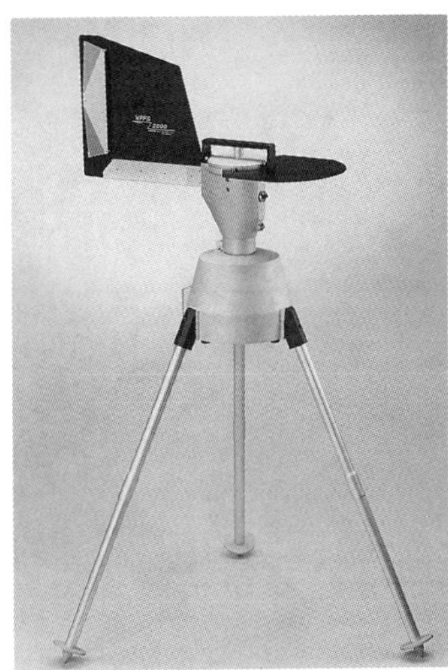

INSTRUMENT 23-7a(ii). Lanzoni 1- to 7-day volumetric pollen and particle sampler.

23-7b. Moving Slide Impactors

23-7b(i). Allergenco Air Sampler - MK-2 (ABP)

Air is drawn at 15 L/min for a preset sampling time of 10 min through a 1- × 14-mm slot and impacted in discrete deposits on a glass slide. Samples can be collected at intervals ranging from 1 min to 24 hrs.

d_{50} cutpoint: 2.0 µm (calculated).

Collection substrate: Adhesive-coated glass slide.

Power: 110/120-V AC power or 12-V DC adapter. Battery rechargeable by AC adapter or solar charger. Indicator lights, digital display.

Materials: Rigid metal case; brass slide-carrier tray.

Dimensions: 13 cm high × 9.5 cm wide × 16 cm front to back.

Weight: 2 kg.

23-7b(ii). Continuous Recording Air Sampler (BMC Sampler 9)

Air is drawn at 10 L/min through a 2- × 14-mm slot and impacted onto a glass slide moving beneath the slot at a rate of 0.2 cm/hr for 24 hrs, 0.4 cm/hr for 12 hrs, or 0.8 cm/hr for 6 hrs (total travel distance: 4.8 cm). Flowmeter available for calibration.

d_{50} cutpoint: 5.2 µm (calculated).

Collection substrate: Adhesive-coated glass slide.

Power: Electrical connection required. Indicator light and timer.

Materials: Rigid metal case; stainless steel moving parts.

Dimensions: 11.5 cm high × 12 cm wide × 21.5 cm front to back.

Weight: 2.6 kg.

INSTRUMENT 23-7b(i). Allergenco moving slide impactor, MK-2; left unit closed, right unit open showing glass slide.

23-7b(iii). Volumetric Pollen and Particle Sampler (L Sampler VPPS 1000)

Air is drawn at 10 L/min through a 2- × 14-mm slot and impacted onto a glass slide moving behind the slot at a rate of 0.2 cm/hr for 24 hrs. Cover protects unit from rain and snow. Flowmeter available for calibration.

d_{50} cutpoint: 10 µm; 70% efficient for 30-µm particles (manufacturer).

Collection substrate: Adhesive-coated glass slide.

Power: Operates off electrical connection, 12-V DC external battery or rechargeable internal battery.

Materials: Stainless steel, brass and aluminium alloy.

Dimensions: 23 cm high × 21 cm wide × 50 cm front to back.

Weight: 6 kg.

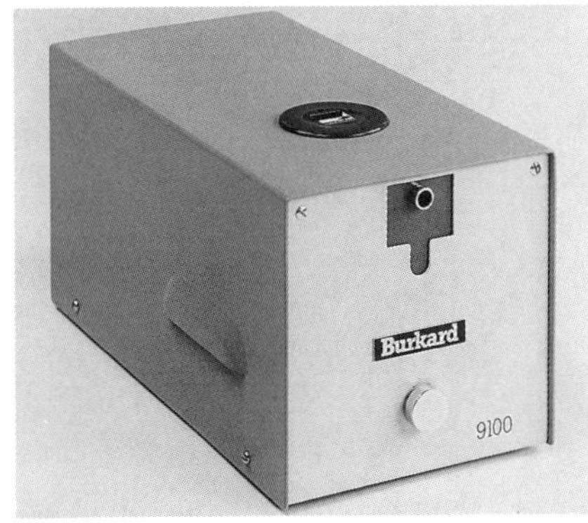

INSTRUMENT 23-7b(ii). Burkard continuous recording air sampler, a moving slide impactor.

23-7c. Stationary Slide Impactor

Personal Volumetric Air Sampler (BMC Sampler 2B)

Air is drawn at 10 L/min through a 2- × 14-mm slot and impacted onto a glass slide. Can be run continuously or using a built-in 1- to 9-min timer. Flowmeter

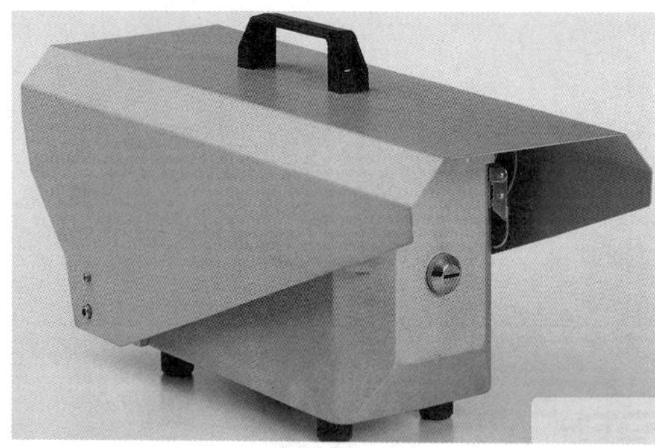

INSTRUMENT 23-7b(iii). Lanzoni volumetric pollen and particle sampler, a moving slide impactor.

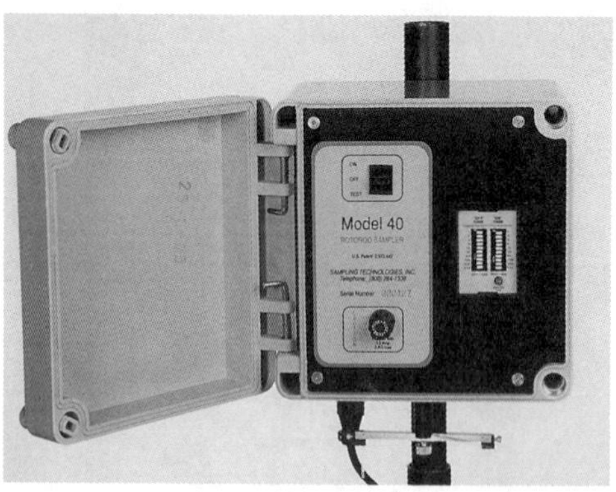

INSTRUMENT 23-7d. Sampling Technologies rotorod sampler (Model 40), a rotating rod impactor; (the left-hand rod can be seen against the power cord below the protective housing).

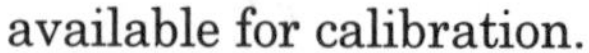

available for calibration.

d_{50} cutpoint: 5.2 µm (calculated).

Collection substrate: Adhesive-coated glass slide.

Power: Rechargeable 6-V battery or AC adaptor. Indicator light and audible signal.

Materials: Light alloy plastic and stainless steel.

Dimensions: 11.5 cm high × 9 cm in diameter.

Weight: 0.64 kg.

23-7d. Rotating Rod Impactors

Rotorod Samplers (STI)

Two vertical rods rotate at a nominal rate of 2400 rpm impacting particles on the leading edges of the rods.

INSTRUMENT 23-7c. Burkard personal volumetric air sampler, a stationary slide impactor.

Three models are available: Model 10 - stationary or hand-held sampler, accepts U or I rods; Model 20 - stationary sampler, accepts H, U, or I rods; Model 40 - stationary area sampler, accepts I rods. Models 10 and 20 accept either fixed or retracting heads; Model 40 accepts retracting head. H rods sample at a nominal rate of 52 L/min, U rods at 120 L/min, and I rods at 45 L/min with retracting head and 48 L/min with fixed head (when 22 mm of rod length is examined). For intermittent operation, Model 20 can be controlled by an external timing device; Model 40 has a programmable internal timer.

d_{50} cutpoint: H rods approximately 100% efficient for particles <5 µm; U and I rods approximately 100% efficient for 20-µm particles (manufacturer).

Collection substrate: Adhesive-coated rods; for culturable bacteria and fungi, H rods - 0.48 × 60 mm or U rods - 1.6 × 60 mm. For microscopic examination, I rods - 1.6 × 32 mm.

Power: Model 10 - 6-V DC; Model 20 - 12-V DC or AC adaptor; Model 40 - 12-V DC or AC adaptor.

Materials: Molded glass fiber cases; H rods stainless steel, U rods brass, I rods clear polystyrene.

Dimensions: Model 10 - 24 × 13 cm; Model 20 - 9 × 16.5 cm (without sampling head); Model 40 - 18 × 20 × 20 cm.

Weight: Model 10 - 1.4 kg; Model 20 - 0.45 kg (without sampling head); Model 40 - 2.7 kg.

TABLE 23-I-1. Manufacturers and Suppliers of Samplers to Collect Bioaerosols

Code	Manufacturer/Supplier
ABP	Allergenco/Bluestone Press P.O. Box 8571 Wainwright Station San Antonio, TX 78208 (210)822-4116 FAX (210)829-1883
AGI	Ace Glass Incorporated P.O. Box 688 1430 Northwest Blvd. Vineland, NJ 08360 (609)692-3333 or (800)223-4524 FAX (800)543-6752
BC	Barramundi Corp. P.O. Drawer 4259 Homosassa Springs, FL 34447 (904)628-0200 FAX (904)628-0203
BDC	Biotest Diagnostics Corporation 66 Ford Rd., Suite 131 Denville, NJ 07834 (201)625-1300 or (800)522-0090 FAX (201)625-9454
BGI	BGI Incorporated 58 Guinan Street Waltham, MA 02154 (617)891-9380 FAX (617)891-8151
BMC	Burkard Manufacturing Co., Ltd. Woodcock Hill Industrial Estate Richmansworth, Hertfordshire England WD3 1PJ (011) +44 (0)923 773134 FAX (011) +44 (0)923 774790
CLL	Casella London Limited Regent House, Wolseley Rd. Kempston, Bedford MK42 7JY England (011) +44 (0)234 841441 FAX (011) +44 (0)234 841490
CC	Corning Costar One Alewife Center Cambridge, MA 02140 (617)868-6200 or (800)492-1110 FAX (617)868-2076
GRA	Graseby Andersen 500 Technology Court Smyrna, GA 30082-5211 (404)319-9999 or (800)241-6898 FAX (404)319-0336
GMW	Graseby GMW General Metal Works, Inc. 145 S. Miami Ave. Cleves, OH 45002 (513)941-2229 FAX (513)941-1977
GS	Gelman Sciences 600 S. Wagner Rd. Ann Arbor, MI 48103-9019 (313)665-0651 or (800)521-1520 FAX (313)761-1208
HG	Hampshire Glassware 77-79 Dukes Rd., Hampshire Southampton SO2 0ST England (011) +44 (0)703 553755 FAX (011) +44 (0)703 553020
L	Lanzoni, S.R.L. Via Zamboni, 6 40126 Bologna Italy (011) +39 (0)51-222456 FAX (011) +39 (0)51-239482
MIL	Millipore Corporation 80 Ashby Road Bedford, MA 01730 (617)533-2125 or (800)645-5476
NBS	New Brunswick Scientific Co., Inc. P.O. Box 4005 44 Talmadge Rd. Edison, NJ 08818-4005 (800)631-5417 FAX (908)287-4222
SKC	SKC, Inc. 863 Valley View Road Eighty Four, PA 15330-9614 (412)941-9701 or (800)752-8472 FAX (412)941-1396
SBI	Spiral Biotech, Inc. 7830 Old Georgetown Rd. Bethesda, MD 20814 (301)657-1620 FAX (301)652-5036
STI	Sampling Technologies, Inc. 10801 Wayzata Blvd. Suite 340 Minnetonka, MN 55305 (612)544-1588 or (800)264-1338 FAX (612)525-3505

Index

A

B

D

E

F

H

J

K

L

M

N

O

Q

R

S

T

U

V

W

X

Y

Z